AMERICAN COUNCIL OF LEARNED SOCIETIES

Dictionary
of Scientific
Biography
cSs

DICTIONARY
OF
SCIENTIFIC BIOGRAPHY

DICTIONARY

OF

SCIENTIFIC BIOGRAPHY

CHARLES COULSTON GILLISPIE

Princeton University

EDITOR IN CHIEF

Volume XIII

HERMANN STAUDINGER – GIUSEPPE VERONESE

CHARLES SCRIBNER'S SONS · NEW YORK

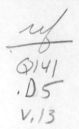
1 3 5 7 9 11 13 15 17 19 MD/C 20 18 16 14 12 10 8 6 4 2

Printed in the United States of America
Library of Congress Catalog Card Number 69-18090
ISBN 0-684-12925-6

Panel of Consultants

GEORGES CANGUILHEM
University of Paris

PIERRE COSTABEL
École Pratique des Hautes Études

ALISTAIR C. CROMBIE
University of Oxford

MAURICE DAUMAS
Conservatoire National des Arts et Métiers

ALLEN G. DEBUS
University of Chicago

MARCEL FLORKIN
University of Liège

JOHN C. GREENE
University of Connecticut

MIRKO D. GRMEK
Archives Internationales d'Histoire des Sciences

A. RUPERT HALL
Imperial College of Science and Technology

MARY B. HESSE
University of Cambridge

BROOKE HINDLE
Massachusetts Institute of Technology

JOSEPH E. HOFMANN
University of Tübingen

REIJER HOOYKAAS
State University of Utrecht

MICHAEL A. HOSKIN
University of Cambridge

E. S. KENNEDY
Brown University

STEN H. LINDROTH
University of Uppsala

ROBERT K. MERTON
Columbia University

JOHN MURDOCH
Harvard University

SHIGERU NAKAYAMA
University of Tokyo

CHARLES D. O'MALLEY
University of California, Los Angeles

DEREK J. DE SOLLA PRICE
Yale University

J. R. RAVETZ
University of Leeds

MARIA LUISA RIGHINI-BONELLI
Istituto e Museo di Storia della Scienza, Florence

DUANE H. D. ROLLER
University of Oklahoma

KARL EDUARD ROTHSCHUH
University of Münster/Westphalia

S. SAMBURSKY
Hebrew University, Jerusalem

GIORGIO DE SANTILLANA
Massachusetts Institute of Technology

AYDIN SAYILI
University of Ankara

ROBERT E. SCHOFIELD
Case Western Reserve University

CHRISTOPH J. SCRIBA
Technical University, Berlin

NATHAN SIVIN
Massachusetts Institute of Technology

BOGDAN SUCHODOLSKI
Polish Academy of Sciences

RENÉ TATON
École Pratique des Hautes Études

J. B. THORNTON
University of New South Wales

RICHARD S. WESTFALL
Indiana University

W. P. D. WIGHTMAN
King's College, Aberdeen

L. PEARCE WILLIAMS
Cornell University

A. P. YOUSCHKEVITCH
Academy of Sciences of the U.S.S.R.

Contributors to Volume XIII

The following are the contributors to Volume XIII. Each author's name is followed by the institutional affiliation at the time of publication and the names of the articles written for this volume. The symbol † means that an author is deceased.

GIORGIO ABETTI
University of Florence
TACCHINI; TOSCANELLI DAL POZZO

MICHELE ALDRICH
Aaron Burr Papers
F. B. TAYLOR

ADEL ANBOUBA
Institut Moderne de Liban
AL-ṬŪSĪ

TOBY A. APPEL
Johns Hopkins University
VALENCIENNES

WILBUR APPLEBAUM
Illinois Institute of Technology
STREETE

A. ALBERT BAKER, JR.
California State University, Fullerton
TIEMANN

JOHN R. BAKER
University of Oxford
TREMBLEY

MARGARET E. BARON
TODHUNTER

DONALD G. BATES
McGill University
SYDENHAM

HANS BAUMGÄRTEL
TSCHERMAK

ROBERT P. BECKINSALE
University of Oxford
K. M. VON STERNBERG

LUIGI BELLONI
University of Milan
TRULLI

OTTO THEODOR BENFEY
Guilford College
F. K. J. THIELE

MICHAEL BERNKOPF
Pace College
STIELTJES

RICHARD BIEBL
University of Vienna
TSCHERMAK VON SEYSENEGG

R. P. BOAS, JR.
Northwestern University
TITCHMARSH

WALTER BÖHM
STEFAN

MARY A. B. BRAZIER
University of California, Los Angeles
UKHTOMSKY

GERT H. BRIEGER
University of California, San Francisco
THAYER

T. A. A. BROADBENT †
VENN

W. H. BROCK
University of Leicester
TILLOCH; E. TURNER

SANBORN C. BROWN
Massachusetts Institute of Technology
B. THOMPSON

THEODORE M. BROWN
City College, City University of New York
STUART

VIGGO BRUN
THUE

JED Z. BUCHWALD
University of Toronto
W. THOMSON

K. E. BULLEN
University of Sydney
H. H. TURNER

VERN L. BULLOUGH
California State University, Northridge
VARENIUS

IVOR BULMER-THOMAS
THEAETETUS; THEODORUS OF CYRENE; THEODOSIUS OF BITHYNIA

WERNER BURAU
University of Hamburg
STAUDT; STUDY; F. O. R. STURM

JOHANN JAKOB BURCKHARDT
University of Zurich
STEINER

JOHN G. BURKE
University of California, Los Angeles
VALMONT DE BOMARE

J. C. BURKILL
University of Cambridge
VALLÉE-POUSSIN

E. ALFRED BURRILL
VAN DE GRAAFF

H. L. L. BUSARD
State University of Leiden
VER EECKE

JAMES H. CASSEDY
National Library of Medicine
STILES

CARLO CASTELLANI
STRUSS; TROJA

ROBERT A. CHIPMAN
University of Toledo
STEINMETZ

STIG CLAESSON
University of Uppsala
SVEDBERG

EDWIN CLARKE
Wellcome Institute for the History of Medicine
TWORT

GEORGE W. CORNER
American Philosophical Society
STREETER

ALBERT B. COSTA
Duquesne University
SWARTS; J. F. THORPE

PIERRE COSTABEL
École Pratique des Hautes Études
VARIGNON

CHARLES COURY †
TESTUT

E. HORNE CRAIGIE
University of Toronto
TÜRCK

J. K. CRELLIN
Wellcome Institute for the History of Medicine
THURNAM

M. P. CROSLAND
University of Kent at Canterbury
THENARD

KARL H. DANNENFELDT
Arizona State University
STEPHANUS OF ALEXANDRIA; SYNESIUS OF CYRENE

STACEY B. DAY
Memorial Sloan-Kettering Cancer Center
STEVENS; TASHIRO

GAVIN DE BEER †
VENETZ

ALLEN G. DEBUS
University of Chicago
VALENTINE

CONTRIBUTORS TO VOLUME XIII

WŁODZIMIERZ HUBICKI
Marie Curie-Skłodowska University
SUCHTEN; THURNEYSSER

KARL HUFBAUER
University of California, Irvine
TROMMSDORFF

G. L. HUXLEY
Queen's University of Belfast
THEON OF SMYRNA; THEUDIUS OF MAGNESIA; THYMARIDAS

REESE V. JENKINS
Case Western Reserve University
TALBOT

RICHARD I. JOHNSON
Museum of Comparative Zoology
STIMPSON

PHILLIP S. JONES
University of Michigan
B. TAYLOR; VANDERMONDE

P. JOVET
Centre National de Floristique
THOUIN; S. VAILLANT

GEORGE KAHLSON
University of Lund
T. L. THUNBERG

T. N. KARI-NIAZOV
Academy of Sciences of the U.S.S.R.
ULUGH BEG

MARSHALL KAY
Columbia University
STILLE

BRIAN B. KELHAM
STONEY

A. G. KELLER
University of Leicester
STELLUTI

HUBERT C. KENNEDY
Providence College
VAILATI

PEARL KIBRE
Hunter College, City University of New York
THOMAS OF CANTIMPRÉ

F. KLEIN-FRANKE
AL-TĪFASHĪ

FRIEDRICH KLEMM
Deutsches Museum
VALTURIO

AKIRA KOBORI
Université Sangyo de Kyoto
TSU CH'UNG-CHIH

M. KOCH †
TREBRA

SHELDON J. KOPPERL
Grand Valley State Colleges
T. E. THORPE; URBAIN

VLADISLAV KRUTA
Purkyně University
TEICHMANN; TIEDEMANN; UNZER

P. G. KULIKOVSKY
Academy of Sciences of the U.S.S.R.
P. K. STERNBERG; SUBBOTIN; TIKHOV; TSERASKY

PAUL KUNITZSCH
University of Munich
AL-ṬŪSĪ

V. I. KUZNETSOV
Academy of Sciences of the U.S.S.R.
VAGNER

I. M. LAMB
Harvard University
THAXTER

EDWIN LAYTON
University of Minnesota
F. W. TAYLOR

JEAN F. LEROY
Muséum National d'Histoire Naturelle
TOURNEFORT

JACQUES R. LÉVY
Paris Observatory
STEPHAN; THOLLON; TISSERAND

E. B. LEWIS
California Institute of Technology
STURTEVANT

G. A. LINDEBOOM
Free University, Amsterdam
F. D. B. SYLVIUS

STEN LINDROTH
University of Uppsala
STELLER; SWEDENBORG

R. BRUCE LINDSAY
Brown University
J. W. STRUTT; SWANN

JAMES LONGRIGG
University of Newcastle Upon Tyne
THALES

JOHN B. McDIARMID
University of Washington
THEOPHRASTUS

ROBERT M. McKEON
Babson College
VERNIER

DUNCAN McKIE
University of Cambridge
TUTTON

VICTOR A. McKUSICK
Johns Hopkins Hospital
SUTTON

SAUNDERS MAC LANE
University of Chicago
VEBLEN

ROY MacLEOD
University of Sussex
TYNDALL

NORA F. McMILLAN
Merseyside County Museums
SWAINSON

M. MALLET
Centre National de Floristique
THOUIN; S. VAILLANT

NIKOLAUS MANI
University of Bonn
SUDHOFF

ARNALDO MASOTTI
Polytechnic of Milan
TARTAGLIA

KIRTLEY F. MATHER
Harvard University
VAN HISE

OTTO MAYR
Smithsonian Institution
STODOLA

GENEVIEVE MILLER
Case Western Reserve University
G. N. STEWART

ERIC L. MILLS
Dalhousie University
STEBBING

M. G. J. MINNAERT †
STEVIN

GIUSEPPE MONTALENTI
University of Rome
VALLISNIERI

ELLEN J. MOORE
U.S. Geological Survey
G. TROOST

J. B. MORRELL
University of Bradford
T. THOMSON

DALE M. J. MUELLER
Texas A&M University
TOZZI

D. MÜLLER
University of Copenhagen
STEENSTRUP

LETTIE S. MULTHAUF
STRATTON

JOHN E. MURDOCH
Harvard University
SWINESHEAD

J. A. NANNFELDT
Institute for Taxonomic Botany, Uppsala
SVEDELIUS

SEYYED HOSSEIN NASR
University of Teheran
AL-ṬŪSĪ

CONTRIBUTORS TO VOLUME XIII

CLIFFORD M. NELSON
University of California, Berkeley
ULRICH

AXEL V. NIELSEN†
STRÖMGREN; T. N. THIELE

W. A. NIEUWENKAMP
State University of Utrecht
VENING MEINESZ

JOHN D. NORTH
University of Oxford
SYLVESTER; TAIT

A. NOUGARÈDE
Faculté des Sciences, Paris
VAN TIEGHEM

MARY JO NYE
University of Oklahoma
L. J. TROOST

ROBERT OLBY
University of Leeds
STAUDINGER; UNGER

C. D. O'MALLEY †
VAROLIO

JANE OPPENHEIMER
Bryn Mawr College
TENNENT

A. PAPLAUSCAS
Academy of Sciences of the U.S.S.R.
URYSON

JOHN PARASCANDOLA
University of Wisconsin
VAN SLYKE

E. M. PARKINSON
Worcester Polytechnic Institute
STOKES

KAI O. PEDERSEN
University of Uppsala
SVEDBERG; TISELIUS

JEAN PELSENEER
University of Brussels
TILLY; VERHULST

ENRIQUE PEREZ ARBELAEZ †
TRIANA

STUART PIERSON
Memorial University of Newfoundland
TILLET

DAVID PINGREE
Brown University
'UMAR IBN AL-FARRUKHĀN AL-ṬABARĪ;
VARĀHAMIHIRA VATEŚVARA

D. ANTON PINSKER, S.J.
Archivar des Österreichischen Provinz des Jesuitenordens, Vienna
STEPLING

M. PLESSNER †
AL-TĪFASHĪ

LORIS PREMUDA
University of Padua
VALSALVA

RHODA RAPPAPORT
Vassar College
A.-R.-J. TURGOT; É.-F. TURGOT

ABRAHAM ROBINSON †
STOLZ; TOEPLITZ

GLORIA ROBINSON
Yale University
STRASBURGER

FRANCESCO RODOLICO
University of Florence
TARGIONI TOZZETTI

B. VAN ROOTSELAAR
State Agricultural University, Wageningen
TURING

PAUL LAWRENCE ROSE
James Cook University
TACCOLA

EDWARD ROSEN
City University of New York
TARDE; VANINI

B. A. ROSENFELD
Academy of Sciences of the U.S.S.R.
THĀBIT IBN QURRA

G. RUDOLPH
TRAUBE

A. S. SAIDAN
Jordanian University
AL-UMAWĪ; AL-UGLĪDISĪ

BETTINA F. SARGEANT
E. I. du Pont de Nemours and Company
STINE

CARL SCHALÉN
University of Lund
SUNDMAN

GUSTAV SCHERZ †
STENSEN

BRUNO SCHOENEBERG
University of Hamburg
STEINITZ

E. L. SCOTT
Stamford High School, Lincolnshire
URE

E. M. SENCHENKOVA
Academy of Sciences of the U.S.S.R.
TIMIRYAZEV; TSVET

ELIZABETH NOBLE SHOR
Scripps Institution of Oceanography
STEJNEGER; F. B. SUMNER

ROBERT R. SHROCK
Massachusetts Institute of Technology
TWENHOFEL

DANIEL M. SIEGEL
University of Wisconsin
B. STEWART

DIANA M. SIMPKINS
Polytechnic of North London
H. H. THOMAS; VAUCHER

W. A. SMEATON
University College, London
VAUQUELIN; VENEL

P. SMIT
G. R. TREVIRANUS; L. C. TREVIRANUS

CYRIL STANLEY SMITH
Massachusetts Institute of Technology
THEOPHILUS

IAN N. SNEDDON
University of Glasgow
M. STEWART

H. A. M. SNELDERS
State University of Utrecht
TEN RHYNE; TROOSTWIJK; VAN'T HOFF

Z. K. SOKOLOVSKAYA
Academy of Sciences of the U.S.S.R.
STRUVE FAMILY

A. I. SOLOVIEV
Academy of Sciences of the U.S.S.R.
TANFILEV

J. W. T. SPINKS
University of Saskatchewan
STEACIE

PIERRE SPEZIALI
University of Geneva
J. C.-F. STURM; J. TANNERY

NILS SPJELDNAES
Aarhus University
STØRMER; SVERDRUP; C. J. THOMSEN;
TILAS

C. G. G. J. VAN STEENIS
Rijksherbarium, Leiden
TREUB

PER STRØMHOLM
University of Oslo
TACQUET; VALERIO

CHARLES SÜSSKIND
University of California, Berkeley
S. P. THOMPSON; E. THOMSON

KENNETH M. SWEZEY †
TESLA

EDITH DUDLEY SYLLA
North Carolina State University at Raleigh
SWINESHEAD

F. SZABADVÁRY
Technical University, Budapest
SZEBELLÉDY; SZILY; THAN

CHARLES H. TALBOT
Wellcome Institute for the History of Medicine
STEPHEN OF ANTIOCH

CONTRIBUTORS TO VOLUME XIII

G. A. TAMMANN
University of Basel
TAMMANN

RENÉ TATON
École Pratique des Hautes Études
P. TANNERY; TINSEAU D'AMONDANS

K. BRYN THOMAS
Royal Berkshire Hospital
W. TURNER

PHILLIP DRENNON THOMAS
Wichita State University
C. W. THOMSON; VARRO

RUTH D'ARCY THOMPSON
D.'A. W. THOMPSON

RONALD C. TOBEY
University of California, Riverside
VERNEUIL

HEINZ TOBIEN
University of Mainz
STUDER

G. J. TOOMER
Brown University
THEON OF ALEXANDRIA

THADDEUS J. TRENN
University of Regensburg
R. J. STRUTT; SUTHERLAND; J. S. E.
TOWNSEND; TRAVERS; TROWBRIDGE

F. G. TRICOMI
Academy of Sciences of Turin
VERONESE

PETER W. VAN DER PAS
South Pasadena, Calif.
SURINGAR; SWIETEN; TULP

GERALD R. VAN HECKE
Harvey Mudd College
TILDEN

STIG VEIBEL
Technical University of Denmark
H. P. J. J. THOMSEN

G. VERBEKE
University of Louvain
THEMISTIUS

JUAN VERNET
University of Barcelona
JACOB BEN MACHIR IBN TIBBON; MOSES
BEN SAMUEL IBN TIBBON; TORRES
QUEVEDO; ULLOA Y DE LA TORRE GIRAL

G. VIENNOT-BOURGIN
Institut National Agronomique
TULASNE

KURT VOGEL
University of Munich
STIFEL

WILLIAM A. WALLACE, O.P.
Catholic University of America
THOMAZ; ULRICH OF STRASBOURG

P. J. WALLIS
University of Newcastle Upon Tyne
STIRLING

E. H. WARMINGTON
University of London
STRABO

CHARLES WEBSTER
University of Oxford
TOWNELEY; W. TURNER

RODERICK S. WEBSTER
Adler Planetarium
TROUGHTON

E. WEGMANN
SUESS

DORA B. WEINER
Manhattanville College
L.-L. VAILLANT

JOHN W. WELLS
Cornell University
VANUXEM

ALWYNE WHEELER
British Museum (Natural History)
J. V. THOMPSON

WESLEY C. WILLIAMS
Case Western Reserve University
TYSON

MARY P. WINSOR
University of Toronto
SWAMMERDAM

A. P. YOUSCHKEVITCH
Academy of Sciences of the U.S.S.R.
STEKLOV; STEPANOV

BRUNO ZANOBIO
University of Pavia
VASTARINI-CRESI

DICTIONARY
OF
SCIENTIFIC BIOGRAPHY

DICTIONARY OF
SCIENTIFIC BIOGRAPHY

STAUDINGER — VERONESE

STAUDINGER, HERMANN (*b.* Worms, Germany, 23 March 1881; *d.* Freiburg im Breisgau, Germany, 8 September 1965), *organic and macromolecular chemistry.*

Staudinger studied at the Gymnasium in Worms. Then, after a brief period at the University of Halle, he transferred to the technical university at Darmstadt when his father, the neo-Kantian philosopher Franz Staudinger, was appointed to a teaching post in that town. Although Staudinger wished to study botany, his parents were advised to give him first a thorough training in chemistry to prepare him for a career in botany. This excellent advice was followed; and from Darmstadt, Staudinger went on to study in Munich and Halle. His dissertation, on the malonic esters of unsaturated compounds, was written under D. Vorländer and was completed in 1903. But it was in Strasbourg, under Johannes Thiele, that Staudinger made his first and unexpected discovery—the highly reactive ketenes. These formed the subject of his *Habilitation* in 1907, the year in which he was appointed associate professor at the Technische Hochschule in Karlsruhe.

Five years later Staudinger succeeded Willstätter at the great Eidgenössische Technische Hochschule of Zurich, where he remained until his call to Freiburg im Breisgau in 1926. Three years after his retirement from the Freiburg chair he was awarded the Nobel Prize in chemistry. It was fitting, although unintentional, that this recognition of his work on macromolecular chemistry should have come in 1953, at a time when the molecular biology that he had glimpsed more than two decades before was taking shape. Staudinger married the Latvian plant physiologist Magda Woit in 1927.

In Karlsruhe, Staudinger achieved a new and simple synthesis of isoprene, from which polyisoprene (synthetic rubber) had previously been formed; and with C. L. Lautenschläger, he synthesized polyoxymethylenes. These discoveries later

served him in his studies of polymer chemistry in Zurich and Freiburg im Breisgau. Staudinger's friends urged him to avoid so difficult a field as the chemistry of polymers, but he was not to be dissuaded. He realized that with polyisoprene he could devise a crucial experiment by which he might be able to confirm either the aggregate or long-chain-molecule theory of the structure of polymers. After synthetic rubber he turned to polyoxymethylene, which he saw as a model for the natural polymer cellulose.

In 1920 Staudinger first expressed his preference for the long-chain-molecule conception of polymers. Six years later he predicted the important role that such macromolecular compounds would be found to play in living organisms, especially in proteins. When he met his future wife, Staudinger's attention was drawn to the role of macromolecules in structural substances like the plant cell-wall constituent, cellulose. Henceforth he sought to introduce the macromolecular concept into biological chemistry.

In the 1920's there existed two conceptions of polymer structure. According to Samuel Pickles and K. Freudenberg, these substances consisted of long-chain molecules held together by "primary" or "Kekulé" bonds; but C. Harries and R. Pummerer believed the real molecules in polymers to be small. These and other authorities held that a polymer is formed by the binding action of the residual forces of unsaturated compounds. These "secondary" valency forces were responsible for the apparent nonstoichiometry and strange physical properties—the nonlinear relation between viscosity and concentration, the tendency to form colloidal solutions, and the failure to yield crystals. Supporters of this aggregate hypothesis argued that the true molecules of a substance like rubber were small and that in the free state they did obey the laws of physical chemistry; in particular, they could be crystallized. Destroy their aggregation and the molecules would be freed. Only thus could the organic chemist be confident that he had a pure compound.

Harries suggested that the secondary forces that held the butadiene molecules together in natural rubber owed their presence to the unsaturated state of these molecules. He stated that hydrogenation of rubber should yield a product with a low boiling point since it would involve saturation of the forces of affinity within the molecules, and this process would destroy the secondary or residual forces between them. In 1922 Staudinger and J. Fritschi produced hydrorubber. Its properties differed little from natural rubber; in particular, it could not be distilled and, like rubber, it gave a colloidal solution. In their paper of that year they used the term "macro-molecular association" for the first time. Two years later Staudinger defined the macromolecule: "For such colloidal particles in which the molecule is identical with the primary particles, in other words, where the single atoms of the colloidal molecule are bound together by normal valency activities, we suggest the term *Makromolekül*."[1] He went on to point out that, since these colloidal particles are the true molecules, no attempts to produce typical, low-molecular solutions with other solvents would succeed.

In the 1920's Staudinger extended these studies to polystyrene and polyoxymethylene, showing that a whole range of products can be produced that, like the members of a homologous series, show a serial order in the viscosity of their solutions. This work was described on three important occasions—in 1924 at the Innsbruck meeting of the Deutsche Naturforscher und Aerzte, in 1925 at a meeting of the Zurich Chemical Society, and in 1926 at the Düsseldorf meeting of the Deutsche Naturforscher und Aerzte. Especially on the occasions in Zurich and Düsseldorf, Staudinger encountered vigorous opposition from the exponents of the aggregate theory. Viscosity measurements, it was argued, did not give direct evidence of molecular weights but, rather, reflected the state of colloidal aggregates in solution. No reliable data on such compounds would be forthcoming until genuine solutions and crystals had been formed. Moreover, the unit cells derived from fiber diagrams of these polymers were far too small to accommodate a macromolecule; and the mineralogist Paul Niggli assured Staudinger that molecules larger than the unit cell did not exist.

It was at this juncture that Theodor Svedberg and Robin Fåhraeus made their first successful measurements of the equilibrium sedimentation of oxy- and carbonylhemoglobin in the ultracentrifuge. The result indicated a molecular weight between 3.73 and 4.25 times the minimum value of 16,700 obtained from elementary analysis.[2] This work laid the basis for the recognition of high-molecular compounds in protein chemistry. Meanwhile, Staudinger battled on against the upholders of the aggregate and micellar theories for synthetic polymers, cellulose, and rubber.

So long as there existed no theoretical relationship between molecular weight and viscosity for nonspherical particles (exhibiting non-Newtonian flow), Staudinger's viscosimetric data were thought to be unsatisfactory as evidence for the existence of macromolecules. But in 1929–1930 R. Nodzu and E. Ochiai, working under Staudinger, showed that for low molecular compounds with linear-shaped molecules the viscosity of their solutions is proportional to the number of residues in the chain.

Staudinger hoped to achieve independent evidence for the macromolecular structure of synthetic and natural polymers by installing an ultracentrifuge in Freiburg, but in 1929 the Notgemeinschaft der Deutsche Wissenschaft refused him the necessary funds. In desperation he returned to viscosimetry and succeeded in deriving a relationship known as the Staudinger law, between specific viscosity η_{sp} and molecular weight, where η_{sp} represents the increase in viscosity of a solvent caused by the addition of solute. The solvent constant Km in the equation was evaluated by using solutes of known molecular weight and was then used for polymers of unknown molecular weight. He took the precaution of extrapolating to infinite dilution.

Here was a simple and quick method for obtaining molecular weights, which, unlike the ultracentrifuge, did not require costly and elaborate apparatus. Although further objections were voiced against it, viscosimetry—as based on Staudinger's law—was widely used in industry wherever polymer research was in progress.

To establish the conception of long-chain molecules by independent lines of evidence, Staudinger asked R. Signer to examine the shape of macromolecules in solution. Signer accomplished this task by using the technique of flow birefringence. He devised a simple apparatus for the rapid measurement of the approximate length:breadth ratio of long-chain molecules.

Meanwhile, Staudinger's conception of macromolecules received further support: X-ray crystallographers realized that the symmetry of crystals could be achieved on the basis of rope-like bundles of chains that stretched in the direction of the fiber axis far beyond a single-unit cell, even beyond a crystallite. Furthermore, in America, W. H. Carothers was achieving polymerization by a condensation reaction in which the eliminated water could be measured and the number of residues in the product estimated.

As early as 1926, Staudinger had appreciated the importance of macromolecular compounds in living organisms. He had seen how the traditional methods of isolation and identification of organic compounds inhibited the study of these sensitive and awkward compounds. Consequently, chemists were only "standing on the threshold of the chemistry of organic compounds."[3] Life processes, he argued, were bound up with high polymers in the shape of proteins and enzymes. In a lecture delivered in Munich in 1936 he returned to this theme. "Every gene macromolecule," he declared, "possesses a quite definite structural plan, which determines its function in life."[4] Such giant protein molecules had innumerable possible structures which chemical techniques were then too crude to reveal.

In 1947, in his book *Makromolekulare Chemie und Biologie*, Staudinger again visualized the molecular biology of the future. He reported the first attempts by Linderstrøm-Lang to arrive at amino acid sequences. This was the kind of problem that Staudinger wished to tackle in his later days, but he found no methods suited to the task. In this book Staudinger computed the molecular weight of a bacterium, from which we may conclude that he did allow his enthusiasm for macromolecules to carry him too far. Long before this time C. F. Robinow had demonstrated an organization in bacteria, including a nuclear structure revealed by differential staining.[5] Such an organism could hardly represent a single macromolecule.

Although Staudinger surely comprehended the conception of chemical individuality, it is understandable that he lacked any appreciation of the nature of information transfer from nucleic acids to proteins or, indeed, of the storage of such information in the nucleic acids rather than in the proteins. Nonetheless, his pioneer work in macromolecular chemistry constituted a major foundation for the molecular biology that was to be built upon it. The debates that took place between Staudinger and the champions of the aggregate theory furnished an interesting conflict of paradigms that only the further development of several sciences could resolve. As a result Staudinger achieved recognition for his work belatedly, receiving the Nobel Prize at the age of seventy-three.

Staudinger tried to produce visual evidence of the existence and form of macromolecules. The ultraviolet phase-contrast microscope and the electron microscope were used to this end in Freiburg. Magda Staudinger began such work in 1937. She and G. A. Kausche described spherical molecules of glycogen two years later. In 1942 Staudinger's colleagues E. Husemann and H. Ruska obtained electron micrographs of glycogen particles with a diameter of 10 mμ. From the osmotic pressure of the corresponding glycogen in solution, they concluded that these were the molecules of glycogen with a molecular weight of one and a half million. This work was brought to an abrupt end when the greater part of the chemistry institute was destroyed during the bombing of Freiburg in 1944. By the time normal working conditions were restored, Staudinger's vigorous powers had been spent; but it was due to him that in 1947 a new journal, *Makromolekulare Chemie*, was published by the firm of Karl Alber in Freiburg; the earlier *Journal für makromolekulare Chemie* appeared only from 1943 to 1945. Both journals were edited by Staudinger. On his retirement in 1951, Staudinger's department became the State Research Institute for Macromolecular Chemistry; five years later an associate professorship in macromolecular chemistry was established for the director of this institute.

NOTES

1. H. Staudinger, "Ueber die Konstitution des Kautschuks," in *Berichte der Deutschen chemischen Gesellschaft*, **57** (1924), 1206.
2. T. Svedberg and R. Fåhraeus, "A New Method for the Determination of the Molecular Weight of the Proteins," in *Journal of the American Chemical Society*, **48** (1926), 430–438.
3. H. Staudinger, "Die Chemie der hochmolekularen organischen Stoffe im Sinne der Kekuléschen Strukturlehre," in *Berichte der Deutschen chemischen Gesellschaft*, **59** (1926), 3019–3043.
4. H. Staudinger, "Ueber die makromolekulare Chemie," in *Angewandte Chemie*, **49** (1936), 801.
5. C. F. Robinow, "A Study of the Nuclear Apparatus of Bacteria," in *Proceedings of the Royal Society*, **130 B** (1942), 299.

BIBLIOGRAPHY

For a comprehensive bibliography of 644 works of Staudinger, see H. Staudinger, *Arbeitserinnerungen* (Heidelberg, 1961), trans. as *From Organic Chemistry to Macromolecules* (New York, 1970).

Staudinger's work on macromolecular chemistry is discussed in several papers: J. T. Edsal, "Proteins as Macromolecules: An Essay on the Development of the

Macromolecule Concept and Some of Its Vicissitudes," in *Archives of Biochemistry and Biophysics*, supp. 1, pp. 12–20; H. Mark, "Polymers—Past, Present and Future," in an unpublished symposium of the Welch Foundation on polymer science (1965); and R. C. Olby, "The Macromolecule Concept and the Origins of Molecular Biology," in *Journal of Chemical Education*, **47** (1970), 168–174; and *The Path to the Double Helix*, chs. 1, 2 (London, 1974).

ROBERT OLBY

STAUDT, KARL GEORG CHRISTIAN VON (*b.* Rothenburg-ob-der-Tauber, Germany, 24 January 1798; *d.* Erlangen, Germany, 1 June 1867), *mathematics.*

Staudt was the son of Johann Christian von Staudt, a municipal counsel, and Maria Albrecht. Rothenburg, famous for its many antiquities, was then a free imperial German city. The family had settled in Rothenburg as craftsmen as early as 1402. Various members became municipal councilmen in the sixteenth century and received a coat of arms. In 1700 Leopold I ennobled the family. Staudt's maternal ancestors, the Albrechts, also served as councilmen and burgomasters in the seventeenth and eighteenth centuries. Staudt's father was appointed a municipal legal officer by the Bavarian government in 1805, the year Rothenburg became part of the Kingdom of Bavaria.

After carefully supervising his early education, Staudt's parents sent him to the Gymnasium in Ansbach from 1814 to 1817. Then, drawn by the great reputation of Gauss, Staudt attended the University of Göttingen from 1818 to 1822. As a student he was surely well acquainted with Gauss's studies in number theory. His chief concern in these years, however, was theoretical and practical astronomy, to which he was also introduced by Gauss, who was then director of the observatory. As early as 1820 Staudt observed and computed the ephemerides of Mars and Pallas. His most comprehensive work in astronomy was the determination of the orbit of the comet discovered by Joseph Nicollet and Jean-Louis Pons in 1821. His precise calculations were highly praised by Gauss, and later observations led to only minor improvements. Staudt never returned to the field of astronomy, but it was on the basis of this early work that he received the doctorate from the University of Erlangen in 1822.

In the same year Staudt qualified at Munich as a mathematics teacher. His first assignment was at the secondary school in Würzburg. But with Gauss's intervention he was also able to lecture at the University of Würzburg. His lectures dealt with rather elementary topics. Because of insufficient support from the university, he transferred in 1827 to the secondary school in Nuremberg and taught there and at the Nuremberg polytechnical school until 1835. He finally achieved his primary goal when, on 1 October 1835, he was appointed full professor of mathematics at the University of Erlangen, where he remained until his death. He was unquestionably the leading mathematician at Erlangen, not least because of his outstanding human qualities. The latter, indeed, brought him many honorary posts in the university administration.

As at most German universities during this period, the level of mathematics instruction at Erlangen was not high, nor did the subject attract many students. It was not yet customary for mathematicians to discuss their own research in the classroom—a practice first introduced by Jacobi, at Königsberg. Accordingly, it was not until 1842–1843 that Staudt gave special lectures on his new geometry of position.

In 1832 Staudt married Jeanette Drechsler. They had a son, Eduard, and a daughter, Mathilde, who became the wife of a burgomaster of Erlangen. Staudt's wife died in 1848, and he never remarried. In his last years he suffered greatly from asthma.

Staudt was not a mathematician who astounded his colleagues by a flood of publications in a number of fields. He let his ideas mature for a long period before making them public, and his research was confined exclusively to projective geometry and to the only distantly related Bernoullian numbers. His fame as a great innovator in the history of mathematics stems primarily from his work in projective geometry, which he still called by the old name of "geometry of position," or *Geometrie der Lage*, the title of his principal publication (1847). This work was followed by three supplementary *Beiträge zur Geometrie der Lage* (1856–1860), which together contain more pages than the original book (396 as compared with 216).

After centuries of dominance, Euclidean geometry was challenged by Poncelet and Gergonne, who created projective geometry during the first third of the nineteenth century. These two mathematicians found that, through the use of perspective, circles and squares and other figures could be transformed into arbitrary conic sections and quadrilaterals and that a metric theorem for, say, the circle could be transformed into a metric theorem for conic sections. The most important contributions made by Poncelet (whose main writings appeared between 1813 and 1822) and Gergonne were the polarity theory of the conic sections and the principle of duality. Jakob Steiner, in his fundamental work *Systematische Entwicklung der Abhängigkeit geometrischer Gestalten voneinander* (1832), then introduced the projective production of conic sections and second-degree surfaces that is now named for him.

In their writings, however, all three of these pioneers failed to adhere strictly to the viewpoint of projective geometry, which admits only intersection, union, and incidence of points, straight lines, and planes. Staudt, in his 1847 book, was the first to adopt a fully rigorous approach. Without exception, his predecessors still spoke of distances, perpendiculars, angles, and other entities that play no role in projective geometry. Moreover, as the name of that important relationship indicates, in accounting for the cross ratio of four points on a straight line, they all made use of line segments. In contrast, Staudt stated in the preface to his masterpiece his intention of establishing the "geometry of position" free from all metrical considerations, and in the body of the book he constructed a real projective geometry of two and three dimensions.

Naturally, in Staudt's book these geometries are not founded on a complete axiom system in the modern sense. Rather, he adopted from Euclid's system everything that did not pertain to interval lengths, angles, and perpendicularity. Although it was not necessary, he also retained Euclid's parallel postulate and was therefore obliged to introduce points at infinity. This decision, while burdening his treatment with a constant need to consider the special positions of the geometric elements at infinite distance, altered nothing of the basic structure of geometry without a metric. Using only union and intersection of straight lines in the plane, Staudt constructed the fourth harmonic associated with three points on a straight line. Correspondingly, with three straight lines or planes of a pencil he was able to construct the fourth harmonic element. Although he did not give the theorem that name, he used Desargues's theorem to prove that his construction was precise.

Using the relationship of four points in general position on a plane to four corresponding points or straight lines on another plane or on the same plane, Staudt defined a collineation—or, as the case may be, a correlation—between these planes. Analogously he also pointed out spatial collineations and correlations. In this instance he made use of Möbius' network construction, which enabled him to obtain, from four given points of a plane, denumerably many points by drawing straight lines through point pairs and by making straight lines intersect. He then associated the points derived in this way with correspondingly constructed points and straight lines of the other plane. Felix Klein later noted that a continuity postulate is still required in order to assign to each of the infinitely many points of the first plane its image point (or image lines) on the other plane.

From the time of his first publications, Staudt displayed a grasp of the importance of the principle of duality. For every theorem he stated its converse. (As was customary, he generally gave the theorem on one half of the page and its converse on the other half.) In discussing the autocorrelations of P_2 and P_3, he succeeded in obtaining the polarities and also the null correlations that had previously been discovered by Gaetano Giorgini and Möbius. For example, he described a plane polarity as a particular type of autocorrelation that yields a triangle in which each vertex is associated with the side opposite. On this basis, Staudt formulated the definition of the conic sections and quadrics that bears his name: they are the loci of those points that, through a polarity, are incident with their assigned straight lines or planes. This definition is superior to the one given by Steiner. For instance, in Staudt's definition the conic section appears as a point locus together with the totality of its tangents. Steiner, in contrast, required two different productions: one for the conic section K and another for the totality of its tangents, that is, for the dual figures associated with K. A conic section defined in Staudt's manner can consist of the empty set; that is, it can contain no real points—accordingly, Klein applied the term *nullteilig* to it.

In a coordinate geometry it is easy to extend the domain of the real points to the domain of the complex points with complex coordinates. Employing the concepts of real geometry, Staudt made an essential contribution to synthetic geometry through his elegantly formulated introduction of the complex projective spaces of one, two, and three dimensions. This advance was the principal achievement contained in his *Beiträge zur Geometrie der Lage*. He conceived of the complex points of a straight line P_1 by means of the so-called elliptic involution of the real range p_1 of P_1, which can also be described as those involuted autoprojectivities of p_1 among which pairs of corresponding points intersect each other. It can be shown by calculation that such an elliptic involution has two complex, conjugate fixed points; and Staudt had to furnish the elliptic involutions with two different orientations, so that ultimately he could interpret the oriented elliptic involutions on the real range of P_1 as points of P_1. The degenerate parabolic involutions are to be associated with the real points of P_1. In this way he also extended the real projective planes p_2 and p_3 to complex P_2 and P_3. He then showed—not an easy feat—that P_2 and P_3 satisfy the connection axioms of projective geometry. Among the lines P_1 of P_3 he found three types: those with infinitely many real points, those with only one real point, and those with no real point. He carefully classified the quadrics of P_3 according to the way in which straight lines of these three types lie on them.

Staudt favored the use of the second type of complex line of P_3 as a model of the complex numbers P_1. He applied the term *Wurf* ("throw") to a point quadruple and gave the procedure for finding sums and products in the set of these throws—or, more precisely, the set of the equivalence classes of projectively equivalent throws. Here he approached the projective foundation of the complex number field and the projective metric determination. Staudt termed certain throws neutral: those with real cross ratio, a property that can be determined computationally. Then, for three given points—A, B, C, in P_1—he designated as a chain the set of all those points of P_1 that form a neutral throw with A, B, C. These sets and their generalization to complex P_n are called "Staudt chains." In part three of the *Beiträge*, Staudt also dealt with third- and fourth-order spatial curves in the context of the theory of linear systems of equations.

At the time of their publication, Staudt's books were considered difficult. This assessment arose for several reasons. First, since he sought to present a strictly systematic construction of synthetic geometry, he did not present any formulas; moreover, he refused to employ any diagrams. Second, he cited no other authors. Finally, although his theory of imaginaries was remarkable, it was extremely difficult to manipulate in comparison with algebraic equations. Accordingly, little significant progress could have been expected from its adoption in the study of figures more complicated than conic sections and quadrics.

Staudt is also known today for the Staudt-Clausen theorem in the theory of Bernoulli numbers. These numbers—B_n ($n = 1, 2, \cdots$)—appear in the summation formulas of the nth powers of the first h natural numbers; they also arise in analysis, for example, in the series expansion $x \cot x$. The B_n are rational numbers of alternating sign, and the Staudt-Clausen theorem furnished the first significant indication of the law of their formation. In formulating the theorem, for the natural number n there is a designated uneven prime number, p, called Staudt's prime number, such that $p - 1$ divides the number $2n$. Then, according to the theorem, $(-1)^n B_n$ is a positive rational number, which, aside from its integral component, is a sum of unit fractions, among the denominators of which appear precisely the number 2 and all Staudt prime numbers for n. Staudt published his theorem in 1840; it was also demonstrated, independently, in the same year by Thomas Clausen, who was working in Altona. Staudt published two further, detailed works in Latin on the theory of Bernoulli numbers (Erlangen, 1845); but these writings never became widely known and later authors almost never cited them.

BIBLIOGRAPHY

I. ORIGINAL WORKS. Staudt's major works are "Beweis eines Lehrsatzes, die Bernoullischen Zahlen betreffend," in *Journal für die reine und angewandte Mathematik*, **21** (1840), 372–374; *Geometrie der Lage* (Nuremberg, 1847), with Italian trans. by M. Pieri (see below); and *Beiträge zur Geometrie der Lage*, 3 vols. (Nuremberg, 1856–1860).

II. SECONDARY LITERATURE. See G. Böhmer, *Professor Dr. K. G. Chr. von Staudt, Ein Lebensbild* (Rothenburg-ob-der-Tauber, 1953); M. Noether, "Zur Erinnerung an Karl Georg Christian von Staudt," in *Jahresbericht der Deutschen Mathematikervereinigung*, **32** (1923), 97–119; "Nekrolog auf K. G. Chr. von Staudt," in *Sitzungsberichte der Bayerischen Akademie der Wissenschaften zu München*, **1** (1868), repr. in *Archiv der Mathematik*, **49** (1869), 1–5; and C. Segre, "C. G. C. von Staudt ed i suoi lavori," in *Geometria di posizione de Staudt*, M. Pieri, ed. and trans. (Turin, 1888), 1–17.

WERNER BURAU

STEACIE, EDGAR WILLIAM RICHARD (*b.* Westmount, Quebec, Canada, 25 December 1900; *d.* Ottawa, Ontario, Canada, 28 August 1962), *physical chemistry.*

Steacie was the only child of Captain Richard Steacie and Alice Kate McWood. His father was born in Ballinasloe, Northern Ireland, from which he emigrated at about the age of twenty to settle in Montreal. Edgar was brought up in comfortable circumstances but was only fourteen when his father died. He was a student at the Royal Military

College in Kingston from 1919 to 1920 and then transferred to McGill University, where he obtained his B.Sc. (1923), M.Sc. (1924), and Ph.D. (1926). He pursued postdoctoral study in Frankfurt and Leipzig and at King's College, London (1934–1935). He was made associate professor at McGill in 1937 but in 1939 he moved to the National Research Council of Canada. He was president of the council from 1952 to 1962.

In 1925 Steacie married Dorothy Catalina Day; they had two children, Diane Jeanette (Mrs. W. A. Magill) and John Richard Brian.

Steacie published many articles in scientific journals and wrote three books: *Introduction to Physical Chemistry*, with O. Maass (1926); *Atomic and Free Radical Reactions* (1946); and *Free Radical Mechanisms* (1946).

In the early stages of his career, Steacie established an enviable reputation in the field of photochemistry, especially in the kinetics of gas reactions and their interpretation by free radical mechanisms. He maintained this interest in photochemistry even after taking up administration duties. A steady stream of postdoctoral fellows came to work in his Ottawa laboratory, and a whole generation of young chemists were strongly influenced by him.

As early as 1934 Steacie used reaction mechanisms involving free radicals to interpret the kinetics of thermal decomposition reactions of organic compounds. In 1937 he obtained further evidence on the mechanisms of organic pyrolyses using deuterated compounds. He then extended his interest in reaction mechanisms to photolytic decompositions of a variety of simple organic compounds and to photosensitization by vapors of metals such as mercury, cadmium, and zinc. Using these various techniques he obtained kinetic data on the rates of elementary chemical processes. The extensive studies by Steacie and his many students formed the basis for his authoritative *Atomic and Free Radical Reactions*.

The development of Steacie's administrative career was linked to the development of the National Research Council of Canada. Founded in 1916, the Research Council underwent an enormous expansion during World War II under the direction of C. J. Mackenzie and emerged with an established reputation for good work. During his tenure as president of the council, Steacie helped bring to fruition long-range plans for the growth of Canadian science, partly by the development of the Research Council laboratories themselves and partly by the encouragement of strong scientific centers in Canadian universities. Here his emphasis was on scholarship programs and the support of qualified individuals doing fundamental research. He will be especially remembered for his enthusiastic support of the postdoctoral fellowship program and for the huge increase in university support that took place under him. As chairman of the council, Steacie handled its proceedings with exceptional skill—never insisting on his own viewpoint but often making a masterly summary of the situation and coming forward with an acceptable proposal at the right time.

Outside the council, Steacie defended the interests of its scientists with great skill and vigor. His presidency coincided approximately with the period in which nations and governments became aware not only of the increasing importance of science to national well-being and security but also of the importance of developing an appropriate relationship between science and government.

BIBLIOGRAPHY

I. ORIGINAL WORKS. L. Marion (see below) lists some 230 scientific papers by Steacie. His works include *Laboratory Exercises in General Chemistry* (Montreal, 1929), written with W. H. Hatcher and N. N. Evans; *An Introduction to the Principles of Physical Chemistry* (New York, 1931; 2nd ed., 1939), written with O. Maass; *Atomic and Free Radical Reactions* (New York, 1946; 2nd ed., 1954); and *Free Radical Mechanisms* (New York, 1946). See also *Science in Canada. Selections From the Speeches of E. W. R. Steacie*, J. D. Babbitt, ed. (Toronto, 1965).

II. SECONDARY LITERATURE. On Steacie and his work, see L. Marion, "E. W. R. Steacie. 1900–1962," in *Biographical Memoirs of Fellows of the Royal Society*, **10** (1964), 257–281, with bibliography; and W. A. Noyes, Jr., convocation address at the opening of the E. W. R. Steacie building for chemistry at Carleton Univ., 22 Oct. 1965.

J. W. T. SPINKS

STEAD, JOHN EDWARD (*b.* Howden-on-Tyne, Northumberland, England, 17 October 1851; *d.* Redcar, Yorkshire, England, 31 October 1923), *metallurgy, analytical chemistry.*

Stead was the younger brother of the journalist W. T. Stead (1849–1912).

Educated privately because he was not robust, Stead was apprenticed at the age of sixteen to John Pattinson, the chemical analyst of Newcastle-upon-Tyne. Three years later he worked at Bolckow, Vaughan and Company, an iron manufacturing firm in Garston, from which post he was able to attend evening classes at Owens College (later the University of Manchester). At the age of twenty-five he became a partner to Pattinson and remained an analyst for the remainder of his life. His original work arose from metallurgical problems encountered in the course of his large commercial practice.

Stead studied eutectics in steels and used his findings to interpret such phenomena as the occurrence of blast-furnace "bears," which were large inclusions of metal formed in the hearth. He also studied the crystalline structure of metals, and was one of the first to recognize the significance of Sorby's work in metallography, which he advanced by such techniques as the heat-tinting of specimens. Stead learned a great deal about the effects of phosphorus on steel. Early in his career he explained the afterblow—essential in the basic Bessemer process, for the complete dephosphorization of phosphoric iron—as a result of the removal of phosphorus by iron oxide after the depletion of all the carbon. Another phenomenon connected with phosphorus was that of "ghosts," superficial markings on forgings, which cause the forgings to be suspect. Stead showed that the markings are due to the difference in solubility of carbon in parts of a steel of different phosphorus content. He also showed that these differences, although visible, are not detrimental in the absence of slag inclusions.

Stead's experimental studies were not confined to the laboratory, and many steelworks on Tyneside offered him facilities for study under working conditions. In 1901 Stead was honored by the Bessemer Medal of the Iron and Steel Institute, and two years later he became a fellow of the Royal Society. He also received honorary doctorates from the universities of Manchester, Leeds, and Sheffield.

BIBLIOGRAPHY

Obituary notices on Stead are H. C. H. Carpenter, in *Proceedings of the Royal Society*, **106A** (1924), i–v, with portrait; and an anonymous author, in *Engineering*, **116** (1923), 598–600, also with portrait.

FRANK GREENAWAY

STEBBING, THOMAS ROSCOE REDE (*b.* London, England, 6 February 1835; *d.* Tunbridge Wells, England, 8 July 1926), *zoology*.

Stebbing called himself "a serf to Natural History, principally employed about Crustacea." He was the fourth son of Henry Stebbing, poet, historian, clergyman, and editor of the *Athenaeum*, and Mary Griffin. Several of the thirteen Stebbing children became writers, and Thomas' brother William, a barrister, was a leader-writer and assistant editor of *The Times* (London).

Beginning his education at King's College School and King's College, London (B.A. 1855), Stebbing matriculated at Lincoln College, Oxford, in 1853 and became a scholar of Worcester College the same year. He received the B.A. in 1857 and the M.A. in 1859, remaining as fellow (1860–1868), tutor (1865–1867), vice-provost (1865), and dean (1866) of Worcester College until resigning his fellowship in 1868. Samuel Wilberforce, bishop of Oxford, ordained him priest in 1859.

When Stebbing took a house for tuition at Reigate, Surrey, in 1863 and met the entomologist William Wilson Saunders, his interest in science began. Upon marrying Saunders' daughter Mary Anne (*d.* 1927), also a naturalist, in 1867, he moved to Torquay, Devon, as a tutor. There, under the influence of the naturalist William Pengelly, he began a long series of writings on natural history, Darwinian evolution, and theology.

In 1877 the Stebbings moved to Tunbridge Wells, Kent, where they lived until their deaths. Although a teacher part of this time, Stebbing devoted most of these years to the study of amphipod Crustacea and to writing. Because of his work on the taxonomy of Crustacea, he became a fellow of the Linnean Society in 1895, fellow of the Royal Society in 1896, and was awarded the Gold Medal of the Linnean Society in 1908.

Stebbing's scientific writings date from 1873; most of them are devoted to the taxonomy of amphipod Crustacea, on which he published about 110 papers and two major monographs. He received the Amphipoda collected by H.M.S. *Challenger* on the recommendation of a marine biologist, the Canon A. M. Norman, and published a large monograph on these creatures in 1888. The 600-page annotated bibliography beginning this work is the definitive history of the classification of Amphipoda and quotes the original definition of each known genus. In a short introduction he discussed the ancestry of the Amphipoda, pointing out how small variations could account for its evolutionary radiation. An ancestor of the group had "simplicity" and "completeness" of characters, that is, structures common in many families and also structures that had disappeared in the more specialized ones. According to his discussion of the known families, the classification of Amphipoda was centered on the ancestral family Gammaridae. Also, among Stebbing's writings are many popular works on Crustacea and other arthropods. He wrote with simplicity, grace, wit, and erudition. His knowledge of Crustacea was widely respected and resulted in a worldwide correspondence with specialists.

Stebbing was an early convert to Darwinism, and many of his essays were written in support of it. He was years ahead of other carcinologists in realizing the importance of Darwinian evolution in the Amphipoda, although this is seldom evident in his routine taxonomic papers. He also subscribed to Herbert Spencer's view that natural selection shaped behavior and accounted for human moral progress. The logic of science was applied by Stebbing to theological dogmas of the Church of England. He doubted the literal truth of Genesis, the accuracy of prophecy, miracles, the doctrine of the Trinity, and many of the Thirty-nine Articles. Shorn of dogma and superstition by science, his religion was based on an omniscient and loving God and on the power of unselfishness. He held this view to be perfectly compatible with the evolutionary science given form by James Hutton, William Smith, Charles Lyell, Charles Darwin, and Herbert Spencer, which was the main philosophy of his life.

BIBLIOGRAPHY

I. ORIGINAL WORKS. Stebbing's works include *Essays on Darwinism* (London, 1871); "Report on the Amphipoda Collected by H.M.S. Challenger During the Years 1873–1876," in *Report on the Scientific Results of the Voyage of H.M.S. Challenger During the Years 1873–1876*, Zoology, XXIX (London, 1888), i–xxiv, 1–1737; *A History of Crustacea. Recent Malacostraca* (London, 1893); "Amphipoda I. Gammaridae," in *Tierreich*, **21** (1906), i–xxix, 1–806; "An Autobiographic Sketch," in *Transactions and Proceedings. Torquay Natural History Society*, **4** (1923), 1–5, with portrait; and *Plain Speaking* (London, 1926).

II. SECONDARY LITERATURE. See W. T. Calman, "T. R. R. Stebbing—1835–1926," in *Proceedings of the Royal Society*, **101B** (1926), xxx–xxxii, with portrait; "Rev. Thomas Roscoe Rede Stebbing," in *Proceedings of the Linnean Society of London*, session 139 (1926–1927), 101–103; and E. L. Mills, "Amphipods and Equipoise. A Study of T. R. R. Stebbing," in *Transactions of the Connecticut Academy of Arts and Sciences*, **44**, 239–256, with portrait.

ERIC L. MILLS

STEENSTRUP, (JOHANNES) JAPETUS SMITH (*b.* Vang, Denmark, 8 March 1813; *d.* Copenhagen, Denmark, 20 June 1897), *zoology.*

Steenstrup was the son of a vicar in northern Jutland; from his youth he hunted, fished, and collected fossils. Although he took no university degree, he taught for six years at the Sorö Academy, where in 1842 he published two works that brought him scientific fame. The first of these, "Geognostisk-geologisk Undersögelse af Skovmoserne Vidnesdam og Lillemose i det nordlige Sjaelland . . .," is a classic work in Scandinavian bog research. In it, Steenstrup compared the results of his own observations on the forest bogs of northern Zealand and on the bogs of the Danish forests, moors, and fens. He noted the postglacial succession and alteration of flora in the bogs and, recognizing that the formation of peat had taken at least five thousand years, was inclined to believe that such changes reflected changes in climate. "We may," he wrote, "consider the bogs as annual reviews in which we can see how the flora and fauna of our country have developed and changed. . . . The further we go back in time, the colder was the climate."

The second major publication of 1842 was *Om Forplantning og Udvikling gjennem vexlende Generationsraekker, en saeregen form for Opfostringen i de lavere Dyreklasser,* Steenstrup's comprehensive presentation of the form of reproduction that he called "alternation of generations," that is, the alternation of asexual and sexual reproduction, or metagenesis. This phenomenon had previously been described by Chamisso, but Steenstrup included a greater number of observations, based on a significantly wider range of subjects, and provided an important chapter on its meaning. Steenstrup's growing reputation, based largely upon these two publications, won him an appointment as professor of zoology at the University of Copenhagen, where he taught from 1846 until 1885.

Steenstrup returned to the study of Scandinavian fossils in 1850 when, with the archaeologist Jens Worsaae, he demonstrated that the shell heaps on the Danish seashores were man-made. He coined the term *Kjökkenmödding* ("kitchen midden") to describe these 4,000–7,000-year-old remains. He also did important taxonomic work on the Cephalopoda, and described many new genera. In a memoir of 1856, "Hektokotyldannelsen hos Octopodslaegterne Argonauta og Tremoctopus . . .," he reported the surprising finding that the arm of the male octopus is modified to fulfill a reproduc-

STEFAN

tive function. In addition, he published a number of short papers on a wide variety of zoological subjects.

It is possible that Steenstrup might have accomplished more if he had chosen to concentrate on fewer topics. His significance to science, however, should not be measured by his writings alone; rather, it should be remembered that for a period of fifty years he initiated and guided Danish research in natural history. His work was influenced strongly by the German school of natural science, and, although he corresponded with Darwin (they had both worked with Cirripedias), Steenstrup was never able to accept Darwin's theory of evolution. In a letter to him of 1881, Darwin expressed disappointment that this should have been so.

BIBLIOGRAPHY

I. Original Works. A list of Steenstrup's writings, containing 239 titles, is S. Dahl, "Bibliographia Steenstrupiana," in H. F. E. Jungersen and J. E. B. Warming, *Mindeskrift i Anledning af Hundredaaret for Japetus Steenstrups Fødsel*, I (Copenhagen, 1914). Among the most important are "Geognostisk-geologisk Undersögelse af Skovmoserne Vidnesdam og Lillemose i det nordlige Sjaelland, ledsaget af sammenlignende Bemaerkninger, hentede fra Danmarks Skov-, Kjaer- og Lyngmoser i Almindelighed," in *Kongelige Danske Videnskabernes Selskabs Skrifter*, 4th ser., **9** (1842), 17–120; *Om Forplantning og Udvikling gjennem vexlende Generationsraekker, en saeregen form for Opfostringen i de lavere Dyreklasser* (Copenhagen, 1842); and "Hektokotyldannelsen hos Octopodslaegterne Argonauta og Tremoctopus, oplyst ved lignende Dannelser hos Blaeksprutterne i Almindelighed," in *Kongelige Danske Videnskabernes Selskabs Skrifter*, 5th ser., **4** (1856), 185–216.

II. Secondary Literature. See C. Lütken, "Steenstrup," in *Natural Science*, **11** (1897), 159–169; and R. Spärck, "Japetus Steenstrup," in V. Meisen, ed., *Prominent Danish Scientists Through the Ages* (Copenhagen, 1932), 115–119.

D. Müller

STEFAN, JOSEF (*b.* St. Peter, near Klagenfurt, Austria, 24 March 1835; *d.* Vienna, Austria, 7 January 1893), *physics*.

Stefan's parents were of Slovene origin. An excellent student at the elementary school and later the Gymnasium in Klagenfurt, he enrolled at the University of Vienna in 1853 and became a *realschule* teacher there four years later. He worked

with Carl Ludwig, in the latter's laboratory, on the flow of water through tubes. In 1858 he qualified as lecturer at the University of Vienna. He became full professor of higher mathematics and physics in 1863, and three years later was appointed director of the Institute for Experimental Physics, founded by Doppler in 1850. Stefan was a brilliant experimenter and a well-liked teacher. He was dean of the Philosophical Faculty in 1869–1870 and *rector magnificus* in 1876–1877. In 1860 he became a corresponding member, and in 1865 member, of the Imperial Academy of Sciences. He was named secretary of the mathematics-science class of the academy in 1875 and served as vice-president from 1885 until his death. In 1883 he presided over the scientific commission of the International Electricity Exhibition in Vienna. Two years later he held the same position at the International Conference on Musical Pitch in Vienna. He also belonged to several foreign scientific academies, held numerous Austrian and foreign honors, and was both royal and imperial privy councillor.

Stefan's most important work deals with heat radiation (1879). Newton had stated a priori a law of cooling for the temperature loss of incandescent iron in a constant stream of air, and Richmann had restated it in the following form: The speed of cooling is proportional to the difference in temperature between the heated body and the surrounding atmosphere. In equal periods of time, Newton stated, equal quantities of air are heated by quantities of heat proportional to those that they remove from the iron (*Opuscula* [1744], II, 423). G. W. Krafft and Richmann verified this law for temperature differences up to 40° or 50°. Yet as early as 1740 George Martine the younger and others realized its inaccuracy and attempted to replace it with another law according to which the heat losses increased more rapidly.

Nevertheless, physicists still considered Newton's law to be exact. Dalton sought to save it by introducing a new temperature scale. F. Delaroche was aware that the heat losses due to radiation increase much more rapidly than in proportion to the temperature difference, but he did not isolate the radiation from the other heat losses—as Dulong and Petit attempted to do. For radiation in empty space they propounded a rather more complicated law, introducing an absolute temperature scale and extending Newton's law. As was later seen, however, their law also possessed only limited validity and did not agree with measured results even up to 300°C. A. Wüllner remarked in his *Lehrbuch der Experimentalphysik*: . . . "the quan-

10

tity of heat emitted increases considerably more quickly than does the temperature, especially at higher temperatures." This followed from Tyndall's experiments on the radiation of a platinum wire heated to incandescence by an electric current. From the weak red glow (about 525°C.) up to the full white glow (about 1200°C.), the intensity of the radiation increases almost twelvefold, from 10.4 to 122 (exactly 11.7-fold).

"This observation," Stefan said, "caused me at first to take the heat radiation as proportional to the fourth power of the absolute temperature." (The ratio of the absolute temperatures 273 + 1200 and 273 + 525 yields, in the fourth power, 11.6.) By means of a thorough discussion of the experiments of Dulong and Petit and of other researchers, Stefan showed that this formula agreed with the results of measurements in all temperature ranges. The theoretical deduction of this relationship was first achieved in 1884 by Boltzmann, who also recognized that it is exact only for completely black bodies (Stefan-Boltzmann law of radiation). Moreover, with the aid of his new formula Stefan could calculate, on the basis of Pouillet's and Violle's actinometric observations, a value for the surface temperature of the sun—approximately 6000°C.

Other important work by Stefan concerns heat conduction in gases, a subject on which reliable measurements were lacking because of extreme experimental difficulties. For this purpose Stefan devised a "diathermometer," which was widely used to measure the heat conductivity of clothing materials. His measurements agreed fairly well with those calculated on the basis of the kinetic theory of gases, especially in the cases of air and hydrogen. Stefan explained the variations as resulting from the movements of the atoms against each other within the molecules. He resumed his investigations on heat conduction in 1876 and 1889. In analogous work on the diffusion of gases (1871, 1872), he calculated the theoretical coefficients of diffusion and of friction and their dependence on the absolute temperature, showing that the calculated values were in agreement with experimental results obtained by Maxwell, Graham, and J. Loschmidt. He also demonstrated that the apparent adhesion of two glass plates is a hydrodynamic phenomenon (1874).

Stefan published further experimental and theoretical works on the kinetic theory of heat: on evaporation (1873, 1881); on heat conduction in fluids, on ice formation, on dissolving (1889); and on diffusion of and in fluids (1878, 1879); and especially on the relationship between surface tension and evaporation, which included "Stefan's number" and "Stefan's law" (1886). He also published many works on acoustics.

In the theory of the mutual magnetic effects of two electric circuits, Stefan succeeded in showing, in opposition to Ampère and Grassmann, that clear results can be achieved only by means of the theory of continuous action. Stefan and Helmholtz were then the the only Continental proponents of the Faraday-Maxwell theory of continuous action. Stefan, in fact, made important calculations in the theory of alternating currents, especially regarding the induction coefficients of wire coils. Many of his experimental and theoretical works dealt with difficult and subtle problems in physics—for example, the discovery of the secondary rings in Newton's experiments and other optical problems.

At the International Conference on Musical Pitch, held at Vienna in 1885 (over which Stefan presided), the proposals of the Austrian commission of experts were generally adopted in central and eastern Europe; the standard pitch was established at 435 cycles per second (as had already been done in France in 1859 and in Austria in 1862). For the production of this tone the conference prescribed, according to Stefan's account, the standard tuning fork constructed to replicate the tuning forks of K. R. König.

BIBLIOGRAPHY

The Royal Society *Catalogue of Scientific Papers*, V, 806; VIII, 1003–1004; XI, 480–481; and XVIII, 921; lists 73 works, most of them published in *Sitzungsberichte der k. Akademie der Wissenschaften in Wien*, Math.-wiss. Kl. See also *Bericht über die von der wissenschaftlichen Commission (der Internationalen Elektrizitätsausstellung, Wien, 1883) an Dynamomaschinen und elektrischen Lampen ausgeführten Messungen* (Vienna, 1886)—the commission was mainly under Stefan's direction; and, for his work in establishing the standard pitch, *Beschlüsse und Protokolle der Internationalen Stimmton-Conferenz 1885* (Vienna, 1885).

For Wüllner's remarks on heat emission, see his *Lehrbuch der Experimentalphysik*, 3rd ed., III (Leipzig, 1875), 214–215.

There are obituaries in *Almanach der Akademie der Wissenschaften in Wien*, 43 (1893), 252–257; *Elektrotechnische Zeitschrift*, 14 (1893), 31; and *Leopoldina*, 29 (1893), 53–54. See also C. von Wurzbach, ed., *Biographisches Lexikon des Kaiserthums Oesterreich*, XXXV (Vienna, 1877), 284–286, with bibliography, and Albert von Obermayer, *Zur Erinnerung an Josef Stefan* (Vienna–Leipzig, 1893).

WALTER BÖHM

STEIN, JOHAN WILLEM JAKOB ANTOON, S. J.
(*b.* Grave, Netherlands, 27 February 1871; *d.*
Rome, Italy, 27 December 1951), *astronomy*.

Stein was the son of Maria Waltéra Boerkamp
and Johan Hendrik Stein, a teacher in Grave. He
entered the Society of Jesus in 1889 and studied
physics and astronomy at the University of Leiden
(1894–1901) under Lorentz. His doctoral dissertation was concerned with the Horrebow method for
determining latitude. In 1901 he taught mathematics and physics at St. Willebrord's College in Kat-
wijk; two years later he was ordained a priest in
Maastricht.

In 1906 Stein was appointed assistant to J. G.
Hagen, S.J., director of the Vatican observatory,
who was then engaged in compiling an atlas of
variable stars. Stein contributed to the studies on
these stars and published papers on variable and
double stars. He became interested in Hagen's
work on the axial rotation of the earth and in 1910
translated into French Kamerlingh Onnes' doctoral
dissertation (1879) on that subject.

Stein left Rome in 1910 to teach mathematics
and physics at St. Ignatius College, Amsterdam.
He remained in close contact with Hagen and in
1924 they published *Die veränderlichen Sterne*, an
authoritative work in two volumes: the second
volume, by Stein, deals with the mathematical-
physical aspect of variable stars. Stein was well
known to professional astronomers in the Netherlands and was a member of many astronomical
societies. He edited the astronomical section of the
journal *Hemel en dampkring* and was known for
his friendly help to amateur astronomers.

In 1930 Stein succeeded Hagen as director of
the Vatican observatory, where his main task was
to supervise its transfer to Castel Gandolfo; the
new observatory with its astrophysical laboratory
was equipped during the years 1932–1935. Stein
continued to direct the work of the observatory
until his death in 1951.

Stein kept up a lifelong interest in the history of
astronomy and in 1910, on the reappearance of
Halley's comet, published new data on the comet
of 1066 from a manuscript found in the cathedral
at Viterbo. Other subjects of his historical research
were the astronomical ideas of Albertus Magnus
and the relationship between Galileo and Clavius.

BIBLIOGRAPHY

I. ORIGINAL WORKS. Stein's major printed works are
Die veränderlichen Sterne, 2 vols., *Mathematisch-phy-
sikalischer*, vol. II (Fribourg, 1924); *Stelle doppie nel
Catalogo . . . Vaticano* (Rome, 1930); *Catalogo di 982
stelle degli ammassi η e χ Persei* (1928); *Atlas Stellarum
Variabilium*, VIII (Rome, 1934), IX (Rome 1941). He
contributed to various astronomical journals; and Poggendorff, V, 1203; VI, 2531, gives an extensive list of
his scientific papers. A more detailed list covering
Stein's publications before 1936 is given in *Notizie e
pubblicazioni scientifiche* (Rome, 1936). Stein contributed 106 articles to the Dutch journal *Hemel en dampkring* between 1910 and 1930. Archival material relating
to Stein is held by the Vatican observatory at Castel
Gandolfo.

II. SECONDARY LITERATURE. Obituary notices include J. de Kort, S.J., in *Specola Vaticana, Ricerche
Astronomiche*, **2**, no. 16 (1952), 372–374, with portrait;
and A. Pannekoek, in *Jaarboek der Koninklijke Nederlandsche akademie van wetenschappen* (1951–1952),
1–4. An account of Stein, with photograph, is found in
Enciclopedia cattolica, XI (1953). An account of the
history of the Vatican Observatory from its inception
until 1951 is found in *La Specola vaticana* (Rome, 1952),
also available in German.

SISTER MAUREEN FARRELL, F.C.J.

STEINER, JAKOB (*b.* Utzensdorf, Bern, Switzerland, 18 March 1796; *d.* Berlin, Germany, 1 April
1863), *mathematics*.

Life. Steiner was the youngest of the eight children of Niklaus Steiner (1752–1826), a small
farmer and tradesman, and the former Anna Barbara Weber (1757–1832), who were married on 28
January 1780. The fourth child, Anna Barbara
(1786–1870), married David Begert; and their
daughter Elisabeth (*b.* 1815) married Friedrich
Geiser, a butcher, in 1836. To this marriage was
born the mathematician Karl Friedrich Geiser
(1843–1934), who was thus a grandnephew of
Steiner.[1]

Steiner had a poor education and did not learn to
write until he was fourteen. As a child he had to
help his parents on the farm and in their business;
his skill in calculation was of great assistance. Steiner's desire for learning led him to leave home,
against his parents' will, in the spring of 1814 to
attend Johann Heinrich Pestalozzi's school at
Yverdon, where he was both student and teacher.
Pestalozzi found a brilliant interpreter of his revolutionary ideas on education in Steiner, who characterized the new approach in an application to the
Prussian Ministry of Education (16 December
1826):

The method used in Pestalozzi's school, treating
the truths of mathematics as objects of independent
reflection, led me, as a student there, to seek other

grounds for the theorems presented in the courses than those provided by my teachers. Where possible I looked for deeper bases, and I succeeded so often that my teachers preferred my proofs to their own. As a result, after I had been there for a year and a half, it was thought that I could give instruction in mathematics.[2]

Steiner's posthumous papers include hundreds of pages of manuscripts containing both courses given by his fellow teachers and his own ideas. These papers include the studies "Einige Gesetze über die Teilung der Ebene und des Raumes," which later appeared in the first volume of Crelle's *Journal für die reine und angewandte Mathematik*. Steiner stated that they were inspired by Pestalozzi's views.

In the application of 1826 Steiner also wrote:

> Without my knowing or wishing it, continuous concern with teaching has intensified by striving after scientific unity and coherence. Just as related theorems in a single branch of mathematics grow out of one another in distinct classes, so, I believed, do the branches of mathematics itself. I glimpsed the idea of the organic unity of all the objects of mathematics; and I believed at that time that I could find this unity in some university, if not as an independent subject, at least in the form of specific suggestions.

These two statements provide an excellent characterization of Steiner's basic attitude toward teaching and research. The first advocates independent reflection by the students, a practice that was the foundation of Steiner's great success as a teacher. At first, in Berlin, he was in great demand as a private teacher; among his students was the son of Wilhelm von Humboldt. Steiner often gave his courses as colloquiums, posing questions to the students. This direct contact with the students was often continued outside the classroom. The second statement expresses the idea that guided all his work: to discover the organic unity of all the objects of mathematics, an aim realized especially in his fundamental research on synthetic geometry. Steiner left Yverdon in the autumn of 1818 and went to Heidelberg, where he supported himself by giving private instruction. His most important teacher there was Ferdinand Schweins, whose lectures on combinatorial analysis furnished the basis for two of Steiner's works.[3]

At this time Steiner also studied differential and integral calculus and algebra. In addition, lectures at Heidelberg stimulated the careful work contained in manuscripts on mechanics from 1821, 1824, and 1825, upon which Steiner later drew for investigations on the center of gravity.[4]

Following a friend's advice, Steiner left for Berlin at Easter 1821. Not having passed any academic examinations, he was now obliged to do so in order to obtain a teaching license. He was only partially successful in his examinations and therefore received only a restricted license in mathematics, along with an appointment at the Werder Gymnasium. The initially favorable judgment of his teaching was soon followed by criticism that led to his dismissal in the autumn of 1822. From November 1822 to August 1824 he was enrolled as a student at the University of Berlin, at the same time as C. G. J. Jacobi. He again earned his living by giving private instruction until 1825, when he became assistant master (and in 1829 senior master) at the technical school in Berlin. On 8 October 1834 he was appointed extraordinary professor at the University of Berlin, a post he held until his death.

Steiner never married. He left a fortune of about 90,000 Swiss francs, equivalent to 24,000 thaler.[5] He bequeathed a third of it to the Berlin Academy for establishment of the prize named for him,[6] and 60,000 francs to his relatives. In addition he left 750 francs to the school of his native village, the interest on which is still used to pay for prizes awarded to students adept at mental computations.[7] Steiner, with a yearly income of between 700 and 800 thaler, amassed this fortune by giving lectures on geometry.[8]

Students and contemporaries wrote of the brilliance of Steiner's geometric research and of the fiery temperament he displayed in leading others into the new territory he had discovered. Combined with this were very liberal political views. Moreover, he often behaved crudely and spoke bluntly, thereby alienating a number of people. Thus it is certain that his dismissal from the Werder Gymnasium cannot have been merely a question of his scholarly qualifications. Steiner attributed this action to his refusal to base his course on the textbook written by the school's director, Dr. Zimmermann. The latter, in turn, reproached Steiner for using Pestalozzi's methods, claiming that they were suitable only for elementary instruction and therefore made Steiner's teaching deficient. Steiner also experienced difficulties at the technical school, where he was expected to follow, without question, the orders of the director, K. F. von Klöden. Klöden, however, felt that Steiner did not treat him with proper respect, and made exacting demands of him that were of a magnitude and severity that even a soldier subject to military discipline could hardly be expected to accept.

Steiner's scientific achievements brought him an honorary doctorate from the University of Königsberg (20 April 1833) and membership in the Prussian Academy of Sciences (5 June 1834). He spent the winter of 1854–1855 in Paris and became a corresponding member of the French Academy of Sciences. He had already been made a corresponding member of the Accademia dei Lincei in 1853. A kidney ailment obliged him to take repeated cures in the following years, and he lectured only during the winter terms.

Mathematical Work. Having set himself the task of reforming geometry, Steiner sought to discover simple principles from which many seemingly unrelated theorems in the subject could be deduced in a natural way. He formulated his plan in the preface to *Systematische Entwicklung der Abhängigkeit geometrischer Gestalten voneinander, mit Berücksichtigung der Arbeiten alter und neuer Geometer über Porismen, Projections-Methoden, Geometrie der Lage, Transversalen, Dualität und Reciprocität* (1832), dedicated to Wilhelm von Humboldt:

> The present work is an attempt to discover the organism [*Organismus*] through which the most varied spatial phenomena are linked with one another. There exist a limited number of very simple fundamental relationships that together constitute the schema by means of which the remaining theorems can be developed logically and without difficulty. Through the proper adoption of the few basic relations one becomes master of the entire field. Order replaces chaos; and one sees how all the parts mesh naturally, arrange themselves in the most beautiful order, and form well-defined groups. In this manner one obtains, simultaneously, the elements from which nature starts when, with the greatest possible economy and in the simplest way, it endows the figures with infinitely many properties. Here the main thing is neither the synthetic nor the analytic method, but the discovery of the mutual dependence of the figures and of the way in which their properties are carried over from the simpler to the more complex ones. This connection and transition is the real source of all the remaining individual propositions of geometry. Properties of figures the very existence of which one previously had to be convinced through ingenious demonstrations and which, when found, stood as something marvelous are now revealed as necessary consequences of the most common properties of these newly discovered basic elements, and the former are established a priori by the latter.[9]

Also in the preface Steiner asserted that this work would contain "a systematic development of the problems and theorems concerning the intersection and tangency of the circle in the plane and on spherical surfaces and of spheres." The plan was not carried out, and the manuscript of this part was not published until 1931.[10] But many of the observations, theorems, and problems included in it appeared in "Einige geometrische Betrachtungen" (1826), Steiner's first long publication.[11]

The earliest detailed account of some of the sources of Steiner's concepts and theorems can be found in the posthumously published *Allgemeine Theorie über das Berühren und Schneiden der Kreise und der Kugeln, worunter eine grosse Anzahl neuer Untersuchungen und Sätze, in einem systematischen Entwicklungsgange dargestellt. . . .*[12] The headings of the sections describe its contents: "I. Of Centers, Lines, and Planes of Similitude in Circles and Spheres. II. Of the Power and the Locus of Equal Powers With Respect to Circles and Spheres. III. Of the Common Power in Circles and in Spheres. IV. Of Angles at Which Circles and Spheres Intersect."

In the foreword to *Allgemeine Theorie*, F. Gonseth stated in current terminology the basic principle on which many of Steiner's theorems and constructions are founded: the stereographic projection of the plane onto the sphere.[13] Section 4 of this work contains the following problem (§ 29, X, p. 167): "Draw a circle that intersects at equal angles four arbitrary circles of given size and position." The new methods were applied to the solution of Apollonius' problem (§ 31, II, p. 175): "Find a circle tangent to three arbitrary circles of given size and position." Another problem (§ 31, III, p. 182) reads: "Find a circle that intersects three arbitrary circles of given size and position at the angles α_1, α_2, α_3." Analogous problems for spheres are given in chapter 2, where the theorems and problems are presented systematically according to the number of spheres involved (from two to eight), with size and position again given—for example (p. 306): "Draw a sphere that intersects five arbitrary spheres of given size and position at one and the same angle" and (p. 333) "Find a sphere that is tangent to a sphere M_1 of given size and position and that cuts at one and the same angle three pairs of spheres, of given size and position, M_2 and M_3, M_4 and M_5, M_6 and M_7, each pair taken singly."

At Berlin, Steiner became friendly with Abel,

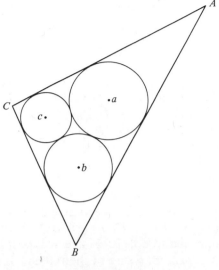

FIGURE 1

Crelle, and Jacobi; and together they introduced a fresh, new current into mathematics. Their efforts were considerably aided by Crelle's founding of the *Journal für die reine und angewandte Mathematik*, to which Steiner contributed sixty-two articles. In the first volume (1826) he published his great work "Einige geometrische Betrachtungen."[14] It contains a selection from the *Allgemeine Theorie* and the first published systematic development of the theory of the power of a point with respect to a circle and of the points of similitude of circles; in his account Steiner mentions Pappus, Viète, and Poncelet. As the first application of these concepts Steiner states, without proof, his solution to Malfatti's problem (§ IV, no. 14). In a given triangle ABC draw three circles a, b, and c that are tangent to each other and such that each is

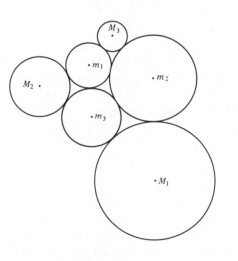

FIGURE 2

tangent to two sides of the triangle (Figure 1). Steiner then remarks that this is a special case of the next problem (no. 15): "Given three arbitrary circles, M_1, M_2, M_3, of specified size and position, to find three other circles m_1, m_2, m_3 tangent to each other and such that each is tangent to two of the given circles, and that each of the given circles M_i is tangent to two of the circles m_k that are to be found" (Figure 2).

Steiner did not prove his solution. Examination of his posthumous papers shows that he knew of the principle of inversion and that he used it in finding and proving the above and other theorems.[15]

It was likewise by means of an inversion that Steiner found and proved his famous theorem on series of circles (§ IV, no. 22; see Figure 3):

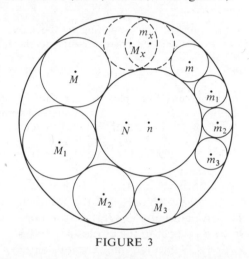

FIGURE 3

Two circles n, N of assigned size and position, lying one within the other, are given. If, for a definite series of circles M, M_1, $\cdots$, M_x, each of which is tangent to n and N unequally and that are tangent to each other in order, the interval between n and N is *commensurable*, that is, if the series consists of $x + 1$ members forming a sequence of u circuits such that the last circle M_x is tangent to the first one M: then this interval is commensurable for any series of circles m, m_1, $\cdots$, m_x; and the latter series also consists of $x + 1$ members forming u circuit, as in the first series.

In this same work (§ VI; see Figure 4), he proves a theorem of Pappus, in the following form:

Given two circles M_1, M_2, of assigned size and position that are tangent to each other in B. If one draws two arbitrary circles m_1, m_2 that are tangent to each other externally in b and each of which is tangent to the two given circles, and if one drops the perpendiculars m_1P_1, m_2P_2 from the centers m_1, m_2 on the axis M_1M_2 of the given circles and divides these perpendiculars by the radii r_1, r_2 of the circles m_1, m_2:

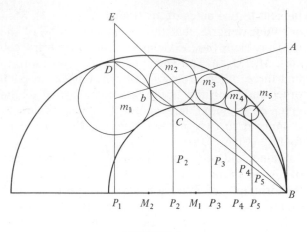

FIGURE 4

then the quotient corresponding to the circle m_2 is greater by 2 than that corresponding to the former; that is, $\dfrac{m_1 P_1}{r_1} + 2 = \dfrac{m_2 P_2}{r_2}$. Or, as Pappus expressed it:

the perpendicular $m_1 P_1$ plus the diameter of the corresponding circle m_1 is to that diameter as the perpendicular $m_2 P_2$ is to the diameter of the corresponding circle m_2—that is, $\dfrac{m_1 P_1 + 2r_1}{2r_1} = \dfrac{m_2 P_2}{2r_2}$.

Steiner furnishes a proof of this proposition, which consists, essentially, of the following steps:

1. The straight line $AB \perp BM_1$ is the line of equal powers with respect to the circles M_1 and M_2.

2. AB passes through the exterior center of similitude A of the circles m_1 and m_2.

3. $Am_2 : Am_1 = r_2 : r_1 = BP_2 : BP_1$ and $AB = Ab$.

4. The points B, C, b, D lie on one straight line.

5. The assertion follows from similarity considerations. In a later paper Steiner applied this "ancient" theorem of Pappus to the sphere.[16]

Also in the first volume of Crelle's *Journal*, Steiner published an expanded version of considerations that stemmed from the period that he was in Yverdon: "Einige Gesetze über die Teilung der Ebene und des Raumes."[17] In it he expressly stated that his ideas were inspired by Pestalozzi's ideas. The simplest result in this paper was presented in the following form:

A plane is divided into two parts by a straight line lying within it; by a second straight line that intersects the first, the number of parts of the plane is increased by 2; by a third straight line that intersects the two first lines at two points, the number is increased by 3; and so forth. That is, each successive straight line increases the number of parts by the number of parts into which it was divided by the preceding straight

lines. Therefore, a plane is divided by n arbitrary straight lines into at most $2 + 2 + 3 \cdots + (n-1) +$

$$n = 1 + \frac{n(n+1)}{2} = 1 + n + \frac{n(n-1)}{1 \cdot 2} \text{ parts.}$$

He then subdivided space by means of planes and spherical surfaces.

In the following years Crelle's *Journal* and Gergonne's *Annales de mathématiques* published many of Steiner's papers, most of which were either problems to be solved or theorems to be proved.[18] In this way Steiner exerted an exceptionally stimulating influence on geometric research that was strengthened by the publication of his first book, *Systematische Entwicklung* (1832).[19] It was originally supposed to consist of five sections, but only the first appeared. Some of the remaining sections were published in the *Vorlesungen*.[20]

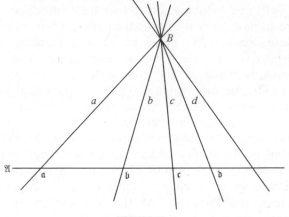

FIGURE 5

Steiner believed that the fundamental concepts of plane geometry are the range of points considered as the totality of points $\mathfrak{a}$, $\mathfrak{b}$, $\mathfrak{c}$, $\cdots$ of a straight line $\mathfrak{A}$ and the pencil of lines a, b, c, $\cdots$ through a point B (Figure 5). Since the latter are the intersection points of a, b, c, $\cdots$ with straight line $\mathfrak{A}$, an unambiguous relationship is established between the pencil of lines and the range, a relationship that he called projectivity. In volume II, § 2, of the *Vorlesungen über synthetische Geometrie* (1867), Steiner expressed this property through the statement that the two constructs are of the same *cardinality*, an expression that Georg Cantor adopted and generalized.[21]

In the first chapter of this part of the *Vorlesungen*, Steiner discusses the elements of projectivity, emphasizing the duality between point and straight line. In particular he proves the harmonic properties of the complete quadrangle and of the complete quadrilateral. In the second chapter he treats the simple elements of solid geometry. At the center of the epochal work stands the theory of conic sections in the third book. Here Steiner proved his fundamental theorem: The intersection points of corresponding lines of two projective pencils of lines form a conic section. In its metric formulation this theorem was essentially known to Jan de Witt and Newton.[22] Steiner, however, was the first to recognize that it was a theorem of projective geometry, and he made it the cornerstone of the projective treatment of the theory of conic sections.

Steiner knew of the significance of his discovery.

The above investigation of projective figures, by placing them in oblique positions deliberately avoided closer research into the laws that govern the projective rays for two straight lines A, A_1 [Figure 6]. We shall now proceed to this examination. It leads, as will be seen, to the most interesting and fruitful properties of curves of the second order, the so-called conic sections. From these almost all other properties of the conics can be developed in a single, comprehensive framework and in a surprisingly simple and clear manner. This examination shows the necessary emergence of the conic sections from the elementary geometric figures; indeed, it shows, at the same time, a very remarkable double production of these [sections] by means of projective figures. . . . When one considers with what ingenuity past and present mathematicians have investigated the conic sections, and the almost countless number of properties that remained hidden for so long, one is struck that, as will be seen, almost all the known properties (and many new ones) flow from their projective generation as from a spring; and this generation also reveals the inner nature of the conic sections to us. For even if properties are known that are similar to those named here, the latter have never, in my opinion, been explicitly stated; in no case, however, has anyone until now recognized the importance that they derive from our development of them, where they are raised to the level of fundamental theorems.[23]

In proposition no. 37 of this volume, Steiner stated and proved his fundamental theorem for the circle (Figure 6): "Any two tangents A, A_1 are projective with respect to the corresponding pairs of points in which they are cut by the other tangents; and the point of intersection $\mathfrak{d}$, e_1, of the tangents corresponds to the points $\mathfrak{d}_1$, e, where they touch the circle." He also gave the dual of this theorem (Figure 7): "Any two points $\mathfrak{B}$, $\mathfrak{B}_1$ of a circle are the centers of two projective pencils of lines, the corresponding lines of which intersect in the remaining points of the circle; and the reciprocal tangents d_1, e at the points $\mathfrak{B}$, $\mathfrak{B}_1$ correspond to the

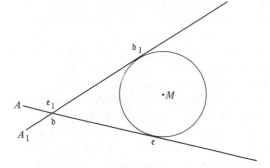

FIGURE 6

lines d, e_1." Applying these theorems to the second-degree cone, Steiner obtained the following result: "Any two tangents of a conic section are projective with respect to the pair of points in which they are intersected by the remaining tangents; and conversely."

Steiner emphasized here that "these new theorems on the second-degree cone and its sections are more important for the investigation of these figures than all the theorems previously known about them, for they are, in the strict sense, the true fundamental theorems."

From these fundamental theorems, Steiner derived consequences ranging from the known theorems on conic sections to the Braikenridge-Maclaurin theorem. Propositions 49–53 deal with the production of projective figures in space. An important group of propositions (54–58) contains previously known "composite theorems and problems" that Steiner was the first to derive in a uniform manner from one basic principle. An example is the following problem taken from Möbius: "Given an arbitrary tetrahedron, draw another the vertices of which lie in the faces of the first and the faces of which pass through the vertices of the

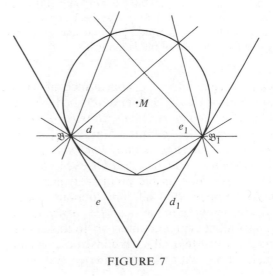

FIGURE 7

first, two vertices of the second tetrahedron being given." Proposition 59, labeled "general observation," contains the "skew projection," a quadratic relationship in space, sometimes called the "Steiner relationship," which had been noted by Poncelet.[24]

The eighty-five "Problems and Theorems" that Steiner appended in a supplement proved especially stimulating to a generation of geometers. They are discussed in the dissertation of Ahmed Karam,[25] who found that, as of 1939, only three problems remained unsolved: no. 70, "What are the properties of a group of similar quadratic surfaces that pass through four or five points of space?"; no. 77, "Does a convex polyhedron always have a topological equivalent that can be either circumscribed about or inscribed in a sphere?"; and no. 76, "If polyhedra are distinguished solely according to their boundary surfaces, there exist only one with four faces, two with five faces, and seven with six faces. How many different bodies are possible with 7, 8, $\cdots$, n faces?"

The last problem was posed by Steiner's teacher at Heidelberg, Ferdinand Schweins.[26] It was partially solved by Otto Hermes in 1903, and further elements of it have been solved by P. J. Frederico.[27]

Of Steiner's work Jacobi stated:

> Starting from a few spatial properties Steiner attempted, by means of a simple schema, to attain a comprehensive view of the multitude of geometric theorems that had been rent asunder. He sought to assign each its special position in relation to the others, to bring order to chaos, to interlock all the parts according to nature, and to assemble them into well-defined groups. In discovering the organism [*Organismus*] through which the most varied phenomena of space are linked, he not only furthered the development of a geometric synthesis; he also provided a model of a complete method and execution for all other branches of mathematics.[28]

Only a year after the appearance of *Systematische Entwicklung*, Steiner published his second book: *Die geometrischen Konstruktionen ausgeführt mittelst der geraden Linie und eines festen Kreises, als Lehrgegenstand auf höheren Unterrichtsanstalten und zur praktischen Benützung* (1833).[29] He took as his point of departure Mascheroni's remark that all constructions made with straightedge and compass can be carried out using compass alone. As a counterpart to this statement, Steiner proved that all such constructions can also be carried out with the straightedge and one fixed circle. To this end he devoted the first chapter to rectilinear figures and especially to the harmonic properties of the complete quadrilateral. In the third chapter he proved his assertion in a way that enabled him to solve eight fundamental problems, to which all others can be reduced. For example (no. 1): "Draw the parallel to a straight line through a point" and (no. 8) "Find the intersection point of two circles." In the intervening chapter 2, he considered centers of similitude and the radical axis of a pencil of circles. This work, which enjoyed great success, contained an appendix of twenty-one problems that were partly taken from *Systematische Entwicklung*. The first one, for example, was "Given two arbitrary triangles, find a third that is simultaneously circumscribed about the first and inscribed in the second."

At this point we shall present a survey of Steiner's further research, published in volume II of the *Gesammelte Werke* (the page numbers in parentheses refer to that volume). A fuller description of its contents can be found in Louis Kollros' article on Steiner, cited in the bibliography.

Steiner pursued the investigation of conic sections and surfaces in some dozen further publications. Sometimes he merely presented problems and theorems without solutions or proofs. In part the material follows from the general projective approach to geometry; but some of it contains new ideas, as the examination of the extreme-value problem: "Determine an ellipse of greatest surface that is inscribed in a given quadrangle" (333 f.) and "Among all the quadrangles inscribed in an ellipse, that having the greatest perimeter is the one the vertices of which lie in the tangent points of the sides of a rectangle circumscribed about the ellipse. There are infinitely many such quadrangles. . . . All have the same perimeter, which is equal to twice the diagonal of the rectangle. All these quadrangles of greatest perimeter are parallelograms; and they are, simultaneously, circumscribed about another ellipse the axes of which fall on the corresponding axes of the given ellipse and that is confocal with the latter. . . . Among all the quadrangles circumscribed about a given ellipse, the one with least perimeter is that in which the normals at the tangent points of its sides form a rhombus" (411–412).

In a paper on new methods of determining second-order curves, Steiner considered pairs of such curves and demonstrated propositions of the following type: "If two arbitrary conic sections are inscribed in a complete quadrilateral, then the eight points in which they are tangent to the sides lie on another conic section" (477 f.). To the theory of second-degree surfaces, he contributed the geometric proof of Poisson's theorem: The attraction of a homogeneous elliptical sheet falls on a point P in the axis of the cone that has P as vertex and is tangent to the ellipsoid.

Steiner dealt on several occasions with center-of-gravity problems. One of the simplest follows.

If, in a given circle $ADBE$, one takes an arc AB, of which one end point, A, is fixed, and lets it increase steadily from zero, then its center of gravity C will describe a curved line ACM. What properties will this barycentric curve possess? . . . The same question can be phrased generally, if instead of the circle an arbitrary curve is given. . . . Questions like those of the above problem occur if one considers the center of gravity of the segment (instead of the arc) ADB. Other questions of the same sort arise regarding the center of gravity of a variable sector AMB, if M is an arbitrary fixed pole and one arm of the sector is fixed, while the other, MB, turns about the pole M [p. 30; see Figure 8].

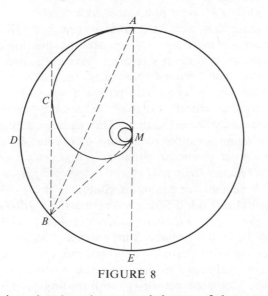

FIGURE 8

Steiner developed a general theory of the center of gravity of mass points in "Von dem Krümmungsschwerpunkt ebener Kurven" (97–159). It led to the pedal curve of a given curve and its area, and was followed by the important memoir "Parallele Flächen" (171–176), which generalized a theorem proved in the preceding paper for plane curves: Let A and B be two parallel polyhedra (surfaces) separated by a distance h. Then it is true for A and B that $B = A + hk + h^2e$; and for the volume I between A and B that $I = hA + h^2k/2 + h^3e/3$, where k is "the sum of the edge curvature" and e "the sum of the vertex curvature."

Steiner's great two-part paper "Ueber Maximum

und Minimum bei den Figuren in der Ebene, auf der Kugelfläche und im Raume überhaupt" (177–308, with 36 figures) was written in Paris during the winter of 1840–1841. It shows the tremendous achievements of which he was still capable—given the necessary time and freedom from distractions. His basic theorem states: "Among all plane figures of the same perimeter, the circle has the greatest area (and conversely)." He gives five ways of demonstrating it, in all of which he assumes the existence of the extremum. All five, moreover, are based on the inequalities of the triangle and of polygons. The first proof proceeds indirectly: Assume that among all figures of equal perimeter the convex figure $EFGH$ possesses the greatest area and that it is not a circle (Figure 9).

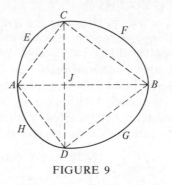

FIGURE 9

Let A and B be two points that bisect the perimeter. Then the surfaces $AEFB$ and $AHGB$ are equal. For if one of them were smaller, then the other could be substituted for it, whereby the perimeter would remain equal and the surface would be increased. These two surfaces should be considered to have the same form; for if they were different, the mirror image of AB could be substituted for one, whereby the perimeter and area would remain the same. According to "Fundamental Theorem II" on triangles, for the extremal figure the angles at C and D must be right angles. Since this consideration holds for every point A of the perimeter, the figure sought is a circle. This is the first occasion on which Steiner employed his principle of symmetrization.

In the fifth proof the basic theorem takes the form that among all plane figures of the same area, the circle has the least perimeter. The principle of the proof is again symmetrization with respect to the axis X.

Steiner next effects the transformation of the pentagon $ABCDE$ (Figure 10) into the pentagon of equal area $abcde$ in such a way that each line segment $B_1B = b_1b$; and bb_1 is bisected by X. As a result, the perimeter decreases. Steiner then turns

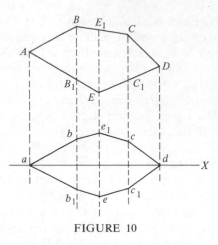

FIGURE 10

to the extremal properties of prisms, pyramids, and the sphere (269–308).

In 1853, while investigating the double tangents of a fourth-degree curve, Steiner encountered a combinatorial problem (435–438): What number N of elements has the property that the elements can be ordered into triplets (t-tuples) in such a way that each two (each t-1) appear in one and only one combination? For the Steiner triple system, N must have the form $6n + 1$ or $6n + 3$, and there

exist $\dfrac{N(N-1)}{2\cdot 3}$ triples, $\dfrac{N(N-1)(N-3)}{2\cdot 3\cdot 4}$ quadruples,

and so on. For example, for $N = 7$ there is only one triple system: 123, 145, 167, 246, 257, 347, 356. For $N = 13$ there are two different triple systems. Steiner was unaware of the work on this topic done by Thomas Kirkman (1847).[30]

In a short paper of fundamental importance, published in 1848 and entitled "Allgemeine Eigenschaften der algebraischen Kurven" (493–500), Steiner first defined and examined the various polar curves of a point with respect to a given curve. He then introduced the "Steiner curves" and discussed tangents at points of inflection, double tangents, cusps, and double points. In particular he indicated the resulting relationships for the twenty-eight double tangents of the fourth-degree curve. Luigi Cremona proved the results and continued Steiner's work in his "Introduzione ad una teoria geometrica delle curve piane."[31]

The desire to find, with the methods of pure geometry, the proofs of the extremely important theorems stated by the celebrated Steiner in his brief memoir "Allgemeine Eigenschaften der algebraischen Kurven" led me to undertake several studies, a sample of which I present here, even though it is incomplete.

In 1851 Steiner wrote "Über solche algebraische Kurven, die einen Mittelpunkt haben . . ." (501–596), a version of which he published in Crelle's *Journal*. In the *Gesammelte Werke* this paper is followed by "Problems and Theorems" (597–601). Steiner's results include the following example: "Through seven given points in the plane there pass, in general, only nine third-degree curves possessing a midpoint." Next follows a discussion of the twenty-eight double tangents of the fourth-degree curve (603–615). In January 1856 Steiner delivered a lecture at the Berlin Academy, "Ueber die Flächen dritten Grades" (649–659), in which he offered four methods of producing these cubic surfaces. The first states: "The nine straight lines in which the surfaces of two arbitrarily given trihedra intersect each other determine, together with one given point, a cubic surface." Aware that Cayley already knew the twenty-seven straight lines of this surface, Steiner introduced the concept of the "nuclear surface" and investigated its properties (656).

Steiner's correspondence with Ludwig Schläfli reveals that the latter discovered his "Doppelsechs" in the course of research on this topic undertaken at Steiner's request.[32] Again, it was Cremona who proved Steiner's theorems in his "Mémoire de géométrie pure sur les surfaces du troisième ordre" (1866).[33] Cremona began his memoir by declaring that "This work . . . contains the demonstration of all the theorems stated by this great geometer [Steiner] in his memoir *Ueber die Flächen dritten Grades*."

A second treatment of Steiner's theorems appeared in Rudolf Sturm's *Synthetische Untersuchungen über Flächen dritter Ordnung* (Leipzig 1867). In the preface Sturm wrote: "Steiner's paper contains a wealth of theorems on cubic surfaces, although, as had become customary with this celebrated geometer, without any proofs and with only few hints of how they might be arrived at." The works of both Cremona and Sturm were submitted in 1866 as entries in the first competition held by the Berlin Academy for the Steiner Prize, which was divided between them.

During his stay at Rome in 1844, Steiner investigated a fourth-order surface of the third class (721–724, 741–742), but it became known only much later through a communication from Karl Weierstrass (1863).[34] The surface, since called the Roman surface or Steiner surface, has the characteristic property that each of its tangent planes cuts it in a pair of conics. On the surfaces there lie three double straight lines that intersect in a triple point of the surface. The surface was the subject of many studies by later mathematicians.

NOTES

1. See F. Bützberger, "Biographie Jakob Steiners."
2. J. Lange, "Jacob Steiners Lebensjahre in Berlin 1821–1863. Nach seinen Personalakten dargestellt"; E. Jahnke, "Schreiben Jacobis . . .," in *Archiv der Mathematik und Physik*, 3rd ser., **4** (1903), 278.
3. *Jacob Steiner's Gesammelte Werke*, K. Weierstrass, ed., I, 175–176, and II, 18.
4. *Ibid.*, II, 97–159.
5. E. Lampe, "Jacob Steiner"; J. H. Graf, "Beiträge zur Biographie Jakob Steiners."
6. K.-R. Biermann, "Jakob Steiner."
7. *Ibid.*
8. J. Lange, *op. cit.*
9. *Gesammelte Werke*, I, 233–234.
10. Steiner, *Allgemeine Theorie über das Berühren und Schneiden der Kreise und der Kugeln*; B. Jegher, "Von Kreisen, die einerlei Kugelfläche liegen. Jakob Steiners Untersuchungen über das Schneiden und Berühren von Kegelkreisen. . . ."
11. *Gesammelte Werke*, I, 17–76.
12. Steiner, *Allgemeine Theorie*.
13. *Ibid.*, xiv–xvi.
14. *Gesammelte Werke*, I, 17–76.
15. See F. Bützburger, "Jakob Steiners Nachlass aus den Jahren 1823–1826," § 11, "Die Erfindung der Inversion"; A. Emch, "The Discovery of Inversion"; and Mautz, *op. cit.*
16. *Gesammelte Werke*, I, 133.
17. *Ibid.*, 77–94.
18. *Ibid.*, 121–228.
19. *Ibid.*, 229–460.
20. The MS material is in Steiner, *Allgemeine Theorie*, and in Jegher, *op. cit.*
21. See G. Cantor, *Gesammelte Abhandlungen* (Berlin, 1932), 151.
22. See W. L. Schaaf, "Mathematicians and Mathematics on Postage Stamps," in *Journal of Recreational Mathematics*, **1** (1968), 208; and I. Newton, *Principia mathematica*, 2nd ed. (Cambridge, 1713), Bk. I, 72; and *Universal Arithmetick* (London, 1728), probs. 57, 95.
23. *Vorlesungen*, II, no. 35.
24. V. Poncelet, *Traité des propriétés projectives des figures* (Paris–Metz, 1822), sec. III, ch. 2.
25. A. Karam, *Sur les 85 problèmes de la "dépendance systématique" de Steiner*. See also L. Kollros, "Jakob Steiner," p. 10.
26. F. Schweins, *Skizze eines Systems der Geometrie* (Heidelberg, 1810), 14–15.
27. See R. Sturm, "Zusammenstellung von Arbeiten, welche sich mit Steinerschen Aufgaben beschäftigen," in *Bibliotheca mathematica*, 3rd ser., **4** (1903), 160–184; P. J. Frederico, "Enumeration of Polyhedra," in *Journal of Combinatorial Theory*, **7** (1969), 155–161.
28. See F. Bützberger, "Biographie Jakob Steiners," 109; and K.-R. Biermann, *op. cit.*, 38.
29. *Gesammelte Werke*, I, 469–522.
30. T. Kirkman, in *Cambridge and Dublin Mathematical Journal*, **2** (1847), 191–204.
31. *Opere matematiche di Luigi Cremona*, I (Milan, 1914), 313–466.
32. See J. H. Graf, *Der Briefwechsel Steiner-Schläfli*.
33. *Opere matematiche di Luigi Cremona*, III (Milan, 1917), 1–121.
34. In *Monatsberichte der Deutschen Akademie der Wissenschaften zu Berlin* (1863), 339, repr. in *Mathematische Werke von Karl Weierstrass*, III (Berlin, 1902), 179–182.

BIBLIOGRAPHY

I. ORIGINAL WORKS. Many of Steiner's writings are in *Jacob Steiner's Gesammelte Werke*, K. Weierstrass, ed., 2 vols. (Berlin, 1881–1882). The major ones include *Jacob Steiners Vorlesungen über synthetische Geometrie*: I, *Die Theorie der Kegelschnitte in elementarer Darstellung*, C. F. Geiser, ed. (Leipzig, 1867; 3rd ed., 1887), and II, *Die Theorie der Kegelschnitte gestützt auf projektive Eigenschaften*, H. Schröter, ed. (Leipzig, 1867; 3rd ed., 1898); *Allgemeine Theorie über das Berühren und Schneiden der Kreise und der Kugeln*, R. Fueter and F. Gonseth, eds. (Zurich–Leipzig, 1931); and Barbara Jegher, "Von Kreisen, die in einerlei Kugelfläche liegen. Jakob Steiners Untersuchungen über das Schneiden und Berühren von Kugelkreisen . . .," in *Mitteilungen der Naturforschenden Gesellschaft in Bern*, n.s. **24** (1967), 1–20.

Two letters from Steiner to Rudolf Wolf, dated 25 July 1841 and 5 Aug. 1848, are in the autograph collection of the Schweizerische Naturforschende Gesellschaft, at the Bern Burgerbibliothek (nos. 110 and 588 under MSS Hist. Helv. XIV, 150).

The following works by Steiner appeared in Ostwald's Klassiker der Exakten Wissenschaften: *Die geometrischen Konstruktionen, ausgeführt mittels der geraden Linie und eines festen Kreises* (1833), no. 60 (Leipzig, 1895), which contains a short biography of Steiner by the editor, A. J. von Oettingen, pp. 81–84; *Systematische Entwicklung der Abhängigkeit geometrischer Gestalten voneinander* (1832), nos. 82–83 (Leipzig, 1896); and *Einige geometrische Betrachtungen* (1826), no. 123, R. Sturm, ed. (Leipzig, 1901).

II. SECONDARY LITERATURE. Undated MS material is F. Bützberger, "Kleine Biographie über Jakob Steiner," Bibliothek der Schweizerischen Naturforschenden Gesellschaft, in the Bern Stadt und Universitätsbibliothek, MSS Hist. Helv. XXIb, 347; "Biographie Jakob Steiners," in the same collection, MSS Hist. Helv. XXIb, 348; and "Jakob Steiners Nachlass aus den Jahren 1823–1826," Bibliothek der Eidgenössischen Technischen Hochschule, Zurich, Hs. 92, pp. 30–223.

On Steiner's youth and years in Yverdon, see especially F. Bützberger, "Zum 100. Geburtstage Jakob Steiners," in *Zeitschrift für mathematischen und naturwissenschaftlichen Unterricht*, **27** (1896), 161 ff.; on the years in Berlin see Felix Eberty, *Jugenderinnerungen eines alten Berliners* (Berlin, 1878; repr. 1925), 238–243; and Julius Lange, "Jacob Steiners Lebensjahre in Berlin 1821–1863. Nach seinen Personalakten dargestellt," in *Wissenschaftliche Beilage zum Jahresbericht der Friedrichs-Werderschen Oberrealschule zu Berlin, Ostern 1899*, Program no. 116 (Berlin, 1899). See also three short obituary notices: C. F. Geiser, "Nekrolog J. Steiner," in *Die Schweiz: Illustrierte Zeitschrift für Literatur und Kunst* (Nov. 1863), 350–355; Otto Hesse, "Jakob Steiner," in *Journal für die reine und angewandte Mathematik*, **62** (1863), 199–200; and Bernhard Wyss, "Nekrolog J. Steiner," in *Bund* (Bern) (9 Apr. 1863).

The first detailed biography of Steiner was written by his grandnephew: Carl Friedrich Geiser, *Zur Erinnerung an Jakob Steiner* (Schaffhausen, 1874). Steiner's correspondence with Schläfli was edited by Schläfli's student J. H. Graf: *Der Briefwechsel Steiner-Schläfli* (Bern, 1896); see also the following three works by Graf: *Der Mathematiker Steiner von Utzensdorf* (Bern, 1897); "Die Exhuminierung Jakob Steiners und die Einweihung des Grabdenkmals Ludwig Schläflis . . . am 18. März 1896," in *Mitteilungen der Naturforschenden Gesellschaft in Bern* (1897), 8–24; and "Beiträge zur Biographie Jakob Steiners," *ibid.* (1905). Another of Schläfli's students, F. Bützberger, examined Steiner's posthumous MSS and reported on them in "Zum 100. Geburtstage Jakob Steiners" (see above) and in his long MS "Jakob Steiners Nachlass aus den Jahren 1823–1826" (see above).

Recent accounts of Steiner's life and work are Louis Kollros, "Jakob Steiner," supp. 2 of *Elemente der Mathematik* (1947), 1–24; and J.-P. Sydler, "Aperçus sur la vie et sur l'oeuvre de Jakob Steiner," in *Enseignement mathématique*, 2nd ser., **11** (1965), 240–257. Valuable corrections of errors in earlier accounts are given by Kurt-R. Biermann, "Jakob Steiner," in *Nova acta Leopoldina*, n.s. **27**, no. 167 (1963), 31–47.

For further information see the following: F. Bützberger, "Jakob Steiner bei Pestalozzi in Yverdon," in *Schweizerische pädagogische Zeitschrift*, **6** (1896), 19–30; and *Bizentrische Polygone, Steinersche Kreis- und Kugelreihen und die Erfindung der Inversion* (Leipzig, 1913); Moritz Cantor, "Jakob Steiner," in *Allgemeine deutsche Biographie*, XXXV (1893), 700–703; A. Emch, "Unpublished Steiner Manuscripts," in *American Mathematical Monthly*, **36** (1929), 273–275; and "The Discovery of Inversion," in *Bulletin of the American Mathematical Society*, **20** (1913–1914), 412–415, and **21** (1914–1915), 206; R. Fueter, *Grosse schweizer Forscher* (Zurich, 1939), 202–203; C. Habicht, "Die Steinerschen Kreisreihen" (Ph.D. diss., Bern, 1904); A. Karam, *Sur les 85 problèmes de la "dépendance systématique" de Steiner* (Ph.D. diss., Eidgenössische Technische Hochschule, Zurich, 1939); E. Kötter, "Die Entwicklung der synthetischen Geometrie. Dritter Teil: Von Steiner bis auf Staudt," in *Jahresbericht der Deutschen Mathematikervereinigung*, **5**, no. 2 (1898), 252 ff.; Emil Lampe, "Jakob Steiner," in *Bibliotheca mathematica*, 3rd ser., **1** (1900), 129–141; Otto Mautz, "Ebene Inversionsgeometric," in *Wissenschaftliche Beilage zum Bericht über das Gymnasium Schuljahr 1908–1909* (Basel, 1909); R. Sturm, "Zusammenstellung von Arbeiten, welche sich mit Steinerschen Aufgaben beschäftigen," in *Bibliotheca mathematica*, 3rd ser., **4**

(1903), 160–184; and a series of articles by Rudolf Wolf in *Vierteljahrsschrift der Naturforschenden Gesellschaft in Zürich*: **9** (1864), 145 ff.; **13** (1868), 110 ff.; **19** (1874), 325 ff.; **25** (1880), 215 ff.; and **35** (1890), 428 ff.

JOHANN JAKOB BURCKHARDT

STEINHEIL, KARL AUGUST (*b.* Rappoltsweiler [now Ribeauvillé], Alsace, 12 October 1801; *d.* Munich, Germany, 12 September 1870), *physics, astronomy.*

Steinheil was the son of Karl Philipp Steinheil, administrator of the estates of a German prince (later Maximilian I of Bavaria), and the former Christine Maria Franziska von Biarowsky. She bore their son after twenty-four years of matrimony. The family moved to Munich in 1807 but the boy did not attend public school because of his delicate health. He was educated by private tutors; and after two years spent at Nancy and Tours with relatives of his mother's, he passed the examination for the school certificate. In 1821 Steinheil began to study law at Erlangen, but in 1823 he turned to science, especially astronomy, at Göttingen and Königsberg. At the latter he received the Ph.D. on 12 October 1825, under Bessel's supervision, for the dissertation "De specialibus coeli chartis elaborantis."

Steinheil continued his astronomical and optical studies at his estate near Munich. He became known to experts in the field for editing three hours of the *Berliner akademische Sternkarten* and, later, for his prize-winning paper "Elemente der Helligkeitsmessungen am Sternenhimmel" (1837). In 1832 he was named ordinary professor of mathematics and physics at Munich University. From 1849 to 1852 he organized telegraph communications in Austria, then returned to Munich, where he worked in the Ministry of Commerce as a technical consultant. Fulfilling a special desire of Maximilian I, Steinheil founded an optical workshop (1854) that was continued by his son and grandson. In his last years he was conservator of the mathematical and physical collections of the Bavarian Academy at Munich.

Steinheil exerted great influence on the scientific life at Munich. He was a keen-witted discoverer and inventor, especially in optics and telegraphy. In 1838 he theorized that the earth could serve as the second half of a telegraphic circuit; and in 1842 he constructed an ingenious photometer. Steinheil also improved the achromatic telescope (some of this work was done with P. L. von Seidel), designed silvered mirrors for reflectors, and stimulated progress in the establishment of standard weights, electrodeposition, daguerreotypy, and fire prevention.

BIBLIOGRAPHY

Steinheil's writings include "Elemente der Helligkeitsmessungen am Sternenhimmel," in *Abhandlungen der Bayerischen Akademie der Wissenschaften*, Math.-phys. Kl., **2** (1837), 1–140; "Über quantitative Analyse durch physikalische Beobachtungen," *ibid.*, **3** (1842), 689–716; "Über die Bestimmung der Brechungs- und Zerstreuungsverhältnisse verschiedene Medien," *ibid.*. **5**. Abt. 2 (1850), 253–268, written with P. L. von Seidel; "Beschreibung und Vergleichung der galvanischen Telegraphen Deutschlands nach Besichtigung vom April 1849," *ibid.*, Abt. 3, 779–840; "Beiträge zur Photometrie des Himmels," in *Astronomische Nachrichten*, **48** (1858), 369–378; "Über Berichtigung des Äquatoreals," *ibid.*, **52** (1860), 129–140; "Das Chronoskop," in *Abhandlungen der Bayerischen Akademie der Wissenschaften*, Math.-phys. Kl., **10**, Abt. 2 (1868), 357–387; and "Methode, eine Grundlinie durch Fortbewegung eines zylindrischen Massstabes in Gestalt eines Rades zu messen," in *Astronomische Nachrichten*, **72** (1868), 369–378.

A biographical notice is in *Allgemeine deutsche Biographie*, XXXV, 720–724.

H.-CHRIST. FREIESLEBEN

STEINITZ, ERNST (*b.* Laurahütte, Silesia, Germany [now Huta Laura, Poland], 13 June 1871; *d.* Kiel, Germany, 29 September 1928), *mathematics.*

Steinitz began the study of mathematics in 1890 at the University of Breslau (now Wrocław, Poland). A year later he went to Berlin and in 1893 returned to Breslau, where he received the Ph.D. in 1894. Two years later he began his teaching career as *Privatdozent* in mathematics at the Technical College in Berlin-Charlottenburg. In 1910 he was appointed professor at the Technical College in Breslau. He assumed a similar post in 1920 at the University of Kiel, where his friend Otto Toeplitz was teaching, remaining there until his death.

In his most important publication, "Algebraische Theorie der Körper" (1910), Steinitz gave an abstract and general definition of the concept of a "field" (*Körper*) as a system of elements with two operations (addition and multiplication) that satisfy associative and commutative laws (which are joined by the distributive law), the elements of which admit unlimited and unambiguous inversion up to division by zero. Steinitz sought to discuss all possible types of fields and to ascertain their relationships. By means of a systematic development of the consequences of the axioms for commutative fields, he introduced a series of fundamental concepts: prime field, separable elements, perfect fields, and degree of transcendence of an extension. His most important achievement was undoubtedly the proof that for every base field K there exist extension fields L in which all polynomials with coefficients in K decompose into linear factors, and that the smallest possible such field is virtually determined up to isomorphism. Because this smallest field possesses no genuine algebraic extension, Steinitz called it algebraically closed, proving its existence with the aid of the axiom of choice; this is now done by means of Zorn's lemma.

In his basic approach Steinitz was influenced primarily by Heinrich Weber and, in his methods, by Leopold Kronecker; Hensel's discovery in 1899 of the field of *p*-adic numbers provided the direct stimulus for his work. His polished and fully detailed treatment of the subject was the starting point for many far-reaching studies in abstract algebra, including those by E. Artin, H. Hasse, W. Krull, E. Noether, and B. L. van der Waerden. The general concept of the derivative or of differentiation, which Steinitz introduced in special cases, is essential in modern algebraic geometry.

In addition to his epochal paper, Steinitz wrote on the theory of polyhedra, a topic of lifelong interest. He gave two lectures on it at Kiel and prepared a comprehensive treatment during his last years. An almost complete manuscript of a planned book was found among his papers; it was completed and edited by Rademacher in 1934. Dealing chiefly with convex polyhedra and their topological types, the book also includes a detailed historical survey of the development of the theory of polyhedra.

BIBLIOGRAPHY

Steinitz' works are listed in Poggendorff, IV, 1435; V, 1203; and VI, 2534. His most important writings are "Algebraische Theorie der Körper," in *Journal für die reine und angewandte Mathematik*, **137** (1910), 137–309, which was also separately published, R. Baer and H. Hasse, eds. (Berlin–Leipzig, 1930; New York [in German], 1950); and *Vorlesungen über die Theorie der Polyeder, unter Einschluss der Elemente der Topologie*, Hans Rademacher, ed. (Berlin, 1934; repr. Ann Arbor, Mich., 1945).

BRUNO SCHOENEBERG

STEINMETZ, CHARLES PROTEUS (*b.* Breslau, Germany [now Wrocław, Poland], 9 April 1865; *d.* Schenectady, New York, 26 October 1923), *engineering.*

Steinmetz' given name was Karl August Rudolf. He was the only son of Karl Heinrich Steinmetz, a government railway employee, and his first wife, Caroline Neubert. After early education at the local Gymnasium, he entered the University of Breslau, where he remained for five years. During this time, he became an ardent socialist. Placed under police surveillance in 1887, he eventually fled to Zurich, shortly before completing the Ph.D. in mathematics, and there studied mechanical engineering.

In 1889 Steinmetz immigrated into the United States and in 1894 became an American citizen, whereupon he took the name Charles Proteus. He never married but in 1905 legally adopted Joseph Le Roy Hayden as his son. Steinmetz received an honorary M.A. from Harvard (1902), and honorary Ph.D. from Union College, and served as president of both the American Institute of Electrical Engineers (1901) and the Illuminating Engineering Society (1915).

Upon entering the United States, Steinmetz was employed as a draftsman by Rudolf Eickemeyer, a prospering manufacturer of motors and machinery and a versatile inventor and pioneer in electrical research. Four years later the newly founded General Electric Company acquired many of Eickemeyer's electrical patents, along with the services of Steinmetz, who by 1892 had already earned a considerable reputation because of two long papers on the mathematical law of magnetic hysteresis, which was praised by contemporaries as "doing for the magnetic circuit what Ohm did for the electric circuit." Steinmetz' first textbook on electricity, *Theory and Calculation of Alternating Current Phenomena* (1897), written with E. J. Berg, described the complex number technique for analyzing alternating-current circuits that he had first presented to the International Electrical Congress in Chicago in 1893. This work played a decisive role in the turn-of-the-century debate between alternating- and direct-current technologies and the technique is still universally used.

To relieve him of administrative duties, Steinmetz was made a consulting engineer at General Electric after 1895. His principal contributions to the advancement of the company in the ensuing twenty-eight years were covered by 195 patents and included the magnetite arc-lamp electrode; two-phase to three-phase transformation; major improvements in motors, generators, and transformers; developments in mercury-arc lighting; and the analysis and design of high-voltage, alternating-current transmission techniques. Transient phenomena in the latter received his particular attention and were explored in a much-publicized, high-voltage "artificial lightning" testing laboratory. He was one of the earliest advocates of atmospheric pollution control, research on solar energy conversion, nationwide electrical networks, electrification of railways, synthetic production of protein, and electric automobiles. While employed by General Electric, Steinmetz also served on the Union College faculty (1903–1913), where he created the electrical engineering department and started his transmission-line research.

Apart from his technical achievements, Steinmetz' unique contribution to the developing electrical engineering profession was his repeated demonstration of the profitability of applying sophisticated mathematical methods to practical problems. Most of his ten technical books were widely used in colleges and had a tremendous influence on curricular development.

Physically small and crippled from birth, like his father and grandfather, Steinmetz had several unusual hobbies and personal idiosyncrasies, about which many legends accumulated. He retained a lifelong interest in socialism; and after the election of a socialist city government in Schenectady in 1911, he served with distinction in several civic positions.

BIBLIOGRAPHY

I. ORIGINAL WORKS. Steinmetz' works include *Theory and Calculation of Alternating Current Phenomena* (New York, 1897), written with E. J. Berg; *Theoretical Elements of Electrical Engineering* (New York, 1901); *General Lectures on Electrical Engineering* (New York, 1908), J. L. Hayden, ed.; *Theory and Calculation of Transient Electrical Phenomena and Oscillations* (New York, 1909); *Radiation, Light and Illumination* (New York, 1909); *Engineering Mathematics* (New York, 1911); *Elementary Lectures on Electrical Discharges, Waves and Impulses and Other Transients* (New York, 1911); *Theory and Calculation of Electric Circuits* (New York, 1917); and *Theory and Calculation of Electric Apparatus* (New York, 1917). The above were published as a nine-volume *Electrical Engineering Library* (New York, 1921).

II. SECONDARY LITERATURE. See Ernest Caldecott and P. L. Alger, *Steinmetz- The Philosopher* (Schenectady, N.Y., 1965); J. W. Hammond, *Charles Proteus*

Steinmetz (New York, 1924); and J. N. Leonard, *Loki, The Life of Charles Proteus Steinmetz* (New York, 1929).

ROBERT A. CHIPMAN

STEJNEGER, LEONHARD HESS (*b.* Bergen, Norway, 30 October 1851; *d.* Washington, District of Columbia, 28 February 1943), *ornithology, herpetology.*

Having left his native country, his father's mercantile business, and his first wife in 1881, Stejneger moved to the United States to seek employment to study his favorite subject, birds. (In 1880 the once prosperous business of his father, Peter Stamer Steineger, had gone into bankruptcy.) At the urging of his mother, Ingeborg Catharina Hess Steineger, Leonhard had aimed toward a medical career but graduated in law (1875) at the University of Kristiania (Oslo). He had long been interested in birds, and first published a work on them when he was nineteen; he also corresponded with ornithologists throughout the world.

After arriving in the United States, Stejneger went directly to Spencer F. Baird at the Smithsonian Institution and was promptly hired to work under the curator of birds, Robert Ridgway. To fill the vacancy left by H. C. Yarrow, Stejneger was appointed acting curator of reptiles and amphibians at the Smithsonian in 1889 and ten years later became curator. From 1911 until his death, he was curator of the department of biology. (He was exempted from retirement by presidential order.)

Stejneger became a citizen of the United States in 1887, and in 1892 he married Helene Maria Reiners. In addition to becoming an honorary member of many scientific societies, Stejneger was elected to the National Academy of Sciences (1923), received an honorary Ph.D. from the University of Oslo, and was elected honorary president for life of the American Society of Ichthyologists and Herpetologists (1931). He was also made a commander of the Royal Norwegian Order of St. Olav (1939), a member of the International Committee on Zoological Nomenclature (1898), and a member of the Permanent Committee of One Hundred of the International Ornithological Congresses (1905). An accomplished linguist, his skills proved useful at the many international meetings to which he was sent.

Stejneger began his extensive collecting in 1882 with a trip to the Komandorskiya Ostrova Islands to help set up weather stations for the United States Signal Service; there, he also gathered bones of the extinct Pallas's cormorant. He returned to these islands during the period 1895–1897 for the International Fur-Seal Commission. Stejneger collected specimens in the American Southwest, in the South Dakota Badlands, in Puerto Rico, and, on a number of trips to Europe for scientific meetings, he collected specimens and made detailed studies of life zones of the Alps.

Stejneger produced a number of descriptive and classificatory publications on birds; but his curatorial appointment turned his interests to reptiles and amphibians, so that he became an expert on the systematics of those groups. With Thomas Barbour, he completed five editions of the highly useful *Check-list of North American Amphibians and Reptiles* (Cambridge, Mass., 1917).

BIBLIOGRAPHY

I. ORIGINAL WORKS. Stejneger's 400 publications are almost equally divided between ornithology and herpetology, but include other subjects as well, for example, a meticulously researched biography of the first Arctic naturalist, Georg Wilhelm Steller (Cambridge, Mass., 1936), and significant publications on fur seals. In 1885 he published "Results of Ornithological Explorations in the Commander Islands and in Kamtschatka," in *Bulletin. United States National Museum,* **29** (1885), 1–382. He contributed extensively to John S. Kingsley, ed., *Natural History of Birds* (Boston, 1885).

In addition to the fifth ed. of Stejneger's *Check-list,* which was in *Bulletin of the Museum of Comparative Zoology at Harvard College,* **93** (1943), 1–260, "Poisonous Snakes of North America," in *Report of the United States National Museum* for 1893 (1895), 337–487, is a classic in herpetology. Regional studies of birds and of reptiles and amphibians are listed in the full bibliography accompanying Wetmore's biography of Stejneger (see below).

II. SECONDARY LITERATURE. Alexander Wetmore wrote an account of Stejneger's life, background, and scientific contributions in *Biographical Memoirs. National Academy of Sciences,* **24** (1945–1947), 143–195, with complete bibliography. A shorter appreciation, with no bibliography, was written by Waldo L. Schmitt, in *Systematic Zoology,* **13,** no. 4 (1964), 243–249. An account of Stejneger's accomplishments and personality, by A. K. Fisher, appeared in a tribute issue of *Copeia,* (Oct. 1931), 75–83.

ELIZABETH NOBLE SHOR

STEKLOV, VLADIMIR ANDREEVICH (*b.* Nizhni Novgorod [now Gorky], Russia, 9 January 1864;

d. Gaspra, Crimea, U.S.S.R., 30 May 1926), *mathematics, mechanics.*

Steklov's father, Andrey Ivanovich Steklov, a clergyman, taught history and was rector of the Nizhni Novgorod seminary; his mother, Ekaterina Aleksandrovna Dobrolyubov, was a sister of the revolutionary-democratic literary critic Nikolay Dobrolyubov. In 1874–1882 Steklov studied at the Alexander Institute in Nizhni Novgorod; after graduation he entered the department of physics and mathematics at Moscow University, transferring a year later to Kharkov. A. M. Lyapunov, who had been lecturing there since 1885, soon became his scientific supervisor. In 1887 Steklov passed his final examinations, and the following summer it was suggested that he remain at the university to prepare for an academic career. He was appointed university lecturer in mechanics in 1891; two years later he presented his master's thesis, and in 1896 he was named extraordinary professor of mechanics. After defending his doctoral dissertation in 1902, Steklov was elected professor; Lyapunov then moved to St. Petersburg, and Steklov obtained the chair of applied mathematics. An active member of the Kharkov Mathematical Society, he served successively as secretary (1891), deputy chairman (1899), and chairman (1902–1906).

In 1906 Steklov transferred to the chair of mathematics at St. Petersburg University. His profound lectures, open sympathy with the aims of progressive students, and acute criticism of the tsarist order—especially at the universities—added new dimensions to the scientific and educational activity of the department of physics and mathematics and attracted numerous students. In St. Petersburg, Steklov laid the foundations of the school of mathematical physics that achieved considerable distinction, particularly after the October Revolution. Among his pupils were such prominent scientists as A. A. Friedman, V. I. Smirnov, and Y. D. Tamarkin.

In 1910 V. Steklov was elected a member of the Academy of Sciences (he had been a corresponding member since 1902), and in 1916 he became a member of its board of directors. From then on, especially after becoming vice-president of the Academy in 1919, Steklov devoted most of his time to that organization. During the civil war, military conflicts, economic decline, and the early phases of reconstruction, he proved to be a brilliant scientific administrator. For eight years he worked tirelessly to maintain, and later to enlarge, the activity of the Academy and to reorganize it in order to bring science and practical requirements closer together. This work embraced all aspects of academic activity, from repairing old buildings and restoring the network of seismic stations to publishing academic proceedings and books, providing foreign periodicals for libraries, and organizing new institutes within the Academy. The Institute of Physics and Mathematics was organized in 1921 on Steklov's suggestion, and he served as its director until his death. In 1934 this institute was divided into the P. N. Lebedev Institute of Physics and the V. A. Steklov Mathematical Institute, both of which became centers of scientific activity.

Along with organizational work, Steklov continued his scholarly pursuits. In his later years he produced a series of articles on the theory of quadratures and on Chebyshev's polynomials, a monograph on mathematical physics, a popular book on the importance of mathematics for mankind, and biographies of Galileo and Newton.

Steklov's early works were devoted mostly to mechanics. In his master's thesis he pointed out the third case in which the integration of equations of a solid body moving in an ideal nonviscous fluid (under certain suppositions) is reduced to quadratures. The two earlier cases were described in 1871 by Rudolf Clebsch, and the fourth (and last) by Lyapunov in 1893. Steklov also treated problems of hydromechanics.

Steklov's principal field of endeavor, however, was mathematical physics and corresponding problems of analysis. Many problems of potential theory, electrostatics, and hydromechanics are reduced to the boundary-value problems of Dirichlet and Neumann when it is necessary to find a solution of Laplace's differential equation satisfying some boundary conditions on a surface S enclosing the region under consideration. Although Neumann, Hermann Schwarz, Poincaré, G. Robin, E. Le Roy, and others had suggested methods of solving such problems, they did not elaborate their rigorous grounding, and their methods were applied to relatively restricted classes of surfaces. The precision of analysis in the general investigation of the problem was first achieved by Lyapunov and Steklov. Steklov presented the first summary of his studies in this field in his doctoral thesis and in the articles "Sur les problèmes fondamentaux de la physique mathématique" and "Théorie générale des fonctions fondamentales." He made a valuable contribution to the theory of fundamental functions (Poincaré's term) or, to use a contemporary expression, the theory of eigen functions depending in a particular way upon the character of the surface S and forming on the surface a normal and orthogonal system; the solution of the boundary-value problems of Dirichlet and Neumann is expressed in terms of these eigen functions. Steklov was the first to demonstrate strictly for a very broad class of surfaces the existence of an infinite sequence of (proper) eigen values and corresponding eigen functions defining them in a way different from Poincaré's. Using a method going back to Fourier, Steklov also solved new problems of the theory of heat conduction subject to some boundary, and initial conditions.

When boundary value problems are considered, an especially difficult problem arises when one wishes to expand an arbitrary function, for example, $f(x)$, subject to certain restrictions, into a convergent series of the form $\sum_{k=0}^{\infty} A_k U_k(x)$ where each A_k is a constant and the eigen functions $U_k(x)$ form a normal and orthogonal system. Particular cases of this kind had occurred since the latter half of the eighteenth century. From 1896, Steklov devoted numerous works to the elaboration of a general method of solving this problem in one, two, and three dimensions; this work resulted in the creation of the general "theory of closedness," the term he introduced in 1910. The condition of closedness established by Steklov is the generalization of Parseval's equality (1805) in the theory of Fourier series. The closed systems are "complete": they cannot be extended by adding new functions without loss of orthogonality; only closed systems may be used for solving the mentioned problem. In the simplest case, when it is necessary to expand a continuous function $f(x)$ on the segment (a, b) into a series of functions of one normal and orthogonal system $\{U_k(x)\}$ with respect to a weight $p(x) \geq 0$, so that $f(x) = \sum_{k=0}^{\infty} A_k U_k$ and the coefficients $A_k = \int_a^b p(x)f(x)U_k(x)dx$, the condition of closedness takes the form $\sum_{k=0}^{\infty} a_k^2 = \int_a^b p(x)f^2(x)dx$. Steklov investigated the closedness of diverse concrete systems and defined certain conditions under which the expansions in question really occur. In 1907 he began to use in the theory of closedness an important "smoothing method," which consisted of replacing the function under study—for example, $f(x)$—with some other mean function—$F_h(x) = \frac{1}{h} \int_x^{x+h} f(t)dt$—that in some sense has more convenient characteristics. For example, it is continu-

ous, whereas $f(x)$ is only integrable. This device is now widely used in mathematical physics. Steklov investigated expansions into series not only with the theory of closedness but also by means of asymptotic methods or by direct evaluation of the remainder term in the series.

The rise of the theory of integral equations at the beginning of the twentieth century, which led to new, general, and effective methods of solving the problems of mathematical physics and expansions of functions on orthogonal systems, inspired Steklov to improve the theory of closedness, although he did not participate in the elaboration of the theory of integral equations itself.

BIBLIOGRAPHY

I. Original Works. Steklov produced 154 works. Bibliographies are in *Pamyaty V. A. Steklova*, G. I. Ignatius, *Steklov* and (most complete) in V. S. Vladimirov and I. I. Markush, *Akademik V. A. Steklov* (see below). Among his writings are *O dvizhenii tverdogo tela v zhidkosti* ("On the Motion of a Solid Body in a Fluid"; Kharkov, 1893), his master's thesis; *Obshchie metody reshenia osnovnykh zadach matematicheskoy fiziki* ("General Methods of Solving Fundamental Problems of Mathematical Physics"; Kharkov, 1901), his doctoral dissertation; "Sur les problèmes fondamentaux de la physique mathématique," in *Annales de l'École normale supérieure*, 3rd ser., **19** (1902), 191–259, 455–490; "Théorie générale des fonctions fondamentales," in *Annales de la Faculté des sciences de Toulouse*, 2nd ser., **6** (1905), 351–475; "Sur les expressions asymptotiques des certaines fonctions définies par les équations différentielles du second ordre et leurs applications au problème du développement d'une fonction arbitraire en série procédant suivant les dites fonctions," in *Soobshchenia Kharkovskogo matematicheskogo obshchestva*, **10** (1907), 97–201; "Problème du mouvement d'une masse fluide incompressible de la forme ellipsoïdale dont les parties s'attirent suivant la loi de Newton," in *Annales scientifiques de l'Ecole normale supérieure*, 3rd ser., **25** (1908), 469–528, and **26** (1909), 275–336; "Une application nouvelle de ma méthode de développement suivant les fonctions fondamentales," in *Comptes rendus . . . de l'Académie des sciences*, **151** (1910), 974–977; "Sur le mouvement d'un corps solide ayant une cavité ellipsoïdale remplie par un liquide incompressible et sur les variations des latitudes," in *Annales de la Faculté des sciences de Toulouse*, 3rd ser., **1** (1910), 145–256; *Osnovnye zadachi matematicheskoy fiziki* ("Fundamental Problems of Mathematical Physics"), 2 vols. (Petrograd, 1922–1923); and *Matematika i ee znachenie dlya chelovechestva* ("Mathematics and Its Importance for Mankind"; Berlin–Petrograd, 1923).

II. Secondary Literature. See G. I. Ignatius, *Vladimir Andreevich Steklov* (Moscow, 1967); V. S.

Vladimirov and I. I. Markush, *Akademik V. A. Steklov* (Moscow, 1973); *Istoria otechestvennoy matematiki* ("History of Native Mathematics"), I. Z. Shtokalo, ed., II and III (Kiev, 1967–1968), see index; *Pamyaty V. A. Steklova* ("Memorial to . . . Steklov"; Leningrad, 1928), with articles by N. M. Gyunter, V. I. Smirnov, B. G. Galiorkin, I. V. Meshchersky, and R. O. Kuzmin–Gyunter's article, "Trudy V. A. Steklova po matematicheskoy fizike" ("Steklov's Works on Mathematical Physics") is reprinted in *Uspekhi matematicheskikh nauk*, **1**, nos. 3–4 (1946), 23–43; Y. V. Uspensky, "Vladimir Andreevich Steklov," in *Izvestiya Akademii nauk SSSR*, 6th ser., **20**, nos. 10–11 (1926), 837–856; and A. Youschkevitch, *Istoria matematiki v Rossii do 1917 goda* ("History of Mathematics in Russia Before 1917"; Moscow, 1968), see index.

A. P. YOUSCHKEVITCH

STELLER, GEORG WILHELM (*b.* Windsheim, Germany, 10 March 1709; *d.* Tyumen, Siberia, Russia, 12 November 1746), *geography, biology.*

Steller (whose real name was Stöller) was born in a small town in Franconia, where his father was an organist. He first studied Lutheran theology at Wittenberg but in 1731 entered the medical faculty of the University of Halle and began to devote himself to botanical research. Apparently he never passed a formal medical examination; but in 1734 he arrived in Danzig via Berlin, was accepted as physician in the Russian army, which was stationed there, and then continued on to St. Petersburg. Steller then worked as an assistant to Johann Amman, a botanist with the Russian Academy of Sciences, and gained a powerful patron in Archbishop Feofan Prokopovich, in whose house he lived.

Steller's desire to join the elaborately planned second Bering expedition as a research member was realized in 1736 when he was nominated a member. In the spring of 1738 he was appointed an assistant at the St. Petersburg Academy and left to join the other members of the expedition. In Yeniseysk, he met the botanist J. G. Gmelin and G. F. Müller. In 1740 they arrived at Okhotsk, and Steller continued with Bering to Kamchatka to study nature and folklore.

In 1741 Steller sailed under Bering's command on the *St. Peter* for America. He was the first natural historian to land on the coast of Alaska, where he collected specimens for several hours before the ship turned west. The return journey met with great difficulties. The crew, decimated by scurvy, was forced to pass the winter under great hard-

ships on Bering Island. Steller survived; and returning to Petropavlovsk in August 1742, he lingered further in Kamchatka, where he pursued his research in natural history and tried to complete his manuscripts. In 1746, en route to St. Petersburg, he was arrested for alleged insubordination as he was approaching the Ural Mountains. He was soon released but died of a fever in the fall of the same year.

Steller was a pioneer in the study of the natural history and geography of Kamchatka and Alaska. His great collections and many manuscripts were sent to the academy in St. Petersburg, and several manuscripts were published posthumously. His *Beschreibung von dem Lande Kamtschatka* (1774) is valuable especially because of his description of the life and habits of the inhabitants and because of his detailed illustrations. His journal of the expedition to Alaska was published by Pallas. On Bering Island, Steller studied the large sea mammals, including the remarkable Steller's sea cow, *Hydrodamalis gigas*, soon to be extinct. Botanical and zoological material from his collections has been published also by Gmelin in his *Flora sibirica* and by Linnaeus and Pallas.

Steller had a difficult and disharmonious character and a violent temper; but as an explorer and field worker, he was rugged, enthusiastic, and indomitable.

BIBLIOGRAPHY

I. ORIGINAL WORKS. Steller's major work is *Beschreibung von dem Lande Kamtschatka* (Frankfurt–Leipzig, 1774; St. Petersburg, 1793). His travel journal with the description of Bering Island and the voyage to Alaska was published by Pallas in *Neue Nordische Beyträge zur physikalischen und geographischen Erd- und Völkerbeschreibung . . .*, **2** (1781), 255–301; **5** (1793), 123–236, also issued separately; and **6** (1793), 1–26. An English trans. is F. A. Golder, *Bering's Voyage . . .*, II (New York, 1925). An abbreviated popular ed. is M. Heydrich, *Von Kamtschatka nach Amerika* (Leipzig, 1926).

Steller's description of the sea animals near Bering Island is "De bestiis marinis," in *Novi Commentarii Academiae Scientiarum Petropolitanae*, **2** (1751), 289–398, with German trans., *Beschreibung von sonderbaren Meerthieren* (Halle, 1753). Letters from Steller to Gmelin are in G. H. T. Plieninger, ed., *Joannis Georgii Gmelini reliquiae quae supersunt* (Stuttgart, 1861).

II. SECONDARY LITERATURE. The major source is Leonhard Stejneger, *Georg Wilhelm Steller, The Pi-*

oneer of Alaskan Natural History (Cambridge, Mass., 1936).

STEN LINDROTH

STELLUTI, FRANCESCO (*b.* Fabriano, Italy, 12 January 1577; *d.* Fabriano, November 1652), *microscopy, scientific organization.*

Stelluti's parents, Bernardino Stelluti and Lucrezia Corradini, belonged to patrician families of Fabriano. They intended him for the law, which subject he went to study at Rome toward the end of the sixteenth century. In Rome he came under the influence of Federico Cesi and Johannes Eck; and with them he helped found the Accademia dei Lincei in August 1603. His academic name was Tardigradus, and his emblem was the planet Saturn, which suggests that he was less quick mentally than his colleagues; he always appears as the loyal helper and companion rather than as the initiator. Stelluti lectured on his specialties, mathematics and astronomy. His classes opened with a general outline of geometry and moved straight on to a mechanized scaling ladder. Stelluti published nothing in mathematics. The Lincei suffered much harassment during their early "secret brotherhood" days, and in 1604 Stelluti was forced to leave Rome for his native Fabriano. He then moved to Parma, attaching himself to the ducal court there.

In October 1605, when Eck returned from his travels, he stayed in Parma with Stelluti, who illustrated the classification of butterflies from the specimens that Eck had brought back with him. This work was Stelluti's introduction to entomology. Once the ground had been cleared for a revival of the Academy, Stelluti and Eck returned to Rome (1608 or 1609).

Stelluti's first reaction to Galileo's *Sidereus nuncius* (1610) was rather disparaging, perhaps out of loyalty to the priority claim made by his colleague Giambattista della Porta. But he was soon won over to wholehearted admiration, and several of his letters to Galileo are preserved. Apart from a few comments on telescopic observations, the letters contain only academic business or personal gossip; Stelluti appreciated the intellectual gap between them and made no attempt to bridge it.

In 1612 Stelluti was elected procurator, or business manager, of the Academy and was entrusted with the negotiations for the purchase of property, where research could be carried on, and the publication of books under the auspices of the Lynxes. He was involved in the publication and distribution of Galileo's *Istoria e dimostrazioni intorno alle macchie solari* and *Il saggiatore* and wrote introductory verses for both.

In 1625 Stelluti made the first microscopic observations to be published, probably with an instrument that Galileo had sent to Cesi in 1624. Cesi had decided to bring out a short treatise on bees, a fragment from his projected encyclopedia, in compliment to Cardinal Francesco Barberini, of whose support the Academy had high hopes. The frontispiece of this *Apiarium* shows three views of a bee (magnified ten times) with insets of the whole head, eye, antenna and mouthparts (displaying the labia and galea), the rear legs, branched hairs, and the sting. Apparently these observations were checked by his fellow Lynx Fabio Colonna. In 1630 Stelluti published his translation, with commentary, of the satires of Persius. A reference to Arezzo, in which the Barberini family supposedly originated, was pretext enough to insert a *Descrizzione dell'ape*, illustrated by woodcuts based on the *Apiarium*, but magnified only six times, with a short account of the organs (shown separately). Persius' allusion to a grain weevil is illustrated by a microscopic representation (magnified ten times); the tip of the snout with its mandibles (magnified twenty times); and a view of the whole (life-size). Although there are numerous medical and botanical footnotes, they evince only casual observation.

When Cesi died in 1630, Stelluti tried to keep the Academy alive by proposing the election of a new prince, possibly Barberini. Although the cardinal was willing to patronize Stelluti, whose books were dedicated to him, he would not help the Academy to continue. In 1637 Stelluti produced synoptic tables of Porta's *De humana physiognomia*. In the introduction he promised that he would later add a treatise on "the hand of man compared to the feet of some quadrupeds and birds"; but this work never appeared. In the same year he published an account of fossilized wood found in the region of Todi. This work was based closely on Cesi's theories of a class of "metallophytes" intermediate between metals and plants. Stelluti explained how he had abandoned his own *prima facie* assumption that these fossils were simply buried, mineralized tree trunks. For most of the latter part of his life Stelluti served as the faithful adviser to Cesi's widow in her various troubles. He had the satisfaction of seeing the descriptions by the Academy of Mexican flora and fauna through the press in 1651. This publication also contained the synoptic tables of Cesi's system of taxonomy, for which Stelluti wrote an introduction, the melancholy last word of the first Academy of the Lynxes.

BIBLIOGRAPHY

I. ORIGINAL WORKS. Stelluti's works are *Persio tradotto in verso sciolto* . . . (Rome, 1630); *Della fisionomia de tutto il corpo humano . . . in tavole sinottiche ridotta et ordinata* (Rome, 1637); and *Trattato del legno fossile minerale nuovamente scoperto* (Rome, 1637).

II. SECONDARY LITERATURE. See G. Gabrieli, "Il carteggio scientifico ed accademico fra i primi Lincei 1603–30," in *Atti della Reale Accademia Nazionale dei Lincei*. Memorie della classe di scienze morali, storiche e filologiche, ser. 6, **1** (1925), 137–219; "Il carteggio linceo della vecchia accademia di Federico Cesi (1603–30)," *ibid.*, **7** (1938–1939), 1–535; G. Gabrieli, "Francesco Stelluti, Linceo Fabrianese," *ibid.*, ser. 7, **2** (1941), 191–233; B. Odescalchi, *Memorie istorico-critiche dell'Accademia dei Lincei* (Rome, 1806); C. Ramelli, "Discorso intorno a Francesco Stelluti da Fabriano," in *Giornale arcadico di scienze, lettere ed arte*, **87** (1841), 106–135; and C. Singer, "The Earliest Figures of Microscopic Objects," in *Endeavour*, **12** (1953), 197.

A. G. KELLER

STENSEN, NIELS, also known as **Nicolaus Steno** (*b.* Copenhagen, Denmark, 1/11 January 1638; *d.* Schwerin, Germany, 25 November/5 December 1686), *anatomy, geology, mineralogy.*

Stensen was the son of Sten Pedersen, who came from a family of preachers and was a goldsmith. After graduating from the Liebfrauenschule, Stensen entered the University of Copenhagen in 1656. There he studied medicine and came under the special influence of Simon Paulli and Thomas Bartholin. The customary study journey took him at the end of March 1660 to Amsterdam and, on 27 July for his matriculation, to the University of Leiden, from which, after three years of diligent research, he was called home because of the death of his stepfather.

The University of Copenhagen failed to enlist Stensen's services, and so he went to Paris; he is known to have been there as late as November 1664 and to have received on 4 December his M.D. from the University of Leiden in absentia. After a fruitful year in the circle of Thévenot, the king's chamberlain, Stensen went in the autumn of 1665 to Montpellier; and from there he went to Pisa, where he stayed until the beginning of March 1666. He remained in Tuscany until July 1668, mostly at the court of Grand Duke Ferdinand II in Florence.

Although he came from a deeply religious Lutheran family, Stensen became a convert to Catholicism on All Souls' Day 1667 during a period of research in anatomy and geology. This research was interrupted, probably by a summons to Denmark, from August 1668 to June 1670. Upon his return to Florence, Stensen again worked in Tuscany, exploring two alpine grottoes at Lake Garda and Lake Como for the Accademia del Cimento.

Following a call to return to Denmark as royal anatomist, Stensen arrived at Copenhagen on 3 July 1672. Here, mostly for a circle of interested friends, he held a series of anatomical demonstrations. But he left his native city on 14 July 1674 to return to Florence, where he was consecrated a priest, probably in the middle of April 1675, and where he worked for two years as educator and tutor of the crown prince. Upon the invitation of Duke Johann Friedrich of Hannover, he went to Rome, where he was appointed apostolic vicar of northern missions by Pope Innocent XI on 21 August 1677 and was consecrated titular bishop of Titiopolis on 19 September. Until the end of June 1680, he ministered to the scattered remnants of Catholicism in northern Germany, Denmark, and Norway. Then after the death of the duke, he was appointed assistant bishop of Münster in Westphalia, where he was very active. On 1 September 1683 he left the city in protest against the simoniac election of the bishop's successor. After two years of apostolic activity in Hamburg and Schwerin, he died in acute pain from gallstones.

Two educational influences upon Stensen's youth deserve special attention. Since his father's goldsmith shop was near the Round Tower, his scientific interest may have been directed at an early age into technical-mathematical channels to which he wished to return even in the midst of his first period of biological investigations in Leiden. He was interested in minerals and metals; in lenses and light refraction; and in telescopes, microscopes, and thermoscopes. Thomas Walgesten, the inventor of the *laterna magica*, belonged to the circle of his acquaintances. Stensen, of course, knew the medical authors Thomas Bartholin, Pierre Borel, Henricus Regius, Paracelsus, Helmont, and Santorio. Stensen's physical-mathematical interests are indicated by his reading not only the works of Galileo (*Sidereus nuncius* [1610]) and Kepler (*De nive sexangula* [1611]) but also those of Gassendi, Clavius, Gaspar Schott, Snel, and Varenius. Stensen had a precocious desire for methodically founded knowledge, and he was critical of analogies and purely authoritarian statements. He also asked for frequent observations and correct conclusions, and he declared himself in favor of Descartes's method in order to secure the greatest possible certainty. Stensen's writings also contain many passages that show a deeply religious nature and a highly ethical character.

During the second half of his life, in which he attained the highest fame and then—for the sake of God and of human souls—renounced his scientific research, there can be differentiated, both in time and in subject matter, four great periods of research. Each period began with almost accidental individual observations but led to an abundance of important discoveries and basic laws, many of which were recognized only in later centuries.

The first of these periods was devoted to the glandular and lymphatic system. In April 1660, three weeks after his arrival at Amsterdam, where he studied under the direction of Gerhard Bläes (Blasius), Stensen made his first known discovery: while dissecting the head of a sheep, he found the duct of the parotid gland (Stensen's duct), which is a principal source of saliva for the oral cavity.

In Leiden, then the most important university on the Rhine, Stensen sought contact with the two leading medical professors: Johannes van Horne, who independently of Pecquet had discovered the chief thoracic lymph passage, and Franciscus Sylvius, famous as an iatrochemist and for his studies on the brain. A warm and stimulating friendship with Jan Swammerdam also began in Leiden. Soon after Stensen's arrival, van Horne demonstrated on humans the course of the parotid duct and declared it to be Stensen's discovery, although Blasius, in his *Medicina generalis* (1661), not only claimed it for himself but incited his friends to slander Stensen, his former student. There ensued a long quarrel that Stensen settled both objectively and devastatingly in his *Apologiae prodromus* (1663).

The controversy spurred Stensen to the further investigation of the glands. He wrote: "I owe much to the famous man Blasius because he not only gave me cause to assert my property rights, but also to discover other new things."

The glands and lymph vessels were then a new and exciting subject for investigation. In 1622 Aselli had demonstrated the lacteal vessels in the mesentery of a dog; in 1642 Johann Georg Wirsung had shown the excreting duct of the pancreas; and in 1651 Pecquet had demonstrated the *cisterna chyli* and its continuation, the thoracic lymph duct; he also had realized that the latter poured its

contents into the veins. In 1653 Thomas Bartholin demonstrated the thoracic lymph passage and the lymphatic system in humans. He also showed that the lymph vessels connecting the liver to the thoracic duct carried lymph away from the liver, thereby throwing doubt on the Galenic doctrine that blood originated in the liver. When Thomas Wharton published his systematic presentation of the contemporary theory of glands in his *Adenographia* (1656), he announced the discovery of the duct of the submaxillary salivary gland; he also designated the brain and tongue as glands.

In contrast, Stensen very soon advanced from his "little discovery," as he called his first one, to a basic understanding of the whole glandular lymphatic system, which he counted among the most sublime artifices of the Creator. Without changing the names of the conglomerate and conglobate glands, the terms by which Sylvius had already distinguished the anatomical form of the real glands from that of the lymph nodes, Stensen distinguished them according to their function. Arguing against such contemporaries as Bils, Anton Deusing, and Everaertz, on the basis of his observations Stensen stated in his Leiden dissertation (1661):

> I gather from this that the saliva consists of the fluid secreted in the oral glands from the arterial blood which is carried through the lymph ducts with the aid of the *Spiritus animales* [a term then used for the nerves] into the mouth and the closely adjoining muscles, but that the round or conglobate glands in the proximity carry the lymphs received from the outer parts back to the veins so that it becomes mixed with the blood streaming back to the heart.

This discovery led Stensen to consider every fluid in the body as a glandular secretion. He then found a series of glands furnishing fluid to each of the body cavities. He likewise sought the afferent and efferent ducts of secretion. Stensen still used the name "lymph" for all watery glandular secretions, because he was not yet able to differentiate between them and to specify them chemically and physiologically.

In the course of this basic research Stensen presented in his Leiden dissertation new discoveries of glands in the cheeks; beneath the tongue; and in the palate, whose structure of veins, arteries, nerves, and lymph vessels he also described. In his *Observationes anatomicae* (1662), dealing with his new discoveries concerning the glands, he described the lachrymal apparatus in great detail. Stensen determined the purpose of the lachrymal fluid—to facilitate the movement and cleansing of the eyelids on the same principle that applied to the saliva and the mucous membrane of the intestinal canals. He grouped the afferent and efferent lachrymal ducts around the tear gland proper and what was then called *glandula lacrimalis*, in the inner eye corner. The moisture of the nose led him, in this connection, to the discovery of the nasal glands. Stensen considered the possibility that the moisture necessary for the nose could come from the ears through the eustachian tubes, and from the eyes through the nasal duct, but decided that the principal source was the nasal glands. He assumed that this fluid disappeared again through the nostrils and also through an opening to the gullet, the *ductus nasopalatini*, also called *ductus Stenoniani*.

In his survey *De musculis et glandulis* (1664) Stensen enumerated all his new observations and individual discoveries, especially those he had made during the first half of his stay in Leiden: earwax duct, ducts of the cheek glands, the smaller gland ducts under the tongue, the glandular ducts of the palate, the glandular ducts of the epiglottis, the nasal gland, the nasal gland peculiar to sheep, the passage from the eyelids to the nose, the lachrymal ducts, and the gland ducts that lubricate the exterior surface of the ray. In 1673 Stensen found, independently of Peyer, the accumulations of lymph follicles in the small intestine (named for Peyer), but published his findings four years later.

The second period of research began with a challenge to the traditional overestimation of the heart: "One has glorified the heart as the sun, even as the king while upon closer examination, one finds nothing but a muscle," which was directed not only against Aristotle, who saw the heart as the seat of the soul, the source of life, and the central organ of all sensation and motion, but also against Galen, who, following the authority of Plato, assigned the life forces of blood motion and heat distribution to the left ventricle. Even Harvey, who first recognized the purely muscle activity of the heart in maintaining the circulation of the blood, did not abandon the idea of a vital warmth within the heart, or did so only very late.

In a letter of 26 August 1662, Stensen told Thomas Bartholin how fascinated he was by the independent motions of the vena cava, which continued even after the stopping of the heartbeat; this stimulated Stensen to make many investigations of the heart and respiratory organs. On 5 March he had spoken of a careful investigation of the heart musculature, and on 30 April he had stated: "As to the substance of the heart, I think I am able to prove that there exists nothing in the heart that is

not found also in a muscle, and that there is nothing missing in the heart which one finds in a muscle."

De musculis et glandis (1664) shows an abundance of new observations and discoveries concerning the anatomy and physiology of individual muscle, and the triangularis, which leads from function of the intercostal muscles, the sacrolumbar muscle, and the triangulararis, which leads from the bony end of the true ribs to the central line of the sternum. He described the role of the diaphragm and several other muscles during respiration; classified the tongue as a muscle; and also described the temporal muscle, and the muscle layer of the esophagus, which has its fibers arranged spirally.

From this research Stensen drew comprehensive conclusions concerning the structure of the muscles: that in each muscle there are arteries, veins, fibers and fibrils, nerves, and membranes; that each muscle fiber ends in a tendon on both sides; that no muscle tissue is a parenchyma (*caro*) but consists instead of closely woven fibers; and that the contractility lies in the muscle substance proper. He then applied all his finding to the heart and proved its muscle structure from both positive and negative evidence. He stated that the heart possesses all the characteristics of a muscle structure and that it is neither the seat of joy nor the source of the blood or of the *spiritus vitales*. The automatic movement, independent of the will, is shared by the heart with other muscles. The findings were new, and even ten years later Bartholin, in a new edition of his *Institutiones anatomicae* (1611), did not accept them. Croone revised his *De ratione motus musculorum* (1664) according to Stensen's findings in the second edition (1670).

The controversy over his views caused Stensen, during his first year in Italy (1666/1667) to publish his *Elementorum myologiae specimen*, which dealt chiefly with the questions: Does the muscle increase in size during contraction? Are hardness and swelling of the muscle signs of an increase in volume? These were acute questions at the time, when even Borelli, one of the leading members of the Accademia del Cimento, still believed that swelling was caused by the influx of nerve fluid. Stensen first provided clear concepts and a clear-cut terminology of the parts of the muscle. Then he characterized the individual muscle fiber and the muscle itself as a parallepiped bordered by six parallelograms. In the second part of the *Elementorum* he dealt with objections against the new knowledge about muscles, and lamented the insufficient knowledge of the muscle fluid. Later, Stensen (before the theory of irritability proclaimed by Haller) discovered that a muscle contraction can also result from direct stimulation of the muscle.

Stensen's muscle research was also a symptom of his philosophical-religious struggle. At the turn of 1662/1663 he had wanted to abandon anatomy for mathematics and physics, a wish probably fostered by the spirit of the times and by his desire for certainty. The need for quantitative knowledge was indicated by Stensen's early enthusiasm for Descartes's method of attaining certainty. During his years in Leiden, Stensen became friendly with Spinoza, whose rationalism may have influenced Stensen so strongly that his Christian belief was endangered. His discovery of the muscle structure of the heart showed him the fallacy of the Cartesian view of the heart as a hearth of fire and made him skeptical of their whole seemingly firmly anchored geometrical philosophy. As he admitted later to Leibniz: "If these gentlemen have been so mistaken with material things which are accessible to the senses, what warranty can they offer that they are not mistaken when they talk about God and the soul?"

The third period of research extended from 1665 to 1667, the last great anatomical-physiological period of his life. The period can be divided into three parts: brain anatomy, embryology, and comparative anatomy.

Stensen's study of brain anatomy was confined almost entirely to his *Discours . . . sur l'anatomie du cerveau* (1669), which he presented in Paris to Thévenot's circle, among whom were many Cartesians. Stensen was stimulated to undertake his brain studies not only by his teacher, the brain anatomist Sylvius, but also by Descartes's *Traité de l'homme*. Vigorously but tactfully, Stensen opposed Descartes's mechanical theory and revealed his anatomical errors, refuting especially his theory concerning the epiphysis. According to Stensen, the epiphysis could not possibly carry out the slightest motion and thereby contribute to one's actions; whereas the Cartesian view was that it inclined itself to one side and then to the other side. In the *Discours* Stensen calls for a sober terminology and proposes new methods of dissection and the preparation of specimens. Stensen demands that the investigation trace the course of the brain fibers and that the investigator strive for a secure knowledge of the anatomical parts before interpreting their functions. In recent times his drawings of the brain have shown that he had a very rich knowledge of its anatomy.

From 1667 to 1669 Stensen contributed two concepts about the ovum and the ovary, oviduct, and uterus. The ovaries were considered to be *testes muliebres*, a type of semen producer. In a recently hatched chick Stensen discovered the oviduct and recognized that it was a canal destined to conduct the yolk directly into the intestine. In the *Elementorum* Stensen says that since he had found the true ova in the female testes, he concluded that they were really ovaries. Johannes Peter Müller credited Stensen with a discovery made by Aristotle but then forgotten: that in the so-called smooth sharks (*Mustelus laevis*) the eggs are not deposited, but the embryos remain connected to the uterus by a placenta, similar to that of mammals. Stensen's embryological observations were not published until 1675, but he had communicated them to De Graaf and Swammerdam. Therefore, the Royal Society of London, in the priority dispute concerning the procreative organs, assigned the credit to Stensen.

Among Stensen's unpublished observations are those on rays and sharks. He established the mucous canal system of these fishes and recognized the significance of the spiral fold in the intestine as a substitute for its greater length in other creatures. He also observed the eyeball stalk, the optical nerve, and the crossing of the optic nerves.

The technical side of Stensen's research was highly developed. He employed simple but effective means, such as the induction of bristles into the gland ducts or the expansion of vessels by inflation. It is not known to what extent he used the microscope, but he knew the optical experts of his time and such microscopists as Swammerdam and Malpighi. He was also a skilled draftsman. His diagram of the blood circulation, which for the first time revealed the heart as two relatively independent hearts or pumps, enabled his pupil Caspar Bartholin, Jr., to develop further the concept of circulation.

The fourth and greatest period of Stensen's research began in Florence at the end of October 1666, when he received the head of a gigantic *Carcharodon rondeletii* that had been caught near Leghorn. He made acute observations of its skin, its canals, the brain and nerves, the Lorenzinian ampullae, and the eyes. The rows of pointed teeth in the mouth, however, led him to a thorough study of their number and substance and also placed immediately before him the question of the relation of these teeth to the so-called *glossopetra* or tongue-stones, which were common on Malta and were considered *lapides sui generis*. Stensen concluded that they were fossil shark's teeth. This led to his paleontological, geological, and mineralogical discoveries.

Scarcely eighteen months later his great work, the *Prodromus*, which outlines the principles of modern geology, was printed. The book presents only the outlines of a discussion, yet almost every sentence or paragraph contains new insights.

After an introductory methodological discussion, Stensen states his purpose: "to find, in the case of a body possessed of a certain shape and produced on the basis of natural laws, the proofs in the body itself which reveal the site and the type of its origin." There follow three important sections: the first concerning the relationship in time between the enclosing body and the body enclosed; the second, the determination of the site and origin of a solid body; and the third, the role of fluids in nature.

In the third section Stensen states such important findings as the fundamental difference between inorganic bodies formed by apposition, and organic bodies formed by internal susception. In the third part the individual enclosing and enclosed bodies are considered. In the central section on geological strata Stensen presents his sediment theory, the time sequence and material of the strata, and data on the site of the stratification. After general observations concerning the effects on the strata of the changes of form through the forces of water and fire, there follows a special section on the origin of mountains. He discusses the sites of ores and minerals and includes an interesting section on crystals. At the end of the section, in drawings and two brief sentences, he states the law of the constancy of crystallic angles. The fourth main part of the work offers an application of the new finding to the geology of Tuscany, which is summarized in six stages of development and illustrated with six drawings. Finally he suggests the possible adaptation of all new findings to the generally prevailing world picture. Although Stensen introduced the concept of chronology and the history of the earth, he had little awareness of the actual duration of geological time.

A glance back to the first main part of the *Prodromus* shows the value of Stensen's methodological directives. He demanded that in the solution of a problem the questions connected with it be considered, that facts be distinguished from assumptions, and that the individual result be examined in connection with the history of science.

In the preface to his last great dissection of a female body (1673) Stensen states the spiritual side of his point of view. He calls the anatomist the index finger of God, addresses science as the servant of life, and declares himself a member of three realms (nature, mind, and faith) and does so in the name of beauty.

BIBLIOGRAPHY

I. ORIGINAL WORKS. Collected works of Stensen's writings are *Nicolai Stenonis opera philosophica*, Vilhelm Maar, ed., 2 vols. (Copenhagen, 1910), which includes the scientific works; *Nicolai Stenonis opera theologica . . .*, Knud Larsen and Gustav Scherz, eds. (Copenhagen, 1941, 1947), the theological and ascetical writings; *Nicolae Stenonis epistolae et epistolae ad eum datae . . .*, Gustav Scherz, ed., 2 vols. (Copenhagen-Fribourg, 1952), which includes Stensen's correspondence with an introduction on the correspondents, notes, and documents; and *Pionier der Wissenschaft, Niels Stensen in seinen Schriften* (Copenhagen, 1963), with a short biography and selected texts with introductions.

Stensen's most important writings include *Observationes anatomicae, . . .* (Leiden, 1662), which consists of four treatises, including Stensen's *Disputatio anatomica de glandulis oris . . .* (1661); *De musculis et glandulis* (Copenhagen, 1664), which includes two letters: "De anatome rajae epistola" and "De vitelli in intestina pulli transitu epistola"; *Elementorum myologiae specimen* (Florence, 1666/1667), also published as *Bibliotheca anatomica* (London, 1709–1714), an abridged English version; *Discours . . . sur l'anatomie du cerveau* (Paris, 1669), also published in G. Scherz, *Nicolaus Steno's Lecture on the Anatomy of the Brain* (Copenhagen, 1965); and *De solido intra solidum naturaliter contento dissertationis prodromus* (Florence, 1669), trans. by H. O[ldenburg], *The Prodromus to a Dissertation Concerning Solids Naturally Contained Within Solids . . .* (London, 1671), and by John G. Winter, *The Prodromus of Nicolas Steno's Dissertation Concerning a Solid Body Enclosed by Process of Nature Within a Solid* (New York, 1916).

See also *Prooemium demonstrationum anatomicarum in Theatro Hafniensi anni 1673*, in *Acata Faniensia* (1673); *Nicolai Stenonis ad novae philosophiae reformatorem de vera philosophia epistola* (Florence, 1675); *Nicolai Stenonis de propria conversione epistola* (Florence, 1677); and *Parochorum hoc age seu evidens demonstratio quod parochus teneatur omnes alias occupationes dimittere et suae attendere perfectioni ut commissas sibi oves ad statum salutis aeternae ipsis a Christo praeparatum perducat* (Florence, 1684).

II. SECONDARY LITERATURE. General biographies about Stensen are M. Bierbaum, *Niels Stensen. Von der Anatomie zur Theologie* (Münster, 1959); R. Cioni, *Niels Stensen. Scientist-Bishop* (New York, 1962); A. D. Jörgensen, *Niels Stensen* (Copenhagen, 1958); and

G. Scherz, *Niels Stensen. Forscher und Denker im Barock* (Stuttgart, 1964). More scholarly works on Stensen include G. Scherz, *Nicolaus Steno and His Indice* (Copenhagen, 1958), with a biography and various studies of Stensen's work; and *Nicolaus Steno and Brain Research in the Seventeenth Century* (London, 1967), from Proceedings of the International Symposium on N. Steno held in Copenhagen, August 1965.

On Stensen's work in anatomy, see P. Franceschini, "Priorita del Borelli e dello Stenone nella conoscenza dell' apparato motore," in *Monitore zoologico italiano* (1948), and in *Rivista di storia delle scienze mediche e naturali* (1951), 1–15; A. Krogh, "Biologen Niels Stensen. Trehundrede År.," in *Nordisk tidsskrift for terapi* (1937), 565–578; V. Maar, "Om Opdagelsen af Ductus Vitello-Intestinalis," in *Kongelige Danske Videnskabernes Selskabs Skrifter* (1908), 233–265; M. T. May, "On the Passage of Yolk Into the Intestines of the Chick," in *Journal of the History of Medicine* (1950), 119–143; H. P. Philipsen, "Ductus parotideus Stenonianus," in *Tendlaegetidende*, **64** (1960), 221–248; C. Schirren, "Niels Stensen entdeckte vor 300 Jahren die später nach Fallot benannte Tetralogie," in *Medizinische Welt* (1965), 278–280; Th. Schlichting, "Das Tagebuch von Niels Stensen," in *Centaurus* (1954), 305–310; C. M. Steenberg, "Niels Stensen som sammenlignende Anatom og Embryolog," in *Naturens Verden* (1938), 202–209; and E. Warburg, "Niels Stensen Beskrivelse af det første publicerede Tilfaelde af Fallcts Tetradé," in *Nordisk medicin*, **16** (1942), 3550.

On Stensen's geological work, see E. Becksmann, "N. Steno (1638–1686) und seine Stellung in der Geschichte der Geologie," in *Zeitschrift der Deutschen geologischen Gesellschaft*, **91** (1939), 329–336; A. Garboe, "Niels Stensens (Stenos) geologiske Arbejdes Skaebne," in *Danmarks geologiske undersøgelse*, **4** (1948), 1–34; A. Johnsen, "Die Geschichte der kristall-morphologischen Erkenntnis," in *Sitzungsberichte der Preussischen Akademie der Wissenschaften zu Berlin* (1932), 404; Hj. Oedum, "Niels Stensens geologiske Syn og videnskabelige Tankesaet," in *Naturens Verden* (1938), 49–60; F. Rodolico, "L'evoluzione geologica della Toscana secondo N. Stenone," in *Memorie della Società toscana di scienze naturali*, **60**, ser. A (1953), 3–7; H. Schenk, "Applied Paleontology," in *Bulletin of the American Association of Petroleum Geologists* (1940), 1752; G. Scherz, "Niels Stensens Smaragdreise," in *Centaurus* (1955), 51–57; and H. Seifert, "Nicolaus Steno als Bahnbrecher der modernen Kristallographie," in *Sudhoffs Archiv für Geschichte der Medizin und der Naturwissenschaften* (1954), 29–47.

The more general works on Stensen and his work are A. Faller, "Die philosophischen Voraussetzungen des Anatomen und Biologen Niels Stensen," in *Arzt and Christ* (Salzburg, 1962); K. Larsen, "Stenos Forfold til Filosofi og Religion," in *Kirkehist. Saml.* (Copenhagen, 1938), 511–553; J. Nordström, "Antonio Magliabechi och Nicolaus Steno," in *Lychnos*, **20** (1962), 1–42; R. Rome, "Nicolas Sténon (1638–1686). Anatomiste,

etc.," in *Revue des questions scientifiques* (1956), 517–572; "Nicolas Sténon et la Royal Society," in *Osiris*, **17** (1956), 244–268; and G. Scherz, "Danmarks Stensen-Manuskript," in *Fund og Forskning* (Copenhagen, 1958–1959), 19–33; and "Niels Stensen's First Dissertation," in *Journal of the History of Medicine and Allied Sciences*, **15** (1960), 247–264.

GUSTAV SCHERZ

STEPANOV, VYACHESLAV VASSILIEVICH (*b.* Smolensk, Russia, 4 September 1889; *d.* Moscow, U.S.S.R., 22 July 1950), *mathematics.*

Stepanov was the son of Vassily Ivanovich Stepanov, who taught history and geography at high schools in Smolensk; his mother, Alexandra Yakovlevna, was a teacher at a girls' school. An honor graduate of Smolensk high school in 1908, Stepanov entered the department of physics and mathematics of Moscow University later that year; his scientific supervisor was Egorov. In 1912, when he was about to graduate, it was suggested that he remain at the university to prepare for a professorship. After spending some time at Göttingen, where he attended lectures by Hilbert and E. Landau, Stepanov returned to Moscow and became lecturer at Moscow University in 1915. At that time he published his first scientific work, an article on Paul du Bois-Reymond's theory of the growth of functions.

From the first Soviet years, Stepanov participated in the organization of new types of university work, especially in the training of young scientists at the Research Institute of Mathematics and Mechanics, established at Moscow University in 1921. He was director of the Institute from 1939 until his death. He was also one of the most influential and active leaders of the Moscow Mathematical Society, owing, among other things, to his exceptional erudition and memory. In 1928 Stepanov became a professor, and in 1946 he was elected corresponding member of the Academy of Sciences of the U.S.S.R.

Stepanov's scientific interests were formed first under the influence of Egorov and Luzin, founders of the Moscow school of the theory of functions of a real variable. In works published in 1923 and 1925 Stepanov established the necessary and sufficient conditions under which a function of two variables, defined on a measurable plane set of finite measure greater than zero, possesses a total differential almost everywhere on that set. These works laid the foundations for the studies of I. Y. Verchenko, A. S. Cronrod, and G. P. Tolstov in the theory of functions of n variables. In his most widely known works, Stepanov treated the theory of almost periodic functions, introduced a short time earlier by H. Bohr; he also constructed and investigated new classes of generalized almost periodic functions.

Stepanov's interest in applications of mathematics and his work at the State Astrophysical Institute in 1926–1936 led him to study the qualitative theory of differential equations. In this field his principal works are related to the general theory of dynamic systems that G. D. Birkhoff elaborated, extending the work of Poincaré. Besides writing articles on the study of almost periodic trajectories and on generalization of Birkhoff's ergodic theorem (which found an important application in statistical physics), Stepanov organized a seminar on the qualitative methods of the theory of differential equations (1932) that proved of great importance for the creation of the Soviet scientific school in this field.

BIBLIOGRAPHY

I. Original Works. Stepanov's writings include "Über totale Differenzierbarkeit," in *Mathematische Annalen*, **90** (1923), 318–320; "Sur les conditions de l'existence de la différentielle totale," in *Matematicheskii sbornik*, **32** (1925), 511–527; "Über einige Verallgemeinerungen der fast periodischen Funktionen," in *Mathematische Annalen*, **95** (1925), 473–498; also in French in *Comptes rendus . . . de l'Académie des sciences*, **181** (1925), 90–94; "Über die Räume der fast periodischen Funktionen," in *Matematicheskii sbornik*, **41** (1934), 166–178, written with A. N. Tikhonov; "Sur une extension du théorème ergodique," in *Compositio mathematica*, **3** (1936), 239–253; *Kachestvennaya teoria differentsialnykh uravneny* (Moscow, 1947; 2nd ed., 1949), written with V. V. Nemytsky, translated into English as *Qualitative Theory of Differential Equations* (2nd ed., Princeton, 1960, 1964); and *Kurs differentsialnykh uravneny* ("Lectures on Differential Equations"; Moscow, 1936; 6th revised ed., 1953), translated into German by J. Auth *et al.* as *Lehrbuch der Differentialgleichungen* (Berlin, 1956).

II. Secondary Literature. See P. S. Aleksandrov and V. V. Nemytsky, *Vyacheslav Vassilievich Stepanov* (Moscow, 1956); *Istoria otechestvennoy matematiki* ("History of Native Mathematics"), I. Z. Shtokalo, ed., III–IV (Kiev, 1968–1970), see index; *Matematika v SSSR za sorok let* ("Forty Years of Mathematics in the U.S.S.R."), 2 vols. (Moscow, 1959), see index; and *Matematika v SSSR za tridtsat let* ("Thirty Years of Mathematics in the U.S.S.R."; Moscow–Leningrad, 1948), see index.

A. P. Youschkevitch

STEPHAN, ÉDOUARD JEAN MARIE (*b.* Ste.-Pezenne, Deux Sèvres, France, 31 August 1837; *d.* Marseilles, France, 31 December 1923), *astronomy.*

Stephan was admitted first in his class to the École Normale Supérieure in 1859. Upon graduating in 1862 he was invited by Le Verrier to the Paris observatory, where he learned observational techniques. At the same time he worked on his doctoral thesis, on second-order partial differential equations, which he defended in 1865.

Around this time Le Verrier had founded a branch of the Paris observatory at Marseilles. The city was selected as the appropriate site for the eighty-centimeter reflecting telescope, for which Léon Foucault had just constructed the mirror. In 1866 Stephan was assigned to equip and direct the observatory, and when it became independent of the Paris observatory in 1873, he was named director. In 1879 he became professor of astronomy at the University of Marseilles, holding both posts until his retirement in 1907. He became a corresponding member of the Bureau des Longitudes in 1875 and a corresponding member of the Académie des Sciences in 1879.

The scientists at the Marseilles observatory devoted their efforts primarily to the exploration of the sky. Stephan's collaborators, Alphonse Borrelly and J. E. Coggia, discovered a great number of asteroids and comets. Stephan directed his attention mainly to the search for nebulae and to the determination of their positions. He discovered approximately 350 of them, including a compact group known as "Stephan's quintet," which consists of five galaxies, one of which has a radial velocity very different from that of the others. The existence of this group poses two problems that are still unsolved: that of the instability of clusters of galaxies and that of abnormal red shifts. For his work as a whole, Stephan was awarded a prize by the Académie des Sciences in 1884.

The first to study stellar diameters, Stephan used a procedure suggested by Fizeau in 1868, in which the surface of the mirror of a telescope is masked by a screen, except for two separated areas that play the role of the slits in Young's experiment. The image of a point source is formed by the superposition of two groups of diffraction fringes; if the source has a perceptible apparent diameter, the fringes disappear when the distance between the areas attains a certain value, which is inversely proportional to this diameter. Stephan employed the procedure with the eighty-centimeter reflector in 1873 and observed the principal bright stars.

The fringes did not disappear, and he concluded that the stellar diameters were less than 0.16″. The experiment was repeated in 1920 by Michelson, whose determinations of diameters confirmed the upper limit obtained by Stephan.

Among his other accomplishments, Stephan contributed to the geodetic connection of Africa and Europe. In collaboration with Maurice Loewy and François Perrier, he determined the differences of longitude between Algiers, Marseilles, and Paris (1874–1876). In this undertaking the astronomical measurements were associated with telegraphic transmissions of time signals.

BIBLIOGRAPHY

I. ORIGINAL WORKS. For Stephan's observations of asteroids and comets, see "Discovery of a New Planet," in *Monthly Notices of the Royal Astronomical Society*, **27** (1867), 15; and "Comet I 1867, Discovered at Marseilles, 27 January 1867," *ibid.*, 255; as well as thirty-five notes in the *Comptes rendus hebdomadaires des séances de l'Académie des sciences*, **63–128** (1866–1899). On the observations of eclipses, see "Voyage de la Commission française . . . éclipse totale de soleil du 19-8-1868," in *Annales scientifiques de l'École normale supérieure*, **7** (1870), 99–162; and four notes in the *Comptes rendus hebdomadaires des séances de l'Académie des sciences*, **99** (1884), **106** (1888), **130** (1900), and **136** (1903). On the positions and discoveries of nebulae, see "Nebulae Discovered at Marseilles," in *Monthly Notices of the Royal Astronomical Society*, **32–34** and **37** (1872–1877); the last article reports on "Stephan's quintet," which is catalogued under the numbers 19–22, corresponding to the objects NGC 7317, 7318 A and B, 7319, and 7320. See also "Note sur les nébuleuses découvertes à l'Observatoire de Marseille," in *Bulletin astronomique*, **1** (1884), 286–290; "Nébuleuses découvertes et observées à l'Observatoire de Marseille," in *Astronomische Nachrichten*, **105** (1883), 81–90, and **111** (1885), 321–330; and eleven notes in *Comptes rendus hebdomadaires des séances de l'Académie des sciences*, **74–100** (1872–1885). For his work on stellar diameters, see "Sur les franges d'interférence . . .," *ibid.*, **76** (1873), 1008–1010; and "Extrême petitesse du diamètre apparent . . .," *ibid.*, **78** (1874), 1008–1012.

Three other publications should be noted: "Équations aux dérivées partielles du second ordre," in *Annales scientifiques de l'École normale supérieure*, **3** (1866), 7–53, his dissertation; "Détermination de la différence des longitudes entre Paris et Marseille et Alger et Marseille," in *Travaux de l'Observatoire de Marseille*, **1** (1878), 1–214, written with M. Loewy; and "Notice sur l'Observatoire de Marseille," in *Bulletin astronomique*, **1** (1884), 122–132.

II. SECONDARY LITERATURE. See J. Bosler, "Édouard Stephan," in *Bulletin astronomique*, **4** (1924), 5–8, with portrait; G. Bigourdan, "Annonce de la mort de Stephan," in *Comptes rendus hebdomadaires des séances de l'Académie des sciences*, **178** (1924), 21–24; and M. Hamy, "La détermination interférentielle des diamètres des astres," in *Annuaire publié par le Bureau des Longitudes* (1919), B9–B15.

JACQUES R. LÉVY

STEPHANUS, CAROLUS. See **Estienne (Stephanus), Charles.**

STEPHANUS (or STEPHEN) OF ALEXANDRIA (*fl.* first half of seventh century A.D.), *philosophy, mathematics, astronomy, alchemy.*

Stephanus was a public lecturer in Constantinople at the court of Emperor Heraclius (A.D. 610–641). Although primarily a mathematician, he apparently also taught philosophy, astronomy, and music in addition to arithmetic and geometry. Commentaries on Aristotle have come down to us under his name, but Stephanus is also reported to have written on other subjects, including astronomy. He has been identified, probably incorrectly, by some authorities with Stephanus of Athens, a medical writer; and commentaries on Galen and Hippocrates have been attributed to both these authors. The *Opusculum apotelesmaticum*, ascribed to Stephanus of Alexandria but probably dating from the eighth century, deals with Islam in astrological terms.

Considerable attention has been given to a long Greek treatise on alchemy, *De chrysopoeia*, which has been ascribed to Stephanus and which was much praised by later alchemists. Consisting of nine mystical lectures, this uncritical, rhetorical, and theoretical document gives no evidence of experimental work. Indeed, in the first lecture the author writes, "Put away the material theory so that you may be deemed worthy to see the hidden mystery with your intellectual eyes." The work may be dated later than the seventh century, but it is mentioned in an Arabic bibliography of A.D. 987, *Kitāb-al-Fihrist*, where the author is known as Stephanus the Elder, who is said to have "translated for Khālid ibn Yāzid alchemical and other works." This Umayyad prince, much interested in science and especially alchemy, died in A.D. 704.

BIBLIOGRAPHY

I. ORIGINAL WORKS. See *Democritus Abderita, De arte magna, sive de rebus naturalibus. Nec non Synesii, et Pelagii, et Stephani Alexandri, et Michaelis Pselli in eundem commentaria,* Dominic Pizimentus, ed. (Padua, 1573); "De chrysopoeia," Julius L. Ideler, ed., in *Physici et medici graeci minores,* II (Berlin, 1842), 199–253; *Opusculum apotelesmaticum,* Hermann Usener, ed. (Bonn, 1879); "In librum Aristotelis de interpretatione commentarium," Michael Hayduck, ed., in *Commentaria in Aristotelem graeca,* XVIII, 3 (Berlin, 1885); "Anonymi et Stephani in artem rhetoricam commentaria," H. Rabe, ed., *ibid.,* XXI, 2 (Berlin, 1896); and "The Alchemical Works of Stephanos of Alexandria," trans. and commentary by F. Sherwood Taylor, in *Ambix, the Journal of the Society for Study of Alchemy and Early Chemistry,* 1 (1937), 116–139; 2 (1938), 38–49.

II. SECONDARY LITERATURE. See Marcellin P. E. Berthelot, *Les origines de l'alchemie* (Paris, 1885), 199–201 and *passim; Introduction à l'étude de la chimie des anciens et du moyen age* (Paris, 1938), 287–301 and *passim;* Lucien Leclerc, *Histoire de la médecine arabe* (Paris 1876; New York, 1961); Hermann Usener, *De Stephano Alexandrino* (Bonn, 1880); Edmund O. von Lippmann, *Enstehung und Ausbreitung der Alchemie* (Berlin, 1919), 103–105; and George Sarton, *Introduction to the History of Science,* I (Baltimore, 1927), 472–473.

KARL H. DANNENFELDT

STEPHEN OF ANTIOCH (*fl.* first half of the twelfth century), *translation.*

According to a gloss on the *Diete universales* of Isaac Judaeus (Isḥāq al-Isrāʿīlī),[1] written by a certain Magister Mattheus F.,[2] Stephen of Antioch was a Pisan who went to Syria, learned Arabic, and translated the *Kitāb al-mālikī* of Haly Abbas (ʿAlī ibn al-ʿAbbās). This work, known more commonly in the medieval period as the *Liber regius,* was called by Stephen *Regalis dispositio.* Stephen undertook this task because, in his opinion, the text had been incompletely translated and grossly distorted by Constantine the African.[3] In order to prevent confusion between his own translation and that of Constantine, Stephen affixed his name to practically every one of the twenty books contained in the *Regalis dispositio,* adding the date on which each part of the work had been completed and several times naming the place where it had been made. Although the dates he gives are conflicting, the year 1127 is constant and can be reliably accepted. The place of translation, Antioch, has been questioned by some writers,[4] but in view of Stephen's remarks at the end of his *Synonima,* "these are the things we have found in Syria," and the description of him as "the nephew of the Patriarch of Antioch,"[5] there can be little doubt

that the place of translation is correct. The Latin patriarch of Antioch at that time was Bernard, previously bishop of Arethusa in Syria, who died in 1134.[6] Antioch also fits in with what we know of the Pisan contribution to the First Crusade and of the existence of a Pisan quarter in Antioch dating from 1108.[7]

In the prologue to the second part of the *Liber regalis* Stephen promised to assist his readers in their understanding of Arab materia medica by compiling a list of synonyms in three columns: Arabic, Latin, and Greek.[8] This list, which can be found in some manuscripts, does not appear in the printed editions and has been supplanted by an alphabetical list compiled by Michael de Capella.[9]

Stephen's probable connection with Salerno is indicated not only by his remark, made at the end of the *Synonima,* that if readers have difficulty in understanding the latinized Arab words they can consult Sicilian and Salernitan scholars who know both Greek and Arabic, but also by several quotations made from his work by Giovanni Platearius in his *Practica*[10] and by the Salernitan treatise *De aegritudinum curatione.*[11]

Stephen's accusation that Constantine the African was a plagiarist and a distorter of Haly Abbas' text has been uncritically accepted by later writers. A close comparison of the two translations reveals that Stephen's slavishly literal and verbose text closely follows its source, while Constantine's free paraphrase is easier to understand, gives better sense, and does great justice to the original.

Since Stephen says that his translation of the work of Haly Abbas was his first undertaking and that he intended to produce others, it has been suggested that he may be identical with a certain Stephanus Philosophus, who wrote several works on astronomy based on Arabic and Greek sources.[12] A comparison of the literary styles and vocabulary of their works makes the suggestion probable, but further investigation is needed.[13]

NOTES

1. W. M. Schum, *Beschreibendes Verzeichniss der Amplonianischen Handschriften-Sammlung zu Erfurt* (Berlin, 1887), 719; Hs. Amplon. O. 62ᵃ, fols. 49–83v.

2. V. Rose, *Verzeichniss der lateinischen Hss. der königlichen Bibliothek zu Berlin,* II, pt. 3 (Berlin, 1905), 1059–1065, expands the letter *F* to Ferrarius.

3. *Liber totius medicine necessaria continens quem sapientissimus Haly filius abbas discipulus abimeher moysi filii seiar edidit: regique inscripsit. vnde et regalis dispositionis nomen assumpsit. Et a Stephano philosophie discipulo ex arabica lingua in latinam satis ornatam reductas . . . .* (Lyons, 1523), fol. 5r, col. 2.

4. See M. Steinschneider, in *Virchows Archiv für patholo-gische Anatomie und Physiologie und für klinische Medizin,* **39** (1867), 333.
5. B. M. Sloane MS 2426, fol. 8r.
6. P. B. G. Gams, *Series episcoporum* (Regensburg, 1873–1886), 433. For the bishopric of Arethusa in Syria, see M. Lequien, *Oriens christianus, in quattuor patriarchatus digestus; quo exhibentur ecclesiae, patriarchae, caeterique Praesules totius Orientis* (Paris, 1740), II, 915; III, 1190–1191.
7. V. Balaguer, *Historia de Cataluña y de la Corona de Aragon,* I (Barcelona, 1863), 620 ff.
8. *Liber regalis* (Lyons, 1523), fol. 136r, col. 1.
9. This list appears at the beginning of the 1523 edition and is not paginated.
10. Printed with *Practica Jo. Serapionis dicta breviarium* (Venice, 1503). The relevant passages can be found on fols. 180r, 180v, cols. 1 and 2, 183v, col. 1.
11. S. de Renzi, *Collectio Salernitana,* II (Naples, 1853), 266, 267, 270, 326–327, with the attribution to M[agister] Platearius.
12. C. H. Haskins, *Studies in Mediaeval Science* (Cambridge, Mass., 1927), 99–103, 135.
13. R. Ganszyniec, "Stephanus de modo medendi," in *Archiv für Geschichte der Medizin,* **14** (1923), 110–113, claims him as the author of a text that appeared in a fifteenth-century MS of Cracow and tries, unconvincingly, to make him a pupil of Copho of Salerno.

CHARLES H. TALBOT

STEPLING, JOSEPH (*b.* Regensburg, Germany, 29 June 1716; *d.* Prague, Bohemia [now Czechoslovakia], 11 July 1778), *astronomy, physics, mathematics.*

Stepling's father came from Westphalia and was a secretary to the Imperial Embassy at Ratisbon (Regensburg). His mother's homeland was Bohemia. After his father's early death, the family moved to Prague. There Stepling began his studies at the Gymnasium run by the Jesuits. He soon demonstrated an extraordinary gift for mathematics, and a certain Father Sykora successfully endeavored to bring out his protégé's talent. When Stepling was only seventeen he calculated with great accuracy the lunar eclipse of 28 May 1733.

Despite a frail physical constitution, Stepling was admitted to the Jesuit order in 1733. After a biennial novitiate at Brno, he attended a three-year course of philosophy (1735 to 1738). His pupil, and later biographer, Stanislaus Wydra, states that Stepling, even in his early studies, transposed Aristotelian logic into mathematical formulas, thus becoming an early precursor of modern logic. Having already adopted the atomistic conception of matter (hyle), he radically refused to accept Aristotelian metaphysics and natural philosophy (the hylomorphic system). From 1738 to 1741 Stepling was a teacher at the Gymnasiums of Glatz (now Kłodzko) and Schweidnitz (now Świdnica). During the period 1741–1743, he devoted himself to special studies in mathematics, physics, and astronomy in Prague. From 1743 to 1747 he studied theology there and in 1745 took holy orders. The last year of his training began a tertianship (special studies of the law of the Jesuit order) in Gitschin (now Jičín), after which he declined a professorship of philosophy at the University of Prague in favor of the chair of mathematics. In 1748, at the request of the Berlin Academy, he carried out an exact observation of a solar and lunar eclipse in order to determine the precise location of Prague.

During Stepling's long tenure at Prague, he set up a laboratory for experimental physics and in 1751 built an observatory, the instruments and fittings of which he brought up to the latest scientific standard. In 1753 the Empress Maria Theresia, as part of her reform of higher education, appointed Stepling director of the faculty of philosophy at Prague. In this capacity he modernized the entire philosophical curriculum, which in those days embraced the natural sciences. He was particularly intent on cultivating the exact sciences, including physics and astronomy; and, following the example of the Royal Society in London, he founded a scientific study group. In their monthly sessions, over which he presided until his death, the group carried out research work and investigations in the field of pure mathematics and its application to physics and astronomy. A great number of treatises of this academy were published.

Stepling corresponded with the outstanding contemporary mathematicians and astronomers: Christian Wolf, Leonhard Euler, Christopher Maire, Nicolas-Louis de Lacaille, Maximilian Heli, Joseph Franz, Rudjer Bošković, Heinrich Hiss, and others. Also, Stepling was particularly successful in educating many outstanding scientists, including Johann Wendlingen, Jakob Heinisch, Johannes von Herberstein, Kaspar Sagner, Stephan Schmidt, Johann Körber, and Joseph Bergmann. After his death, Maria Theresia ordered a monument erected in the library of the University of Prague.

BIBLIOGRAPHY

I. ORIGINAL WORKS. Stepling's works include *Eclipsis lunae totalis Pragae octava Augusti 1748 observata* (Prague, 1748); *De actione solis in diversis latitudinibus* (Prague, 1750); *Exercitationes geometrico-analyticae de angulis aliisque frustis cylindrorum, quorum bases sunt sectiones conicae infinitorum generum* (Prague, 1751); *Observationes baroscopicae, thermoscopicae, hyetome-*

tricae (Prague, 1752); *De pluvia lapidea anni 1753 ad Strkow et ejus causis* (Prague, 1754); *Brevicula descriptio speculae astronomicae Pragae instructae* (Wittenberg, 1755); *De terrae motus causa discursus* (Prague, 1756); *Liber II. Euclidis algebraice demonstratus* (Prague, 1757); *Solutio directa problematis de inveniendo centro oscillationis* (Prague, 1759); *Contra insignem superficiei oceani et marium cum eo communicantium inaequalitatem a V. Cl. Henrico Kuehnio assertam* (Prague, 1760); *Beantwortung verschiedener Fragen über die Beschaffenheit der Lichterscheinung Nachts den 28 Hornungstage, und über die Nordlichter* (Prague, 1761); *De aberratione astrorum et luminis; item de mutatione axis terrestris historica relatio* (Prague, 1761); *Adnotationes in celebrem transitum Veneris per discum solis anno labente 6. Jun. futurum* (Prague, 1761); *De terrae motibus . . . adnexa est meditatio de causa mutationis Thermarum Töplicensium . . .* (Prague, 1763); *Vergleichungstafeln der altböhmischen Maasse und deren Preis mit den neu Oestreichischen und deren Preis* (Prague, 1764); *Differentiarum minimarum quantitatum variantium calculus directus, vulgo differentialis* (Prague, 1765); and *Clarissimi ac magnifici viri Iosephi Stepling . . . litterarum commercium eruditi cum primum argumenti* (Prague, 1782).

Stepling published many papers in *Nova acta eruditorum* (1750, 1761), and *Abhandlungen einer Privatgesellschaft in Böhmen zur Aufnahme der Mathematik, der vaterländischen Geschichte, und der Naturgeschichte* (1775–1784).

A bibliography appears in Poggendorff, II, 1004.

II. SECONDARY LITERATURE. On Stepling and his work, see Ludwig Koch, S.J., *Jesuitenlexikon* (Paderborn, 1934), cols. 1692–1693; Franz Martin Pelzel, *Boehmische, Maehrische und Schlesische Gelehrte und Schriftsteller aus dem Orden der Jesuiten* (Prague, 1786), 227–230; Carlos Sommervogel, S.J., *Bibliothèque de la Compagnie de Jésus*, VII (Brussels, 1896), cols. 1564–1568; Stanislaus Wydra, *Laudatio funebris Jos. Stepling coram senatu populoque academico . . . dicta* (Prague, 1778); *Vita Admodum Reverendi ac magnifici viri Iosephi Stepling* (Prague, 1779); and *Oratio ad monumentum a Maria Theresia Aug. Josepho Stepling erectum . . .* (Prague, 1780); and *Abbildungen böhmischer und Mährischer Gelehrter und Künstler nebst kurzen Nachrichten von ihren Leben und Werken*, IV (Prague, 1782), 164–172, which appeared without the name of the author but has the printed signature "Franz Martin Pelzel und die übrigen Verfasser" on the dedication page.

D. ANTON PINSKER, S.J.

STERN, OTTO (*b.* Sohrau, Upper Silesia, Germany [now Zory, Poland], 17 February 1888; *d.* Berkeley, California, 17 August 1969), *physics.*

Stern was the oldest of five children (two sons and three daughters) of Oskar Stern and Eugenie Rosenthal. Before he reached school age, the family moved to Breslau (now Wrocław, Poland), where Otto received his primary and secondary education at the Johannes Gymnasium. After graduating in 1906, he continued his studies at the universities of Freiburg im Breisgau, Munich, and Breslau, from which he received the Ph.D. in physical chemistry in 1912.

Stern's parents belonged to a prosperous Jewish family of grain merchants and flour millers who were content to let their children satisfy their thirst for knowledge without immediate, professional goals. Even while attending the Gymnasium, which emphasized the classics at the expense of mathematics and the sciences, Stern supplemented his education by perusing various books that his father put at his disposal; and during his university studies, he explored several fields of science before deciding on a career. This approach to learning was in accordance with German academic tradition in the period before World War I, when young men of means could migrate from one university to another and attend lectures on a variety of subjects without regard to curricula or to the time needed for completion of promotion requirements. Thus, Stern attended lectures on theoretical physics by Arnold Sommerfeld, one of the most brilliant lecturers of his generation, and on experimental physics by Otto Lummer and Ernst Pringsheim, both of whom were famous for their elegant research on blackbody radiation.

Stern's real interest, however, was aroused more by his private readings than by his formal studies. The books of Boltzmann on molecular theory and statistical mechanics and of Clausius and Nernst on thermodynamics appear to have greatly influenced his choice of career. Returning to Breslau to complete his university studies, Stern decided to major in physical chemistry because two professors in that department, R. Abegg and O. Sackur, were more closely concerned with his interest in thermodynamics and molecular theory than were the professors of physics. His doctoral dissertation on the osmotic pressure of carbon dioxide in concentrated solutions was both theoretical and experimental and set the style for his future research, which he himself later described as that of an "experimenting theoretician."

Stern's scientific activity can be divided into two distinct periods: the theoretical (1912–1919) and the experimental (1919–1945). During the first period, he was strongly influenced by his contacts with Einstein, whom he joined as a postdoctoral associate in Prague immediately after graduating from Breslau and with whom he moved to Zurich in 1913; by Ehrenfest and Laue, with whom he became acquainted in Zurich; and finally, but to a lesser extent, by Max Born, with whom he began to work after his return to Frankfurt in 1919. During these years, he took advantage of his financial independence, which allowed him to select a place of work without regard to the availability of a remunerative position. He received the *venia legendi* at the Eidgenössische Technische Hochschule in Zurich in 1913 and transferred it to the University of Frankfurt in 1914, thus achieving the status of *Privatdozent*, which carried the right to lecture in the university without salary. From the outbreak of the war in August 1914 until the German defeat in 1918, he served in the German army, first as a private and later as a noncommissioned officer, in various technical assignments. After his demobilization he returned to Frankfurt.

This period can best be described as Stern's *Lehr- und Wanderjahre*. Its most important result was not the production of scientific papers, although Stern's papers published during these years were by no means negligible, but the development of a certain attitude toward the selection of research problems. As Stern told this writer, he was less attracted to Einstein because of his spectacular achievement in formulating the theory of relativity than by his work in molecular theory, particularly the application of the then imperfectly understood quantum concepts to the explanation of the curious temperature behavior of the specific heat of crystalline bodies.

An early paper published with Einstein contributed to one aspect of this problem, namely, the question of the existence of the so-called zero-point energy: Are the atoms of a body at rest at the absolute zero of temperature, or do they oscillate around their equilibrium positions with an energy of $h\nu/2$? But what Stern really learned from Einstein was the evaluation of the importance of current physical problems, which questions to ask, and what experiments should be undertaken at a given time. His association with Einstein developed into a lifelong friendship and planted the seed for the major accomplishments of Stern's later career, culminating in his winning the Nobel Prize in physics for 1943.

Stern's work during the years 1912–1918 was concerned with various problems in statistical thermodynamics. Two papers published during this period are worthy of mention, one because of its scientific merit and the other because of the unusual circumstances of its origin. The first dealt with the absolute entropy of a monoatomic gas. The expression for the entropy of a gas obtained by classical theories contains an arbitrary constant that cannot be computed but that greatly affects such properties as the vapor pressure of a solid or the chemical equilibrium of reacting gases. The importance of this constant had been pointed out by Nernst in the formulation of the third law of thermodynamics (also known as Nernst's theorem).

It was fairly obvious that quantum theory held the key to the solution of this problem, but the methods for the application of quantum concepts to a perfect gas had not yet been discovered. Otto Sackur and Tetrode had already published papers giving a theoretical expression for the entropy constant; and while their result was correct, their derivation was open to justifiable criticism. Stern avoided the need of applying quantum theory to a gas by considering the equilibrium of a solid crystal with its vapor at a high temperature. Under these conditions it was perfectly correct to use classical statistical mechanics for the gas and to apply quantum concepts only to the solid, where the theory provided the necessary guidance. Using Einstein's theory of the specific heat and Nernst's theorem, Stern obtained the same result as Sackur and Tetrode, but this time the derivation was unobjectionable.

The second paper carries the dateline "Lomsha, Russian Poland," probably the only scientific paper that ever originated in this small town. Stern was stationed there during 1916 as a military weather observer, and his duties of recording twice daily the readings of a few instruments left him plenty of free time. To escape boredom he tackled the tedious problem of calculating the energy of a system of coupled mass points — doing all the computations in longhand.

During the last years of the war, many German physicists and physical chemists were assigned to military research at Nernst's laboratory at the University of Berlin. There Stern met James Franck and Max Volmer, both excellent experimenters; and it is very probable that his shift from theoretical to experimental work was due to the influence of these two scientists, who also became his lifelong friends.

After returning to Frankfurt, Stern continued to work on similar theoretical problems; and he published a paper on the surface energy of solids with Max Born, director of the Institute for Theoretical Physics, to which Stern was attached. Shortly thereafter, Stern felt compelled to provide experimental proof for the fundamental concepts used in molecular theory. For this purpose, he began to develop the molecular-beam method. In 1911 Dunoyer had shown that atoms or molecules introduced into a high-vacuum chamber travel along straight trajectories, forming beams of particles that in many respects are similar to light beams. His work had been practically forgotten until Stern realized that it was a very powerful tool for the investigation of properties of free atoms. Thus began the second period of Stern's scientific career, which secured for him a place of honor in the history of physics.

The first application of this method was still concerned with molecular theory, namely, the measurement of molecular velocities in a gas. These quantities had been computed theoretically around 1850; and although the result had been generally accepted, no one had succeeded in providing experimental proof. In 1919 Stern performed an elegant experiment, using beams of silver atoms, and confirmed the theoretical values within the limits of experimental error. Although a nice achievement, it was not exactly world-shaking. Its real importance was that it demonstrated the usefulness of the method and encouraged its further application. (Einstein's teaching of how to recognize the really important problems is clearly visible in this work.)

At that time, Bohr's theory of the atom had undergone rapid development, particularly in the hands of Sommerfeld, who concluded that certain atoms—for example, those of hydrogen, the alkali metals, or silver—should possess magnetic moments of the magnitude of

$$M = \frac{eh}{4\pi mc},$$

where e is the electronic charge, m is the mass of an electron, c is the velocity of light, and h is Planck's constant. Moreover, if such an atom were placed in a magnetic field, it should be able to assume only two distinct orientations, with its axis and magnetic moment either parallel or opposed to the direction of the field. (A third possible orientation—magnetic moment perpendicular to the field—was forbidden by a special selection rule.) While the first conclusion was at least compatible with the classical theory, the second was not, and very few physicists of that time were inclined to take this spatial quantization seriously. Stern recognized that the molecular-beam method was capable of giving a clear yes-or-no answer to this question: If the classical theory were correct, a narrow beam of silver atoms should be broadened

when passing through a nonhomogeneous magnetic field; but if the spatial quantization theory were correct, the beam should be split into two separate beams.

In 1920 this experiment, although simple in concept, was difficult to perform. Not particularly skillful in handling experimental techniques (as opposed to designing experiments), Stern asked Walther Gerlach, a colleague at the Institute for Experimental Physics in Frankfurt, to join in this work. Together they succeeded in proving the reality of space quantization and in measuring the magnetic moment of the silver atom. The five papers reporting this work, which soon became known as the Stern-Gerlach experiment, received wide attention and established Stern's rank among physicists.

In 1921, when these experiments were practically completed, Stern received his first formal academic appointment as associate professor of theoretical physics at the University of Rostock. There he was joined by this writer, who had just completed his doctorate under Stern's friend Max Volmer. At that time, an appointment in Rostock was mainly a stepping-stone to greener pastures, and it was not long before Stern received a call to the University of Hamburg as professor of physical chemistry and as director of the Institute for Physical Chemistry, still to be erected. In the meantime, Stern and this writer, who were later joined by a few additional assistants, postdoctoral guests, and graduate students, were assigned temporary quarters in the Institute for Experimental Physics.

The period 1923–1933 marks the peak of Stern's contributions to physics. Shortly after assuming his post at Hamburg on 1 January 1923, he set out to organize a laboratory specially equipped for molecular-beam research and to devise a program for conducting this research, which was executed, to a large degree, with remarkable success. The first part of the program was concerned with completing and expanding Stern's previous work and with developing new and improved techniques; the second, with demonstrating the wave nature of particles—a revolutionary assumption introduced in 1924 by Louis de Broglie that became the foundation of modern quantum mechanics; and the third, with measuring the magnetic moment of the proton and deuteron. The significance of the work on the wave nature of particles is similar to that of the Stern-Gerlach experiment: each provided unambiguous, direct, and thoroughly convincing proof of revolutionary concepts introduced into the foundations of physics. These experiments were essential for the acceptance of new ideas that had previously been regarded with considerable skepticism.

The last part of Stern's program had a completely different outcome. Dirac had promulgated a theory according to which the ratio of the magnetic moment of the proton to that of the electron should have been the same as the inverse ratio of their masses. This theory was believed so generally that when Stern, O. R. Frisch, and this writer began the very difficult experiments, they were told more than once by eminent theoreticians that they were wasting their time and effort. But Stern's perseverance paid off. Measurements showed a proton magnetic moment two or three times larger than expected. While that result has since been reproduced with greater accuracy, a really satisfactory theoretical explanation is still outstanding. It is this work that was specifically mentioned in Stern's Nobel Prize citation.

With the advent of the Nazi regime in 1933, the work in Hamburg came to an abrupt end. Several of Stern's closest collaborators, who happened to be of Jewish origin, were summarily dismissed, and in protest Stern submitted his resignation before his own foreseeable dismissal. Stern and this writer received invitations to come to the United States, to the Carnegie Institute of Technology, where they began to build a molecular-beam laboratory. Stern was appointed research professor of physics, but the means put at his disposal during the depression years were rather meager. The momentum of the Hamburg laboratory was never regained, although a number of significant papers originated at Carnegie. Stern retired in 1946 to Berkeley, California, where he continued to maintain some contact with local physicists but shunned public appearances. Stricken by a heart attack, he died on 17 August 1969 at the age of eighty-one.

Stern was a member of both the National Academy of Sciences and the American Philosophical Society in 1945 after having received the Nobel Prize. He was also a member of the Royal Danish Academy and received honorary doctorates from the University of California and the Eidgenössiche Technische Hochschule in Zurich.

BIBLIOGRAPHY

I. Original Works. A complete bibliography of the papers published by Stern and his associates between 1926 and 1933 is listed in Estermann (see below). His early paper on the absolute entropy of a monoatomic gas is "Zur kinetischen Theorie des Dampfdrucks einatomiger fester Stoffe und über die Entropiekonstante einatomiger Gase," in *Physikalische Zeitschrift*, **14** (1913), 629–632; the memoir on the energy of a system of coupled mass points is "Die Entropie fester Lösungen," in *Annalen der Physik*, 4th ser., **49** (1916), 823–841. Subsequent works cited above are "Über die Oberflächenenergie der Kristalle und ihren Einfluss auf die Kristallgestalt," in *Sitzungsberichte der Preussischen Akademie der Wissenschaften zu Berlin* (1919), 901–913, written with Max Born; and "Eine direkte Messung der thermischen Molekulargeschwindigkeit," in *Zeitschrift für Physik*, **2** (1920), 49–56, and **3** (1920), 417–421.

The results of the Stern-Gerlach experiment were reported in "Ein Weg zur experimentellen Prüfung der Richtungsquantelung im Magnetfeld," *ibid.*, **7** (1921), 249–253; "Der experimentelle Nachweis des magnetischen Moments des Silberatoms," *ibid.*, **8** (1921), 110–111, written with W. Gerlach; "Der experimentelle Nachweis der Richtungsquantelung im Magnetfeld," *ibid.*, **9** (1922), 349–352, written with Gerlach; "Das magnetische Moment des Silberatoms," *ibid.*, 353–355, written with Gerlach; and "Über die Richtungsquantelung im Magnetfeld," in *Annalen der Physik*, 4th ser., **74** (1924), 673, written with Gerlach.

Stern's Nobel Prize lecture, "The Method of Molecular Rays," is in *Nobel Lectures 1942–1962 (Physics)* (Amsterdam–London–New York, 1964), 8–16, with biography on 17–18.

II. Secondary Literature. See I. Estermann, "Molecular Beam Research in Hamburg, 1922–1933," in his *Recent Research in Molecular Beams* (New York–London, 1959), 1–7, with bibliography.

I. Estermann

STERNBERG, KASPAR MARIA VON (*b*. Prague, Bohemia [now in Czechoslovakia], 6 January 1761; *d*. Březina castle, Radnice, 20 December 1838), *botany, geology, paleontology.*

Sternberg was the scion of an old landed family that took its title from Sternberg castle in the Sázava valley forty-five kilometers southeast of Prague. His eldest brother, Joachim, was fond of mathematics; he also founded an iron factory and took a keen interest in mining and metallurgy, on which he wrote prolifically. Strongly influenced by the activities and philanthropy of his family, Sternberg studied theology at first privately and later at Rome. He then pursued a celibate ecclesiastical career, being appointed successively canon and counselor to the court of the prince-bishop of Regensburg. In 1791 he was nominated counselor to the court at Freisingen.

His duties at Regensburg involved the control of

woods and forests and induced him to study botany and later to found a botanical garden there. In 1805 and 1806 he accompanied the prince-bishop to Paris, where he met many prominent scientists including Faujas de Saint-Fond, who initiated him in the study of fossil plants. Here he received and studied carefully, with the aid of collections in Paris, Ernst von Schlotheim's book (1804) on fossil plant impressions in Coal Measures. In 1808 he inherited the family estate at Radnice with Březina castle and thereafter devoted himself to botanical studies and the promotion of natural science in Bohemia. When, shortly before his death thirty years later, he presided over a large congress of naturalists at Prague, he and Brongniart were recognized as the two leading paleobotanists in the world.

Sternberg studied especially the Carboniferous phytopaleontology but he also published some papers dealing with the trilobites and Pleistocene fauna. He had ready access to fossils and fossil impressions found in the coalfields on his own estate and in the "transitional rocks" near Prague. He tried to interpolate the species of fossil plants into the botanical system by discarding the old names given to the fossil forms and applying existing botanical correlations to them. Thereby he greatly increased the proper botanical significance of fossil floras and paved the way for a scientific treatment of paleobotany. His chief work, the seven-volume *Versuch einer geognostisch-botanischen Darstellung der Flora der Vorwelt* (1820–1833), described two hundred fossil species of plants with the aid of sixty folio plates. The ideas expressed in this work expanded those of Ernst von Schlotheim but were based on a narrower range of material than that contained in the contemporary publications of Brongniart, one of the Paris naturalists who helped to turn Sternberg to botanical pursuits. William Buckland sized up the situation fairly when he wrote: "We owe to the labours of Schlotheim, Sternberg and Ad. Brongniart the foundation of such a systematic arrangement of fossil plants, as enables us to enter, by means of the analogies of recent plants, into the difficult question of the Ancient Vegetation of the Earth, during those periods when the strata were under the process of formation" (*Geology and Mineralogy*, I [London, 1837], 454).

Sternberg's name is commemorated in the technical terminology for fossil organisms, both animal and vegetable, *Sternbergia*, *Sternbergella*, and *Parasternbergella*. The plants include several small crocuslike species native to Europe, such as

Sternbergia lutea. The mineral sternbergite is a natural sulfide of silver and iron ($AgFe_2S_3$) crystallized in orthorhombic prisms and first discovered in the mines at Joachimsthal (Jachymov), Bohemia.

In 1818–1821 Sternberg was one of the chief founders of the Bohemian National Museum, Prague. He acted as its president from 1822 to his death and bequeathed his library and his geological and botanical collections to it. He had close dealings with Goethe and their correspondence has been published. Today his botanical, geological, and paleontological collections remain in the National Museum. His written works are in the Museum of National Literature, Prague, and his diplomas, correspondence, and other literary remains are in the department of the State Archives at Benešov.

BIBLIOGRAPHY

I. Original Works. Sternberg wrote all his books and articles in German. F. Palacký, *Leben des Grafen K. Sternberg . . .* (see below), contains a bibliography with 74 titles, among which the most important are *Galvanische Versuche in manchen Krankheiten; herausgeben mit einer Einleitung in Bezug auf die Erregungstheorie von J.-U.-G. Schaeffer* (Regensburg, 1803); *Botanische Wanderungen in den Böhmerwald . . .* (Nuremberg, 1806); *Reisen in die rhaetischen Alpen, vorzüglich in botanischer Hinsicht* (Nuremberg–Regensburg, 1806); *Reise durch Tyrol in die Oesterreichischen Provinzen Italiens in Frühjahr 1804 . . .* (Regensburg, 1806); *Revisio saxifragarum iconibus illustrata* (Regensburg, 1810, 1822); *Abhandlung über die Pflanzenkunde in Böhmen*, 2 vols. (Prague, 1817–1818); *Versuch einer geognostisch-botanischen Darstellung der Flora der Vorwelt . . .*, 7 vols. (Leipzig–Prague, 1820–1833); and *Umrisse einer Geschichte der böhmischen Bergwerke*, 2 vols. (Prague, 1836–1838). His correspondence with Goethe was published as *Briefwechsel zwischen Goethe und Kaspar Graf von Sternberg (1820–1832)*, F. T. Bratranek, ed. (Vienna, 1866).

II. Secondary Literature. The chief biographies are F. Palacký, *Leben des Grafen K. Sternberg . . . nebst einem akademischen Vortrag über der Grafen K. und F. Sternberg Leben und Wirken . . .* (Prague, 1868), and V. Zázvorka, "Kašpar Maria hrabě Šternberk, jeho život a význam," in *Zvlástni otisk z časopisu Národniho musea*, **113** (Prague, 1939), 1–22, with portraits. See also W. Whewell, in *Proceedings of the Geological Society* (London), **3** (1838–1842), 72–74; and C. von Wurzbach, *Biographisches Lexikon des kaiserthums Oesterreich*, XXXVIII (Vienna, 1879), 252–266.

Robert P. Beckinsale
Jan Krejčí

STERNBERG, PAVEL KARLOVICH (*b.* Orel, Russia, 2 April 1865; *d.* Moscow, U.S.S.R., 31 January 1920), *astronomy, gravimetry.*

The son of a petty tradesman, Sternberg became interested in astronomy as a child; at fifteen, having received a spyglass as a gift, he converted it into a telescope and began observations. After graduating from the Orel Gymnasium in 1883, he entered the Faculty of Physics and Mathematics of Moscow University. In his first year he began regular observations at Moscow observatory. Its director, F. A. Bredikhin, attracted Sternberg to his program of cometary research. In his final year Sternberg received the gold medal of the faculty for his paper "O prodolzhitelnosti vrashchenia Krasnogo pyatna Yupitera" ("On the Duration of Rotation of the Red Spot of Jupiter"). After graduating in 1887 with the degree of candidate in mathematical sciences, he remained at the university to prepare for an academic career. In March 1888 he became a supernumerary assistant at the observatory and subsequently participated in Bredikhin's gravimetric expeditions in European Russia.

In 1890 Sternberg was confirmed as astronomer-observer at Moscow observatory. In 1903, after defending his thesis, "Shirota Moskovskoy observatorii v svyazi s dvizheniem polyusov" ("The Latitude of the Moscow Observatory in Relation to the Motion of the Poles"), he was awarded the master's degree. Ten years later, for his dissertation "Nekotorye primenenia fotografii k tochnym izmereniam v astronomii" ("Certain Uses of Photography for Precise Measurements in Astronomy"); Sternberg received the doctorate in astronomy. In July 1916 he succeeded V. K. Tserasky as director of the university observatory.

Sternberg's teaching career had begun in 1887 at the private Kreiman Gymnasium, where he taught physics until 1909. In 1890, as a *Privatdozent* at the University of Moscow, Sternberg gave his first course, on the general theory of planetary perturbations, which was later followed by courses in celestial mechanics, advanced geodesy, spherical astronomy, and descriptive astronomy. From 1901 to 1917 Sternberg was on the staff of the higher courses for women, organized in St. Petersburg, Moscow, and Kiev by groups of progressive professors in the 1870's because tsarist law did not permit women to study at the universities. In 1914 he was elected extraordinary professor of astronomy and geodesy, and the following year he was named honored professor.

From 1905 Sternberg was an active Social Democrat (Bolshevik) and was a member of the clandestine Military-Technical Bureau, which undertook technical preparation for an armed uprising. Only after February 1917 was he openly involved in the political struggle, and in October 1917 he led the revolutionary forces of the Zamoskvoretsky district of Moscow. After the establishment of Soviet power in Moscow, Sternberg was named military commissar. Later he became a member of the Board of the People's Commissariat of Education and was active in preparing for the reform of higher education. In the fall of 1918 he traveled to the Eastern Front as a political commissar of the Second Army, and in 1919 he covered the entire Eastern Front. Having caught a cold during the forced crossing of the Irtysh River near Omsk, he became seriously ill and was evacuated to Moscow, where after two operations he died.

Sternberg was a distinguished researcher and innovator in three fields: gravimetry, the variations of latitude in relation to the motion of the earth's poles, and photographic astrometry.

His numerous gravimetric expeditions, lectures, and practical studies with students aided the formation of a scientific school in Moscow, which after Sternberg's death carried out a wide-ranging gravimetric study of the Soviet Union, development of the theory, and gravimetric prospecting for useful fossils.

During many years of measuring the latitude of the Moscow observatory, Sternberg carefully and precisely investigated the motion of the poles and recommended the organization of a network of stations forming an "international service of polar altitude." This has become the International Latitude Service.

As a pioneer in the use of photography for precise measurements of stellar position, Sternberg used the fifteen-inch double astrograph of the Moscow observatory for an extremely comprehensive study of the possibilities of the new method and the possible sources of systematic errors.

In April 1917, Sternberg was elected president of the All-Russian Congress of Astronomers. In 1931 his name was given to the astronomical institute at Moscow University, which brought together three scientific institutions, including the university observatory.

BIBLIOGRAPHY

I. ORIGINAL WORKS. Sternberg's writings include "Sur la durée de la rotation de la tache rouge de Jupiter," in *Annales de l'observatoire astronomique de Mos-*

cou, 2nd ser., **1**, no. 2 (1888), 91–128; "Observations faites à l'aide du pendule à réversion de Repsold," *ibid.*, **2**, nos. 1–2 (1890), 94–132; "Observations photographiques de l'étoile γ Virginis," *ibid.*, **3**, no. 1 (1893), 120–123; "Dvizhenia zemnykh polyusov" ("The Motion of the Earth's Poles"), in *Nauchnoe slovo*, **3** (1903), 112–115; "Shirota Moskovskoy observatorii v svyazi s dvizheniem polyusov" ("The Latitude of the Moscow Observatory in Relation to the Motion of the Poles"), *Uchenye zapiski Moskovskogo universiteta*, Fiz.-mat. otd. (1904), no. 22; "Application de la photographie aux mesures des étoiles doubles," in *Annales de l'observatoire astronomique de Moscou*, 2nd ser., **5** (1911), 42–71; "Nekotorye primenenia fotografii k tochnym izmereniam v astronomii" ("Some Applications of Photography to Precise Measurements in Astronomy"); *Bulletin de la Société des naturalistes de Moscou* for 1913, nos. 1–3 (1914), his doctoral dissertation; *Kurs sfericheskoy astronomii . . .* ("Course in Spherical Astronomy . . ."; Moscow, 1914), compiled by a student with the initials L. D. from lectures given by Sternberg at Moscow University in the academic year 1913–1914; *Kurs opisatelnoy astronomii* ("Course in Descriptive Astronomy"; Moscow, 1915), compiled by A. A. Sokolov from a course of lectures by Sternberg; "Détermination relative de la pesanteur à Moscou," in *Annales de l'observatoire astronomique à Moscou*, 2nd ser., **8**, no. 1 (1925), 3–17; and "Sila tyazhesti v Moskovskom rayone i ee anomalii" ("The Force of Gravitation in the Moscow Region and Its Anomaly"), *ibid.*, nos. 2–3 (1926), 43–83, observations of Sternberg, edited by I. A. Kazansky.

II. SECONDARY LITERATURE. See S. N. Blazhko, "Pamyati P. K. Sternberga" ("Recollections of Sternberg"); in *Mirovedenie*, **25**, no. 2 (1936), 81–89; O. A. Ivanova, "Moskovskoe voenno-tekhnicheskoe byuro RSDRP (1906–1907)" ("Moscow Military-Technical Bureau . . ."), in *Moskva v trekh revolyutsiakh* ("Moscow in Three Revolutions"; Moscow, 1959); 108–127; Yu. G. Perel, ed., in S. N. Blazhko, *Vydayushchiesya russkie astronomy* ("Outstanding Russian Astronomers"; Moscow, 1951), 141–175; K. A. Timiryazev, "Ucheny-geroy. Pamyati P. K. Sternberga" ("A Scientist-Hero. Recollections of Sternberg"), in his *Sochinenia* ("Works"), IX (Moscow, 1939), 415–424; and P. G. Kulikovsky, *Pavel Karlovich Sternberg. 1865–1920* (Moscow, 1965).

P. G. KULIKOVSKY

STEVENS, EDWARD (*b.* St. Croix, Virgin Islands, ca. 1755; *d.* St. Croix, 26 September 1834), *medicine, physiology*.

Stevens' father, Thomas, a prosperous merchant, was reputedly also the father of Alexander Hamilton. Nothing is known of his mother. In his youth Stevens moved with his family to New York. He graduated A.B. from King's College (now Columbia University) in 1774; and the following year he began studies at the University of Edinburgh, enrolling in the medical school in 1776 and again in 1777. He graduated M.D. on 12 September 1777.

Stevens' inaugural dissertation, "De alimentorum concoctione," presented with ingenuity and insight his experiments and observations on gastric digestion, and clearly confirmed him as the first investigator to isolate human gastric juice. It removed the confusion and contradictions presented in the doctrines of fermentation and trituration, the latter championed by Leeuwenhoek, Borelli, Pitcairne, and Pecquet, and decried by Astruc and Stephen Hales. It also repudiated such views as those of John Pringle and David Macbride. Stevens' work formed a vital bridge linking the experiments of Réaumur before him and Spallanzani and later workers after him. Réaumur had shown, in 1752, that digestion was due to the solvent power of gastric juice. Stevens confirmed this, isolated human gastric juice, and performed experiments both *in vitro* and *in vivo* in man and animals.

Stevens was admitted to the Royal Medical Society (Edinburgh) on 20 January 1776 and served as its president in 1779 and 1780. At Edinburgh he was awarded the Harveian prize for an experimental inquiry on the red color of the blood. He returned to St. Croix about 1783 and practiced medicine there for ten years. In 1793 Stevens moved to Philadelphia, where he received public support from Alexander Hamilton and became embroiled in a controversy with Benjamin Rush over methods of treating yellow fever in the great epidemic of that year. On 18 April 1794 he was admitted to the American Philosophical Society, and the following year he was appointed professor of the practice of medicine in King's College (later Columbia University). It is probable that Stevens' presence and reputation in Philadelphia, as well as his contributions in gastric physiology, contributed to the marked interest in gastric studies that took place round the turn of the century in that city. Of these studies, that of John R. Young is best-known. He undoubtedly was familiar with Stevens' work; indeed, his experiments with bullfrogs and small frogs are reminiscent of Stevens' observations of partially digested small fish inside larger ones.

Stevens was United States consul-general to Santo Domingo from 1799 to 1800. His consular dispatches to Timothy Pickering, Adams, Jefferson, and other leaders, revealing a critical, observant mind, outlined the geopolitical problems facing the United States in the Caribbean at that time. Controversy marred his political life, however, and he returned to the United States in 1801. He made appearances at the American Philosophical Society meetings in 1803 and 1804, probably returning to St. Croix shortly thereafter. Little is known of Stevens' last years. David Hosack wrote to him in St. Croix on yellow fever in 1809, and in 1823 he wrote Hosack a letter introducing his son, who had also graduated at Edinburgh.

Stevens' fundamental and sound gastric studies were confirmed by Spallanzani, who augmented and added to them in masterly fashion, assuring that from then on, gastric physiology would be a well-founded science.

BIBLIOGRAPHY

I. ORIGINAL WORKS. "Dissertatio inauguralis de alimentorum concoctione" (1777) is transcribed, in the original Latin, in *Thesaurus Medicus*, III (Edinburgh, 1785), a selection of medical dissertations from Edinburgh, repr. by William Smellie. An incomplete English trans. of the experimental section is appended to Spallanzani's *Dissertations Relative to the Natural History of Animals and Vegetables* (London, 1784). In 1778 Stevens read a paper to the Royal Medical Society of Edinburgh entitled "What Is the Cause of the Increase of Weight Which Metals Acquire During Their Calcination." A MS copy is in the library of Edinburgh University. No copy appears to have survived of Stevens' Harveian prize thesis, "An Experimental Inquiry Concerning the Red Colour of the Blood."

II. SECONDARY LITERATURE. Stevens has received remarkably little attention. Stacey B. Day appears to be the only one who has endeavored to piece together his life and to correct the fragmentary and incorrect notes that are commonly found. See Stacey B. Day and Roy A. Swanson, "The Important Contribution of Dr. Edward Stevens to the Understanding of Gastric Digestion in Man and Animals," in *Surgery*, **52**, no. 5 (1962), 819–836. The most comprehensive account available is Stacey B. Day, *Edward Stevens, Gastric Physiologist, Physician and American Statesman, With a Complete Translation of His Inaugural Dissertation De Alimentorum Concoctione and Interpretive Notes on Gastric Digestion Along with Certain Other Selected and Diplomatic Papers* (Cincinnati–Montreal, 1969), which presents most of the biographical details of Stevens' life known today. Possibility of his kinship with Alexander Hamilton is examined. The book presents the first complete English trans. of "De alimentorum concoctione"; a trans. of the German précis by Friedrich August Weiz (1782); the exchange of letters between Stevens and Benjamin Rush; the controversy between these two

physicians over the treatment of yellow fever; and a review of Stevens' role as United States consul-general in Santo Domingo. The book provides reference sources: Jefferson MSS, Pickering MSS, Hamilton Papers, Stephen Girard Papers, National Archives records, and source materials in Edinburgh and elsewhere.

STACEY B. DAY

STEVIN, SIMON (*b.* Bruges, Netherlands [now Belgium], 1548; *d.* The Hague, Netherlands, *ca.* March 1620), *mathematics, engineering.*

Stevin was the illegitimate son of Antheunis Stevin and Cathelijne van de Poort, both wealthy citizens of Bruges. There is little reliable information about his early life, although it is known that he worked in the financial administration of Bruges and Antwerp and traveled in Poland, Prussia, and Norway for some time between 1571 and 1577. In 1581 he established himself at Leiden, where he matriculated at the university in 1583. His religious position is not known, nor is it known whether he left the southern Netherlands because of the persecutions fostered by the Spanish occupation. At any rate, in the new republic of the northern Netherlands Stevin found an economic and cultural renaissance in which he at once took an active part. He was first classified as an "engineer," but after 1604 he was quartermaster-general of the army of the States of the Netherlands. At the same time he was mathematics and science tutor to Maurice of Nassau, prince of Orange, for whom he wrote a number of textbooks. He was often consulted on matters of defense and navigation, and he organized a school of engineers at Leiden and served as administrator of Maurice's domains. In 1610 he married Catherine Cray; they had four children, of whom one, Hendrick, was himself a gifted scientist who, after Stevin's death, published a number of his manuscripts.

Stevin's work is part of the general scientific revival that resulted from the commercial and industrial prosperity of the cities of the Netherlands and northern Italy in the sixteenth century. This development was further spurred by the discovery of the principal works of antique science—especially those of Euclid, Apollonius, Diophantus, and Archimedes—which were brought to western Europe from Byzantium, then in a state of decline, or from the Arabic centers of learning in Spain. A man of his time, Stevin wrote on a variety of topics. A number of his works are almost wholly original, while even those that represent surveys of science as it existed around 1600 contain his own interpretations; all are characterized by a remarkably lucid and methodical presentation. Stevin chose to write almost all of his books in the vernacular, in accordance with the spirit of self-confidence of the newly established republic. In the introduction to his *De Beghinselen der Weeghconst* of 1586, he stated his admiration for Dutch as a language of wonderful power in shaping new terms; and a number of the words coined by Stevin and his contemporaries survive in the rich Dutch scientific vocabulary.

Stevin's published works include books on mathematics, mechanics, astronomy, navigation, military science, engineering, music theory, civics, dialectics, bookkeeping, geography, and house building. While many of these works were closely related to his mercantile and administrative interests, a number fall into the realm of pure science. His first book, the *Tafelen van Interest* (1582), derives entirely from his early career in commerce; in it Stevin set out the rules of single and compound interest and gave tables for the rapid computation of discounts and annuities. Such tables had previously been kept secret by big banking houses, since there were few skilled calculators, although after Stevin's publication interest tables became common in the Netherlands.

In *De Thiende*, a twenty-nine-page booklet published in 1585, Stevin introduced decimal fractions for general purposes and showed that operations could be performed as easily with such fractions as with integers. He eliminated all difficulties in handling decimal fractions by interpreting 3.27, for example, as 327 items of the unit 0.01. Decimal fractions had previously found only occasional use in trigonometric tables; although Stevin's notation was somewhat unwieldy, his argument was convincing, and decimal fractions were soon generally adopted. At the end of the tract, Stevin went on to suggest that a decimal system should also be used for weights and measures, coinage, and divisions of the degree of arc.

In *L'arithmétique*, also published in 1585, Stevin gave a general treatment of the arithmetic and algebra of his time, providing geometric counterparts. (An earlier work, the *Problemata geometrica* of 1583 had been entirely devoted to geometry; strongly marked by the influence of Euclid and Archimedes, it contained an especially interesting discussion of the semi-regular bodies that had also been studied by Dürer.) Stevin was of the opinion that all numbers—including squares, square roots, and negative or irrational quantities—were of the same nature, an opinion not shared by contemporary mathematicians but one that was vindicated in

the development of algebra. Stevin introduced a new notation for polynomials and gave simplified and unified solutions for equations of the second, third, and fourth degrees; in an appendix published at a later date he showed how to approximate a real root for an equation of any degree.

De Deursichtighe is a mathematical treatment of perspective, a subject much studied by artists and architects, as well as mathematicians, in the fifteenth and sixteenth centuries. Stevin's book gives an important discussion of the case in which the plane of the drawing is not perpendicular to the plane of the ground and, for special cases, solves the inverse problem of perspective, that is, of finding the position of the eye of the observer, given the object and the perspective drawing of it. A number of other works are also concerned with the application of mathematics to practical problems, and in these the instances in which Stevin had to perform what amounts to an integration are particularly interesting. While mathematicians up to his time had followed the Greek example and given each proof by *reductio ad absurdum*, Stevin introduced methods that, although still cumbersome, paved the way toward the simpler methods of the calculus.

De Beghinselen der Weeghconst is Stevin's chief work in mechanics. Published in 1586, some fifty years before Galileo's discoveries, it is devoted chiefly to statics. From the evidence that it provides, Stevin would seem to be the first Renaissance author to develop and continue the work of Archimedes. The book contains discussions of the theory of the lever, the theorems of the inclined plane, and the determination of the center of gravity; but most particularly it includes what is perhaps the most famous of Stevin's discoveries, the law of the inclined plane, which he demonstrated with the *clootcrans*, or wreath of spheres.

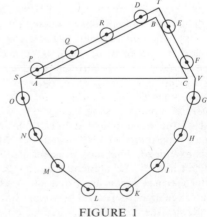

FIGURE 1

The *clootcrans*, as conceived by Stevin, consists of two inclined planes (*AB* and *BC*), of which one is twice the length of the other. A wreath of spheres placed on a string is hung around the triangle *ABC*, all friction being disregarded. The wreath will not begin to rotate by itself, and the lower section *GH* ··· *MNO*, being symmetrical, may be disregarded. It is thus apparent that the pull toward the left exerted by the four spheres that lie along *AB* must be equal to the pull to the right exerted by the two spheres that lie along *BC*—or, in other words, that the effective component of gravity is inversely proportional to the length of the inclined plane. If one of the inclined planes is then placed vertically, the ratio between the component along the inclined plane and the total force of gravity becomes obvious. This is, in principle, the theory of the parallelogram of forces.

Beneath his diagram of the *clootcrans* Stevin inscribed a cherished maxim, "Wonder en is gheen wonder"—"What appears a wonder is not a wonder" (that is, it is actually understandable), a rallying cry for the new science. He was so delighted with his discovery that he used the diagram of his proof as a seal on his letters, a mark on his instruments, and as a vignette on the title pages of his books; the device also appears as the colophon of this *Dictionary*.

Stevin's next work on mechanics, *De Beghinselen des Waterwichts*, is the first systematic treatise on hydrostatics since Archimedes. In it, Stevin gave a simple and immediately comprehensible explanation for the Archimedean principle of displacement; before a body *C* is immersed, consider a volume of water equal to that of *C*. Since the latter body was at rest, it must have experienced, on displacement, an upward force equal to its weight, while *C* itself will, upon being placed in the water, experience the same degree of buoyancy. Stevin similarly chose to explain the hydrostatic paradox by imagining parts of the water to be solidified, so that neither equilibrium nor pressure was disturbed. He also wrote a number of shorter works in which he applied the principles of mechanics to practical problems of simple machines, balances, the windlass, the hauling of ships, wheels powered by men, the block-and-tackle, and the effect of a bridle upon a horse.

Stevin's chief book on astronomy, *De Hemelloop*, was published in 1608; it is one of the first presentations of the Copernican system, which Stevin unconditionally supported, several years before Galileo and at a time when few other scientists could bring themselves to do likewise. Calling the Copernican hypothesis "the true theory," Stevin demonstrated that the motions of the planets can be inductively derived from observations; since there were no complete direct observations, he used the ephemerides of Johann Stadius in their stead. He first explained the Ptolemaic model (in which the earth is at the center and the sun and planets move in epicycles) by this means, then offered a similar explanation of the Copernican system, in which he improved on the original theory in several minor points.

In a seafaring nation like the Dutch republic matters of navigation were, of course, of great importance. In addition to his astronomical works, Stevin gave a theory of the tides that was—as it must have been, fifty years before Newton—purely empirical. He also, in a short treatise entitled *De Havenvinding*, approached the subject of determining the longitude of a ship, a problem that was not fully solved until the nineteenth century. Several previous authors had suggested that longitude might be determined by measuring the deviation of the magnetic needle from the astronomical meridian, a suggestion based on the assumption that the earthwide distribution of terrestrial magnetism was known. Since the determination of latitude was well known, such a measurement would allow the sailor to chart longitudinal position against the latitudinal circle.

Stevin, in his booklet, gave a clear explanation of this method; he differed from Petrus Plancius and Mercator in that he did not rely upon a priori conceptions of the way in which geomagnetic deviation depends upon geographical position. Although he was willing to offer a conjecture about this dependence, Stevin insisted on the necessity of collecting actual measurements from all possible sources and urged the establishment of an empirical, worldwide survey. His method was sound, although as data began to accumulate it became clear that the magnetic elements were subject to secular variation. The problem of determining longitude was at last solved more simply by the invention of the ship's chronometer.

In *Van de Zeijlstreken*, Stevin set out a method, based on one proposed by Nuñez in 1534, of steering a ship along a loxodrome, always keeping the same course, to describe on the globe a line cutting the meridians at a constant angle. Although the feat was beyond the grasp of the seaman of Stevin's time, his exposition nonetheless contributed to a clear formulation of the principles upon which it was based and helped make the method itself better known both in the Netherlands and abroad.

A considerable body of Stevin's other work developed from his military duties and interests. The Dutch army had been completely reorganized through the efforts of Maurice and counts William Louis and John of Nassau; their innovations, which were widely adopted by other countries, included the establishment of regular drills and maneuvers, the development of fortifications (combined with new methods of attacking a besieged city), and army camps planned after those of the Romans. As quartermaster general, Stevin observed these reforms, as well as actual battles, and wrote in detail, in his usual lucid and systematic style, of sieges, camps, and military equipment.

Stevin's *De Sterctenbouwing* is a treatise on the art of fortification. Although cost prohibited the implementation of the ideas Stevin set out in it, these notions were put to practical effect a century later by Vauban and Coehoorn. *De Legermeting* is a less theoretical work, a description of field encampment during Maurice's campaigns, with the encampment before the Battle of Juliers (in 1610) as a particular example. Stevin gave an account of the layout of the camp, inspired by the writings of Polybius (since later Roman authors were not then known), together with the modifications made by Maurice. He listed all the equipment required in the campaign, and gave detailed instructions concerning the building of huts and the housing of dependents and suppliers. In the last section of the work he made a comparative study of the different methods of deploying soldiers in files and companies, and again recommended distribution by a decimal system. All told, his book gives a vivid impression of the army life of his period.

Of his works on engineering, two books are devoted to the new types of sluices and locks that Stevin himself had helped to devise. He cites their particular usefulness in scouring canals and ditches through the use of tidal action, and cites their application for the waterways of Danzig and other German coastal cities. In these short works he also discusses the formation of sandbanks, peat and quicksand, and the modifications of the course of a river; his explanation of the changes of the surface of the earth, which he attributes to natural forces only, is quite modern.

In *Van de Molens*, Stevin discusses wind-driven drainage mills, crucially important to the flat regions of the Netherlands. Stevin proposed the construction of a new type of mill with more slowly revolving scoop wheels and a smaller number of wider floats, and he further modified the means of transmission of power by making use of conical toothed wheels. A number of mills were built or rebuilt according to his specifications; that they were not completely successful may lie in imperfections in the execution of his design. Stevin also applied the principles of mechanics to windmills, in a series of computations that allowed him to determine, given the size and the number of the cogs, both the minimum wind pressure required on each square foot of the sails to lift the water to the necessary height and how much water is raised by each revolution of the sails. He gave the results of his measurement of fifteen mills.

In another book, *Van de Spiegeling der Singconst*, Stevin turned to the theory of musical tuning, a subject that had enthralled mathematicians from antiquity on. Musicians had also long been concerned with devising a scale in which the intervals of the pure octave (2:1), the pure fifth (3:2), and the pure third (5:4) could be rigorously combined. The chief problem lay in the resolution of the progression by four fifths (96:144:216: 324:486) and the interval with the double octave ($96 \times 2 \times 2 = 384$); this ratio, which should be the third, 480:384, is rather the imperfect ratio 486:384. While a number of other mathematicians and musicians had attempted to reach a resolution by minor modifications in the scale, Stevin boldly rejected their methods and declared that all semitones should be equal and that the steps of the scale should each correspond to the successive values of $2^{n/12}$; he dismissed the difference between the third and the fifth as unimportant. Stevin's scale is thus the "equal temperament" now in general use; at the time he proposed it he had been anticipated only by Vicenzo Galilei (1581) and the Chinese prince Chi Tsai-Yü (1584). It is unlikely that Stevin knew the latter's work.

Another of Stevin's many publications was a book on civic life, *Het Burgherlick Leven*. The work is a handbook designed to guide the citizen through periods of civil disorder, a matter of some concern in a nation that had only recently won its freedom through rebellion, and in which religious freedom was still a matter for discussion. Stevin only rarely refers to these circumstances in his book, however; he rather presents his precepts as being completely objective and derived from common sense. The first of his tenets is that the citizen should obey anyone in a position of *de facto* authority, no matter how this authority has been obtained. Since history consists of a succession of princes, Stevin questions how historical rights can be established, then goes on to state that the citizen's duty is to obey the laws, no matter if they appear wrong or unjust. He cites the necessity of religion as a means of instilling virtue in children, but adds that if a man's religion is different from that of his countrymen, the dissenter should either conform or leave. All told, his views are typical of those current in a post-revolutionary period in which consolidation was more important than individual freedoms.

In the last years of his life, Stevin returned to the study of mathematics. He reedited his mathematical works and collected them into the two folio volumes of his *Wisconstighe Ghedachtenissen* (published in 1605–1608). These mathematical memoirs were also published, at almost the same time, in Latin and French translations.

Stevin's writings in general are characterized by his versatility, his ability to combine theory and practice, and the clarity of his argument. They demonstrate a mind confident of the prevalence of reason and common sense and convinced of the comprehensibility of nature. His style, especially the personal way in which he addresses the reader, is particularly charming.

BIBLIOGRAPHY

I. ORIGINAL WORKS. A committee of Dutch scientists has edited *The Principal Works of Simon Stevin*, 5 vols. (Amsterdam, 1955–1968), which contains a bibliography and extensive introductions to each of the works.

Stevin's major works include *Tafelen van Interest* (Antwerp, 1582; Amsterdam, 1590), a French trans. of which appears in *De Thiende* (Leiden, 1585); *Problematum geometricorum-Libri V* (Antwerp, 1583); and *De Thiende* (Leiden, 1585; Gouda, 1626, 1630; Antwerp–The Hague, 1924). Translations of *De Thiende* are H. Gericke and K. Vogel, *De Thiende von Simon Stevin* (Frankfurt am Main, 1965); Robert Norton, *Disme, the Art of Tenths* (London, 1608); J. Tuning, "La disme," in *Mémoires mathématiques* (Leiden, 1608), also reprinted in *Isis*, **23** (1925); Henry Lyte, *The Art of Tenths* (London, 1619), and "The Disme of Simon Stevin," in *Mathematics Teacher*, **14** (1921), 321, also in D. E. Smith, *Source Book of Mathematics* (New York–London, 1929).

Subsequent writings include *L'arithmétique* (Leiden, 1585, 1625), which contains French translations of *Tafelen van Interest* and *De Thiende*; *Vita Politica, Het Burgherlick Leven* (Leiden, 1590; Amsterdam, 1939); *De Stercktenbouwing* (Leiden; 1594; Amsterdam, 1624), also trans. by G. A. von Dantzig (Frankfurt, 1608, 1623), and by Albert Girard, *Les oeuvres mathématiques de Simon Stevin* (Leiden, 1634); *Castrametatio, Dat is legermeting. Nieuwe Maniere van Sterctebou door Spilseuysen* (Rotterdam, 1617), trans. in French (Leiden–Rotterdam, 1618) and in Albert Girard, trans.,

Les oeuvres mathématiques de Simon Stevin (Leiden, 1634), and in German (Frankfurt, 1631); *Van de Spiegeling der Singconst. Van de Molens* (Amsterdam, 1884).

II. SECONDARY LITERATURE. A bibliography of Stevin's works is in *Bibliotheca Belgica. Bibliographie générale des Pays-Bas*, ser. 1, XXIII (Ghent–The Hague, 1880–1890). On Stevin and his work, see R. Depau, *Simon Stevin* (Brussels, 1942), which is in French and contains a bibliography of the articles on Stevin; E. J. Dijksterhuis, *Simon Stevin* (The Hague, 1943), in Dutch, with bibliography of Stevin's works, and which is in an abbreviated English version: R. Hooykaas and M. G. J. Minnaert, eds., *Simon Stevin: Science in the Netherlands Around 1600* (The Hague, 1970); and A. J. J. van de Velde, "Simon Stevin 1548–1948," in *Mededelingen Kongelige Vlaamse Academie*, **10** (1948), 10.

M. G. J. MINNAERT

STEWART, BALFOUR (*b.* Edinburgh, Scotland, 1 November 1828; *d.* Drogheda, Ireland, 19 December 1887), *physics, meteorology, terrestrial magnetism.*

Son of William Stewart, a tea merchant, and named Balfour after his grandmother's family, Balfour Stewart was educated at the universities of St. Andrews and Edinburgh, and then embarked upon a mercantile career. His interest in the physical sciences had, however, been sparked in the natural philosophy class of James D. Forbes at Edinburgh; and after ten years in the business world, Stewart sought a career in science—first, briefly, as an assistant at the Kew observatory and then as an assistant to Forbes at Edinburgh, where he soon made original contributions to the study of radiant heat. In 1859 Stewart returned to Kew as director; and for twelve years he was involved with the continuing missions of that institution, including the study of meteorology, solar physics, and terrestrial magnetism. During this period he was elected a fellow of the Royal Society of London; he married Katharine Stevens, daughter of a London lawyer; and he was awarded the Rumford Medal by the Royal Society for his earlier work on radiant heat. In 1870 Stewart was appointed professor of natural philosophy at Owens College, Manchester. He was subsequently president of the Manchester Literary and Philosophical Society, the Physical Society, and the Society for Psychical Research.

The heart of Stewart's contributions to the study of radiant heat (infrared radiation), and to thermal radiation in general, came in "An Account of Some Experiments on Radiant Heat, Involving an Extension of Prévost's Theory of Exchanges"

(1858). Building in part on suggestions by Forbes and results of Macedonio Melloni and others, he had investigated the abilities of various materials to emit and absorb radiation of various wavelengths. Stewart found, in particular, that a material that radiates heat of a certain wavelength preferentially tends also to absorb heat of that same wavelength preferentially. He dealt with these results by extending a theory that had been developed by Pierre Prevost in the years around 1800. Considering thermal equilibrium to be dynamic, involving continual exchange of the heat substance between the bodies in equilibrium, Prevost had been able to derive relationships between the emissive and reflective powers of surfaces. Extending these arguments from surfaces to volumes, and specializing to individual wavelengths, Stewart derived from the "theory of exchanges" a result in accord with his experimental data on the emissive and absorptive powers of thin plates of various materials: "The absorption of a plate equals its radiation [emission], and that for every description [wavelength] of heat" ("Account," Brace ed., p. 39).

Unfortunately, this original and significant work had little influence on the subsequent development of science. Two years after Stewart's paper had been submitted to the Royal Society of Edinburgh, Gustav Kirchhoff, not knowing Stewart's work and proceeding from experiments on optical spectra, came to similar conclusions. Kirchhoff's results were more solid: the experiments were cleaner, the derivations more rigorous, and the results more clearly and generally stated. Moreover, the particular experimental context of Kirchhoff's work suggested immediate and extremely important applications in chemistry and astronomy. Thus, although Stewart's work was meritorious and prior, as he and his supporters vigorously argued for decades after, it was Kirchhoff's work that had decisive influence throughout the physical sciences.

Upon becoming director of the Kew observatory, Stewart turned his attention to the continuing missions of that institution. (In 1867 Kew was designated the central meteorological observatory of Great Britain; and the annual operating grant from the British Association was then augmented by direct governmental support of the meteorological activities, bringing the yearly budget over £1,000.) Extending investigations of the relationships between terrestrial magnetism and the sunspot cycle, he also studied correlations of these phenomena with various other terrestrial and "cosmical" cycles. Later, in an influential review article on ter-

restrial magnetism (published in the *Encyclopaedia Britannica*), Stewart proposed mechanisms for some of these correlations. In particular, certain variations in the geomagnetic field were to be referred to varying electric currents in the upper atmosphere: Assuming that the rarefied air of the upper atmosphere possessed appreciable electrical conductivity, thermal and tidal air currents, moving the conducting air through the earth's magnetic field, would generate electric currents. By this mechanism the well-known daily variation of the geomagnetic field was explained. Also explained were seasonal variations of the geomagnetic field, analogies between global wind patterns and global magnetic patterns, and lunar correlations. Stewart's hypotheses informed subsequent research in geomagnetism, and strong confirmation ensued.

In later years at Owens College, Stewart lectured on elementary physics and established a teaching laboratory; J. J. Thomson, one of his most illustrious students, traced his initial enthusiasm for research to that laboratory. Textbooks and popularizations by Stewart were widely read; Ernest Rutherford, at age ten, owned one of them. Another widely read book, written in collaboration with Peter Guthrie Tait, was intended to demonstrate the compatibility between science and religion. Entitled *The Unseen Universe*, the book argued that the individual soul was immortal, existing after death in the context of the subtle media of nineteenth-century physics, including the luminiferous ether, the ultramundane (gravitation-causing) particles of Le Sage, and the ubiquitous fluid substratum of William Thomson's vortex atoms; thermodynamics and evolution also supported the argument.

"Have great [physical] vitality, restless," but "no power of great amount of [mental] work," Stewart wrote of himself (Hilts, "Guide"). In the domain of science broadly defined, he participated in many institutions, programs, and discoveries but left no single monument.

BIBLIOGRAPHY

I. ORIGINAL WORKS. The following are representative of Stewart's publications: "An Account of Some Experiments on Radiant Heat, Involving an Extension of Prévost's Theory of Exchanges," in *Transactions of the Royal Society of Edinburgh*, **22** (1857–1861), 1–20, repr. in D. B. Brace, ed., *The Laws of Radiation and Absorption: Memoirs by Prévost, Stewart, Kirchhoff, and Kirchhoff and Bunsen* (New York, 1901), 21–50; *The Unseen Universe: or Physical Speculations on a Future*

State (London, 1875), written with P. G. Tait; and "Terrestrial Magnetism," an appendix to the article on meteorology in *Encyclopaedia Britannica*, 9th ed., XVI, 159–184.

II. SECONDARY LITERATURE. A list of Stewart's publications, as well as a review of his scientific career, is furnished in Arthur Schuster, "Memoir of the Late Professor Balfour Stewart, LL.D., F.R.S.," in *Memoirs and Proceedings of the Manchester Literary and Philosophical Society*, 4th ser., **1** (1888), 253–272. See also Philip J. Hartog, "Balfour Stewart," in *Dictionary of National Biography*.

Aspects of Stewart's activities are treated in the following: Joseph Agassi, "The Kirchhoff-Planck Radiation Law," in *Science*, **156** (1967), 30–37; Sydney Chapman and Julius Bartels, *Geomagnetism*, II (Oxford, 1940), 750–752; P. M. Heimann, "*The Unseen Universe*: Physics and the Philosophy of Nature in Victorian Britain," in *British Journal for the History of Science*, **6** (1972), 73–79; Victor L. Hilts, "A Guide to Francis Galton's *English Men of Science*," in *Transactions of the American Philosophical Society* (in press); Hans Kangro, "Kirchhoff und die spektralanalytische Forschung," editor's *Nachwort* in Gustav Robert Kirchhoff, *Untersuchungen über das Sonnenspectrum und die Spectren der chemischen Elemente und weitere ergänzende Arbeiten aus den Jahren 1859–1862*, Milliaria, no. 17 (Osnabrück, 1972), 17–26; Robert H. Scott, "The History of the Kew Observatory," in *Proceedings of the Royal Society*, **39** (1885), 37–86; Daniel M. Siegel, "Balfour Stewart and Gustav Kirchhoff: Two Independent Approaches to 'Kirchhoff's Radiation Law,' " in *Isis* (in press); and J. J. Thomson, *Recollections and Reflections* (New York, 1937), 18–22.

A large collection of unpublished source materials is held at the Royal Society.

DANIEL M. SIEGEL

STEWART, GEORGE NEIL (*b.* London, Ontario, 18 April 1860; *d.* Cleveland, Ohio, 28 May 1930), *physiology*.

Although Stewart, the son of James Innes and Catherine Sutherland Stewart, was born in Canada, his parents returned to Scotland and he grew up in Lybster, a fishing village in Caithness. His studies at the University of Edinburgh included classics, philosophy, history, and mathematics, the latter leading him to physics and, in 1879, an assistantship with Peter Guthrie Tait. His introduction to physiology came from William Rutherford. Being especially interested in electrophysiology, Stewart spent 1886–1887 studying with du Bois-Reymond at Berlin. After receiving the M.A., B.S., and D.Sc. (1887) degrees at Edinburgh, he became senior demonstrator of physiology at Owens College, Victoria University, Man-

chester (1887–1889), where he learned from William Stirling the value of the illustrative experiment in teaching science.

His decision to study medicine led to the M.B. and M.D. at Edinburgh (1889, 1891) and the D.P.H. at Cambridge (1890) while he was George Henry Lewes student at Downing College (1889–1893). He was also an examiner in physiology at Aberdeen (1890–1894). In 1893, at Henry P. Bowditch's invitation, Stewart went to Harvard as instructor in physiology; the following year he was appointed professor of physiology and histology at Western Reserve University School of Medicine, in Cleveland, where with the exception of four years (1903–1907) as professor of physiology at the University of Chicago, he remained for the rest of his life. In 1907 he became professor of experimental medicine and director of the H. K. Cushing Laboratory.

Stewart's major contribution was in transmitting modern methods of teaching and research in physiology to American medical education. During his first year in Cleveland, using improvised laboratory equipment, he began illustrating lectures with experiments; simultaneously he wrote a 796-page *Manual of Physiology* (1895), in which, for the first time, practical exercises for students were appended to each chapter and experiments on mammals were included. The practice spread to other schools, and the *Manual* became a standard text.

After earlier work on color vision, electrophysiology, Talbot's law, cardiac nerves, otoliths, muscle proteins, and permeability of blood corpuscles, Stewart later experimentally investigated such clinical problems as the effect of total anemia on the brain, resuscitation, the measurement of blood flow by the calorimetric method, and the estimation of pulmonary blood capacity and cardiac output by indicator-dilution techniques. With Julius M. Rogoff he studied the functions of the adrenal medulla and cortex, including the epinephrine output and the usefulness of cortex extracts to treat Addison's disease. They discovered that the adrenal cortex was indispensable to the life of higher animals. Stewart was described as a brilliant teacher, witty, and possessed of prodigious energy and an amazing memory. A perfectionist, he had little pleasure outside his laboratory. The University of Edinburgh awarded him the honorary LL.D. in 1920.

Pernicious anemia and progressive spinal degeneration afflicted Stewart during his later years; but he remained mentally alert until the end, making notes about his own condition.

BIBLIOGRAPHY

Stewart's major work was *A Manual of Physiology With Practical Exercises* (London, 1895; 8th ed., 1918).

Secondary literature includes Torald Sollmann, "George Neil Stewart, Physiologist, April 18, 1860, to May 28, 1930," in *Science*, **72** (1930), 157–162; and Carl J. Wiggers, "The Evolution of Experimental Physiology at the University of Michigan and Western Reserve University," in *Bulletin of the Cleveland Medical Library*, **10** (1963), 14–15. See also the faculty minutes and biography file of the Case Western Reserve University Archives.

Genevieve Miller

STEWART, MATTHEW (*b.* Rothesay, Isle of Bute, Scotland, January 1717; *d.* Catrine, Ayrshire, Scotland, 23 January 1785), *geometry, astronomy, natural philosophy.*

Stewart's father, Dugald, was minister of the parish of Rothesay; his mother was Janet Bannatyne. Intending to follow his father's career, he entered the University of Glasgow in 1734, soon coming under the influence of Robert Simson, professor of mathematics, and Francis Hutcheson, professor of moral philosophy.

Simson was then attempting to reconstruct Euclid's lost book on porisms; and he communicated his enthusiasm for this project—and for the study of Greek mathematics in general—to Stewart, who soon developed his own approach to the subject. Aware that new horizons were opening in mathematics, Simson conscientiously instructed his students in the newer subjects of calculus and analytical geometry. It was at his suggestion that Stewart went to the University of Edinburgh to work under Colin Maclaurin, himself a pupil of Simson's. Although he was studying calculus, higher plane curves, and cosmogony with Maclaurin, Stewart continued to correspond with Simson and, under his general direction, to carry on his work in pure geometry.

Simson's investigations were slow and laborious, and he was disinclined to publish findings that he regarded as incomplete—after the publication of a paper on porisms in 1723, nothing by him on the subject was published until eight years after his death—but he made his work freely available to Stewart. He actively encouraged Stewart to publish his celebrated series of geometrical propositions, *General Theorems*, in 1746 because the chair of mathematics at Edinburgh was vacant as a result of Maclaurin's service with the government

troops in the Jacobite Rebellion of 1745 and subsequent death from an illness contracted during that campaign. Stewart was then largely unknown in Scottish academic circles; and the chair was offered to James Stirling, who already enjoyed a European reputation as a mathematician of distinction. Stirling declined the invitation; and when the electors to the chair re-assessed the situation at the end of 1746, the reception accorded the publication of Stewart's book had been so favorable that they were encouraged to offer him the chair. Stewart had only recently (May 1745) been ordained minister of the parish of Roseneath, Dunbartonshire, on the nomination of the Duke of Argyll; but he had no hesitation in changing his career and was duly elected to the chair of mathematics at Edinburgh in September 1747.

Stewart's reputation as a mathematician was established overnight by the publication of the *General Theorems*. John Playfair, himself a scientist of distinction, claimed that Stewart's results were "among the most beautiful, as well as most general propositions known in the whole compass of geometry, and are perhaps only equalled by the remarkable *locus* to the circle in the second book of Apollonius, or by the celebrated theorems of Mr. Cotes. . . . The unity which prevails among them is a proof that a single though extensive view guided Mr. Stewart in the discovery of them all" ("Memoir of Matthew Stewart," 59–60). Simson's influence is obvious throughout the work. Several of Stewart's theorems are in fact porisms, although he refrains from calling them by that name, probably through fear of seeming to anticipate Simson. Several of their contemporaries assert in their memoirs that Simson, singularly lacking in personal ambition, was so keen for Stewart to succeed to Maclaurin's chair that he allowed him to incorporate in his book results that were originally Simson's; it is fairly clear that what is usually described as "Stewart's theorem" was demonstrated in lectures by Simson several years before the publication of Stewart's book.

After his election to the chair, Stewart's interests turned to astronomy and natural philosophy; and he displayed great ingenuity in devising purely geometrical proofs of results in these subjects that had previously been established by the use of algebraic and analytical methods. Examples of this kind are to be seen in his *Tracts, Physical and Mathematical* (1761). In a work published in 1763 he extended these methods to provide a basis for the approximate calculation of the distance of the earth from the sun. He derived a value of 29,875 radii of the earth for this distance—a result that was shown shortly afterward (1768) by John Dawson to be greatly in error; Stewart's mistake had been his failure to realize that his geometrical methods did not indicate how small arithmetical errors could grow in the course of his calculation.

Stewart bore the attacks on this work rather badly, and as a result his health began to fail. In 1772 he retired to his country estate at Catrine in Ayrshire, leaving the duties of his chair to his son Dugald, who was elected joint professor with him in 1775.

BIBLIOGRAPHY

I. ORIGINAL WORKS. Stewart's books include *General Theorems of Considerable Use in the Higher Parts of Mathematics* (Edinburgh, 1746); *Tracts, Physical and Mathematical . . .* (Edinburgh, 1761); *Distance of the Sun From the Earth . . .* (Edinburgh, 1763); and *Propositiones geometricae more veterum demonstratae ad geometriam antiquam illustrandam et promovendam idoneae* (Edinburgh, 1763).

II. SECONDARY LITERATURE. See John Playfair, "Memoir of Matthew Stewart," in *Transactions of the Royal Society of Edinburgh*, **1** (1788), 57–76; and Matthew Stewart, *Memoir of Dugald Stewart* (Edinburgh, 1838).

IAN N. SNEDDON

STIELTJES, THOMAS JAN (*b.* Zwolle, Netherlands, 29 December 1856; *d.* Toulouse, France, 31 December 1894), *mathematics.*

To the majority of mathematicians, Stieltjes' name is remembered in association with the Stieltjes integral,

$$\int_a^b f(u)\,dg(u),$$

a generalization of the ordinary Riemann integral with wide applications in physics. Yet in his own day, he was renowned as a versatile mathematician whose publications include papers in almost every area of analysis. He is the father of the analytic theory of continued fractions, and his integral was developed as a tool for its study.

Stieltjes, the son of a distinguished Dutch civil engineer, received his principal schooling at the École Polytechnique in Delft. He left the École in 1877 to take up a post at the observatory in Leiden, where he served six years. Evidently he

kept up his mathematical studies, since he left Leiden to accept a chair in mathematics at the University of Groningen. Honors came to Stieltjes early. In 1884 the University of Leiden awarded him an honorary doctorate, and in 1885 he was elected to membership in the Royal Academy of Sciences of Amsterdam. Disappointed at Groningen, Stieltjes went to live in Paris, where he received his doctorate of science in 1886. In the same year he was appointed to the faculty at the University of Toulouse, where he remained until his death eight years later. Although not elected to the Academy of Sciences in Paris, Stieltjes was considered for membership in 1892 and won its Ormoy Prize in 1893 for his work on continued fractions.

Stieltjes' published work encompasses almost all of analysis of his time. He made contributions to the theory of ordinary and partial differential equations, studied gamma functions and elliptical functions, and worked in interpolation theory. His thesis was on asymptotic series. A special and increasing interest was the evaluation of particular integrals such as

$$\int_0^\infty \frac{\sin(xu)}{1+u^2}\,du$$

or

$$\int_0^\infty \frac{u\cos(xu)}{1+u^2}\,du$$

and series of the general form $\sum\limits^{\infty} a_n/x^n$, which arise in a natural way from such integrals. These series also occur in the study of continued fractions, and this may have led Stieltjes to analytic continued fraction theory.

His first paper on continued fractions, published in 1884, proves the convergence of

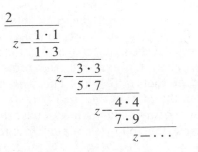

$$\cfrac{2}{z-\cfrac{1\cdot 1}{1\cdot 3}}$$

in the slit complex z-plane excluding the interval $(-1,1)$, with use of the series in decreasing powers of z. This convergence, which is locally uniform, was established by transforming the fraction into a definite integral.

Yet Stieltjes' monument is his last memoir, "Recherches sur les fractions continues," written just before he died, and published in two parts (*Annales de la Faculté des sciences de l'Université de Toulouse pour les sciences mathématiques et physiques*, **1**, ser. 1 [1894], 1–122; **1**, ser. 9 [1895], 5–47), the second posthumously. In it he polished and refined all of his previous work on the subject, and here is the first appearance of his integral. The memoir is a beautiful piece of mathematical writing—clear, self-contained, almost lyric in its style.

In this paper the fraction

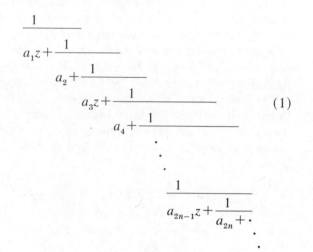

$$\cfrac{1}{a_1z+\cfrac{1}{a_2+\cfrac{1}{a_3z+\cfrac{1}{a_4+\cfrac{1}{\ddots\cfrac{1}{a_{2n-1}z+\cfrac{1}{a_{2n}+\ddots}}}}}}} \qquad (1)$$

is considered. The a_i's are assumed to be known real positive quantities, and z is a complex variable. Fraction (1) will be said to converge, or otherwise, according to the convergence or not of the sequence of "approximates" $P_n(z)/Q_n(z)$. Each approximate is the rational function formed by considering only the first n terms of (1) and simplifying the resulting compound fraction. Thus, $Q_{2n}(z)$ and $P_{2n+1}(z)$ are polynomials of degree n in z, while P_{2n} is of degree $n-1$, and Q_{2n+1} is of degree $n+1$.

Stieltjes began by studying the roots of the polynomials $P_n(z)Q_n(z)$, which are all real. He proved a whole series of theorems concerning the interlacing of their roots; for example, the roots of $Q_{2n}(z)$ separate the roots of $Q_{2n-2}(z)$. This was then used to prove that the roots of $P_n(z)$ and $Q_n(z)$ ($n=1, 2, \cdots$) are all nonpositive and distinct. Thus, the approximates have the following partial fraction decomposition:

$$\frac{P_{2n}(z)}{Q_{2n}(z)}=\sum_{k=1}^{n}\frac{M_k}{z+x_k} \qquad (2)$$

$$\frac{P_{2n+1}(z)}{Q_{2n+1}(z)}=\frac{N_0}{z}+\sum_{k=1}^{n}\frac{N_k}{z+y_k}, \qquad (3)$$

where in (2) $\{x_1, x_2, \cdots, x_n\}$ are the (positive) roots of $Q_{2n}(-z)$ and in (3) $\{0, y_1, y_2, \cdots, y_n\}$ are the roots of $Q_{2n+1}(-z)$.

Next Stieltjes was able to show that

$$\frac{P_n(z)}{Q_n(z)}=\sum_{k=1}^{n}(-1)^{k-1}\frac{c_{k-1}}{z^k}+\sum_{k=n+1}^{\infty}\frac{\alpha_{n,k-1}}{z^k}, \qquad (4)$$

where the $\{c_k : k = 1, 2, \cdots, n\}$ depend only upon the original fraction (1) and not upon n. Formula (4) led to the definition of the development of (1) in decreasing powers of z:

$$\sum_{k=1}^{\infty}(-1)^{k-1}\frac{c_{k-1}}{z^k} \qquad (5)$$

The c_k are all real and positive, and

$$\frac{c_{n+1}}{c_n}<\frac{c_{n+2}}{c_{n+1}}. \qquad (6)$$

Either the sequences of ratios is unbounded, in which case (5) diverges for all z, or (6) is bounded, in which case there is a $\lambda > 0$ with the property that (5) converges for all z satisfying $|z| > \lambda$. Stieltjes then proved that, in the latter case, if the (necessarily positive) roots of $Q_n(-z)$ are ordered according to size, and if the largest is, say, $x_{n,k}$, then $\lim_{n\to\infty} x_{n,k} = \lambda$.

oscillation of (1). Here Stieltjes showed that for all z with positive real part,

$$\lim_{n\to\infty}\frac{P_{2n+1}(z)}{Q_{2n+1}(z)}=F_1(z) \qquad (7)$$

and

$$\lim_{n\to\infty}\frac{P_{2n}(z)}{Q_{2n}(z)}=F(z). \qquad (8)$$

Furthermore, for z real ($=x$), $F(x)$ and $F_1(x)$ are real, and $F_1(x) \geq F(x)$. Equality in the right half plane, including the positive real axis, was proved to hold if and only if the series

$$\sum_{k=1}^{\infty}a_k \qquad (9)$$

formed from the terms of fraction (1) is divergent. (Recall that the a_k are all positive.) Also, since the convergence of (7) and (8) is locally uniform, the functions $F(z)$ and $F_1(z)$ are analytic in the right half plane. Thus, to sum up, Stieltjes had shown that the continued fraction (1) was convergent when and only when the series (9) diverged; otherwise the fraction oscillated. The remaining problem was to extend this result to the z in the left half plane, except for certain points on the negative real axis.

To this end, Stieltjes showed that the limits

$$\lim_{n\to\infty} P_{2n}(z) = p(z) \qquad \lim_{n\to\infty} P_{2n+1}(z) = p_1(z)$$

$$\lim_{n\to\infty} Q_{2n}(z) = q(z) \qquad \lim_{n\to\infty} Q_{2n+1}(z) = q_1(z)$$

all exist, that p, q, p_1, q_1 are all analytic, and that

$$p_1(z)q(z) - p(z)q_1(z) \equiv 1.$$

Then, again he supposed that the roots $\{x_{n,1}, x_{n,2}, \cdots, x_{n,n}\}$ of $Q_{2n}(-z)$ were ordered according to increasing size for each n. Stieltjes then proved that $\lim_{n\to\infty} x_{nk} = \lambda k$, that $\{\lambda_k; k = 1, 2, \cdots\}$ are all distinct real and positive, and that the λ_k are the only zeros of $q(z)$. Similar results hold for $q_1(z)$, $p(z)$, and $p_1(z)$. Next, μ_k is defined by

$$\mu_k = \frac{p(-\lambda_k)}{q'(-\lambda_k)}, \tag{10}$$

and it was proved that $\mu_k = \lim_{n\to\infty} M_k$ ($k = 1, 2, \cdots$), where the M_k are from expression (2). Furthermore,

$$S(z) = \sum_{k=1}^{\infty} \frac{\mu_k}{z + x_k} \tag{11}$$

is meromorphic in the plane, $S(z) = F(z)$ (see [8]), and finally that for each i

$$c_i = \sum_{k=1}^{\infty} \mu_k \lambda_k^{\,i}, \tag{12}$$

where the c_i's are from (5).

In precisely the same way, an infinite set of pairs of positive real numbers similar to $\{(\mu_k, \lambda_k)\}$ above was associated with the sequence $\{p_{2n+1}(z)/Q_{2n+1}(z)\}$. In particular $F_1(z)$ was shown to be meromorphic, and if $\nu_k = \lim_{n\to\infty} N_k$ ($k = 0, 1, 2, \cdots$); see [3]), and if $\theta_k = \lim_{n\to\infty} y_{n,k}$ ($k = 1, 2, \cdots$), then

$$c_0 = \sum_{k=0}^{\infty} \nu_k \text{ and } c_i = \sum_{k=1}^{\infty} \nu_k \theta_k^{\,i} \ (i = 1, 2, \cdots), \text{ and}$$

$$F(z) = \frac{\nu_0}{z} + \sum_{k=1}^{\infty} \frac{\nu_k}{z + \theta_k}. \tag{13}$$

In this way he established the analyticity of $F_1(z)$ and $F(z)$ in the slit plane.

Observe that the above systems (12) (or [13]) can be considered as the equations of the moments of all orders of a system of masses μ_k (or ν_k) placed at a distance λ_k (or θ_k) from the origin, and that in either case the ith moment is c_i. Of course, if Σa_k is divergent, $\nu_k = \mu_k$ and $\lambda_k = \theta_k$ for all k, since $F(z)$

and $F_1(z)$ are the same function. But if Σa_k is convergent, the equalities do not hold, even though the c_i are the same in each case.

The further study of the nature of $F_1(z)$ and $F(z)$ in more detail led Stieltjes to the "moment problem": that is, to find a distribution of mass (an infinite set of ordered pairs of positive numbers) whose moments of all orders are known. If this problem can be solved, then $F_1(z)$ and $F(z)$ will be known, since the c_i's can be calculated from the a_k's of fraction (1). However, it is immediately evident that if Σa_k is convergent, there can be no unique solution, as there are at least two. But Stieltjes was able to show (later on) that if Σa_k diverges, there is a unique solution.

It was to solve the moment problem that Stieltjes introduced his integral. First he considered an increasing real-valued function φ defined on the positive real axis, and gave a lengthy discussion of one-sided limits. For example, he showed that φ is continuous at x, if and only if $\varphi^+(x) = \varphi^-(x)$. Only bounded functions with countably many discontinuities on the positive axis were considered. Next he supposed that φ was a step function, with $\varphi(0) = 0$. Then a finite mass condensed at each point of discontinuity can be given by $\varphi^+(x) - \varphi^-(x)$, and $\varphi(b) - \varphi(a)$ is the total mass between a and b; in particular $\varphi(x)$ is the total mass between x and the origin. Also, changing the value of φ at a point of discontinuity does not change the associated mass distribution there.

Stieltjes then defined the integral

$$\int_a^b f(x)\,d\varphi(x) \tag{14}$$

to be the limit, as $\max (x_{i+1} - x_i) \to 0$ of

$$\sum_{i=1}^{n} f(\zeta_i)[\varphi(x_i) - \varphi(x_{i-1})], \tag{15}$$

where $a = x_0 < x_i < \cdots < x_n = b$ and $x_{i-1} \le \zeta_i \le x_i$. Stieltjes then established the formula for integration by parts

$$\int_a^b f(x)\,d\varphi(x) =$$

$$f(b)\varphi(b) - f(a)\varphi(a)$$

$$- \int_a^b \varphi(x)\,df(x),$$

defined the improper integral $\int_a^\infty f(a)\,d\varphi(x)$ in the usual way, and established many properties of the integral.

57

Next he considered the function φ_n defined from the even-order approximates by

$$\varphi_n(0) = 0 \quad 0 \le u < x_1$$

$$\varphi_n(u) = \sum_{i=1}^{k} M_i \quad x_k \le u < x_{k+1} (1 \le k \le n-1)$$

$$\varphi_n(u) = \sum_{i=1}^{n} M_i = \frac{1}{a_1} \quad x_n \le u < \infty,$$

where the M_i and the x_k are defined as in (2), and where a_1 is the first term of (1). After a lengthy discussion of "lim inf" and "lim sup" (the ideas were new then), he defined, for each u: $\psi(u) = \lim$ sup $\varphi_n(u)$, $\chi(u) = \lim \inf \varphi_n(u)$, and $\Phi(u) = \frac{1}{2}(\psi(u) + \chi(u))$. Φ was shown to have the property that

$$F(z) = \int_0^\infty \frac{d\Phi(u)}{z+u}$$

and also that the distribution of mass represented by Φ solved the moment problem, since

$$c_k = \int_0^\infty u^k d\Phi(u).$$

A function $\Phi_1(u)$ with similar properties was constructed from the odd-order approximates. He also undertook the study of the inverse problem; that is, given an increasing function $\psi(u)$, with $\psi(0) = 0$, then, by setting

$$c_k = \int_0^\infty u^k d\varphi(x)$$

a fraction like (1) can be determined with the property that

$$F(x) \le \int_0^\infty \frac{d\psi(u)}{x+u} \le F_1(x).$$

Stieltjes' paper, of which only a portion has been summarized here, is a mathematical milestone. The work represents the first general treatment of continued fractions as part of complex analytic function theory; previously, only special cases had been considered. Moreover, it is clearly in the historical line that led to Hilbert spaces and their generalizations. In addition, Stieltjes gave a sort of respectability to discontinuous functions and, together with some earlier work, to divergent series. All together these were astonishing accomplishments for a man who died just two days after his thirty-eighth birthday.

BIBLIOGRAPHY

All Stieltjes' published papers, with some letters, notes, and incomplete works found after his death, are in *Oeuvres complètes de Thomas Jan Stieltjes* (Groningen, 1914–1918). An annotated bibliography of his published works appears with his obituary in *Annales de la Faculté des sciences de l'Université de Toulouse pour les sciences mathématiques et physiques*, **1**, ser. 1 (1895), 1–64.

MICHAEL BERNKOPF

STIFEL (STYFEL, STYFFEL, STIEFFELL, STIFELIUS, or STIEFFEL), MICHAEL (*b.* Esslingen, Germany, *ca.* 1487; *d.* Jena, Germany, 19 April 1567), *mathematics, theology.*

Stifel was the son of Conrad Stifel. Nothing is known about his education except that, on his own testimony, he knew no Greek.[1] He was a monk at the Augustinian monastery of Esslingen, where he was ordained priest in 1511. Reacting to the declining morality of the clergy and the abuses committed in the administration of indulgences, Stifel became an early follower of Luther. While studying the Bible he came upon the numbers in Revelation and in the Book of Daniel.[2]

After 1520 he became increasingly preoccupied with their cabalistic interpretation, for which he used a "word calculus" (*Wortrechnung*). In the malevolent great beast designated in Revelation by the number 666 he saw Pope Leo X.[3] Stifel aroused the suspicion of the bishop of Constance and of his vicar-general by giving absolution without receiving indulgence money and by composing a song in honor of Luther.[4] Realizing that his life was in danger, Stifel escaped in 1522 to Kronberg in the Taunus Mountains, seeking refuge in the castle of a knight named Hartmut, a relative of Franz von Sickingen. He soon had to flee again[5] and went to Wittenberg, where Luther lodged him in his own house. The two became friends, and in 1523 Luther obtained Stifel a post as pastor at the court of the count of Mansfeld. Two years later Stifel became pastor and tutor at Castle Tollet in Upper Austria, in the service of the widow of a nobleman, Wolfgang Jörger.[6] The persecution unleashed by Ferdinand I of Bohemia against the new religious teaching forced Stifel to return to Luther, who procured him a parish at Annaberg. Luther accompanied Stifel there on 25 October 1528 and married him to the widow of the previous incumbent.

At Annaberg, Stifel resumed his dabbling in number mysticism, an activity that, if nothing else, revealed his skill in detecting number-theory relationships. From his reading of the Bible, he thought that he had discovered the date of the end of the world; and in *Ein Rechen-büchlin Vom End Christ* (1532) he prophesied that the event would occur at 8 o'clock on 18 October 1533.[7] On 28 September 1533 Luther implored him not to spread his fantastic notions. Stifel could not be dissuaded, however; and as he vainly warned his assembled congregation of the coming of the end, he was arrested and subsequently dismissed from his post.[8] Through the intervention of Luther—who forgave his "little temptation" (*kleine Anfechtlein*) —and Melanchthon, he finally received another parish, at nearby Holzdorf, in 1535.

Now cured of prophesying, Stifel devoted himself to mathematics. He enrolled at, and received his master's degree from, the University of Wittenberg, where Jacob Milich was lecturer on mathematics.[9] Stifel gave private instruction in mathematics, and among his pupils was Melanchthon's son-in-law Kaspar Peucer. The years at Holzdorf were Stifel's most productive period. At the urging of Milich he wrote *Arithmetica integra* (1544), in which he set forth all that was then known about arithmetic and algebra, supplemented by important original contributions.[10] In his next work, *Deutsche arithmetica* (1545), Stifel sought to make his favorite branch of mathematics, the coss (algebra) or "artful calculation" (*Kunstrechnung*), more accessible to German readers by eliminating foreign words.[11] His last book written at Holzdorf was *Welsche Practick* (1546).[12]

The peaceful years in Holzdorf ended suddenly after the Schmalkaldic War (1547), for the "Hispanier" drove off all the inhabitants.[13] Stifel fled to Prussia, where he finally found a position in 1551 as pastor at Haberstroh, near Königsberg.[14] He lectured on theology and mathematics at the University of Königsberg and brought out a new edition of Christoph Rudolff's *Coss*, which first appeared in 1525 and had since become unavailable. He undertook the republication at the request of a businessman named Christoff Ottendorffer, who paid the printing costs. Stifel reproduced Rudolff's text in its entirety, as well as all 434 problems illustrating the eight rules of the *Coss*. To each chapter of the original text he appended critical notes and additional developments, most of which he drew from his *Arithmetica integra*.[15] Stifel's additions are much longer than the corresponding sections of Rudolff's book.[16]

Stifel returned to playing with numbers, as is evident from his next published book, *Ein sehr wunderbarliche Wortrechnung* (1553).[17] At odds with his colleagues, especially Andreas Osiander, as a result of theological controversies, and urged to return to Holzdorf by his former congregation, he returned to Saxony in 1554. His first post there was as pastor at Brück, near Wittenberg. He then went to Jena, following his friend Matthias Flacius,[18] and lectured on arithmetic and geometry at the university. In 1559 he was mentioned in the register as "senex, artium Magister et minister verbi divini."[19] By this time he apparently had given up his pastorate. Stifel's life in Jena was made difficult by theological disputes until Flacius, from whom Stifel had become alienated, found a successor (Nikolaus Selnecker) for him in 1561.[20] Stifel bequeathed the latter a long work on *Wortrechnung* that was never printed.[21]

In his books Stifel offered more than a methodical exposition of existing knowledge of arithmetic and algebra:[22] he also made original contributions that prepared the way for further progress in these fields. A principal concern was the establishment of generally valid laws. He contended that to improve algebra, it was necessary to formulate rules the validity of which was not limited to special cases, and which therefore could advance the study of the entire subject.[23] He was, in fact, the first to present a general method for solving equations, one that replaced the twenty-four rules traditionally given by the cossists (and the eight that appeared in Rudolff's *Coss*).[24] For example, he pointed out that basically there was nothing different about problems with several unknowns, a type for which Rudolff had introduced a special name.[25] Similarly, he asserted that the symbol "dragma" for the linear member could simply be omitted.[26] Stifel introduced into western mathematics a general method for computing roots that required, however, the use of binomial coefficients. He had discovered these coefficients only with great difficulty, having found no one to teach them to him nor any written accounts of them.[27] Stifel also surpassed his predecessors in the division of general polynomials and extraction of their roots, as well as in computing with irrational numbers.

The second chapter of *Arithmetica integra* is devoted entirely to the numerical treatment of Euclidean irrationals (binomials, residues, and so forth), a topic that Fibonacci had planned to discuss.[28] Stifel's exceptional skill in number theory is evident in his investigation of numerical relationships in number sequences, polygonal numbers, and magic squares.[29] Particularly noteworthy is his contribution to the preliminary stages of logarithmic computation. The starting point for this type of computation was attained by correlating a geometric series with an arithmetic series. This can be seen in Stifel's explanation of the cossists' symbols:

$$0 \cdot 1 \cdot 2 \cdot 3 \cdot 4 \cdot 5 \cdot 6 \cdot 7$$
$$1 \cdot 1x \cdot 1z \cdot 1c \cdot 1zz \cdot 1\beta \cdot 1zc \cdot 1b\beta.$$

On this occasion Stifel introduced the term "exponent" for the numbers of the upper series.[30] In correlating the two number sequences he extended the use of exponents to the domain of the negative numbers in the manner shown below.

−3	−2	−1	0	1	2	3	4	5	6
$\frac{1}{8}$	$\frac{1}{4}$	$\frac{1}{2}$	1	2	4	8	16	32	64

Stifel suspected the importance of his innovation, stating: "A whole book might be written concerning the marvellous things relating to numbers, but I must refrain and leave these things with eyes closed."[31] He did, however, provide a table that made it possible to carry out logarithmic calculations. Stifel approached the concept of the logarithm from another direction as well. He was aware of both inversions of the power, the root, and the "logarithmus." He discussed "division" of a ratio by a number, obtaining, for example, in the case of (27:8) "divided" by 3/4: $\sqrt[3/4]{27:8} = \sqrt[3]{(27:8)^4} = 81:16$.[32] In contrast, Stifel saw the "division" of a ratio by a ratio as a way of finding exponents. Thus, by means of continuous "subtraction," he obtained from the equality $(729:64) = (3:2)^x$ the "quotient" $x = 6$; and in the case of $(2187:128) = (27:8)^x$, the result was $x = 2 \, 1/3$.[33]

Stifel was also a pioneer in the development of algebraic symbolism. To designate the unknowns he used A, B, C, D, and F, as well as the traditional x.[34] For the powers he employed Az, $x^3 = AAA$, $x^4 = FFFF$, and so forth—not just the traditional z (census).[35] He simplified the square root sign from $\sqrt{z}$ to $\sqrt{.}$, and later to $\sqrt{}$ alone.[36] In one instance he closely approached modern symbolism, writing $\sqrt[11]{38}$ as $11\sqrt{38}$.[37] Other, more cumbersome designations for unknowns and the root used in Deutsche arithmetica were not adopted by later mathematicians.[38] The only operational signs that Stifel employed were + and −; other operations were indicated verbally. Equality was designated either in words or by a point, as in $1x . \sqrt{48}$.[39]

Stifel made a thorough study of magic squares and polygonal numbers for a nonmathematical purpose.[40] He correlated the twenty-three letters of the alphabet with the first twenty-three triangular numbers, thereby establishing connections between words and numbers.[41] He called such Wortrechnung "the holy arithmetic of numbers."[42] For example, from the number 666 he derived the sentence "Id bestia Leo"; and the equality 2.5 ages = 1,260 days that he found in the book of Daniel yielded the sentence "Vae tibi Papa, vae tibi." Although Stifel's work at Holzdorf is most admired today, he declared that he valued his "word calculus" above all the computations he had ever made.[43]

The development of Stifel's scientific ideas was decisively influenced by Jacob Milich, who recommended that he study Campanus of Novara's translation of Euclid.[44] He also proposed that Stifel write a comprehensive work on arithmetic and algebra (which became Arithmetica integra).[45] To prepare for the latter project Stifel worked through Rudolff's Coss without assistance.[46] He had already studied proportions in the writings of Boethius, and had long been acquainted with contemporary arithmetic books, such as the Margarita phylosophica of Gregor Reisch (1503) and the works of Peter Apian (Eyn newe unnd wolgegründete Underweysung aller Kauffmanns Rechnung, 1527) and Adam Ries (Rechnung auf der Lynihen un Federn in Zalmass und gewicht auff allerley handierung gemacht, 1522).[47] (He especially admired Ries's book.)[48] Stifel conscientiously named the authors from whom he had taken examples and never neglected to express his appreciation.[49] The enthusiasm with which he followed Milich's advice[50] to collect mathematical writings is obvious from the large number of authors he cited.[51]

Stifel's achievements were respected and adopted by contemporary mathematicians, although, like Clavius, they often did not cite him.[52] The last edition of Arithmetica integra appeared in 1586, and the last of the Coss in 1615. After that, mathematicians surpassed Stifel's level of knowledge in symbolism and logarithms, and they opened new fields of research. It is for both these reasons that his work fell into neglect. He was, in fact, the greatest German algebraist of the sixteenth century.

NOTES

1. Stifel admitted that he was "ignarus linguae graecae." Since he knew Euclid only from the translations of Campanus

and Zamberti, he turned to other scholars for assistance. See *Arithmetica integra* (cited below as *AI*), fol. 143v.

2. In these numbers Stifel saw "sealed words" (*versiegelte Worte*). See *Wortrechnung* (cited below as *WR*), fol. B2^r.

3. The numbers (LDCIMV) that Stifel obtained from the name "Leo DeCIMVs" yielded 1656, 1,000 too much and 10 too little; but he manipulated them to obtain 666 by the addition of *decimus* = 10 and by setting M = *Mysterium*.

4. "Von der Christförmigen rechtgegründten leer Doctoris Martini Luthers . . ." (1522).

5. The castle was besieged by Franz von Sickingen's enemies and was taken on 15 Oct. 1522. A sermon that Stifel gave on 8 Sept. is still preserved; see J. E. Hofmann, "Michael Stifel, 1487?–1567," n. 14.

6. In the Grieskirchen congregation; see Ritter's *Geographisch-statistisches Lexicon*, II (Leipzig, 1906), 1051.

7. On the Biblical passages see J. E. Hofmann, "Michael Stifel," in n. 43. Other dates also were mentioned: 3 Oct. (J. H. Zedler, *Universallexikon*, XL [1744], 22); 16 Oct. (see Treutlein, p. 17, and Poggendorff, II, 1010–1011); and 19 Oct. (Giesing, p. 11). *Der Biograph*, p. 473, mentions the 282nd day and the 42nd week of the year.

8. For an eyewitness report in a letter from Petrus Weller to Ioannes Briessmann, see Strobel, pp. 74–84; the German trans. of the letter is given by Grosse, pp. 19 ff.

9. With Luther and Melanchthon, Milich was also friendly with Stifel at Annaberg and acted as the family's physician. See *AI*, fol. (α4)r, entry of 25 Oct. 1541, *Album der Universität Wittenberg*, I (Leipzig, 1841), 195a: "Gratis inscripti . . . Michael Stifel pastor in Holtzdorff."

10. A detailed description of the contents of the book can be found in Kaestner, *Geschichte der Mathematik*, I, 112 ff.; and in Treutlein; in Cantor; and in Hofmann, *op. cit.*

11. Stifel stated that the *regula falsi* is related to the coss as a point is to a circle. *AI*, 227r.

12. In the *Welsche Practick* (cited below as *WP*) Stifel objected to Apian's problems, which were correct but not comprehensible to everyone. He did not wish to blame Apian but to "diligently expound" his work (see pp. 293, 337). Stifel also drew on the "*praxis italica*" in *AI*, fols. 83v ff.

13. See *WR*. fol. A(1)v.

14. He went to Memel in 1549 and to Eichholz in 1550.

15. The title page bears the date 1553, the preface 1552, and the *explicit* 1554. Stifel made changes in the course of the printing, and thus the table of contents must be corrected. See *Coss*, fol. 179r.

16. Rudolff's 208 pages grew to 494 in Stifel's edition.

17. Osiander wrote on 19 Feb. 1549: ". . . Commentus est novos alphabeti numeros scil. triangulares et delirat multo ineptius quam antea" ("He has devised new numbers for the alphabet, namely the triangular numbers, and his fantasies are more absurd than before"). See B. F. Hummel, *Epistolarum historico-ecclesiasticarum saeculo XVI a celeberrimis viris scriptorum semicenturia altera* (Halle, 1780), 70 ff.

18. Like Stifel and Ottendorffer, Flacius was an opponent of Osiander.

19. Entry in *Die Matrikel der Universität Jena*, I (Jena, 1944), 320.

20. See J. E. Hofmann, "Michael Stifel," p. 59.

21. The MS, "Explicatio apocalypseos," is now in the Karl Marx University Library, Leipzig. The Lutheran congregation of Kronberg possesses a microfilm copy of the work. See W. Meretz, "Aus Stiefels Nachlass," p. 5.

22. The first book of *AI* is devoted to the fundamental operations—including roots, properties of numbers, series, magic squares, proportions, the rule of three, false substitution, and the Welsh practice; the second book treats computation with irrationals, corresponding to the tenth book of Euclid; the third book takes up algebra and equations of higher degree, such as were found in the work of Rudolff

and Cardano and that could be solved by employing certain devices.

The first part of the *Deutsche arithmetica* (cited below as *DA*) is devoted to "household computations" (*Hausrechnung*): carrying out on the abacus fundamental operations and the rule of three using whole numbers. The second part is concerned with computation with fractions, with the German *Coss* or "Kunstrechnung," and with extracting roots on the abacus. The third part, on "church computations" (*Kirchrechnung*), treats the division of the church year.

The division of the *Coss* is the same as in Rudolff's original edition. Stifel also reproduced Rudolff's *Wortrechnung*, but he did not agree with its contents. Among the new elements that he added were remarks on the higher-degree equations that Rudolff had presented; on the rules of the *Cubicoss* formulated by Scipione dal Ferro and Cardano that had been published in the meantime; and a procedure for computing

$$\sqrt[3]{a + \sqrt{b}}$$

Stifel's edition of the *Coss* also contained diagrams for verifying solutions. These had been drawn by Rudolff but did not appear in the original edition. Stifel obtained them from Johann Neudörfer, a brother-in-law of the printer Johannes Petrejus. See *Coss*, fol. 172r.

23. *DA*, fol. 72v.

24. Stifel reduced the three cases of the quadratic equation, $x^2 + a = b$, $x^2 + b = ax$, and $x^2 = ax + b$, to the standard form $x^2 = \pm ax \pm b$. By "extracting roots with cossic numbers" he obtained his rule called AMASIAS: $x = \sqrt{\left(\frac{a}{2}\right)^2 \pm b} \pm \frac{a}{2}$, where the plus and minus signs correspond to those of the standard form. See *AI*, fols. 240r f.; and Treutlein, *op. cit.*, 79. Stifel knew of the double solution only for $x^2 + b = ax$ (*AI*, fol. 243v). He avoided negative solutions, although he recognized negative numbers as those less than zero. (*AI*, fol. 48r.) An equation of which the solution happened to be zero can be found in *AI*, fol. 283r.

25. For the term *quantitas*, see *AI*, fol. 257v; it was also used by Cardano (see *AI*, fol. 252r).

26. *DA*, fol. 17v.

27. *Ibid.*, fol. 72v. The table with binomial coefficients can be found in *AI*, fol. 44v; *DA*, fol. 71v; and *Coss*, fol. 168r.

28. See article on Fibonacci in this Dictionary, IV, 612, n. 7.

29. A detailed account is given by Hofmann in "Michael Stifel 1487?–1567," 13 ff.

30. *AI*, fol. 235.

31. "Posset hic fere novus liber integer scribi de mirabilibus numerorum sed oportet ut me hic subducam et clausis oculis abeam" (*AI*, fol. 249v). Translation from D. E. Smith, *History of Mathematics*, II (New York, 1925), 521.

32. Stifel distinguished between fraction (*Bruch*) and ratio (*Verhältnis*), and wrote the latter as a fraction without a fraction line. Nevertheless, he conceived of the ratio as a fraction; the quotient was its "name." Thus, 4:3 had the name 1 1/3. See *WP*, pp. 36 ff.; and *Coss*, fol. 135v.

33. First Stifel obtained, as the result of two "subtractions," $(2187:128) = (27:8)^2 (3:2)$ and then, because $(3:2) = (27:8)^{1/3}$, $(2187:128) = (27:8)^{2\ 1/3}$. The details are in *AI*, fols. 53v ff. On computation with fractional power exponents and fractional radical indices, see *Coss*, fols. 138r f.

34. *AI*, fol. 254r.

35. *DA*, fol. 74v.

36. As Rudolff originally had it in the *Coss*.

37. *DA*, fol. 71r.

38. See *DA*, fol. 61v. Stifel extended the cumbersome symbols for the square root ($\sqrt{}$) and cube root ($\sqrt[3]{}$) as far as the sixth root (*DA*, fol. 62r). The designations for the unknowns in the *DA* (see fols. 20 ff.) are $x = 1$ Sum:or 1 Sum A:, $x^2 = 1$ Sum:Sum; and so on, up to x^{11} (*DA*, fol. 70v).

39. *Coss*, fol. 351v. He also uses points to indicate inclusion of

several elements in the same operation, as in $\sqrt{z}.\ 6+\sqrt{z2}.=\sqrt{6+\sqrt{2}}$. *AI*, fol. 112v.

40. The number 666 of the "great beast" appeared in *Ein Rechen Büchlin vom End Christ* (fols., H 4v and 5r) as the sum of all the cells of a magic square.
41. See *WR*, fol. D2r. For Stifel, i = j and u = v = w; Rudolff's alphabet, however, had twenty-four letters, since he included w.
42. See *WR*, fol. A(1)r.
43. See *Coss*, fol. 487v.
44. See *AI*, fol. 226v.
45. *AI*, fols. (α4)v.
46. See *WR*, fol. B(1)r; *Coss*, fol. A2r.
47. *AI*, fols. 55 f., 250r: *Coss*, fol. 23r; *AI*, fol. 102r; *WP*, fol. A2v.
48. *AI*, fol. 226v; *DA*, fol. 31r.
49. The problems come from Peter Apian, Cardano, Johann Neudörfer, Adam Ries, Adamus Gigas, Rudolff, and Widmann.
50. *AI*, fol. (α4)v.
51. Stifel names the following: Apian, Boethius, Campanus, Cardano, Nicholas Cusa, Dürer, Euclid, Gemma Frisius, Faber Stapulensis, Jordanus de Nemore, Neudörfer, Ptolemy, Reisch, Ries, Rudolff, Sacrobosco, Schöner, Theon of Alexandria, Zamberti, and Widmann.
52. See Hofmann, "Michael Stifel 1487?–1567," 31, n. 94.

BIBLIOGRAPHY

I. ORIGINAL WORKS. Stifel's works include *Ein Rechen Büchlin vom End Christ, Apocalypsis in Apocalypsin* (Wittenberg, 1532); *Arithmetica integra*, with preface by Melanchthon (Nuremberg, 1544; 1545; 1546; 1548; 1586); *Deutsche arithmetica, inhaltend Haussrechnung, deutsche Coss, Kirchrechnung* (Nuremberg, 1545); *Rechenbuch von der welschen und deutschen Practick . . .* (Nuremberg, 1546); *Ein sehr wunderbarliche Wortrechnung. Sampt einer mercklichen Erklärung ettlicher Zahlen Danielis unnd der Offenbarung Sanct Iohannis* ([Königsberg], 1553); and *Die Coss Christoffs Rudolffs. Die schönen Exempeln der Coss. Durch Michael Stifel gebessert und sehr gemehrt* (Königsberg, 1552–1553 [colophon dated 1554], 1571; Amsterdam, 1615).

Lists of Stifel's theological writings and songs are in J. E. Hofmann, "Michael Stifel 1487?–1567" (see below), and in the articles by G. Kawerau and W. Meretz cited below. Illustrations of the title pages of Stifel's books are given by Hofmann and Meretz.

II. SECONDARY LITERATURE. See *Allgemeine deutsche biographie*, VI (1893), 208–216; *Der Biograph*, VI (Halle, 1807), 458–488; F. J. Buck, *Lebensbeschreibung der preussischen Mathematiker* (Königsberg, 1764), 34–38; M. Cantor, *Vorlesungen über Geschichte der Mathematik*, 2nd ed., II (Leipzig, 1913), 430–449; C. J. Gerhardt, *Geschichte der Mathematik in Deutschland* (Munich, 1877), 60–74; J. Giesing, *Stifels Arithmetica integra* (Döbeln, 1879); J. Grosse, "Michael Stiefel, der Prophet," in *Westermanns Monatshefte*, no. 85 (Oct. 1863), 1–40; J. E. Hofmann, "Michael Stifel 1487?–1567," *Sudhoffs Archiv . . .*, supp. no. 9 (1968); and "Michael Stifel," in *Jahrbuch für Geschichte der Oberdeutschen Reichsstädte*, Esslinger Studien, **14**

(1968), 30–60; G. Kawerau, "Stiefel (Styfel)," in *Realencyclopädie für protestantische Theologie und Kirche*, 3rd ed., X (Leipzig, 1907), 74–88, and XXIV (Leipzig, 1913), 529; A. G. Kaestner, *Geschichte der Mathematik*, I (Göttingen, 1796), 112–128, 163–184; W. Kaunzner, "Deutsche Mathematiker des 15. und 16. Jahrhunderts und ihre Symbolik," *Veröffentlichungen des Forschungsinstitutes des Deutschen Museums für die Geschichte der Naturwissenschaften und der Technik*, ser. A, no. 90 (1971); W. Meretz, "Uber die erste Veröffentlichung von Kronbergs erstem Pfarrer Michael Stiefel," in *Jahresberichte des Kronberger Gymnasiums, die Altkönigsschule* (Jan. 1969), 15–20; and "Aus Stiefels Nachlass," *ibid.* (Feb. 1969), 5–6; J. E. Montucla, *Histoire des mathématiques*, 2nd ed., I (Paris, 1799), 614; G. C. Pisansky, *Historia litteraria Prussiae* (Königsberg, 1765), 228; G. T. Strobel, *Neue Beiträge besonders zur Literatur des 16. Jahrhunderts*, I, pt. 1 (Nuremberg–Altdorf, 1790), 3–90; P. Treutlein, "Das Rechnen im 16. Jahrhundert," in *Abhandlungen zur Geschichte der Mathematik*, **2** (1879), 1–124, esp. 17 f., 33 ff., 42 f., 48 ff., 77 ff.; and F. Unger, *Die Methodik der praktischen Arithmetik* (Leipzig, 1888), see index, 239. Concerning a MS from 1599 with solutions to problems from the *Coss*, see D. E. Smith, *Rara arithmetica* (Boston–London, 1908), 493.

For further bibliographical information, see especially Hofmann, Kawerau, and Meretz.

KURT VOGEL

STILES, CHARLES WARDELL (*b.* Spring Valley, New York, 15 May 1867; *d.* Baltimore, Maryland, 24 January 1941), *zoology, public health.*

Stiles was the son of Samuel Martin Stiles, a Methodist minister, and Elizabeth White Stiles, both of whom belonged to old New England families. After attending high school in Hartford, Connecticut, he attended Wesleyan University for one year before going to Europe in 1886. General studies in Paris and Göttingen, and science studies at the University of Berlin, were followed by a concentration in zoology at the University of Leipzig with the parasitologist Rudolf Leuckart. After receiving the Ph.D. at Leipzig in 1890, Stiles studied in several important European laboratories before returning to the United States in 1891 to work in Washington as principal zoologist at the Bureau of Animal Industry of the Department of Agriculture.

At the Bureau of Animal Industry, Stiles's work included investigation of a wide range of animal parasites. Among these, his studies of trichinosis led to his assignment in 1898 and 1899 as science attaché at the American embassy in Berlin to investigate German allegations that imported American pork was unhealthy. Meanwhile, in 1893 and 1894 Stiles was instrumental in organizing the contingent of American scientists in residence at the Naples zoological station, and he served as secretary of its advisory committee for many years. Also during the 1890's he introduced medical zoology into the curricula of several Eastern medical schools. This and other health-related work led to Stiles's transfer in 1902 from the Bureau of Animal Industry to the Hygienic Laboratory of the United States Public Health Service, where he remained as chief of the division of zoology for the next thirty years.

Stiles's preeminent contributions to health were made in connection with hookworm disease. In 1902 he not only discovered a new variety of hookworm (*Uncinaria americana* [or *Necator americanus*]) but also showed it to be endemic among poor whites of the South. His subsequent efforts to obtain action against the parasite resulted in formation of the Rockefeller Sanitary Commission in 1909. With Stiles as medical director, the commission conducted a five-year campaign that resulted in noticeably improved sanitation and health. In this and in his later public health work, Stiles effectively combined the roles of health educator and epidemiologist with his principal work as a laboratory investigator.

As virtual successor to Joseph Leidy, Stiles contributed to both basic and applied zoology. A prodigious worker and keen observer, he systematically rearranged the principal American helminthological collections, and also identified and reported many new species of parasitic worms. Elected to the International Commission on Zoological Nomenclature in 1895, and its secretary from 1898 to 1936, he exerted great influence on the orderly development of the field. Of even greater importance was his publication, with Albert Hassall, of the monumental *Index-catalogue of Medical and Veterinary Zoology*, which, with its associated key catalogs of insects, parasites, protozoa, crustacea, and arachnids, was a continuing task from the 1890's until the mid-1930's.

BIBLIOGRAPHY

I. ORIGINAL WORKS. Relatively few of Stiles's personal papers have come to light thus far. MSS pertaining to certain aspects of his career are to be found, however, in the archives of the Smithsonian Institution; and there is also some material in the United States National Archives (Department of State files). Much of Stiles's voluminous scientific writing is in the form of reports or other official publications of the Bureau of Animal Industry, the Public Health Service, and the Rockefeller Sanitary Commission. See especially C. W. Stiles and Albert Hassall, *Index-catalogue of Medical and Veterinary Zoology* (Washington, D.C., 1908–   ). A short autobiographical account is "Early History, in Part Esoteric, of the Hookworm (*Uncinariasis*) Campaign in Our Southern United States," in *Journal of Parasitology*, **25** (1939), 283–308.

II. SECONDARY LITERATURE. While there is no book-length study of Stiles, several articles are available. Among the fullest are F. G. Brooks, "Charles Wardell Stiles, Intrepid Scientist," in *Bios* (Mt. Vernon, Iowa), **18** (1947), 139–169; and Mark Sullivan, *Our Times*, III (New York, 1930), 290–332. Shorter accounts are in *National Cyclopaedia of American Biography*, Current vol. D (1934), 62–63; *Who Was Who in America, 1897–1942*; and *New York Times*, 25 Jan. 1941, 15.

Studies of particular phases of Stiles's career include James H. Cassedy, "The 'Germ of Laziness' in the South 1900–1915: Charles Wardell Stiles and the Progressive Paradox," in *Bulletin of the History of Medicine*, **45** (1971), 159–169; and "Applied Microscopy and American Pork Diplomacy: Charles Wardell Stiles in Germany 1898–1899," in *Isis*, **62** (1971), 4–20; and Benjamin Schwartz, "A Brief Résumé of Dr. Stiles's Contributions to Parasitology," in *Journal of Parasitology*, **19** (1933), 257–261.

JAMES H. CASSEDY

STILLE, WILHELM HANS (*b.* Hannover, Germany, 8 October 1876; *d.* Hannover, 26 December 1966), *tectonic geology*.

Stille was the son of Eduard and Meta Hankes Stille. His father was an army officer and later a manufacturer in Hannover. Hans married Hanna Touraine, of Huguenot ancestry, in 1903; their sons were Wilhelm, a lawyer, and Hans, a banker. Stille was a man of sturdy physique and vigorous health.

He began his studies of stratigraphy and tectonics near his home, continuing fieldwork in the area, with few interruptions, until later in life. Exploration in Colombia when he was a young man introduced him to a continent to which he devoted particular attention. He spent little time in research abroad but directed studies by many students in the western Mediterranean region. His wide and thorough reading helped him to become the leader in synthesizing global tectonics and to recognize some significant relationships.

Stille graduated from the Leibniz School in Hannover in 1896. He entered the Technische Hochschule there as a chemistry student but soon transferred to the University of Göttingen, where, under the influence of Adolf von Koenen, he studied geology until his graduation in 1899. He then worked for the Prussian Geological Survey until 1908, when he was summoned to teach in Hannover. In 1912 he replaced H. Credner as professor of geology and director of the Royal Saxon Geological Survey at Leipzig. The following year he was appointed successor to Koenen in Göttingen, where he established a reputation as an outstanding teacher and philosopher of global tectonics. He was named professor at the University of Berlin in 1932, remaining until he became emeritus in 1950.

Stille was a leader in German geology, an outstanding investigator and collator of the history of global tectonic events, and a highly admired teacher. From the time of his doctorate, he was interested in the chronological sequence of mountain-building events in time; his dissertation concerned late Jurassic orogeny in the Teutoburg Forest region. His concern was to date unconformities as evidence of orogenic events; he considered his "geotectonic classification of geologic history" to be his major contribution. From a review of world literature and his observations, Stille listed some fifty orogenic phases in Paleozoic and later time. He thought each to be essentially synchronous throughout the earth. The phases were smaller pulses in his tectonic eras—Precambrian Assyntic, Caledonic, Variscic, and Neoidic or Alpidic. Each orogenic phase made a part of the crust less mobile, the consolidations progressively enlarging the continents. He referred to progressive stages of European consolidation as Ur-, Pal-, Meso- and Neoeuropa.

Stille's synthesis of global tectonics has been considered a worthy successor to that of Eduard Suess. Stille conceived of the crust as separated into mobile orthogeosynclinal belts with marginal oceanic low cratons and continental high cratons, the latter with subsiding regions that he called parageosynclinal. Thus he had more intense "alpinotype" or orthotectonic deformation contrasting with the "germanotype" or paratectonic, which characterized western Germany. The terms were subsequently misconstrued. Stille later divided his original orthogeosynclinal zones into eugeosynclinal (the pliomagmatic zones or internides) and the relatively amagmatic miogeosynclinal zones (the externides). Although he coined the terms in 1941, he used them very rarely. His magmatic or volcanic geosynclinal belts of the earth (eugeosynclinal belts) gained wide application. During his lifetime it was generally accepted that the low cratons

(ocean basins) were essentially permanent, in contrast with the present view of their more dynamic and transient nature. Stille thought that some ocean basins might be foundered continental "high cratons" but that the Pacific was permanent. In his later years he accepted the idea of large-scale underthrusting of oceanic regions beneath the continents, as on the Pacific margin of South America.

Study of eugeosynclinal belts led to interest in their magmatic history. The progression that Stille described passed from an "initial" basic submarine volcanism (the extrusion of ophiolites) through successive sialic magmatic intrusions during and following deformation, and culminated in the final extrusion of surficial volcanic rocks on consolidated craton.

Pulses of Stille's orogenic time scale are recognized locally, but establishment of the universality of the many phases is beyond the resolution of present stratigraphic methods. Stille astutely recognized the restriction of magmatism to orogenic belts and the magmatic succession through time, although this latter was not wholly a novel concept. He accepted the growth of continents by consolidation of mobile belts, but he was hampered by the conventional dogma of the stability of oceanic cratons. As a pioneer in many aspects of relating the larger tectonic features of the earth, Stille directed attention to the explanation of relationships among large crustal features that are now becoming understood through the advent of geophysical techniques that he did not possess.

Stille received honorary doctorates from the universities of Bucharest, Hannover, Jena, Sofia, and Tübingen, and was elected to honorary membership in many academies of science, geological societies, and other scientific organizations. He was honorary president of the German Geological Society, which awarded him its Leopold von Buch Medal and established the Hans Stille Medal in his honor.

BIBLIOGRAPHY

I. ORIGINAL WORKS. Stille wrote 200 publications. His reputation was most firmly established by *Grundfragen der vergleichenden Tektonik* (Berlin, 1924). A second large work, *Einführung in den Bau Amerikas* (Berlin, 1941), was distributed to only a few close friends; although it is rarely seen, the conclusions were rather widely disseminated in other publications.

Stille's principal field studies were on the region of moderate folding in western Germany; an early work on this region was his doctoral dissertation, *Der*

Gebirgsbau des Teutoburger Waldes zwischen Altenbecken und Detmold (Berlin, 1900). He expressed his first interest in South America in *Geologische Studien im Gebiete des Rio Magdalena* (Stuttgart, 1907). Discussion of larger problems in tectonics include *Tektonische Evolutionen und Revolutionen in der Erdrinde* (Leipzig, 1913); *Die Begriffe Orogenese und Epirogenese* (Berlin, 1919); and "Present Tectonic State of the Earth," in *Bulletin of the American Association of Petroleum Geologists*, **20** (1936), 847–880. "Die Entwicklung des amerikanischen Kordillerensystems in Zeit und Raum," in *Sitzungsberichte der preussischen Akademie der Wissenschaften zu Berlin*, Math.–Phys. Kl. (1936), 134–155, was one of several papers concerned with the Americas. Later histories of specific regional tectonic systems are "Die assyntische Ära und der vormit-, und nachassyntische Magmatismus," in *Zeitschrift der Deutschen geologischen Gesellschaft*, **98** (1948); *Die saxonische Tektonik im Bilde Europas* (Hannover, 1949); and *Der Geotektonische Werdegang der Karpaten* (Hannover, 1953).

II. SECONDARY LITERATURE. The full bibliography through 1955 was published in *Geotektonisches Symposium zu Ehren von Hans Stille*, Franz Lotze, ed. (Stuttgart, 1956), on his eightieth birthday; S. von Bubnoff prepared an appreciative note in *Geologie*, **5** (1956), 528–529: and A. Pilger, on his ninetieth birthday, in *Geologisches Jahrbuch*, **84** (1967), i–vii. H. J. Margini wrote an obituary in *Geologisches Jahrbuch*, **84** (1967), viii–ix; W. Carle, in *Jahresberichte und Mitteilungen des oberrheinischen geologischen Vereins*, **49** (1967), 17–19; and Roland Brinkmann, in *Proceedings. Geological Society of America* for 1967 (1970), 263–267. Later publications are listed in a short biographical note by Hans Hitlermann in *Berliner Naturhistorische Gesellschaft*, **112** (1968), 5–8. Stille directed more than 100 research students, of whom the earlier are listed in *Festchrift zum 60. Geburtstag von Hans Stille* (Stuttgart, 1936).

MARSHALL KAY

STIMPSON, WILLIAM (*b.* Roxbury, Massachusetts, 14 February 1832; *d.* Ilchester, Maryland, 26 May 1872), *marine zoology.*

Stimpson was the son of Herbert Hawthorne Stimpson and Mary Ann Devereau Brewer. The Stimpsons were an Episcopalian family which had settled in Massachusetts during the seventeenth century. The Brewers were an old Virginia family. During the middle of the nineteenth century the father was a prosperous stove merchant in Boston, having invented the "Stimpson range," which became well-known throughout New England. Stimpson's boyhood was spent near Harvard College in Cambridge, which was then a village with

green fields and shaded groves. Here he developed such an interest in natural history that, at the age of fourteen, he presented himself to Augustus A. Gould, the author of the *Invertebrata of Massachusetts* (1841). Gould was so impressed with young Stimpson that he gave him a copy of his book and brought him to the attention of Louis Agassiz, William G. Binney, and other members of the Boston Society of Natural History. He soon began assisting Binney in the study of land snails.

Stimpson graduated from Cambridge High School in 1848, winning the school's highest academic award. Stimpson's father, a practical man with little education, could not envision the study of natural history as a profession. William therefore went to work for a firm of civil engineers, but his employer reported that he was too fond of collecting land snails to make a good surveyor. He then spent one year at the Cambridge Latin School. After a trip to the island of Grand Manan, New Brunswick, to dredge for marine invertebrates, he was reluctantly permitted to become a special student in Agassiz's laboratory at Harvard College in October 1850. On 4 December 1850 he was appointed curator of mollusks at the Boston Society of Natural History. He held this post until 18 May 1853, when, at the age of twenty-one, he was chosen as naturalist for the United States North Pacific Exploring and Surveying Expedition, commanded by Cadwalader Ringgold and, later, by John Rodgers.

The expedition, which lasted until 1856, visited Madeira, South Africa, Australia, the Coral Sea, Hong Kong, Japan, and the Aleutian Islands. Stimpson collected over 5,000 specimens, mostly invertebrates, and made notes and drawings of over 3,000 of them. From the time the expedition returned until 1865, he was in charge of the invertebrate section of the Smithsonian Institution. Stimpson described the Crustacea and other invertebrates collected by the expedition except for the mollusks, which were sent to A. A. Gould. In 1860, Columbia University awarded Stimpson an honorary M.D. in recognition of his knowledge of marine invertebrates. Five years later, he was appointed director of the Chicago Academy of Sciences, which was then moving into a new fireproof building.

Stimpson took with him to Chicago ten thousand jars of Crustacea, at that time the largest collection of its kind in the world: the invertebrates, except mollusks, of the North Pacific Exploring and Surveying Expedition, including the types of J. D. Dana; and his own collection of shells dredged from Maine to Texas; he later received the United States Coast Survey collection of deep-sea Crustacea and mollusks dredged in the Gulf Stream by L. F. de Pourtalès in 1867 and 1868. All these, including Stimpson's notes and drawings and the plates and text of the reports that were to augment the brief descriptions of the northern Pacific Crustacea and Mollusca, which he and Gould had published without figures, were destroyed in the Chicago fire of 1871.

Stimpson's health had never been very good, and he succumbed to tuberculosis in 1872, at the age of forty. He was survived by his wife, Annie Gordon, and a son, Herbert.

Aside from his faunal studies and monographs, Stimpson is remembered as the first naturalist to dredge systematically along the Atlantic coast and for the description of 948 new species of marine invertebrates.

BIBLIOGRAPHY

I. ORIGINAL WORKS. An annotated list of Stimpson's published works is available in Mayer (see below). Among his more important works are "Synopsis of the Marine Invertebrata of Grand Manan; or the Region About the Mouth of the Bay of Fundy, New Brunswick," *Smithsonian Contributions to Knowledge*, **6**, no. 5 (1854); "Researches Upon Hydrobiinae and Allied Forms," Smithsonian Miscellaneous Collection, **7**, no. 4; "Preliminary Report on the Crustacea Dredged in the Straits of Florida, by L. F. de Pourtalès, Pt. 1, Brachyura," in *Bulletin of the Museum of Comparative Zoology at Harvard College*, **2** (1871), 109–160.

II. SECONDARY LITERATURE. See W. H. Dall, "Some American Conchologists," in *Proceedings of the Biological Society of Washington*, **4** (1888), 129–133; W. K. Higley, "Historical Sketch of the Academy," in *Special Publications of the Chicago Academy of Sciences*, no. 1 (1902), 14–26; R. I. Johnson, "The Recent Mollusca of Augustus A. Gould," in *Bulletin. United States National Museum*, no. 239 (1964), 19–28, which contains excerpts from Stimpson's unpublished journal made on the North Pacific Exploring and Surveying Expedition; and A. G. Mayer, "Biographical Memoir of William Stimpson," in *Biographical Memoirs. National Academy of Sciences*, **8** (1918), 419–433.

RICHARD I. JOHNSON

STINE, CHARLES MILTON ALTLAND (*b.* Norwich, Connecticut, 18 October 1882; *d.* Wilmington, Delaware, 28 May 1954), *organic chemistry*.

Stine was the elder son of Milton Henry Stine, a Lutheran clergyman, and Mary Jane Altland Stine. He attended Gettysburg College, from which he received the B.A. in 1901, the B.S. in 1903, the M.A. in 1904, and the M.S. in 1905. He was awarded the Ph.D. by Johns Hopkins University in 1907, the same year in which he joined E. I. du Pont de Nemours and Company. During the early years of his lifelong association with Du Pont, Stine developed a number of products and processes in organic chemistry. He was one of the few American researchers familiar with the German synthetic dye process and his expertise enabled Du Pont to build, during World War I, a dye intermediates plant that was the first major synthetic organic chemical facility in the United States.

Stine became assistant chemical director of Du Pont in 1919; he was made director five years later. He had long been convinced that the company should undertake a program of fundamental research like those sponsored by the German chemical industry. Such programs were at that time virtually unknown in the United States outside the universities, and Stine—having developed research curricula in organic chemistry, chemical engineering, and catalytic processes, and having built a staff of exceptional men—was able to establish, by 1927, the research policy that made Du Pont an industrial pioneer in American science. Within a decade Du Pont's chemical department, under Stine's direction, had produced neoprene, the first general-purpose synthetic rubber, and nylon, the first noncellulosic synthetic fiber. More important, Stine's program gave new impetus and practical application to polymer chemistry and led to the creation of whole new families of fibers, films, plastics, paints, and elastomers and related products.

Stine was named vice-president and Executive Committee adviser on research in 1930. During his tenure he inaugurated and promoted research in agriculture and in animal nutrition and medicine. The animal research facilities that were completed in 1952 near Newark, Delaware, were named in his honor. He retired as vice-president in 1945, because of ill-health, but remained as a director of Du Pont until his death from a heart attack nine years later. He was survived by his wife, Martha E. Molly, whom he had married in 1912, and by their two daughters.

Stine's ability to organize and direct research on a wide variety of subjects brought him international recognition. He was a member of many scientific organizations, and particularly active in the American Association for the Advancement of Science, the American Chemical Society, the American

Institute of Chemical Engineers, and the Franklin Institute. He was a member of Phi Beta Kappa and a trustee of Gettysburg College and the University of Delaware, from both of which he received honorary degrees. The American Section of the Society of the Chemical Industry awarded Stine its Perkin Medal for 1939, "for valuable work in applied chemistry."

BIBLIOGRAPHY

I. ORIGINAL WORKS. Stine's writings include "Effect of One Salt on Hydrating Power of Another Salt Present in the Same Solution," in *American Chemical Journal*, **39** (1908), 313–402, written with Harry C. Jones; "Organic Synthesis and the du Pont Company," in *Chemical and Metallurgical Engineering*, **19** (1918), 569–571, written with C. L. Reese; "Chemical Engineering in Modern Industry," in *Transactions of the American Institute of Chemical Engineers*, **21** (1928), 45–54; "The Chemist's Aid to Agriculture," in *Chemicals*, **30**, no. 25 (1928), 7–9, and no. 26 (1928), 7–8; "Industrial Chemistry," in F. W. Wile, ed., *A Century of Industrial Progress* (Garden City, N.Y., 1928), 335–359; "Recovery of Bromine From Sea Water," in *Industrial and Engineering Chemistry*, **21** (1929), 434–442; "Structure of an Industrial Research Organization," *ibid.*, 657–659; "The Use of Power in Chemical Industries," in *Chemical Age* (London), **21** (1929), 237, also in *National Engineer*, **33** (1929), 273–274; "Chemical Research: A Factor of Prime Importance in American Industry," in *Journal of Chemical Education*, **9** (1932), 2032–2039; "Coordination of Laboratory and Plant Effort," in *Industrial and Engineering Chemistry*, **24** (1932), 191–193; and "Fundamental and Applied Chemical Research," in Malcolm Ross, ed., *Profitable Practice in Industrial Research* (New York–London, 1932), 104–118.

See also "Relation of Chemical to Other Industry," in *Industrial and Engineering Chemistry*, **25** (1933), 487–495; "Approach to Chemical Research Based on a Specific Example," in *Journal of the Franklin Institute*, **218** (1934), 397–410; "The Place of Fundamental Research in an Industrial Research Organization," in *Transactions of the American Institute of Chemical Engineers*, **32** (1936), 127–137; "The Value of Fundamental Research to Industry," in Carnegie Institute of Technology, Coal Research Laboratory, *Proceedings of Technical Meeting . . . December 3, 1936* (Pittsburgh, 1937), 48; "Training Tomorrow's Industrial Leaders," in *Transactions of the American Institute of Chemical Engineers*, **34** (1938), 643–656; and "The Rise of the Organic Chemical Industry in the United States," in *Smithsonian Report* for 1940 (1941), 177–192, reprinted as *Smithsonian Institution Publication* no. 3611 (1941).

II. SECONDARY LITERATURE. See A. D. McFadyen, "Personalities in Chemistry (Charles M. A. Stine)," in *Chemical Industries*, **46**, no. 6 (June 1940), 742; and

"Perkin Medal," in *Industrial and Engineering Chemistry*, **32**, no. 2 (Feb. 1940), 137.

BETTINA F. SARGEANT

STIRLING, JAMES (*b*. Garden, Stirlingshire, Scotland, 1692; *d*. Edinburgh, Scotland, 5 December 1770), *mathematics*.

Stirling was the third son of Archibald Stirling and his second wife, Anna Hamilton, and grandson of Lord Garden of Keir. The whole family supported the Jacobite cause, and Archibald Stirling was in prison on a charge of high treason (of which he was later acquitted) while his son attended Glasgow University. James Stirling matriculated at Balliol College, Oxford, in 1711, without taking the oath. He himself was acquitted of the charge of "cursing King George" at the assizes. He seems to have left Oxford in 1716, after refusing to take the oaths needed to continue his scholarship. He did not graduate.

The previous year John Keill had mentioned Stirling's achievements in a letter to Newton, and at about the same time Stirling became acquainted with John Arbuthnot, the well-known mathematician, physician, and satirist. Such connections enabled him to publish (in Oxford) his first book, *Lineae tertii ordinis Neutonianae, sive illustratio tractatus D. Neutoni de enumeratione linearum tertii ordinis* (1717). The eight-page subscription list included Newton himself, besides many Oxford men. The book was dedicated to Nicholas Tron, the Venetian ambassador, who had become a fellow of the Royal Society in 1715, the same year in which Newton's correspondent, the Abbé Conti, was also elected. Stirling may then have held a teaching appointment in Edinburgh,[1] but the fame brought him by his book and the influence of his Venetian friends soon secured him a post in Venice. In 1718 Stirling submitted, through Newton, his first Royal Society paper, "Methodus differentialis Newtoniana illustrata," and in August 1719 he wrote from Venice thanking Newton for his kindness and offering to act as intermediary with Nikolaus I Bernoulli.

Little else is known about Stirling's stay in Venice, although his return to Britain is supposed to have been hastened because he had learned some secrets of the glass industry and may have feared for his life. By mid-1724 he had returned to Scotland, and a few months later he settled in London. In 1726 Newton helped secure Stirling's fellowship in the Royal Society and at about this time

Stirling succeeded Benjamin Worster as one of the partners of the Little Tower Street Academy,[2] conducted by William Watts. This was one of the most successful schools in London; and, although he had to borrow money to pay for the mathematical instruments he needed, Stirling's finances improved. He helped to prepare *A Course of Mechanical and Experimental Philosophy* (to give it the title of a syllabus published in 1727) that included mechanics, hydrostatics, optics, and astronomy, a course very much in the tradition of Keill and Desaguliers, the leading scientific lecturer at that time. Stirling gave up some of his leisure to write his main work, *Methodus differentialis*, which appeared in 1730. A little later, through his friend Arbuthnot, Stirling was brought in as an adviser to Henry St. John, Lord Bolingbroke, since he was considered to be one of the few persons capable of understanding the financial calculations of Sir Robert Walpole. The latter's electoral victory of 1734 led to Bolingbroke's retirement to France.[3]

Given his reputation it was not surprising that Stirling was asked to reorganize the work of the Scottish Mining Company in the lead mines at Leadhills, Lanarkshire, near the border with Dumfries. Stirling was a successful administrator and spent most of his time after 1735 in the remote village. He married Barbara Watson of Thirtyacres, near Stirling; their only child, a daughter, married her cousin Archibald Stirling, who succeeded Stirling as manager at Leadhills.

Although Stirling continued his mathematical correspondence—with John Machin, Alexis-Claude Clairaut, Leonhard Euler, and Martin Folkes, among others—it is clear that most of his energy was spent in mining affairs. His most influential mathematical correspondent, Colin Maclaurin, died in 1746, largely as a result of his efforts in defending Edinburgh against the Jacobite rebellion of the preceding year; Stirling's own political principles prevented him from succeeding to the Edinburgh chair left vacant at Maclaurin's death.[4] In 1748 Stirling was elected to the Berlin Academy of Sciences, even though his directly mathematical activities had ceased; he resigned his fellowship in the Royal Society in 1754. In 1752 he was presented with a silver teakettle for conducting the first survey of the Clyde by the town council of Glasgow, where he also apparently acted as a teacher of bookkeeping, navigation, geography, practical mathematics, and French.[5] In his later years he became too frail to move about easily; he died on a visit to Edinburgh for medical treatment.

Stirling's *tractatus* of 1717 won him a considerable reputation. In it, after a considerable amount of introductory material, Stirling proved Newton's enumeration of seventy-two species of cubic curves and added four more. François Nicole and Nikolaus I Bernoulli then added two more curves, in 1731 and 1733, respectively, the latter in a letter to Stirling.

Stirling next turned from cubics to differences, the other main topic of Newton's *Analysis* (1711). But these studies were interrupted by his moving from Oxford to Venice, from which he wrote to give permission for publication (without an intended supplement) of his 1719 paper "Methodus differentialis." This paper should not be confused with a later book of similar title, but it may be considered a precursor to it, since the book represents the further development and fuller treatment of the same ideas. Some of the same results are given in both; the so-called Newton-Stirling central difference formula,[6] which was also discussed by Cotes, is especially noteworthy.

The *Methodus differentialis: sive tractatus de summatione et interpolatione serierum infinitarum* of 1730 consists of a relatively brief introduction followed by two parts, on summation and interpolation. The work was sufficiently important to be reprinted twice during Stirling's lifetime, in 1753 and 1764, and to be published in an English translation in 1749.[7] The translation was made by Francis Holliday, who was then master of a grammar school near Retford, Nottinghamshire, as well as editor of *Miscellanea curiosa mathematica*, one of a number of relatively short-lived popular mathematical serials[8] published during the mid-eighteenth century. (The translator's preface shows that Holliday had originally intended to publish the translation in his serial and indicates that he planned to follow *The Differential Method* with other translations of Stirling's work as well; perhaps the reception of the book was insufficiently favorable for these other plans to materialize.)

In his preface, Stirling indicated that Newton, too, had considered the problem of speeding the convergence of series by transformations involving differences. De Moivre had made progress with a recurring series, but his methods could be generalized to other series in which "the relation of the terms is varied according to some regular law." The most useful representation of terms was in a series of factorials, positive or negative. Manipulation often required conversion of factorials into powers, and Stirling gave tables of the coefficients for this conversion. He then showed that the columns of the tables gave the coefficients for the inverse expressions, of powers in factorials; those for positive (negative) powers are now called "Stirling Numbers of the first [or second] kind" in his honor.[9] The so-called Stirling series

$$\frac{1}{x-a}=\frac{1}{x}+\frac{a}{x(x+1)}+\frac{a(a+1)}{x(x+1)(x+2)}+\cdots$$

is equivalent to the expansion of $(z^2 + nz)^{-1}$ in negative factorials, which is the last example given in his introduction.

Stirling explained that part one of the *Methodus differentialis*, "on the summation of series," was designed to show how to transform series in order to make them converge more rapidly and so to expedite calculation. As an example[10] he gave the series

$$\sum_{1}^{\infty} 1/(2n-1)2n,$$

studied by Brouncker in connection with the quadrature of the hyperbola; Stirling concluded that "if anyone would find an accurate value of this series to nine places . . . they would require one thousand million of terms; and this series converges much swifter than many others. . . ." Another example[11] was the calculation—"which Mr. Leibnitz long ago greatly desired"—of

$$\frac{\pi}{4}=1-\frac{1}{3}+\frac{1}{5}-\frac{1}{7}+\cdots.$$

Stirling's sixth proposition was effectively an early example of a test for the convergence of an infinite product; he gave many examples of problems, now solved by the use of gamma functions, that illustrated his aim. The last section of the first part of the book contains an incomplete development of De Moivre's principles used in recurring series; for linear relations with polynomial coefficients connecting a finite number of terms, Stirling reduced the solution to that of a corresponding differential equation.

Stirling continued to show his analytical skill in part two, on the interpolation of series. As an example[12] of interpolation at the beginning of a series, he took the gamma series $T_{n+1} = nT_n$, with $T_1 = 1$, to find the term $T_{3/2}$ intermediate between the two terms T_1 and T_2 and calculated the result to ten decimal places: his result is now written $\Gamma(1/2) = \sqrt{\pi}$. Stirling's other results are now expressed using gamma functions or hypergeometric series. He also discussed[13] the sum of any number of logarithms of arguments in arithmetical progression and obtained the logarithmic equivalent of the result, sometimes called Stirling's theorem, that

$$n! \sim n^{n+1/2}e^{-n}.$$

Just before leaving London, Stirling contributed a short article to the *Philosophical Transactions of the Royal Society* entitled "Of the Figure of the Earth, and the Variation of Gravity on the Surface." In it he stated, without proof, that the earth was an oblate spheroid, supporting Newton against the rival Cassinian view. This paper was unknown to Clairaut, who submitted a paper partly duplicating it from Lapland, where he was part of the expedition under Maupertuis that proved Newton's hypothesis.[14] Although Stirling contributed another technical paper ten years later, it is clear that his new post in Scotland did not give him an opportunity to pursue his mathematical activities in any depth and that his significant work was confined to the 1720's and 1730's.

NOTES

1. W. Steven, *History of George Heriot's Hospital*, F. W. Bedford, ed. (Edinburgh, 1859), 307, mentions James Stirling as assistant master, elected 12 August 1717.
2. N. Hans, *New Trends in Education in the Eighteenth Century* (London, 1951), 82–87, gives the best account of the Academy, but his dates for Stirling and Patoun are unreliable.
3. The connection with Bolingbroke is given by Ramsay (see bibliography), 308–309, but is ignored in most accounts.
4. A. Grant, *The Story of the University of Edinburgh*, II (London, 1884), 301.
5. Glasgow City Archives and *Glasgow Courant*, Nov. 1753, Nov. 1754, and Nov. 1755, reported by M. J. M. McDonald and J. A. Cable respectively.
6. D. T. Whiteside, ed., *The Mathematical Papers of Isaac Newton*, IV (Cambridge, 1971), 58, n. 19.
7. The Latin and English versions had 153 and 141 pages, respectively; references in Tweedie to the Latin ed. can be converted to those to the latter, given here, by subtracting about ten.
8. R. C. Archibald, "Notes on some Minor English Mathematical Serials," in *Mathematical Gazette*, **14**, no. 200 (April 1929), 379–400.
9. Stirling, *Differential Method*, 17, 20. A useful, modern textbook, C. Jordan's *Calculus of Finite Differences*, 2nd ed. (New York, 1947), devotes ch. 4 to Stirling's numbers. Jordan and Tweedie give details of the articles by N. Nielsen that stress the significance of Stirling.
10. *Differential Method*, 23–25.
11. *Ibid.*, 27–28.
12. *Ibid.*, 99–103.
13. *Ibid.*, 123–125.
14. I. Todhunter, *A History of the Mathematical Theories of Attraction*, I (London, 1873), ch. 4.

BIBLIOGRAPHY

I. ORIGINAL WORKS. Stirling's works are listed in the text. His major work is *Methodus differentialis: sive tractatus de summatione et interpolatione serierum infinitarum* (London, 1730). The family papers are at the General Register House, Edinburgh; they contain disappointingly few mathematical papers, but more about Stirling's mining activities.

II. SECONDARY LITERATURE. The main authority is the unindexed volume C. Tweedie, *James Stirling: A Sketch of His Life and Works Along With His Scientific Correspondence* (Oxford, 1922); also J. O. Mitchell's *Old Glasgow Essays* (Glasgow, 1905), repr. from "James Stirling Mathematician," *Glasgow Herald* (1886); and J. Ramsay's *Scotland and Scotsmen in the Eighteenth Century*, A. Allardyce, ed., II (Edinburgh, 1888), 306–326. Other works are detailed in the notes and in Tweedie.

P. J. WALLIS

STOCK, ALFRED (*b.* Danzig, West Prussia [now Gdansk, Poland], 16 July 1876; *d.* Aken, Germany, 12 August 1946), *chemistry.*

The son of a bank executive, Stock received a Gymnasium education in Berlin. He developed an interest in science as a schoolboy and matriculated as a chemistry student at the University of Berlin in 1894. Attracted to Emil Fischer's institute, he began his doctoral research in 1895 under Oscar Piloty. Following his graduation, magna cum laude, in 1899, Stock spent a year in Paris as an assistant to Moissan. On 21 August 1906 he married Clara Venzky, who bore him two daughters. Stock pioneered in the development of the chemistry of the boron and silicon hydrides, developed the chemical high-vacuum technique, held numerous high positions in chemical organizations and educational institutes, and made important contributions to chemical education and nomenclature. Some of his work had important technological applications. His intensive investigations into the pathology and detection of mercury were prompted by his desire to spare others the suffering he endured from the effect of chronic mercury poisoning.

Stock devoted the first nine years (1900–1909) of his professional career at the University of Berlin to the preparation and characterization of the modifications of phosphorus, arsenic, and antimony, and their compounds with hydrogen, sulfur, and nitrogen. He identified an unstable yellow form of antimony, and a new polymeric hydride (P_2H_9) and nitride (P_3N_5) of phosphorus. His research on the phosphorus-sulfur system resolved many ambiguities in the literature and established the existence of three of the four well-established phosphorus sulfides. His study of the kinetics of the decomposition of antimony hydride was a classic example of an autocatalytic, heterogeneous decomposition.

In July 1909, Stock was appointed to organize and direct the new Inorganic Chemistry Institute at Breslau, where he began an experimental program inspired by the belief that boron ought to have an extensive and diverse chemistry analogous to that of the hydrocarbons. Previous attempts, by Ramsay and others, to produce hydroboranes by the reaction of magnesium boride with mineral acids had led to incomplete and erroneous conclusions because of the difficulty of isolating and characterizing the small amounts of volatile, unstable, and highly reactive compounds formed. The problem was complicated by the presence of silanes and other gases in the reaction mixture. Stock devised a high-vacuum apparatus that permitted the quantitative manipulation and fractionation of small amounts of gaseous and volatile materials in the absence of air and lubricating greases. He soon established the existence of three boranes—B_2H_6, B_4H_{10}, $B_{10}H_{14}$—and produced evidence for others that later proved to be B_5H_9 and B_6H_{10}.

In 1916 Stock moved to the Kaiser Wilhelm Institute in Berlin. During this time he concerned himself with problems related to the war and to the restoration of German chemistry afterward. His research efforts were devoted primarily to the study of the reactive and volatile silicon hydrides. At the time of Stock's entry into this field, only SiH_4 had been well characterized. His high-vacuum technique enabled him to purify and characterize Si_2H_6 and two new silanes, Si_3H_8 and Si_4H_{10}, and to establish the existence of Si_5H_{12} and Si_6H_{14}. Stock prepared numerous halogen derivatives of these compounds that in turn were used to produce many new and interesting compounds, such as siloxanes, silyl amines and amides, and alkyl silanes. Supported by the experimental knowledge obtained through work on the silanes, he prepared very pure samples of B_2H_6 and B_4H_{10} and isolated B_5H_9 and B_6H_{10}. In 1924 he discovered yet another borane, B_5H_{11}.

Ever since his early postdoctoral years, Stock had suffered from headaches, vertigo, numbness, catarrhs, poor hearing, and ailments of the upper respiratory tract that would not respond to any medical treatment. During 1923 he suffered an almost total loss of memory and hearing. In March 1924, after an unbearable winter, he discovered that his difficulties stemmed from mercury poisoning, caused by prolonged exposure to mercury vapors (several micrograms of mercury per cubic meter) in poorly ventilated laboratories. After a brief rest Stock began a program of research into

70

the analysis and pathology of mercury that continued to the end of his active life. He devised techniques capable of detecting 0.01 microgram of mercury, which he used to determine mercury concentrations in natural materials and common reagents. He examined the modes of ingestion of mercury and traced its path through the body and its accumulation in various organs, often using himself as an experimental subject. He wrote numerous articles warning of the dangers of mercury and suggested precautionary measures.

After his appointment as director of the Chemical Institute at Karlsruhe in October 1926, Stock constructed a model chemical laboratory designed to minimize mercury contamination. Here he determined the genetic relationships between the boranes and developed more effective preparation techniques; studied the reactions of boranes with active metals and prepared compounds that were later recognized as borohydrides, now an important class of reducing agents in organic chemistry; and prepared borazine $B_3N_3H_6$, an important inorganic analogue of benzene.

In addition to his hydride research, Stock investigated a number of compounds of carbon with oxygen, sulfur, selenium, and tellurium; introduced many improvements in apparatus, including the mercury valve, automatic Töpler pump, vaportension thermometer, zinc arc, and gas buoyancy balance; and devised numerous accessories for the widely used Stock high-vacuum technique. He drew up a system of chemical nomenclature that has been universally adopted by inorganic chemists. Stock perfected an instructional epidiascope that could project chemical demonstrations on a large screen by means of incident or reflected light. Some of his research led to industrial applications: P_4S_3 was used as a substitute for phosphorus in matches, and P_3N_5 was used to remove traces of oxygen from incandescent lamps. His technique for the electrolytic preparation of beryllium became the basis for the first commercial production of that metal. His work on silicon helped establish the chemical foundations for the technologically important silicone plastics.

Stock not only opened up two important fields of chemistry but also devised apparatus and techniques of great versatility and exactness that made the achievement possible, and established the associated health hazards and precautionary measures necessary for safety. E. Wiberg described him as punctual, neat, exact, and patient, yet witty and sociable. Although his work stimulated a great deal of theoretical speculation, and in some cases led to practical applications, Stock always remained an experimentalist who was driven by the pure joy of discovery. He placed as little value on speculative opinion as he did on seeking practical applications of his research.

Stock received many honors, including the presidency of both the Verein Deutscher Chemiker (1926–1929) and the Deutsche Chemische Gesellschaft (1936–1938). He was appointed to many major policy committees and represented Germany at several international conferences. His deteriorating health and increasing difficulties with political authorities caused him to retire in October 1936, at the age of sixty. He returned to Berlin, where he continued his research on mercury. By 1940 his movements had become so restricted by the onset of myogelosis (hardening of the muscles) that he was almost completely confined to his home. In May 1943 he gave up his small laboratory, which was needed for war work, and retired to Bad Warmbrunn in Silesia. With Russian cannon rumbling in the distance, he and his wife packed the few belongings they could carry and undertook a grueling train trip to Aken, a small city on the Elbe. Stock died there in obscurity, after a life of great accomplishment and tragic suffering.

BIBLIOGRAPHY

I. ORIGINAL WORKS. A complete bibliography of Stock's 274 publications is in Wiberg (see below). His books include *Praktikum der quantitativen anorganischen Analyse* (Berlin, 1909), written with Arthur Stähler; *Ultra-Strukturchemie* (Berlin, 1920); and *Hydrides of Silicon and Boron* (Ithaca, N.Y., 1933).

II. SECONDARY LITERATURE. The major biography is E. Wiberg, "Alfred Stock," in *Chemische Berichte*, **83** (1950), xix–lxxvi; a short summary of this article is in E. Farber, ed., *Great Chemists* (New York, 1961), 1423–1432.

JOHN E. FREY

STOCK, CHESTER (*b.* San Francisco, California, 28 January 1892; *d.* Pasadena, California, 7 December 1950), *paleontology.*

Stock's parents, John Englebert Stock and the former Maria Henriette Meyer, were natives of Germany; and he attended a Gymnasium as well as public schools until the earthquake and fire of 1906 destroyed the family home and business and obliged him to go to work. In 1910 he entered the University of California, where the odors of the zoology laboratory discouraged him from premedical studies and John C. Merriam's lectures whetted his interest in prehistoric animals. He published a paper on the ground sloths from the tar pits of Rancho La Brea before graduating in 1914; in 1917 he received the Ph.D. and joined the university faculty. When Merriam left Berkeley in 1921, Stock, by then assistant professor, took over his courses. He was called to a professorship at California Institute of Technology in Pasadena in 1926, and in 1947 he became chairman of its Division of Earth Sciences. He also served on the staff of the Los Angeles County Museum, becoming senior curator of earth sciences in 1944 and chief of the Science Division in 1949.

Stock married Clara Margaret Doud in 1921; they had a daughter, Jane Henriette, and a son, John Chester. His wife died in 1934; and in 1935 he married Margaret Wood, by whom he had a second son, James Ellery.

Stock's early studies were on Pleistocene vertebrates, especially ground sloths, on which he published a major monograph in 1925; he also collaborated with John C. Merriam in a monographic study of saber-toothed cats. He continued Merriam's program of exploration for vertebrate fossils in the Great Basin as well as along the Pacific coast, and extended these studies into northern Mexico. Stock's discovery of Eocene land mammals in the Sespe formation of the Ventura basin and near San Diego, and his description of Oligocene mammals from Death Valley, extended the record of land animals on the Pacific coast far earlier than previously known Miocene remains.

Stock's scientific publications consist largely of meticulous descriptions of fossil material, including careful documentation of its geologic occurrence and sound systematic conclusions. He also published several interpretive studies of the Rancho La Brea fauna and of various earlier mammalian assemblages.

Stock attracted many more students than could enter the field of vertebrate paleontology. He was always eager to explain his work to nonprofessional audiences; and his enthusiasm for the life of the past and his warm, cheerful personality won him many friends, within and outside the geological profession, who often supplied him with leads to new fossil occurrences. At the Los Angeles County Museum he was particularly concerned with developing an exhibition of fossil bones in situ at the tar pits in Hancock Park and with plans for the Hall of Evolving Life.

Stock's honors included membership in the National Academy of Sciences and presidencies of the Paleontological Society of America (1945), the Society of Vertebrate Paleontology (1947), and the Geological Society of America (1950), the latter a few weeks before his death.

BIBLIOGRAPHY

I. ORIGINAL WORKS. Stock's writings include "Cenozoic Gravigrade Edentates of Western North America With Special Reference to the Pleistocene Megalonychinae and Mylodontinae of Rancho La Brea," which is *Carnegie Institution of Washington Publication* no. 331 (1925); "Rancho La Brea, a Record of Pleistocene Life in California," which is *Los Angeles County Museum Publication* no. 1 (1930); 6th ed., 1956); and "The Felidae of Rancho La Brea," which is *Carnegie Institution of Washington Publication* no. 422 (1932), written with John C. Merriam. His technical publications on Tertiary and Pleistocene faunas are in *University of California Publications in Geological Sciences* and *Carnegie Institution at Washington Contributions to Paleontology*. Eocene fossils are described in *Proceedings of the National Academy of Sciences of the United States of America*. Full bibliographies are given in Simpson and in Woodring (see below).

II. SECONDARY LITERATURE. See John P. Buwalda, in *Bulletin of the American Association of Petroleum Geologists*, **35** (Mar. 1951), 775–778, with portrait; R. W. Chaney, in *Yearbook. American Philosophical Society* for 1951 (1952), 304–307; Hildegard Howard, in *News Bulletin. Society of Vertebrate Paleontology*, **31** (1951), 32–34, and in *Quarterly. Los Angeles County Museum*, **8**, nos. 3–4 (1951), 15–18, with portrait; George G. Simpson, in *Biographical Memoirs. National Academy of Sciences*, **27** (1952), 335–362, with portrait; and Wendell P. Woodring, in *Proceedings. Geological Society of America* for 1951 (1952), 49–50, 149–156.

JOSEPH T. GREGORY

STODOLA, AUREL BOLESLAV (*b.* Liptovský Mikuláš, Hungary [now Czechoslovakia], 10 May 1859; *d.* Zurich, Switzerland, 25 December 1942), *mechanical engineering.*

Stodola was born in a small Slovakian town at the foot of the High Tatra mountains, the second son of a leather manufacturer, Andreas Stodola, and his wife, Anna Kovač. After attending secondary school, he studied at the Budapest Technical University (1876–1877), the University of Zurich (1877–1878), and the Eidgenössische Technische Hochschule (1878–1880), from which he graduated as a mechanical engineer. He completed his theoretical and practical education informally: he spent two years as a volunteer in the machine factory of the Hungarian State Railways, studied in Berlin (1883) and Paris (1884), and worked in his father's factory and in a machine shop in Brno. In his first permanent position (1886–1892), as chief engineer with Ruston & Co. in Prague, Stodola was responsible for the design of a great variety of steam engines. In 1892 the Eidgenössische Technische Hochschule of Zurich, where his exceptional performance as a student was still remembered, appointed him to its newly founded chair for thermal machinery. Stodola held this position until his retirement in 1929, after which he remained in Zurich. He was married to Darina Palka in 1887; they had two daughters.

During his lifetime Stodola's reputation was very great. In the technical sense his role is best described by saying that during the decades of the main growth of the steam turbine, he was the leading authority on that machine. He also had remarkable personal charm. The importance of his accomplishments, the broad range of his learning, his friendly but aristocratic personality, and his ascetic appearance made him seem the embodiment of the central European ideal of a professor; the loyalty of his friends (among them Einstein) and disciples was extraordinary; and the eulogistic writing devoted to him is not only remarkable in quantity but also uncommonly persuasive.

In Stodola's academic career teaching, industrial consultation, engineering design, and scientific research were intimately blended; perhaps most important was his scientific work, which was characterized by a combination of high mathematical competence with an explicit devotion to practical utility.

Stodola's first publications dealt with the theory of automatic control. He derived the differential equations for the speed-regulating systems of hydroelectric power plants, analyzing them with respect to dynamic stability and checking his results at the power plant itself. In this work he enlisted the help of a colleague, Adolf Hurwitz, who was led through it to the discovery (1895) of the stability criterion named after him.

At the turn of the century Stodola's attention shifted to the steam turbine, which, after its invention in the 1880's, was gradually coming into industrial use and was soon to displace the reciprocating steam engine. It became the subject of his lifework. A lecture given in 1902 before the Society of German Engineers became the book *Die Dampfturbinen und die Aussichten der Wärmekraftmaschinen* (1903), which in later editions, enti-

tled *Dampf- und Gasturbinen*, developed into an authoritative work that holds a unique place in the literature of engineering. Although Stodola also published many articles, most results of his researches were incorporated directly into the various editions of this book.

Perhaps the book's most important innovation concerned the basic thermodynamic treatment of the flow of steam through the turbine. It had become clear that it was impractical to describe the properties of steam, which changed with temperature and pressure, in terms of mathematical formulas; instead these data, which were determined empirically, were presented in graphic charts and printed tables. Recognizing the superiority of entropy charts, which were easy to manipulate and at the same time facilitated the comparison of actual and ideal processes, Stodola was the first to base the analysis of heat engines upon these charts. After having first used the older temperature-entropy charts, he soon turned to the more convenient enthalpy-entropy charts proposed by Richard Mollier (1904). Shortly thereafter this approach was adopted universally.

Stodola also did pioneer work in the flow of steam through Laval nozzles. The possibility of supersonic flow in divergent nozzles was then still a matter of controversy. In careful experiments Stodola studied the conditions under which supersonic flow does occur and obtained results that for the first time could be reconciled with theoretical predictions. Through this line of inquiry he also became one of the first to investigate shock waves.

Although thermodynamics and fluid mechanics and their applications were Stodola's true domain, he also did original work in pure mechanics. He investigated, for example, the strength of disks rotating at high speed and problems of vibration and critical speed.

Stodola's innumerable more technical contributions to steam turbine design are reflected in the fact that the Swiss steam turbine manufacturers, who retained him as a consultant and employed his students, became international leaders in this field. They were also among the pioneers of the gas turbine, a machine in which Stodola had been interested since the beginning of his career, when its prospects had seemed dim indeed.

Stodola had a strong sense of social responsibility. During World War I he worked on the problem, totally unrelated to his basic interests, of improving artificial limbs. Social responsibility is also shown in a later philosophical and reflective work, *Gedanken zu einer Weltanschauung vom Stand-*

punkt des Ingenieurs (1931), which went through several editions.

BIBLIOGRAPHY

I. ORIGINAL WORKS. Stodola's publications are listed in Poggendorff, VI, 2551, and VIIa, pt. 4, 550; in his *Festschrift* (see below), xxi–xxiii; and in *Schweizerische Bauzeitung*, **121** (1943), 77–78. His major book is *Die Dampfturbinen und die Aussichten der Wärmekraftmaschinen* (Berlin, 1903), 5th ed. retitled *Dampf- und Gasturbinen* (Berlin, 1922; 6th ed., 1925); 1st ed. translated by Louis C. Lowenstein as *Steam Turbines, With an Appendix on Gas Turbines, and the Future of Heat Engines* (New York, 1905; 2nd ed., 1906), and the 5th ed. by Lowenstein as *Steam and Gas Turbines* (New York, 1927) and by E. Hahn as *Turbines à vapeur et à gaz*, 2 vols. (Paris, 1925). Other books are *Gedanken zu einer Weltanschauung vom Standpunkt des Ingenieurs* (Berlin, 1931); and *Geheimnisvolle Natur: Weltanschauliche Betrachtungen* (Zurich, 1937).

II. SECONDARY LITERATURE. The most useful biographical treatments of Stodola are the following, listed chronologically: W. G. Noack, "Prof. Dr. Aurel Stodola," in E. Honegger, ed., *Festschrift Prof. Dr. A. Stodola zum 70. Geburtstag* (Zurich–Leipzig, 1929), ix–xx; G. Eichelberg, "Aurel Stodola," in *Schweizerische Bauzeitung*, **121** (1943), 73–74; H. Quiby, "Aurel Stodola, sein wissenschaftliches Werk," *ibid.*, 74–77; E. Sörensen, "Aurel Stodola," in *Zeitschrift des Vereins deutscher Ingenieure*, **87** (1943), 169–170; Anton Turecký, ed., *Aurel Stodola 1859–1942, pamiatke storočnice narodenia* (Bratislava, 1959); C. Keller, "Zum 100. Geburtstag von Aurel Stodola am 10. Mai 1959," in *Zeitschrift des Vereins deutscher Ingenieure*, **101** (1959), 558–560; and A. Sonntag, "Aurel Stodola 1859/1942," in *Brennstoff-Wärme-Kraft*, **11** (1959), 211–212.

OTTO MAYR

STOKES, GEORGE GABRIEL (*b*. Skreen, County Sligo, Ireland, 13 August 1819; *d*. Cambridge, England, 1 February 1903), *physics, mathematics.*

Stokes was born into an Anglo-Irish family that had found its vocation for a number of generations in the established Church of Ireland. His father, Gabriel Stokes, was the rector of the parish of Skreen in County Sligo. His mother, Elizabeth Haughton, was the daughter of a rector. The youngest of six children, Stokes had three brothers, all of whom took holy orders, and two sisters. He received his earliest education from his father and the parish clerk in Skreen. Stokes then attended school in Dublin before going to Bristol

College in Bristol, England, to prepare to enter university. Later in life Stokes recalled that one of his teachers at Bristol, Francis William Newman, a classicist and mathematician, had influenced him profoundly. In 1837 Stokes entered Pembroke College, Cambridge, where during his second year he began to read mathematics with William Hopkins, an outstanding private tutor whose influence on Stokes probably far outweighed that of the official college teaching. When he graduated as senior wrangler and first Smith's prizeman in 1841, Pembroke College immediately elected him to a fellowship.

Stokes became the Lucasian professor at Cambridge in 1849, rescuing the chair from the doldrums into which it had fallen, and restoring it to the eminence it had when held by Newton. Since the Lucasian chair was poorly endowed, Stokes taught at the Government School of Mines in London in the 1850's to augment his income. He held the Lucasian chair until his death in 1903. In 1857 he married Mary Susanna, daughter of the Reverend Thomas Romney Robinson, the astronomer at Armagh Observatory in Ireland. Stokes had to relinquish his fellowship to marry, but under new regulations he held a fellowship again from 1869 to 1902. A very active member of the Cambridge Philosophical Society, he was president from 1859 to 1861. Always willing to perform administrative tasks, Stokes became a secretary for the Royal Society of London in 1854, conscientiously carrying out his duties until 1885 when he became president of the society, a post he held until 1890. The society awarded him the Copley Medal in 1893. From 1887 to 1891 he represented the University of Cambridge in Parliament at Westminster; and from 1886 to 1903 he was president of the Victoria Institute of London, a society founded in 1865 to examine the relationship between Christianity and contemporary thought, especially science. Stokes was universally honored, particularly in later life, with degrees, medals, and membership in foreign societies. He was knighted in 1889. The University of Cambridge lavishly celebrated his jubilee as Lucasian professor in 1899, and three years later Pembroke College bestowed on him its highest honor by electing him master.

As William Thomson commented in his obituary of Stokes, his theoretical and experimental investigations covered the entire realm of natural philosophy. Stokes systematically explored areas of hydrodynamics, the elasticity of solids, and the behavior of waves in elastic solids including the diffraction of light, always concentrating on physically important problems and making his mathematical analyses subservient to physical requirements. His few excursions into pure mathematics were prompted either by a need to develop methods to solve specific physical problems or by a desire to establish the validity of mathematics he was already employing. He also investigated problems in light, gravity, sound, heat, meteorology, solar physics, and chemistry. The field of electricity and magnetism lay almost untouched by him, however; he always regarded that as the domain of his friend Thomson.

After graduating, Stokes followed Hopkins' advice to pursue hydrodynamics, a field in which George Green and James Challis had recently been working at Cambridge. Thus in 1842 Stokes began his investigations by analyzing the steady motion of an incompressible fluid in two dimensions. In one instance, for motion symmetrical about an axis, he was able to solve the problem in three dimensions. In the following year he continued this work. Some of the problems that Stokes tackled had already been solved by Duhamel in his work on the permanent distribution of temperature in solids. Despite this duplication, which Stokes mentioned, he deemed the application of the formulas to fluid flow instead of heat flow sufficiently different to warrant publication. Stokes had not yet analyzed the motion of a fluid with internal friction, later known as viscosity, although references to the effects of friction continually appear in his papers. The problem, however, of the motion of a fluid in a closed box with an interior in the shape of a rectangular parallelepiped, which Stokes solved in 1843, was attacked partly with an eye to possible use in an experiment to test the effects of friction. By 1846 he had performed the experiment, but to Stokes's disappointment the differences between the experimental results and the theoretical calculations that excluded friction were too small to be useful as a test of any theory of internal friction.

Stokes's analysis of the internal friction of fluids appeared in 1845. Navier, Poisson, and Saint-Venant had already derived independently the equations for fluid flow with friction, but in the early 1840's Stokes was not thoroughly familiar with the French literature of mathematical physics, a common situation in Cambridge. Stokes said that he discovered Poisson's paper only after he had derived his own equations. He insisted, however, that his assumptions differed sufficiently from Poisson's and Navier's to justify publishing his own results. One novel feature of Stokes's derivation was that instead of using the Frenchmen's ultimate molecules he assumed that the fluid was infinitely

divisible, for he was careful not to commit himself to the idea that ultimate molecules existed. Another novel feature was his treatment of the relative motion of the parts of the fluid. He was able also to use these equations and the principles behind them to deduce the equations of motion for elastic solids, although he introduced two independent constants for what were later called the moduli of compression and rigidity, instead of one independent constant to describe elasticity as Poisson had. Stokes noted that the equations of motion he obtained for an elastic solid were the same as those that others had derived for the motion of the luminiferous ether in a vacuum. He then justified the applicability of these equations to the ether partly on the basis of the law of continuity, which permitted no sharp distinction between a viscous fluid and a solid, and which he believed held throughout nature.

Stokes became well known in England through a report on recent developments in hydrodynamics, which he presented in 1846 to the British Association for the Advancement of Science. So perceptive and suggestive was his survey that it immediately drew attention to his abilities and further enhanced his reputation as a promising young man. The report shows Stokes's increasing familiarity with the French literature on hydrodynamics and reveals his admiration for the work of George Green.

Stokes then pursued (1847) the topic of oscillatory waves in water, which he had suggested in his report merited further investigation. Poisson and Cauchy had already analyzed the complicated situation in which waves were produced by arbitrary disturbances in the fluid, but Stokes ignored the disturbances to examine the propagation of oscillatory waves the height of which is not negligible compared with their wavelength. Much later, in 1880, Stokes examined the shape of the highest oscillatory waves that could be propagated without changing their form. He showed that the crest of these waves enclosed an angle of 120°, and proposed a method for calculating the shape of the waves.

In one of his most important papers on hydrodynamics, presented in 1850, Stokes applied his theory of the internal friction of fluids to the behavior of pendulums. Poisson, Challis, Green, and Plana had analyzed in the 1830's the behavior of spheres oscillating in fluids, but Stokes took into account the effects of internal friction, including both spherical bobs and cylindrical pendulums. He then compared his theoretical calculations with the results of experiments conducted by others, including Coulomb, Bessel, and Baily. In the same paper he showed that the behavior of water droplets in the atmosphere depended almost completely on the internal friction of air and so explained how clouds could form in the atmosphere of the earth.

On account of his theoretical analysis and experimental observations of pendulums combined with his study of gravity at the surface of the earth, Stokes became the foremost British authority on the principles of geodesy. In his study of 1849 he related the shape of the surface of the earth to the strength of gravity on it without having to adopt any assumptions whatsoever about the interior of the earth. He obtained Clairaut's theorem as a particular result. Stokes assumed merely that the earth has a surface of equilibrium, one perpendicular to the gravity on it, whereas previously assumptions about the distribution of matter in the earth were always introduced to derive Clairaut's theorem. One result of his analysis was an explanation of the well-known observation that gravity is less on a continent than on an island. When the pendulum observations for the Great Trigonometrical Survey of India were conducted from 1865 to 1873, his expertise, together with his position as secretary to the Royal Society, made him an obvious person for the surveyors to turn to for advice, even though numerical calculations based on some of Stokes's own formulas would have been too laborious to carry out.

Occasionally Stokes studied problems in sound, which he considered a branch of hydrodynamics. In 1848 and 1849 he replied to Challis' claim of a contradiction in the commonly accepted theory, and in doing so Stokes introduced surfaces of discontinuity in the velocity and density of the medium. But later, on the basis of the argument by William Thomson and Lord Rayleigh that the proposed motion violated the conservation of energy, he retracted the idea that such motion, later called shock waves, could take place. (Stokes frequently crossed swords with Challis publicly in the *Philosophical Magazine*. They disagreed over the basic equations of fluid flow [1842, 1843, 1851], the theory of aberration [1845, 1846, 1848], and the theory of colors [1856].) In 1857 Stokes explained succinctly the effect of wind on the intensity of sound. Also, using a sphere to represent a bell and an infinite cylinder to represent a string or wire, he analyzed mathematically the production of sound by the transmission of motion from a vibrating body to a surrounding gas (1868). Poisson had already solved the case of the sphere, but Stokes

was quick to point out that Poisson had examined a different problem. Stokes's analysis explained John Leslie's observation that hydrogen or a mixture of hydrogen and air transmitted the sound of a bell feebly, and why sounding boards were necessary for stringed instruments to be heard, the vibrations being communicated to the board and then to the air. In a manner typical of Stokes, he then proceeded to explain how sound was produced by telegraph wires suspended tightly between poles.

The wave theory of light was well established at Cambridge when Stokes entered the university, and he seems to have embraced it right from the beginning of his studies. His earliest investigations in this field centered on the nature of the ether, beginning in 1845 with a proof that the wave theory was consistent with a theory of aberration in which the earth dragged along the ether instead of passing freely through it, as Fresnel had suggested. In 1846 Stokes showed that when the motion of the earth through the ether was not ignored, the laws of reflection and refraction remained unchanged in his own theory as well as in Fresnel's theory, thus offering no way to decide between the two theories of the interaction of the ether with the earth. In 1848 Stokes examined mathematically the properties of the ether, and by analogy with his own theory of the motion of fluids with internal friction he combined in his ether the seemingly contradictory properties of fluidity and solidity. He maintained that to examine the motion of the earth, the ether must be viewed as a very rarefied fluid, but to examine the propagation of light the same ether must be regarded as an elastic solid. To illustrate his view Stokes suggested that the ether is related to air in the same way as thin jelly is to water. Also in 1848 Stokes employed the wave theory of light to calculate the intensity of the central spot in Newton's rings beyond the critical angle of the incident light at which the rings vanish, leaving only the central black spot. He also examined the perfectly black central spot that results when the rings are formed between glasses of the same material. Fresnel had already analyzed this phenomenon, but Stokes's assumptions and derivation differed from his.

In a major paper on the dynamical theory of diffraction (1849), Stokes treated the ether as a sensibly incompressible elastic medium. Poisson had already calculated the disturbance at any point at any time resulting from a given initial disturbance in a finite portion of an elastic solid; but Stokes presented a different derivation, which he deemed simpler and more straightforward than Poisson's. Stokes also determined the disturbance in any direction in secondary waves, upon which the dynamical theory of diffraction depends, not limiting himself, as others had, to secondary waves in the vicinity of the normal to the primary wave. Moreover, by comparing his theory with the results of diffraction experiments that he conducted with a glass grating, Stokes answered the vexing question about the direction of vibrations of plane-polarized light by concluding that they were perpendicular to the plane of polarization.

At this time, both Stokes's theoretical analyses and his experiments covered a broad area of optics. In addition to his experiments on diffraction, he conducted experiments on Talbot's bands (1848), on the recently discovered Haidinger's brushes (1850), on phase differences in streams of plane-polarized light reflected from metallic surfaces (1850), and on the colors of thick plates (1851). Occasionally he invented and constructed his own instruments, as he did to facilitate measurements of astigmatism in the human eye (1849). In 1851 Stokes devised and largely constructed an instrument for analyzing elliptically polarized light. Here we see an excellent example of his theoretical studies complementing his experimental and instrumental work. In 1852 he published a mathematical analysis of the composition and resolution of streams of polarized light originating from different sources; the four parameters by which he characterized polarized light in this study became known as the Stokes parameters.

Stokes's explanation of fluorescence, published in 1852, for which the Royal Society awarded him the Rumford Medal, arose from his investigations begun the previous year into the blue color exhibited at the surface of an otherwise colorless and transparent solution of sulfate of quinine when viewed by transmitted light. Sir John Herschel had described this phenomenon in 1845, and Sir David Brewster had also examined it. Stokes, who had started by repeating some of Herschel's experiments and then had devised his own, rapidly concluded that light of a higher refrangibility, which corresponded to light of a higher frequency, produced light of lower refrangibility in the solution. Thus the invisible ultraviolet rays were absorbed in the solution to produce blue light at the surface. Stokes named this phenomenon fluorescence. Always looking for applications of optics, he quickly devised a method for exhibiting the phenomenon that did not require direct sunlight and so would render a chemist independent of the fickle

British weather in utilizing fluorescence to distinguish between various chemicals. In opening up the entire field of fluorescence to investigation, Stokes showed how it could be used to study the ultraviolet segment of the spectrum. By 1862 Stokes was using the spark from an induction coil to generate the spectra of various metals employed as electrodes. The invisible rays of the spectra were then examined and recorded systematically by means of fluorescence, although Stokes knew that photography was already beginning to replace fluorescence as a tool for mapping out spectra. Through his studies on fluorescence Stokes in 1862 began to collaborate with the Reverend W. Vernon Harcourt, who was one of the few people at that time attempting to vary the chemical composition of glass to produce new glasses with improved optical properties. Hoping to make glasses that would allow them to construct a perfectly achromatic combination, they collaborated until Harcourt's death in 1871.

While studying spectra by means of fluorescence, Stokes speculated on the physical principles of spectra, a topic of growing interest in the 1850's. Although Stokes always disclaimed priority in developing the principles of spectrum analysis, William Thomson insisted vigorously that Stokes taught him the principles in their conversations no later than 1852. They were discussing the topic in their correspondence in 1854 and speculating on the possibility of employing spectra to identify the chemical constituents of the sun. But Stokes did not publish anything on these ideas at that time, so the credit for the development of the principles of spectrum analysis went later to Kirchhoff and Bunsen.

Stokes's use of fluorescence in the 1850's as a tool for investigation typified his increasing emphasis on the exploitation of light to study other aspects of nature than light itself. In the 1860's, for instance, he drew the attention of chemists to the value of optical properties such as absorption and colored reflection as well as fluorescence in discriminating between organic substances. He was also a pioneer in combining spectrum analysis with chemical reactions to study blood.

Stokes's final major mathematical study on light was his classic report of 1862 on the dynamical theory of double refraction, presented to the British Association. He reviewed the theories of Fresnel, Cauchy, Neumann, Green, and MacCullagh, showing his preference for the ideas of Green and pointing out that he thought the true dynamical theory had not yet been discovered. Continuing his study of the dynamical theories, Stokes later showed experimentally that double refraction could not depend on differences of inertia in different directions, an idea W. J. M. Rankine, Lord Rayleigh, and Stokes had all entertained. He concluded that Huygens' construction for the wave fronts should be followed. A very brief summary of his experiments and conclusion was published in 1872, but a detailed account that he promised to present to the Royal Society was never published.

Stokes's papers on pure mathematics were tailored to his requirements for solving physical problems. His paper on periodic series (1847) consisted of an examination of various aspects of the validity of the expansion of an arbitrary function in terms of functions of known form. The expansions are now called Fourier series. In the paper Stokes applied his findings to problems in heat, hydrodynamics, and electricity. In 1850 he calculated the value

of $\int_0^\infty \cos \frac{\pi}{2}\left(x^3 - mx\right) dx$, when m is large and real,

an integral that had arisen in the optical studies of G. B. Airy. The method employed by Stokes for expanding the integral in the form of power series that initially converge rapidly and ultimately diverge rapidly was the one he afterward used in 1850 to determine the motion of a cylindrical pendulum in a fluid with internal friction. In 1857 he solved the

equation $\frac{d^2w}{dz^2} - 9zw = 0$ in the complex z-plane,

which was equivalent to calculating the definite integral above. He also showed that the arbitrary constants forming the coefficients of the linear combination of the two independent asymptotic solutions for large $|z|$ were discontinuous, changing abruptly when the amplitude of z passed through certain values. The discontinuous behavior became known as the Stokes phenomenon, and the lines for which the amplitude of z has a constant value at which the discontinuities occur became known as the Stokes lines. He later examined (1868) a method of determining the arbitrary constants for the asymptotic solutions of the Bessel

equation, $\frac{d^2y}{dx^2} + \frac{1}{x}\frac{dy}{dx} - \frac{n^2}{x^2}y = y$, where n is a real

constant. These studies in mathematics, however, formed only one small area of Stokes's publications.

In the early years of his career, through the Cambridge Philosophical Society, his teaching, and the examinations he composed, Stokes was a pivotal figure in furthering the dissemination of French mathematical physics at Cambridge. Partly because of this, and because of his own researches,

Stokes was a very important formative influence on subsequent generations of Cambridge men, including Maxwell. With Green, who in turn had influenced him, Stokes followed the work of the French, especially Lagrange, Laplace, Fourier, Poisson, and Cauchy. This is seen most clearly in his theoretical studies in optics and hydrodynamics; but it should also be noted that Stokes, even as an undergraduate, experimented incessantly. Yet his interests and investigations extended beyond physics, for his knowledge of chemistry and botany was extensive, and often his work in optics drew him into those fields.

Stokes's output of papers dropped rapidly in the 1850's, while his theoretical studies gradually gave way to experimental investigations. This occurred partly when he became a secretary to the Royal Society in 1854 and partly after he married in 1857. He often took on heavy administrative duties, which prevented him from conducting any research; and so from the 1860's many of his publications related to points arising from his official duty of reading papers submitted to the Royal Society. Stokes's papers eventually became a guide to other people's problems and interests. This is also seen in his correspondence with Thomson, for whom Stokes was a lifelong sounding board.

Throughout his life Stokes invariably took time to reply in detail to private as well as official requests for aid in solving problems, a frequent occurrence. A good example is his paper (1849) on the solution of a differential equation representing the deflection of iron railroad bridges, which Robert Willis, who was on a royal commission looking into the behavior of iron in various structures, had asked him to examine.

Although Stokes never fulfilled the expectations of his contemporaries by publishing a treatise on optics, his Burnett lectures on light, delivered at the University of Aberdeen from 1883 to 1885, were published as a single volume. The Gifford lectures on natural theology, which he delivered at Edinburgh in 1891 and 1893, were also published. A devoutly religious man, Stokes was deeply interested in the relationship of science to religion. This was especially true toward the end of his life, although he did not feel qualified to do justice to his Gifford lectureship.

BIBLIOGRAPHY

I. ORIGINAL WORKS. A comprehensive list of Stokes's papers appears in the Royal Society *Catalogue of Scientific Papers*, V, 838–840; VIII, 1022–1023;

XI, 505–506; XVIII, 977. Almost all of his published papers are included in *Mathematical and Physical Papers*, 5 vols. (Cambridge, 1880–1905); vols. I–III were edited by Stokes, and vols. IV–V posthumously by Sir Joseph Larmor. Vol. V also contains a previously unpublished MS on waves in water, as well as Smith's Prize examination papers and mathematical tripos papers set by Stokes at Cambridge.

A list of lectures and addresses on scientific topics, which were not printed in *Mathematical and Physical Papers*, is included in Larmor's preface to vol. V. A second ed. with a new preface by C. Truesdell appeared as *Mathematical and Physical Papers by the Late Sir George Gabriel Stokes, Bart. . . . Second Edition, Reprinting the Former of 1880–1905, Prepared by the Author (Volumes 1–3) and Sir J. Larmor (Volumes 4–5). With Their Annotations and the Obituary Notices by Lord Kelvin and Lord Rayleigh, and Also Including the Portions of the Original Papers Which Were Omitted From the Former Edition . . .* , 5 vols. (New York–London, 1966). *Memoirs and Scientific Correspondence of the Late Sir George Gabriel Stokes . . . Selected and Arranged by Joseph Larmor . . .* , 2 vols. (Cambridge, 1907; repr., New York–London, 1971), contains selected correspondence of Stokes, memoirs by his daughter Mrs. Laurence Humphrey and some of his colleagues, and miscellaneous material about Stokes's life and work.

Cambridge University Library, England, holds an extensive collection of Stokes's MSS, especially the Stokes Papers, which include his scientific, miscellaneous, family, Royal Society, and religious correspondence; notes for lectures; notes taken in lectures; and material concerning university administration. Add. MS 7618 at Cambridge contains the Stokes-Kelvin correspondence. The Scientific Periodicals Library, Cambridge, holds a number of Stokes's notebooks, some containing records of his experiments.

From the journal's inception in 1857 to 1878, Stokes, with A. Cayley and M. Hermite, assisted editors J. J. Sylvester and N. M. Ferrers of the *Quarterly Journal of Pure and Applied Mathematics* (London). He contributed articles, mostly on physical optics, and revised others on physical topics taken from the *Penny Cyclopaedia*, for *The English Cyclopaedia. A New Dictionary of Universal Knowledge. Conducted by Charles Knight. Arts and Sciences*, 8 vols. (London, 1859–1861). The three series of Burnett lectures were issued separately, and then published together as *Burnett Lectures. On Light. In Three Courses Delivered at Aberdeen in November, 1883, December, 1884, and November, 1885* (London–New York, 1887; 2nd ed., 1892), with a German trans. by O. Dziobek appearing as *Das Licht* (Leipzig, 1888).

Apart from his contributions to the *Journal of the Transactions of the Victoria Institute* (London), Stokes's principal writings on religion and on aspects of its relationship to science are *Natural Theology. The Gifford Lectures Delivered Before the University of Edinburgh in 1891* (London, 1891), *Natural Theology.*

The Gifford Lectures . . . 1893 (London, 1893), and *Conditional Immortality. A Help to Sceptics. A Series of Letters Addressed . . . to James Marchant (With a Prefatory Note by the Latter)* (London, 1897).

The *Transactions of the Cambridge Philosophical Society*, **18** (1900), consists of memoirs presented to the society to celebrate Stokes's jubilee as Lucasian professor.

II. SECONDARY LITERATURE. The two most important obituaries assessing Stokes's scientific work are Lord Kelvin, in *Nature*, **67** (1903), 337–338, also in *Mathematical and Scientific Papers*, 2nd ed., V, xxvii–xxxii, and Lord Rayleigh, *Proceedings of the Royal Society*, **75** (1905), 199–216, repr. in both eds. of *Mathematical and Physical Papers*, V, ix–xxv.

Since these obituaries and Larmor's *Memoir and Scientific Correspondence . . .* , little has been published on Stokes's scientific work. A few recent accounts are Truesdell's preface to the *Mathematical and Physical Papers*, 2nd ed., I, IVA–IVL; I. Grattan-Guinness, *The Development of the Foundations of Mathematical Analysis From Euler to Riemann* (Cambridge, Mass.–London, 1970), 113–120; and David B. Wilson, "George Gabriel Stokes on Stellar Aberration and the Luminiferous Ether," in *British Journal for the History of Science*, **6** (1972–1973), 57–72.

E. M. PARKINSON

STOLETOV, ALEKSANDR GRIGORIEVICH (*b.* Vladimir, Russia, 10 August 1839; *d.* Moscow, Russia, 27 May 1896), *physics*.

Stoletov came from a merchant family that had been exiled to Vladimir for sedition by Ivan the Terrible. His father, Grigory Mikhailovich, owned a small grocery store and a tannery; his mother, Aleksandra Vasilievna, was intelligent and well-read. While still a schoolboy he studied French, English, and German.

In 1856 Stoletov entered the Faculty of Physics and Mathematics at Moscow University as one of the first students from the merchant class to receive a government scholarship. His instructors in physics were M. F. Spassky and N. A. Lyubimov; and he received solid mathematical preparation under N. E. Zernov and N. D. Brashman. After graduating in 1860, he remained in the physics department to prepare for an academic career.

In 1862 Stoletov traveled abroad on a fellowship and spent three and a half years in Germany, where he attended the lectures of Helmholtz, Kirchhoff, and Wilhelm Weber and worked in H. G. Magnus' laboratory. At the end of 1865 he became a physics teacher at Moscow University. Four years later he defended his master's thesis, "Obshchaya zadacha elektrostatiki i privedenie ee k prosteyshemu vidu" ("The General Problem of Electrostatics and Its Reduction to the Simplest Form").

In 1871 Stoletov completed plans for his doctoral dissertation, which was based on his experimental research on the magnetic properties of iron. Since there was no laboratory at Moscow University—although Stoletov tried to have one established—he was again obliged to go abroad. At Heidelberg, Kirchhoff offered him the necessary conditions for working on his dissertation, which he defended in Moscow the following year, "Issledovanie o funktsii namagnichenia myagkogo zheleza."

He became extraordinary professor, and since a physics laboratory had in the meantime been opened at the university, he did his research there. In addition to his lectures, Stoletov also popularized science through his work in the Society of Amateurs of Science, the Society of Amateurs of Natural Sciences, and the Russian Physical-Chemical Society. He attracted a large group of talented young people to the physics laboratory and was the first to organize systematic training of scientific teams in physics. His protracted efforts to establish a physics institute at Moscow University were finally realized in 1887.

In his master's thesis Stoletov examined the theoretical equilibrium of electricity in an arbitrary number of isolated conductors (continuous and field) in an arbitrarily given field created by arbitrarily complex stationary electric poles. He continued to develop the mathematical method of successive approximation of Robert Murphy, Lipschitz, and William Thomson (Lord Kelvin) for the case of an arbitrary number of conductors. Stoletov had already written his thesis when Lipschitz's work on the same subject appeared abroad, but the latter was significantly less complete.

In his doctoral dissertation Stoletov examined the relation of the magnetization of iron to the strength of the external magnetic field. Although it was then known that the course of magnetization is not linear, the form of the function in the area of relatively weak fields remained unexplained. A thorough analysis of the experimental material led Stoletov to conclude that previous investigations, carried out in cylindrical models, could not yield satisfactory results because of the demagnetizing effect of the flat end. His use of Kirchhoff's theory led to the possibility of studying the true relation of magnetization to the field in closed rings magnetized along the perimeter. For this investigation Stoletov developed the method now generally accepted for measuring induction in rings with the aid of a ballistic galvanometer. He was the first to show that magnetic permeability of a ferromagnet increases in proportion to the intensification of the magnetizing field, attains a maximum, and then decreases. Stoletov emphasized the importance of applying these results to electrotechnology.

In his most distinguished work, *Aktinoelektricheskie issledovania* ("Actinoelectric Investigations," 1889), Stoletov experimentally established the basic laws of the external photoelectric effect and certain fundamental regularities of electrical discharge in rarefied gases. The first to develop an experimental method of studying the photoeffect, he showed that during the illumination of metals by ultraviolet light, there is a loss of negative electrical charge. By illuminating the negative plate of a condenser through a latticed-plate positive electrode, he observed a continuous electrical current in the circuit containing the condenser, a cell battery, and a galvanometer. The strength of the current appeared to be proportional to the intensity of the incident light and to the area illuminated. In 1888–1889 Stoletov was the first to show that through the presence of contact difference in potentials between the lattice and the plate, the photoelectric apparatus can, without a supplementary battery, serve as the source of current, converting light energy into electricity. This was the first photoelement, but Stoletov did not patent his invention. In 1890 the German physicists Elster and Geitel independently had the same idea, and received a patent for the photoelement and several of its applications.

Investigating the relation of the photocurrent to the external difference in potential, Stoletov discovered the existence of a saturation current. Further experimental study of this phenomenon at different degrees of rarefaction of air led him to discover an important regularity. If p_m is the pressure of gas at which the current attains the maximum value, l the distance between electrodes, and v the potential difference between them, then,

$$\frac{p_m l}{v} = \text{constant}.$$

The theory of this phenomenon was provided in 1910 by Townsend, who proposed calling the quantity the Stoletov constant.

In his important four-part *O kriticheskom sostoyanii tel* ("On the Critical State of Bodies," 1882–1894), Stoletov thoroughly analyzed the experimental data and the theoretical opinions of various authors, introduced clarity into the discussion of the critical state, and showed the correctness of the ideas of Thomas Andrews and van der Waals.

Stoletov's interest in the history of physics was reflected in an extensive study, *Ocherk razvitia nashikh svedeny o gazakh* ("Sketch of the Development of Our Information on Gases," 1879), and in articles on Newton, da Vinci, and others.

BIBLIOGRAPHY

Stoletov's writings were published as *Sobranie sochineny* ("Collected Works"; Moscow, 1941) and *Izbrannye sochinenia* ("Selected Works"), A. K. Timiryazev, ed. (Moscow, 1950). The Royal Society *Catalogue of Scientific Papers*, VIII, 1024; XI, 507; XII, 707; and XVIII, 978–980, lists 29 of his memoirs and several obituary notices.

On his life and work, see A. I. Kompaneets, *Mirovozrenie A. G. Stoletova* ("The World View of A. G. Stoletov"; Moscow, 1956), with a comprehensive bibliography of his writings and correspondence, pp. 281–286; M. S. Sominsky, *Aleksandr Grigorievich Stoletov* (Leningrad, 1970); and G. M. Teplyakov and P. S. Kudryavtsev, *Aleksandr Grigorievich Stoletov* (Moscow, 1966).

J. G. DORFMAN

STOLZ, OTTO (*b.* Hall [now Solbad Hall in Tirol], Austria, 3 July 1842; *d.* Innsbruck, Austria, 25 October 1905), *mathematics*.

Stolz was the son of a physician who later achieved some prominence as a psychiatrist. After graduating from the Gymnasium at Innsbruck, he studied mathematics and natural sciences at the University of Innsbruck and later at Vienna. In 1864 he received the Ph.D. at the University of Vienna, where he was subsequently a *Privatdozent* until 1869, when he obtained a scholarship for further study at Berlin and Göttingen.

From 1869 to 1871 Stolz attended courses given by Weierstrass, Kummer, and Kronecker at Berlin and by Clebsch and Klein at Göttingen. Weierstrass made the greatest impression on him and led him to extend his research from geometry to analysis.

In July 1872 Stolz was appointed associate professor at the University of Innsbruck. He became a full professor in 1876 and married in the same year. He remained in Innsbruck for the rest of his life.

Stolz's earliest papers were concerned with analytic or algebraic geometry, including spherical trigonometry. He later dedicated an increasing part of his research to real analysis, in particular to convergence problems in the theory of series, including double series; to the discussion of the limits of indeterminate ratios; and to integration. Stolz was the first to formulate the counterpart, for double series, of Cauchy's necessary and sufficient condition for convergence. He also generalized Abel's theorem on the behavior of a power series in radial approach to the circle of convergence ("regularity of Abelian summability") to approach in an angular region with a vertex on the circle of convergence.

During his lifetime, and for some time afterward, Stolz was known as the author of several carefully written textbooks, of which *Vorlesungen über allgemeine Arithmetik* (1885–1886) and *Theoretische Arithmetik* (1900–1902) in particular gained wide recognition. The latter work was written with his student J. A. Gmeiner. Stolz is known today for his contributions to many questions of detail rather than for any major single achievement. For example, he is credited by K. Knopp with having been the first to show that every irrational number has a unique representation in decimal notation.

Stolz was greatly interested in the history of mathematics. After the Weierstrass ϵ,δ approach had found general acceptance in the early 1870's, he was the first to point out that Bolzano had suggested essentially the same approach even before Cauchy introduced his own, less rigorous method. Under the influence of P. du Bois-Reymond, Stolz also reexamined the theory of infinitely small and infinitely large quantities that had been used, on shaky foundations, until the advent of Weierstrass' method.

BIBLIOGRAPHY

I. ORIGINAL WORKS. Stolz's writings include "Beweis einiger Sätze über Potenzreihen," in *Zeitschrift für Mathematik und Physik*, **20** (1875), 369–376; "B. Bolzano's Bedeutung in der Geschichte der Infinitesimalrechnung," in *Mathematische Annalen*, **18** (1881), 255–279; *Vorlesungen über allgemeine Arithmetik*, 2 vols. (Leipzig, 1885–1886); and *Theoretische Arithmetik*, 2 vols. (Leipzig, 1900–1902), written with J. A. Gmeiner.

II. SECONDARY LITERATURE. See J. A. Gmeiner, "Otto Stolz," in *Jahresberichte der Deutschen Mathematikervereinigung*, **15** (1906), 309–322; and K. Knopp, *Theorie und Anwendung der unendlichen Reihen*, Grundlehren der mathematischen Wissenschaften in Einzeldarstellungen, no. 2 (Berlin, 1922).

ABRAHAM ROBINSON

STONEY, GEORGE JOHNSTONE (*b*. Oakley Park, Kingstown [now Dún Laoghaire], County Dublin, Ireland, 15 February 1826; *d*. London, England, 5 July 1911), *mathematical physics*.

Stoney was the eldest son of George Stoney and his wife, Anne, who were Protestant landowners. The family was a talented one: Stoney's younger brother, Bindon Blood Stoney (1828–1909); his son, George Gerald Stoney (1863–1942); and his nephew, George Francis Fitzgerald (1851–1901), made significant contributions to science and technology, and were fellows of the Royal Society.

Stoney graduated from Trinity College, Dublin, in 1848 and became assistant to Lord Rosse in his observatory at Parsonstown (now Birr). After failing to obtain a fellowship at Trinity College, he obtained the chair of natural philosophy at Queen's College, Galway, which he held for five years. In 1857 he returned to Dublin as secretary to Queen's University, in which post he spent the rest of his working life. Stoney was a member of the Royal Irish Academy and the Royal Dublin Society, and was secretary of the latter for over twenty years. In 1893 he moved to London and became involved in the affairs of the Royal Society, of which he had been elected a fellow in 1861; in 1898 he was vice-president and a member of the Council.

Stoney had an interest in all fields of science and, like many of his Irish contemporaries, applied mathematics to the solution of scientific problems. He was particularly interested in spectrum analysis. A paper he wrote in 1868 suggested that spectral lines were due to periodic motions inside the atom rather than to the translational motion of molecules. Stoney continued this line of thought for a number of years and, as a result, put forward important ideas on atomic structure. In 1891 he explained the presence of double and triple lines in spectra by apsidal and precessional motions of orbital electrons.

Since his early work in Rosse's observatory, Stoney maintained an interest in astronomy and wrote many papers on the subject. Using the kinetic theory as a basis of his work, he reached certain conclusions concerning the atmospheres of planets. Stoney's paper of 1897 suggested that if the velocity of molecules exceeded a limit set by the force of gravity, then the molecules would fly off into space. By this means he explained the absence of an atmosphere on the moon.

Stoney probably is best-known for having coined the term "electron." He hoped that by a careful choice of fundamental units, science would be simplified; and at the 1874 meeting of the British Association, he presented the paper "On the Physical Units of Nature." One of the basic units he suggested was the charge carried on a hydrogen ion, which he determined from experimental data. The weight of hydrogen liberated on electrolysis by a given quantity of electricity was known; and by calculating the number of atoms associated with this weight of hydrogen, Stoney found the electric charge associated with each atom. A similar theory of electrical atomicity was advanced by Helmholtz in his Faraday lecture in 1881, and ten years later Stoney introduced the word "electron" for this fundamental unit. The term later came to be used for the "corpuscles" discovered by J. J. Thomson.

BIBLIOGRAPHY

I. ORIGINAL WORKS. Stoney's writings include "The Internal Motions of Gases Compared With the Motions of Waves of Light," in *Philosophical Magazine*, 4th ser., **36** (1868), 132–141; "On the Physical Units of Nature," *ibid*., 5th ser., **11** (1881), 381–389; "On the Cause of Double Lines and of Equidistant Satellites in the Spectra of Gases," in *Scientific Transactions of the Royal Dublin Society*, **4** (1891), 563–608; "Of the 'Electron' or Atom of Electricity," in *Philosophical Magazine*, 5th ser., **38** (1894), 418–420; and "Of Atmospheres Upon Planets and Satellites," in *Scientific Transactions of the Royal Dublin Society*, **6** (1897), 305–328.

II. SECONDARY LITERATURE. Biographies are by F. T. Trouton in *Nature*, **87** (1911), 50–51; and by an anonymous author in *Proceedings of the Royal Society*, **86** (1912), xx–xxv.

BRIAN B. KELHAM

STØRMER, FREDRIK CARL MÜLERTZ (*b*. Skien, Norway, 3 September 1874; *d*. Oslo, Norway, 13 August 1957), *mathematics, geophysics*.

Størmer's father, Georg Størmer, was a pharmacist; his mother was the former Elisabeth Mülertz. When he was twelve, the family moved to Oslo (then Christiania). As a young boy he was interested in botany, which remained a lifelong hobby. During his high school years, Størmer's interest and ability in mathematics became apparent; and through a friend of the family, who was a professor of mathematics at the University of Oslo, he received instruction in that science. His first publication was published while he was still in high school (1892). Størmer entered the University of Oslo in 1892, received the master's degree in 1898, and was awarded the doctorate in 1903. In the latter year he became professor of pure mathematics, a post he held until his retirement in 1944.

Størmer's first papers were on number theory; but in 1903 he met the physicist Kristian Birkeland, who studied the polar aurora. Birkeland approached the problem experimentally, by bombarding a magnetic sphere in a vacuum with cathode rays. In this way it was possible to observe phenomena resembling the polar aurora. Størmer made the field observations and the theoretical calculations of the charged particles. The observations of the polar aurora were made photographically, by taking parallactic pictures along a base line. Størmer thus accumulated an enormous amount of observational material, not only on the altitude but also on the size, shape, and periodicity of the polar aurora. In the course of this work he also acquired interesting information on noctilucent and mother-of-pearl (nacreous) clouds. He constructed the instruments and worked out the procedures for these observations himself, showing a gift for experimentation that is rare among pure mathematicians.

Størmer's other approach to the study of the polar aurora was a mathematical analysis of the trajectories of charged particles in the earth's dipole magnetic field. It included the numerical integration of series of differential equations—an enormous task before the advent of electronic computers—in which Størmer was assisted by many of his students. His analysis showed that only some trajectories are possible, others being "forbidden." Størmer was also led to postulate a circular electric current in the equatorial plane of the earth and showed that electrons may be trapped into oscillatory trajectories in the earth's dipole field. Although his calculations were made in the course of studying the polar aurora, they became important for other areas of cosmic geophysics. When the latitudinal variation in cosmic radiation was discovered in the 1930's, it could be explained by Størmer's calculations; and the discovery of the Van Allen belts confirmed, to a surprising degree, his theoretical analysis of the trajectories of charged particles from the sun in the dipole field of the earth.

Størmer was an old-fashioned scientist who worked by himself. He mastered the field and often did the manual labor connected with his experiments and calculations. His last book, *The Polar Aurora* (1955), is not only his final summary, but also an up-to-date and authoritative study. Størmer

had no direct followers; but he exerted a profound influence during his forty-one-year teaching career. He also was an excellent popularizer.

BIBLIOGRAPHY

Most of Størmer's scientific publications appeared in the *Norske Videnskabsakademiets Skrifter*; lists can be found in *Årbok. Norske videnskapsakademi i oslo* (1892–1953). His books include *Fra verdensrummets dybder til atomenes indre* (Oslo, 1923), which went through 4 eds. in Norwegian and was translated into 5 foreign languages; and *The Polar Aurora* (Oxford, 1955).

An obituary is L. Harang, "Minnetale over professor Carl Størmer," in *Årbok. Norske videnskapsakademi i Oslo* (1958), 81–85.

NILS SPJELDNAES

STRABO (*b*. Amasia, Asia Minor, 64/63 B.C.; *d*. Amasia, *ca*. A.D. 25), *history, geography.*

Strabo was the son of wealthy parents. He was Greek by language and education; in his youth he studied under the rhetorician Aristodemus at Nysa in Caria, and he may also have known the Stoic polymath Posidonius. In about 44 B.C. he went to Rome to study with the geographer Tyrannion and the philosopher Xenarchus. He became a convert to Stoicism, probably through the offices of the philosopher Athenodorus Cananites, the friend and teacher of the emperor Augustus, although he continued to distrust popular religion (however useful it might be) and to believe in Providence as a first cause. He was again in Rome in 35 B.C. and in 31 B.C. He visited Crete, journeyed through Corinth in 29 B.C., and spent five years, from 25 to 20 B.C., in Alexandria, where he may have studied in the great library. In 25 or 24 B.C., he made a journey from Alexandria up the Nile to Aswan and the Ethiopian frontier in the company of the Roman governor, Marcus Aelius Gallus.[1]

An admirer of the Roman empire, Strabo may have been politically motivated in the writing of his works, although they also contain a great deal of knowledge presented for its own sake. Of these works, only one, the *Geographica*, is extant. It is known that Strabo composed a number of historical works, including a *Hypomnemata historica* in which he recounted incidents in the lives of famous men. He intended a fuller work, incorporating some of the same material, to be a continuation of the work of Polybius, whose history concluded with the years 146/145 B.C. Strabo's work appeared in either forty-three or forty-seven books, and brought Polybius up to date at least as far as the troubles following the assassination of Julius Caesar in 44 B.C.; it may even have extended to about 27-25 B.C.[2]

Strabo apparently published some of his surviving *Geographica* about 7 B.C.; a partially revised version of this appeared in about A.D. 18, and a finished but still incompletely revised work in seventeen books was published later, perhaps after Strabo's death. The place of its publication must have been far from Rome, since the work was not known there; indeed, it was not generally known until the fifth century. It was addressed to men in elevated stations in life; although Strabo stated that it should be of some general interest, he particularly recommended it to statesmen, rulers, and soldiers, as well as to those who wanted an account of known lands (especially those prominent in the history of civilization).

Although by his own statement Strabo traveled from Armenia to Etruria, and from the Black Sea to Ethiopia—and although he knew many parts of Asia Minor from Pontus to Syria—his *Geographica* was based less upon his personal observations than on his reading. He knew little of Italy, except for the areas along the Roman roads in the southern and central parts, and he took little advantage of Roman sources, although he knew Caesar; Calpurnius Piso Frugi,[3] governor of Libya; Aelius Gallus; and an unnamed, but probably Roman, chorographer. He was apparently unfamiliar with Marcus Vipsanius Agrippa's chart of the Roman empire and its adjacent countries.

The bulk of Strabo's material came (although it is not possible to ascertain how directly) from a number of Greek sources that are now lost. Among other writers Strabo drew upon Eratosthenes for mathematical geography and cartography and information about India; upon Eudoxus of Cnidus for astronomy; on Hipparchus, whose astronomical material Strabo used only for mathematical cartography; on Posidonius, especially for information on Spain and Gaul; on Polybius, especially for material concerning Europe; on Artemidorus, for Asia Minor and Egypt; and on Apollodorus of Athens, perhaps for Greece (of which Strabo knew less than he did of Italy). Despite his borrowings from mathematicians and astronomers, and despite his recognition of the importance of the principles of mathematics and physics,[4] Strabo's scientific skills were limited, and he tended to underestimate science, being more sympathetic to "human" interests.

The first two books of the *Geographica* contain a somewhat rambling but still useful survey of earlier geographic theories and serve as an introduction to the rest of the work, wherein Strabo attempted to set out an account of the physical features, products, and national character of each country. His presentation is at once mathematical, chorographical, topographical, physical, political, and historical. He was, of course, dealing with the known world; much of northern Europe and of Africa south of the Mediterranean coastal regions and Egypt was still unexplored, while Asia was known only as far as India and Ceylon. He therefore ignored the great unknown stretches of eastern and northern Asia, and treated Africa as an area smaller than Europe, lying wholly north of the equator; outside Egypt, he noted, it was largely desert.[5]

Within these limitations, and given his reliance on reports of varying degrees of accuracy, Strabo produced an excellent account of parts of western Europe, Asia Minor, and Egypt. He was also good on Gaul, although he relied too little on recent Roman records (including the narratives of Caesar) and made the Pyrenees run from north to south, while the coast (largely because Strabo distrusted the explorer Pytheas, discoverer of Britain) runs northeast from the Pyrenees to the Rhine. His account of the British Isles is understandably weak, as is his treatment of the Baltic region and Scandinavia. His account of Greece is also disappointing.

Strabo followed Eratosthenes in showing the known world as a single ocean-girt landmass (*oikoumene*, that is, inhabited) composed of Europe, Asia, Africa, and their associated islands. The *oikoumene* occupies less than one-half of one quadrilateral on a sphere (about 25,200 geographical miles in circumference, according to Eratosthenes' good calculation) that remains motionless within a revolving spherical universe. Strabo represented the *oikoumene* as being entirely north of the equator of the sphere, occupying one-quarter of the whole; but he surmises that there may be other inhabited land continents, as yet unknown.[6]

Strabo stated that the *oikoumene* should be drawn on one-quarter of a globe not less than ten feet in diameter in order to render it in sufficient detail. He further discussed projecting the *oikoumene* on a plane surface, noting that it made little difference whether the meridians remained parallel to each other, since it was scarcely worthwhile to make them converge even slightly toward the pole. He relied upon established astronomical observations and conclusions to fix the equator, the ecliptic, and the tropics, and was aware that longitudes could be determined accurately only through comparing observations made during a suitable eclipse. He accepted the system of dividing the equator into 360 degrees and of establishing, by astronomical observations, parallels of north latitude, including a main one that intersects, at Rhodes, a main meridian line of longitude.[7] He also adopted the notion of five zones or "belts" in latitude: north frigid (uninhabitable), north temperate (inhabited), torrid (partly uninhabited—Strabo rejected the idea that the unknown southern part of this zone might be habitable), south temperate (habitable), and south frigid (uninhabited).[8]

Strabo represented the *oikoumene* itself as mantle-shaped, tapering toward the east and west. He showed it as extending in length for about 7,000 miles along a parallel drawn from Spain, through Rhodes, and to the Ganges, and in breadth for about 3,000 miles along the main meridian drawn through Rhodes (these distances were an unwise reduction of those set out by Eratosthenes). The encircling ocean intrudes into the landmass in a number of gulfs, especially the Caspian Sea (this error was not originally Strabo's), the Persian Gulf, the Arabian Gulf (the Red Sea), and, largest of all, the "Inside Sea," or "Our Sea" the Mediterranean.[9] It is interesting in this context to note that Strabo considered a long, varied coastline, together with a temperate climate, to be one of the factors important to the rise of civilization; for this reason the Mediterranean lands, especially Greece, developed a culture superior to lands at the outer edges of the *oikoumene*, where the coastline, although extensive, lacks variety of contour.

Strabo devoted much discussion to the forces that had formed the *oikoumene*. A number of conclusions that he recorded had probably derived from Posidonius; he was also interested in Aristotle's theories about earthquakes and volcanic activity, and in Strato's notion that the Mediterranean had once been a lake that, overfilled by rivers, broke through the Straits of Gibraltar. Strabo suggested that some islands were torn from the mainland by earthquakes, while others (including Sicily) were thrown up by volcanic action. He gave examples of both local and widespread land subsidence and alluded to the uprising of seabeds with consequent flooding; he further described the silting of rivers that form alluvial plains and deltas. His acceptance of the long-held notion that inland regions containing salt marshes, salt beds, sand, and seashells and other marine débris had arisen from the bottom of the sea led him to conclude that Egypt—and the greater part of the *oikoumene*—had once been submerged.[10]

Strabo's whole work is not orderly, perhaps because he was not able to give it a final form. He was fond of historical and mythological digressions, and on some subjects argumentative and obsessive. The *Geographica* is nonetheless highly valuable in its exposition of the development of geography. It marked the first attempt to assemble all available geographical knowledge into a single treatise. A philosophy of geography, it is utterly unlike the mathematical geography of Ptolemy, the geographical parts of Pliny the Elder's *Natural History*, or, indeed, any other surviving work of ancient geography.

NOTES

1. On his birthplace, see Strabo, *Geography*, 12.3.39, and Stephen of Byzantium, under Ἀμάσεια; on his ancestry, Strabo, 10.4.10, 11.2.18, 12.3.33, 12.3.53; on his education and philosophy, 14.1.48, 14.5.4, 12.6.2, 12.3.16, 13.1.54, 16.2.24, 7.3.4, 1.2.34, 2.3.8, 16.4.21, 1.2.8, 17.1.36, 4.1.14—also Athenaeus, *Deipnosophistae*, 14.75.657, and Stephen of Byzantium, *loc. cit.*; on his admiration of Rome, 6.4.2, 1.1.16, 3.2.5; on his travels, 2.5.11; to Rome, 6.2.6, 8.6.23, 5.3.8—compare Dio Cassius, L.10; to Corinth, 10.4.10 and 10.5.3; in Egypt, 2.3.5, 2.5.12, 11.11.5, 17.1.24, 17.1.50, 15.1.45; to Italy, 2.5.11 and 5.2.6.
2. 1.1.22–23, 2.1.9, 11.9.3; Plutarch, "Lucullus," 28; "Sulla," 26; *Suda Lexicon*, "Λούκουλλος"; Flavius Josephus, *Antiquities*, 13.286–287, 319, 347.14.35, 68, 104, 111, 114, 118, 138–139, 15.9–10; and *Contra Apionem*, 2.84.
3. Calpurnius Piso: Strabo, 2.5.33.
4. Strabo, 1.1.16–18, 1.1.22–23, 2.5.1.
5. See especially 2.5.26–33; 17.3.1.
6. 1.1.8; compare 1.4.6, 2.3.6, 2.5.5–7, 2.5.34.
7. 2.5.10, 1.4.1 ff., 1.1.12, 2.1.1, 2.1.10, 2.1.12–13, 2.5.4, 2.5.34–42.
8. 2.3.1–2, 2.5.3, 2.5.5. A zone in latitude must not be confused with a κλίμα "clima" in latitude, which was the "inclination" of a place's horizon to the earth's axis.
9. 2.5.6–9, 2.5.14, 2.5.18.
10. 1.3.4–5, 1.3.8, 1.3.10, 5.4.8, 2.5.18.

BIBLIOGRAPHY

I. ORIGINAL WORKS. Strabo's history, now lost, consisted of historical sketches (or memoirs), Ὑπομνήματα Ἱστορικά, of which he cites his "Deeds of Alexander" as an example, and a continuation of Polybius, probably entitled Ἱστορίαι or Ἱστορία, in 43 or 47 bks., of which bk. 2 was identical with bk. 6 of the sketches. The geography, which is extant, was entitled Γεωγραφικά ("Geography" or "Matters Geographical"), and is in 17 bks.

The *Geography* was little read until the late fifth century, and even then copies were rare. We do have in three portions (Codex Vat. gr. 2306, Codex Crypt. Ζα xliii, and Codex Vat. 2061A) a palimpsest written at that time and still showing legible remains of the original text of Strabo; we also have quotations by Stephen of Byzantium from another early source. All extant later MSS of Strabo's text and direct medieval quotations are derived from a lost archetype of about the mid-ninth century. For the first nine bks. Codex Parisinus gr. 1397 (late tenth century) is the best MS but lacks bks. 10–17, for which the best MSS are Codex Vat. gr. 1329 (lacking bks. 10, 11, and beginning of 12; late thirteenth or early fourteenth century) and Codex Marc. gr. 640 (A.D. 1321).

The latest treatment of the early tradition is by F. Lasserre in Germaine Aujac and F. Lasserre, *Strabon, Géographie*, I, pt. 1 (Paris, 1969), xlviii ff., which is criticized by D. R. Dicks in *Classical Review*, n.s. **21** (1971), 188 ff.

The 1st ed., the Aldine (Venice, 1516), is based on the corrupt Codex Parisinus gr. 1393. The eds. by Guilielmus Xylander (Basel, 1549, 1571) were revised with commentary by I. Casaubon (Geneva, 1587), who later (Paris, 1620) issued his own ed. with Latin translation by Xylander and notes by F. Morrellius. The pages of his text are often cited (C and a numeral) in references to Strabo's text, rather than those of T. J. van Almaloveen's reissue of Casaubon's ed. (Amsterdam, 1707). Casaubon's was the base for further eds.: L. G. de Bréquigny (Paris, 1763), bks. 1–3 only; J. P. Siebenkees, 7 vols. (Leipzig, 1796–1818); T. Falconer, (Oxford, 1807); and the outstanding one of Adamantios Corais (Coraës, Coray), 3 vols. of text and 1 vol. of notes in modern Greek (Paris, 1815–1819). G. Kramer put the text on a better basis in 3 vols. (Berlin, 1844–1852). Also important are the eds. of A. Meineke, 3 vols. (Leipzig, 1852, 1866–1877) and of C. Müller and F. Dübner, 2 vols. (Paris, 1853–1858).

Several important series are in progress. W. Aly, *Strabonis Geographica in 17 Büchern*, IV, *Strabon von Amaseia. Untersuchungen über Text, Aufbau, und Quellen der Geographica* (Bonn, 1957), is one of several vols. planned to include text, translation, and commentary; *Strabonis Geographica*, I, text of bks. 1 and 2 (Bonn, 1968), was edited after his death by E. Kirsten and F. Lapp. F. Sbordone was responsible for *Strabonis Geographica*, I, bks. 1 and 2 (Rome, 1963). The following have appeared in the Budé series, giving introductions, text, French translation, and short notes; Germaine Aujac and F. Lasserre, I, pt. 1, intro. and bk. 1 (Paris, 1969); Germaine Aujac, I, pt. 2, bk. 2 (Paris, 1969); F. Lasserre, II, bks. 3 and 4 (Paris, 1966); III, bks. 5 and 6 (Paris, 1967); VII, bk. 10 (Paris, 1971).

Still appreciated are the French translations by A. Coray and G. La Porte du Theil (bks. 1–15) and A. Letronne (bks. 16 and 17) (Paris, 1805–1819). The German translation of C. G. Groskurd, 4 vols. (Berlin–Stettin, 1831–1834), is monumental. English translations include those of H. C. Hamilton and W. Falconer, 3 vols. (London, 1892–1893), and of H. L. Jones, with text, in the Loeb Classical Library series, 8 vols. (London, 1917–1932).

Much other modern work on Strabo, which has been done and is being done, is recorded yearly in J. Marouzeau, *L'année philologique*. Fragments of Strabo's historical work were edited by P. Otto in *Leipziger Studien zur classischen Philologie*, **11** (1889); and are also in C. Müller, *Fragmenta historicorum Graecorum*, III (Paris, 1841), 490 ff., and in F. Jacoby, *Die Fragmente der griechischen Historiker*, IIA (Berlin, 1926), 430–436, and II C (Berlin, 1926), 291–295.

II. SECONDARY LITERATURE. For further study of Strabo, see Germaine Aujac, *Strabon et la science de son temps* (Paris, 1966); H. Berger, *Geschichte der wissenschaftlichen Erdkunde der Griechen* (Leipzig, 2nd ed., 1903), 327–582; E. H. Bunbury, *History of Ancient Geography*, II (London, 1879; 2nd ed., New York, 1959), 209–337; A. Calzon, *Conception de la géographie d'après Strabon* (Fribourg, 1940); M. Dubois, *Examen de la Géographie de Strabon* (Paris, 1891); W. Heidel, *The Frame of Ancient Greek Maps* (New York, 1937), *passim*, but 30–46, 104–122; E. Honigmann, in Pauly-Wissowa, *Real-Encyclopädie der classischen Altertumswissenschaft*, IVa, pt. 1 (1931), 76–155; J. O. Thomson, *History of Ancient Geography* (Cambridge, 1948), 182–186, 286–289, 188–198; H. F. Tozer, *Selections from Strabo* (Oxford, 1893), with intro.; and *A History of Ancient Geography*, 2nd ed., by M. Cary (Cambridge, 1935), 238–260.

E. H. WARMINGTON

STRACHEY, JOHN (*b.* Sutton Court, Chew Magna, Somerset, England, 10 May 1671; *d.* Greenwich, England, 11 June 1743), *geology.*

Strachey was the only son of John and Jane Strachey. He inherited his father's estate when three years old. Little is known about his education and early life. On 26 November 1686, he matriculated at Trinity College, Oxford, but left to study law at Middle Temple, London, in 1687. In 1692 Strachey married Elizabeth Elletson, who bore him eighteen children, and, two years after her death in 1722, Christina Stavely, by whom he had a son. He resided mainly at Sutton Court but spent the latter part of his life in Edinburgh. In 1719 he was elected fellow of the Royal Society.

In the early eighteenth century there were several coal mines near Sutton Court; and it was probably Strachey's interest in them that led him to study geology, for he published two geological papers and a pamphlet, all relative to occurrences of coal in Somerset and elsewhere. In the first two he included diagrams showing a cross section several miles long of the strata in the region of Sutton

Court, based on an intimate knowledge of the coal workings and an examination of rock outcrops in the surrounding countryside. They showed nearly horizontal Jurassic, Triassic, and (in his 1725 paper) Cretaceous strata resting on steeply inclined Coal Measures (Pennsylvanian). This was the first clear demonstration by a British author of an angular unconformity. Within the Coal Measures he recorded seven named seams, one of which was characterized by the fossil shells and plants occurring above it, a very early use of fossils to identify a specific horizon. The diagram also showed the effect of a fault on the continuity of the coal seams.

In his 1727 pamphlet Strachey restated his earlier observations and added details of the strata in other coalfields in England and Scotland, based partly on his own observations. He described the lithological characteristics of the coal seams and associated sediments, but seems to have had little idea how they were formed and hence did not realize the significance of the unconformity he recorded. Strachey recognized the importance of dip and strike, noting that across a broad belt of England, strata in general dip to the east and southeast. To account for it he accepted the suggestion already made by some British authors that all rock formations continue downward to the center of the earth, as a result of the west-to-east rotation of the earth acting on strata that originally were soft and unconsolidated.

Strachey left a number of unpublished manuscripts, one of which, since published, "Of Stones," is of considerable geological interest as a record of early eighteenth-century mining and quarrying operations in England. He also published a map of Somerset showing the sites of coal and metalliferous mines.

Strachey's work is of value as an early attempt to establish a stratigraphical succession, but the importance of the unconformity he recorded was not realized until much later.

BIBLIOGRAPHY

I. ORIGINAL WORKS. Strachey's writings include "A Curious Description of the Strata Observ'd in the Coal-Mines of Mendip in Somersetshire," in *Philosophical Transactions of the Royal Society*, **30** (1719), 968–973; "An Account of the Strata in Coal-Mines, &c.," *ibid.*, **33** (1725), 395–398; *Observations on the Different Strata of Earths, and Minerals. More Particularly of Such as Are Found in the Coal-Mines of Great Britain* (London, 1727); *Somersetshire Survey'd and Protracted* (London, 1736), a map of Somerset, on the scale of about 1/2 inch to the mile; and "Of Stones" (*ca.* 1736), from the MS of John Strachey's proposed "Somersetshire Illustrated," annotated by R. D. Webby, in *Proceedings of the Bristol Naturalists' Society*, **31**, no. 3 (1967), 311–330. Strachey's MSS are preserved in the Somerset Record Office, Taunton, England.

II. SECONDARY LITERATURE. See J. G. C. M. Fuller, "The Industrial Basis of Stratigraphy: John Strachey, 1671–1743, and William Smith, 1769–1839," in *Bulletin of the American Association of Petroleum Geologists*, **53**, no. 11 (1969), 2256–2273; and J. D. Webby, "Some Early Ideas Attributing Easterly Dipping Strata to the Rotation of the Earth," in *Proceedings of the Geologists' Association*, **80**, pt. 1 (1969), 91–97.

V. A. EYLES

STRASBURGER, EDUARD ADOLF (*b.* Warsaw, Poland, 1 February 1844; *d.* Poppelsdorf, Germany, 19 May 1912), *botany, plant cytology*.

Strasburger, who clarified the phenomena of cell division and the role of the nucleus and chromosomes in heredity, was born in Warsaw, when the city was under Russian rule. He was the eldest son of Eduard Gottlieb Strasburger, a merchant, and Anna Karoline von Schütz. Both parents were of German descent. He received his early schooling in Warsaw and, upon completing his Gymnasium studies, went to Paris in 1862 and studied for two years at the Sorbonne. He continued in botany under Hermann Schacht at the University of Bonn and gained the technical skill in microscopy that proved invaluable to him. Julius von Sachs lectured at the Agricultural Academy at Poppelsdorf, a suburb of Bonn, providing further stimulus to Strasburger's botanical interests. Strasburger met Nathanael Pringsheim when the latter visited Bonn. Upon the unexpected death of Schacht, Strasburger decided to go to Jena and accept an offer to become an assistant in Pringsheim's laboratory.

Pringsheim in time became his friend as well as his teacher, and Strasburger valued his critical mind; but his imagination was taken by the more speculative approach of the professor of zoology, Ernst Haeckel, especially by Haeckel's enthusiasm for Darwin's theory of evolution. Haeckel's lectures and their long discussions on development determined the direction of Strasburger's work, and he always recalled the influence of Darwin's *Origin of Species*. Thereafter Strasburger was an evolutionist and applied phylogenetic interpretations to the structure and developmental history of plants.

As Pringsheim's student, Strasburger also studied chemistry and zoology. He received the doctorate at Jena in 1866 with the thesis "Asplenium bulbiferum, ein Beitrag zur Entwicklungsgeschichte des Farnblattes mit besonderer Berücksichtigung der Spaltöffnungen und des Chlorophylls." The dissertation was not published, but his results appeared that year in an article in Pringsheim's *Jahrbuch für wissenschaftliche Botanik* and were used when he habilitated in 1867 at the University of Warsaw as *Privatdozent.*

Through the offices of Haeckel, Strasburger was appointed professor extraordinarius at Jena following Pringsheim's retirement and was made director of the botanical gardens; he became full professor two years later, at twenty-seven. In 1870 he married Alexandrine Wertheim, from Warsaw; they had a daughter and a son, Julius, later professor of medicine at Breslau. Strasburger accompanied Haeckel on a scientific trip to Egypt and the Red Sea in 1873, and it was Haeckel who first described to Strasburger the beauties of the Italian Riviera, where he later vacationed. Always interested in the plants of the regions he visited, Strasburger wrote popular articles and a book, *Streifzüge an der Riviera* (Berlin, 1895, Jena, 1904), which was later translated as *Rambles on the Riviera* (London, 1906).

During his twelve years at Jena, Strasburger published his botanical investigations. The development of his cytological observations can be followed in the three editions of his *Zellbildung und Zelltheilung* (1875, 1876, 1880).

Strasburger succeeded Johannes von Hanstein at the University of Bonn as ordinary professor, and in 1881 he transferred to Bonn his morphological and physiological work and investigations of plant reproduction and cytology. He spent the rest of his career there, and his laboratory became the leading center for the study of plant cytology.

Strasburger noted the appearance of plant cells even in his early research, reporting in his doctoral thesis that in the cells of a fern he had seen the nucleus divide during cell division. At that time the nucleus of the dividing cell was generally thought to disappear. The year he came to Jena he published a book on fertilization in conifers, but although his investigations followed upon Wilhelm Hofmeister's work on the alternation of generations, Strasburger wrote, "I was never closely associated with Hofmeister. Unfortunately, during the latter part of his life, Hofmeister became very sensitive and was angry because in 1869 in my work on *Befruchtung bei den Coniferen* I sought to prove that the 'corpuscula' do not correspond to the embryo sacs of angiosperms, but are archegonia" (Chamberlain, *Botanical Gazette*, **54** [1912], 70).

In *Die Coniferen und die Gnetaceen* (1872), Strasburger discussed the morphology of the flower and the origin of tissues. While zoologists independently observed and described the stages of cell division in 1873, using animal cells that were especially suitable because of their transparency, Strasburger, studying the embryogeny of the Coniferae, noticed and followed the formation of the nuclear spindle. He pioneered methods of fixing and hardening tissues, using pure alcohol. His observations on the phenomena of plant cells were included in his *Zellbildung und Zelltheilung,* (1875–1880), and in such papers as "Über Befruchtung und Zelltheilung" (1877) and "Über Polyembryonie" (1878).

The embryo sacs of certain plants permitted numerous nuclei to be seen at the same time in different phases of division. In his illustrations and descriptions, he noted the formation of the equatorial plate, the longitudinal extension of rods that met at the two poles, and the succession of events that paralleled the phenomena being reported by his colleagues in the division of animal cells. This suggested to Strasburger the common descent of vegetable and animal cells, which Haeckel had maintained. As he examined *Spirogyra* and other simple forms, he was again impressed by the difficulties in differentiating the plant from the animal kingdom. He was also carrying on physiological experiments, studying the reactions of swarm spores when he changed the conditions of light and temperature. Strasburger originated a number of terms in the course of his work, among them "phototaxis" and "chloroplast" and later, "cytoplasm," "nucleoplasm," "haploid," and "diploid." He saw the relation between his physiological and morphological investigations. He no doubt had his swarm spore researches in mind when in 1894 he reported that he had unsuccessfully tried to arrest the division of nuclei by lowering the temperature or varying the light. He felt that they might thus be more conveniently observed, especially in multinucleate forms, than when the successive stages of division occurred at chance times.

In 1875 Strasburger thought that free cell formation took place; in the 1880 edition of *Zellbildung und Zelltheilung* he no longer held this view. Meanwhile, in the 1870's there had been a continuing series of observations: Oscar Hertwig in 1875 had seen the spermatozoon as it entered the ovum and inferred that the fusion of the nuclei was the aim of fertilization; and Walther Flemming, aided by stains that distinguished the fibrils within the nucleus, had described in 1879 the nuclear threads with illustrations, and had clearly shown that these chromatin-staining bodies split longitudinally during division. In 1880 Strasburger still maintained that there was a transverse division of the bodies within the nucleus (first to be called chromosomes by Wilhelm Waldeyer in 1888), but as he often did when the evidence required, he changed his interpretation. Wilhelm Pfitzner in 1882 showed in detail the longitudinal segmentation, and the next year Wilhelm Roux pointed out the implications of the process—then called indirect division—for heredity.

In 1884, from his observations of plants, Strasburger independently concluded, as did Hertwig, August Weismann, and Albert von Koelliker at about the same time, that the nucleus was responsible for heredity, and that it contained within the filaments the substance that was divided in halves between the daughter cells and bore the characters of the parents and earlier ancestors.

For Strasburger the fertilization processes of the phanerogams demonstrated the role of the nucleus of the spermatozoon. He considered the male and female germ cells to be equivalent and the bearers of heredity. He now maintained that the longitudinal splitting assured the proportionate distribution of the substances in the nuclear threads, setting forth his views in "Die Controversen der Indirecten Kerntheilung" and *Neue Untersuchungen über den Befruchtungsvorgang bei den Phanerogamen als Grundlage für eine Theorie der Zeugung* (Jena, 1884). Strasburger gathered observations from his own and other researches to show that "fertilization depends only on the cell nuclei." He believed that there was a reciprocal dynamic action between the cell nucleus and the surrounding cytoplasm, but although both exerted influence, the nucleus in a way governed the cytoplasm and controlled metabolism and growth, among other processes.

Strasburger studied the formation of the cell plate in plant material and the growth of the cell wall, which he considered to occur through apposition. Throughout his life he continued his cytological researches; he was interested in the role of the centrosome and the problem of protoplasmic connections between cells; and he proposed (1892) that protoplasm was composed of structurally different substances, a more active kinoplasm in the fibrils and other structures, and trophoplasm, which was more concerned with nutrition.

Strasburger investigated reproduction in plants from algae and mosses to cryptogams and phanerogams, and from an evolutionary standpoint viewed asexually reproducing organisms as the earlier forms from which sexually differentiated organisms descended (although some forms again lost this differentiation). He presented his ideas in his article "Ueber periodische Reduktion der Chromosomenzahl im Entwicklungsgang der Organismen" (*Biologische Centralblatt*, **14** [1894]). From the life histories of plant forms, and from the simpler to more complex sequences in which sexual or asexual generations developed, Strasburger inferred the courses through which the plants must have evolved. He pointed out the advantages of asexual reproduction under favorable external conditions for the rapid increase of individuals of the species, while sexual reproduction provided for the species to meet unfavorable conditions, and he interpreted the significance of the alternation of generations as it appeared in the higher plants.

Strasburger investigated the anatomy, life history, and aspects of physiology of plants. References to his extensive and careful work can be found throughout the botanical literature of his day and afterward. His textbooks appeared in many editions and translations, and have been revised in recent years. He also carried on investigations of the movement of sap, and in 1891 he studied the movement of sap in trees and the forces propelling it.

Strasburger's famous laboratory at the Botanical Institute of the University of Bonn was housed in the former palace of the electors of Cologne, in Poppelsdorf. The Institute also provided a residence for the professor of botany, with a laboratory and library. Strasburger directed the botanical gardens, which included outdoor collections, arboretums, and greenhouses, and sections containing special displays in which plants were grouped with reference to the solution of certain biological problems.

Under Strasburger, Bonn was foremost in plant cytology. Students came to his laboratory from all over Europe and as far away as Japan; but over half of the foreign students were American, in whom Strasburger took a special interest. They included Douglas H. Campbell, Charles J. Chamberlain, and B. M. Duggan. Bent from long hours spent over the microscope, Strasburger was an impressive teacher who gave each student his careful attention, yet steadily continued his own research. His clear and thoughtful lectures, his comprehensive views both of the broad principles and the fine details of morphology, his active involvement in the problems of the day, and his grasp of plant physiology exerted a lasting influence on the younger botanists. In addition, the laboratory and his textbooks provided methods and techniques essential to accurate experiment and observation. His texts included *Das botanische Practicum*, first published in 1884, and his renowned *Lehrbuch der Botanik für Hochschulen*, written with F. Noll, H. Schenck, and Andreas Schimper (Jena, 1894, and subsequent editions).

Strasburger had many interests beyond the Botanical Institute. He was rector of the University of Bonn in 1891–1892 (his inaugural address was entitled "Das Protoplasma und die Reizbarkeit"). Pringsheim died in 1894, and Strasburger became coeditor with Wilhelm Pfeffer of the *Jahrbücher für wissenschaftliche Botanik*. He belonged to the German Botanical Society, the Prussian Academy of Sciences, and many other scientific societies in Germany. He was a foreign member of the Royal Society of London, the Linnean Society, the American Academy of Arts and Sciences, and learned societies in Italy, France, Belgium, and Ireland.

The government honored Strasburger with the title of *Geheimer Regierungsrat* in 1887, and he received honorary degrees in medicine from the University of Göttingen (1887) and in law from the University of Oxford (1894). The Linnean Society of London awarded Strasburger a medal in 1905 for his contributions to botanical histology and morphology and another medal three years later at the Darwin-Wallace celebration, in recognition of his contribution to the study of evolution. Strasburger was still teaching and engaged in research, with especial interest in questions of sex determination, when he died in 1912. He had been active in research and teaching for nearly fifty years and had linked his extensive botanical and cytological observations to the solution of central problems of heredity and evolution.

BIBLIOGRAPHY

I. ORIGINAL WORKS. For a retrospective view of Strasburger's thought on the cell, see "The Minute Structure of Cells in Relation to Heredity," in *Darwin and Modern Science*, A. C. Seward, ed. (Cambridge, 1909), 102–111. Strasburger's many publications are listed by Beauverie, Tischler, and Küster, and by Cle-

mens Müller (appended to Karsten's obituary in the *Berichte der Deutschen botanischen Gesellschaft*, 80–86), in the articles cited below.

For Strasburger's address upon accepting the Darwin-Wallace medal in 1908, see *The Darwin-Wallace Celebration Held on Thursday, 1st July, 1908, by the Linnean Society of London* (London, 1908), 22–24. A letter to Haeckel, recalling his debt to his teacher upon Haeckel's sixtieth birthday, is found in Uschmann (see below), pp. 67–68. Strasburger's autobiographical letter (Chamberlain, p. 70, see below) recounts his differences with Hofmeister and is a short but interesting personal account.

II. SECONDARY LITERATURE. For discussions of Strasburger and his work, see J. Beauverie, "Édouard Strasburger," in *Revue générale de botanique*, **24** (1912), 417–452, 479–493; Charles Chamberlain, "Eduard Strasburger," in *Botanical Gazette*, **54** (1912), 68–72; Bradley M. Davis, "Eduard Strasburger," in *Genetics*, **36** (1951), 1–3; L. F., "Professor Dr. Eduard Strasburger," in *Lotos*, **60** (1912), 170–171; and J. B. F., "Prof. Eduard Strasburger," in *Nature*, **80** (1912), 379–380.

For a student's description of Strasburger as a teacher and of the laboratory at Bonn, see James Ellis Humphrey, "Eduard Strasburger," in *Botanical Gazette*, **19** (1894), 401–405. Other accounts of Strasburger, his life and work, are B. D. J., "Eduard Strasburger," in *Proceedings of the Linnean Society of London* (1911–1912), 64–66; G. Karsten, "Eduard Strasburger," in *Berichte der Deutschen botanischen Gesellschaft*, **30** (1912), 61–80; and "Eduard Strasburger," in *Biographisches Jahrbuch und Deutscher Nekrolog*, XVII (Berlin, 1915), 25–39; Ernst Küster, "Eduard Strasburger," in *Muenchener medizinische Wochenschrift*, **59** (1912), 1445–1447; and obituary in *Sitzungsberichte der Niederrheinischen Gesellschaft für Natur- und Heilkunde zu Bonn* (1912), 5–18. See also W. J. V. Osterhout, "Eduard Strasburger (1844–1912)," in *Daedalus*, **51** (1916), 927–928; G. Tischler, "Eduard Strasburger," in *Archiv für Zellforschung*, **9** (1913), 1–40; and Georg Uschmann, *Geschichte der Zoologie und der zoologischen Anstalten in Jena 1779–1919* (Jena, 1959), 60–61, 67–69.

A contemporary account of Strasburger's and his colleagues' botanical work is Sydney Howard Vines, *Lectures on the Physiology of Plants* (Cambridge, 1886), 658–660. A valuable overview placing Strasburger's cytological contributions in the context of his time is William Coleman, "Cell, Nucleus, and Inheritance: An Historical Study," in *Proceedings of the American Philosophical Society*, **109** (1965), 124–158, esp. pp. 126, 128–133, 145, 149–151, for Strasburger's work and the development of his thought on the cell. Further background is Arthur Hughes, *A History of Cytology* (London, 1959), 62–63, 65–66, 71–72, 82, 134.

GLORIA ROBINSON

STRATO OF LAMPSACUS (*b.* Lampsacus, Mysia; *d.* Athens, 271/268 B.C.), *natural philosophy.*

Very little is known of Strato's life. His father was Arcesilaus. His birthplace, a small town on the Asian coast of the Hellespont (Dardanelles), had a certain tradition of philosophical studies: Anaxagoras (*d. ca.* 428 B.C.) spent his last years there and may have founded a school, and Epicurus taught there for some years before founding his school at Athens in 306 B.C. Thus the first impulse to scientific work may have come to Strato in his native town. The dominant influence on his thought was that of Aristotle's school at Athens. It is not known when he joined it, but he must have spent a considerable time studying there under Theophrastus; it is just possible, but unlikely, that Aristotle was still at Athens when he entered. The next known event in Strato's life was his appointment as tutor to the future Ptolemy II Philadelphus, who ruled Egypt from 283 to 246 B.C.; this implies a period of residence at Alexandria, where he may have been concerned in the establishment of the museum and perhaps met such important intellectual figures as Diodorus Cronus, the "Megarian" philosopher, and the anatomist and surgeon Herophilus. Strato seems to have maintained a correspondence with Ptolemy and his queen Arsinoë after his return to Athens. On Theophrastus' death *ca.* 287, Strato was elected to succeed him as head of the Lyceum, a position he held until his death eighteen years later.

Since Strato's writings are not extant, knowledge of his work is derived from later sources. These fall into two classes. The first consists of passages in later authors where Strato is quoted or referred to by name; they are mostly quite short and generally report his conclusions without the reasoning that led to them. The most important are in a commentary on Aristotle's *Physics* by Simplicius, a Neoplatonist writing in the sixth century A.D.

The second consists of writings in which Strato is not named but which can be shown to be derived from his work. The importance of these sources is that some of them have preserved the reasoning by which Strato arrived at his theories. The most important texts of this class are the introduction to the *Pneumatica* of Hero of Alexandria and a long extract from a book *On Sounds* (Περὶ Ἀκουστῶν), wrongly attributed to Aristotle, included in Porphyry's commentary on the *Harmonica* of Ptolemy (third century). They are supported by shorter texts from the pseudo-Aristotelian *Problems*, the Greek commentators on Aristotle, and others. The

evidence in favor of attributing their contents to Strato is so strong as to make this virtually certain. Nevertheless, in the following reconstruction of Strato's teaching, the two kinds of evidence will be distinguished as far as possible.

From an incomplete list of his books preserved by Diogenes Laërtius (5.59 ff.), we learn that Strato wrote on logic, ethics, cosmology (including meteorology), psychology, physiology, zoology, and even a book on inventions—in fact, on most of the subjects included in the Aristotelian corpus. But his interest was centered on physics, in the wide sense the ancients gave to that word—the study of the natural world in all its aspects. All his significant work was done in this field, and it is the only part of his teaching about which we have any real information. Strato's preoccupation with this kind of work, in an age when philosophers generally were more concerned with problems of ethics and the theory of knowledge, earned him the sobriquet ὁ φυσικός to distinguish him from others of the same name.

Modern historians generally have represented Strato as an eclectic trying to combine elements from the systems of Aristotle and Democritus. Nothing could be further from the truth. In reality his thought was a one-sided but legitimate, consistent, and often brilliant development of Aristotle's views, along lines that to a large extent had been marked out by Theophrastus. The occasional resemblances between Strato's doctrine and that of the atomists are fortuitous. What Strato did was to strip the Aristotelian world picture of its transcendental elements—or, to put it another way, he refused to acknowledge the reality of anything not subject to the natural laws seen to apply in the sublunary world. In doing this he was carrying to its logical conclusion a process begun by Aristotle himself.

Aristotle had criticized Plato's conception of a world of Forms above and behind the sensible world on the ground that he had failed to show how these two systems were related. Nevertheless, he continued to teach the existence of an Unmoved Mover outside the physical world and above its laws; and within the physical world he distinguished two systems subject to different laws, one extending from the center of the universe to the sphere of the moon's revolution, the other embracing the heavenly bodies. The difficulties entailed by the second division can be seen by studying Aristotle's *Meteorologica*; those involved by the first were stated by Aristotle's pupil Theophrastus in his *Metaphysica*, in which the Unmoved Mover and the teleological view of the world are subjected to a critique that in many ways is a continuation of Aristotle's critique of the Platonic Forms.

It was left to Strato, however, to construct a new cosmology in which the world was explained as the product of immanent forces only. The ancient authorities tried to express this by saying that "everything that exists is the result of natural weights and movements" (fr. 32, from Cicero); that "all divine power is contained in nature, which contains in itself the causes of coming-into-being, growth and decay, but has no consciousness or shape" (fr. 33, from Cicero); that "natural processes are governed by 'what happens spontaneously' (τὸ αὐτόματον)" (fr. 35, from Plutarch); and even that Strato regarded heaven and earth as gods (frs. 37 and 39, both derived from Seneca). The preference for an explanation of the world that does not depend on transcendent causes was shared by Strato with the other chief philosophical schools of his day, the Stoics and the Epicureans; but their teaching was in some ways more naïve and less radical. Strato differed from the Stoics in denying that nature is conscious and provident, and from the atomists in positing a regulating principle to which all the processes that constitute the world are somehow subordinated.

The tendency to bring all reality under the same laws appears again in Strato's description of the physical universe. Like Aristotle, he seems to have regarded it as unique and finite; at least we are told he believed that "void can exist within the universe, but not outside it" (frs. 54–55). But he rejected Aristotle's doctrine of "natural places," and said that all bodies have weight, a natural tendency toward the center of the universe (frs. 50–53); light substances move away from the center because they are "squeezed out" by the heavier. (This was also the view of the atomists and is the only point of any substance on which Strato and they agreed.) The stars are composed of fiery stuff, not, as Aristotle thought, of the mysterious "fifth substance," and are subject to the same laws of gravitation as everything else (fr. 84); a different report, according to which Strato held that the stars derive their light from the sun (fr. 85), probably refers to the moon and planets only.

The immediate cause of physical phenomena is the interplay of natural forces, especially the traditional elementary forces hot, cold, moist, and dry; the hot had a special preeminence. Strato, like Theophrastus, tended to identify these forces with the substances in which they inhere, and treated even heat and light as material emanations (frs. 42–49, 65). Aristotle's distinction between matter and form was blurred in theory by Strato's argument that in any process, the starting point and end point (the formal element), as well as the substrate, are subject to movement (fr. 72; against Aristotle, *Physics*, 224b4), and was ignored in practice. Strato's approach is revealed very clearly in his doctrine of animal reproduction. Aristotle had taught that the male parent contributes the active, formal principle and the female, the material principle. Since the perfection of anything depends on the dominance of form over matter, and males are more perfect than females, the offspring would be male if the (father's) formal principle completely mastered the material contributed by the mother, female if it did not. Strato, however, held (frs. 94–95) that both parents produce "semen" (γονή, the word used by Aristotle to denote the male active-formal principle only), and that the offspring would be male if the father's, female if the mother's "semen" predominated; he also believed that the "power" (δύναμις) of the semen is material, being "of the nature of breath" (πνευματική). Thus the Aristotelian interplay of form and matter was replaced by a tug-of-war between forces, which, although opposed, were fundamentally of the same kind.

Another feature that distinguished Strato's theory from Aristotle's was his belief that bodies are not continuous but consist of tiny particles with void interstices where the particles do not fit together exactly. This scheme was used to account for compression and rarefaction, and for the ability of one substance to penetrate another. Material substances could act on each other only if they first interpenetrated; surface contact was not enough, in Strato's view, to ensure a reaction. Thus the interactions of substances were determined by two factors, their dynamic compatibility and their structure. The same idea is found in some of the writings of Theophrastus; but whereas Theophrastus apparently thought that only solids have this discrete structure, Strato extended it to all bodies, including liquids and gases—even light rays, he says, must consist of particles separated by void, for they are seen to interpenetrate (fr. 65). The existence of void was, however, closely circumscribed. Hero tells us that bodies tend naturally to fill all empty space; no "continuous void" can exist naturally in the world or, as we have seen, outside it. Void interstices or "pores" are found in nature only where the shape of the particles composing bodies does not allow them to fit together exactly. A large void can, however, be produced artificially, as when air is sucked out of a sealed container and, conversely, some bodies can be compressed, that is, their particles can be made to pack more closely into their "pores." But both conditions are unnatural, and the bodies concerned will return to their normal state as soon as the force that produced the artificial conditions is removed. This is the famous law of *horror vacui*, which Hero—or, rather, the engineering school of Ctesibius, of which Hero is a late representative— took from Strato as the theoretical basis for the construction of hydropneumatic machines.

Since Strato's admission of void has been taken as chief evidence for direct atomist influence, it is necessary to emphasize the difference between his doctrine and atomism. This can be expressed by saying that the atoms and void were the starting point of atomist physics, while the particles and interstices were the end point of Strato's. Instead of being the eternal prime constituents of the world, Strato's particles were mere divisions of matter, with no stable individual existence; the qualities hot, cold, moist, and dry, which Strato regarded as primary, were for the atomists epiphenomena of the shapes and sizes of atoms; the void, which for the atomists was infinite in extent and within which the atoms moved freely, existed in Strato's world only as discrete interstices, imprisoned in matter like the bubbles in foam rubber; lastly, the Democritean atoms are in constant movement and tend to repel each other, while Strato's particles hang closely together unless forcibly separated.

To complete the framework of his cosmology, Strato criticized and modified Aristotle's teaching about place, time, and motion. The most fundamental change concerned the nature of place, which Aristotle had defined as the boundary at which a containing body is in contact with a body it contains (*Physics*, 212a6). This definition had been criticized by Theophrastus (frs. 21–22), and Strato went back to an earlier conception that Aristotle had considered and rejected: the place of anything is the hypothetical space between the extremities of that thing. Space is coextensive with the universe; qua space it is empty, but in fact all space is always filled with matter of some kind (frs. 59–60). In this definition Strato seems to have disregarded the existence of void interstices in bodies, presumably because he considered them as part of the substances in which they occur. In regard to motion and time he made only minor changes. He emphasized the continuity of both and the uniformity of time, and stressed that time is a concomitant of physical things, not an independently existing reality. He also seems to have replaced Aristotle's explanation of the "unnatural" movement of bodies through space with one that closely approximates the modern theory of inertia, and demonstrated experimentally that freely falling bodies accelerate (fr. 73).

Most of our information about the detailed working of Strato's system comes from Hero. Like Aristotle, Strato believed that one element can be "overpowered" and changed into its opposite, a process that can be observed in combustion, evaporation, condensation, and the absorption of water by earth. This occurs on a cosmic scale in the "exhalation" from the earth produced by subterranean heat, which gives rise to wind, rain, and most other meteorological phenomena. Another principle that played a major part in Strato's meteorology was the "antiperistasis," or "circular displacement" of heat and cold, which is explained by Seneca in a passage referring specifically to Strato (fr. 89):

> Hot and cold always go in opposite directions and cannot be together; the cold gathers in places from which the hot has departed, and vice versa. . . . Wells and underground cavities are hot in winter when there is cold on the surface of the earth, because the hot has taken refuge there, yielding the upper regions to the cold to occupy; the hot for its part, when it has entered the lower regions and penetrated there as far as possible, becomes all the more powerful for being concentrated.

If such a concentration of heat is disturbed by an influx of cold, it will break out violently. This can happen in the earth, causing earthquakes, or in clouds, causing lightning, thunder, and typhoons. Probably Strato thought that the "exhalation" from the earth was produced by heat concentrated underground by "antiperistasis" when the surface of the earth cools at night. The direction of winds apparently was governed by *horror vacui*: when the "exhalation" disturbs the overlying air and produces pockets of high and low density, the operation of this law ensures that air flows into the low-pressure areas.

While many elements of Strato's theory, including the "exhalation" and "antiperistasis," had already appeared in the teaching of Aristotle and Theophrastus, Strato's account is distinguished by being based on a limited number of principles, which—unlike some of those invoked by Aristotle—are natural laws in the modern sense. He succeeded in giving a unified explanation that was flexible enough to account for the phenomena in all their variety.

Strato seems to have devoted a good deal of attention to the nature of light and sound. Light, in his view, is a material emanation, which travels through the "pores" of air and other transparent substances and is reflected by any solid particles in its path, being modified by the colors of the surfaces from which it is reflected and probably also those of the media through which it passes. Transparency is a function of structure: bodies are transparent if they have continuous straight "pores" for light to pass through; provided this condition is satisfied, their density is immaterial. Strato's explanation of sound is more interesting. He discovered that each sound is the result of many separate beats in a stationary medium (usually air), its pitch being governed by the frequency of the beats; thus he anticipated the true account in the most important respects. We do not know how he came to this conclusion; but he could have done so by reinterpreting, in the light of accurate observations of lyres and other sounding objects, Aristotle's doctrine that sound is a "movement of alteration" traveling through a stationary medium from the object to the ear.

Strato's psychology is consistent with his cosmology. He denied the existence of an immaterial or immortal soul—he argued at considerable length against the doctrine of Plato's *Phaedo* (frs. 118, 122–127)—or even of a transcendent element in the soul such as Aristotle's "Active Reason"; he insisted, rather, that mental activity is not essentially different from any other kind of movement (fr. 74). The carrier of all psychic activity is the "breath" or "spirit" ($\pi\nu\epsilon\hat{v}\mu\alpha$), which has its center in the brain behind the eyebrows and spreads to all parts of the body. The soul is a single entity. All mental processes, including sensation, take place at the center; the sense organs, which Strato described as "windows" of the soul, only receive and transmit stimuli; and when the act of perception is complete, the sensation is projected back to the organ where the stimulus originated in the same way as sounds are located at their points of origin (frs. 108–112). Sleep is due to the temporary withdrawal of the "spirit" from the extremities of the body to the psychic center; the complete withdrawal of the "spirit" results in death (frs. 128–129). Dreams are caused by residual movements in the "spirit" arising from past stimuli (frs. 130–131). As usual, most of the constituents of Strato's

doctrine have precedents in the Peripatetic school. The concept of the "Active Reason" had been questioned, but not definitely abandoned, by Theophrastus. The theory of "pneuma" had been originated by Aristotle and further developed by Theophrastus and by Diocles of Carystus, a famous physician and pupil of Aristotle. Only the location of the psychic center in the brain was entirely new; it came from Herophilus, the discoverer of the nervous system.

A noteworthy feature of Strato's work was his extensive use of experiments. While not the first to perform them, he was the first to use experiments systematically to establish a fundamental cosmological doctrine. Strato's experiments are not isolated, but form a progressive series in which each is based on the result of the previous one. Also characteristic of Strato are the care taken to define the conditions in which the experiment takes place and to eliminate all possible alternative explanations of the result, and the practice of pairing controlled experiments with observations of similar phenomena occurring under natural conditions. His purpose presumably was to avoid the charge that his experiments distorted nature.

That Strato's system was in many ways a continuation of those of Aristotle and Theophrastus should not be allowed to obscure his very real originality. This lay in his ability to combine philosophical and scientific reasoning to produce a unified explanation of the world in which theories were shaped by observed facts and the facts themselves interpreted in the light of simple and consistent theories. The need for such a synthesis was particularly acute in the early third century B.C., a time when, largely as a result of Aristotle's teaching and example, factual knowledge was increasing immensely and the natural sciences were asserting their independence. Nevertheless, Strato's influence was limited. The centrifugal tendency among the sciences could not be arrested, and philosophical cosmology came to be dominated increasingly by religious considerations. Signs of a reaction against Strato in his own school appear in the last chapter of the pseudo-Aristotelian *De spiritu*, perhaps written within thirty years of his death. A few Peripatetics of the first century B.C. are reported to have held views similar to some of Strato's; but it is not clear whether they were influenced by his writings, and it is very unlikely that they tried to revive his system as a whole. His name occurs rarely in the extant remains of philosophical writers belonging to other schools. The only pupils of

Strato who made fruitful use of his ideas seem to have been the scientists of Alexandria, Ctesibius the engineer and Erasistratus the physician, and perhaps the astronomer Aristarchus of Samos.

BIBLIOGRAPHY

I. ORIGINAL WORKS. Editions of Strato's works are F. Wehrli, *Die Schule des Aristoteles*, V (Basel, 1950; 2nd ed., 1969), which includes the named fragments and a selection of the others (references in this article are to this ed.); and H. B. Gottschalk, "Strato of Lampsacus: Some Texts," in *Proceedings of the Leeds Philosophical and Literary Society*, Lit.-Hist. Sec., 11, pt. 6 (1965), 95–182, which deals chiefly with the longer texts in which Strato's name is not mentioned. Both eds. include a commentary and bibliography.

The best text of the *De audibilibus* is in I. Düring, "Porphyrius' Kommentar zur Harmonielehre des Ptolemaios," in *Göteborgs högskolas årsskrift* (1932), pt. 2, 67–77. The authorship of this work has been discussed by H. B. Gottschalk, "The De Audibilibus and Peripatetic Acoustics," in *Hermes*, 96 (1968), 435–460.

II. SECONDARY LITERATURE. See W. Capelle, "Straton 13," in Pauly-Wissowa, *Real-Encyclopädie der classischen altertumswissenschaft*, 2nd ser., IVa (1931), 278–315; and M. Catzemeier, *Die Naturphilosophie des Str. von L.* (Meisenheim, 1970). The older literature has been superseded, but the following article is still worth reading: H. Diels, "Ueber das physikalische System des Straton," in *Sitzungsberichte der Preussischen Akademie der Wissenschaften zu Berlin*, Phil.-hist. Kl. (1893), 101–127, also available in *Kleine Schriften zur Geschichte der antiken Philosophie* (Hildesheim, 1969), 239–265.

H. B. GOTTSCHALK

STRATTON, FREDERICK JOHN MARRION (*b.* Birmingham, England, 16 October 1881; *d.* Cambridge, England, 2 September 1960), *astronomy*.

After attending school in Birmingham, Stratton entered Gonville and Caius College, Cambridge. He was third wrangler in the mathematical tripos of 1904 and in the same year was elected a fellow of his college. His first paper, "On Planetary Inversion" (1906), was essentially a mathematical work concerned with the possibility that tidal forces can produce substantial changes in the obliquities of planetary orbits. Subsequently, however, Stratton joined the Cambridge observatory as an honorary member and worked on the proper motions of faint stars. In 1913 he was appointed assistant director of the Solar Physics Observatory at Cambridge. His astronomical work was interrupted by the First World War, in which he served with great distinction. At the end of the war Stratton relinquished his position at the observatory to become a tutor at Gonville and Caius College. This post gave him the opportunity to direct bright young men into astronomy; and eventually the offices of astronomer royal, astronomer royal for Scotland, and H.M. astronomer at the Cape of Good Hope were filled with Gonville and Caius men.

Stratton went on an expedition to Sumatra with C. R. Davidson to observe the total solar eclipse of 14 January 1926. They obtained excellent spectra of the chromosphere and conducted observations of the intensity of the Balmer lines and of the distribution of intensity of the corona. His report was published in 1929.

In 1928 Stratton succeeded Newall as professor of astrophysics and director of the Solar Physics Observatory. He also was active in the organization of science and was general secretary of the British Association for the Advancement of Science from 1930 to 1935 and general secretary of the International Astronomical Union from 1925 to 1935.

BIBLIOGRAPHY

Stratton's published works include "On Planetary Inversion," in *Monthly Notices of the Royal Astronomical Society*, 66 (1906), 374–402; "Proper Motions of Faint Stars in the Pleiades," in *Memoirs of the Royal Astronomical Society*, 57 (1908), 161–184; "The Constants of the Moon's Physical Libration," *ibid.*, 59 (1909), 257–290; "On Possible Phase-Relations Between the Planets and Sun-Spot Phenomena," in *Monthly Notices of the Royal Astronomical Society*, 72 (1912), 9–26; "Preliminary Note on the Later Spectrum of Nova Geminorum No. 2," *ibid.*, 73 (1913), 72; "On Enhanced (Spark) Lines in the Early Spectra of Nova Geminorum No. 2," *ibid.*, 380–382; "The Spectrum of Nova Geminorum II, 1912," in *Annals of the Solar Physics Observatory* (Cambridge), 4, pt. 1 (1920), 1–71; *Astronomical Physics* (London–New York, 1925); "Das Sternsystem, zweiter Teil," VI, pt. 2 of *Handbuch der Astrophysik* (Berlin, 1928); "Report on the Total Solar Eclipse of 1926 January 14," in *Memoirs of the Royal Astronomical Society*, 64 (1929), 105–148, written with C. R. Davidson; "The Absorption Spectrum of Nova Herculis, 1934: The First Phase," in *Annals of the Solar Physics Observatory* (Cambridge), 4, pt. 4 (1936), 131–161; "On Some Spectrograms of Nova Persei 1901," *ibid.*, pt. 2 (1936), 73–84; "The History of the Cambridge Observatories," *ibid.*, **1** (1949), 1–26; "Prof. Megh Nad Saha, F. R. S.," in *Nature*, **177** (1956), 917; "Thomas Royds," in *Monthly Notices of the Royal Astronomical Society*, **116** (1956), 156–158; "John Evershed," in *Biographical Memoirs of Fellows of the Royal Society*, **3** (1957), 41–48; and "Henry Norris Russell," *ibid.*, 173–185.

Stratton was editor of *Scientific Papers by Sir George Howard Darwin*, 5 vols. (Cambridge, 1907–1916); and coeditor of *Observatory*, **36–48** (1913–1925).

Richard v. d. R. Woolley's obituary in *Quarterly Journal of the Royal Astronomical Society*, **2** (1961), 44–49, served as the main basis of this article.

LETTIE S. MULTHAUF

STREETE, THOMAS (*b.* Cork, Ireland [?], 15 March 1622; *d.* Westminster, London, England, 27 August 1689), *astronomy*.

Streete spent most of his life in London, where he was employed as a clerk in the Excise Office under Elias Ashmole. He frequented Gresham College and numbered the leading astronomers both in England and abroad among his friends and acquaintances, often assisting them in observing eclipses, transits, comets, and other unusual astronomical phenomena. For many years Streete published highly regarded ephemerides and worked intensively on the problem of determining longitude at sea. After the great fire of 1666, he was engaged in the resurvey of London.

Streete's most important work was *Astronomia Carolina* (1661). One of the most popular expositions of astronomy in the second half of the seventeenth century, it served as a textbook for Newton, Flamsteed, and Halley. Its tables, constructed from a large number of observations, were generally conceded to be the best of their time. The lunar tables, in particular, were felt to mark an advance over previous ones. The book went through many editions and continued in use well into the eighteenth century.

The *Astronomia Carolina* was an important vehicle for the dissemination of Kepler's astronomical ideas, which were as yet by no means generally accepted. Kepler's first and third laws of planetary motion were clearly stated, and it was from the *Astronomia* that Newton learned of them. In place of Kepler's second law, however, Streete, using as a basis the planetary theories of Seth Ward and Ismael Boulliau, developed an equant construction in which the planets generate equal angles in equal times about the "empty" focus of the elliptical orbit. His explanation of the physical cause of planetary motion employed both Cartesian vortices and

Kepler's concept of quasi-magnetic solar attraction.

BIBLIOGRAPHY

Streete's major works are *Astronomia Carolina: A New Theorie of the Celestial Motions* (London, 1661); *An Appendix to Astronomia Carolina* (London, 1664); and *The Description and Use of the Planetary Systeme* (London, 1674).

There is no adequate and reliable extended account of his life and work.

WILBUR APPLEBAUM

STREETER, GEORGE LINIUS (*b.* Jamestown, New York, 12 January 1873; *d.* Gloversville, New York, 27 July 1948), *embryology*.

Streeter, the son of George Austin Streeter, a glove manufacturer, and Hannah Green Anthony Streeter, was graduated from Union College in 1895 and from the College of Physicians and Surgeons of Columbia University, where he took his M.D. degree, in 1899. After an internship at Roosevelt Hospital in New York City, he became assistant to Henry Hun, a prominent neurologist, in Albany and also taught anatomy at Albany Medical College. In 1902 he studied at Frankfurt with Ludwig Edinger and at Leipzig with Wilhelm His. Under the latter's influence Streeter devoted himself thereafter to embryology and particularly to the development of the human nervous system.

Returning to the United States in 1904, Streeter joined the department of anatomy of the Johns Hopkins Medical School in Baltimore, under the leadership of Franklin P. Mall. There he published his first contribution to embryology, on the development of the cranial and spinal nerves of the human embryo. In this work he showed a talent for three-dimensional analysis of complex microscopic structures, accurate observation, and skilled draftsmanship. His only experimental investigation was a study of the early development of the internal ear in frog embryos (tadpoles) by removal and transplantation of the ear vesicles. His interest in the auditory apparatus led to many years' work on the embryology of the human ear, crowned in 1918 by publication of a distinguished monograph on the development of the labyrinth.

In 1906–1907 Streeter was assistant professor at the Wistar Institute of Anatomy and Biology in Philadelphia and then went to the University of Michigan as professor of anatomy. There he continued his embryological research on the human brain and auditory apparatus with such success that he was recalled to Baltimore to join Mall in the newly organized department of embryology of the Carnegie Institution, located at the Johns Hopkins Medical School. When Mall died in 1917, Streeter succeeded him as director, taking over a well-organized laboratory with the world's largest collection of human embryological material. Continuing Mall's program, he not only carried on his own wide-ranging investigations but also, with generous and enthusiastic leadership, promoted the work of a highly competent staff and numerous guest investigators.

Streeter's paper on the weight and dimensions of human embryos and fetuses at successive stages of development (1920) is the classic account of this subject. His comprehensive chapter on the development of the human brain in Franz Keibel and Mall's *Manual of Human Embryology* (1912) has not been superseded. Mall had been deeply interested in the pathological aspects of human prenatal development. Working before the great twentieth-century advance of genetics, he attributed prenatal retardation, malformation, and intrauterine death to defects or disease of the uterine environment. Streeter, on the other hand, tended to attribute these disasters to genetic factors. It is now known that both environmental and genetic causes are operative in prenatal pathology, but Streeter's skilled exposition of his views was valuable in turning the attention of physicians and biologists to the importance of genetic factors.

Although primarily a morphologist, Streeter always saw the embryo as a living, growing individual, and its organs and tissues as carrying on physiological functions appropriate to its stage of growth. He therefore opposed the kind of embryology represented in its extreme form by Haeckel's law of recapitulation, which regarded every embryonic structure as no more than a record of phylogeny. He was especially critical of the concept of the mammalian branchial arches as merely rudimentary gills rather than as preliminary stages of the external ears and other definitive parts of the head and neck; and he denied the supposed metamerism of the early vertebrate brain. To combat these older ways of thinking, often supported by oversimplified diagrams, he illustrated his own descriptions as far as possible by photomicrographs or realistic drawings based on actual sections.

Streeter's joint studies of the early embryology of the pig, with Chester A. Heuser, and of the rhesus monkey, with Heuser and Carl G. Hartman,

published in the *Contributions to Embryology* of the Carnegie Institution between 1927 and 1941, are among the most accurate descriptions of early mammalian development ever published and stand in the front rank of American scientific achievements. With his great descriptive talent, his long experience in the most exacting kind of morphological study, and the skilled assistance of a technical staff that he himself had largely trained, Streeter was well fitted to begin (about 1935) the great advance in early human embryology made by his staff in cooperation with John Rock and Arthur T. Hertig of Boston. Before this time the human embryo was known only after about the eleventh day following conception. New specimens obtained by Hertig and Rock carried the story back to the beginning and made the earliest stages of human development as well known as the earliest stages of other mammals.

Streeter's last major undertaking, unfinished at his death, was a systematic catalog and analytic description of the human embryo, classified by stages up to the end of the embryonic period— about the forty-eighth day of gestation. The "developmental horizons," as he called them, were published, as far as completed, in the Carnegie Institution *Contributions to Embryology* from 1942 to 1951.

Devoting his entire career to intensive research in a difficult field, Streeter had little time or inclination for popularizing his findings or for general scientific affairs. He published no textbooks nor comprehensive reviews; his talents for exposition were demonstrated largely through numerous papers presented at professional meetings. He was elected to the National Academy of Sciences in 1931 and to the American Philosophical Society in 1943, and was president of the American Association of Anatomists in 1926–1928. He married Julia Allen Smith of Ann Arbor, Michigan, in 1910. Their son and one daughter became physicians, and the other daughter took her doctorate in chemistry.

Streeter retired in 1940 from the directorship of the Carnegie department of embryology but continued his work on human embryology until, with his microscope and drawing board at hand and another section of "Horizons of Human Development" in preparation, he died suddenly of coronary occlusion at the age of seventy-five.

BIBLIOGRAPHY

A complete bibliography of Streeter's more than 130 publications follows the obituary by George W. Corner,

"George Linius Streeter, 1873–1948," in *Biographical Memoirs. National Academy of Sciences*, **28** (1954), 261–287, with portrait.

GEORGE W. CORNER

STRÖMBERG, GUSTAF BENJAMIN (*b.* Göteborg, Sweden, 16 December 1882; *d.* Pasadena, California, 30 January 1962), *astronomy*.

Strömberg spent thirty years, the greater part of his working life, at the Mount Wilson observatory. His main contributions to astronomy were statistical analyses of stellar motions, made at a time when both the size and the manner of rotation of our galaxy were still uncertain quantities.

The son of Bengt Johan Gustaf Lorentz Strömberg and Johanna Elisabeth Noehrman, Strömberg prepared in Göteborg for study at the universities of Kiel and Stockholm. He was an assistant in the Stockholm observatory for eight years, ending in 1914, the year he married Helga Sofia Henning. In 1916, at age thirty-three, he obtained a Ph.D. from the University of Lund; his dissertation was written under the direction of Carl Vilhelm Ludwig Charlier.

In June 1916 Strömberg arrived at Mount Wilson. He served one year as a volunteer assistant in stellar spectroscopy and then was appointed to the staff as astronomer, a position he held until his retirement in 1946. The director in 1916 was Walter S. Adams, who had just developed a technique for estimating a star's distance from its spectrum—referred to as a spectroscopic parallax—thus providing for the first time a way to convert large numbers of stellar brightnesses as observed into intrinsic luminosities, that is, absolute magnitudes. Strömberg's first assignment was to help Adams analyze data on some 1,300 stars, looking for a statistically valid relation between motions through space and absolute magnitudes. They found that faint dwarf stars seemed to move faster than bright giant stars of the same spectral class.

Strömberg continued to analyze the wealth of observational material being obtained at Mount Wilson, and also took his turn at the telescope acquiring it. He was looking for large-scale preferential motions of stars. Having obtained a statistical estimate of how the sun moves through space, he used this to calculate the peculiar motions of stars (across the line of sight), and also the so-called K-term in radial velocities, which for any selected group of stars refers to a net speed either toward or away from us. His discovery of what was

referred to at the time as "Strömberg's asymmetry" confirmed tentative conclusions reached earlier by Boss, by Adams, and by Joy; he found that stars in the plane of the Milky Way had a marked preferential motion, directed around a galactic center approximately coincident with the one proposed by Shapley in 1918. Strömberg thus provided an early confirmation of Shapley's theory, and also supplied the basic data to be used by Lindblad and by Oort in developing the presently accepted picture of galactic rotation.

BIBLIOGRAPHY

Strömberg's publications include "The Relationship of Stellar Motions to Absolute Magnitude," in *Astrophysical Journal*, **45** (1917), 293–305, written with Walter S. Adams; "A Determination of the Solar Motion and the Stream-Motion From Radial Velocities and Absolute Magnitudes of Stars of Late Spectral Types," *ibid.*, **47** (1918), 7–37; "Space Velocities of Long-Period Variable Stars of Classes Me and Se," *ibid.*, **59** (1924), 148–154, written with Paul W. Merrill; "The Asymmetry in Stellar Motions and the Existence of a Velocity-Restriction in Space," *ibid.*, **59** (1924), 228–251; "Analysis of Radial Velocities of Globular Clusters and Non-Galactic Nebulae," *ibid.*, **61** (1925), 353–362; and "The Asymmetry in Stellar Motions as Determined From Radial Velocities," *ibid.*, **61** (1925), 363–388.

Strömberg also wrote two books dealing with the philosophical implications of science: *The Soul of the Universe* (New York, 1940; 2nd ed., 1948) and *The Searchers* (New York, 1948).

Eighty-seven publications by Strömberg are listed in the *Yearbook of the Carnegie Institution of Washington*, **15** (1916)–**46** (1946–1947). In addition Strömberg wrote "Angenäherte allgemeine Störungen des Planeten 471 Papagena und 123 Brunhild," in *Astronomische Nachrichten*, **195** (1913), cols. 129–140, written with Vilhelm Hernlund; Strömberg's dissertation, "On a Method for Studying a Certain Class of Regularities in a Series of Observations, With Application to the Temperature Curve of Uppsala" (Lund, 1915); and the two books mentioned above.

SALLY H. DIEKE

STRÖMGREN, SVANTE ELIS (*b.* Hälsingborg, Sweden, 31 May 1870; *d.* Copenhagen, Denmark, 5 April 1947), *astronomy*.

Strömgren studied astronomy at the University of Lund, where he received his doctorate in 1898. He spent the years 1901–1907 at Kiel, as assistant to the editor of *Astronomische Nachrichten*, and beginning in 1904 he was a lecturer at Kiel University. From 1907 to 1940 he was professor of astronomy at Copenhagen University and director of the observatory. Strömgren's research belongs to the tradition of classical celestial mechanics, even though he used elaborate mathematical apparatus to make numerical computations more than most members of this school did.

In his dissertation Strömgren derived the definitive orbit of Comet 1890 II, which, like most comets, followed an approximately parabolic path relative to the sun. This investigation was the first of a series of papers on the original orbits of such comets—open or closed—and was crucial for work on the cosmogony of comets. In "Ueber den Ursprung der Kometen" (1914), Strömgren concluded that all comets of which the orbits had been determined with sufficient accuracy for a decision about their return to be possible, have followed closed orbits; the hyperbolic motion derived for several comets was a consequence of the perturbations of the large planets during their passage through the internal regions of the solar system. About thirty years later his investigations formed the starting point for J. H. Oort's and A. J. J. van Woerkom's "discovery" of the comet cloud far outside the planetary orbits.

Strömgren's survey of the three-body problem was concerned with two equal masses moving in circular orbits around a common center of gravity and with a body without mass—a *problème restreint*. The movement of the third body was derived by numerical integration with the aim of determining the orbits, which are periodic relative to the coordinate system, in which the main bodies are relatively at rest. With J. Fischer-Petersen and J. P. Møller, Strömgren pointed out a number of groups of simple-periodic orbits. Strömgren's pioneer work has recently been the starting point for further surveys because electronic computers have greatly simplified the routine computational work. In "Connaissance actuelle des orbites dans le problème des trois Corps" (1935), Strömgren gave a general view of the work done at Copenhagen.

Strömgren held a major position in international astronomical collaboration. From 1922 to 1947 he was director of the telegram bureau for astronomical news sponsored by the International Astronomical Union; and as early as 1914, at the outbreak of World War I, Strömgren had established a "neutral bureau" at the Copenhagen observatory, as a branch of the old Kiel bureau. During World War II he maintained the news service at the Lund observatory as a neutral branch bureau. From 1921 to 1930 he was president of the Astronomische Gesellschaft.

Strömgren's textbook of astronomy for students at Copenhagen University was translated into German and enlarged by Bengt Strömgren in 1933. Unique for its time, the work deals with both classical and modern stellar astronomy and astrophysics. From 1920 to 1947 Strömgren was president of the Astronomisk Selskab (Copenhagen) and was editor-in-chief of *Nordisk astronomisk tidsskrift*. He also took a strong interest in the Variable Star Section sponsored by the Astronomisk Selskab. A distinguished Latin scholar, Strömgren had a major role in the translation into modern languages of Tycho Brahe's book on his own instruments and of Peder Horrebow's description of Ole Römer's instruments.

BIBLIOGRAPHY

I. ORIGINAL WORKS. A bibliography of Strömgren's papers and books (1896–1940) was edited by K. Lundmark in *Astronomical Papers, Dedicated to Elis Strömgren* (Copenhagen, 1940). His principal works are "Ueber den Ursprung der Kometen," in *Kongelige Danske Videnskabernes Selskabs Skrifter*, 7th ser., Naturv.-mathem. Afd., **11**, p. 4 (1914), 189–251; "Connaissance actuelle des orbites dans le problème des trois corps," in *Bulletin astronomique*, 2nd ser., **9** (1935), 87–130; and *Ole Rømer som Astronom* (Copenhagen, 1944).

With Bengt Strömgren he was coauthor of *Lehrbuch der Astronomie* (Berlin, 1933); and with Bengt Strömgren and Hans Raeder, *Tycho Brahe's Description of His Instruments and Scientific Work . . .* (Copenhagen, 1946).

See also *Publikationer og mindre Meddelelser fra Kjøbenhavns Observatorium* (1910–1947) and "Tre Aartier celest Mekanik paa Kjøbenhavns Observatorium," in *Festskrift, Copenhagen University* (Nov. 1923).

II. SECONDARY LITERATURE. Obituaries are J. M. V. Hansen, in *Nordisk astronomisk tidsskrift* (1947), 41–43; in *Observatory*, **67** (1947), 142–143; and in *Popular Astronomy*, **55** (1947), 341–343; B. Lindblad, in *Nordisk astronomisk tidsskrift* (1947), 43; and in *Populär astronomisk tidsskrift*, **28** (1947), 59–60; K. Lundmark, in *Monthly Notices of the Royal Astronomical Society*, **108** (1948), 37–41; and N. E. Nørlund, in *Festskrift, Copenhagen University* (Nov. 1947), 149–152; and in *Oversigt over det K. Danske Videnskabernes Selskabs Forhandlinger* (1948), 73–77. See also R. Grammel, "E. Strömgrens Arbeiten zum Dreikörperproblem," in *Vierteljahrsschrift der Astronomischen Gesellschaft*, **64** (1929), 90–100.

AXEL V. NIELSEN

STRUSS (or **STRUTHIUS**), **JÓZEF** (*b.* Poznan, Poland, 1510; *d.* Poznan, 6 March 1568), *medicine.*

The son of Nicolas Strusiek, a wealthy comb manufacturer, Struss completed his primary education at the parish school of St. Mary Magdalene in Poznan, then went on to Lubranski College, a secondary school of arts. He next moved to Cracow, where in 1531, after seven years of study, he obtained a diploma in the seven liberal arts. In particular Struss had studied Greek and classical philosophy, subjects that then included material of a more strictly scientific nature, and thus was able to increase his knowledge of Aristotle's mathematical and astrological works. At the same time he also studied medicine; but since the University of Cracow did not confer degrees in that subject, he went to Padua, where many Polish and German medical students completed their studies. Vesalius was his fellow pupil and later his teacher there.

Struss's graduation in medicine on 26 October 1535 is recorded in documents preserved in the Old Archive of the University of Padua. He began to teach theoretical medicine at that university on 12 November and remained there until 1537, when he was asked to teach medicine at the University of Cracow, with the particular task of illustrating Galen's *De differentiis morborum* for his students. Struss soon left Cracow; his precise destination is not known but he probably returned to Padua, since it was there, at about this time, that some of his works were published. About 1540 he was again in Poznan, where he had entered the court of Andrei Gorka, then the governor of Greater Poland. The following year he accompanied Gorka to Hungary on a mission of mediation between Ferdinand I of Hungary and Isabella, the widow of John Zápolya, king of Hungary, who was besieged in Buda. On this occasion Struss was called upon to treat both Isabella and Sultan Suleiman I. In 1545 he returned to Poznan, where he established a successful practice and became personal physician to King Sigismund Augustus.

Struss's main work is *Sphygmicae artis*, an accurate clinicophysiological study of the pulse and its alterations; it was perhaps the first work in the history of medicine that suggested the pulse as a reliable source of clinical data and of diagnostic and prognostic information. The physiology on which Struss's study is based is Galen's, as are the plan and framework. But Struss maintained an independent judgment, often contradicting Galen's teaching and following concepts and approaches that were entirely new. *Sphygmicae artis* is a classic example of the clinical concept of medicine that was then developing in Padua.

According to Manget (*Bibliotheca scriptorum medicorum* . . ., XI [Geneva, 1731], 330) and other writers, the work was first published in 1540, but there is no trace of this edition; and it is more likely, also on the basis of internal evidence, that the first edition was produced at Basel in 1555. In addition to his editions and translations of various classical medical works of Galen and treatises, Struss also published literary works.

BIBLIOGRAPHY

I. ORIGINAL WORKS. Struss's writings include *Ad medicum hisce temporibus maximum atque celeberrimum D. Cyprianum de Lowicz de medica arte excellentis carmen elegiacum authore Josepho Struthio Posnaniense* (Cracow, 1529); *Sanctissimi Petris et Domini d. Joannis a Lasco archiepiscopi et primatis regni Epicedion elegiacis versibus confectum* (Cracow, 1531); *Sphygmicae artis iam mille ducentos annos perditae et desideratae libri V* (Padua, 1540 [?]; Basel, 1555); and *Giuseppe Struzio: Dell'arte sfigmica*, C. Castellani and G. Invernizzi, eds. (Turin, 1961), which includes the Latin text, an Italian translation, an introduction, and notes on cardiology and on the history of medicine.

II. SECONDARY LITERATURE. See H. Barycz, *Historja Uniwersytetu Jagiellońskiego w epoce humanizmu* (Cracow, 1935), 241–242; W. Bugiel, *Un célèbre médecin polonais au XVI siècle: Joseph Struthius* (Paris, 1901); and G. Sterzi, *Josephus Struthius, lettore nello studio di Padova* (Venice, 1910).

CARLO CASTELLANI

STRUTT, JOHN WILLIAM, THIRD BARON RAYLEIGH (*b.* Langford Grove, near Maldon, Essex, England, 12 November 1842; *d.* Terling Place, Witham, Essex, England, 30 June 1919), *experimental and theoretical physics.*

Lord Rayleigh (as he is universally known in scientific circles) was one of the greatest ornaments of British science in the last half of the nineteenth century and the first two decades of the twentieth. A peer by inheritance, he took the unusual course of devoting himself to a scientific career and maintained his research activity continuously from the time of his graduation from Cambridge University in 1865 until almost literally the day of his death. Rayleigh's investigations, reported in 430 scientific papers and his monumental two-volume treatise *The Theory of Sound* (1877–1878), covered every field of what in the twentieth century is commonly referred to as "classical" physics; at the same time he kept abreast of, and made incisive critical comments on, the latest developments of quantum and relativistic physics. Not in any sense a pure mathematician, Rayleigh applied mathematics with great skill and accuracy to a host of problems in theoretical physics. In addition he was an ingenious and resourceful experimentalist, with the uncanny ability to extract the most from the simplest arrangements of apparatus. The discovery and isolation of argon, usually considered by the lay public as his greatest scientific achievement, was a triumph of both careful logical reasoning and patient and painstaking experimentation.

At Cambridge, Strutt became a pupil of the mathematician E. J. Routh and profited greatly from his thorough coaching. This and the inspiration gained from the lectures of Sir George Stokes, at that time Lucasian professor of mathematics, paved the way in part at least for Strutt's emergence as senior wrangler in the mathematical tripos as well as Smith's Prizeman. He became a fellow of Trinity College, Cambridge, in 1866; and from that time on, there was no doubt that he was headed for a distinguished scientific career.

Strutt varied the usual custom of a tour of the Continent after graduation with a visit to the United States, then recovering from the Civil War. On his return to England in 1868 he purchased a set of experimental equipment and proceeded to carry out some investigations at the family seat in Terling Place. This was the genesis of the famous laboratory in which most of his later scientific work was done. Strutt early formed the habit of getting along with very simple scientific apparatus and made much of it himself. It is clear that he was considered somewhat of a freak by members of his family and friends for his determination not to be contented with the life of a country gentleman. It is equally clear that Strutt did not feel he was violating any strongly entrenched custom. He simply wanted to be a scientist; and with typical British stubbornness he pursued this course, feeling that there was nothing unusual or blameworthy in his action.

In 1871 Strutt married Evelyn Balfour, sister of Arthur James Balfour, who became a celebrated scholar, philosopher, and statesman. A serious attack of rheumatic fever occurred shortly after the marriage, and as a recuperative measure Strutt undertook a trip up the Nile. It was on this journey that the *Theory of Sound* had its genesis, although the first volume was not completed and published until 1877. Shortly after returning to England in 1873, Strutt succeeded to the title and took up residence at Terling. He then began serious experimental work in the laboratory attached to the manor house. He had already developed considerable theoretical interest in radiation phenomena and had published papers on acoustics and optics in the late 1860's and early 1870's. One of these, on the theory of resonance, extended in important fashion the work of Helmholtz and established Rayleigh as a leading authority on sound. Another paper from this early period resolved a long-standing puzzle in optics, the blue color of the sky. In this research, published in 1871, Rayleigh derived the well-known law expressing the scattering of light by small particles as a function of the inverse fourth power of the wavelength of the incident light. It is of interest to note that in this work he used the elastic-solid theory of light and not the recently introduced electromagnetic theory of Maxwell.

In his laboratory at Terling, Rayleigh embarked on a series of experimental studies of optical instruments that apparently originated in his attempts to manufacture cheap diffraction gratings by photographic means. Although not very successful, these early experiments led him to the very important study of the resolving power of gratings, a matter that was then poorly understood by optical experts. It seems clear that Rayleigh was the first to publish formally a clear definition of resolving power of an optical device. He proved that the resolving power of a plane transparent grating is equal to the product of the order of the spectrum and the total number of lines in the grating. This work was continued with a series of fundamental researches on the optical properties of the spectroscope, an instrument that in the late 1870's was becoming increasingly important in the study of the solar spectrum as well as of the spectra of the chemical elements. In his study of optical diffraction and interference, Rayleigh anticipated the French physicist Charles Soret in the invention of the optical zone plate, with its interesting light-focusing property.

During the late 1870's Rayleigh's laboratory in his home at Terling became well established as the seat of his researches, and it appeared likely that he would spend the rest of his career there without serious interruption. The fates decreed otherwise, however, for in 1879 James Clerk Maxwell, the first Cavendish professor of experimental physics at Cambridge, died. Sir William Thomson (later Lord Kelvin), at that time professor of natural philosophy at the University of Glasgow, refused to be considered for the post in succession to Maxwell. Rayleigh, the next obvious choice, accepted the appointment in December 1879—not without some reluctance, since his natural preference was to continue the Terling routine. The professorial salary was not unwelcome, however, in the face of falling revenues from his estate due to the severe agricultural depression then prevailing in Britain.

Rayleigh remained as professor at Cambridge until 1884. Although admittedly not a brilliant lecturer, he was an effective instructor and, moreover, succeeded in putting laboratory instruction in elementary physics on a firm basis. This was a revolutionary accomplishment in England, and the influence of Rayleigh's pioneer efforts was ultimately felt in higher educational institutions throughout the country. A rather elaborate research program was also set up with the help of his assistants Glazebrook and Shaw, both of whom later became scientists of note. This program involved the redetermination of three electrical standards: the ohm, the ampere, and the volt. Work of this sort had already been started by Maxwell for the British Association for the Advancement of Science. Rayleigh's continuation and development demanded the construction of more precise equipment than Maxwell's, as well as meticulous care and patience in its use. When the investigation was completed in 1884, the results stood the test of time remarkably well. The realization of the importance of standards in physical measurements that this work implied undoubtedly influenced Rayleigh favorably toward the establishment of a government standards laboratory in Britain, which eventually (1900) took the form of the National Physical Laboratory at Teddington, Middlesex.

In 1884 Rayleigh served as president of the British Association for the Advancement of Science, which held its annual meeting that year in Montreal, the first outside the United Kingdom. It provided the occasion for a second trip to the North American continent, and Rayleigh took advantage of it to increase his acquaintance with prominent physicists in the United States and Canada. Immediately after his return to Britain he resigned his professorship at Cambridge and retired to his laboratory at Terling, which remained his scientific headquarters for the rest of his life. Rayleigh did accept a professorship at the Royal Institution of Great Britain in London, and served from 1887 to 1905. This post, however, involved residence in London for only a short time each year and the presentation of a certain number of

lectures on topics of his research interest. It did not seriously disturb the continuity of his research program at Terling.

The late 1880's saw the establishment of a more or less definite pattern of research activity. Preferring to have several irons in the fire at the same time, Rayleigh divided his time rather evenly between experimental work in the laboratory and theoretical investigations in his study. An avid reader of the technical literature, he found the origin of many of his researches in questions suggested to him by his reading. He had an uncanny knack of putting his finger on a weak or difficult point in another man's research results and of building an important contribution of his own on it. Rayleigh's grasp of such widely diverse fields as optics and hydrodynamics, acoustics and electromagnetic theory, was phenomenal; and only Maxwell, Kelvin, and Helmholtz came near him in this aspect of his genius.

During the middle and late 1880's Rayleigh's increasing tendency to extend his research net became apparent. His published papers from this period report results of experimental and theoretical work on radiation both optical and acoustical, electromagnetism, general mechanical theorems, vibrations of elastic media, capillarity, and thermodynamics. To this period belongs his pioneer work on the filtration (selective transmission) of waves in periodic structures, as well as his first precise measurements of the density of gases, which led to the discovery of argon. It was also the period in which Rayleigh apparently first became interested in the problem of the complete radiation law, which governs the distribution of energy in the spectrum of blackbody radiation. His work here was tentative, but he fully recognized the physical significance of this puzzling problem to which Planck, Wien, and others were devoting considerable attention. What is now known as the Rayleigh-Jeans law was first enunciated by Rayleigh in 1900.

The discovery and isolation of argon was undoubtedly Rayleigh's most dramatic and famous accomplishment. It emerged as the solution to a scientific puzzle, and Rayleigh was usually at his best when faced by a puzzle. The difficulty was encountered in high-precision measurements of the density of nitrogen, undertaken in the first instance with the aim of obtaining better values of the atomic weight of that element. It was found that the density of nitrogen prepared from ammonia was about one part in two hundred less than the density of nitrogen obtained from air. Repeated reweighings only confirmed the difference and led to Rayleigh's publishing in *Nature* (1892) a short note citing the apparent dilemma and asking for suggestions for its resolution. In a certain sense this was unfortunate, in the light of the priority problem involved in the subsequent discovery. It does, however, illustrate Rayleigh's single-minded devotion to science as a social profession and what may appropriately be called his scientific unselfishness.

The ultimate solution to the peculiar problem of the density of nitrogen was suggested by the reading of a paper published by Henry Cavendish in 1795. He had oxidized the nitrogen in a given volume of air by sparking the air with a primitive static machine. Cavendish found that no matter how long he conducted the sparking, there was always a small residue of gas that apparently could not be further oxidized. He abandoned the research at that point. Had he continued, he presumably would have been the discoverer of argon. Rayleigh decided to push Cavendish's experiment to a conclusion, acting finally on the conviction that there really was another constituent of atmospheric air in addition to the commonly accepted ones.

Rayleigh used an induction coil to provide the electrical discharge for the oxidation of nitrogen, but the process of accumulating enough of the new gas to test its properties was a slow one. In the meantime Sir William Ramsay, having noted Rayleigh's nitrogen-density problem, proceeded to attempt the isolation of the unknown gas by much faster chemical means. Ramsay kept Rayleigh thoroughly informed of his activities, but some confusion and uncertainty still exist over whether Rayleigh actually gave Ramsay his scientific blessing. In the end both shared in the recognition for the discovery of argon and presented their results in a joint paper. There was the usual skepticism over the validity of the result, especially on the part of chemists, who found it hard to believe that a genuinely new element could have remained undetected for so long. The relative chemical inertness of argon was, of course, the explanation. Sooner or later spectroscopic analysis would in any case have revealed its existence. Rayleigh and Ramsay were led to take the hard way in its recognition.

It was largely because of this discovery that Rayleigh was awarded the Nobel Prize in physics in 1904, while Ramsay received the Nobel Prize in chemistry the same year. It is rather ironic that Rayleigh received the prize for work as relevant for chemistry as for physics, when he never felt he had much competence as a chemist. And indeed

there seems little question that his other contributions to physics were vastly more significant than the discovery of argon. The latter caught both the scientific and the popular fancy, however. Although Rayleigh took the discovery very seriously—as he did all his research—and worked very hard at it, it seems clear that once the existence of the new gas and the demonstration of its properties were irrefutably established, Rayleigh was disinclined to go on with this kind of research. Even during the three years of the argon research (1892–1895) he found time to contribute to the scientific literature some twelve papers dealing with the interference and scattering of light, the telephone and its technical problems, and the measurement of the minimum audible intensity of sound.

An illustration of Rayleigh's uncanny ability to forecast developments in physics is provided by his 1899 paper "On the Cooling of Air by Radiation and Conduction and on the Propagation of Sound." In this he faced the problem of the anomalously high sound attenuation observed in air (much greater than that predicted by the transport properties of viscosity and heat conduction). He predicted that the solution to the difficulty might well be found in a relaxation mechanism involving reciprocal transfer of energy between translational and internal energy states of the molecules of the gas through which the sound passes. This suggestion was adopted by various later investigators and has led to the establishment of the vigorous field of molecular acoustics, which by the second half of the twentieth century has thrown new and important light not only on ultrasonic propagation but also on the structure and interaction of molecules.

Any appraisal of Rayleigh's scientific achievements must include mention of his relation to modern physics and, in particular, to the formulation and development of quantum and relativity theories. This poses an interesting but somewhat puzzling problem. In his reading and his association with other scientists, Rayleigh kept fully abreast of all the important activity in physics. He keenly realized the difficulties that classical physics (electromagnetic theory, thermodynamics, and statistical mechanics) was encountering near the end of the nineteenth century in the attempt to explain the experimental phenomena of radiation spectra. But he refused to give up hope that adequate solutions would be forthcoming within the framework of traditional physical theories. Revolutionary ideas evidently were distasteful to him. He could never develop much enthusiasm for Planck's quantum theory and its subsequent development. He never attacked the theory with any vehemence but simply felt it was not to his taste.

His derivation of what came later to be called the Rayleigh-Jeans radiation law (published in 1900, a few months before Planck's famous paper on the distribution law) reflects Rayleigh's general attitude very well. The statistical principle of equipartition of energy among resonators worked very well for long wavelengths. One has the impression that Rayleigh felt a secret longing that with some ingenious maneuvering it might be made to work for the short wavelengths as well. Of course it never has! But he certainly cannot be accused of allowing any nostalgia for traditionalism in physics to keep him from seriously considering the problem and its importance.

Somewhat similar remarks apply to the problem of the unraveling of the intricacies of atomic spectra. Rayleigh fully realized the ultimate significance of this in connection with atomic constitution and tried his hands at numerous calculations of vibratory systems that might possess frequencies in accord, for example, with the Balmer formula for the emission spectrum of hydrogen. He admitted freely that the failures of these attempts indicated the need for new approaches. At the same time Bohr's theory was too radical and revolutionary for his liking.

Rayleigh also was much concerned with the physical problems that ultimately led to the theory of relativity. As far back as 1887 he was interested in astronomical aberration and its bearing on the theory of a luminiferous ether. At that time he indicated a preference for Fresnel's assumption of a stationary ether, despite the presumably null results of Michelson's famous 1881 experiment. Rayleigh was skeptical of the validity of Michelson's early work. Here again it seems clear that he was much disturbed by the possibility that the ether would have to be abandoned as an unworkable hypothesis. His loyalty to the classical wave theory of light was very great. Rayleigh saw the necessity for further experiments, however, and in 1901 undertook to detect possible double refraction in a material medium due to motion through a presumptive stationary ether. The negative results added to the mounting evidence that no physical phenomenon can enable one to distinguish between the motion of two inertial systems so as to say that one is at rest while the other is moving in an absolute sense. Rayleigh contributed nothing to the Einstein theory of relativity as such, although it is evident that he followed its developments with in-

terest. Here again his rather conservative nature asserted itself.

The pace of Rayleigh's research activity did not slacken as he approached his later years. In the last fifteen years of his life he produced ninety papers, of which some reported notable work. For example, to this period belongs a paper on sound waves of finite amplitude, in which the earlier investigations of W. J. M. Rankine and Hugoniot on what came to be called shock waves were much extended. This laid the groundwork for much future development. Other important contributions to acoustics after 1905 were concerned with the binaural effect in human hearing, in which Rayleigh's pioneer investigations paved the way for the relatively enormous amount of interest in this problem in the later twentieth century, and with the filtration and scattering of sound.

The Theory of Sound was kept up-to-date with appropriate revisions and is still a vade mecum in every acoustical research laboratory. The scattering of light from a corrugated surface also provided new insight into a difficult problem.

Along with this intense research activity, Rayleigh devoted considerable attention to professional scientific societies and governmental applied science. The details of the life of a research scientist working at his desk or in his laboratory often seem to offer little of dramatic character. But Rayleigh became an important public figure in his lifetime and devoted much energy to the promotion of science as a whole and physical science in particular. He early became interested in the affairs of the British Association for the Advancement of Science. His first research results were presented at a meeting of the Association at Norwich in 1868, and he served as president of Section A (Mathematics and Physics) at the Southampton meeting in 1882. His presidency of the entire Association for the Montreal meeting in 1884 has already been mentioned.

Elected to the Royal Society in 1873, Rayleigh served as secretary (succeeding to Sir George Stokes) from 1885 to 1896. He took his duties very seriously and made some interesting discoveries in the archives of the Society, including the neglected paper by the Scottish engineer J. J. Waterston, pioneer in the molecular theory of gases. In 1905 Rayleigh was elected president of the Royal Society and served until 1908. Because he never treated any organizational post as a sinecure, he was much in demand when advice and active work on difficult problems were sought.

In 1896 Rayleigh accepted appointment as scientific adviser to Trinity House, a post Michael Faraday had held some sixty years previously. This organization, dating to the time of Henry VIII, has as its function the erection and maintenance of such coastal installations as lighthouses and buoys. Rayleigh served this organization for fifteen years. Much of his later work in optics and acoustics was suggested by problems arising in connection with tests of fog signals and lights. This work for Trinity House is an illustration of his willingness to give freely of time and energy to scientific committees of government and professional organizations in the interests of applied science. A leader in the movement culminating in the establishment of the National Physical Laboratory at Teddington (the British counterpart of the United States National Bureau of Standards), he presided over its executive committee until shortly before his death. Other examples of Rayleigh's public service are his chairmanships of the Explosives Committee of the War Office and his long tour of duty as chief gas examiner of the London gas supply.

Despite the relative shortness of his own career as a university teacher, Rayleigh took a great interest in educational problems and served on the governing boards of several educational institutions. From 1908 to his death in 1919 he served as chancellor of Cambridge University.

The bulk of Rayleigh's experimental notebooks, calculations, and the original MSS of his published papers have been acquired by the United States Air Force Cambridge Research Laboratories in Bedford, Massachusetts, and are now housed there as the Rayleigh Archives. Photostat copies have been distributed to other libraries, particularly the Niels Bohr Library of the American Institute of Physics in New York, and are available for scholarly study.

Public recognition of his scientific achievements came to Rayleigh in full measure. After receiving the Nobel Prize in 1904, he donated its cash award, amounting to about $38,500, to Cambridge University to improve the Cavendish Laboratory and the University Library. Rayleigh was one of the first members of the new Order of Merit when it was established in 1902. He also became a privy councillor in 1905. He was the recipient of thirteen honorary degrees and held honorary memberships in, or received special awards from over fifty learned societies.

Rayleigh may justly be considered the last great polymath of physical science. He outlived his closest rivals Helmholtz, Gibbs, Kelvin, and Poincaré

by a measurable span of years and remained professionally active to the end of his life. At the time of his death he left three completed professional papers unpublished. The amount of work he accomplished in the roughly fifty-five years of his professional career can only be regarded as prodigious. By nature he was not a profoundly or boldly imaginative scientist who would initiate a wholly new idea like the electromagnetic theory of radiation, the quantum theory, or relativity. In this respect he differed from Maxwell, Planck, Bohr, and Einstein. But he did advance enormously the power and scope of applicability of practically every branch of classical physics. He was admired and respected for his sound scientific judgment and his ability to penetrate to the heart of any scientific problem he encountered. Above all, Rayleigh was a modest man. Typical of this was the remark he made in his speech accepting the Order of Merit: "The only merit of which I personally am conscious is that of having pleased myself by my studies, and any results that may have been due to my researches are owing to the fact that it has been a pleasure to me to become a physicist."

BIBLIOGRAPHY

I. ORIGINAL WORKS. Lord Rayleigh's complete bibliography includes one book and 430 articles. All the articles have been published in his *Scientific Papers*, 6 vols. (Cambridge, 1899–1920), repr., 3 vols. (New York, 1964). The scope of Rayleigh's research activity is indicated by the following. His book is *The Theory of Sound*, 2 vols. (London, 1877–1878). His articles include "On Some Electromagnetic Phenomena Considered in Connexion With the Dynamical Theory," in *Philosophical Magazine*, **38** (1869), 1–14; "On the Theory of Resonance," in *Philosophical Transactions of the Royal Society*, **161** (1870), 77–118; "On the Light From the Sky, Its Polarization and Colour Appendix," in *Philosophical Magazine*, **41** (1871), 107–120, 274–279; "On the Scattering of Light by Small Particles," *ibid.*, 447–454; "Investigation of the Disturbance Produced by a Spherical Obstacle on the Waves of Sound," in *Proceedings of the London Mathematical Society*, **4** (1872), 253–283; "On the Application of Photography to Copy Diffraction-Gratings," in *British Association Report* (1872), 39; "On the Diffraction of Object-Glasses," in *Astronomical Society Monthly Notes*, **33** (1872), 59–63; "Some General Theorems Relating to Vibrations," in *Proceedings of the London Mathematical Society*, **4** (1873), 357–368; "On the Manufacture and Theory of Diffraction-Gratings," in *Philosophical Magazine*, **47** (1874), 81–93, 193–205; "General Theorems Relating to Equilibrium and Initial and Steady Motions," *ibid.*, **49** (1875), 218–224; "On the Dissipation of Energy," in *Nature,* **40** (1875), 454–455; "On Waves," in *Philosophical Magazine,* **1** (1876), 257–259; "Our Perception of the Direction of a Source of Sound," in *Nature,* **41** (1876), 32–33; "On the Application of the Principle of Reciprocity to Acoustics," in *Proceedings of the Royal Society,* **25** (1876), 118–122; "Acoustical Observations. I," in *Philosophical Magazine,* n.s. **3** (1877), 456–464; "Absolute Pitch," in *Nature,* **17** (1877), 12–14; "On the Relation Between the Functions of Laplace and Bessel," in *Proceedings of the London Mathematical Society,* **9** (1878), 61–64; "On the Capillary Phenomena of Jets," in *Proceedings of the Royal Society,* **29** (1879), 71–97; and "Acoustical Observations. II," in *Philosophical Magazine,* **7** (1879); 149–162.

Later articles are "On Reflection of Vibrations at the Confines of Two Media Between Which the Transition is Gradual," in *Proceedings of the London Mathematical Society,* **9** (1880), 51–56; "On the Resolving-Power of Telescopes," in *Philosophical Magazine,* **10** (1880), 116–119; "On the Electromagnetic Theory of Light," *ibid.,* **12** (1881), 81–101; "On the Determination of the Ohm [B.A. Unit] in Absolute Measure," in *Proceedings of the Royal Society,* **32** (1881), 104–141, written with Arthur Schuster; "Experiments to Determine the Value of the British Association Unit of Resistance in Absolute Measure," in *Philosophical Transactions of the Royal Society,* **173** (1882), 661–697; "On the Specific Resistance of Mercury," *ibid.,* **174** (1882), 173–185, written with Mrs. H. Sidgwick; "Address to the Mathematical and Physical Science Section of the British Association," in *British Association Report* (1882), 437–441; "On an Instrument Capable of Measuring the Intensity of Aerial Vibrations," in *Philosophical Magazine,* **14** (1882), 186–187; "On the Maintained Vibrations," *ibid.,* **15** (1883), 229–235; "Distribution of Energy in the Spectrum," in *Nature,* **27** (1883), 559–560; "On the Crispations of Fluid Resting Upon a Vibrating Support," in *Philosophical Magazine,* **16** (1883), 50–58; "On Laplace's Theory of Capillarity," *ibid.,* 309–315; "On the Circulation of Air Observed in Kundt's Tubes and on Some Allied Acoustical Problems," in *Philosophical Transactions,* **175** (1883), 1–21; "The Form of Standing Waves on the Surface of Running Water," in *Proceedings of the London Mathematical Society,* **15** (1883), 69–78; "On the Constant of Magnetic Rotation of Light in Bisulphide of Carbon," in *Philosophical Transactions of the Royal Society,* **76** (1884), 343–366; "On Waves Propagated Along the Plane Surface of an Elastic Solid," in *Proceedings of the London Mathematical Society,* **17** (1885), 4–11; "On the Maintenance of Vibrations by Forces of Double Frequency and on the Propagation of Waves Through a Medium Endowed With a Periodic Structure," in *Philosophical Magazine,* **24** (1887), 145–159; "On the Relative Densities of Hydrogen and Oxygen (Preliminary Notice)," in *Proceedings of the Royal Society,* **43** (1887), 356–363; "On the Free Vibrations of an Infinite Plate of Homogeneous Isotropic Elastic Matter," in *Proceedings of the London Mathematical Society,* **20** (1889), 225–234; "On the Character of the Complete Radiation at a Given Temperature," in *Philosophical Magazine,* **27** (1889), 460–469; "Foam," in *Proceedings of the Royal Institution,* **13** (1890), 85–97; "On the Tension of Water Surfaces, Clean and Contaminated, Investigated by the Method of Ripples," in *Philosophical Magazine,* **30** (1890), 386–400; "On The Theory of Surface Forces," in *Philosophical Magazine,* **30** (1890), 285–298, 456–475; "On the Virial of a System of Hard Colliding Bodies," in *Nature,* **45** (1891), 80–82; "On the Relative Densities of Hydrogen and Oxygen. II," in *Proceedings of the Royal Society,* **50** (1892), 448–463; and "On the Physics of Media That are Composed of Free and Perfectly Elastic Molecules in a State of Motion," in *Philosophical Transactions of the Royal Society,* **183A** (1892), 1–5.

See also "Density of Nitrogen," in *Nature,* **46** (1892), 512–513; "On the Reflection of Sound or Light From a Corrugated Surface," in *British Association Report* (1893), 690–691; "On an Anomaly Encountered in Determinations of the Density of Nitrogen Gas," in *Proceedings of the Royal Society,* **55** (1894), 340–344; "An Attempt at a Quantitative Theory of the Telephone," in *Philosophical Magazine,* **38** (1894), 295–301; "On the Amplitude of Aerial Waves Which Are But Just Audible," *ibid.,* 365–370; "Argon, a New Constituent of the Atmosphere," in *Philosophical Transactions of the Royal Society,* **186A** (1895), 187–241, written with William Ramsay; "Argon," in *Proceedings of the Royal Institution,* **14** (1895), 524–538; "On the Propagation of Waves Upon the Plane Surface Separating Two Portions of Fluid of Different Vorticities," in *Proceedings of the London Mathematical Society,* **27** (1895), 13–18; "On Some Physical Properties of Argon and Helium," in *Proceedings of the Royal Society,* **59** (1896), 198–208; "On the Propagation of Waves Along Connected Systems of Similar Bodies," in *Philosophical Magazine,* **44** (1897), 356–362; "Note on the Pressure of Radiation, Showing an Apparent Failure of the Usual Electromagnetic Equations," *ibid.,* **45** (1898), 522–525; "On the Cooling of Air by Radiation and Conduction and on the Propagation of Sound," *ibid.,* **47** (1899), 308–314; "On the Transmission of Light Through an Atmosphere Containing Small Particles on Suspension, and On the Origin of the Blue of the Sky," *ibid.,* 375–384; "On the Calculation of the Frequency of Vibration of a System in Its Gravest Mode, With an Example from Hydrodynamics," *ibid.,* 566–572; "The Law of Partition of Kinetic Energy," *ibid.,* **49** (1900), 98–118; "Remarks Upon the Law of Complete Radiation," *ibid.,* 539–540; "On the Magnetic Rotation of Light and the Second Law of Thermodynamics," in *Nature,* **64** (1901), 577–578; "On the Pressure of Vibrations," in *Philosophical Magazine,* **3** (1902), 338–346; "Is Rotatory Polarization Influenced by the Earth's Motion?" *ibid.,* **4** (1902), 215–220; "Does Motion Through the Aether Cause Double Refraction?" *ibid.,* 678–683; "On the Bending of Waves Round a Spherical Obstacle," in *Proceedings of the Royal Society,* **72** (1903), 401–441; "On the

Acoustic Shadow of a Sphere," in *Philosophical Transactions of the Royal Society*, **203A** (1904), 87–110; "The Dynamical Theory of Gases and of Radiation," in *Nature*, **71** (1905), 559; **72** (1905), 54–55, 243–244; "On Electrical Vibrations and the Constitution of the Atom," in *Philosophical Magazine*, **11** (1906), 117–123; "On the Experimental Determination of the Ratio of the Electrical Units," *ibid.*, **12** (1906), 97–108; "On Our Perception of Sound Direction," *ibid.*, **13** (1907), 214–232; "Note As to the Application of the Principle of Dynamical Similarity," in *Report of the Advisory Committee for Aeronautics* (1909–1910), 38; "Aerial Plane Waves of Finite Amplitude," in *Proceedings of the Royal Society*, **84A** (1910), 247–284; "On the Propagation of Waves Through a Stratified Medium, with Special Reference to the Question of Reflection," in *Proceedings of the Royal Society*, **86A** (1912), 207–266; "On the Motion of a Viscous Fluid," in *Philosophical Magazine*, **26** (1913), 776–786; "The Pressure of Radiation and Carnot's Principle," in *Nature*, **92** (1914), 527–528; "Some Problems Concerning the Mutual Influence of Resonators Exposed to Primary Plane Waves," in *Philosophical Magazine*, **29** (1915), 209–222; "The Principle of Similitude," in *Nature*, **95** (1915), 66–68, 644; "The Theory of the Helmholtz Resonator," in *Proceedings of the Royal Society*, **92A** (1915), 265–275; "The Le Chatelier-Braun Principle," in *Transactions of the Chemical Society*, **91** (1917), 250–252; "The Theory of Anomalous Dispersion," in *Philosophical Magazine*, **33** (1917), 496–499; "On the Pressure Developed in a Liquid During the Collapse of a Spherical Cavity," *ibid.*, **34** (1917), 94–98; "On the Scattering of Light by a Cloud of Similar Small Particles of Any Shape and Oriented at Random," *ibid.*, **35** (1918), 373–381; "Propagation of Sound and Light in an Irregular Atmosphere," in *Nature*, **101** (1918), 284; "On the Problem of Random Vibrations, and of Random Flights in One, Two, or Three Dimensions," in *Philosophical Magazine*, **37** (1919), 321–347; "Presidential Address," in *Proceedings of the Society for Psychical Research*, **30** (1919), 275–290; and "On Resonant Reflexion of Sound From a Perforated Wall," in *Philosophical Magazine*, **39** (1920), 225–233.

II. SECONDARY LITERATURE. See the obituary notice by Sir Arthur Schuster, in *Proceedings of the Royal Society*, **98A** (1921), 1; Robert John Strutt, *Life of John William Strutt, Third Baron Rayleigh, O.M., F.R.S.* (London, 1924); 2nd augmented ed. with annotations by the author and foreword by John N. Howard (Madison, Wis., 1968); and R. Bruce Lindsay, *Lord Rayleigh, the Man and His Works* (Oxford–London, 1970).

R. B. LINDSAY

STRUTT, ROBERT [ROBIN] JOHN, FOURTH BARON RAYLEIGH (*b.* Terling Place, Witham, Essex, England, 28 August 1875; *d.* Terling, 13 December 1947), *physics*.

Rayleigh is best-known for his work on atmospheric optics. The first child of the renowned physicist J. W. Strutt, third Baron Rayleigh, he attended Eton from 1889 and matriculated at Trinity College, Cambridge, in 1894. After studying experimental physics, he began research at the Cavendish Laboratory in 1899 and published his first scientific paper. Strutt was elected a fellow of the Royal Society in 1905; and from 1908 he was professor of physics at Imperial College, London, until becoming Baron Rayleigh in 1919.

Strutt's early research was on radioactivity. In 1900 he had suggested that alpha radiation might consist of charged particles, a fact verified in 1902 by E. Rutherford. From measurements on the helium content of minerals, Strutt proved that their minimum age was significantly greater than that allowed by Kelvin's geological timetable. Following up the 1884 observations of Emil Warburg on the afterglow in electric discharge and the assertion in 1900 by E. Percival Lewis that the cause of the airglow was nitric oxide, Strutt in 1911 confirmed that discharge airglow was due to a chemically active modification of nitrogen, which he called "active nitrogen." His suggestion that the effect was an atomic phenomenon was not accepted until about 1925. The Lewis-Rayleigh afterglow opened up an important line of optical research.

By comparing absorption spectra, Strutt and Alfred Fowler confirmed in 1916 the presence of ozone in the atmosphere. Strutt investigated its optical effects, and from the nonuniform density distribution he estimated the upper boundary of high-altitude ozone. He examined luminous glows in other gases and metallic vapors and investigated the airglow of the night sky. Strutt determined that this effect was not due to (third Baron) Rayleigh-scattered sunlight and that it had a green line spectrum, later shown to be characteristic of a transition of atomic oxygen.

Rayleigh distinguished the atmospheric airglow generally observable, especially at low latitudes, from the high-latitude night glow associated with magnetic disturbances and auroral phenomena. Because of his pioneering quantitative research, the unit of sky brightness is called the rayleigh; the order of magnitude for the airglow is less than 10^2 rayleighs and that for auroral phenomena lies between 10^2 and 10^4 rayleighs.

Until his death Rayleigh was occupied with matters pertaining both to science and to his many public duties, serving as foreign secretary of the Royal Society, president of the Royal Institution, and chairman of the governing board of Imperial College.

BIBLIOGRAPHY

Rayleigh published over 300 scientific papers. A complete list, in John N. Howard, ed., *Summaries and Abstracts of the Scientific Writings of Robert John Strutt, Fourth Baron Rayleigh, From Notes Written by Him, 1945–1947* (Bedford, Mass., 1969), 63–88, is based on the bibliography included in Alfred C. Egerton, "Lord Rayleigh, 1875–1947," in *Obituary Notices of Fellows of the Royal Society of London*, 6 (1949), 503–538. A selected list is in Charles R. Strutt, "The Optics Papers of Robert John Strutt, Fourth Baron Rayleigh," in *Applied Optics*, 3 (1964), 1116–1119.

Additional biographical material dealing with his family life and background is in Guy Robert Strutt, "Robert John Strutt, Fourth Baron Rayleigh," *ibid.*, 1105–1112. An expanded version of this appeared in John N. Howard, ed., *The Airglow Rayleigh; Robert John Strutt, Fourth Baron Rayleigh, A Memoir by Guy Robert Strutt* (Bedford, Mass., 1969), 1–24. Howard included several contemporary biographical notes relating to Rayleigh that appeared in *Nature*, 125 (1930), 420, and 140 (1937), 456; *The Times* (London) (15 Dec. 1947), 6d; *Proceedings of the Society for Psychical Research*, 48 (1948), 330–331; and *Proceedings of the Royal Institution of Great Britain*, 34 (1948), 156–158. See also A. C. Egerton's notice, in *Dictionary of National Biography* (1959), 850–852.

From personal recollection Sydney Chapman contributed "On the Influence of the Fourth Baron Rayleigh on Air Glow and Auroral Research," in John N. Howard, ed., *The Rayleigh Archives Dedication*, Air Force Cambridge Research Laboratories, Special Report no. 63 (Bedford, Mass., 1967), 46–53. Charles R. Strutt wrote "The Optics Research of Robert John Strutt, Fourth Baron Rayleigh," in *Applied Optics,* 3 (1964), 1113–1115. The results of Strutt and Lewis are contrasted in E. P. Lewis, "The Origin of the Bands in the Spectrum of Active Nitrogen," in *Philosophical Magazine*, 25 (1913), 826–832.

Howard has brought together nearly all the primary and secondary literature pertaining to Strutt in "The Scientific Papers of the Lords Rayleigh," in *Actes du XIe congrès international d'histoire de sciences, 1965*, IV (1968), 315–318. A short obituary notice in *Isis*, 39 (1948), 69, refers to a review by N. R. Campbell, *ibid.*, 8 (1926), 177–181, of Strutt's model scientific biography of his father. This biography, *Life of John William Strutt: Third Baron Rayleigh, O.M., F.R.S.*, was reedited by John N. Howard (Madison, Wis., 1968) and includes 33 pages of annotations by R. J. Strutt keyed to the text.

The early research of R. J. Strutt was considered by C. T. R. Wilson in Cavendish Laboratory, *A History of the Cavendish Laboratory 1871–1910* (London, 1910), 211–215. Part of Strutt's work in its larger scientific context is considered in A. N. Wright and C. A. Winkler, *Acitve Nitrogen* (London, 1968), *passim*. The technical context is considered in F. E. Roach and J. L. Gordon, *The Light of the Night Sky* (Dordrecht, 1973). L. Badash deals with Strutt's helium method of geological dating in "Rutherford, Boltwood and the Age of the Earth: The Origin of Radioactive Dating Techniques," in *Proceedings of the American Philosophical Society*, 112 (1968), 157–169. See also S. I. Levy, *The Rare Earths* (London, 1915), ch. 8. John N. Howard described the 22 notebooks of the fourth Baron Rayleigh including over 4,000 experiments from 1916 to 1944 in "The Rayleigh Notebooks," in *Applied Optics*, 3 (1964), 1132–1133.

Several previously unpublished MSS and the text of Strutt's House of Lords debates and letters to the *Times* (London) are included in John N. Howard, ed., *Robert John Strutt, Fourth Baron Rayleigh, Unpublished Manuscripts and Reviews of His Work* (Bedford, Mass., 1971), which also contains contemporary reviews of Strutt's four books. Additional correspondence of Strutt is in the Lodge collection, Library, University College, London.

THADDEUS J. TRENN

STRUVE, FRIEDRICH GEORG WILHELM (or **Vasily Yakovlevich**) (*b.* Altona, Germany, 15 April 1793; *d.* Pulkovo, Russia, 23 November 1864), *astronomy, geodesy.*

Struve's father, Jacob Struve, came from a peasant family, but by diligence and ability was able to graduate from the University of Göttingen. He held a number of teaching positions in various German towns and then, after ten years, settled in Altona as professor in the Christianeum classical Gymnasium, a school that he had himself attended. He was made principal after three years, and retained that post for about forty years more. Struve's mother, Maria Emerenzia Wise, was the daughter of a preacher. There were six other children.

When Struve reached the age of conscription his parents decided to send him out of Germany. He thus went to Dorpat, Russia, where his older brother Karl had been living for some time. In 1810 he graduated from the University of Dorpat with a degree in philology, but he was not enthusiastic about becoming a teacher of that subject and proposed instead to devote himself to the study of mathematics, astronomy, and geodesy. With the support of the rector of the university and several of its professors, he received permission to work in the university observatory, where he in-

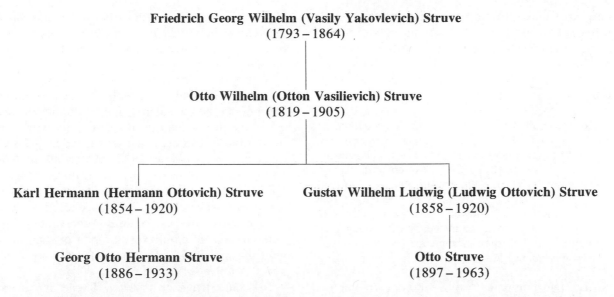

Friedrich Georg Wilhelm (Vasily Yakovlevich) Struve
(1793 – 1864)

Otto Wilhelm (Otton Vasilievich) Struve
(1819 – 1905)

Karl Hermann (Hermann Ottovich) Struve   **Gustav Wilhelm Ludwig (Ludwig Ottovich) Struve**
(1854 – 1920)   (1858 – 1920)

Georg Otto Hermann Struve   **Otto Struve**
(1886 – 1933)   (1897 – 1963)

The Struve family, four generations of astronomers who conducted research in Germany, Russia, and the United States for a period of more than 150 years.

stalled a number of previously purchased new instruments and carried out observations by which he was able to make an accurate determination of the latitude and longitude of the building. In 1813 he was awarded the doctorate for this work and was appointed professor extraordinarius of mathematics and astronomy and observing astronomer.

Struve thus began a teaching career that lasted twenty-five years, during which he delivered at Dorpat many courses of lectures on different astronomical and mathematical subjects; he also gave widely popular public lectures and often taught astronomy and geodesy at the general staff headquarters of the Corps of Military Topographers and at the Hydrographic Department. In addition to his teaching, Struve's research was also significant in a number of areas, notably observation of double stars; determination of stellar parallaxes and distribution of stars in space; observation of planets, the moon, comets, and auroras; meridian measurements; statistical techniques; and the design and refinement of astronomical and geodetic instruments.

In January 1814 Struve began to make systematic observations with a transit that he had installed. His results in the next two years were included in the first volume of the *Observationes astronomicas institutas in specula universitatis caesareae Dorpatensis*, published in 1817. (Seven other volumes followed, containing Struve's own observations and those of his assistants and students, which he revised and edited.) He devised new methods of observation that were later widely adopted, and he

improved the Dorpat facility, adding a meridian circle constructed by Georg von Reichenbach in 1822 and a nine-inch refracting telescope made by Fraunhofer (the largest in existence) in 1824.

These efforts brought Struve considerable recognition, and he was invited by the St. Petersburg Academy of Sciences to carry out the organization of a new main observatory, to be constructed at Pulkovo, near St. Petersburg. A preliminary plan for the new observatory had been drawn up by the physicist G. F. Parrot and reviewed by a special commission, of which Struve was a member. The design was approved in April 1834, and the architect A. P. Bryllov was put in charge of construction. Struve himself was appointed director of the new installation, and in June of the same year he went abroad to buy the best instruments to be found. He discussed the new observatory with Bessel, Humboldt, Lindenau, Olbers, Steinheil, H. C. Schumacher, and others, and ordered instruments to be made by Ertel, Repsold, Mertz, Plössl, Pistor, Throughton, and Dent. Among his purchases was a fifteen-inch refractor, the largest made.

The observatory was opened with great ceremony on 19 August 1839, and soon achieved worldwide fame. In 1845 Struve published a detailed description of the installation, including a complete catalog of the instruments, with remarks on their installation, application, and testing procedures. Appended to this description was a catalog of the library of the observatory, enumerating 5,411 astronomical works, of which 3,869 dated from the fifteenth to the seventeenth centuries. In a supplement, Struve analyzed the collection and discussed the history of the library; a second edition of the catalog, prepared by Struve's son Otto Struve and published in 1860, listed 18,890 titles. In a letter to Schumacher, published in 1855, George Airy wrote that

> No astronomer can claim a complete acquaintance with the practical aspect of our science at its present stage of development until he makes a diligent and thorough study of all the treasures kept in Pulkovo; the researches carried out by the Pulkovo astronomers and their precise methods of observation are most instructive, as is the very construction of the observatory building and the installation, selection, and characteristics of the instruments [*Vestnik estestvennykh nauk*, no. 19, 596].

Struve had completed some of his own important research while he was still at Dorpat. He studied the results of Herschel's work on double stars and in 1814 discovered the motions of the satellite of Castor and of η Cassiopeiae by comparing his own recent observations with those made by Herschel between 1780 and 1800. By 1820 he had determined the revolutions of P Ophiuchi and ξ Ursae Majoris, nearly completed since Herschel's observations of 1780. In 1822 he published a catalog of all known double stars, which contained 795 items. He went on to observe some 122,000 stars over two-thirds of the celestial sphere from the north pole to 15° south declination, among which he detected 3,112 double stars, which he classified according to their angular separation. These were incorporated into a new catalog of double stars that he published in 1827.

Struve then undertook to make micrometric measurements of these celestial objects and on 14 November 1834 reported to the St. Petersburg Academy of Sciences that he had so measured 2,736 double stars. He published these results, together with those of a further series of observations, in a paper of 1837 entitled *Stellarum duplicium et multiplicium mensurae micrometricae*. Bessel characterized this paper as "a magnificent work ranking among the greatest performed by astronomical observers in recent times." By 1842 Struve and his assistants had observed the entire northern sky. In addition to the 18,000 stars known, they discovered 518 multiple stars that had not been reported previously, and Struve published data on 514 of them the following year. In 1852, having compared his data with those obtained by James Bradley, Lalande, Piazzi, and Stephen

Groombridge, Struve published his *Stellarum fixarum imprimis duplicium et multiplicium positiones mediae*, which included 2,874 double and fundamental stars.

Struve consistently paid special attention to stellar parallaxes, and may, with Bessel and Thomas Henderson, be considered one of the first to make a reliable determination of them. This work made it possible to calculate the actual values of stellar distances. As early as 1822, Struve attempted to estimate the parallaxes of several dozen stars and published his finding that the parallaxes he derived for twenty-seven stars did not exceed 0.5″. Although most of his findings represented linear combinations of parallaxes of a pair of stars, he did give the individual parallaxes of δ Ursae Majoris and α Aquilae.

In 1836 Struve observed α Lyrae and a small star of 10.5 magnitude, at a distance of 43″. From these observations he derived a series of general conclusions about the parallaxes of fixed stars that he reported to the Academy on 13 January 1837 and included in his *Stellarum duplicium et multiplicium mensurae micrometricae*, presented later that year. "My observations for seventeen dates," he wrote, "show the distance and direction (position angles) of the two stars from which, by calculation using thirty-four equations by the method of least squares, the parallax for the main star proves to be 0.125″, or 1/8 second, with a probable error of 0.055″, or 1/18 second." This result is very close to the modern value of 0.121″, but in the course of verifying his data Struve later reached the less accurate value of $+0.2613'' \pm 0.0254''$.

Struve also conducted investigations on stellar distribution to determine whether there is a statistical dependence between the brightness of stars and their distances. To this end he organized work at Pulkovo on a new star catalog, which he studied closely for changes in the visible star density in the field of the Milky Way. He was thereby led to maintain that the sun was not the center of this system, but lay above its main plane. He was also able to substantiate earlier suggestions by Loys de Chésaux and Olbers that the interstellar medium is incompletely transparent and to determine the value of the obscuration effect in outer space, results that he published in the preface to Maximilian Weisse's star catalog of 1846 and in his own *Études d'astronomie stellaire* of 1847.

In connection with this study, Struve analyzed the observations that Herschel had made with a twenty-foot telescope and compared the number of stars that Herschel had observed with a theoretical figure to conclude that "the range of Herschel's telescope, determined by observing the sky, scarcely exceeds one-third of the range corresponding to its optical resolution." The reason for this limitation, Struve stated emphatically, is that "the intensity of light decreases in a greater proportion than the ratio of the inverse square of the distance, which means that there is a loss of light, an extinction when it passes through celestial space." This conclusion testified to the presence of rarefied matter in space; in an approximate calculation, Struve also estimated that "The light in passing the same distance of a first-magnitude star is extinguished by almost one-hundredth—in other words, it loses 1/107th of its intensity." The value that he thus obtained is in fair agreement with the currently accepted mean value for absorption near the galactic plane.

Throughout his career Struve was also active in geodetic studies. In 1816 he began three years' work on the triangulation of Livonia, at the request of the Livonian Economic Society, and with K. I. Tenner he sponsored the joint Russian-Scandinavian measurement of 25°20' of the arc of meridian. He personally supervised the measurement of 9°38' of the Finnish-Livonian arc between the Dvina and Tornio rivers, and advised Tenner on the measurement of the large and difficult section of the arc (11°10') between the Dvina and the Danube. The 3°13' of the arc that lies between the Tornio and Belatsvar, in Sweden, was measured under the supervision of N. C. Zeelander, while the measurement of 1°46' of the arc in Sweden, between Atjik and Cape Fuglnes, was carried out under the guidance of Hansteen. The entire project was finished by 1855, and Struve played a large part in organizing and processing the data for publication between 1856 and 1857.

The Russian-Scandinavian measurements were of great value to geodesy and practical astronomy, to which Struve made other important contributions. In 1837 he was involved in determining the difference in level between the Black and Caspian seas, and organized an expedition that investigated some 800 kilometers to yield not only fairly reliable results (26.04 ± 0.25 meters) concerning the difference in level, but also furnished data on terrestrial refraction and produced the first accurate determination of altitude for Mounts Elbrus, Kazbek (eastern and western), Besh-Tau, and Bezymyannaya. Struve's methods of geodetic construction are of considerable interest, and his work on

the altimetry of the Caspian Sea represents the first application of the technique of parallactic polygonometry that was later developed by V. V. Danilov.

Struve further discovered rational methods for the determination of latitude, time, and azimuth that allowed him to eliminate many systematic errors. He participated in a number of chronometric expeditions, among them one conducted by F. F. Schubert for the purpose of correcting the map of the Baltic Sea (1833), in which he was responsible for the astronomical observations. In 1842 he himself organized an expedition that set out from Pulkovo to observe the solar eclipse at Lipetsk— an expedition that, according to Struve, completely eliminated uncertainties about the values for longitudes determined by chronometers that had been transported over long distances by land. In 1843 and 1844 he conducted two other expeditions, between Pulkovo and Altona and between Altona and Greenwich. They established the longitudinal connection between the Pulkovo and Greenwich observatories.

Struve's work brought him international fame, and he was a member of more than forty scientific academies, learned societies, and universities. In particular, he was a corresponding member of the St. Petersburg Academy of Sciences from 1822 and a full member and honorary member for more than forty years. He was also a founding member of the Russian Geographical Society and chairman of its department of mathematical geography.

In 1814 Struve married Emily Wall, the daughter of an Altona merchant; they had twelve children. A year after his first wife died in 1834, Struve married her friend Johanna Bartels, daughter of the mathematician J. M. C. Bartels; they had six children. Twelve of Struve's children survived him, and his son Otto collaborated in his work for a number of years and carried it on after his death.

BIBLIOGRAPHY

I. ORIGINAL WORKS. There is a complete bibliography of Struve's publications (272 titles) in Novokshanova (see below). They include, in addition to works cited in the text, *De geographica positione speculae astronomicae Dorpatensis* (Mitau, 1813), his doctoral thesis: "Catalogus stellarum duplicium a 20° decl. Austr. ad 90° decl. Bor. pro anno 1820," in *Observationes astronomicas institutas in specula universitatis caesareae Dorpatensis*, **3** (1822), 15–24; "Additamentum I. De numero constanti aberrationis et parallaxi annua fixarum ex observationibus stellarum circumpolarium in ascensione oppositarum," *ibid.*, 51–90; "Observationes stellarum duplicium per micrometrum filare Fraunhoferianum tubo mobili Troughtoniano 5 pedum abhibitum," *ibid.*, **4** (1825), 175–195; *Beschreibung des auf der Sternwarte der Kaiserlichen Universität zu Dorpat befindlichen grossen Refractors von Fraunhofer* (Dorpat, 1825); "Micrometer-Beobachtungen des Planeten Saturn mit dem grossen Refractor von Fraunhofer in Dorpat angestellt," in *Astronomische Nachrichten*, **5** (1827), 7–14; **6** (1828), 389–392; "Micrometer-Messungen des Jupiters und seiner Trabanten mit dem grossen Refractor von Fraunhofer angestellt," *ibid.*, **5** (1827), 13–16; *Catalogus novus stellarum duplicium et multiplicium* (Dorpat, 1827); and "Disquisitio de refractione astronomica, stellarum que primariarum declinationibus et ascensionibus rectis, quales sequuntur ex observationibus anni 1822 ad 1826," in *Observationes astronomicas institutas . . . Dorpatensis*, **6** (1830).

Subsequent works are *Anwendung des Durchgangsinstruments für die geographische Ortsbestimmung* (St. Petersburg, 1833); "Expédition organisée par l'Académie impériale des sciences, dans le but de déterminer la différence de niveau de la Mer Noire et de la Mer Caspienne," in *Bulletin scientifique publié par l'Académie impériale des sciences de St.-Pétersbourg*, **1** (1837) 79–80; **2** (1837), 254–270; **3** (1838), 27–31, 127–132, 366–368; "Additamentum in mensuras micrometricas stellarum duplicium editas anno 1837, exhibens mensuras Dorpati annis 1837 et 1838 institutas. Adjecta est disquisitio de parallaxi annua stellae α Lirae," in *Mémoires de l'Académie impériale des sciences de St.-Pétersbourg*, Sciences math. et phys., 6th ser., **2**, no. 4 (1840), 337–358; "Sur les constantes de l'aberration et de la nutation," in *Bulletin scientifique publié par l'Académie impériale des sciences de St.-Pétersbourg*, **8**, no. 13 (1841), 199–206; *Catalogue de 514 étoiles doubles et multiples découvertes sur l'hémisphère céleste boréal . . . et catalogue de 256 étoiles doubles principales où la distance des composantes est de 32″ à 2′ et qui se trouvent sur l'hémisphère boréal* (St. Petersburg, 1843); "Mémoire sur le coefficient constant dans l'aberration des étoiles fixes," in *Bulletin de la classe physique-mathématique de l'Académie impériale des Sciences de St.-Pétersbourg*, **1**, nos. 17–18 (1843), 257–260; and "Table des positions géographiques principales de la Russie," *ibid.*, nos. 19–21 (1843), 289–306.

See also *Expédition chronométrique exécutée entre Poulkova et Altona pour la détermination de la longitude géographique relative de l'observatoire central de Russie* (St. Petersburg, 1844); *Description de l'observatoire astronomique central de Poulkova* (St. Petersburg, 1845), with *Appendice: Catalogus librorum in bibliotheca speculae Pulcovensis contentorum*, 2 vols. (St. Petersburg, 1845; 2nd ed., 1860); "Notice sur la comète à courte période découverte par M. Faye à Paris, d'après les observations faites à l'observatoire de Poulkova," in *Bulletin de l'Académie des sciences de St.-Pétersbourg*,

Cl. phys.-math., **3**, no. 18 (1845), 273–280; "Ueber die im Jahre 1845 auszuführende Chronometer-Expedition ins Innere Russlands," *ibid.*, **4**, no. 3 (1845), written with Otto Struve; *Expédition chronométrique entre Altona et Greenwich pour la détermination de la longitude géographique de l'observatoire central de Russie* (St. Petersburg, 1846); "Obzor geograficheskikh rabot v Rossii" ("Survey of Geographical Work in Russia"), in *Zapiski Russkogo geograficheskogo obshchestva*, **1** (1846) 43–58; *Études d'astronomie stellaire. Sur la Voie Lactée et sur la distance des étoiles fixes* (St. Petersburg, 1847), also in Russian (Moscow, 1953); "Observations de la nouvelle planète (Astrée) faites à l'observatoire central, à l'aide des instruments du méridien, éléments de l'orbite de la planète," in *Bulletin de l'Académie des sciences de St.-Pétersbourg*, Cl. phys.-math., **5**, no. 13 (1847), 193–196; and *Arc du méridien de 25°20′ entre le Danube et la Mer Glaciale, mesuré, depuis 1816 jusqu'en 1855*, 2 vols. (St. Petersburg, 1856–1857; ed. 2, 1861; Moscow, 1957).

II. SECONDARY LITERATURE. Z. K. Novokshanova, *Vasily Yakovlevich Struve* (Moscow, 1964) is the most complete biography and includes a bibliography of 272 original works (pp. 249–273) and 89 sources. See also A. A. Mikhaylov, ed., *Vasily Yakovlevich Struve. Sbornik statey i materialov k 100-letiyu so dnya smerti* (". . . . Collected Papers and Materials on the Centennial of His Death"; Moscow, 1964). Earlier sources (listed chronologically) are A. N. Savich, *Vospominania o V. Y. Struve. Torzhestvennoe sobranie Akademii nauk 29 dekabrya 1864 g.* ("Memoirs of V. Y. Struve. Grand Meeting of the Academy of Sciences of 29 December 1864"; St. Petersburg, 1865); E. F. Litvinova, *V. Y. Struve, ego zhizn i nauchnaya deyatelnost* ("V. Y. Struve, His Life and Scientific Activity"; St. Petersburg, 1893); A. A. Tillo, "O geograficheskikh zaslugakh V. Y. Struve" ("On the Geographical Merits of V. Y. Struve"), in *Izvestiya Russkogo geograficheskogo obshchestva*, **29**, no. 3 (1893), 151–164; and Otto Struve, *Wilhelm Struve. Zur Erinnerung an den Vater den Geschwistern dargebracht* (Karlsruhe, 1895).

More recent studies include B. A. Vorontsov-Belyaminov, *Zvezdno-statisticheskie raboty V. Struve* ("V. Struve's Works on Stellar Statistics"), in *Trudy soveshchania po istorii estestvoznania 24–26 dekabrya 1946 g.* ("Proceedings of the Conference on the History of Natural Science, 24–26 December 1946"; Moscow–Leningrad, 1948), 132–144; A. N. Deutsch, "Pervoe opredelenie V. Y. Struve parallaksa α Liry" ("V. Y. Struve's First Determination of the Parallax of α Lyrae"), in *Astronomicheskii zhurnal*, **29**, no. 5 (1952), 597–601; B. A. Orlov, "Vasily Yakovlevich Struve," in V. Y. Struve, *Etyudy zvezdnoy astronomii* ("Essays on Stellar Astronomy"; Moscow, 1953), 171–208; T. Rootsmyae, "Akademik V. Y. Struve i ego deyatelnost v Tartuskom universitete" (". . . and His Activity at the University of Tartu"), in *Uchenye zapiski Tartuskogo gosudarstvennogo universiteta*, no. 37 (1955), 30–69;

O. Struve, "The First Determination of Stellar Parallax," in *Sky and Telescope*, **16** (1956), 9–12, 69–72; N. P. Erpylev, "Razvitie zvezdnoy astronomii v Rossii v XIX veke" ("The Development of Stellar Astronomy in Russia in the Nineteenth Century"), in *Istoriko-astronomicheskie issledovaniya*, no. 4 (1958), 43–130; Y. G. Perel, "Vasily Yakovlevich Struve," in *Lyudi russkoy nauki* ("People of Russian Science"; Moscow, 1961), 94–103; and Z. K. Sokolovskaya, "Pervye opredelenia zvezdnykh parallaksov" ("The First Determinations of Stellar Parallax"), in *Vestnik Akademii nauk SSSR*, no. 3 (1972), 132–136.

Works on the Struve family are E. B. Frost, "A Family of Astronomers," in *Popular Astronomy*, **29**, no. 9 (1921), 536–541; A. F. Marshal, "Une dynastie d'astronomes. Les Struve," in *Industrie* (Brussels), **17**, no. 12 (1963), 833–839; and P. van de Kamp, "The Struve Succession," in *Journal of the Royal Astronomical Society of Canada*, **59**, no. 3 (1965), 106–114.

Z. K. SOKOLOVSKAYA

STRUVE, GEORG OTTO HERMANN (*b*. Pulkovo, Russia, 29 December 1886; *d*. Berlin, Germany, 10 June 1933), *astronomy*.

Struve was born at Pulkovo while his father, Karl Hermann Struve, was adjunct astronomer there. He was taken to Königsberg in 1895, when the elder Struve was appointed director of the observatory of that university, and attended the Königsberg Gymnasium, from which he graduated in 1905. He then studied at the universities of Heidelberg and Berlin; in 1910 he was awarded the Ph.D. for a dissertation entitled *Die Darstellung der Pallasbahn durch die Gausssche Theorie für den Zeitraum 1903 bis 1910*, which he had dedicated to the memory of his grandfather Otto Struve. During the next two years he worked as an assistant at the Bonn Observatory, in his father's observatory in Berlin, and at the Bergedorf Observatory, then, in 1913, became astronomer at the Wilhelmshaven naval observatory, where he was placed in charge of chronometers and compasses. In the last post he utilized his spare time and the observatory's meridian circle (made by Repsold) to make observations of Saturn and its satellites, an interest that he shared with his father.

Beginning in 1917 Struve published some ten works on Saturn, including one on the determination of its equator and the orbits of its satellites (1917), an analysis of observations performed by other researchers (1918), an observation of periodic disappearance of some of its rings (1921), the results of observations of its ring system that he

had carried out in South America (1927), and a comparison of the results of both visual and photographic observations of its satellites (1928). This work was summarized in five issues of the sixth volume of the *Veröffentlichungen der Universitätssternwarte zu Berlin-Babelsberg*, published between 1924 and 1933. Struve had begun working as an observer at that observatory in 1919; he became professor there in 1929, and held that post until his death.

In addition to his work on Saturn, Struve also observed the eclipse of Jupiter's satellites and measured the diameter of Venus, applying the theory of contrasts to determine its irradiation. Toward the end of his career he also made observations of Uranus and its satellites, Oberon and Titania, and studied other minor planets, especially Eros, of which an opposition occurred in 1930–1931. He supplemented his data with those that he collected on visits to the Johannesburg Observatory in South Africa, and to the Lick and Yerkes observatories in the United States.

BIBLIOGRAPHY

I. ORIGINAL WORKS. The most complete bibliography of Struve's works (26 titles) is Poggendorff, V, 1224; and VI, 2570–2571. His most important writings are *Die Darstellung der Pallasbahn durch die Gausssche Theorie für den Zeitraum 1903 bis 1910* (Berlin, 1911); "Neue Elemente der inneren Saturnstrabanten," in *Abhandlungen der Preussischen Akademie der Wissenschaften*, Math.-Naturwiss. Kl. (1918), no. 1; and "Neue Untersuchungen im Saturn System," in *Veröffentlichungen der Universitätssternwarte zu Berlin-Babelsberg*, **6**, no. 4 (1930), 82.

II. SECONDARY LITERATURE. There are obituaries by J. Dick, in *Vierteljahrsschrift der Astronomischen Gesellschaft*, **69** (1934), 2–8; and by P. Guthnick, in *Astronomische Nachrichten*, **251**, no. 6003 (1934), 47.

Z. K. SOKOLOVSKAYA

STRUVE, GUSTAV WILHELM LUDWIG (or **Ludwig Ottovich**) (*b*. Pulkovo, Russia, 1 November 1858; *d*. Simferopol, Russia, 4 November 1920), *astronomy, geodesy*.

Struve completed his Gymnasium studies at Vyborg in 1876, then entered the University of Dorpat, where he graduated in 1880 to become a part-time astronomer at Pulkovo Observatory. In 1883 he defended a dissertation entitled "Resultate aus den in Pulkowa angestellten Vergleichungen von Procyon mit benachbarten Sternen," then was sent abroad to work at the observatories of Bonn, Milan, and Leipzig. In 1885 he participated in the general session of the German Astronomical Society held in Geneva and visited the observatories of Paris, Greenwich, Leiden, and Potsdam before returning to Russia in October of the same year. He worked briefly at Pulkovo before assuming the post of observational astronomer at the University of Dorpat. There he received, in 1887, the doctorate in astronomy for his "Bestimmung der Constante der Präcession und der eigenen Bewegung des Sonnensystems."

At Dorpat Struve's chief interest was in the positions and motions of stars. He collaborated with the German Astronomical Society in compiling a catalog of stars between 70° and 75° north declination and later, at Kharkov, in cooperation with N. N. Evdokimov and B. I. Kudrevich, he observed zodiacal stars, reference stars for Eros, and circumpolar stars from 79° to the pole. Many of his publications were concerned with the precession and motion of the solar system.

In 1887 Struve adopted the hypothesis that the rotation of a galaxy is similar to that of a solid body, and derived an angular rotation rate of $-0.41'' \pm 0.42''$ in each hundred years (a value that may be compared to the current one of $-0.028''$ at the distance of the sun from the center of the galaxy). Between 1884 and 1888 he also carried out observations of the occultation of the stars by the moon during total lunar eclipses in the interest of determining the radius of the moon. These results were published in 1893 and earned Struve the first prize of the Russian Astronomical Society. The Society also awarded him its Glazenap Prize for his response (the only one submitted, as it happened) to a competition set, in 1910, on the subject "Treatment of Observations of the Occultation of Stars During the Lunar Eclipses of 1891, 1895, 1898, and 1910." Reviewing Struve's researches, which were published in 1915, F. F. Witram noted that Struve "must be considered the most competent scholar in this field."

In autumn of 1894 Struve moved to Kharkov, where he was first professor extraordinarius and then (from 1897 to 1919) full professor of astronomy and geodesy. He was simultaneously director of the university observatory and, from 1912 until 1919, dean of the faculty of mathematical and physical sciences. He took active part in a number of geodetic projects, including the leveling by which the Kharkov observatory was made part of the Russian state network of altitudes.

In 1919 Struve moved with his family to the Crimea, on the advice of doctors who were treating the illness of his seventeen-year-old son Werner. He became professor of the Tauris University at Simferopol, but his health was weakened by family misfortunes—Werner Struve and a six-year-old daughter died, an elder daughter became ill, and his son Otto had been recalled into the White Army under General Denikin, who was then retreating through the Crimea. Struve died while attending a meeting of the Tauris Learned Association, where he was to have read his paper on the new star in Cygni. His son Otto survived to carry on the family profession.

BIBLIOGRAPHY

I. ORIGINAL WORKS. There is a bibliography of Struve's writings (22 titles) in Slastenov (see below), 171–172. His most important works are "Resultate aus den in Pulkowa angestellten Vergleichungen von Procyon mit benachbarten Sternen," in *Mémoires de l'Académie impériale des sciences de St.-Pétersbourg*, 7th ser., **31**, no. 2 (1883), his master's thesis; "Bestimmung der Constante der Präcession und der eigenen Bewegung des Sonnensystems," *ibid.*, **35**, no. 3 (1887), his doctoral diss.; "Bearbeitung der während der totalen Mondfinsternisse 1884 Oct. 4 und 1888 Jan. 28 beobachteten Sternbedeckungen," in *Beobachtungen der K. Universitäts-Sternwarte zu Jurjew* (Dorpat), **20** (1893), 1–30; *Soedinenie Kharkova s russkoy nivelirnoy setyu tochnoy nivelirovkoy, proizvedennoy professor om L. O. Struve v 1895 i 1899 gg.* ("The Connection of Kharkov With the Russian Vertical Control Network by the Accurate Leveling Made by Professor L. Struve in 1895 and 1899"; St. Petersburg, 1902); and *Obrabotka nablyudeny pokryty zvezd Lunoyu vo vremya polnykh lunnykh zatmeny* ("The Reduction of Observations of the Occultation of Stars by the Moon During Total Lunar Eclipses"; Petrograd, 1915).

II. SECONDARY LITERATURE. On Struve and his work, see A. I. Slastenov, *Astronomia v Kharkovskom universitete za 150 let* ("Astronomy at the University of Kharkov for 150 years"; Kharkov, 1955), 171–172. There are obituaries in *Nauka i ee rabotniki*, no. 3 (1921), 37; by L. Courvoisier, in *Astronomische Nachrichten*, **212** (1921), 351–352; and by N. N. Evdokimov, in *Nauka na Ukraine*, no. 4 (1922), 428–430. On Struve's work in the prize contest of the Russian Astronomical Society, see F. F. Witram, "Otzyv" ("Review"), in *Izvestiya Russkago astronomicheskago obshchestva*, **21**, no. 6 (1915), 144–149.

Z. K. SOKOLOVSKAYA

STRUVE, KARL HERMANN (or **Hermann Ottovich**) (*b.* Pulkovo, Russia, 30 October 1854; *d.*

Neubabelsberg, near Potsdam, Germany, 12 August 1920), *astronomy*.

Hermann Struve received his early education in the Gymnasiums of Karlsruhe (during the winter of 1862–1863) and Vyborg; he took his final examinations in Reval (now Tallin, Estonian S.S.R.) and, in 1872, entered the University of Dorpat. After graduating from the university in 1877 he was admitted to Pulkovo Observatory, where he had passed his childhood. He was then sent to Paris, Strasbourg, Berlin, and Graz to further his education. In Graz, he worked under Boltzmann, who directed his dissertation, "Fresnels Interferenzerscheinungen; theoretisch und experimentell Bearbeitet," which he wrote in the summer of 1881 and submitted to the University of Dorpat soon thereafter. The following year he received the doctorate in astronomy from Dorpat with a study entitled "Über den Einfluss der Diffraktion an Fernröhren auf Lichtscheiben."

In 1874 Struve took part in B. Hasselberg's expedition to eastern Siberia and to the port of Posyet to observe the transit of Venus. In 1877 he became part-time astronomer at Pulkovo; in 1883 he was made adjunct astronomer; and from 1890 until 1895, he served as senior astronomer. Among the works that he published during this tenure, "Bestimmung der Elemente von Japetus und Titan aus der Verbindung dieser Satelliten untereinander" represents an exposition of his method for the micrometric measurement of the satellites of Saturn. He also made thorough investigations of Neptune, Mars, and Jupiter, observed double stars, and wrote a number of theoretical articles on optics.

In 1895, perhaps influenced by his father's move to Germany upon his retirement, Struve accepted a post as director of the observatory at the University of Königsberg. His most important work, "Beobachtungen der Saturnstrabanten am 30-zölligen Pulkowaer Refractor," published in 1898, draws upon the data that he had obtained in his earlier post, and contains, among other things, a list of all the basic constants of Saturn's ring system. Most of Struve's later work on Saturn represents developments of the concepts he presented there.

Struve was awarded the Damoiseau Prize by the Paris Académie des Sciences in 1897 and received the gold medal of the Royal Astronomical Society in 1903. In 1904 he was appointed director of the Berlin-Babelsberg Observatory, and from 1913 until his death he was director of the Neubabelsberg Observatory, which he had helped to found.

Struve was married to Olga Struve, the daughter of his father's cousin. Of their twin sons, one, Georg, also became an astronomer.

BIBLIOGRAPHY

I. ORIGINAL WORKS. The most complete bibliography of Struve's works (60 titles) is in Poggendorff, III, 1308; IV, 1457–1458; and V, 1225. They include "Bestimmung der Elemente von Japetus und Titan aus der Verbindung dieser Satelliten untereinander," in *Astronomische Nachrichten*, **111** (1885), 1–10; "Beobachtungen der Saturnstrabanten. Abt. I. Beobachtungen am 15-zölligen Refractor," in *Observations de Poulkova*, supp. 1 (1888); "Beobachtungen des Neptunstrabanten am 30-zölligen Pulkowaer Refractor," in *Mémoires de l'Académie imperiale des sciences de St.-Pétersbourg*, 7th ser., **42**, no. 4 (1894); "Beobachtungen der Saturnstrabanten am 30-zölligen Pulkowaer Refractor," in *Publications de l'Observatoire central (Nicolas) à Poulkova*, 2nd ser., **11** (1898); "Mikrometermessungen von Doppelsternen, ausgefuhrt am 30-zölligen Refractor zu Pulkowa," *ibid.*, **12** (1901); and *Die neue Berliner Sternwarte in Babelsberg* (Berlin, 1919).

II. SECONDARY LITERATURE. There are obituaries of Struve by F. S. Archenhold. Geh. Reg.-Rat. in *Weltall*, **21**, nos. 5–6 (1920), 35–36; B. Wanach, in *Vierteljahrsschrift der Astronomischen Gesellschaft*, **56** (1921), 4–12; and L. Courvoisier, in *Astronomische Nachrichten*, **212** (1921), 33–38.

Z. K. SOKOLOVSKAYA

STRUVE, OTTO (*b.* Kharkov, Russia, 12 August 1897; *d.* Berkeley, California, 6 April 1963), *astronomy*.

Struve was the son of Gustav Wilhelm Ludwig Struve, professor of astronomy and geodesy and director of the observatory at the University of Kharkov. He graduated from the Kharkov Gymnasium with honors in 1914, then entered the university. His studies were interrupted by World War I, and on his father's advice he went to Petrograd in 1915 to enroll in artillery school. He was sent to the Turkish front as a junior officer in the following year. When Russia withdrew from the war in 1918, Struve returned to Kharkov to resume his education, and soon caught up with his former classmates to take a first-class degree in astronomy. He became an instructor at the university, but when civil war broke out in Russia was recalled into the army under General Denikin, who was then retreating before the advancing Red Army.

In 1920 Struve was evacuated from the Crimea, along with the remnants of Denikin's army, and placed on a ship full of starving and dysentery-ridden refugees; no country would admit them, but Turkey allowed them a small territory in which the emigrants lived in tents during the winter of 1920–1921. Struve went to Constantinople in spring of the latter year, but was unable to find housing or employment, since the city was crowded with Russian emigrants.

While in Turkey, Struve, seeking news of his relatives in Russia, wrote to his uncle Georg Hermann Otto Struve, who was then in Berlin. Hermann Struve had died, but his widow wrote to his colleagues of their nephew's plight, and E. B. Frost, director of the Yerkes Observatory in Williams Bay, Wisconsin, invited him to come to the United States as an assistant observer in stellar spectroscopy. After surmounting considerable difficulties—he had no money and no visa—Struve left Turkey and reached Yerkes in November 1921. On Frost's advice, he immediately began spectral investigations of stars and continued his studies and improved his English. In 1923 he received the Ph.D. from the University of Chicago and in the following year became an instructor at the observatory. In 1927 he became an American citizen.

Struve quickly rose to prominence at Yerkes, becoming assistant professor in 1927, associate professor in 1930, assistant director in 1931, and, on Frost's retirement, director in 1932. He held the last post until 1947, when he became chairman and honorary director, a position he held until 1950. From 1932 until 1947 he also served as professor of astrophysics at the University of Chicago, which administered Yerkes.

Struve was also concerned with the founding of the McDonald Observatory in Texas. As he himself recounted, in an article published in *Sky and Telescope* (volume 24 [1962], 316–317),

> After becoming a staff member at Yerkes Observatory in 1921, I was most closely associated with George Van Biesbroeck. Together we determined many comet and asteroid positions with the 24-inch reflector. . . . But my main task was observing the spectra of *B* and *A* stars, following a program prepared by Director Edwin B. Frost. . . . It soon became apparent to Van Biesbroeck and me that very faint asteroids and comets could not be observed with the 24-inch. I also realized that the Bruce spectrograph was not suitable for medium or high-dispersion spectra of stars. . . . No wonder Van Biesbroeck and I spent many cloudy night hours trying to think how we could secure a moderately large reflector, preferably in some other location that had more clear nights. . . . Since we were thinking of a small observ-

ing station, equipped with a 60-inch telescope and operated from Yerkes, we wanted it to be not too far from headquarters. We consulted weather data, and noted a good location in the high plains of the Texas Panhandle, near Amarillo.

These plans were not immediately implemented, and it was only in 1932, after Struve had been invited to become assistant director of the Harvard Observatory, that the officials of the University of Chicago decided to offer him what he wanted. Struve became Yerkes' director in the same year, and the university appropriated $15,000 toward a new observatory—far less than the required amount.

The situation was soon resolved, however. A few years earlier, a banker from Paris, Texas, had left $800,000 to the state university at Austin to build and equip a new observatory; his will was contested in the courts for six years, but the money was available to the university by 1932, and Struve, who knew of the bequest, persuaded Robert M. Hutchins, president of the University of Chicago, to meet with the president of the University of Texas to discuss the construction of an observatory in common. "Within ten minutes," according to Struve, "the two university presidents had agreed upon a broad plan of cooperation, whereby Texas would pay for the telescope and retain ownership of it, while Chicago would pay all salaries and most of the operating expenses." Struve himself was to be director of the new observatory, and in the summer of the same year he took part in selecting a site on top of a double hill (named Mt. Locke, after the donor of the land) in west Texas. He immediately began writing to the directors of other large observatories, soliciting their suggestions, and to telescope-makers, asking for bids and proposals.

By 1936 the eighty-two-inch telescope, then the second-largest in the world, was nearly completed; Struve had assembled most of his staff, including C. T. Elvey, Morgan Kuiper, P. Swings, B. G. D. Strömgren, S. Chandrasekhar, and J. L. Greenstein. The observatory was dedicated on 5 May 1939, although a good deal of work was already under way there. Struve remained as its director until 1947, at which time he became honorary director and chairman of the astrophysics department, positions that he held for another two years. In the years just after World War II, he was able to recruit a number of distinguished European scientists, to whom he offered professorships at McDonald or Yerkes.

In 1950 Struve had begun to suffer from overwork and insomnia, and left McDonald and Yerkes to accept a less demanding appointment as head of the department of astronomy at the University of California at Berkeley, and director of its affiliated Leuschner Observatory. He proved to be a gifted teacher, especially of graduate students, and was able to continue his own research, including projects as a guest investigator at Mt. Wilson. He missed the autonomy and the direct access to the president he had had at Yerkes, however, and in 1959 he returned to that institution. In the same year he was offered the post of director of the new National Radio Astronomical Observatory, which was nearly completed at Green Bank, West Virginia, with its giant eighty-five-foot radio telescope. He took the job willingly, in part from a sense of moral obligation—he had himself written of the need to accept "those laborious and often thankless jobs that are needed for the general advancement of science." Within three years he had made the observatory, despite its geographic isolation, a first-rate scientific institution, staffed by a loyal and dedicated group of young scientists.

By 1962, Struve's health forced him to resign from the new observatory, but he was unable to remain idle for long, and soon accepted a joint professorship at the Institute of Advanced Study, Princeton, and the California Institute of Technology. He died soon after, survived by his mother, who had followed him to the United States in 1923, and by his wife, Mary Martha Lanning, a singer whom he had married in 1925. They had no children.

Although much of Struve's career was devoted to organization and administration, he nevertheless found time to conduct his own investigations. T. G. Cowling, in the memorial sketch of Struve published in the *Biographical Memoirs of Fellows of the Royal Society*, cites Swing's account of Struve's demanding schedule:

> While at Yerkes he used to start very early in the morning, finish late and take hardly any time for his meals. At McDonald he could relax somewhat from his administration duties, hence was eager to spend as much time as possible at the telescope. He loved challenges, physical as well as intellectual, and I have often seen him actively measuring at the microscope after only a few hours' sleep following a long winter night at the 82-inch. Occasionally he would drive from Williams Bay to Chicago in the morning, fly from Chicago to Big Spring [Texas], drive then (over 200 miles) to McDonald, and be ready for a whole night's work at the 82-inch.

Struve's chief astronomical and astrophysical interests lay in spectroscopic investigations of binary and variable stars and researches into stellar atmospheres, stellar rotation, the gaseous constituents of cosmic matter, and stellar evolution. The nature of his work was strongly influenced by Henry Norris Russell, and particularly by Russell's "Some Problems of Sidereal Astronomy," published in 1919. As Struve later wrote (in "The General Needs of Astronomy"), "My own work in astrophysics was stimulated and directed by this article, and even today [1955] it forms one of the most inspiring pieces of astronomical literature."

Struve's work in stellar spectroscopy was based upon protracted observations of minute changes in stellar spectra—widened and shifted lines, distortions of their contours, variations in linear intensities, the appearance of new lines and absorption bands and the disappearance of existing ones. From these observations he was able to derive a great number of spectral regularities and to point out the exceptional usefulness of the technique. He himself provided the means for further exploitation of the method by developing a means for obtaining wide-scale images of the spectra; he also, with Elvey, invented a nebular spectrograph that allows the photographic magnification of the contrast lines of weak diffuse nebulae, the spectra of which are not normally visible against the sky.

Struve investigated the gaseous constituents of cosmic matter throughout his career. As early as 1925 he showed that the stationary interstellar lines of calcium, which had been discovered by Harry Plaskett in the preceding year, are created by absorption in the extended gas clouds that are concentrated in the plane of the Milky Way. He demonstrated that these lines become more intense with distance, and, in the 1930's, working in collaboration with B. P. Gerasimovich, found the value for the density of the interstellar gaseous substratum to be 10^{-26} g./cm.^{3}, and its total mass to represent less than one percent of the complete stellar mass per unit of volume. In 1938, using his nebular spectrograph (which had been installed in both the Yerkes and McDonald observatories), Struve discovered the presence of areas of ionized hydrogen in interstellar space, a discovery crucial to modern radio astronomy. He also did research on the influence upon stellar spectra of the physical processes occurring in the stellar atmospheres, and used the division of separate spectral lines to determine that intermolecular electric fields act within the atmosphere of type A and B hot stars, and that gas turbulence also occurs there.

In 1928, in collaboration with G. A. Shayn, Struve confirmed the axial rotation of single stars that had been suggested as early as the time of Galileo. With Elvey, he investigated the rotation of several thousand stars, and established the relationship between the velocity of stellar rotation and spectral type. He paid particular attention to stars that exhibit an irregular variation in brightness, and attributed their instability to physical processes (for example, flashes, ejection of matter, or pulsation) occurring in either the stars themselves or in their surrounding atmospheres; he further maintained that the rapid rotation (more than 3,000 km./sec.) of certain extremely hot stars produces the effect that a fraction of the stellar atmosphere is thrown by centrifugal force toward the equator of the star. This condition might be expected to produce gaseous rings, and Struve discovered such rings for some stars in 1931. He then, from 1939 until 1949, made a series of meticulous studies of the formation of the gaseous ring around Pleione, in the Pleiades, and was able to detect its pulsation and rapid scattering.

Like his forebears, Struve was interested in double stars; indeed, his first scientific publication, in 1923, was an article "On the Double Star 9 Argus." It contained a considerable amount of data on the masses of components of this visually and spectroscopically binary star; two other articles published by Struve in the following year were devoted to the orbit of the spectroscopically binary star 43 Orionis and to the nature of binary stars of short period. In an article published in 1927 in the Russian journal *Mirovedenie*, Struve noted the time and effort required in observing binary stars, but went on to emphasize the value of such observations. By 1944, he was able to determine the statistical dependence between the periodicity and amplitude of the curve of distribution of line-of-sight velocity of 144 spectroscopically binary stars with periods of longer than 2.4 days. From these data Struve estimated the mean value of the stellar masses to be equivalent to about three solar masses, and he deduced a criterion for distinguishing RR Lyrae variable stars from true binary stars. He also made a study of close pairs and noted that the components of these unstable binary systems are elliptical in shape because of their mutual gravitation.

In his investigations of α Lyrae, Struve found it to be a closely paired, eclipsing binary system composed of a massive, hot, rapidly rotating blue giant and its smaller, cooler yellow satellite, in which the flow of gas from the hotter to the cooler

body surrounds the stars in a kind of circular envelope that extends into space and is partially dispersed there. In a more general investigation conducted with Su-Shu Huang, Struve concluded that the formation of binary stars is accompanied by a partial loss of mass by the parent body and by an exchange of mass and momentum. His observations of close pairs and irregular stars gave him considerable insight into nonstationary star processes and provided him an approach to problems of stellar evolution, an approach that he characterized in the preface to his *Stellar Evolution* of 1950:

> The purpose of observational research in astrophysics is to present a unified picture of a series of phenomena and to explain it in terms of a theory or hypothesis. The temptation is always to accumulate more and more factual data and to delay the process of interpretation because we rarely, if ever, feel satisfied that we have enough information to justify a generalization. . . . The Vanuxem Lectures at Princeton in 1949 presented a favorable occasion for taking stock in one field of astrophysics—that of the origin and evolution of single stars and, more especially, of close double stars. This subject has been treated before by other workers, but since their observational basis was different from mine I thought that it would be interesting to present this subject in the light of my own experience at the telescope. . . . I am, however, conscious of the fact that of necessity there is a great deal of speculation in any attempt to discuss the evolution of the stars. . . . The history of previous evolutionary hypotheses teaches us that most of them were wrong. Yet, they have contributed to our understanding of the universe and have, in almost every case, left a permanent imprint upon later hypotheses.

Although Struve's general hypothesis of stellar formation was not widely accepted, a number of aspects of his supporting research were greeted enthusiastically by his fellow astronomers. In particular, his demonstration of the interdependence of the velocity of stellar rotation and other stellar features—especially the positions of stars on the Hertzsprung-Russell diagram—and his detection of a correlation between speed of rotation and the distribution of stars within a cluster, the latter being an indication of the age of these stars, provided astrophysicists with the suggestion that rapid stellar velocities represent the residual motions of the turbulent vortices within the condensing diffuse medium from which the stars had arisen.

Struve was always glad to share his results with fellow workers. He considered international cooperation a necessity, since astronomy is a science of global scope, dependent upon observations made from all over the earth. In a presidential speech before the Dublin meeting of the International Astronomical Union, Struve in 1955 emphasized the problems of the development of an astronomy that would be practical for the launching of man-made satellites and space journeys. He pointed out the growing importance of sophisticated astronomical instrumentation and technology, but maintained that the most important tools of the science are the astronomers themselves.

Struve was also concerned with popularization and with communication among astronomers. From 1932 until 1947 he served as editor-in-chief of the *Astrophysical Journal*, and for more than forty years, from 1923 to 1963, was one of its most prolific authors as well. Between 1949 and 1963 Struve wrote an additional 152 articles (of which fourteen were published in two successive issues) for the more popular *Sky and Telescope*. He there demonstrated his ability to present complicated concepts of astrophysics so as to make them clear to the lay reader—although his pieces were also of interest to professional astronomers. A number of these writings were devoted to the history of science, a bent also apparent in *Stellar Evolution* and in *Astronomy of the Twentieth Century* (1962); and a number concerned the lives and careers of fellow scientists, including E. E. Barnard, the astronomer Charles Darwin, G. A. Shayn, and M. A. Kovalsky. (It may be noted that Struve was careful to acknowledge the work of his colleagues and to assign it its proper value; in particular he considered Barnard, an astronomer who worked at Yerkes until his death in 1923, as "the most capable and productive astronomical observer in the world.")

For several years Struve edited articles and compiled abstracts for *Astronomical Newsletter*. He was especially concerned with Russian works, since he always took a keen interest in developments there, and was vigorous in expounding Russian research.

Struve participated in the activities of many scientific institutions and societies. In addition to the International Astronomical Union, of which he was elected vice-president in 1948 and president in 1952, he held prominent posts in the National Academy of Science, the American Astronomical Society, the American Philosophical Society, and the National Scientific Council. He was a member of the Royal Astronomical Society of London, the Royal Astronomical Society of Canada, the Royal Astronomical Society of New Zealand, and the academies of science of Denmark, Amsterdam, Norway, Sweden, Belgium, and France. He re-

ceived honorary doctorates from more than ten universities.

In 1944 the Royal Astronomical Society of London gave Struve its highest award, the Gold Medal; he was the fourth member of his family to win it in some 118 years. In presenting the medal, the Society's president, E. A. Milne, noted that the awards council had been "totally uninfluenced by the glamour that surrounds the name Struve. . . . Professor Otto Struve . . . has earned this distinction in his proper right, by the overwhelming significance and value of his brilliant observational and interpretational work in stellar and nebular spectroscopy."

BIBLIOGRAPHY

I. ORIGINAL WORKS. The most complete bibliography of Struve's writings (six books and 446 articles) follows A. Unsöld's obituary in *Mitteilungen der Astronomischen Gesellschaft* (1963), 11–22; it does not, however, include Struve's more than 180 popular scientific articles in *Sky and Telescope*, 6–25 (1946–1963) and *Popular Astronomy*, 32–59 (1924–1951), or his 45 book reviews in *Astrophysical Journal*, 60–110 (1924–1949). His books are *Stellar Evolution. An Exploration From the Observatory* (Princeton, 1950); *The Astronomical Universe* (Eugene, Ore., 1958); *Elementary Astronomy* (New York, 1959), written with B. Lynds and H. Pillans; *The Universe* (Cambridge, Mass., 1961); *Astronomy of the Twentieth Century* (New York–London, 1962), written with V. Zebergs; and *Stellar Spectroscopy*, 2 vols. (Trieste, 1969–1970), written with M. Hack.

II. SECONDARY LITERATURE. There are notices and obituaries on Struve by B. V. Kukarin and P. G. Kulikovsky, in *Astronomicheskii zhurnal*, **40**, no. 6 (1963), 1126–1129; G. J. Odgers, in *Journal of the Royal Astronomical Society of Canada*, **57**, no. 4 (1963), 170–172; C. Payne-Gaposchkin, in *Sky and Telescope*, **25**, no. 6 (1963), 308–310; J. Sahade, in *Ciencia e investigación*, **19** (1963), 195–198; S. Chandrasekhar, in *Astrophysical Journal*, **139**, no. 2 (1964), 423; T. G. Cowling, in *Biographical Memoirs of Fellows of the Royal Society*, **10** (1964), 283–304; L. Goldberg, in *Quarterly Journal of the Royal Astronomical Society*, **5**, no. 3 (1964), 284–290; and P. Swings, in *Bulletin de l'Académie r. de Belgique. Classe des sciences*, 5th ser., **49**, no. 6 (1964), 523–524.

Other sources on Struve's life and work (listed chronologically) are E. A. Milne, "Address. Delivered . . . on the Award of the Gold Medal to Professor Otto Struve," in *Monthly Notices of the Royal Astronomical Society*, **104**, no. 2 (1944), 112–120; A. I. Eremeeva, "Otto Ludwig Struve," in *Vydayushchiesya astronomy mira* ("The World's Leading Astronomers"; Moscow, 1966), 348–357; M. Hack, ed., *Modern Astrophysics*

(Paris – New York, 1967), a memorial volume of collected works dedicated to Struve; P. G. Kulikovsky, *O. Struve i V. Zebergs. Astronomia XX veka* (". . . Twentieth-Century Astronomy"; Moscow, 1968), 5–11; and G. H. Herbig, ed., *Spectroscopic Astrophysics. An Assessment of the Contribution of Otto Struve* (Berkeley, Calif., 1970).

Z. K. SOKOLOVSKAYA

STRUVE, OTTO WILHELM (or **Otton Vasilievich**) (*b.* Dorpat, Russia [now Tartu, Estonian S.S.R.], 7 May 1819; *d.* Karlsruhe, Germany, 14 April 1905), *astronomy, geodesy.*

The son of F. G. W. Struve and his first wife, Emily Wall, Struve entered the University of Dorpat in 1834 and three years later, while still a student, began to work as an assistant at the university observatory, where he carried out observations under the guidance of his father. In 1839 he graduated with a dissertation entitled "Reduction der am 19/7 März in Dorpat beobachten Plejadenbedeckung" and became adjunct astronomer at the new Pulkovo Observatory, of which his father was director. He himself spent fifty years at Pulkovo, becoming vice-director in 1848 and director in 1862.

Struve shared his father's broad astronomical and geodetic interests and collaborated with him on a number of projects, especially during his early years at Pulkovo. He participated in the systematic survey of all the stars from the north pole to 15° south declination and discovered and described several hundred of the double stars that were included in the *Catalogue revu et corrigé des étoiles doubles et multiples découvertes à l'observatoire central de Poulcova*, published in 1853. He simultaneously began the investigation of the motion of binary and multiple stars that occupied him for almost forty years, during which time he made 6,080 micrometric observations of more than 905 systems. The results of these studies were published in the ninth volume of *Observations de Poulkova* in 1878; in a preface, Struve described his research on systematic errors of micrometric measurements and described the formula he had worked out for their correction by means of a model of double star systems. His work on astronomical constants led him to the determination, in the 1850's, of a value for the constant of precession that was used throughout the world until 1895, when Simon Newcomb derived a more accurate one. This work won Struve the gold medal of the Royal Astronomical Society.

In taking up his father's work on stellar parallaxes, Struve chose to concentrate on those stars — α Lyrae, 61 Cygni, η and μ Cassiopeiae, α Aurigae, and α Aquilae, for example — of which the great motion was assumed to account for their relative closeness to the earth. He was also concerned with the structure of the universe and adhered to William Herschel's theories of the development of stars from nebulae. The great variety of nebula forms, he believed, might represent various stages of star formation, and for this reason he paid particularly close attention to nebulae — such as those in Orion — that are relatively close to stars. Struve maintained that a direct physical link existed among stars which appear to be in the center of nebulae and those which had originated from nebular material. Some of his conclusions are obviously wrong, as for example his belief that only one stellar system could exist in the admittedly infinite universe and that this system — the Milky Way — must be a uniform kinematic entity, having no central body and extending, probably infinitely, into the unknown.

Struve took part in a number of scientific expeditions. In 1842 he went with his father to Lipetsk to observe the solar eclipse and to carry out chronometric observations, while in 1842 and 1843 he participated in the elder Struve's expeditions to Altona and Greenwich, by which the longitudinal relationship of the Pulkovo and Greenwich observatories was established. He himself made further trips between 1846 and 1857 to determine the longitudinal relationships of Pulkovo and Moscow, Warsaw, Kazan, Dorpat, and Arkhangelsk, and observed two other solar eclipses (at Lomge in 1851 and at Pobes, Spain, in 1860). From the latter he was led to conclude that the protuberances visible on the solar surface during eclipses originate on the sun itself.

Much of Struve's geodetic work was conducted in the 1850's, prior to his succession to the directorship of the Pulkovo Observatory. He served as astronomical adviser to the Military Topographic Department of General Staff Headquarters in St. Petersburg from 1847 until 1862 and to the Hydrographic Department of the Marine Ministry from 1854 until 1864. In these posts he dealt with problems of practical astronomy, geodesy, and hydrography, particularly those of latitudinal and longitudinal measurement, accurate altimetric measurement of European Russia, and the improvement of instrumentation. He supported the United States' proposal to introduce a common prime meridian, and discussed this project with American scientists in 1884 when he went to the United States to commission a large refractor for the Pulkovo Observatory from Alvan Clark. His interest in instrumentation extended to spectroscopy and photography, and under his guidance an astrophysical laboratory was established at Pulkovo.

Struve took an active part in the affairs of the Russian Geographical Society, and he served as chairman of its department of mathematical geography from 1860 to 1866; he was also a member of the commission that equipped expeditions to the North Urals and to Central Asia to study the old bed of the Amu-Darya River. He was a member of the St. Petersburg Academy of Sciences and of the French Académie des Sciences; an enthusiastic advocate of international scientific cooperation, he was from 1867 to 1878 chairman of the German Astronomical Society. He was also chairman of the Paris congress on establishing the standard meter (1872) and of the International Commission on Sky Photography (1887).

In 1889, at the end of fifty years of service to the Pulkovo Observatory, Struve resigned as director and went to Karlsruhe, where other members of his family were living. Despite his advanced age, he frequently lectured at the Naturalists' Society of the Technische Hochschule there. He was married twice, first to Emily Dirssen and then, following her death, to Emma Yankovskaya. He had seven children, of whom two sons, Hermann and Ludwig Struve, carried the family profession into a new generation.

BIBLIOGRAPHY

I. ORIGINAL WORKS. Struve's more than 130 published works include "Bestimmung der Constanten der Praecession, mit Berücksichtigung der eigenen Bewegung des Sonnensystems," in *Mémoires de l'Académie impériale des sciences de St.-Pétersbourg*, Ser. sci. math. et phys., 6th ser., **5**, no. 1 (1844), 17–124; "Catalogue revu et corrigé des étoiles doubles découvertes à Poulkova," *ibid.*, 6th ser., **7**, no. 4 (1853), 385–405; "Issledovanie o kompensatsii khronometrov" ("Studies on the Compensation of Chronometers"), in *Morskoi sbornik*, **21**, no. 4 (1856), 52–93; "Nouvelle détermination de la parallaxe annuelle des étoiles α Lyrae et 61 Cygni," in *Mémoires de l'Academie impériale des sciences de St.-Pétersbourg*, 7th ser., **1**, no. 1 (1859), 1–51: "O zvezdnykh sistemakh i tumannykh pyatnakh" ("On Stellar Systems and Nebular Spots"), in *Zapiski Imperatorskoi akademii nauk*, **1**, no. 2 (1862), 145–161; and *Obzor deyatelnosti Nikolaevskoy Glavnoy (Pulkovskoy) observatorii v prodolzhenie pervykh 25 let ee sushchestvovania* ("Survey of the Activities of the Nikolaev Main [Pulkovo] Observatory During Its First Twenty-Five Years"; St. Petersburg, 1865).

Subsequent works include "Résultats de quelques observations supplémentaires faites sur des étoiles doubles artificielles," in *Bulletin de l'Académie impériale des sciences de St.-Pétersbourg*, **12** (1867), 73–95; "O pervom meridiane" ("On the Prime Meridian"), in *Izvestiya Imperatorskogo Russkogo geograficheskogo obshchestva*, **6**, sec. 2 (1870), 1–14; "Ob uslugakh, okazannykh Petrom Velikim matematicheskoy geografii Rossii" ("On the Service of Peter the Great to the Mathematical Geography of Russia"), in *Zapiski Imperatorskoi akademii nauk*, **20**, no. 1 (1872), 1–19; "O resheniakh, prinyatykh na Vashingtonskoy konferentsii otnositelno pervogo meridiana i vselenskogo vremeni" ("On the Resolutions Adopted at the Washington Conference Regarding the Prime Meridian and Universal Greenwich Civil Time," *ibid.*, **50**, supp. 3 (1885), 1–25; "Die Photographie im Dienste der Astronomie," in *Bulletin de l'Académie impériale des sciences de St.-Pétersbourg*, **30** (1886), 484–500; and "Mesures micrométriques des étoiles doubles," in *Observations de Poulkova*, **10**, pt. 2 (1893), 1–226.

II. SECONDARY LITERATURE. On Struve and his work, see *Otton Vasilievich Struve. Materialy dlya biograficheskogo slovarya deystvitelnykh chlenov Imperatorskoy Akademii nauk* (" . . . Materials for the Biographical Dictionary of Full Members of the Imperial Academy of Sciences"), pt. 2 (Petrograd, 1917), 177–182, which includes a bibliography of 131 of his works; D. I. Dubyago, "O nauchnykh zaslugakh akademika Ottona Vasilievicha Struve" ("On the Scientific Merits of Academician Otton Vasilievich Struve"), in *Sobranie protokolov Obshchestva estestvoispytateley pri Kazanskom universitete*, **5** (1887), 141–151.

There are obituaries by M. Nyren, in *Vierteljahrsschrift der Astronomischen Gesellschaft*, **40** (1905), 286–303; and by A. A. Ivanov, in *Izvestiya Russkago astronomicheskago obshchestva*, **11**, nos. 5–6 (1905), 222–224.

Z. K. SOKOLOVSKAYA

STUART, ALEXANDER (*b*. Aberdeen [?], Scotland, 1673; *d*. London [?], England, September 1742), *physiology*.

Stuart, in 1738 the first Croonian lecturer on muscle physiology at the Royal Society, was a Scotsman of obscure origin and uncertain early history. After receiving his M.A. from Marischal College, Aberdeen, in 1691, he enrolled as a medical student at Leiden, on 14 December 1709, at the age of thirty-six, and graduated M.D. two years later. Appointed physician to Westminster Hospital, London, upon its creation in 1719, he was admitted licentiate of the College of Physicians in June 1720. In 1728 he was designated physician to the queen, admitted to the M.D. at Cambridge (Comitiis Regiis), and elevated to a fellowship in the College of Physicians. Stuart achieved some prominence in the College, serving as censor in 1732 and again in 1741. He was also elected fellow of the Royal Society in 1714, was a recipient of its Copley Medal many years later for his work on muscles, and achieved membership in the Académie Royale des Sciences.

Prior to the publication of his Croonian lectures as a special supplement to the *Philosophical Transactions of the Royal Society* in 1739, Stuart had contributed three well-received papers to the same journal. Two of these papers considered the role of bile as a stimulus to the peristaltic motion of the intestines and raised general questions regarding the "animal oeconomy," and the third reported experiments attempting to demonstrate the existence of a fluid in the nerves. Stuart also published in 1738 a substantial essay on the structure and function of muscles: *Dissertatio de structura et motu musculari*. This essay was an expanded version of his inaugural dissertation for the M.D. at Leiden, presented in 1711.

Stuart's principal concern both in his *Dissertatio*, and in the Croonian lectures based closely on it, was to demonstrate that a strict hydraulic iatromechanism was the best theory by which to account for muscular motion. Unlike contemporary British writers who in the 1730's advanced theories of muscular action based on the wavelike movement of animal spirits and the jiggling of elastic nerve fibers, Stuart insisted that the mechanics of sanguinary and nervous fluids, and of their vessels, alone governs the action of the muscles. The forceful flow of blood in the arteries and veins and the trickle of liquid juice through the nerves suffice to cause and control muscular motion.

Stuart saw the muscles as an elaborate network of vessels and open spaces, in basic design not unlike the lungs. The proximate cause of systole is the elastic restitution of the walls of the muscular blood vessels, which had been expanded in a preceding diastole.[1] Alternate systole and diastole accelerates and retards blood flow through the capillary vessels. This effect in turn allows small quantities of nervous juice to exercise a large control over blood flow and, hence, over systole and diastole. Nervous control is concentrated in the neural fiber, which Stuart thought of as "a chain of distensile vesicles whose sides are covered with a net-work of elastic longitudinal and transverse blood-vessels."[2] Since blood flow is particularly difficult when the capillary vessels have been longi-tudinally stretched and their transverse diameters shortened, the dripping of nerve juice into the vesicles (around which the capillaries are woven) can quickly reverse the hydraulic circumstances. The dimensions of the neural vesicles will subtly alter with the addition of nerve juice, and this modification will cause capillary diameters to alter too. This latter alteration can quickly intensify because the pressure of inflowing blood will multiply the initial effect. Dramatic alterations of blood flow within the muscles can throw them from systole to diastole, or vice versa. Antagonist muscles can thus be seen as if poised in a fine static balance, with the blood mass shared between them via commonly connected vessels ready to switch from one "balance pan" to another nearly instantaneously.[3] The trickle of nerve juice, initiated by the immaterial spirit or mind, can therefore cause the elevation or depression of the muscle balance pans, that is, the systole and diastole of muscle pairs.

Stuart quite possibly derived his theory from analogous ideas on heartbeat and its nervous control introduced by Boerhaave in his *Institutiones medicinae*.[4] Stuart also resorted to several kinds of direct empirical evidence. He explored muscular anatomy through the microscope and with the help of excarnation and injection techniques.[5] He tried to prove the elasticity of the blood vessels by tying arteries, veins, and nerves next to one another onto a wooden board and watching the blood vessels but not the nerves contract.[6] He dissected out a demonstration muscle pair and attendant vessels; common blood vessels and individual nerve supplies were clearly indicated in the special preparation.[7] Finally, Stuart tried to demonstrate his basic theory of muscle action by suspending a decapitated frog by its forelegs in a frame and then pushing down on the exposed spinal cord with a blunt probe. The hind legs of the frog twitched, and Stuart explained this by claiming that the probe forced a small quantity of nerve juice from the spinal cord into the appropriate muscles, the small increment of nervous liquid being sufficient mechanically to trip muscle contraction.[8]

It was for the decapitated "spinal frog" experiment that Stuart was most widely known by his eighteenth-century successors. It did not, however, originate with him. Decapitated spinal frog experiments can easily be traced into the seventeenth century and, in one form, perhaps even as far back as Leonardo da Vinci.[9] Robert Whytt credited the experiment to Stephen Hales, a contemporary of Stuart and a correspondent of Whytt.[10] But it was

Stuart, because of the presumptive importance of the experiment to his iatromechanical theory, who gave it greatly enhanced attention and by doing so fixed the decapitated frog in the imagination of later eighteenth-century physiologists. Albrecht von Haller, at any rate, referred to Stuart's "very useful facts,"[11] and Robert Whytt often mentioned Stuart's work.[12] Both Whytt and Haller focused on the phenomena and largely ignored Stuart's hypotheses. The experiment was borrowed, repeated, and made increasingly more sophisticated. The clarifying articulation of reflex theory in the latter half of the eighteenth century thus owes an unintended but considerable debt to Stuart, for as J. F. Fulton suggested, the decapitated frog became in that period ". . . one of the first martyrs of science."[13]

NOTES

1. Alexander Stuart, *Dissertatio de structura et motu musculari* (London, 1738), p. 120.
2. Alexander Stuart, *Three Lectures on Muscular Motion,* . . . (London, 1739), p. xiii.
3. *Ibid.*, p. vii.
4. *Dr. Boerhaave's Academical Lectures on the Theory of Physic*, II (London, 1743), pp. 75, sect. 190.
5. See, for example, *Dissertatio*, pp. 36 and 47.
6. *Three Lectures*, p. iii.
7. *Ibid.*, p. vi.
8. *Ibid.*, pp. xxxvii–xxxix.
9. See, for example, Georges Canguilhem, *La formation du concept de réflexe* (Paris, 1955), p. 91.
10. See R. K. French, *Robert Whytt, the Soul, and Medicine* (London, 1969), p. 86.
11. Albrecht von Haller, "A Dissertation on the Sensible and Irritable Parts of Animals," Owsei Temkin, ed., in *Bulletin of the History of Medicine*, **4** (1936), 694.
12. French, *op. cit., passim.*
13. Quoted in Canguilhem, *op. cit.*, p. 89.

BIBLIOGRAPHY

I. ORIGINAL WORKS. Stuart's two principal extant works are *Dissertatio de structura et motu musculari* (London, 1738); and *Three Lectures on Muscular Motion, Read Before the Royal Society in the Year 1738* (London, 1739). The *British Museum Catalogue* also lists *Dissertatio medica inauguralis de structura et motu musculari, etc.* (Leiden, 1711), and *New Discoveries and Improvements in Anatomy and Surgery . . . With Cases and Cures* (London, 1738).

Three of Stuart's major papers are "An Essay Upon the Use of the Bile in the Animal Oeconomy, Founded on an Observation of a Wound in the Gallbladder," in *Philosophical Transactions of the Royal Society*, **36** (1729–1730), 341–363; "Experiments to Prove the Existence of a Fluid in the Nerves," *ibid.*, **37** (1731–1732), 327–331; and "Explanation of an Essay on the Use of the Bile in the Animal Oeconomy," *ibid.*, **38** (1733–1734), 5–25.

II. SECONDARY LITERATURE. Stuart has rarely been studied, although in recent years he has been receiving increasing notice. Biographical essentials can be found in Robert W. Innes-Smith, *English-Speaking Students of Medicine at the University of Leyden* (Edinburgh, 1932), 226; and more extensively in William Munk, *The Role of the Royal College of Physicians of London*, II (London, 1878), 109. More than passing mention of Stuart's work is made in R. K. French, *Robert Whytt, the Soul, and Medicine* (London, 1969), 90, 150–151; Karl E. Rothschuh, *History of Physiology*, Guenter B. Risse, trans. (Huntington, N.Y., 1973), 138, 183; and Robert Schofield, *Mechanism and Materialism: British Natural Philosophy in an Age of Reason* (Princeton, 1970), 192–193. Also of considerable utility in setting the eighteenth-century context for Stuart's work are E. Bastholm, *The History of Muscle Physiology* (Copenhagen, 1950); and Georges Canguilhem, *La formation du concept de réflexe* (Paris, 1955).

THEODORE M. BROWN

STUDER, BERNHARD (*b.* Büren, Switzerland, 21 August 1794; *d.* Bern, Switzerland, 2 May 1887), *geology.*

Studer, the son of Samuel Studer, a Protestant pastor, spent most of his youth in Bern, where his father had been appointed professor of practical theology in 1796 at the Bern Academy. To please his family, Studer agreed to study theology, although at the same time he became increasingly interested in mathematics and science. After earning his theology degree, he decided to study these subjects, first at Bern and then, from 1816 to 1818, at Göttingen. He then returned to Bern to teach mathematics at the municipal Gymnasium. He was later given a post at the Bern Academy, where, in addition to mathematics, he taught physics, mathematical geography, and mineralogy. His teaching and publications made him well known, and, shortly after its founding in 1834, the University of Bern offered him the professorship of geology and mineralogy, which he held until his retirement in 1873.

Studer's scientific writings are devoted to the geology of Switzerland, particularly to the Swiss Alps. In his first major work, on the Molasse (1825), he showed himself to be a master of careful, precise observation and clear presentation. His other major publications include *Geologie der westlichen Schweizer Alpen* (1834) and "Die Gebirgsmasse von Davos" (1837). With Arnold Escher von der Linth, his lifelong friend and collaborator,

Studer wrote *Geologische Beschreibung von Mittel-Bündten* (1839). This work, as well as a number of subsequent ones, culminated in 1853 in a further collaboration with Escher: the first geological map of Switzerland. (It was on a scale of 1:380,000; a second edition was published in 1869.) The map was based on painstakingly detailed observations and thorough preliminary studies made throughout the country. Before its appearance, Studer published a text designed to accompany it, entitled *Geologie der Schweiz* (1851–1853); together, map and text constitute the crowning achievement of Studer's scientific work. The *Geologie* contains the first comprehensive description of the structure of the Swiss Alps, which have been of extraordinary importance for understanding the formation of the former and existing mountains of the world, and represents the point of departure for all later synthetic accounts.

In the following years Studer devoted great energy to editing a geological map of Switzerland on a scale of 1:100,000, four times greater than his earlier map. The research on this map, which was based on Dufour's excellent topographical map, was conducted by a geological commission created for this purpose and placed under Studer's direction. (This commission still exists as the Swiss Geological Commission and is responsible for national geological surveys.) The new map ultimately consisted of twenty-one sheets, the first appearing in 1865, the last in 1887, on the day of Studer's death.

Besides his geological works, Studer wrote textbooks on physics and mechanics and on mathematical and physical geography. He was also the author of an extensive history of the physical geography of Switzerland. With Escher, he was one of the founders of modern Alpine geology in Switzerland.

BIBLIOGRAPHY

I. ORIGINAL WORKS. Besides many articles and papers, Studer published a number of larger works: *Beyträge zu einer Monographie der Molasse . . .* (Bern, 1825); *Geologie der Westlichen Schweizer Alpen* (Heidelberg, 1834), with 5 plates and a geological map; "Die Gebirgsmasse von Davos," in *Neue Denkschriften der Allgemeinen schweizerischen Gesellschaft für die gesamten Naturwissenschaften*, **1** (1837), with 3 plates; *Geologische Beschreibung von Mittel-Bündten* (Bern, 1839), with 2 plates and 3 maps, written with A. Escher von der Linth; *Geologie der Schweiz*, 2 vols. (Bern–Zurich, 1851–1853); *Einleitung in das Studium der Physik und Elemente der Mechanik* (Bern, 1859); *Ge-*

schichte der physischen Geographie der Schweiz bis 1815 (Bern–Zurich, 1863); and *Index der Petrographie und Stratigraphie der Schweiz und ihrer Umgebungen* (Bern, 1872).

II. SECONDARY LITERATURE. On Studer and his work, see A. Daubrée, "Notice sur les travaux de M. Studer," in *Comptes rendus hebdomadaires des séances de l'Académie des sciences*, **104** (1887), 1203–1205; C. W. von Gümbel, in *Neue deutsche Biographie*, XXXVI (Leipzig, 1893), 731–734; Albert Heim, *Geologie der Schweiz*, I (Leipzig, 1919), 7–8, with portrait; H. Hölder, *Geologie und Paläontologie in Texten und ihrer Geschichte* (Freiburg im Breisgau–Munich, 1960), *passim*; J. W. Judd, "B. Studer," in *Quarterly Journal of the Geological Society of London*, **44** (1888), 49–50; R. Lauterborn, "Der Rhein. Naturgeschichte eines deutschen Stromes . . .," in *Berichte der Naturforschenden Gesellschaft zu Freiburg im Breisgau*, **33** (1934), 110–113; L. Rütimeyer, "Prof. Bernhardt Studer," in *Verhandlungen der schweizerischen naturforschenden Gesellschaft*, **70** (1887), 177–205; R. Wolf, "Notizen zur schweizerischen Kulturgeschichte," in *Vierteljahrsschrift der Naturforschenden Gesellschaft in Zürich*, **32** (1887), 90–104; and K. A. von Zittel, *History of Geology and Palaeontology*, Maria M. Ogilvie-Gordon, transl. (London, 1901), *passim*.

H. TOBIEN

STUDY, EDUARD (*b.* Coburg, Germany, 23 March 1862; *d.* Bonn, Germany, 6 January 1930), *mathematics*.

Study, the son of a Gymnasium teacher, studied mathematics and science, beginning in 1880, at the universities of Jena, Strasbourg, Leipzig, and Munich. One of his favorite subjects was biology, and even late in life he investigated entomological questions and assembled an imposing butterfly collection. He received the doctorate from the University of Munich in 1884 and the following year became a *Privatdozent* in mathematics at Leipzig, where he was influenced chiefly by Paul Gordan, an expert in invariant theory.

In 1888 Study left this post to take a similar one at Marburg. From July 1893 to May 1894 he lectured in the United States, mainly at the Johns Hopkins University. He was appointed extraordinary professor at Göttingen in 1894 and full professor at Greifswald in 1897. In 1904 he succeeded Lipschitz at Bonn, where he remained until his retirement in 1927; he died of cancer three years later.

Study was largely self-taught in mathematics, and his writings reflect a highly individual way of thinking. He worked in many areas of geometry but did not accept the geometric axiomatics that Pasch and Hilbert were then developing. (On this point see Study's remarks in his more philosophical writings [1, 2].) Study mastered Grassmann's *Ausdehnungslehre*, Lie's theory of continuous groups, and the calculus of invariant theory; he was highly skilled at employing related algebraic techniques in the solution of geometric questions.

It was then usual for geometers to state their findings with little concern for exactitude in individual aspects of problems, and many theorems were labeled simply "in general," without any indication of the scope of their validity. Questions concerning real numbers, for example, were not carefully distinguished from those concerning complex numbers. Many of Study's papers were addressed to drawing such distinctions. His objections, buttressed by counterexamples, to Schubert's principle of the conservation of number were particularly well known, and the principle was eventually firmly established with suitable restrictions on its range of applicability [3].

In his own work Study demonstrated what he considered to be a thorough treatment of a problem. Moreover, a number of the problems he chose to discuss—for example, Apollonius' tangent problem [4] and Lie's straight-line–sphere transformation [5]—had long been thought resolved. Study was the first to show how the totality of the conic sections of the plane—that is, the conic sections considered as unions of elements—can be mapped into a point set M_5 of P_{27} [6].

With Corrado Segre, Study was one of the leading pioneers in the geometry of complex numbers. He systematically constructed the analytic geometry of the complexly extended Euclidean spaces R_2 and R_3; and, with Fubini, he was the first to introduce metrics for these spaces [7]. His contributions to complex differential geometry include the first systematic studies of isotropic curves and the introduction of isotropic parameters [8].

Adept in the methods of invariant theory—which are almost completely forgotten today—Study, employing the identities of the theory, sought to demonstrate that geometric theorems are independent of coordinates. This undertaking was not a simple one, but he achieved a number of successes. In a long work [9] he derived the formulas of spherical trigonometry from a new point of view, and in the process created many links between trigonometry and other branches of mathematics. He wrote other works on invariant theory, but they provoked little response even at the time of their publication [10].

Study was the first to investigate systematically all algebras possessing up to four generators over R and C [11], including W. R. Hamilton's quaternions, which interested him chiefly because of their applications to geometry and Lie groups. In his long work *Geometrie der Dynamen* [12] Study made a particularly thorough examination of Euclidean kinematics and the related subject of the mechanics of rigid bodies. Unfortunately, because of its awkward style and surfeit of new concepts, this work has never found the public it merits.

BIBLIOGRAPHY

I. ORIGINAL WORKS.
[1] *Die realistische Weltansicht und die Lehre vom Raume* (Brunswick, 1914; 2nd ed. 1923).
[2] *Denken und Darstellung in Mathematik und Naturwissenschaften*, 2nd ed. (Brunswick, 1928).
[3] "Über das sogenannte Prinzip von der Erhaltung der Anzahl," in *Archiv der Mathematik und Physik*, 3rd ser., **8** (1905), 271–278.
"Das Prinzip der Erhaltung der Anzahl," in *Berichte über die Verhandlungen der K. Sächsischen Gesellschaft der Wissenschaften zu Leipzig*, Math.-phys. Kl., **68** (1916), 65–92.
[4] "Das Apollonische Problem," in *Mathematische Annalen*, **49** (1897), 497–542.
[5] "Vereinfachte Begründung von Lie's Kugelgeometrie," in *Sitzungsberichte der Preussischen Akademie der Wissenschaften zu Berlin*, **27** (1926), 360–380.
[6] "Über die Geometrie der Kegelschnitte, insbesondere Charakteristikenproblem," in *Mathematische Annalen*, **27** (1886), 58–101.
[7] "Kürzeste Wege im komplexen Gebiet," *ibid.*, **60** (1905), 327–378.
[8] "Zur Differentialgeometrie der analytischen Kurven," in *Transactions of the American Mathematical Society*, **10** (1909), 1–49.
[9] "Sphärische Trigonometrie, orthogonale Substitutionen und elliptische Funktionen," in *Abhandlungen der Sächsischen Akademie der Wissenschaften*, **20** (1893), 83–232.
[10] *Methoden zur Theorie der ternären Formen* (Leipzig, 1889); and *Einleitung in die Theorie der invarianten linearen Transformationen auf Grund der Vektorrechnung* (Brunswick, 1923).
[11] "Theorie der gemeinen und höheren komplexen Grössen," in *Encyklopädie der mathematischen Wissenschaften*, I, pt. 4 (Leipzig).
[12] *Geometrie der Dynamen . . .* (Leipzig, 1903).
II. SECONDARY LITERATURE. See F. Engel, "Eduard Study," in *Jahresberichte der Deutschen Mathematikervereinigung*, **40** (1931), 133–156; and E. A. Weiss, "Eduard Study, ein Nachruf," in *Sitzungsberichte der Berliner mathematischen Gesellschaft*, **10** (1930), 52–77; "Eduard Study's mathematischen Schriften," in

Jahresberichte der Deutschen Mathematikvereinigung, **43** (1934), 108–124, 211–225.

WERNER BURAU

STURGEON, WILLIAM

STURGEON, WILLIAM (*b.* Whittington, Lancashire, England, 22 May 1783; *d.* Prestwick, Manchester, England, 4 December 1850), *physics.*

Sturgeon's father, John Sturgeon, is described as an ingenious but idle shoemaker who poached fish and raised gamecocks. His mother, Betsy Adcock, was the daughter of a small shopkeeper.

After a disagreeable apprenticeship to a shoemaker, beginning in 1796, Sturgeon in 1802 joined the militia and two years later enlisted in the Royal Artillery. He was stationed at Woolwich, where he studied natural science at night and performed occasional electrical experiments, which attracted some attention. He left the service in 1820, at the age of thirty-seven, and took up the trade of bootmaker in Woolwich. About 1804 he married a widow named Hutton; they had three children who died in infancy. In 1829 he married Mary Bromley of Shrewsbury; they had one child who died in infancy and one adopted child, Sturgeon's niece.

Sturgeon had developed mechanical skills useful for making scientific apparatus, and he lectured on science to schools and other groups. He was a member of the Woolwich Literary Society and in 1824 was appointed lecturer in science and philosophy at the East India Company Royal Military College of Addiscombe. In 1832 he was on the lecture staff of the short-lived Adelaide Gallery of Practical Science, and in 1840 he went to Manchester to become superintendent of the Royal Victoria Gallery of Practical Sciences. He held this last post for four years, after which he supported his family from his income as an itinerant lecturer. He was a member of the Manchester Literary and Philosophical Society and through the influence of its president received a grant of £200 from Lord John Russell and later, in 1849, an annuity of £50.

Sturgeon's major achievements concerned electromagnetism. In 1825 he received a silver medal and thirty guineas from the Society of Arts in recognition of his electromagnetic apparatus, including his important refinement of the design of the electromagnet. He placed a bar of soft iron in a solenoid and found that the magnetic effect was greatly increased. A coating of shellac on the bar served as insulation between it and the bare wires; Joseph Henry later insulated the wires themselves, thus allowing many more turns and an additional increase in the magnetic force.

Sturgeon's other contributions were mainly designs of apparatus for displaying electromagnetic phenomena. In this respect he exemplified that small but important group of instrumentmakers and lecturers who sought means of exhibiting electrical science in graphic and exciting ways.

In 1836 Sturgeon established a monthly periodical, *Annals of Electricity*, which lasted through ten volumes until 1843, when he founded a successor journal, *Annals of Philosophical Discovery and Monthly Reporter of the Progress of Science and Art*. This journal was terminated at the end of the same year.

BIBLIOGRAPHY

I. ORIGINAL WORKS. Sturgeon's works include *Experimental Researches in Electromagnetism, Galvanism . . .* (London, 1830); *Lectures on Electricity Delivered in The Royal Victorian Gallery, Manchester* (London, 1842); *Twelve Elementary Lectures on Galvanism* (London, 1843); and *Scientific Researches* (Manchester, 1850), which contains all of his important works. In 1843 he edited a reissue of William Barlow's *Magnetical Advertisements* (London, 1616).

Sturgeon's articles, which number about seventy, are listed in the Royal Society *Catalogue of Scientific Papers*, V, 876–878. The description of his magnet appears in "Account of an Electromagnetic Apparatus," in *Annals of Philosophy*, **12** (1826), 357–361. Apparently none of his manuscripts or apparatus has been preserved.

II. SECONDARY LITERATURE. A relatively lengthy entry by William Dee appears in the *Dictionary of National Biography* and a *Biographical Note* by S. P. Thompson was privately printed in 1891. Other, shorter notices are mentioned in Dee's account.

BERNARD S. FINN

STURM, CHARLES-FRANÇOIS

STURM, CHARLES-FRANÇOIS (*b.* Geneva, Switzerland, 29 September 1803; *d.* Paris, France, 18 December 1855), *mathematics, physics.*

Sturm's family, originally from Strasbourg, had lived in Geneva since the middle of the eighteenth century. He was the elder son of Jean-Henri Sturm, a teacher of arithmetic, and Jeanne-Louise-Henriette Gremay. Sturm at first studied classics, a field in which he displayed considerable ability. For example, at age sixteen he improvised Greek and Latin verses without the aid of a dictionary. In order to perfect his German, he attended the Lutheran church to hear sermons given in that language. In 1819, the year of his father's death, Sturm abandoned his literary studies and devoted himself to mathematics. At the Geneva Academy he attended the mathematics lectures of Simon L'Huillier and the physics lectures of Marc-Auguste Pictet and Pierre Prevost. L'Huillier, who in 1821 was preparing to retire, soon discovered Sturm's abilities; he encouraged Sturm, offered him advice, and lent him books. His influence, however, was less decisive than that of his successor, Jean-Jacques Schaub.[1] Sturm also attended a course in mathematics given by Baron Jean-Frédéric-Théodore Maurice and one in astronomy taught by Alfrède Gautier. Among Sturm's fellow students were Auguste de La Rive, Jean-Baptiste Dumas, and Daniel Colladon, his best friend.[2]

Having completed his studies at the Academy, Sturm moved early in May 1823 to the château of Coppet, about fifteen kilometers from Geneva, as tutor to the youngest son of Mme de Staël.[3] About ten people lived at the château, including Duke Victor de Broglie, his wife, the former Albertine de Staël, and their three children. Sturm's duties as tutor left him sufficient free time to write his first articles on geometry, which were published immediately in *Annales de mathématiques pures et appliquées*, edited by J. D. Gergonne. Toward the end of the year, he accompanied the duke's family to Paris for a stay of approximately six months. Through de Broglie's assistance he was able to enter the capital's scientific circles.

During this period Sturm wrote to Colladon: "As for M. Arago, I have two or three times been among the group of scientists he invites to his house every Thursday, and there I have seen the leading scientists, MM Laplace, Poisson, Fourier, Gay-Lussac, Ampère, etc. Mr de Humboldt, to whom I was recommended by Mr de Broglie, has shown an interest in me; it is he who brought me to this group. I often attend the meetings of the Institut that take place every Monday."[4]

In May 1824 Sturm returned to Coppet with the de Broglie family, but toward the end of that year he gave up teaching in order to devote himself to scientific research. With Colladon he undertook a study of the compression of liquids, which had just been set by the Paris Academy as the subject of the grand prize in mathematics and physics for the following year. They decided to measure the speed of sound in water—Lake Geneva was nearby—and then to seek the coefficient of compressibility of water, introduce this coefficient into Poisson's formula for the speed of sound, and compare their results with those predicted by the formula. The project did not, however, yield the desired results. In addition, Colladon seriously injured his hand during the tests.

On 20 December 1825 Sturm and Colladon left for Paris with the intention of attending physics courses and of finding the instruments needed for the experiments that would enable them to complete their memoir. Arago often invited them to his house, and for a time Sturm gave mathematics lessons to his eldest son. In addition, Ampère offered them the use of his physics laboratory.

At the Sorbonne and at the Collège de France, Sturm and Colladon attended the lectures of Ampère and Gay-Lussac in physics and of Cauchy and Lacroix in mathematics. They also were present during the tests on steam engines that Arago and Dulong conducted near the Paris observatory. In addition they visited Fourier, who at this time was engaged in research on heat. Fourier asked Colladon to measure the thermal conductivity of various substances and, recognizing Sturm's inclination and talent for theoretical work, suggested that the latter make a thorough study of a certain procedure in analysis, later called harmonic analysis, that Fourier believed would be of great use in theoretical physics.

Sturm and Colladon finished their paper on the compression of liquids and submitted it to the Academy, which eventually decided that none of the memoirs it had received merited the prize and that the the same subject would be set for the 1827 award. Meanwhile, Sturm and Colladon had been appointed assistants to Ampère, who suggested that they collaborate on a major treatise on experimental and theoretical physics (the project was never undertaken). In November 1826 Colladon returned to Geneva and measured the speed of sound in water between Thonon and Rolle, situated on opposite banks of Lake Geneva. He obtained a value of 1,435 meters per second. The agreement was good with the theoretical speed determined by Poisson's formula, which gave 1,437.8 meters per second. Upon his return to Paris, he and Sturm completed the new version of their memoir. This time it won the grand prize of 3,000 francs, a sum that enabled them to pay the costs of their experiments and to prolong their stay in Paris.

Henceforth their scientific careers diverged. Even in his physical research, however, Sturm continued to obtain interesting results in geometry, notably on the theory of caustic curves of reflection, the poles and polars of conic sections, Desargues's theorem, and involutions.

In 1829, through Ampère's influence, Sturm was appointed chief editor for mathematics of the *Bulletin des sciences et de l'industrie*. On 13 May of that year he presented to the Academy "Mémoire sur la résolution des équations numériques," containing the famous theorem that perhaps did more to assure his reputation than the rest of his writings together. The founder of the *Bulletin*, André Étienne, Baron d'Audebard de Férussac, invited his principal collaborators to assemble at his Paris residence once a week; and it is possible that Sturm met Niels Abel and Évariste Galois there, as well as Cournot, Coriolis, Duhamel, Hachette, and Lacroix.[5]

Sturm and Colladon wished to obtain posts in the state school system; but even though they had the backing of several influential members of the Academy, they were unsuccessful because they were foreigners and Protestants. The revolution of July 1830 proved beneficial to their cause: Arago was able to have Sturm named professor of *mathématiques spéciales* at the Collège Rollin and Colladon, professor of mechanics at the École Centrale des Arts et Manufactures. (Colladon returned to Geneva in 1839.) It is interesting that the minister of public education after the revolution was Duke Victor de Broglie.[6]

Sturm became increasingly interested in the theory of differential equations; and in September 1833, six months after he had acquired French citizenship, he read a memoir on this subject before the Academy. About this time the Geneva Academy considered offering him a post, and in October 1833 he received official notification through La Rive. But Sturm declined it, for his decision to remain in France was irrevocable. He also rejected an offer from the University of Ghent.

Upon the death of Ampère, a seat in the Académie des Sciences became vacant. On 28 November 1836 Sturm was nominated to it by Lacroix; the other candidates were Liouville, Duhamel, Lamé, and Jean-Louis Boucharlat. At the following meeting, it was announced that Liouville and Duhamel had withdrawn their names, considering it right that the seat go to Sturm; he was elected by forty-six of the fifty-two votes cast.

Sturm's career now progressed rapidly; in 1838 he was named *répétiteur* of analysis in Liouville's course at the École Polytechnique, where he became professor of analysis and mechanics in 1840. Also that year he assumed the chair of mechanics formerly held by Poisson at the Faculty of Sciences. In 1837 Sturm became *chevalier* of the Legion of Honor, and in 1840 he won the Copley Medal of the Royal Society and was elected a member of that body. He was already a member of the Berlin Academy (1835) and the Academy of St. Petersburg (1836).

Sturm was obliged to spend much time preparing his courses on differential and integral calculus and on rational mechanics. An excellent lecturer, he was admired for both his personal qualities and his knowledge. Sturm dedicated his remaining time to research. From analysis he turned to optics, particularly to vision, and to mechanics, in which, independently and by a new method, he derived one of Duhamel's theorems on the variation in *vis viva* resulting from a sudden change in the links of a moving system.

Around 1851 Sturm's deteriorating health obliged him to arrange for a substitute at the Sorbonne and at the École Polytechnique. He became obese, had a nervous breakdown, and no longer derived pleasure from intellectual work. His doctors ordered him to walk a great deal and to move to the country. Two years later Sturm resumed some of his teaching duties, but the illness returned—probably with other complications, the nature of which is not known—and it slowly took his life.

On 20 December 1855 a crowd of scientists, friends, and students accompanied Sturm's body to the cemetery of Montparnasse. Moving speeches were given by a Protestant minister and by Liouville, who called Sturm "a second Ampère: candid like him, indifferent to wealth and to the vanities of the world."[7]

Sturm's moral qualities, his innate sense of duty and of honor, and his devotion to the ideals of friendship brought him the esteem and affection of all who knew him. His life, like his writings, was a model of clarity and rigor. Favorable circumstances smoothed the way and permitted him to display his genius; but his long friendship with Colladon and the patronage of such highly placed persons as de Broglie, Arago, and Ampère are also inseparable from his career and should be taken into account in explaining his success.

In the rest of the article we shall not consider Sturm's earliest works nor, in particular, his many articles on plane geometry—in each of which he made a valuable, original contribution. The essential features of his work in this area were incorporated in later works on geometry, often without mention of their origin. We shall, instead, examine rather closely three other important aspects of his work.

Sturm's Theorem. Although the problem of finding the number of real roots of the equation $f(x) = 0$ had already been encountered by Descartes and by Rolle, it was not investigated systematically until the mid-eighteenth century. Gua de Malves made the first significant attempts in 1741, and in 1767 Lagrange approached the problem by forming the transform with the squares of the differences of the zeroes of the polynomial. Later, Fourier considered the sequence formed by the first member of the equation and its successive derivatives. Poisson suggested the problem to Cauchy, who in 1813 sent three notes on the subject to the Academy and in 1815 discussed it at length in his "Mémoire sur la détermination du nombre de racines réelles dans les équations algébriques."[8] By successive eliminations, Cauchy established a system of rational functions of the coefficients of the given polynomial; and from the sign of these functions he deduced the number of zeroes. His was the first complete solution, but the calculations involved are so long and laborious that it was never adopted.

Sturm used Fourier's method, as well as some unpublished results that Fourier had communicated to him. (Sturm credited Fourier for these in the article published in *Bulletin des sciences et de l'industrie*.) But instead of working with the successive derivatives, he was able to develop his method by using only the first derivative. The essential part of the argument is as follows:[9]

Let $V = 0$ be an equation of arbitrary degree with distinct roots, and let V_1 be the derivative of V. One proceeds as in finding the greatest common divisor of V and V_1, the sole difference being that it is necessary to change the signs of all the remainders when they are used as divisors. Let $Q_1, \cdots, Q_{r-1}$ be the quotients and $V_2, \cdots, V_{r-1}$ the remainders, V_r being a constant. One therefore has

$$V = V_1 Q_1 - V_2$$
$$V_1 = V_2 Q_2 - V_3$$
$$\cdots \cdots$$
$$V_{r-2} = V_{r-1} Q_{r-1} - V_r.$$

The statement of the theorem then reads:

Let us substitute two arbitrary numbers a and b, positive or negative, for x in the sequence of functions $V, V_1, V_2, \cdots, V_{r-1}, V_r$. If a is smaller than b, the number of the variations in the sequence of the signs of these functions for $x = b$ will, at most, be equal to the number of the variations in the sequence of the signs of these same functions for $x = a$. And if it is less, the difference will be equal to the number of real roots of the equation $V = 0$ between a and b.

"Variation" in this statement means "change of sign." The demonstration, which includes an examination of two cases, a scholium, and two corrolaries, requires several pages. Sturm's discovery elicited great excitement, and he became famous as the mathematician who had filled a lacuna in algebra. It was not long, however, before voices were raised in support of Cauchy—that, for example, of Orly Terquem, editor of the *Nouvelles annales de mathématiques*, who accorded priority to Cauchy while recognizing that Sturm had found a simpler method. Cauchy himself later asserted his priority. As for Sturm, he was satisfied to speak of the "theorem of which I have the honor to bear the name." Charles Hermite made the following assessment: "Sturm's theorem had the good fortune of immediately becoming classic and of finding a place in teaching that it will hold forever. His demonstration, which utilizes only the most elementary considerations, is a rare example of simplicity and elegance."[10]

Cauchy subsequently found a way to determine the number of imaginary roots of an equation; but here, too, Sturm arrived at the same results by a shorter and more elementary method. The proof of this "Cauchy theorem" was published in *Journal de mathématiques pures et appliquées* for 1836 in an article signed by Sturm and Liouville.

The functions $V, V_1, \cdots, V_r$ are called Sturm functions. J. J. Sylvester discussed them in two articles and expressed them by means of the roots of the given equation.[11]

Differential Equations and Infinitesimal Geometry. On 28 September 1833 Sturm presented a memoir on second-order differential equations to the Académie des Sciences, but it was not published until three years later, in *Journal de mathématiques*. In this work Sturm studied equations of the form

$$L\frac{d^2V}{dx^2} + M\frac{dV}{dx} + N \cdot V = 0,$$

where L, M, and N are given functions of x, and V is the unknown function. The integration is, in general, impossible. Sturm's insight was to determine the properties of V without assigning it in advance to any class. Although used today, this method of proceeding was not at all common at that time. Sturm started by writing the given equation as

$$\frac{d}{dx}\left(K\frac{dV}{dx}\right) + G \cdot V = 0,$$

where K and G are new functions of x that can be determined subsequently. This type of differential equation is encountered in several problems of mathematical physics.

Liouville maintained a special interest in this area of Sturm's research, to which he himself made several important additions in two notes to the Academy in 1835 and 1836. Further, in his *Journal* he published a work written with Sturm on the expansion of functions in series; their paper begins with the differential equation

$$\frac{d}{dx}\left(K\frac{dV}{dx}\right) + (gV - l) = 0.$$

Maxime Bôcher, professor at Harvard University, gave a series of lectures at the Sorbonne in the winter of 1913–1914 on the use of Sturm's methods in the theory of differential equations.

In infinitesimal geometry, Sturm examined the problem of finding the surface of revolution that is at the same time a minimal surface. Delaunay had demonstrated that it is generated by the rotation of the curve described by the focus of an ellipse or of a hyperbola that rolls without sliding on a straight line. His method consisted in imposing on the differential equation of minimal surface the condition that it be a surface of revolution. Sturm handled the problem in another way. He began with an arbitrary surface of revolution; calculated its volume; and sought to determine, with the aid of the calculus of variations, in which cases this volume could become minimum. He thus arrived at the differential equation of the meridian and showed that it is indeed that of the curve described by the focus of a conic section. Furthermore, he demonstrated that in the case of the parabola, the meridian is a catenary curve. He then generalized the question and determined the curve that must be rolled on a straight line in order for a certain point of the plane of this curve to describe another curve the differential equation of which is known. Sturm's solution appeared in Liouville's *Journal* of 1841.

Experimental and Mathematical Physics. Sturm and Colladon's prizewinning "Mémoire sur la compression des liquides et la vitesse du son dans l'eau" consists of three parts. The first contains a description of the apparatus used to measure the compression of liquids, an account of the experiments concerning the compressibility of glass, and the tables of the results for mercury, pure water and water saturated with air, alcohol, sulfuric ether, ethyl chloride, acetic ester, nitrous ester, sulfuric acid, nitric acid, acetic acid, essence of turpentine, carbon disulfide, water partially saturated with ammonia gas, and seawater. The second part records the experiments to measure the heat emitted by liquids following the application of strong and sudden pressures, as well as tests made to determine the influence of mechanical compression on the electrical conductivity of several highly conductive liquids. The third part gives the details of Colladon's experiments on the propagation of sound in water and compares the values obtained experimentally with those resulting from the insertion of the measurements of compressibility in Poisson's formula.

Sturm also published many articles on mechanics and analytical mechanics. Three of the most important deal, respectively, with a theorem of Sadi Carnot's on the loss of *vis viva* in a system of which certain parts are inelastic and undergo sudden changes in velocity; with the motion, studied by Poinsot, of a solid about a fixed point; and with a way of shortening the calculations of W. R. Hamilton and Jacobi for integrating the equations of motion. Further, Sturm's *Cours de mécanique*, like his *Cours d'analyse*, was used by many students and remained a classic for half a century.

In addition to the memoir of 1838 on optics, Sturm earlier wrote many articles and notes on caustics and caustic surfaces. His studies on vision culminated in a long work that displayed a profound knowledge of physiology.

Fourier's influence on Sturm is reflected in a memoir of 1836 on a class of partial differential equations. In it Sturm considers the distribution of heat in a bar, either straight or curved, that is composed of a homogeneous or nonhomogeneous substance, and is of constant or variable thickness but of small dimensions. Under these conditions it may be assumed that all the points of a plane section perpendicular to the axis of the bar are at the same temperature at the same instant. In this work, one of his longest and most important, Sturm exhibits such a richness of ideas and skill in handling mathematics as an instrument for solving a problem in theoretical physics that he may unhesitatingly be placed on the same level as his teacher Fourier.

Sturm, who was so adept at combining mathematics with physics in his work, appears today, by virtue of his modes of thinking, as a very modern scientist. Since 1900 there has been growing interest in his mathematical work, especially in the United States. His contribution to physics, on the other hand, has not yet received the examination it merits. There is still no thorough, full-scale study of his life and work based on the unpublished documents.

NOTES

1. Jean-Jacques Schaub (1773–1825) left MSS on the theory of numerical approximations and on the elementary concepts of the calculus of quaternions. His greatest importance for the history of mathematics is that he was the teacher and patron of Sturm, whose family found itself in financial difficulties after the death of the father.
2. Daniel Colladon (1802–1893), who studied law before turning to physics, played an important role in Sturm's life. A skillful experimenter and brilliant inventor, he conceived the idea of illuminated fountains, which were immediate successes in Paris, London, and Chicago. His research on the action of compressed air led him to construct drilling machines for boring tunnels, and he participated in the cutting of the Mont Cenis and St. Gotthard tunnels. He also was an expert in the building of gasworks.
3. See Countess Jean de Pange, Le dernier amour de Madame de Staël (Geneva, 1944). The author, who died at Paris in 1972, at the age of eighty-four, was the sister of Louis de Broglie.
4. This six-page letter of 26 Apr. 1824 is reproduced in D. Colladon, Souvenirs et mémoires (Geneva, 1893). The original is at the Bibliothèque Publique et Universitaire, Geneva, MS 3255, fols. 219–222.
5. See R. Taton, "Les mathématiques dans le Bulletin de Férussac," in Archives internationales d'histoire des sciences, 1 (1947), 100–125.
6. There is a passage concerning Sturm in Souvenirs du duc de Broglie (Paris, 1886), II, 454. published by his son, C. J. V. A. Albert de Broglie.
7. The complete text of Liouville's speech is in E. Prouhet, "Notice sur la vie et les travaux de Ch. Sturm." On the same day Colladon, who hurriedly left Geneva to attend his friend's funeral, sent Auguste de La Rive a long letter containing much information on Sturm; this unpublished letter is MS fr. 3748, fols. 206–207, at the Bibliothèque Publique et Universitaire, Geneva.
8. Journal de l'École polytechnique, 10 (1815), 457–548; see also Oeuvres de Cauchy, 2nd ser., I, 170–257; II, 187–193; XV, 11–16.
9. The statement of the theorem and the notation we follow is Mayer and Charles Choquet, Traité élémentaire d'algèbre (Paris, 1832). Sturm had given them permission to publish the results of his research.
10. A full study, already outdated, of Sturm's theorem is in Charles de Comberousse, Cours de mathématiques, 2nd ed., IV (Paris, 1890), pt. 2, 442–460.
11. "Memoir on Rational Derivation From Equations of Coexistence, That Is to Say, a New and Extended Theory of Elimination," in Philosophical Magazine, 15 (July–Dec. 1839), 428–435; and "On a Theory of the Conjugate Relations of Two Rational Integral Functions, Comprising an Application to the Theory of Sturm's Functions, and That of the Greatest Algebraic Common Measure," in Abstracts of Papers Communicated to the Royal Society of London, 6 (1850–1854), 324–327.

BIBLIOGRAPHY

I. Original Works. Sturm's books, both published posthumously, are Cours d'analyse de l'École polytechnique, 2 vols. (Paris, 1857–1859), prepared by E. Prouhet, 8th and subsequent eds. prepared by A. de Saint-Germain—the 14th ed. appeared in 1909—translated into German by Theodor Fischer as Lehrbuch der Analysis (Berlin, 1897–1898); and Cours de mécanique de l'École polytechnique, 2 vols. (Paris, 1861), prepared by E. Prouhet, 5th ed. rev. and annotated by A. de Saint-Germain (Paris, 1905).

Sturm's articles, notes, memoirs, and reports are listed below according to the journal in which they appeared.

In Annales de mathématiques pures et appliquées, edited by J. D. Gergonne: "Extension du problème des courbes de poursuite," 13 (1822–1823), 289–303. In Mémoires présentés par divers savants à l'Académie royale de France: "Mémoire sur la compression des liquides," 2nd ser., 5 (1838), 267–347, written with D. Colladon, who republished it thirty-two years after Sturm's death with his own paper of 1841, "Sur la transmission du son dans l'eau," as Mémoire sur la compression des liquides et la vitesse du son dans l'eau (Geneva, 1887); and "Mémoire sur la résolution des équations numériques," 6 (1835), 271–318, the complete text of the work containing the statement and demonstration of Sturm's theorem.

In Nouvelles annales de mathématiques or Journal des candidats aux écoles polytechnique et normale, edited by Orly Terquem and Camille Christophe Gerono: "Sur le mouvement d'un corps solide autour d'un point fixe," 10 (1851), 419–432.

The Bibliothèque Publique et Universitaire, Geneva, has nine original letters (plus one copy) sent by Sturm to Colladon, La Rive, and other Genevans. Colladon's correspondence contains sixteen letters directly concerning Sturm; among recipients are J. Liouville, Baron J.-F.-T. Maurice, Louis-Albert Necker, and Sturm's sister. All these documents are unpublished, except for two letters from Sturm to Colladon.

II. Secondary Literature. The first work on Sturm, appearing a year after his death, was E. Prouhet, "Notice sur la vie et les travaux de Ch. Sturm," in Bulletin de bibliographie, d'histoire et de biographie mathématiques, 2 (May–June 1856), 72–89; repr. in Cours d'analyse, 5th ed. (1877), I, xv–xxix. This article leaves much to be desired: the biographical data are incomplete and the analysis of Sturm's work is superficial; and although the list of writings is complete, it contains many errors. A fuller source is the autobiography of Daniel Colladon, Souvenirs et mémoires (Geneva, 1893), which contains long passages on Sturm's life and on their joint work, as well as the complete text of two long letters from Sturm (Coppet, 1823; Paris, 1824).

See also M. B. Porter, "On the Roots of Functions Connected by a Linear Recurrent Relation of the Second Order," in Annals of Mathematics, 2nd ser., 3 (1901), 55–70, in which the author discusses Sturm's first memoir on second-order homogeneous differential equations (which appeared in *Journal de mathématiques pures et appliquées*, **1** [1836], 106–186); J. E. Wright, "Note on the Practical Application of Sturm's Theorem," in *Bulletin of the American Mathematical Society*, **12** (1906), 246–347; and F. H. Safford, "Sturm's Method of Integrating $dx/\sqrt{X} + dy/\sqrt{Y} = 0$," *ibid.*, **17** (1910–1911), 9–15. With respect to the last article, it may be noted that one of the simplest methods for obtaining the addition theorem for the elliptic integrals of the first type is based on a procedure that appears in Sturm's *Cours d'analyse*, 5th ed., II (1877), 340–343.

Maxime Bôcher, "The Published and Unpublished Work of Charles Sturm on Algebraic and Differential Equations," in *Bulletin of the American Mathematical Society*, **18** (1911–1912), 1–18, is the best study on this subject. See also Bôcher's "Charles Sturm et les mathématiques modernes," in *Revue du mois*, **17** (Jan.–June 1914), 88–104; and *Leçons sur les méthodes de Sturm dans la théorie des équations différentielles linéaires et leurs développements modernes*, Gaston Julia, ed. (Paris, 1917). Gaspare Mignosi, "Theorema di Sturm e sue estensioni," in *Rendiconti del Circulo matematico di Palermo*, **49** (1925), 1–164, is the most complete study of Sturm's theorem from both the theoretical and the historical points of view. It includes a long historical and critical introduction on works concerning the theorem and a chronological list of 65 notes and memoirs (pp. 152–158).

Gino Loria, "Charles Sturm et son oeuvre mathématique," in *Enseignement mathématique*, **37** (1938), 249–274, with portrait, is very good and, despite its title, also deals with Sturm's works on mechanics, optics, and the theory of vision. Loria's chronological list of Sturm's works is partly based on that of Prouhet; although superior, it still contains several errors. Giorgio Vivanti, "Sur quelques théorèmes géométriques de Charles Sturm," *ibid.*, 275–291, was inspired by Sturm's article on regular polygons in *Annales mathématiques*, **15** (1825), 250–256. The first of the three theorems treated was developed by L'Huillier.

See also Henri Fehr, "Charles Sturm 1803–1855," in *Pionniers suisses de la science* (Zurich, 1939), 210–211, with portrait; and Pierre Speziali, *Charles-François Sturm (1803–1855). Documents inédits*, Conférences du Palais de la Découverte, ser. D, no. 96 (Paris, 1964). The latter is fully documented, especially with regard to Sturm's biography; it includes a reproduction of a profile of Sturm at age nineteen, based on a pencil drawing by Colladon. The portrait in the articles by Loria and Fehr was based on this drawing. There are no other likenesses of Sturm.

One may also consult the chapter on the Sturm-Liouville theory of differential equations in Garrett Birkhoff, *A Source Book in Classical Analysis* (Cambridge, Mass., 1973), 258–281.

PIERRE SPEZIALI

STURM, FRIEDRICH OTTO RUDOLF (*b.* Breslau, Germany [now Wrocław, Poland], 6 January 1841; *d.* Breslau, 12 April 1919), *mathematics*.

The son of a Breslau businessman, Sturm attended the St. Maria Magdalena Gymnasium. In the winter semester of 1859 he began to study mathematics and physics at the University of Breslau, where in the summer of 1863 he received his doctorate of philosophy. From then until 1872 he worked as a teaching assistant, part-time teacher, and (from 1866) science teacher in Bromberg (now Bydgoszcz, Poland). With the Easter semester of 1872 he became professor of descriptive geometry and graphic statics at the Technical College in Darmstadt. In 1878 he was appointed full professor at Münster, and in 1892 he accepted a similar post at Breslau, where he taught until his death.

Sturm's principal interest was in pure synthetic geometry. Following Poncelet, Steiner, and von Staudt, the practitioners of this field sought to work with very few or no formulas. At Breslau, Sturm had the good fortune to be taught by Heinrich Schroeter, who, as a student of Steiner, strongly encouraged Sturm to take up this type of geometry. Since at Darmstadt, Sturm was required to teach descriptive geometry and graphic statics, he directed his efforts to these subjects and as early as 1874 wrote *Elemente der darstellenden Geometrie* (Leipzig, 1874, 1900), a textbook on descriptive geometry for his students. Except for this book and another such textbook that he published later, *Maxima und Minima in der elementaren Geometrie* (Leipzig–Berlin, 1910), his work was devoted entirely to synthetic geometry. His first studies in this area concerned the theory of third-degree surfaces in their various projective representations. In his dissertation, "De superficiebus tertii ordinis disquisitiones geometricae," Sturm proved a number of properties of these representations that Steiner had stated without proof. In 1864 Sturm shared with Luigi Cremona the Steiner Prize of the Berlin Academy for further investigations of surfaces, all of which are collected in *Synthetische Untersuchungen über Flächen*, his first textbook on the subject.

Sturm was a prolific writer, but there is no need to mention his many journal articles individually, since he later collected almost all of them in two multivolume textbooks (*Die Lehre von den geometrischen Verwandtschaften*, I, II [Leipzig 1908], III, IV [Leipzig, 1909]) on line geometry and geometric transformations. The three-volume work on line geometry is the most extensive ever written on this specialty. Like Plücker, the author of the first systematic treatment of line geometry in algebraic form, Sturm sought to develop subsets of straight lines of P_3. Accordingly, in the first two volumes Sturm treated linear complexes, congruences, and the simplest ruled surfaces up to tetrahedral complexes, all of which can be particularly well handled in a purely geometric fashion. He did not systematically investigate the remaining quadratic complexes until volume three, where the difficulties of his approach—as compared with an algebraic treatment—place many demands on the reader. Sturm rejected as "unintuitive" the interpretation proposed in the nineteenth century by Felix Klein and C. Segre, who held that the line geometry of P_3 could be considered a point geometry of a quadric of P_5.

Sturm's *Lehre von den geometrischen Verwandtschaften*, which appeared in four volumes with more than 1,800 pages, was even larger than *Liniengeometrie*. In Sturm's use of the expression, geometric relationships encompassed, first, all collineations and correlations of projective spaces (extended to both real and complex numbers) of three dimensions at the most. The work, however, is much more than a textbook of projective geometry; it also contains many chapters on algebraic geometry, and among "geometric relationships," Sturm included correspondences, Cremona transformations, and plane projections of the simplest types of rational surfaces. Volume I deals with (1,1) relationships and also with (a,b) correspondences on straight lines, spheres, and the constructs generated from them. Volume II contains a description of collineations and correlations between two-step constructs; Volume III provides a similar treatment for three-step constructs; and Volume IV is devoted to Cremona transformations, several plane projections of rational surfaces, and a number of spatial correspondences. Frequently in the work Sturm touches upon questions related to Schubert's enumerative geometry, for example in the treatment of problems of plane and spatial projectivities.

In *Lehre von den geometrischen Verwandtschaften* synthetic geometry in the style of Sturm and his predecessors was developed virtually as far as it could be. During the final years of Sturm's life, mathematicians became markedly less interested in the large number of detailed geometric questions that are discussed in his writings. Consequently, although he trained many doctoral candidates in the course of his career, Sturm had no successor to continue his mathematical work.

BIBLIOGRAPHY

I. ORIGINAL WORKS. A list of Sturm's works is in Poggendorff III, 1312–1313; IV, 1462; V, 1227–1228; VI, 2576.

Sturm's major works are "De superficiebus tertii ordinis disquisitiones geometricae" (Ph.D. diss., Bratislava, 1863); *Synthetische Untersuchungen über Flächen* (Leipzig, 1867); *Elemente der darstellenden Geometrie* (Leipzig, 1874, 1900); *Die Gebilde 1. und 2. Grades der Liniengeometrie in synthetischer Behandlung*, 3 vols. (1892–1896); *Die Lehre von dem geometrischen Verwandtschaften*, I, II (Leipzig, 1908), III, IV (Leipzig, 1909); and *Maxima und Minima in der elementaren Geometrie* (Leipzig–Berlin, 1910).

II. SECONDARY LITERATURE. For works about Sturm, see W. Lorey, "Rudolf Sturm zum Gedenken," in *Zeitschrift für mathematischen und naturwissenschaftlichen Unterricht*, **50** (1919), 289–293; and W. Ludwig, "Rudolf Sturm," in *Jahresbericht der Deutschen Mathematikervereinigung*, **34** (1926), 41–51.

WERNER BURAU

STURTEVANT, ALFRED HENRY (*b.* Jacksonville, Illinois, 21 November 1891; *d.* Pasadena, California, 5 April 1970), *genetics.*

Sturtevant was the youngest of six children of Alfred Henry Sturtevant and Harriet Evelyn Morse. His grandfather Julian M. Sturtevant graduated from Yale Divinity School and was a founder and later president of Illinois College. Sturtevant's father taught mathematics for a time at Illinois College but subsequently turned to farming, first in Illinois and later in southern Alabama, where the family moved when Sturtevant was seven. His early education was in Alabama in a one-room country school, but for the last three years of high school he went to a public school in Mobile.

In the fall of 1908 Sturtevant entered Columbia University. The choice, a crucial one, was made because Sturtevant's oldest brother, Edgar, was then teaching Latin and Greek at Barnard College; Edgar and his wife made it possible for Sturtevant to attend the university by taking him into their home. Sturtevant was greatly influenced by Edgar, from whom he learned the aims and standards of scholarship and research.

As a boy Sturtevant had drawn up the pedigrees of his father's horses and of his own family. He pursued this interest as a hobby while he was at Columbia. Edgar encouraged him to read works on heredity and to learn more about the meaning of pedigrees. As a result Sturtevant read a book on Mendelism by Punnett that greatly stimulated his interest, since he saw how Mendel's principles could be used to explain the pattern of inheritance of certain coat colors in horses. Edgar suggested that Sturtevant work out the genetic relationships, write an account of his findings, and submit it to Thomas Hunt Morgan, who held the chair of experimental zoology at Columbia and from whom Sturtevant had already taken a course. Morgan clearly was impressed, since he not only encouraged Sturtevant to publish the account, which appeared in *Biological Bulletin* in 1910, but also, in the fall of that year, gave Sturtevant a desk in his laboratory, which came to be known as the "fly room." Only a few months before, Morgan had found the first white-eyed mutant in *Drosophila* and had worked out the principles of sex linkage.

After completing his doctoral work with Morgan in 1914, Sturtevant remained at Columbia as a research investigator for the Carnegie Institution of Washington. He was a member of a research team that Morgan had assembled a few years earlier and that consisted principally of two other students of Morgan's, C. B. Bridges and H. J. Muller. The "fly room" in which they conducted all of their experiments was only sixteen by twenty-three feet, and at times as many as eight people had desks in it. According to Sturtevant, the atmosphere was one of high excitement, each new idea being freely put forth and debated. Morgan, Bridges, and Sturtevant remained at Columbia until 1928; Muller left the group in 1921 to take a position at the University of Texas.

In 1922 Sturtevant married Phoebe Curtis Reed; and in the same year they made their first trip to Europe, visiting museums and laboratories in England, Norway, Sweden, and Holland. They had three children.

In 1928 Sturtevant moved to Pasadena to become professor of genetics in the new division of biology that Morgan had established in that year at the California Institute of Technology. Much of the same stimulating atmosphere and unpretentious way of conducting science that Morgan and his students had practiced at Columbia was transferred to the new Kerckhoff Laboratory at Caltech. Sturtevant became the acknowledged and natural leader of the new genetics group established there. He maintained an active research program in which he often collaborated with other members of the genetics staff, including George W. Beadle, Theodosius Dobzhansky, Sterling Emerson, and Jack Schultz. He gave lectures in the general biology course and taught elementary and advanced courses in genetics and, on occasion, a course in entomology. He remained at Caltech until his death except for a year in England and Germany in 1932, as visiting professor of the Carnegie Endowment for International Peace, and shorter periods when he held visiting professorships at a number of American universities. He received many honors, including the National Medal of Science in 1968.

In addition to his principal publications dealing with the genetics and taxonomy of *Drosophila*, Sturtevant contributed papers on the genetics of horses, fowl, mice, moths, snails, iris, and especially the evening primroses (*Oenothera*). Although his chief contributions are in genetics, he was also a leading authority on the taxonomy of several groups of Diptera, especially the genus *Drosophila*, of which he described many new species. He was much interested in the social insects and published several papers on the behavior of ants.

Sturtevant had a prodigious memory and truly encyclopedic interests. He had a natural bent for mathematics but little formal training in it. He especially enjoyed, and was expert at solving, all kinds of puzzles, especially those involving geometrical situations. For him scientific research was an exciting and rewarding activity not unlike puzzle-solving. A common theme of his investigations was an effort to analyze and explain exceptions to established principles.

Sturtevant knew how to design and execute simple, elegant experiments, describing the results in concise, lucid prose. He set high standards for his own research and expected others to do the same.

Sturtevant's discoveries of the principle of gene mapping, of the first reparable gene defect, of the principle underlying fate mapping, of the phenomena of unequal crossing-over, and of position effect were perhaps his greatest scientific achievements. The account of these and some of his other major contributions to science is arranged in approximate chronological order.

Mendel had found that all of the hereditary factors with which he worked assorted independently of one another at the time of gamete formation. Exceptions to this second Mendelian law began to accumulate in 1900–1909. Morgan was the first to provide a satisfactory explanation for such exceptions in terms of a hypothesis, which assumes that genes tending to remain together in passing from one generation to the next must be located in the same chromosome. He further postulated that the extent to which such linked genes recombine at meiosis is a relative measure of their physical distance.

Sturtevant introduced the concept that the frequency of crossing-over between two genes furnishes an index of their distance on a linear genetic map. He proposed that 1 percent of crossing-over be taken as equal to one map unit. He then reasoned that if the distance between two genes, A and B, is equal to x map units and the distance between B and a third gene, C, is equal to y map units, then the distance between A and C will be $x + y$ if B is the middle gene; $x - y$ if C is the middle gene, and $y - x$ if A is the middle gene. The germ of this idea occurred to Sturtevant in conversation with Morgan. In his *History of Genetics*, Sturtevant recorded that he "went home, and spent most of the night (to the neglect of my undergraduate homework) in producing the first chromosome map, including the linked genes, y, w, v, m, and r, in that order, and approximately the relative spacing, as they still appear on the standard maps" (p. 47).

Sturtevant devised a crucial test of the principles of mapping genes by constructing crosses in which all three genes were segregating simultaneously. In the progeny of such "three-factor" crosses, Sturtevant discovered that double crossing-over can occur and that its frequency is equal to, or less than, the product of the two single crossing-over frequencies. Conversely, the frequency of double crossing-over can be used to deduce the order of the three genes. Sturtevant showed that the order obtained from two-factor crosses was fully confirmed and that the three-factor crosses provided a more powerful method of ordering and mapping genes than did two-factor crosses. He published these findings in 1913. His principles and methods of chromosome mapping have enabled geneticists to map the chromosomes of a wide variety of higher organisms, including man.

Sturtevant was as much concerned with the role of genes in development as with the laws governing their transmission from one generation to the next. In 1915 he published an account of the sexual behavior of *Drosophila* that included a study of sexual selection based on the use of specific mutant genes that altered the eye color or body color of the fly. This work was the forerunner of an extensive line of research by others and constituted one of the first examples of the use of specific mutant genes to dissect the behavior of an organism.

One of the more conspicuous roles that genes play in development is their control of the processes of sexual differentiation. In 1919 Sturtevant reported the first case in which intersexuality could be shown to result from the presence of specific recessive genes. Years later he found a similar type of gene that resulted in the virtually complete transformation of females into males. Mutants of still other "sex genes" have been found in *Drosophila* and in many other organisms, including man. As a result, sex has come to be viewed as a complex trait controlled by a number of different genes, mutants of which can be expected to produce various grades of intersexuality.

Sturtevant pioneered in providing experimental approaches to a central problem in biology—how genes produce their effects. An important breakthrough came in 1920, with his discovery of the first reparable gene defect. In studying gynandromorphs of *Drosophila* in which there was somatic mosaicism for the vermilion eye-color mutant, he noticed that the eyes developed the dark red color of the wild type instead of the bright red color of the vermilion mutant, even when the eye could be shown to be genetically vermilion. Evidently, vermilion eye tissue lacked some substance that could be supplied by genetically nonvermilion tissue from another portion of the body. As G. W. Beadle pointed out, much of modern biochemical genetics stems directly from this early work.

Sturtevant had shown in 1913 that for each of the major chromosomes of *Drosophila* there is a corresponding linkage map. He and others had noticed, however, that excessive variation in the amount of crossing-over sometimes occurs. The factors responsible were isolated by Sturtevant and by Muller around 1915 and were shown to act as dominant cross-over suppressors. The first clue to the nature of these factors came in 1921, when Sturtevant compared the chromosome maps of *Drosophila melanogaster* with those of *D. simulans*, a closely related species that he had first described in 1919. These maps closely paralleled one another except for a region of the third chromosome, in which it appeared likely that the two species differed by an inversion in their gene sequences. It was only later that sufficient numbers of mutants were obtained in the various inversion-containing chromosomes of *D. melanogaster* for Sturtevant to establish that the dominant cross-over suppressors were indeed inversions. What had first been a disturbing exception to the generality of Sturtevant's principles of chromosome mapping became, in his hands, another demonstration of their validity. In 1935, after the discovery of the giant salivary gland chromosomes of the Diptera by Emile Heitz and H. Bauer (1933), T. S. Painter, C. B. Bridges, and others demonstrated the existence of inversions and their points of rearrangement by direct microscopic analysis. These cytological studies fully confirmed the standard and inverted sequences that Sturtevant had deduced by purely abstract genetic analysis.

In 1923 Sturtevant provided the first satisfactory explanation of the puzzling pattern of inheritance that others had found for direction of shell-coiling in snails. He showed that it was sufficient to assume a simple Mendelian gene, with dextrality being determined by the dominant allele and with the direction of coiling in the individual being determined not by its own genetic constitution but by that of its mother. He pointed out that such characters are "fundamental," in the sense that they are impressed on the egg by the action of genes in the mother. In 1946 he showed that intersexuality in a species hybrid—that of the *repleta* and *neorepleta* species of *Drosophila*—is an unusually subtle case of maternal inheritance conditioned by an autosomal dominant gene.

In the early 1920's Sturtevant and Morgan had begun a study of the unstable *Bar* mutant of *Drosophila* in order to learn more about the nature of mutations and the mechanisms by which new ones arise. It was known by then that mutations, in the sense of simply inherited changes, could take the form of changes in numbers of chromosomes (such as trisomy or polyploidy), changes involving several genes at a time (deficiencies or duplications), or changes that appeared to be within the gene (point mutations). Efficient methods for the experimental induction and detection of mutations had yet to be worked out, however. Moreover, spontaneous mutants were too rare, for the most part, to permit practical study of specific genes, except in the case of *Bar*. This small-eye mutant had already been found by C. Zeleny to mutate occasionally to either reverted *Bar*, with eyes of normal size, or *Ultra-Bar*, with eyes distinctly smaller than those of *Bar*. In 1925 Sturtevant demonstrated that these derivatives of *Bar* arise at meiosis and are associated, at the time of their origin, with an unusual type of recombination process that he termed "unequal crossing-over." He postulated that the reverted type had lost the *Bar* gene and that *Ultra-Bar* was a tandem duplication for the *Bar* gene.

After the discovery of the giant salivary gland chromosomes, it was shown by H. J. Muller and A. A. Prokofieva, and by C. B. Bridges, that *Bar* itself is a small tandem duplication of a short section of the sex chromosome of *Drosophila*. The exact nature of the unequal crossing-over process then became evident. If the chromosome containing the *Bar* mutant is symbolized as ABCBCDE · · ·, where BC is a small segment that has become tandemly repeated, then, in the germ cells of an individual homozygous for such a chromosome, the leftmost BC region of one chromosome may occasionally come to pair with the rightmost BC region of the other chromosome. If a crossing-over then occurs within such unequally paired BC regions, it is evident that two new types of chromosome sequences will be produced: ABCDE · · · and ABCBCBCDE · · · ·. The former sequence corresponds to reverted *Bar* and the latter to *Ultra-Bar*. Thus, orthodox crossing-over within unequally paired, tandemly duplicated chromosomal segments accounts for the instability of the *Bar* mutant and provides a mechanism for progressively increasing the number of genes in a chromosome.

The process of unequal crossing-over has come to assume increasing prominence in biology as possibly one of the main forces of evolution. To illustrate, this process may have been involved in the evolution of the cluster of closely linked genes controlling the production of the β, γ, and δ polypeptide chains of the human hemoglobin molecule. The extremely close similarity of these chains at the molecular level strongly implies that the genes determining them all arose from a single ancestral gene, presumably by repeated unequal crossing-over. In turn, the resultant duplicated genes evidently diverged gradually from one another by mutation until the gene cluster acquired its present form.

Sturtevant realized that *Bar* and its derivatives provided a unique opportunity to determine whether the position of a gene in the chromosome can affect its function. He devised a critical test that consisted of comparing the sizes of the eyes of two types of flies: homozygotes for *Bar*, the genetic composition of which can be symbolized as BCBC/BCBC; and heterozygotes for reverted *Bar* and *Ultra-Bar*, of composition BC/BCBCBC. He compared the eye sizes by counting the number of facets and showed that the second type of fly had significantly fewer facets than did the first. Since the total content of genic material in the two chromosomes is the same in both cases, the observed differences in eye size constitute a demonstration that the effect of the *Bar* gene (or *Bar* region) does indeed depend upon the position of that gene in the chromosome. Sturtevant's discovery of this phenomenon of "position effect" was the first demonstration that primary genic interactions occur at the site of the genes in the chromosome, as opposed to elsewhere in the nucleus or cytoplasm.

The position effect was shown by H. J. Muller, J. Schultz, and others to take many forms. Moreover, the more primitive the organism, the more prominent (apparently) is the role played by position effect. Thus, in bacteria the chromosome consists of a series of gene clusters, or operons, that are examples par excellence of the position-effect phenomenon, in the sense that the order of the genes in an operon, as François Jacob and Jacques Monod first showed, directly determines the order in which those genes are expressed.

As is often the case in basic science, Sturtevant's discovery of the position effect of *Bar* was a by-product of another study, in this case of the mutations of *Bar*. His accounts of the quite separate phenomena of unequal crossing-over and of position effect were published in 1925 in a paper that bore the modest title "The Effects of Unequal Crossing Over at the Bar Locus in *Drosophila*."

Sturtevant was able to exploit his early use of somatic mosaics to study the developmental effects of genes when he discovered a way of producing them in large numbers. He found that females homozygous for the claret eye-color mutant of *D. simulans* produce a high proportion of gynandromorphs and other mosaics in their offspring. With the aid of this mutant he showed in 1929 that the degree of resemblance in genetic composition between two tissues in a somatic mosaic can serve to measure the degree to which those tissues have a common embryological origin. This principle, which underlies a kind of embryological-genetic mapping process now known as "fate mapping," has been widely exploited and has become a powerful tool of developmental and behavioral genetics.

In 1929 Sturtevant and S. Emerson showed that much of the extraordinarily complex genetics of the evening primrose (*Oenothera*) could be interpreted on a translocation hypothesis that had first been elaborated by John Belling for the jimsonweed, *Datura*. Many of the puzzling and bizarre "mutations" that Hugo de Vries and others had found in this organism remained disturbing thorns in the side of established genetic theory until Sturtevant and Emerson provided a detailed demonstration that they were not genuine mutations but, rather, the expected segregation products from the complex translocations of chromosome arms that are peculiar to, and widespread in, *Oenothera*.

Sturtevant and Dobzhansky collaborated in studying the plethora of inversions that occur in wild strains of many species of *Drosophila*, especially *pseudoobscura*. This work culminated in a paper (1936) that propounded an ingenious method by which inversions could be used as probes to trace phylogenetic relationships. They then successfully applied the method to constructing a detailed phylogeny of various strains and races of *pseudoobscura*.

In 1936 Sturtevant and Beadle published the results of an exhaustive study of the effects of inversions in *Drosophila* on crossing-over and disjunction. In this work they provided the first satisfactory explanation of the frequency and fate of certain aberrant chromosome types that arise as the result of crossing-over in inversion heterozygotes.

Sturtevant always maintained a keen interest in evolution and constantly examined the consequences for evolutionary theory of each new discovery in the rapidly developing science of genetics. He was an excellent naturalist and, as already noted, a taxonomist in his own right. In 1937 he published three "Essays on Evolution" in *Quarterly Review of Biology*. The first dealt with the effect of selection for mutator genes on the mutation rate of a species. The second pointed out some of the special problems of selection that are presented by the existence of sterile workers among the social insects. In the third essay he formulated a general scheme for interpreting one of the great puzzles of evolutionary theory—the origin of the sterility of hybrids.

In 1941 Sturtevant and Edward Novitski brought together the then-known mutational parallels in the genus *Drosophila*. Their results showed that the major chromosome arms of this organism tend to remain intact throughout the speciation process, although the specific order of genes within an arm gradually becomes scrambled, evidently by successive fixations of inversions.

The tiny fourth chromosome of *Drosophila* for many years resisted all efforts to map it genetically, until Sturtevant discovered special conditions that stimulated recombination to occur in that chromosome. His map of that chromosome appeared in 1951.

After 1951 Sturtevant's publications consisted mainly of original contributions to the genetics of iris; general articles on such topics as genetic effects of high-energy irradiation on human populations, the social implications of human genetics, and the theory of genetic recombination; and several taxonomic studies, including a major monograph, written with Marshall R. Wheeler, on the taxonomy of the Ephydridae (Diptera).

In 1954, in his presidential address before the Pacific Division of the American Association for the Advancement of Science, Sturtevant warned of the genetic hazards of fallout from atmospheric testing of atomic bombs. He felt that although there might be a need for bomb testing, the public should be given the best scientific estimate of the biological hazards of fallout.

Sturtevant's last published work on *Drosophila* (1956) was an account of his discovery of a remarkable mutant gene that was without any obvious effect on the fly by itself but that, in combination with another specific mutant gene (determining a prune-colored eye), killed the organism at an early stage of development. In addition to posing a challenging problem in developmental genetics, such highly specific complementary lethal systems provide an opportunity for effecting the self-destruction of certain undesirable classes of flies.

Sturtevant's last major work, *A History of Genetics* (1965), was the outgrowth of a series of lectures given at several universities and of a lifelong interest in the history of science. True to his early love of pedigrees, he presents, in an appendix to that book, detailed intellectual pedigrees of geneticists of his day.

BIBLIOGRAPHY

I. ORIGINAL WORKS. A complete bibliography of Sturtevant's publications through 1960 can be found in the appendix to *Genetics and Evolution* (see below). A collection of thirty-three of his more important papers, reprinted in 1961 to honor Sturtevant on his seventieth birthday, includes brief annotations written by him in 1961 for several articles: *Genetics and Evolution, Selected Papers of A. H. Sturtevant*, E. B. Lewis, ed. (San Francisco, 1961).

Sturtevant was the author of *An Analysis of the Effects of Selection*, Carnegie Institution Publication no. 264 (1918); and *The North American Species of Drosophila, ibid.*, no. 301 (1921); and *A History of Genetics* (New York, 1965). His other works include *The Mechanism of Mendelian Heredity* (New York, 1915; New York, 1972), written with T. H. Morgan, H. J. Muller, and C. B. Bridges; *The Genetics of Drosophila* (Amsterdam, 1925), written with T. H. Morgan and C. B. Bridges; and *An Introduction to Genetics* (New York, 1939), written with G. W. Beadle.

Background material can be found in Sturtevant's *A History of Genetics* and his articles "Thomas Hunt

Morgan," in *Biographical Memoirs. National Academy of Sciences*, **33** (1959), 283–325; and "The Early Mendelians," in *Proceedings of the American Philosophical Society*, **109** (1965), 199–204.

II. SECONDARY LITERATURE. There are biographical accounts of Sturtevant by G. W. Beadle, in *Yearbook. American Philosophical Society* (1970), 166–171; and by Sterling Emerson, in *Annual Review of Genetics*, **5** (1971), 1–4. For a discussion of Sturtevant's work in Morgan's laboratory, see G. E. Allen, "Thomas Hunt Morgan," in *DSB*, IX, 515–526.

E. B. LEWIS

SUBBOTIN, MIKHAIL FEDOROVICH (*b.* Ostrolenka [now Ostroleka], Lomzhinsk province, Russia [now Poland], 29 June 1893; *d.* Leningrad, U.S.S.R., 26 December 1966), *astronomy, mathematics*.

Subbotin was the son of an army officer. In 1910 he entered the mathematics section of the Faculty of Physics and Mathematics of Warsaw University, where he received the Copernicus stipend, awarded in competition for works on a subject set by the department. In 1912, while still a student, Subbotin worked as a supernumerary calculator at the university astronomical observatory; and after graduating in 1914, he was promoted to junior astronomer. The following year Subbotin was evacuated with the university to Rostov-on-Don; and from there he went to the Polytechnic Institute in Novocherkassk, where he worked until 1922, first as an assistant, then as a docent, and, finally, as professor of mathematics. His first scientific works of this period are mathematical. In 1917 Subbotin passed his master's examination at Rostov-on-Don.

In 1921 Subbotin was invited to work at the Main Russian Astrophysical Observatory, which soon became the State Astrophysical Institute, in Moscow. Ten years later this institute became part of the P. K. Sternberg Astronomical Institute. Subbotin moved to Tashkent in 1922 and became director of the Tashkent division of the State Astrophysical Institute, created on the basis of the old Tashkent observatory. In 1925 the observatory again became independent, with Subbotin as its director; and until 1930 he did much to revitalize and equip it. On his initiative the Kitab international latitude station was created.

From 1930 Subbotin directed the department of astronomy at Leningrad University. From 1935 to 1944 he was chairman of the department of celestial mechanics; from 1931 to 1934, head of the theoretical section of Pulkovo observatory; and from 1934 to 1939, head of the astronomical observatory at Leningrad University. Seriously ill and emaciated from hunger, Subbotin was evacuated in February 1942 from besieged Leningrad to Sverdlovsk, where, after treatment and convalescence, he accepted an invitation to work at the Sternberg Institute, which had been evacuated from Moscow. He traveled several times to Saratov to lecture and consult at Leningrad University, which had been evacuated there. At the end of 1942 Subbotin was named director of the Leningrad Astronomical Institute, which on his recommendation was reorganized in 1943 as the Institute of Theoretical Astronomy of the U.S.S.R. Academy of Sciences and became the main scientific institution in the Soviet Union for problems of celestial mechanics and ephemerides. On his return to Leningrad, Subbotin continued his professorial activity at the university and also taught at the Institute of Theoretical Astronomy.

From 1928 Subbotin was a member of the International Astronomical Union and, from 1933, president of the Commission on Theoretical Astronomy of the Astronomical Council of the U.S.S.R. Academy of Sciences. In 1946 he was elected corresponding member of the Academy of Sciences of the U.S.S.R. In 1963 he was awarded the Order of Lenin.

Subbotin's first scientific work was devoted to the theory of functions and the theory of probability. Several early articles deal with astrometry, particularly the creation of a catalog of faint stars. Later, however, his attention was devoted entirely to celestial mechanics and theoretical astronomy and to related areas of mathematics. He also wrote valuable works in the history of astronomy.

Subbotin began research on celestial mechanics by dealing with the theory of unperturbed motion. His new and original method of computing elliptical orbits from three observations was based on the solution of the Euler-Lambert equation. The solution of the modified equation yielded a semimajor axis, and then the remaining orbital elements were found. A number of Subbotin's works were devoted to the improvement of orbits on the basis of extensive observations. The last of these works included calculations destined to be carried out by electronic computers. In other writings Subbotin not only showed the possibility of improving the convergence of the trigonometric series by which the behavior of perturbing forces is represented, but also gave an expression for determining Laplace coefficients and presented formulas for computing the coefficients of the necessary members of the trigonometric series.

Subbotin also proposed a new, two-parameter form of equation of the Kepler ellipse, the various values of which lead to a number of anomalies, including one that changes with time more uniformly than the true and eccentric anomalies. This greatly simplified the computational integration of the equation of motion, which was particularly important for comets having large orbital eccentricities.

Subbotin's important three-volume course in celestial mechanics embraced all the basic problems of this science: unperturbed movement, the theory of perturbation and lunar theory, and the theory of figures of celestial bodies.

BIBLIOGRAPHY

I. ORIGINAL WORKS. Subbotin's writings include "Ob opredelenii osobykh tochek analiticheskikh funktsy" ("On the Determination of Singular Points of Analytic Functions"), in *Matematicheski sbornik*, **30** (1916), 402–433; "Sur les points singuliers de certaines équations différentielles," in *Bulletin des sciences mathématiques*, 2nd ser., **40**, no. 1 (1916), 339–344, 350–355; "O forme koeffitsientov stepennykh razlozheny algebraicheskikh funktsy" ("On the Form of Coefficients of Exponential Expansion of Algebraic Functions"), in *Izvestiya Donskogo politekhnicheskogo instituta, Novocherkassk*, **7** (1919); "Determination of the Elements of the Orbit of a Planet or Comet by Means of the Variation of Two Geocentric Distances," in *Monthly Notices of the Royal Astronomical Society*, **82** (1922), 383–390; "On the Law of Frequency of Error," in *Matematicheski sbornik*, **31** (1923), 296–300, in English; "On the Solar Rotation Period From Greenwich Sunspot Measures 1886–1909," in *Astronomische Nachrichten*, **218** (1923), 5–12; "Novaya forma uravnenia Eylera-Lamberta i ee primenenie pri vychislenii orbit" ("New Form of the Euler-Lambert Equation and Its Application in the Calculation of Orbits"), in *Russkii astronomicheskii zhurnal*, **1**, no. 1 (1924), 1–28; "A Proposal for a New Method of Improving the Fundamental Starplaces and for Determining the Constant of Aberration," in *Astronomische Nachrichten*, **224** (1925), 163–172; and "Proper Motions of 1186 Stars of the Cluster NGC 7654 (M52) and the Surrounding Region (First Catalogue)," in *Trudy Tashkentskogo gosudarstvennogo universiteta*, 5th ser. (1927), no. 1, 3–32.

Later works are "Sur les propriétés-limites du module des fonctions entières d'ordre fini," in *Mathematische Annalen*, **104** (1931), 377–386; "O chislennom integrirovanii differentsialnykh uravneny" ("On the Numerical

Integration of Differential Equations"), in *Izvestiya Akademii nauk SSSR*, Otd. matem. i estest. nauk, 7th ser. (1933), no. 7, 895–902; *Nebesnaya mekhanika* ("Celestial Mechanics"), 3 vols. (Leningrad–Moscow, 1933–1949; I, repr. 1941), also *Prilozhenie: Vspomogatelnye tablitsy dlya vychisleny orbit i efemerid* ("Appendix: Supplementary Tables for Computation of Orbits and Ephemerides"; 1941); "O novoy anomalii, zaklyuchayushchey kak chastnye sluchai ekstsentricheskuyu, istinnuyu i tangentsialnuyu anomalii" ("On a New Anomaly, Including Particular Cases of Eccentric, True, and Tangential Anomalies"), in *Doklady Akademii nauk SSSR*, n.s. **4**, no. 4 (1936), 167–169, also in *Trudy Astronomicheskoi observatorii Leningradskogo gosudarstvennogo universiteta*, **7** (1937), 9–20; "Astronomicheskie raboty Lagranzha" ("Astronomical Work of Lagrange"), in A. N. Krylov, ed., *Zhozef Lui Lagranzh (1736–1813). K 200-letiyu so dnya rozhdenia* (". . . Lagrange. . . . On the 200th Anniversary of His Birth"; Moscow–Leningrad, 1937), 47–84; and "Nekotorye soobrazhenia po voprosu o postroenii fundamentalnogo kataloga" ("Some Considerations on the Question of the Structure of the Fundamental Catalog"), in *Astronomicheskii zhurnal*, **14**, no. 3 (1937), 228–245.

Other works are *Mnogoznachnye tablitsy logarifmov* ("Multidigit Tables of Logarithms"; Moscow–Leningrad, 1940); "O nekotorykh svoystvakh dvizhenia v zadache *n*-tel" ("On Certain Properties of Motion in the *n*-Body Problem"), in *Doklady Akademii nauk SSSR*, **27**, no. 5 (1940), 441–443; "K voprosu ob orientirovke fundamentalnogo kataloga slabykh svezd" ("Toward the Question of the Orientation of the Fundamental Catalog of Faint Stars"), in *Uchenye zapiski Kazanskogo gosudarstvennogo universiteta*, **100**, no. 4 (1940), 138–141; "Sur le calcul des inégalités séculaires. I. Solution nouvelle du problème de Gauss," in *Journal astronomique de l'URSS*, **18**, no. 1 (1941), 35–50; "Ob odnom sposobe uluchshenia skhodimosti trigonometricheskikh ryadov, imeyushchikh osnovnoe znachenie dlya nebesnoy mekhaniki" ("On One Method of Improving the Convergence of Trigonometric Series of Basic Importance for Celestial Mechanics"), in *Doklady Akademii nauk SSSR*, **40**, no. 8 (1943), 343–347; *Proiskhozhdenie i vozrast Zemli* ("Origin and Age of the Earth"; Moscow, 1945; 1947; 1950); and "Uluchshenie skhodimosti osnovnykh razlozheny teorii vozmushchennogo dvizhenia" ("Improvement in the Convergence of the Basic Expansions of the Theory of Perturbed Motion"), in *Byulleten Instituta teoreticheskoi astronomii*, **4**, no. 1 (1947), 1–16.

Writings from late in Subbotin's life are "Differentsialnoe ispravlenie orbity s ekstsentrisitetom, malo otlichayushchimsya ot edinitsy" ("Differential Correction of the Orbit With an Eccentricity Slightly Different From Unity"), in *Byulleten Instituta teoreticheskoi astronomii*, **7**, no. 6 (1959), 407–415; "O vychislenii parabolicheskikh orbit" ("On the Calculation of Parabolic Orbits"), *ibid.*, 416–419; "Raboty Mukhammeda Nasireddina po teorii dvizhenia solntsa i planet" ("Work of

Muhammed Nasīr al-Dīn on the Theory of Motion of the Sun and Planets"), in *Izvestiya Akademii nauk Azerbaidzhanskoi SSR* (1952), no. 5, 51–58; "Astronomicheskie i geodezicheskie raboty Gaussa" ("Astronomical and Geodesical Works of Gauss"), in *100 let so dnya smerti (1855–1955)* ("100th Anniversary of His Death . . ."; Moscow, 1956), 241–310; "Raboty Anri Paunkare v oblasti nebesnoy mekhaniki" ("Works of Henri Poincaré in the Area of Celestial Mechanics"), in *Voprosy istorii estestvoznaniya i tekhniki* (1956), no. 2, 114–123; and "Astronomicheskie raboty Leonarda Eylera" ("Astronomical Works of Leonhard Euler"), in *Leonard Eyler. K 250-letiyu so dnya rozhdenia* (". . . Euler. On the 250th Anniversary of His Birth"; Moscow, 1958), 268–376.

II. SECONDARY LITERATURE. See G. A. Merman, "Ocherk matematicheskikh rabot Mikhaila Fedorovicha Subbotina" ("Sketch of the Mathematical Works of . . . Subbotin"), in *Byulleten Instituta teoreticheskoi astronomii*, **7**, no. 3 (1959), 233–255, with a bibliography; and N. S. Yakhontova, "Mikhail Fedorovich Subbotin (k 70-letiyu so dnya rozhdenia)" (". . . Subbotin [on the 70th Anniversary of His Birth]"), *ibid.*, **10**, no. 1 (1965), 2–5.

P. G. KULIKOVSKY

SUCHTEN (or **Zuchta**), **ALEXANDER** (*b.* Tczew [?], Poland, *ca.* 1520; *d.* Bavaria, 1590 [?]), *chemistry, medicine*.

Suchten's father, George Suchten, was an assessor for the Gdańsk town court; his mother was Eufemia Schultze. The Suchtens were an important family, possessing houses in Gdańsk and an estate near Tczew, where Alexander was probably born. An uncle, Christopher Suchten, was a secretary to King Sigismund I Jagiello; a grandfather and another uncle had been mayors of Gdańsk. In 1521–1522 an "Alexius Zuchta de Gedano alias etiam Suchten, dictus Kaszuba Polonus" lectured at the University of Cracow, where he held the post of *Extraneus de Facultate*. This academic was certainly a cousin of Alexander Suchten, who pursued his own studies in the years 1535–1539 in Elblag.

Suchten's fortunes were greatly influenced by his maternal uncle, Alexander Schultze (or, in Latin, Sculteti), a canon of Frombork and a friend of Copernicus, who resigned his canonry, with consent from Rome, in favor of his nephew. Since (according to a decree of the bishop of Warmia, Joannes Dantiscus) the higher clerical positions could be filled only by those who had studied at a foreign university for three years and had taken a doctorate, Suchten went to Louvain, where he studied medicine, and then to Rome, Ferrara, Bologna, and Padua. In Padua he received the doctorate with a dissertation entitled "Galeni placita." During this time, Suchten's uncle, a follower of Heinrich Bullinger, was accused of heresy and his estate was confiscated. Suchten became involved in his uncle's trial and in 1545 was deprived not only of his canonicate but also of his paternal inheritance. He then went to Königsberg and was poet and physician at the court of Duke Albrecht of Prussia.

In 1549 Suchten went to the Rhineland, where he was both physician and librarian to the elector of the Palatinate, Ottheinrich, a noted bibliophile and collector of alchemical books. While there Suchten became acquainted with the treatises of Paracelsus. He also became a friend of Michael Schütz, known as Toxites, who shared Suchten's interest in poetry, medicine, and alchemy. In 1554 he returned to Poland and was named physician to Sigismund II Augustus. Despite his influential position, he was unable to recover his property.

About 1564 Suchten wrote his two treatises *De tribus facultatibus* and *Decem et octo propositiones*, which created a storm of protest in the medical world. In them, Suchten stated that doctors of medicine who had obtained degrees from the universities of Bologna, Padua, Ferrara, Paris, Louvain, and Wittenberg were nothing but common frauds, and himself endorsed the medical views of Paracelsus. It is not known whether these tracts were manuscripts or whether they were also printed, since they survive only in later editions. At any rate, they were severely criticized by a number of famous physicians, including Konrad Gesner, Thomas Erastus, Crato von Krafftheim, Lukas Steglin, and Achilles Gasser, whose indignation must have come to the attention of Sigismund II, since Suchten was dismissed from his post.

Suchten went for a short time to Königsberg, as physician to Duke Albrecht, then to the court of the German magnate Johann von Seebach in Bavaria. In 1570 he was in Strasbourg, where he published his *Liber unus de secretis antimonii*. During his stay in the Palatinate, Suchten married; he eventually settled somewhere in Bavaria.

Suchten was a distinguished Paracelsian, who dedicated himself to attacking deceit and charlatanism in medicine. He also wrote on the history of chemistry, perhaps the first scholar to do so, and demonstrated, with the aid of scales, that the transmutation of metals into gold is impossible, so that all claims for "successful" transmutations must be fraudulent. He had a considerable reputation as a Latin poet, and his *Dialogus* seems to be autobiographical. A number of his manuscripts were published only after his death.

BIBLIOGRAPHY

I. ORIGINAL WORKS. A complete bibliography of Suchten's published works is in W. Haberling (see below). His works include *Liber unus de secretis antimonii* (Strasbourg, 1570), with English trans. as *Alex. Van Suchten, of the Secrets of Antimony* (London, 1670); *Clavis alchimiae* (Mümpelgardt, 1604); *Dialogus de hydrope* (Mümpelgardt, 1604); *Concordantia chimica* (Mulhouse, 1606); *Colloquia chemica* (Mulhouse, 1606); *De tribus facultatibus explicatio tincturae Theophrasti Paracelsi, de vera medicina* in Benedictus Figulus's *Pandora* (Strasbourg, 1608) and *Opera omnia*, U. von Dagitza, ed. (Hamburg, 1680). "De lapide philosophorum," a verse in Latin against the possibility of the transmutation of metals into gold, is in Michael Toxites' *Raymundi lullii . . . vade mecum* (Basel, 1572). Suchten's greatest poetical work, on the mythical Polish princess Wanda, is in his *Vandalus* (Königsberg, 1547).

II. SECONDARY LITERATURE. See Wilhelm Haberling, "Alexander von Suchten . . .," in *Zeitschrift des Westpreussischen Geschichtsvereins*, **69** (1926), 177–230, with bibliography; Włodzimierz Hubicki, "Doktor Aleksander Zuchta. Zapomniany polski chemik, lekarz i poeta XVI wieku," in *Studia i materiały z dziejów nauki polskiej*, **1** (1953), 102–120; "Alexander von Suchten," in *Sudhoffs Archiv für Geschichte der Medizin un der Naturwissenschaften*, **44** (1960), 54–63; and "Chemistry and Alchemy in Sixteenth Century Cracow," in *Endeavour*, **17** (1958), 204–207. Earlier literature is cited by John Ferguson in *Bibliotheca chemica*, II (Glasgow, 1906), 417.

WŁODZIMIERZ HUBICKI

SUDHOFF, KARL FRIEDRICH JAKOB (*b.* Frankfurt am Main, Germany, 26 November 1853; *d.* Salzwedel, Germany, 8 October 1938), *history of medicine.*

Sudhoff, the son of a Protestant minister, attended the elementary school and Gymnasium in Frankfurt until his family moved to Zweibrücken and then to Kreuznach, where he finished his secondary education. He studied medicine at the universities of Erlangen, Tübingen, and Berlin, taking the M.D. in 1875, then did postgraduate work in the hospitals of Augsburg and, for a short time, Vienna. In 1878 he established a general practice in Bergen, near Frankfurt; in 1883 he moved to

Hochdahl, near Düsseldorf, where he practiced until 1905.

During the twenty-seven years of his medical practice Sudhoff devoted his spare time to the study of the history of medicine. His own first major contribution to the field was his two-volume *Bibliographia Paracelsica* (1894–1899), an indispensable guide to the Paracelsian printed and manuscript source material. This work brought him some fame, and Sudhoff in 1901 became instrumental in founding the German Society for the History of Medicine and Science. In 1905 he was offered the chair in the history of medicine at the University of Leipzig that had been endowed by the widow of Theodor Puschmann, who had left her entire fortune to that university for the promotion of the study of medical history. Sudhoff left Hochdahl for Leipzig in the same year, and began to develop the first German department for the history of medicine. He further contributed to this field by editing a series of important periodicals, including the *Mitteilungen zur Geschichte der Medizin und der Naturwissenschaften* (from 1902), the *Studien zur Geschichte der Medizin* (from 1907), and *Sudhoffs Klassiker der Medizin* (from 1910). The *Archiv für Geschichte der Medizin und der Naturwissenschaften* (later called *Sudhoffs Archiv*), of which he was founder and to which he contributed heavily, first appeared in 1907.

Sudhoff's own historical researches were concerned chiefly with the fields of ancient, medieval, and Renaissance medicine and with epidemiology. In 1909 he published *Aerztliches aus griechischen Papyrus-Urkunden*, in which he considered ancient materials concerning water supply, housing conditions, clothing, gymnastics, and cosmetics, as well as medical topics; the following year he brought out *Aus dem antiken Badewesen*, a detailed discussion of ancient hygienic practices. He also traveled widely throughout Europe to examine medieval manuscripts, which he photographed and edited; he was particularly concerned with medical and anatomical iconography, and traced the ramifications of the iconographical tradition back to the early Middle Ages. He edited a large number of medieval texts on medicine, surgery, dietetics, and anatomy, and demonstrated the significance of the Salernitan school as the center of medical lore and training in the Latin West. In Renaissance studies, he returned to the works of Paracelsus in 1922 and began the critical edition that he finished eleven years later; he also published facsimile editions of the anatomical tables of Vesalius and Jost de Neg-

ker. In epidemiology, Sudhoff edited important source materials on the early history of syphilis and the plague.

Sudhoff also wrote two textbooks, an innovative history of dentistry and a medical history that continued Pagel's introduction to the subject. But although his publications and editions were vastly consequential, Sudhoff's chief contribution to science lies in his espousal of a strict historical method, based upon an objective and thorough study of original sources, to which he dedicated both himself and his students. His institute at the University of Leipzig was a center of medico-historical research and served as a model for other such departments both in Europe and elsewhere. Upon his retirement from the university in 1925, he was succeeded by Henry Sigerist, but when Sigerist went to the Johns Hopkins University in 1932 Sudhoff returned as acting director, a post in which he remained until 1934.

BIBLIOGRAPHY

I. ORIGINAL WORKS. A complete list of Sudhoff's writings, compiled by G. Herbrand-Hochmuth, is "Systematisches Verzeichnis der Arbeiten Karl Sudhoffs," in *Sudhoffs Archiv für Geschichte der Medizin und der Naturwissenschaften*, **27** (1934), 131–186; with additions, *ibid.*, **31** (1938), 343–344, and **32** (1939), 279–284.

Of his individual works, see especially *Bibliographia Paracelsica*, 2 vols. (Berlin, 1894–1899); *Kurzes Handbuch der Geschichte der Medizin* (Berlin, 1922), which was a new ed. of J. L. Pagel, *Einführung in die Geschichte der Medizin; Iatromathematiker vornehmlich im 15. und 16. Jahrhundert* (Breslau, 1902); *Tradition und Naturbeobachtung in den Illustrationen medizinischer Handschriften und Frühdrucke vornehmlich des 15. Jahrhunderts* (Leipzig, 1907); *Ein Beitrag zur Geschichte der Anatomie im Mittelalter speziell der anatomischen Graphik und Handschriften des 9. bis 15. Jahrhunderts* (Leipzig, 1908); *Ärztliches aus griechischen Papyrus-Urkunden* (Leipzig, 1909); *Aus dem antiken Badewesen* (Berlin, 1910); *Aus der Frügeschichte der Syphilis* (Leipzig, 1912); *Beiträge zur Geschichte der Chirurgie im Mittelalter*, 2 vols. (Leipzig, 1914–1918); *Des Andreas Vesalius sechs anatomische Tafeln vom Jahre 1538* (Leipzig, 1920), written with M. Geisberg; *Geschichte der Zahnheilkunde* (Leipzig, 1921); *Zehn Syphilisdrucke aus den Jahren 1495–1498*, Monumenta medica, 3 (Milan, 1924); *Erstlinge der pädiatrischen Literatur* (Munich, 1925); *Die ersten gedruckten Pestschriften* (Munich, 1926), written with A. Klebs; and *Die anatomischen Tafeln des Jost de Negker*, 1539 (Munich, 1928), written with M. Geisberg. Sudhoff's critical edition of Paracelsus is *Theophrast von Hohen-*

heim . . . Medizinische, naturwissenschaftliche und philosophische Schriften, 14 vols. (Munich-Berlin, 1922–1933).

A selection of Sudhoff's work, compiled by H. E. Sigerist, is "Ausgewählte Abhandlungen zum 75. Geburtstage," in *Sudhoffs Archiv für Geschichte der Medizin und der Naturwissenschaften*, **21** (1929), 1–332; an autobiographical note is "Aus meiner Arbeit. Eine Rückschau," *ibid.*, 333–387.

II. SECONDARY LITERATURE. Poggendorff, VIIa, 4, 602, gives a comprehensive list of biographical and bibliographical materials concerning Sudhoff and his work. See also W. Artelt, "Karl Sudhoff," in *Janus*, **43** (1939), 84–91; P. Diepgen, "Zur hundertsten Wiederkehr des Geburtstages von Karl Sudhoff am 26. November 1953," in *Archives internationales d'histoire des sciences*, **6** (1953), 260–265; and "Leben und Wirken eines grossen Meisters," in *Wissenschaftliche Zeitschrift der Karl Marx Universität, Leipzig*, **5** (1955–1956), 23–25; F. H. Garrison, "Karl Sudhoff as Editor and Bibliographer," in *Bulletin of the Institute of the History of Medicine*, **2** (1934), 7–9; J. R. Oliver, "Karl Sudhoff as a Classical Philologian," *ibid.*, 10–15; H. E. Sigerist, "Karl Sudhoff, the Man and the Historian," *ibid.*, 3–6; and "Karl Sudhoff, the Mediaevalist," *ibid.*, 22–25; and O. Temkin, "Karl Sudhoff, the Rediscoverer of Paracelsus," *ibid.*, 16–21.

NIKOLAUS MANI

SUESS, EDUARD (*b.* London, England, 20 August 1831; *d.* Marz, Burgenland, Austria, 26 April 1914), *geology*.

Although the name Suess had been known in Vienna since the fifteenth century, Eduard's family came from Vogtland, a region surrounded by Bohemia, Saxony, and Bavaria. His father was the son of a minister at Bobenneukirchen, near the Bavarian frontier; his mother, Eleonore Zaekauer, was the daughter of a Prague banker. Suess's father established a wool business in London, where Eduard, the couple's second child, was born. The family left England in 1834 and traveled from the coast of the Netherlands to Prague by horse and carriage. As a child Eduard spoke English, and in order to preserve this knowledge he had an English instructor as well as German and French tutors. He therefore was able to enter the Gymnasium at an exceptionally early age.

In 1845 Suess's father took over a leather factory, located near Vienna, which belonged to an ailing brother-in-law. During the revolutionary disturbances of 1848, Suess participated in demonstrations and joined the Légion Académique. He was elected to its committee and represented it on the Committee of Public Safety (*Sicherheits-

ausschuss*), of which he was the youngest member. His frequent participation in arbitration enabled him to learn to make decisions, assume responsibility for them, and justify them.

Treatment for an abscess on his foot obliged Suess to go to Prague, where he lived in his grandparents' house. He thus escaped the upheaval in Vienna that put an end to the Metternich era.

While continuing his university studies at Prague, Suess also frequented the museums and made geological excursions to nearby fossil-rich areas. The samples he collected so stimulated his interest that he devoted himself increasingly to geology. When he returned to Vienna, he presented a manuscript on the graptolites to the Society of the Friends of Science, of which the leading member was Wilhelm Haidinger. This scientific work, Suess's first, involved him in a minor dispute with the paleontologist Joachim Barrande; but their difference of opinion ended in friendship. Suess took charge of the society's foreign correspondence and a portion of that of the Museum of Natural History. This work brought him valuable international contact.

A liver ailment compelled Suess to take a cure at Carlsbad (now Karlovy Vary). The region spurred him to analyze its differences from the countrysides around Prague and Vienna. (Comparisons of this sort long held Suess's interest.) He studied the granites and sketched the shapes of columns. As a result he was invited to write the chapter on geology for a tourist guide, his first published work.

Suess was imprisoned on 16 December 1850, probably as a result of a denunciation, but was released at the request of Haidinger, director of the Geological Survey. He then found regular studies at the Technical University to be impossible and devoted himself instead to geology at the Geological Survey and at the Imperial Mineralogical Collection, where he was assigned to classify the brachiopods and was appointed a paid assistant on 10 May 1852. During the summer he was in charge of surveys for the Semmering Tunnel and in the Mur Valley.

In 1853 Franz von Hauer undertook to make a geological profile across the Eastern Alps from Passau to Duino. Suess asked to be made responsible for the highest section, that of the Dachstein. With a guide he reached the summit, where he enjoyed a vast panorama which he compared with the countrysides around Vienna, Prague, and Carlsbad; the differences were puzzling, and he decided to devote himself to elucidation of this problem.

On 12 June 1855 Suess married Hermine Strauss, the niece of the director of the Museum of Natural History and the daughter of a prominent Viennese physician. Fearing that he would not be able to support a family, his father agreed to the marriage on the condition that his son work at the leather factory in the afternoon, while the mornings were devoted to the classification of brachiopods and alpine rocks. In 1856 Suess applied for the post of *Privatdozent* at the University of Vienna but, lacking the doctorate, he failed to qualify. At the recommendation of Haidinger, the minister of education circumvented this difficulty by naming Suess extraordinary professor of paleontology, thereby freeing him from work at the factory. He became full professor of geology five years later.

Looking back on his life, Suess realized that these youthful years had been decisive. The experiences and impressions determined the goals he was to pursue and the means by which he attained them. The outlook of the high bourgeoisie in a multinational empire favored intellectual life and research. A classical and technical education and the consciously exercised gift of presenting and explaining his ideas so as to make them comprehensible had prepared Suess for a manifold career. His knowledge of languages early brought him wide-ranging personal and literary associations. He made geological excursions with researchers from Switzerland (from 1854), France (from 1856), Germany (from 1856), England (from 1862), and Italy (from 1867). Suess thus had the opportunity to visit important regions in the company of those who had explored them, and to discuss his findings and make comparisons. At an advanced age he learned Russian in order to be able to consult the original literature.

Suess took an early interest in education, at first promoting the popular university (from 1855), and then studying conditions at all levels of the educational system. As a result of his work in education, Suess was elected to the Vienna city council (1863–1886), to the provincial diet (1869–1896), and to Parliament (1872–1896). He was even approached to become secretary of state for education, but he preferred to remain a professor of geology. His vast knowledge enabled him to study conditions in other countries, to compare them with those in the empire, and to propose solutions. Investigating the conditions of workers in Great Britain, he offered predictions about the future status of labor in Austria and attempted to prepare the way for change. His recommendations influenced the passage of social legislation and the appointment of labor inspectors (1873).

On 20 December 1857 the dismantling of the bastions and fortifications of the old city of Vienna was begun, to make way for new neighborhoods and official buildings. Using the exposures presented by the excavations, Suess studied the city's subsoil and in 1862 published *Der Boden der Stadt Wien.*

Two difficult projects brought Suess great fame and the gratitude of his fellow citizens: the diversion of drinking water from the mountains to Vienna and the Danube Canal.

A great part of Vienna was supplied with water from wells. Epidemics, particularly of typhoid fever, were frequent and claimed numerous victims. In 1863 Suess was elected to the city council and was named head of a commission to study the water supply. Of fifty-three competing projects, Suess's proposal, which was one of the boldest, was chosen: it called for bringing water from mountain springs by an aqueduct. Three reasons determined its selection: mountain regions received more precipitation than the plains, they were sparsely populated, and the water could flow by gravity. Suitable springs existed in the Alps only seventy miles from Vienna, and their owner was ready to sell them. After convincing the taxpayers and their representatives, it was necessary to plan and direct the construction of the aqueduct, which began operation on 17 October 1873. The number of deaths from typhoid fever subsequently dropped from 34 to 9 per 1,000.

The low-lying sections of Vienna were often flooded. In 1869 Suess was appointed to a commission for the control of the Danube; and although he was an educational inspector busily engaged in reorganizing public instruction, he accepted. In November of that year he was a member of a delegation accompanying the emperor to Egypt to attend the opening of the Suez Canal. Noting the relevance of the canal to his own project, Suess discussed the technical problems of dredging with the head of these operations. He hired this official to come to Vienna in 1870, with his crew and machinery, to excavate the bed of the Danube Canal. Many difficulties arose, some unpredictable, such as the variations in the river's flow. On 15 April 1875 the canal was opened, and there have been no major floods in Vienna since 1876.

After the Universal Exposition of 1873 a chain of financial failures and misfortunes began. Suess attempted to clarify the phenomena by linking political, economic, and geological problems in a new fashion. He also studied the problems associated with gold (1877) and silver (1892). His book on silver, translated into English at the initiative of the United States government, was published in America.

Suess also played an important role in what is now called the politics of science. In 1860 he was named a corresponding member of the Imperial Academy and a full member in 1867; he was elected vice-president in 1893 and president in 1898. He resigned in 1911, having reorganized the Academy into a more effective body for scientific research. Skilled in obtaining funds for important projects, Suess arranged archaeological expeditions to Egypt and oceanographic cruises in the Mediterranean and the Red Sea. He organized the union of German-language academies that later became the Union Mondiale des Académies; and he was able to orient and direct their collaboration toward great common goals, such as the *Thesaurus linguae latinae.*

Suess likewise wielded great influence at the University of Vienna. He was occupied both with the organization of the curriculum and the location and construction of the new university. Although Suess was a Protestant, his election as rector was supported by the votes of the Catholic faculty. Yet the greater part of his political and technical activities gradually yielded to geology and teaching, and Suess declined very attractive offers in order to devote himself to what he considered his principal responsibility. After reaching retirement age, he gave all his time to his fundamental work.

Suess emphasized the joy derived from contact with nature, considering it a relic of the savage state that had passed through the filter of civilization. It is, he believed, only in nature that the geologist can grasp the scale of the mountains and can immerse himself in their disposition, that he learns to read the explanation of their structure and of its development.

Suess knew most of the European geologists of the older generation—that of Élie de Beaumont, Haidinger, and Escher—as well as those of his own and the following one. He often experienced the strength of scientific ties, even across political frontiers. His friendship with the Italian geologist Quintino Sella (who also was the first minister of finance of the kingdom of Italy) was based on their common views on both science and the conduct of affairs of state.

Each summer was dedicated to geological expeditions. In autumn Suess often participated in meetings and geological excursions with foreign colleagues in the Swiss Alps, Italy, and other countries. All his field excursions were carefully planned and formed part of a flexible research program. Suess also emphasized that his work on cataloging the mineralogical collections and in the library of the Museum of Natural History had enabled him to become familiar with groups of fossil forms from different strata and with the literature. Indeed, his knowledge of the geological literature and his gift for locating information in obscure publications was highly impressive.

Suess began his scientific career as a paleontologist. Graptolites, brachiopods, ammonites, and the mammals of the Tertiary especially attracted his attention. He studied their anatomy and compared their modes of life with those of existing species, engaging in what is now called paleobiology. Emphasizing the unity of the living world, in 1875 he created the concept of the biosphere. Earlier, in 1860, Suess had attempted to use the Paleozoic brachiopods to determine the depth of water at the time of sedimentation. He enlarged the goals of Lyell's stratigraphy by comparing series deposited in different regions, on forelands and in mountain chains, and by distinguishing epicontinental and geosynclinal series. Accordingly, his studies gradually shifted from stratigraphy to tectonics, of which he must be considered a creator.

Suess received no formal training in paleontology or geology. An autodidact, he increased his knowledge through contact with his seniors, friends, and students. In 1865 he was commissioned to write a treatise on the geology of the Austrian Empire, for which project he obtained a leave of absence and funds to travel. He undertook long tours on foot. The comparative method, so advantageous in anatomy, appeared of increasing importance to him. After observing asymmetry in the Carpathians, the Sudetes, and the Apennines, he located it again in the Alps. The initial result of these peregrinations was *Die Entstehung der Alpen* (1875), which contained many of his governing ideas in embryonic form. Rather than a geological description of the Alps, it was an overall view of the genesis and structure of mountain chains.

During this period the ideas of Leopold von Buch and Élie de Beaumont still largely determined the image of mountain chains. For Buch, eruptive rocks were the active elements in mountain chains; they raised the central zones and exerted lateral pressures against the two sides, thereby causing folds and other dislocations. Élie de Beaumont determined the folds of various ages and made a first attempt at a global tectonics. Lack of information obliged him to make extrapolations, such as his proposed system of the pentagonal dodecahedron, the directions of which supposedly corresponded to the ages of the folds.

Suess accepted neither the idea of the raising of the central zone by crystalline rocks nor the notion of symmetry with respect to that zone. He distinguished a foreland and a hinterland, between which movements were tangential and unilateral. There were, in his view, no rectilinear directions, but only an ensemble of curved lines. The mountain chains formed garlands and festoons, and their convex side was usually directed toward the exterior. The curves and the disposition of the folds depended on the form of the foreland and on the resistance of the materials. The crystalline rocks of the central zones were passive.

One of the first tasks of the geologist was to trace the contours of the festoons and garlands and to ascertain their internal organization. A hierarchy of features was thus discerned, enabling him to grasp the geometric anatomy and to locate its details. Next he had to reconstruct the movements that had caused these structures, in order to visualize the youth, maturity, and old age of the chain.

This work marked the beginning of the extraordinary development of tectonics and made possible the work of Marcel Bertrand, Pierre Termier, Hans Schardt, Maurice Lugeon, and Emile Argand. The point was stressed by Bertrand in his preface to the French translation of *Das Antlitz der Erde* when he gave an example of this fruitfulness that has become classic. In 1846 Arnold Escher recognized the great extent of the Permian overthrust on the Tertiary of the Glarus Alps. His student and successor Albert Heim extended the study and in 1870 constructed the "Glarus double fold" (*Glarner Doppelfalte*), thrust from both north and south, a phenomenon that aroused a heated polemic throughout Europe and pitted the partisans of overthrusts against those who interpreted the phenomenon as a stratigraphic superposition. Basing his argument on the principle of asymmetry, Bertrand interpreted the ensemble as a single nappe with a root lying to the south and a head plunging toward the north, a view incorporated into Lugeon's synthesis of the Northern Alps (1902). (This was the origin of the modern concept of the nappe or decke.)

Studies conducted in the Alps and in Calabria convinced Suess that earthquakes are manifesta-tions of mountain chains in motion and are produced along great faults. Volcanoes and intrusions are only accessory phenomena, most often occurring at the interior of arcs.

The concept of the geosyncline, elaborated in the United States by James Hall and James Dana, had been introduced to Europe. Suess stressed not only the difference in thicknesses, but also the diverse evolution of the stratigraphic series of the forelands and of the folded and overthrust zones from the point of view of lithology and of the facies. This was the first rational classification of the features of terrestrial physiognomy and an attempt to interpret and synthesize them that Suess later took up in greater detail.

In 1883 Suess signed a publication contract for his masterpiece, *Das Antlitz der Erde*, scheduled to appear in three volumes. The first fascicle was published the same year, and the entire work was completed in 1909. Certain of the notions, principles, and ways of reasoning presented in the work have entered so profoundly into the thinking of geologists that many are unaware of their origin and consider them archetypes. It is therefore worth mentioning a few examples.

Suess avoided dogmatism in presenting his views. He sought to assimilate and coordinate a century of observations, attempting to extract order from chaos by means of several governing ideas. Field experience since his youth developed in Suess a profound grasp of the relations between major outlines and details, between the structures and the behavior of materials, and between assemblages of facies and their position in the whole. He thus was able to assimilate observations in the literature, most of which were made from different viewpoints. According to his contemporaries, Suess knew the literature better than any other scientist of his time and was familiar with sources that were difficult to obtain even in major libraries. The result was a three-dimensional picture on which he superposed changes through time.

Because *Das Antlitz der Erde* was the first presentation of global views of this type, it was necessary for Suess to create an appropriate language; and his book therefore contains a considerable number of new terms, many of which are still in use.

The principal value of the "great mosaic" method consists of its manner of observing, of representing, and of transmitting—in a language developed especially for the purpose—the ensemble that is the face of the earth, a multidimensional ensemble of forms and contours arranged hierarchically on different scales. The principal features emerged from a host of details, communicating the author's enthusiasm to the reader. Enthusiasm for his discoveries did not, however, render Suess a prisoner of his ideas: over the years he reworked his syntheses and hypotheses. Some of the views presented in the first volumes are contradicted in the last, a circumstance Suess explained by invoking the image of a mountain climber: as an alpinist climbs from rock to rock, the scientist goes from error to error; and even if he does not reach the summit, at each stage his view encompasses more territory.

At the beginning and at the end of this masterpiece the entire earth revolves before the reader's eye as Suess attempts to show its history by deciphering the features of its surface. He distinguished five ancient continents: Laurentia, Fennoscandia (a term created by Wilhelm Ramsay), Angaraland, Gondwanaland, and Antarctica. Between Eurasia and the Indo-African lands there extended a series of recently joined mountain chains that had originated in an ancient Mediterranean, called Tethys by Suess, extending from Central America to the Sunda Islands. These chains were generally concave toward the north in Asia and toward the south in Europe. Another series of mountain chains in festoons and garlands surrounded the Pacific Ocean. Suess distinguished three principal epochs of folding in Europe, evidence of which can be found in the more resistant rock massifs. Their age decreases as one goes from north to south. The most recent chains, bordering on the Mediterranean, are already subsiding. The ancient chains, eroded and covered by more recent deposits, can be reactivated and are therefore posthumous. Suess compared subsidences and giant grabens to tangential dislocations (folds and overthrusts), believing that subsidences characterize an important part of the surface of the earth.

The evolution of the concept of marine oscillations is an interesting example of the way in which Suess conceived a seminal idea, gathered observations to support it, followed its ramifications and weighed its consequences before proposing it, and, finally, set it against the image of nature at the time.

In 1860 and 1861 Suess studied the littoral formation deposited by the Tertiary Mediterranean on the border of the Bohemian massif north of Vienna. Following these ancient shorelines, he speculated that the observed regularity of their elevations was due not to an uplift of the massif but to a lowering of the sea level. From then on, he gathered observations relevant to this subject. After his visit to the region of the Suez Canal in 1869, Suess asserted that the isthmus was the result not of an elevation but of a relatively recent lowering of the waters. He decided at that time to examine the vestiges of the similar shores of northern Norway but was not able to do so until the summer of 1885, when he made two trips to the interior from Tromsö. He described the countryside, including the solifluction phenomena, in minute detail. The stepped terraces on the flanks of the fjords and valleys strongly impressed him. Trusting his own eye and dispensing with leveling, Suess concluded that the terraces are horizontal and do not intersect. They indicate successively lower sea levels without elevation of the shield. Suess not only studied the terraces but also investigated the Scandinavian literature on the subject dating as far back as the eighteenth century.

From his conclusion that the ancient massifs have remained stable ($\varepsilon\nu\sigma\tau\acute{\alpha}\sigma\varepsilon\iota\alpha$), Suess deduced that it was the level of the sea that had varied; as a result he proposed the principle of eustatic levels (*Das Antlitz der Erde*, II, 680). Theoretically, these levels should be found on the peripheries of all seas and oceans, with the exception of some interior seas, such as the Baltic. Suess probably would not have been as affirmative regarding the stability of the old shields had he leveled the traces of the ancient sea levels or had he taken into account the measurements of others.

He did, however, reflect for more than fifteen years on the consequences of this concept. In his view the changes in level resulted from deformations of the ocean floor: "The earth yields; the ocean follows" (*ibid.*). A multitude of phenomena, even the form of the continents, tapered toward the south and were connected to the stated principles. Sedimentary deposits in the seas displace the waters and cause them to rise, and major subsidences lower them. Suess traced the history of the great transgressions since the Silurian, concentrating especially on that of the Middle Cretaceous. "The history of the continents," he wrote, "results from that of the seas" (II, 700). The virtual similarity of the great transgressions on all the continents would explain why the limits of the formations (recognized by William Smith and corresponding to interruptions of sedimentation) are found in so many localities.

In his attempt to learn more about the little-known sea floor Suess was forced to extrapolate from structures known on land. He distinguished the Atlantic coastal type from the Pacific, the former interrupting the structural lines and the latter being more or less parallel to them. Although Suess supposed that the great oceanic basins were formed by collapse between stable blocks, he was aware of the contradiction between the hypotheses of collapse and of contraction, and discussed the problem.

Volcanological studies led Suess to posit that oceanic waters result from the degasification of the earth (III, pt. 2, 631). He introduced the distinction between juvenile and vadose waters (III, pt. 2, p. 630). Juvenile gases and, higher in the earth's crust, thermal waters not only displace and concentrate numerous chemical elements; they are also important in the transport of terrestrial heat. Juvenile gases, Suess thought, originate under the siliac crust, a term created to indicate that silicon and aluminum are the principal and characteristic elements of this terrestrial layer (III, pt. 2, 626). Under this first sphere would be that of sima (characterized by silicon and magnesium) and finally the barysphere or nife (nickel and iron), which is primarily metallic. Studies of abyssal rocks sometimes suggested the presence of a "crofesima" or "nicrofesima" (III, pt. 2, 627). Suess thought that juvenile gases also played a role in lunar volcanism (III, pt. 2, 689).

In a final chapter of *Das Antlitz der Erde* Suess discussed life and its distribution on the earth. The old shields provided refuge for the terrestrial faunas, sheltering them during marine transgressions. The history of communications between the ancient lands and of the invasions and exchanges of faunas constitutes an important chapter that completes the study of the formation of mountain chains and of marine transgressions.

The results of many later methods were not at Suess's disposal for this synthesis, but those that did exist were employed to best advantage so that his work remains the structural model for such a project. His accomplishment is still more impressive when it is appreciated that one man was able to create such a panorama. Suess stressed several times that certain problems could be solved only by new techniques—for example, when he regretted the lack of methods for determining absolute ages (II, 703).

Such a critical analysis combined with a synthesis of broad compass strongly impressed his contemporaries and is reflected in the literature of the period. Marcel Bertrand wrote: "It would almost appear to us that he would be the most advanced in our science who has best understood this book. . . . It is not only a question of making known the origin of ideas that will have an important place in the history of our science; it is also a matter of bringing within the reach of a great number of readers an almost inexhaustible mine of documents, the primary material in every kind of research and new discoveries. At first readers have been struck by an initial flowering of ideas; others remain in embryo on the same pages." Diverse and insular branches of the earth sciences were linked; and regional geologies were fitted into greater ensembles, thus forming new units that often transcended national frontiers.

The newly created field of structural geology was tied by many threads to stratigraphy—once the central concern of geology—and to geomorphology. Many paths of communication were opened toward the understanding of terrestrial substances and of their behavior, composition, origin, and evolution. Friedrich Becke, another Viennese professor, had developed links to petrography by defining the families of Atlantic and Pacific rocks and especially by creating the notion of zones of depth of metamorphism and the principle of diaphtoresis, thereby making it possible to grasp the upward motion of certain metamorphic rocks. Bruno Sander at Innsbruck and Schmidt at Leoben established relations between the deformations and fine structures of rocks and between internal displacement and mineralogical evolution.

In 1912 Alfred Wegener outlined in several lectures his new global kinematics and mobilism. As Bertrand had affirmed, Suess's work was not an end, for it opened many paths toward new knowledge and explanations. The impetus given in different directions to Austrian science and to the international scientific community can still be detected in the greater part of the earth sciences.

BIBLIOGRAPHY

I. ORIGINAL WORKS. Suess's memoirs, *Erinnerungen* (Leipzig, 1916), discuss his family origins as well as his scientific and political activities to the age of sixty and offer valuable insight into the development of his concepts and the reasoning and motivation for his accomplishments.

His separately published works include *Über das Wesen und den Nutzen palaeontologischer Studien* (Vienna, 1857); *Der Boden der Stadt Wien nach seiner Bildungsweise* (Vienna, 1862); *Die Entstehung der Alpen* (Vienna, 1875); *Die Zukunft des Goldes* (Vienna, 1877); and *Die Zukunft des Silbers* (Vienna, 1892), translated into English as *The Future of Silver* (Washington, 1893).

Das Antlitz der Erde, 3 vols. (Prague – Vienna – Leipzig, 1883 – 1909), was translated into French as *La face de la terre*, 4 vols. (Paris, 1897 – 1918), and into English as *The Face of the Earth*, 5 vols. (Oxford, 1904 – 1924).

The Royal Society *Catalogue of Scientific Papers* lists 81 memoirs published before 1900: V, 883 – 884; VIII, 1043 – 1044; XI, 530; and XVIII, 1034. See also Poggendorff, III, 1313 – 1314; IV, 1464; and V, 1230.

II. SECONDARY LITERATURE. Biographical studies of Suess include the notices by A. Geikie, in *Nature*, **72** (1905), 1 – 3; C. F. Parona, in *Atti dell'Accademia delle scienze* (Turin), **49** (1913 – 1914), 959 – 966; E. von Koerber, in *Almanach der Akademie der Wissenschaften in Wien*, **64** (1914), 349 – 362; N. Krebs, in *Mitteilungen der Geographischen Gesellschaft in Wien*, **57** (1914), 296 – 311; R. Michael, in *Zeitschrift der Deutschen geologischen Gesellschaft*, **66** (1914), 260 – 264; and P. Termier, in *Revue générale des sciences pures et appliquées*, **25** (1914), 546 – 552, translated into English in *Smithsonian Annual Report* for 1914 (Washington, 1915), 709 – 718.

On his importance in the history of geology, see G. Sarton, "La synthèse géologique de 1775 à 1918," in *Isis*, **2** (1914 – 1919), 381 – 392.

E. WEGMANN

AL-ṢŪFĪ, ABU'l-ḤUSAYN ʿABD AL-RAḤMĀN IBM ʿUMAR AL-RĀZĪ (*b.* Rayy, Persia, 903; *d.* 986), *astronomy.*

Little is known of al-Ṣūfī's life and career. He seems to have been closely associated with members of the Buwayhid dynasty in Iran and Baghdad, especially ʿAḍud al-Dawla (*d.* 983); besides that of ʿAḍud al-Dawla, names of three other members of the dynasty occur in connection with some of al-Ṣūfī's writings. Occasionally he mentions a "master" (*ustādh*) and "chief" (*raʾīs*) Abuʾl-Faḍl Muḥammad ibn al-Ḥusayn, in whose company he visited Dīnawar in 946/947 and Isfahan in 948/949. This person obviously is Ibn al-ʿAmīd (*d.* 970), vizier of ʿAḍud al-Dawla's father. Rukn al-Dawla, who had contributed a foreword to al-Ṣūfī's book on the astrolabe (which was dedicated to one of ʿAḍud al-Dawla's sons, Sharaf al-Dawla).

Al-Ṣūfī is most renowned for his observations and descriptions of the fixed stars. The results of his investigations in this field are presented in his *Kitāb ṣuwar al-kawākib al-thābita* ("Book on the Constellations of the Fixed Stars"), in which he gives a critical revision of Ptolemy's star catalog, adding the differing or additional results of his own observations. The first such revision of Ptolemy's findings, the work became a classic of Islamic

astronomy for many centuries; it even found its way into medieval Western science, where al-Ṣūfī became known as Azophi. In the "Book on the Constellations" the series of the forty-eight Ptolemaic constellations are dealt with according to the following scheme: first, there is a general discussion of all the stars of each constellation, in which al-Ṣūfī introduces his own criticism, mostly concerning positions, magnitudes, and colors; second, an identification of Arabic star names with the stars of the Ptolemaic stellar system contained in that constellation; third, two drawings of the constellation, as it is seen in the sky and as it is seen on the celestial globe; and fourth, a table of the stars of the constellation, giving longitude, latitude, and magnitude for each star. The epoch of the star table is the beginning of the year 1276 of Alexander (1 October 964), adding a constant of 12°42′ to Ptolemy's longitudes (adopting a precession of one degree in sixty-six years, in accordance with the *Zīj al-Mumtaḥan*, the *Tabulae probatae*, which were prepared in 829/830 by order of the caliph al-Maʾmūn in order to improve certain parameters in the classical tradition). The magnitudes represent the results of al-Ṣūfī's own observations.

The scientific significance of this work lies in the valuable records of real star observations – in contrast with those of most other medieval astronomers, who merely repeated the Ptolemaic star catalog, adding constant values to his longitudes. There is also another important aspect: the exact astronomical identification of the several hundred old Arabic star names, which had been registered and transmitted only in philological works that completely omitted the exact astronomical considerations. Al-Ṣūfī did his best to identify them astronomically, although he was not always successful. His identifications were adopted by most later Islamic writers on astronomy and even penetrated modern stellar terminology: from T. Hyde's quotations from al-Ṣūfī and his follower Ulugh Beg, G. Piazzi selected ninety-four star names and introduced them into common use through his *Praecipuarum stellarum inerrantium positiones . . .* (1814).

Al-Ṣūfī also wrote a rather long and detailed *Kitāb al-ʿamal biʾl-asṭurlāb* ("Book on the Use of the Astrolabe"), an "Introduction to the Science of Astrology" (extant only in manuscript), and a "Book on the Use of the Celestial Globe" (also unpublished). He seems to have constructed astronomical instruments as well, for a silver celestial globe of his manufacture is said to have been extant in Egypt around 1043.

A poem on the constellations, in the *radjaz* meter ("Urjūza fī ṣuwar al-kawākib al-thābita"), by Abū ʿAlī ibn Abi'l-Ḥusayn al-Ṣūfī should be mentioned. He usually is referred to as Ibn al-Ṣūfī, the son of al-Ṣūfī. There is, however, sufficient reason to assume that he could not have been a son of the subject of this article, for the person to whom the poem is dedicated was obviously a prince reigning in the middle of the twelfth century.

BIBLIOGRAPHY

I. ORIGINAL WORKS. Al-Ṣūfī's most widely known work is *Kitāb ṣuwar al-kawākib al-thābita* ("Book on the Constellations of the Fixed Stars"). The Arabic text was widely used and was quoted several times by T. Hyde in the commentary to his ed. of Ulugh Beg's star catalog, *Tabulae longitudinis et latitudinis stellarum fixarum ex observatione Ulugh Beighi* (Oxford, 1665), 2nd ed. by G. Sharpe in *Syntagma dissertationum* (Oxford, 1767). L. Ideler drew many quotations from Hyde in his *Untersuchungen über den Ursprung und die Bedeutung der Sternnamen* (Berlin, 1809). Al-Ṣūfī's intro. appears in French trans. by J. J. A. Caussin de Perceval in *Notices et extraits des manuscrits*, XII (Paris, 1831), 236 ff.; the entire book in French, with selected portions in Arabic and the drawings, was edited from two MSS by H. C. F. C. Schjellerup as *Description des étoiles fixes par Abd-al-Rahman Al-Sûfi* (St. Petersburg, 1874); the complete Arabic text was edited from five MSS and was augmented by the "urjūza" poem of Ibn al-Ṣūfī at the Osmania Oriental Publications Bureau (Hyderabad, India, 1954), with intro. in English by H. J. J. Winter.

Naṣīr al-Dīn al-Ṭūsī translated the book into Persian in 1250 but his translation has not been published. By order of Alfonso X of Castile, an adaptation of the work, in Castilian, was completed around the middle of the thirteenth century and was edited by Manuel Rico y Sinobas as *Los libros del saber de astronomia*, I (Madrid, 1863). There is a critical ed. of the star nomenclature in this Castilian version (and in a succeeding Italian trans.) by O. J. Tallgren as "Los nombres árabes de las estrellas y la transcripción alfonsina," in *Homenaje a R. Menéndez Pidal*, II (Madrid, 1925), 633 ff., with "Correcciones y adiciones" in *Revista de filología española*, 12 (1925), 52 ff.

Traces of al-Ṣūfī's star catalog are also found in some Latin MSS, but there is no trans. of the complete text. See P. Kunitzsch, "Ṣūfī Latinus," in *Zeitschrift der Deutschen Morgenländischen Gesellschaft*, 115 (1965), 65 ff. Peter Apian sometimes quotes al-Ṣūfī, but detailed investigations are still required in order to determine whether he quoted from the Arabic or from a translation.

For medieval Arabic criticism of al-Ṣūfī (by al-Bīrūnī and Ibn al-Ṣalāḥ), see P. Kunitzsch, ed., *Ibn aṣ-Ṣalāḥ. Zur Kritik der Koordinatenüberlieferung im Sternkata-*log *des Almagest* (Göttingen, 1975), 21, 109–111; and the places from p. 38 to 74 given in the name index *s.v.* aṣ-Ṣūfī.

Al-Ṣūfī's other published work is *Kitāb al-ʿamal bi'l-asṭurlāb* ("Book on the Use of the Astrolabe"). The Arabic text, in 386 chapters, was edited from a Paris MS by the Osmania Oriental Publications Bureau (Hyderabad, India, 1962). An intro. in English, by E. S. Kennedy and M. Destombes, was printed separately (Hyderabad, India, 1967). For a geometrical treatise of al-Ṣūfī see F. Sezgin, *Geschichte des arabischen Schrifttums*, V (Leiden, 1974), 309–310.

II. SECONDARY LITERATURE. See C. Brockelmann, *Geschichte der arabischen Litteratur*, 2nd ed., I (Leiden, 1943), 253–254, and *Supplement*, I (Leiden, 1937), 398; and C. A. Storey, *Persian Literature*, II, pt. 1 (London, 1958), 41–42. For Ibn al-Ṣūfī, see Brockelmann, *Supplement*, I, 863, no. 4a. See also A. Hauber, "Die Verbreitung des Astronomen Ṣūfī," in *Islam*, 8 (1918), 48 ff.; M. Shermatov, "Ash-Shirazi's comments on the star catalogue of as-Sufi," in *Uchenye zapiski Dushanbin. gos. ped. in-t.*, 81 (1971), 73–83 (in Russian); S. M. Stern, "ʿAbd al-Raḥmān al-Ṣūfī," in *Encyclopaedia of Islam*, new ed., I (Leiden–London, 1960), 86–87; J. Upton, "A Manuscript of 'The Book of the Fixed Stars' by ʿAbd Ar-Raḥmān Aṣ-Ṣūfī," in *Metropolitan Museum Studies*, 4 (1933), 179–197; E. Wellesz, *An Islamic Book of Constellations* (Oxford, 1965); H. J. J. Winter, "Notes on Al-Kitab Suwar Al-Kawakib," in *Archives internationales d'histoire des sciences*, 8 (1955), 126 ff. For critical remarks on al-Ṣūfī's attitude and method in identifying the ancient Arabic star nomenclature, see P. Kunitzsch, *Untersuchungen zur Sternnomenklatur der Araber* (Wiesbaden, 1961), 10, 14 ff., 31; and also *Arabische Sternnamen in Europa* (Wiesbaden, 1959), 230–231. A sky map, including the Arabic stellar nomenclature according to al-Ṣūfī, was printed as *Supplément* to *Le Mobacher* (Algiers, Sept. 1881).

PAUL KUNITZSCH

SUMNER, FRANCIS BERTODY (*b.* Pomfret, Connecticut, 1 August 1874; *d.* La Jolla, California, 6 September 1945), *biology.*

Sumner spent a lonely childhood in the bare hills near Oakland, California, to which his parents, Arthur Sumner and Mary Augusta Upton, moved a few months after he was born. His father had been a schoolteacher before taking up, unsuccessfully, small-scale farming. He educated his two sons himself until Francis was ten, and he encouraged their collection and observation of the local wildlife.

In 1884 the family moved to Colorado Springs, Colorado, where Francis discovered himself to be a surprisingly good student. He also became conscious of his lack of social accomplishment, which deficiency he later declared, not quite accurately, a lifelong shortcoming. When the family moved to Minneapolis in 1887, Sumner attended high school and in 1894 received the B.S. at the University of Minnesota. He collected fishes in the remote streams and lakes of that state, under the direction of Henry F. Nachtrieb.

At Columbia University, where he went for graduate work in 1895, Sumner was attracted to zoology by Bashford Dean, Edmund B. Wilson, and Henry Fairfield Osborn, although he was always interested in philosophy as well. He received the Ph.D. in 1901 with a thesis on fish embryology that was written under Dean, who had arranged for Sumner's participation in a disastrous Nile expedition (1899) to collect *Polypterus*. For the next seven years Sumner taught natural history at the College of the City of New York and spent most of his summers at Woods Hole, Massachusetts.

In 1903 Sumner married Margaret Elizabeth Clark; in the same year he took up a summer appointment as director of the laboratory of the United States Bureau of Fisheries at Woods Hole. For three years he conducted a detailed biological survey of that area, working with others in collecting and classifying, and himself summarizing the correlations and drawing generalizations. Sumner concluded that the varying distribution of closely related species is a result of environmental differences. In 1911, as naturalist aboard the *Albatross*, he conducted a similar survey of San Francisco Bay for the Bureau of Fisheries.

In 1913 Sumner went to La Jolla, California, to work at the Scripps Institution for Biological Research. The director of the Institution, William E. Ritter, became interested in Sumner's proposed population studies of the deer mouse, *Peromyscus*, and encouraged him to undertake them. Sumner collected many distinctive subspecies of *Peromyscus* extensively in California and to a lesser degree in other states, to breed through a number of generations in a uniform climate, in order to determine whether they would tend to become less variable. He found that through as many as twelve generations the colors and other measurable characters continued to be distinctive. Reluctantly, he concluded that Mendelian inheritance, which he called "a fad," was a more likely cause of speciation by means of minute, cumulative genetic changes than was the environment.

When the Scripps Institution of Oceanography succeeded the former institution for biological research, Sumner's studies turned from mice to the pigments of fishes, a field in which he had done significant research during a six-month visit in 1910 to the Zoological Station in Naples. His original experiments with a variety of fishes proved the direct effect of the albedo upon the deposition of melanin and of guanine within the chromatophores of the skin. Always engrossed singlemindedly in one subject at a time, he did no further work on *Peromyscus*, but his stocks of mice and unpublished material on them were transferred to Lee Raymond Dice at the University of Michigan.

Sumner was a member of the National Academy of Sciences, the Philadelphia Academy of Sciences, the American Philosophical Society, and Phi Beta Kappa.

BIBLIOGRAPHY

I. ORIGINAL WORKS. Sumner was a prolific writer on a variety of biological subjects. Of his major researches, the biological survey at Woods Hole was reported in "A Biological Survey of the Waters of Woods Hole and Vicinity," in *Bulletin of the Bureau of Fisheries* for 1911, **31** (1913), pts. 1–2, written with R. G. Osburn, L. J. Cole, and B. M. Davis. The results of the survey of San Francisco Bay appeared in "A Report Upon the Physical Conditions in San Francisco Bay, Based Upon the Operations of the United States Fisheries Steamer Albatross, During the Years 1912 and 1913," in *University of California Publications in Zoology*, **14** (1914), 1–198, written with G. D. Louderback, W. L. Schmitt, and E. C. Johnston. In addition to many shorter papers on *Peromyscus*, he summarized the results of his fifteen-year study in "Genetic, Distributional and Evolutionary Studies of the Subspecies of Deer-mice (*Peromyscus*)," in *Bibliographia genetica*, **9** (1932), 1–106.

Sumner's early work on pigments of fishes is described in "The Adjustment of Flatfishes to Various Backgrounds," in *Journal of Experimental Zoology*, **10** (1911), 409–479. His later studies were reported in a number of papers, the most significant being "Quantitative Changes in Pigmentation, Resulting From Visual Stimuli in Fishes and Amphibia," in *Biological Reviews*, **15** (1940), 351–375. A candid account of Sumner's life and convictions is given in his self-critical autobiography, *The Life History of an American Naturalist* (Lancaster, Pa., 1945).

II. SECONDARY LITERATURE. A complete bibliography and review of Sumner's researches is in Charles Manning Child, "Biographical Memoir of Francis Bertody Sumner," in *Biographical Memoirs. National Academy of Sciences*, **25** (1948), 147–173. Letters and personal memorabilia are in the library of the Scripps Institution of Oceanography, La Jolla, California.

ELIZABETH NOBLE SHOR

SUMNER, JAMES BATCHELLER (*b.* Canton, Massachusetts, 19 November 1887; *d.* Buffalo, New York, 12 August 1955), *biochemistry.*

The son of Charles and Elizabeth Rand Sumner, James Sumner grew up in a well-to-do New England family engaged in manufacturing and farming. As a boy, he was an enthusiastic hunter, and in consequence of a shooting accident lost the use of his left arm—a misfortune all the more serious because he had been left-handed. With perseverance and ingenuity, he trained himself to use his right hand not only in normal activities but also in sports; he became an expert tennis player and continued to play into his sixties. In 1915 Sumner married Bertha Louise Ricketts; they had five children. After their divorce in 1930, he married Agnes Pauline Lundquist the following year. His second marriage also ended in divorce, and in 1943 Sumner married Mary Morrison Beyer; they had two children.

Upon completing his schooling at the Eliot Grammar School and the Roxbury Latin School, Sumner entered Harvard College in 1906 to study electrical engineering, but shifted to chemistry before graduating in 1910. He then worked briefly in his uncle's textile plant and taught chemistry at Mount Allison University, Sackville, New Brunswick, and at the Worcester Polytechnic Institute in Massachusetts. He returned to Harvard in 1911 to pursue graduate studies. He received the A.M. degree in 1913 and the Ph.D. degree in biological chemistry in 1914; his dissertation, "The Formation of Urea in the Animal Body," was based on research he conducted under the supervision of O. Folin and in association with C. H. Fiske.

In 1914 Sumner became assistant professor of biochemistry at the Ithaca division of the Cornell University Medical College, and in 1929 he was promoted to full professor. After the division was discontinued in 1938, he was successively a member of the department of zoology and of the department of biochemistry and nutrition in the Cornell School of Agriculture. In 1947 a laboratory of enzyme chemistry was established in the latter department, with Sumner as its director.

Sumner decided, in 1917, to isolate an enzyme; his earlier interest in urea metabolism led him to select urease, which catalyzes the cleavage of urea to ammonia and carbon dioxide. He found this enzyme to be present in relatively large amounts in the jack bean (*Canavalia ensiformis*); because of his conviction that enzymes are proteins, he concentrated on the fractionation of the proteins of this material. After nine years of effort he succeeded in obtaining a crystalline globulin with high urease activity. He published this result in 1926, a time at which Willstätter was advocating the view that enzymes were low-molecular-weight substances readily adsorbed upon such carrier colloids as proteins. Because of Willstätter's eminence in chemistry (he had won the Nobel Prize in 1915 for his work on chlorophyll), Sumner's claim that urease is a protein was not generally accepted by the scientific community. Although he published a series of papers during the years 1926–1930 providing additional data in support of his position, it was not until J. H. Northrop announced, in 1930, the isolation of pepsin in the form of a crystalline protein that the merit of Sumner's work began to be recognized.

By 1937 several other enzymes had been obtained in crystalline form, and convincing data had been offered for the view that the catalytic activity of enzymes is associated with the integrity of individual proteins. Furthermore, W. M. Stanley had isolated, from plants infected with tobacco mosaic, a crystalline protein (later shown by F. C. Bawden and N. W. Pirie to be a nucleoprotein) that carried the infectivity of the virus. The recognition of Sumner's achievement was underlined in 1946 by the decision of the Nobel Committee in chemistry to award him one-half of the prize for that year for "his discovery that enzymes can be crystallized," the other half being shared by Northrop and Stanley.

Because the Willstätter group emphasized the importance of low-molecular-weight substances as bearers of the catalytic activity of enzymes, the iron-porphyrin-containing enzymes peroxidase and catalase were considered around 1930 to represent examples of the adsorption of such small catalytic substances to protein carriers. In 1937 Sumner (with his student A. L. Dounce) reported the crystallization of catalase, and he later provided data to demonstrate its protein nature. During the succeeding years, he published valuable reports on peroxidases, lipoxidase, and other enzymes.

Sumner's scientific career exemplifies the persistence of the investigator who stubbornly treads a path that his more influential contemporaries consider to be a blind alley. As matters turned out, it was they who were going in the wrong direction, and it was Sumner who had chosen the road that led to the great achievements in enzyme chemistry after 1930.

BIBLIOGRAPHY

I. ORIGINAL WORKS. Sumner's books include *Textbook of Biological Chemistry* (New York, 1927); *Chemistry and Methods of Enzymes* (New York, 1943; 2nd ed., 1947; 3rd ed., 1953), written with G. Fred Somers; and *Laboratory Experiments in Biological Chemistry* (New York, 1944; 2nd ed., 1949), also written with Somers. With Karl Myrbäck, Sumner edited the treatise *The Enzymes, Chemistry and Mechanism of Action*, 2 vols. (New York, 1950–1952). Sumner published about 125 research articles; among the most important are "The Isolation and Crystallization of the Enzyme Urease (Preliminary Paper)," in *Journal of Biological Chemistry*, **69** (1926), 435–441; and "Crystalline Catalase," *ibid.*, **121** (1937), 417–424, written with Alexander L. Dounce.

II. SECONDARY LITERATURE. An appreciation of Sumner's life and work is L. A. Maynard's article in *Biographical Memoirs. National Academy of Sciences*, **31** (1958), 376–396, with portrait and bibliography.

JOSEPH S. FRUTON

SUNDMAN, KARL FRITHIOF (*b*. Kaskö, Finland, 28 October 1873; *d*. Helsinki, Finland, 28 September 1949), *astronomy*.

After studying at the University of Helsinki and the Pulkovo Observatory, Sundman was appointed assistant professor at Helsinki in 1902 and later, in 1907, associate professor. In 1918 he was made full professor and director of the Helsinki observatory, which positions he held until his retirement in 1941.

Sundman's scientific work was devoted principally to problems of celestial mechanics, and his name is connected with two important achievements. First, he extended Laplace's propositions concerning the convergence of the series in unperturbed elliptic motion to the perturbation problem. His second achievement concerned the fundamental problem of celestial mechanics, the so-called three-body problem, which he reported in two papers (1907, 1909) and summarized, in 1912, in "Mémoire sur le problème des trois corps." The method he used results in a general solution to the three-body problem because the series developments he derived of the coordinates of the three bodies represent the future motion even if the convergence of the series becomes slower with increasing time.

Sundman's later papers include a description of a machine for the computation of planetary perturbations (1915), studies of the invariability of the axes of planetary orbits (1940), and a numerical calculation of the motion of the sun and the moon at the time of the total solar eclipse on 9 July 1945 (1948).

Although Sundman's main interest lay in theoretical astronomy, he promoted practical work at the Helsinki observatory. He also continued the work on the photographic star catalogue that had been initiated by his predecessor, A. Donner.

BIBLIOGRAPHY

I. ORIGINAL WORKS. Sundman's works include "Utvecklingarna af *e* och *e*^{2} uti kedjebråk med alla partialtäljare lika med ett," in *Öfversikt af Finska Vetenskapssocietetens förhandlingar*, **38** (1896); "Om den personliga eqvationen vid ringmikrometerobservationer," *ibid.*; "Über die Störungen der kleinen Planeten, speciel derjenigen, deren mittlere Bewegung annähernd das Doppelte Jupiters beträgt" (1901), Sundman's dissertation; "Über eine direkte Herleitung der Gyldén'schen A- und B-Koeffizienten als Funktionen von Θ-Transcendenten," in *Förhandlingar vid Nordiska naturforskare-och läkarmötet* (1902); "Recherches sur le problème des trois corps," in *Finska Vetenskapssocietetens Acta*, **34** (1907), 6; "Nouvelles recherches sur le problème des trois corps," *ibid.*, **35** (1909), 9; "Om planeternas banor," in *Öfversikt af Finska Vetenskapssocietetens forhandlingar*, **51C** (1909), 3; and "Sur les singularités réelles dans le problème des trois corps," in *Comptes rendus du Congrès des mathematiciens scandinaves* (1910).

See also "Mémoire sur le problème des trois corps," in *Acta mathematica*, **36** (1912); "Theorie der Planeten," in *Encyklopädie der mathematischen Wissenschaften*, **6** (1915), 2; "Plan d'une machine destinée à donner les perturbations des planètes," in *Festskrift für A.S. Donner* (1915); "Sur les conditions nécessaires et suffisantes pour la convergence du développement de la fonction perturbatrice dans le mouvement plan," in *Öfversikt af Finska Vetenskapssocietetens förhandlingar*, **58A** (1916), 24; "Observations de l'éclipse du soleil à Kumlinge le 21 août 1914," *ibid.*, **59A** (1916), 1; "Étude d'un cliché pris avec le tube polaire de l'observatoire de Helsingfors," *ibid.*, **59A** (1916), 5; "Om de astronomiska rörelseteorierna," *ibid.*, **61C** (1919), 4; "Uber die Richtungslinien für fortgesetzte Untersuchungen in den Planet- und Trabanttheorien," in *Redog. f. 5 Skand. Matem. Kongr. 1922* (1923); "La gravitation universelle et sa vitesse de propagation," in *Festskrift till Ernst Lindelöf* (1929); "Über die Bestimmung geradliniger Bahnen," in *Vierteljahrsschrift der Astronomischen Gesellschaft*, **70** (1935); "Démonstration nouvelle du théorème de Poisson sur l'invariabilité des grands axes," in *Festschrift für Elis Strömgren* (1940), 263; and "The Motions of the Moon and the Sun at the Solar Eclipse of 1945, July 9th," in

L'activité de la Commission géodésique Baltique pendant les années 1944–47 (1948).

C. Schalén

SURINGAR, WILLEM FREDERIK REINIER (*b.* Leeuwarden, Netherlands, 28 December 1832; *d.* Leiden, Netherlands, 12 July 1898), *botany.*

Suringar was the eldest son of Gerard Tjaard Nicolaas Suringar, a book dealer and publisher, and Alida Boudina Koopmans. The family probably belonged to the Dutch Reformed Church. Suringar received his secondary education at Oostbroek, near The Hague, and at the Gymnasium of Leeuwarden. In 1850 he enrolled at the University of Leiden, planning to study medicine, but soon turned to botany. In 1855 he was awarded a gold medal by the university for an essay on the algae of the Netherlands; the work was the basis for his dissertation in natural philosophy, for which he received his doctorate on 13 March 1857. In November of that year he was appointed extraordinary professor of botany at the University of Leiden, substituting for de Vriese, who was on an extended study trip in the Dutch East Indies. De Vriese died shortly after his return, and in May 1862 Suringar succeeded him as professor, occupying the chair until his death in 1898.

In 1857 Suringar was appointed *conservator herbarii* of the Netherlands Botanical Society and coeditor of its journal, *Nederlandsch kruidkundig archief.* In 1868 he became director of the national herbarium. As director of these institutions, Suringar was a leading plant taxonomist of the Netherlands. Although not published under his name, the *Prodromus florae Batavae* could not have been compiled without Suringar's assiduous work at the herbaria. Intended as a preliminary study for an extensive, national flora of the Netherlands to be published by the Netherlands Botanical Society, the work went through two editions (1850–1866, 1901–1916) but was never completed. Suringar's own flora of the Netherlands, first published in 1870 and frequently reprinted, was the leading work until the turn of the century. The planned national flora was not begun until the 1970's, as it seemed no longer needed after the publication of the floras of Oudemans (1859–1862), Suringar, Heimans and Thysse (1899), and Heukels (1900).

Suringar sustained a continuing interest in algae; and his monograph on Japanese algae, written in 1870, was based on herbarium material available in Leiden. His brief concern with bacteriology was reflected in the publication of his study on *Sarcina ventriculi* (1865), for which he was awarded an honorary doctorate by the University of Munich in 1872. He subsequently investigated the cactus family (Cactaceae), especially the genus *Melocactus*, on which he began a monograph that was never completed. According to his student Hugo de Vries, he also contributed studies of the carpels of Cruciferae, polycephaly of Compositae, pitcher formation of *Ulmus* leaves, and peloric flowers of *Digitalis.*

A long-standing opponent of the theory of evolution, Suringar surprised his friends with *Het plantenrijk* (1895), published shortly before his death. In it he discussed the evolution of plants, based on the work of Darwin and his followers, in addition to his own ideas.

Suringar's students included Melchior Treub, who became director of the botanical garden in Buitenzorg, Java [now Bogor, Indonesia], in 1880. Under Treub's leadership, this institution became one of the world's most important centers of botanical research. Many important posts at Buitenzorg were held by Suringar's pupils, for example, J. G. Boerlage, W. Burck, and J. van Breda.

BIBLIOGRAPHY

I. Original Works. There is apparently no complete bibliography of Suringar's works. His more important books include *Dissertatio botanica inauguralis continens observationes phycologicae in floram Batavam* (Leeuwarden, 1857), his doctoral diss.; *De beteekenis der plantengeographie en de geest van haar onderzoek* (Leeuwarden, 1857), Suringar's inaugural diss. as professor of botany; *De Sarcine (Sarcina ventriculi, Goodsir)* (Leeuwarden, 1865); *De kruidkunde in hare betrekking tot de maatschappij en de hoogeschool* (Leeuwarden, 1868); *Algae japonicae musei botanici Lugduno-Batavorum* (Haarlem, 1870); *Illustration des algues du Japan*, Musée botanique de Leide, I (Leiden, 1872), 63–69; II (Leiden, 1874), 1–15; *Handleiding tot het bepalen van de in Nederland wild groeiende planten* (Leeuwarden, 1870–1873), the flora of the Netherlands, which went through at least 13 eds.; *De kruidkunde in Nederland* (Leiden, 1889); *Het plantenrijk, philogenetische schets* (Leeuwarden, 1895); and *Illustrations du genre Melocactus*, 5 pts. (Leiden, 1897–1905), continued by his son, J. Valckenier Suringar.

Suringar's memoirs are listed in the Royal Society *Catalogue of Scientific Papers*, V, 888; VIII, 1046; XI, 530; XII, 711; and XVIII, 1039–1040. They include a series of papers on *Melocactus*, in *Verslagen en mededeelingen der K. Akademie van Wetenschappen*, Afd. Natuurkunde, 3rd ser., **2** (1886), 183–195; **6** (1889), 408–437, 438–461; **9** (1892), 406–412; and in *Versla-*

gen van de zittingen der wis- en natuurkundige afdeeling der K. Akademie van Wetenschappen, **4** (1896), 251–252; **5** (1897), 1–46; and **6** (1898), 178–192.

II. SECONDARY LITERATURE. On Suringar's life and work, see the notices by K. Schumann, in *Verhandlungen des Botanischen Vereins der Provinz Brandenburg,* **40** (1898), cxvii–cxviii; and *Monatsschrift für Kakteenkunde,* **8** (1898), 134–137; J. Valckenier Suringar, in *Nieuw nederlandsch biografisch woordenboek,* X (Leiden, 1937), 990–995; and H. G. van de Sande Bakhuysen, in *Verslagen van de gewone vergadering der afdeeling natuurkunde, K. Akademie van wetenschappen te Amsterdam,* **7** (1899), 129–130.

Other notices are by Hugo de Vries, in *Eigen Haard,* **23** (1897), 724–727; and *Berichte der Deutschen botanischen Gesellschaft,* **17** (1899), 220–224; L. Vuyck, in *Nederlandsch kruidkundig archief,* 3rd ser., **1** (1899), i–x; and H. Witte, in *Tijdschrift voor tuinbouw,* **4** (1899), 1–5. Two unsigned articles are "Biographische Mitteilungen (Suringar)," in *Leopoldina,* **34** (1898), 144; and "Necrologio (W. F. R. Suringar)," in *Nuova notarisia,* **10** (1899), 45–46.

PETER W. VAN DER PAS

SUTER, HEINRICH (*b.* Hedingen, Zurich canton, Switzerland, 4 January 1848; *d.* Dornach, Switzerland, 17 March 1922), *mathematics, Oriental studies.*

Suter was the son of a farmer and a keeper of posthorses. In 1875 he married Hermine Frauenfelder, sister of a famous philanthropist and preacher of Schaffhausen cathedral, Eduard Frauenfelder; they had three daughters.

Beginning in 1863 Suter attended the Zurich cantonal school, where he learned Latin and Greek. At the University of Zurich and at the Eidgenössische Technische Hochschule he studied mathematics, physics, and astronomy under Christoffel, K. T. Reye, C. F. Geiser, and Rudolf Wolf; he then completed his training under Kronecker, Kummer, and Weierstrass at the University of Berlin, where he also attended lectures on history and philology. Suter received the doctorate from the University of Zurich in 1871 for the dissertation *Geschichte der mathematischen Wissenschaften,* I; *Von den ältesten Zeiten bis Ende des 16. Jahrhunderts,* in which the significance of mathematics for cultural history was emphasized. Although Suter set forth the goal of treating the history of mathematics in terms of the history of ideas, he was prevented from attaining it because of the paucity of available data.

Following a temporary appointment at the Wettingen teachers' training college (Aargau canton)

and as a part-time teacher at the Gymnasiums in Schaffhausen (1874) and St. Gall (1875), Suter taught mathematics and physics at the cantonal schools of Aargau (1876) and Zurich (1886–1918). At the latter he acquired a thorough knowledge of Arabic under the Orientalists Steiner and Hausheer. His chief studies, in addition to numerous minor publications that appeared mainly in *Bibliotheca mathematica* (1889–1912), are "Das Mathematiker-Verzeichnis im Fihrist des . . . an-Nadîm" and "Die Mathematiker und Astronomen der Araber und ihre Werke." The outstanding expert of his time on Muslim mathematics, Suter was awarded an honorary doctorate of philosophy by the University of Zurich shortly before his death.

BIBLIOGRAPHY

I. ORIGINAL WORKS. Suter's writings include *Geschichte der mathematischen Wissenschaften,* I, *Von den ältesten Zeiten bis Ende Des 16. Jahrhunderts* (2nd rev. ed., Zurich, 1873), and II, *Vom Anfange des 17. bis gegen Ende des 18. Jahrhunderts* (Zurich, 1875); "Die Mathematiker auf den Universitäten des Mittelalters," in *Wissenschaftliche Beilage zur Programm der Kantonsschule* (Zürich, 1887); "Das Mathematiker-Verzeichnis im Fihrist des . . . an-Nadîm," in *Abhandlungen zur Geschichte der mathematischen Wissenschaften,* **6** (1892); "Die Mathematiker und Astronomen der Araber und ihre Werke," *ibid.,* **10** (1900); his edition of "Die astronomischen Tafeln des Muhammad ibn Mûsâ al-Khwârizmî," in *Kongelige Danske Videnskabernes Selskabs Skrifter,* 7th ser., **3,** no. 1 (1914); and "Beiträge zur Geschichte der Mathematik bei den Griechen und Arabern," J. Frank, ed., in *Abhandlungen zur Geschichte der Naturwissenschaften und der Medizin* (1922), no. 4, with autobiographical sketch.

II. SECONDARY LITERATURE. See E. Beck, "Heinrich Suter," in *Jahresberichte des Gymnasiums Zürich* for 1921–1922; J. Ruska, "Heinrich Suter," in *Isis,* **5** (1923), 408–417, with portrait and bibliography; and C. Schoy, "Heinrich Suter," in *Neue Zürcher Zeitung* (8 Apr. 1922), also in *Vierteljahrsschrift der Naturforschenden Gesellschaft in Zürich,* **67** (1922), 407–413, with bibliography.

J. E. HOFMANN

SUTHERLAND, WILLIAM (*b.* Dumbarton, Scotland, 4 August 1859; *d.* Melbourne, Australia, 5 October 1911), *theoretical physical chemistry, molecular physics.*

One of five sons of a Scottish woodcarver, Sutherland immigrated to Sydney in 1864 and settled in Melbourne in 1870. Educated locally at Wesley

College, in 1876 he matriculated in the University of Melbourne, graduating B.A. in 1879. In July, Sutherland left for England. He entered University College, London, on a science scholarship and studied under G. Carey Foster, graduating B.Sc. in 1881 with first-class honors in experimental physics. In 1882 Sutherland returned to Melbourne, where he received the M.A. in 1883. Supporting himself by part-time literary activities, he devoted himself to scientific research.

Although Sutherland remained indirectly attached to the University of Melbourne, he held no regular appointment. From 1885 he published about two or three major scientific articles per year, mostly in the *Philosophical Magazine*. He investigated such interrelated topics as the viscosity of gases and liquids, molecular attraction, valency, ionization, ionic velocities, and atomic sizes. His results were internationally recognized and highly valued.

In 1893 Sutherland introduced a quickly accepted dynamical explanation of the hitherto problematic relationship between the viscosity of a gas and its temperature. The Sutherland constant C increases in general with the size of the molecule and is a measure of the strength of the mutual molecular attraction. From 1900 he put forward the theory that the magnetism of the earth results from its rotating electrostatic field. His calculations were later confirmed by L. A. Bauer. Sutherland speculated in 1901 that the spectra of the elements were a function of their rigidity, and in 1902 he published his electric-doublet theory. His heterodox views (1902) regarding the complete dissociation of strong electrolytes at all concentrations were elaborated by S. R. Milner a decade later and by 1923 had become an integral part of the Debye-Hückel theory. Sutherland's later research dealt chiefly with the electronic theory of matter.

Although J. J. Thomson had, in 1899, disputed Sutherland's electron conceived as a disembodied charge, Sutherland's continued efforts to prove that the various properties of matter were essentially electrical in origin were later eulogized by Thomson for their significance.

BIBLIOGRAPHY

Correspondence from Sutherland during the period 1905–1907 is in the Bragg Collection at the Royal Institution, London; additional material is available at the National Library of Australia, Canberra.

A list of Sutherland's sixty-nine major scientific publications is given in W. A. Osborne, *William Sutherland. A Biography* (Melbourne, 1920), reviewed by G. Sarton in *Isis*, **4** (1922), 328–330. Additional articles are F. Johns, in *Australian Biographical Dictionary* (Melbourne, 1934), 346–347, and in *Australian Encyclopedia*, VIII (Sydney, 1965), 372; and P. Serle, in *Dictionary of Australian Biography*, II (Sydney, 1949), 394–395. The Sutherland constant is discussed in A. von Engel, *Ionized Gases* (Oxford, 1965), 31. Sutherland's speculation on complete dissociation in strong electrolytes at all concentrations is considered in its historical and scientific context by N. Feather, *Electricity and Matter* (Edinburgh, 1968), 218–219. His electrical theory of the atom and eccentric symbolism are considered in N. Feather, "A History of Neutrons and Nuclei," in *Contemporary Physics*, **1** (1960), 191–193.

THADDEUS J. TRENN

SUTTON, WALTER STANBOROUGH (*b.* Utica, New York, 5 April 1877; *d.* Kansas City, Kansas, 10 November 1916), *biology, medicine.*

Sutton was the fifth of the seven sons of William Bell Sutton and Agnes Black Sutton. His father, a farmer, moved from New York to Russell County, Kansas, when Sutton was ten years old. He was educated in the local public schools and entered the engineering school of the University of Kansas at Lawrence in 1896. The death of a younger brother from typhoid fever in the summer of 1897 decided Sutton on a career in medicine. He transferred to the school of arts (later the college of liberal arts) the following fall and embarked on biological studies. Under the influence of Clarence Erwin McClung, then an instructor in zoology, he began cytologic work. He received the B.A. degree in 1900 and, working as McClung's first graduate student, earned the M.A. degree in 1901. In the fall of that year he went to Columbia University to work with Edmund Beecher Wilson. Although Sutton never completed a Ph.D. thesis, during the years 1901–1903 he formulated the theory of the chromosomal basis of Mendelism, his most noteworthy contribution to science.

After two years as foreman in the oil fields of Chautauqua County in southeastern Kansas (1903–1905), Sutton returned to the College of Physicians and Surgeons of Columbia University and completed the requirements of the M.D. degree (1907). He spent the following two years in a surgical house officership at Roosevelt Hospital in New York City. From 1909 until his premature death from a ruptured appendix, he practiced surgery privately in Kansas City, Kansas, and in Kansas City, Missouri.

Sutton was of impressive physical appearance, standing six feet tall and weighting 215 pounds — the basis for his nickname "Bill Taft." E. B. Wilson [9] described "his quiet steadfastness and force and a quality of serenity . . . his clear, direct gaze, his self-possessed and tranquil manner." He was elected to Phi Beta Kappa and to Sigma Xi. At the time of his death, he was an associate professor of surgery at the University of Kansas and a fellow of the American College of Surgeons. He never married.

As a farmboy, Sutton displayed great skill in the repair and operation of agricultural equipment. He also built his own camera, thereby prefiguring his later professional use of photography, and he was adept at drawing. His ingenuity was often evident in the laboratory and in his surgical practice.

In his first publication, "The Spermatogonial Divisions of *Brachystola magna*" [1], Sutton used specimens of grasshoppers that he had collected during the summer of 1899 as he rode the "header box" in the wheat fields of his father's farm. With McClung, he discovered the value of this species for cytologic study, since the large size of its cells made it "one of the finest objects thus far discovered for the investigation of the minutest details of cell-structure." The paper was the basis for his subsequent deductions about the role of the chromosomes in heredity.

By the fall of 1902 Sutton had been associated with E. B. Wilson for a year; they had spent the preceding summer collecting and studying marine specimens in North Carolina and Maine. Sutton's intimate familiarity with the meiotic process, together with the expositions of Bateson, the ardent English protagonist of the newly rediscovered Mendelism, crystallized in his mind the relationship between the behavior of the chromosomes at meiosis and Mendelian segregation and assortment. (Bateson himself was slow to accept the chromosomal basis of Mendelism.) Thus, in a second paper on the chromosomes of the grasshopper [2], published in December 1902, Sutton wrote:

> I have endeavored to show that the eleven ordinary chromosomes (autosomes) which enter the nucleus of each spermatid are selected from each of the eleven pairs which make up the double series of the spermatogonia. . . . I may finally call attention to the probability that the association of paternal and maternal chromosomes in pairs and their subsequent separation during the reducing division as indicated above

may constitute the physical basis of the Mendelian law of heredity.

Cytologists had been aware for some time that at one phase of meiosis whole chromosomes separate, or segregate (the "reducing division" of August Weismann). In 1901 Thomas Montgomery had concluded that "in the synapsis stage is effected a union of paternal with maternal chromosomes." It was known, furthermore, that in fertilization chromosomes are contributed in equal numbers by the two gametes (Van Beneden's law).

On 19 December 1902 Wilson published a short note in *Science* proposing a relationship between the phenomena of meiosis and Mendel's laws. He stated the following reason for the note: "Since two investigators, both students in the University, have been led in different ways to recognize this clue or explanation, I have, at their suggestion and with their approval, prepared a brief note in order to place their independent conclusions in proper relation to each other and call attention to the general interest in the subject." Sutton's fellow student William Austin Cannon, later professor of botany at Stanford University, was working with fertile hybrid cotton plants and had found separation of paternal and maternal elements in meiosis.

Wilson [9] later wrote: "I well remember when, in the early Spring of 1902, Sutton first brought his main conclusion to my attention. . . . I also recall that at that time I did not at once fully comprehend his conception or realize its entire weight." Of their work together in the summer of 1902, Wilson wrote, "It was only then in the course of our many discussions, that I first saw the full sweep, and the fundamental significance of his [Sutton's] discovery." A year or so before, the work of several other cytologists had brought them to the verge of the chromosomal theory. "Sutton, however, was the first clearly to perceive and make it known. . . ."

Sutton's "The Chromosomes in Heredity" (1903) is a major landmark in the biologic literature [3]. Like his 1902 paper, it was intended as a preliminary report. Complete, although concise, it displayed model clarity and logic. Sutton built his argument on six components, of which three were corroborations of the findings or suspicions of his predecessors, while three others were uniquely his own, as was the synthesis. The six points are:

(1) That the somatic chromosomes comprise two equivalent groups, one of maternal derivation and one of paternal derivation;

(2) That synapsis consists of pairing of corre-

sponding (homologous) maternal and paternal chromosomes;

(3) That the chromosomes retain their morphologic and functional individuality throughout the life cycle;

(4) That the synaptic mates contain the physical units that correspond to the Mendelian allelomorphs; that is, the chromosomes contain the genes;

(5) That the maternal and paternal chromosomes of different pairs separate independently from each other—"The number of possible combinations in the germ-products of a single individual of any species is represented by the simple formula 2^n in which n represents the number of chromosomes in the reduced series"; and

(6) That "Some chromosomes at least are related to a number of different allelomorphs . . . [but] all the allelomorphs represented by any one chromosome must be inherited together. . . . The same chromosome may contain allelomorphs that may be dominant or recessive independently."

Sutton thus predicted genetic linkage and pointed out that Bateson and Saunders, in their experiments with *Matthiola*, had detected "two cases of correlated qualities which may be explained by association of their physical bases in the same chromosome." (Bateson himself had an alternative and incorrect explanation.) Although Sutton observed and pictured chiasmata, their specific delineation and the suggestion that parts are exchanged between homologous chromosomes are attributed to F. A. Janssens (1909); the relation to genetic recombination was discovered by Thomas Hunt Morgan and his students.

Cytologists had suspected for fifteen or twenty years before Sutton that hereditary factors are carried by the nucleus and even by chromatin, but Sutton's demonstration of the relationship between the behavior of the chromosomes in meiosis and Mendel's two laws was the first strong evidence specifically in support of the theory. Wilson [9] wrote that subsequent to the appearance of Sutton's papers, Theodor Boveri had stated that he himself had already arrived at the same general conclusion. Consequently, the chromosomal theory of inheritance is sometimes called the Sutton-Boveri theory.

None of Sutton's surgical contributions rank with his main contribution to biology. He did, however, introduce colonic administration of ether for surgery of the head and neck and was further responsible for a number of minor technical innovations.

BIBLIOGRAPHY

[1]. Sutton, "The Spermatogonial Divisions of *Brachystola magna*," in *Kansas University Quarterly*, **9** (1900).

[2]. Sutton, "Morphology of the Chromosome Group in *Brachystola magna*," *ibid.*, **4** (1902).

[3]. Sutton, "The Chromosomes in Heredity," *ibid.*, **4** (1903), 231–251. repr. in J. A. Peters, ed., *Classic Papers of Genetics* (Englewood Cliffs, New Jersey, 1959).

[4]. A. Hughes, *A History of Cytology* (London–New York, 1959).

[5]. The anonymous "Walter Stanborough Sutton," in *Journal of the American Medical Association*, **67** (1916).

[6]. *Walter Stanborough Sutton, April 5, 1877–November 10, 1916* (Kansas City, 1917), published by his family and available from the Library of Kansas University School of Medicine.

[7]. V. A. McKusick, "Walter S. Sutton and the Physical Basis of Mendelism," in *Bulletin of the History of Medicine*, **34** (1960), 487–497.

[8]. B. R. Voeller, ed., *The Chromosome Theory of Inheritance. (Classic Papers in Development and Heredity)* (New York, 1968).

[9]. E. B. Wilson, see [6].

VICTOR A. MCKUSICK

SVEDBERG, THE (THEODOR) (*b.* Fleräng, Valbo, near Gävle, Sweden, 30 August 1884; *d.* Örebro, Sweden, 25 February 1971), *physical chemistry*.

Svedberg was the only child of Elias Svedberg and Augusta Alstermark. His father, a civil engineer, was a very active man with many interests besides his profession. He was strongly attracted to the study of nature and made long excursions with his son, who shared his enthusiasm. He worked as a manager of iron works in Sweden and Norway, but the family suffered economic problems from time to time. As a Gymnasium student Svedberg was especially interested in chemistry, physics, and biology, especially botany, and finally decided to study chemistry, believing that many unsolved problems in biology could be explained as chemical phenomena. In January 1904 he enrolled at the University of Uppsala, with which he remained associated for the rest of his life. He passed the necessary courses and examinations in record time and received the B.Sc. in September 1905; his first scientific paper was published that December. Two years later he defended his dissertation, "Studien zur Lehre von den kolloiden Lösungen," for the doctorate of philosophy and became docent in chemistry. In 1912 he was appointed to the first Swedish chair of physical chemistry.

When, in August 1949, Svedberg reached the mandatory retirement age for a university professor, a special ruling, unique in Swedish academic administration, allowed him to become head of the new Gustaf Werner Institute of Nuclear Chemistry and to retain that post as long as he desired. He resigned in 1967.

Svedberg enjoyed good health throughout his active life, going for long walks almost every day. He loved making excursions in the open country and collecting wild flowers throughout Sweden. This remained his lifelong hobby, and his herbarium finally contained a complete collection of all the phanerogams in Sweden. His botanical excursions extended as far north as Greenland and Svalbard.

Svedberg received the 1926 Nobel Prize in chemistry for his work on disperse systems and was awarded honorary doctorates by the universities of Groningen, Wisconsin, Uppsala, Harvard, Oxford, Delaware, and Paris. He was elected member or honorary member of more than thirty learned societies, including the Royal Society, the National Academy of Sciences (Washington), and the Academy of Sciences of the U.S.S.R.

Svedberg was little interested in university politics and seldom attended faculty meetings. On the other hand, he was very active in promoting research activities both in industry and at the universities. He played an important role in the creation of the first research council in Sweden, the Research Council for Technology (1942), of which he was a member until 1957. He was also a member of the Swedish Atomic Research Council from its foundation in 1945 to 1959 and, from 1947 to 1956, a member of the board of AB Atomenergi, a company partly owned by the Swedish government.

Very early in his chemical studies Svedberg came across books that greatly stimulated his scientific thought: the 1903 edition of Nernst's *Theoretische Chemie*, in which he found the sections on colloids, osmotic pressure, diffusion, and molecular weights the most interesting; Zsigmondy's *Zur Erkenntnis der Kolloide*; and Gregor Bredig's *Anorganische Fermente*. Svedberg was fascinated by the new field of colloid chemistry, which became the main subject of his scientific activity for almost two decades. He began by studying the electric synthesis of metal sols in organic solvents. Bredig had prepared metal sols by letting a direct-

current arc burn between metal electrodes under the surface of a liquid. The sols obtained were, however, rather coarse, polydisperse, and contaminated. Svedberg introduced an induction coil with the discharge gap placed in the liquid. The results were striking. He was able to prepare a number of new organosols from more than thirty different metals, and they were more finely dispersed and much less contaminated. In addition, the method was reproducible, making it possible to use the sols for exact quantitative physicochemical studies. With the ultramicroscope Svedberg began studying the Brownian movements of the particles in these sols and determined the influence of solvent, viscosity, temperature, and other factors. In 1906 these studies provided an experimental confirmation of Einstein's and of Smoluchowski's theories on Brownian movement.

Svedberg retained a lifelong interest in radioactive processes. With D. Strömholm he carried out a pioneering investigation on isomorphic coprecipitation of radioactive compounds. Different salts were crystallized in solutions of various radioelements, and it was determined whether or not the radioelement crystallized out with the salts. Their discovery that thorium X, for example, crystallized with lead and barium salts, but not with others, indicated to them the existence of isotopes before that conception was introduced into chemistry by Soddy.

In his Nobel lecture Soddy referred to these experiments, the results of which were published in 1909: "Strömholm and Svedberg were probably first to attempt to fit a part of the disintegration series into the Periodic Table." Referring to their last paper of that year, he added:

Nevertheless, in their conclusion, is to be found the first published statement that the chemical nonseparability found for the radio-elements may apply also to the non-radioactive elements in the Periodic Table. Remarking on the fact that, in the region of the radio-elements, there appear to be three parallel and independent series, they then say "one may suppose that the genetic series proceed down through the Periodic Table, but that always the three elements of the different genetic series, which thus together occupy one place in the Periodic System, are so alike that they always occur together in Nature and also not have been able to be appreciably separated in the laboratory. Perhaps, one can see, as an indication in this direction, the fact that the Mendeleev scheme is only an approximate rule as concerns the atomic weight, but does not possess the exactitude of a natural law; this would not be surprising if the elements of the scheme were mixtures of several homogeneous elements of similar but not completely identical atomic weight." Thus Strömholm and Svedberg were the first to suggest a general complexity of the chemical elements concealed under their chemical identity.[1]

During these highly productive years prior to 1914 Svedberg published many scientific papers and two monographs: one (1909) on methods for preparing colloidal solutions of inorganic substances, the other (1912) describing his own experimental contribution to the prevailing but almost resolved discussion of whether molecules existed as particles or as a mathematical conception.

From 1913 to 1923 Svedberg continued his studies of the physicochemical properties of colloidal solutions with various co-workers. Toward the end of this period photochemical problems connected with the formation and growth of the latent image in the photographic emulsion also aroused his interest.

For some time it had been evident to Svedberg that, in order to gain further insight into the properties of colloidal solutions, he would need to know not only the mean sizes of their particles but also the frequency distribution of the particle sizes. For this purpose he and H. Rinde developed a method by which the variation in concentration with height in small sedimenting systems could be followed by optical means. The smallest particles that this method allowed them to determine in their metal sols were on the order of 200 mμ in diameter. Svedberg was interested in studying the formation and the growth of the colloidal particles, however, and thus the very small particles were especially important. To study them it would be necessary to increase the rate of sedimentation, which could be done by introducing centrifugal methods. The first attempt to do so was made in 1923, when Svedberg and J. B. Nichols constructed the first optical centrifuge in which the settling of the particles could be followed photographically during the run. No proper determination of the particle sizes could be made, however, because the particles were carried down both by sedimentation in the middle part of the cell and by combined convection and sedimentation along the cell walls in the nonsectorshaped cell. These experiments were carried out while Svedberg was guest professor at the University of Wisconsin at Madison. In recognition of his earlier work he had been invited by Professor J. H. Mathews to spend eight months in Madison giving lectures and organizing research in colloid chemistry. He accepted this invitation with enthusiasm. It gave him the opportunity to work in a very stimulating atmosphere and proved to be a turning point in his scientific career.

Returning to Uppsala with many new ideas and great enthusiasm, Svedberg started a more extensive research program, including centrifugation, diffusion, and electrophoresis as methods for studying fundamental properties of colloidal systems. The most urgent problem was to improve and reconstruct the optical centrifuge to render it suitable for quantitative measurement of the sedimentation during the run of the centrifuge. With Rinde he introduced a sector-shaped cell for the solution, one of the requirements for obtaining convection-free sedimentation in a revolving centrifuge cell. They derived the important square-dilution law for sedimentation under these conditions. At first they still had great trouble with heat convection currents in the rotating solutions; in the spring of 1924, however, when the rotor was allowed to spin in a hydrogen atmosphere, the problem disappeared and a new tool was introduced into the study of colloidal solutions. This centrifuge made it possible to follow optically the sedimentation of particles too small to be seen even in the ultramicroscope. In analogy with the ultramicroscope and ultrafiltration, Svedberg and Rinde proposed the name "ultracentrifuge" for the new instrument. This first ultracentrifuge could produce a centrifugal field of up to 5,000 times the force of gravity, and the rate of sedimentation of gold particles could be determined for particles as small as about 5 mμ in diameter. The studies of the metal sols by this method were continued by Svedberg's pupils, especially by Rinde.

Svedberg's interest was now focused on determining whether his ultracentrifuge could be used in the study of other colloidal systems, such as proteins. Convinced that they were polydisperse, he sought to determine the frequency distribution of their particle sizes in solutions. The first experiments were disappointing; no sedimentation could be observed in solutions of egg albumin. Later experiments, conducted in the autumn of 1924, with native casein from milk showed a very broad frequency distribution, with coarse particles having diameters on the order of 10 to 70 mμ.

With Robin Fåhraeus, Svedberg tested hemoglobin, which actually sedimented (October 1924). After about two days of centrifugation, the first sedimentation equilibrium of a protein was established. A molecular weight of about 68,000 could be calculated from the variation in the hemoglobin concentration between the meniscus and the bottom of the cell. Combined with the known analytical value for the iron content of hemoglobin, it showed the presence of four iron atoms in the hemoglobin molecule; and within the experimental error of the method, the molecular weight was found to be constant throughout the cell. This finding came as a great surprise to Svedberg. Was it possible that the protein had a well-defined molecular weight? How could he test this hypothesis? Sedimentation equilibrium measurements might give some indication of the uniformity of the particles, but this method made it difficult to obtain more detailed information about the homogeneity of a dissolved protein. If the sedimentation velocity method could be used, an analysis of the shape of the boundary would reveal the presence of inhomogeneous material. This would demand a considerably increased centrifugal field, however; about 70,000 to 100,000 times the gravitational field would be necessary for a reasonable sensitivity. This involved increasing the centrifugal force then available by fifteen to twenty times. An entirely new type of centrifuge had to be constructed; and a number of new problems, concerning technique and safety, had to be discussed and solved.

On 10 January 1926 the new high-speed oil-turbine ultracentrifuge was ready. The test was disappointing; instead of the desired 40,000–42,000 rpm, only 19,000 rpm was reached. During the next three months the main troubles were overcome; and although a number of minor problems remained, Svedberg could start making routine runs with hemoglobin in the centrifuge and could work on the general question of the uniformity of the protein molecules. From these sedimentation velocity experiments he again concluded that hemoglobin in solution gave monodisperse particles. In the following years a number of different types of proteins were studied in the ultracentrifuge, and in many cases they were found to be paucidisperse (two or more distinctly different size classes were present). By fractionation or changes in pH such solutions often yielded monodisperse proteins. Besides casein, only one polydisperse protein was found: gelatin, which often was used as a "model protein" at that time. The most astonishing result was obtained, according to Svedberg, when the hemocyanin from the land snail *Helix pomatia* was centrifuged. From its copper content a minimum molecular weight of 15,000–17,000 had been calculated. It was expected, therefore, that a gradual change in the concentration in the cell should occur during the run, leading to a sedimentation equilibrium. But, on the contrary, the hemocyanin sedimented rapidly with a knife-sharp boundary,

indicating that the particles from this protein were giant molecules and all of the same size. The molecular weight was found to be on the order of five million.

After some years studying various proteins, Svedberg concluded that certain rules existed for the molecular weights of the proteins. In a letter to *Nature* (8 June 1929) he wrote:

> Our work has been rewarded by the discovery of a most unexpected and striking general relationship between the mass of the molecules of different proteins and the mass of the molecules of the same protein at different acidities, as well as of a relationship concerning the size and shape of the protein molecules.
>
> It has been found that all stable native proteins so far studied, can with regard to molecular mass be divided into two large groups: the haemocyanins with molecular weights of the order of millions and all other proteins with molecular weights from about 35,000 to about 210,000. Of the group of the haemocyanins only two representatives, the haemocyanin from the blood of *Helix pomatia* with a spherical molecule of weight 5,000,000 and a radius of 12.0 $\mu\mu$, and the haemocyanin from the blood of *Limulus polyphemus* with a non-spherical molecule of weight 2,000,000 have been studied so far.
>
> The proteins with molecular weights ranging from about 35,000 to 210,000 can, with regard to molecular weight, be divided into four sub-groups. The molecular mass, size, and shape are about the same for all proteins within such a sub-group. The molecular masses characteristic of the three higher sub-groups are—as a first approximation—derived from the molecular mass of the first sub-group by multiplying by the integers *two*, *three* and *six*.[2]

Many new proteins were subsequently studied, and it was found that some had molecular weights lower than 35,000, previously considered the lowest weight unit. An extended study of pH-influenced dissociation-association reactions also was carried out, particularly with the hemocyanins for which molecular weights in the range of millions were found—a startling discovery at that time.

> Moreover the weights of all the well-defined haemocyanin molecules seem to be simple multiples of the lowest among them. In most cases the haemocyanin components of a certain species are interconnected by reversible, pH-influenced dissociation-association reactions. At certain pH values a profound change in the number and percentage of the components take place. The shift in pH necessary to bring about reaction is not more than a few tenths of a unit. Consequently the forces holding dissociable

parts of the molecule together must be very feeble.

Not only the molecular weight of the haemocyanins, but also the mass of most protein molecules, even those belonging to chemically different substances, show a similar relationship. This remarkable regularity points to a common plan for the building up of the protein molecules. Certain aminoacids may be exchanged for others, and this may cause slight deviations from the rule of single multiples, but on the whole only a very limited number of masses seems to be possible. Probably the protein molecule is built up by successive aggregation of definite units, but that only a few aggregates are stable. The higher the molecular weight, the fewer are the possibilities of stable aggregation. The steps between the existing molecules therefore become larger and larger as the weight increases.[3]

With the new results the basic unit was assumed to be about 17,600 instead of 35,000; and the multiples were 2, 4, 8, 16, 24, 48, 96, 192, and 384.

Svedberg's discovery that in most cases the soluble proteins had molecules with a well-defined, uniform size was received with skepticism by many scientists. Traditionally the proteins had been regarded as colloids and as very complicated substances. Svedberg's hypothesis of the multiple law for the molecular weights of proteins elicited even greater skepticism, and some scientists wondered whether Svedberg and his co-workers were measuring artifacts. At the beginning of the 1930's, however, protein studies by other methods began to corroborate the finding that these substances had well-defined, uniform molecules. Later studies have confirmed the homogeneity of the proteins to an even greater extent than Svedberg had anticipated.

In the late 1930's and early 1940's, when studies of proteins other than the respiratory ones became more extended, severe criticism was raised against the multiple law. Many proteins were found, at Uppsala and elsewhere, with molecular weights considerably lower than 17,600. Other proteins that were studied did not fit into the system of multiples. Eventually it became evident that the multiple law did not have the generality that Svedberg had expected. This hypothesis was very important to the development of protein chemistry, however, especially in the 1930's and early 1940's. It initiated greater interest in proteins among chemists and provided an impetus for new work. The introduction of sedimentation velocity ultracentrifugation, and later of the Tiselius electrophoresis technique, made it possible to visualize much more directly to what extent the isolation of an individual protein had been successful.

Svedberg remained intensively engaged in the development of his ultracentrifuge. For the study of the homogeneity of the proteins he needed a centrifuge that could yield a higher centrifugal field than the 100,000 g attained with the earliest (1926) type of high-speed ultracentrifuge. Furthermore, he was anxious to see to what extent the ultracentrifuge method could be developed. Starting in 1930, the ultracentrifuge machinery was completely reconstructed. Until 1939 its rotors were gradually improved, most of the development being concentrated on those of standard size. The following values for the centrifugal field were attained; 200,000 g (1931), 300,000 g (1932), and 400,000 g (1933). Svedberg then sought to determine whether it was possible to make sedimentation studies in still more intense centrifugal fields, at one million g. In order to do so, it would be necessary to increase the speed of the rotor considerably; this could not be done with the standard-size rotors, because they would break long before the necessary speed was reached.

In 1933 and 1934 experiments were made with three smaller rotors. The first exploded during the test runs. With the second rotor a few successful runs were made at 900,000 g before it exploded. The third rotor was used for a few runs at 710,000 g and for many runs at 525,000 g (120,000 rpm). The solution cells gradually became greatly deformed in the high centrifugal fields, and the use of this rotor was discontinued.

Suspending further work on the small rotors, Svedberg now concentrated on the standard-size ones. The cell holes in the early rotors became deformed during the test runs and had to be ground to cylindrical form before being used for routine runs. Even so, a gradual deformation of the cell holes occurred during the use of the rotor and increased with time. A number of different rotor designs were constructed and tested before a satisfactory type was finally achieved in January 1939. Of the twenty-two rotors previously tested, seven standard-size and two small ones had exploded. After such explosions Svedberg was sometimes about to give up; there seemed to be no hope of finding a satisfactory design, and he wondered whether it was really worthwhile to devote further work to improving the ultracentrifuge, or whether it might not be better to concentrate on other problems. His interest in the proteins and his anxiety to prove or disprove his hypothesis of the multiple system for their molecular weights, however, inspired him to continue; and after his retirement he described this period as the happiest of his scientific life.

Toward the end of the 1930's, Svedberg extended his interest in macromolecules of biological origin to include the polysaccharides. With N. Gralén he found that the sap of the bulbs from various species of Liliifloreae contained soluble high-molecular-weight substances. The various species yielded widely different sedimentation diagrams because they contain proteins and polysaccharides of different properties and in different proportions. Two classes of carbohydrates could be distinguished by their sedimentation behavior, and a similarity among the species of the same genus was generally found with regard to the content of high-molecular-weight material that could elucidate problems in systematic botany.

In the 1940's Svedberg and his co-workers extended their investigations to other natural polysaccharides, primarily to determine parameters of molecular size and shape. The gradual shift of his interest to the study of cellulosic materials, particularly wood cellulose and cellulose nitrates, led to close cooperation with the research laboratories of the biggest cellulose manufacturers in Sweden.

The outbreak of World War II forced Svedberg to take up activities connected with the war. Owing to the blockade, no oil-resistant rubber could be obtained from abroad; and Svedberg was charged with developing Swedish production of synthetic rubber (polychloroprene). For several years more than half of the research facilities of his laboratory was used for this development and for pilot plant work. The project was successful and led to a small production plant in northern Sweden. The government and other state agencies demanded much of Svedberg's time. Institutes and industries closely related to war materials sought his help and his advice. The planning necessary for combining these activities with the work at his institute gave him fewer opportunities than before for his own experimental work and for contact with his co-workers and students.

In connection with the work on synthetic rubber, Svedberg took physicochemical studies on other synthetic polymers. He was always looking for new experimental techniques to be used in the study of these high polymers and of cellulose. With I. Jullander he developed an osmotic balance by means of which low osmotic pressures could be determined by weighing. Electron microscopy was

introduced into the study of the structure of native and regenerated celluloses. X-ray techniques were used for cellulosic fibers and electron diffraction for investigation of micelles and crystallites.

Svedberg's interest in radiation chemistry was revived in the late 1930's with investigations using hemocyanins to study the effect of ultraviolet light, α particles, and ultrasonics on solutions of these proteins. In the 1940's, a small neutron generator was built by one of his collaborators, H. Tyrén, to study the action of an uncharged particle on proteins. After being completed, however, it was used mainly for the production of a small amount of radiophosphorus and a few other radioactive isotopes needed at some of the medical institutes at Uppsala. The question soon arose of how to increase the capacity for making radioactive isotopes. The construction of a cyclotron at Uppsala would immensely increase that capacity and would open new fields for research in radiation chemistry there.

One of Svedberg's old friends at the Medical Faculty proposed that he approached Gustaf Werner, a wealthy industrialist in Göteborg, about the possibility of obtaining financial help to build a large cyclotron. The response was very positive, partly because of Werner's interest in the possible medical application of such research. In the spring of 1946, he promised to give one million Swedish crowns for the construction of a cyclotron. Svedberg immediately made plans for the cyclotron and for the building of an adjoining research institute. He even obtained extra funds from the government, and construction of the building was started in February 1947. Svedberg had now decided to devote his time to the creation of this new research institute and to the planning of the work with the cyclotron. In December 1949, some months after his retirement from the chair of physical chemistry, the Gustaf Werner Institute of Nuclear Chemistry was officially inaugurated, and Svedberg received permission to continue his activities as head of that institute. It took another two years, however, before some important model experiments with the magnet and the oscillator were satisfactory and the final installations could be made. In the late fall of 1951, the necessary equipment had been acquired, and the 185 MEV synchro-cyclotron was in full operation.

Although Svedberg had brought a few co-workers from his old institute, he had to assemble a new staff and find students in order to build the research organization for his new institute. Many different problems were studied. One group worked mainly on the biological and medical application of the cyclotron; others investigated the effect of radiation on macromolecules, problems in radiochemistry, and radiation physics. The institute soon became the center in Sweden for research in the area between high-energy physics, chemistry, and biology. Svedberg's own interest in research remained intense throughout his life, and he followed all the work in progress and advised his students and collaborators. He even took active part in some research projects. The last publication bearing his name (1965) deals with recent developments in high-energy proton radiotherapy.

NOTES

1. *Nobel Lectures in Chemistry 1901–1921* (Amsterdam, 1966), 381.
2. *Nature*, **123** (1929), 871.
3. *Ibid.*, **139** (1937), 1061.

BIBLIOGRAPHY

I. ORIGINAL WORKS. Svedberg published 240 papers and books, only a few of which can be mentioned here. A complete bibliography is in the biography by Claesson and Pedersen (1972). His first paper was "Ueber die elektrische Darstellung einiger neuen colloidalen Metalle," in *Berichte der Deutschen chemischen Gesellschaft*, **38** (1905), 3616–3620. His early work on colloids was summarized in his dissertation, "Studien zur Lehre von den kolloiden Lösungen," in *Nova acta Regiae societatis scientiarum upsaliensis*, 4th ser., **2**, no. 1 (1907), 1–160. His contribution to the preparation of colloidal solutions was given in *Die Methoden zur Herstellung kolloider Lösungen anorganischer Stoffe* (Dresden–Leipzig, 1909; 3rd ed., 1922). The work on isomorphic coprecipitation of radioactive compounds is "Untersuchungen über die Chemie der radioaktiven Grundstoffe. I–II," in *Zeitschrift für anorganische Chemie*, **61** (1909), 338–346, and **63** (1909), 197–206, written with D. Strömholm. His experimental contributions to the discussion of whether molecules exist as particles were published in *Die Existenz der Moleküle* (Leipzig, 1912). The first papers dealing with centrifugal methods were "The Determination of the Distribution of Size of Particles in Disperse Systems," in *Journal of the American Chemical Society*, **45** (1923), 943–954, written with H. Rinde; "Determination of Size and Distribution of Size of Particle by Centrifugal Methods," *ibid.*, 2910–2917, written with J. B. Nichols; and "The Ultra-Centrifuge, a New Instrument for the Determination of Size of Particle in Amicroscopic Colloids," *ibid.*, **46** (1924), 2677–2693, written with H. Rinde.

Svedberg's Wisconsin lectures were published in *Col-loid Chemistry* (New York, 1924; 2nd ed., rev. and enl. in collaboration with Arne Tiselius, New York, 1928). The first ultracentrifugal determination of the molecular weight of a protein appeared in "A New Method for the Determination of the Molecular Weight of the Proteins," in *Journal of the American Chemical Society*, **48** (1926), 430–438, written with Robin Fåhraeus. Svedberg's Nobel lecture was originally published in Swedish as "Nobelföredrag hållet i Stockholm den 19 maj 1927," in *Les prix Nobel en 1926* (Stockholm, 1927), 1–16; an English version is "The Ultracentrifuge," in *Nobel Lectures in Chemistry 1922–1941* (Amsterdam, 1966), 67–83. The first paper dealing with the hypothesis of the multiple system for the molecular weights of the proteins is "Mass and Size of Protein Molecules," in *Nature*, **123** (1929), 871; two later papers dealing with the same hypothesis are "The Ultracentrifuge and the Study of High-Molecular Compounds," *ibid.*, **139** (1937), 1051–1062; and "A Discussion on the Protein Molecule," in *Proceedings of the Royal Society*, **A170** (1939), 40–56, also *ibid.*, **B127** (1939), 1–17. A comprehensive account of the ultracentrifuge is given in *The Ultracentrifuge* (Oxford, 1940; repr. New York, 1959), written with K. O. Pedersen. The detailed study of the polysaccharides appeared in "Soluble Reserve-Carbohydrates in the Liliifloreae," in *Biochemical Journal*, **34** (1940), 234–238, written with N. Gralén. The osmotic balance was first reported in "The Osmotic Balance," in *Nature*, **153** (1944), 523, written with I. Jullander. The work on cellulose is described in "The Cellulose Molecule. Physical-Chemical Studies," in *Journal of Physical and Colloid Chemistry*, **51** (1947), 1–18.

II. SECONDARY LITERATURE. A complete bibliography of Svedberg's books and papers is in S. Claesson and K. O. Pedersen, "The Svedberg 1884–1971," in *Biographical Memoirs of Fellows of the Royal Society*, **18** (1972), 595–627. Other publications dealing with Svedberg's life are N. Gralén, "The Svedberg 1884–," in S. Lindroth, ed., *Swedish Men of Science 1650–1950* (Stockholm, 1952), 271–279; P.-O. Kinell, "Theodor Svedberg. Kolloidchemiker-Molekülforscher-Atomfachmann," in H. Scherte and W. Spengler, eds., *Forscher und Wissenschaftler im heutigen Europa—Weltall und Erde* (Oldenburg, 1955), 191–198; A. Tiselius and S. Claesson, "The Svedberg and Fifty Years of Physical Chemistry in Sweden," in *Annual Review of Physical Chemistry*, **18** (1967), 1–8; and A. Tiselius and K. O. Pedersen, eds., *The Svedberg 1884–1944* (Uppsala, 1944), published in honor of Svedberg's sixtieth birthday.

STIG CLAESSON
KAI O. PEDERSEN

SVEDELIUS, NILS EBERHARD (*b.* Stockholm, Sweden, 5 August 1873; *d.* Uppsala, Sweden, 2 August 1960), *phycology.*

Svedelius' father, Carl, was a Supreme Court justice; and his father's family included numerous intellectuals, clergymen, governmental officials, army officers, scholars, and teachers. His mother, Ebba Katarina Skytte of Sätra, belonged to the untitled nobility. At a young age he showed keen interest in botany; and in 1891 he entered the University of Uppsala, where K. F. Kjellman was one of his teachers. The marine algal flora of high latitudes was a main interest of Kjellman, who had been the botanist of the *Vega* expedition, which in 1878–1880 accomplished the Northeast Passage. In Sweden the marine algae had been studied mainly at the North Sea coast, whereas the depauperated flora of the Baltic Sea had been neglected. Svedelius therefore selected as the topic for his doctoral dissertation the algal flora of the southern Baltic coast of Sweden, with special emphasis on their morphological and ecological responses to the decreased salinity. In 1901 he received the doctorate and became a docent the following year. Svedelius was appointed professor of botany in 1914 and retired in 1938. Although he retained a lifelong interest in the algae of the Baltic, Svedelius made his contributions of fundamental importance in a totally different branch of phycology—in the elucidation of the various life cycles in the red algae (Florideae) and their evolutionary value.

In 1902–1903 Svedelius visited the tropics, spending most of his time in Ceylon, particularly at Galle, which has a large coral reef where he surveyed the marine algae and their taxonomy, ecology, and distribution. Rather little was ever published from this journey; but it focused his interest on the red algae, and his experiences in Ceylon were in many ways valuable to his later investigations.

The introduction of the microtome and fixing and staining techniques at that time opened a new era in biology. The alternation between a gametophytic and a sporophytic generation had long been known in ferns and mosses, as had the existence of different kinds of reproductive bodies in algae; but no regular pattern could be discerned in the latter group. In 1904 J. L. Williams established the alternation between two externally similar generations in a brown alga, and two years later S. Yamanouchi found it in a red alga, the formation of tetraspores being preceded by meiosis. Realizing that the technical means were now at hand, Svedelius decided to investigate reproduction in the red algae. After establishing one more case of regular alternation, he turned to *Nitophyllum punctatum* (1914), in which tetraspores were known to occur

both on special (sporophytic) and on gametophytic individuals. The latter were, as expected, haploid. Their apparent tetraspores were formed without meiosis and thus were not true tetraspores, but a kind of accessory spore. In 1915 Svedelius showed that *Scinaia furcellata*, a species without tetraspores, does not possess independent alternating generations because the first nuclear division after fertilization is meiotic and the carpospores thus become haploid. For the rest of his life (his last paper was written in 1955) he continued along these lines, studying additional species, finding new complications and modifications in the life cycles, and trying to trace their phylogenetic connections. All his publications are exhaustive, detailed, exact, and profusely illustrated by his own instructive and beautiful drawings.

From the beginning of his life-cycle studies Svedelius was interested in the general significance of the alternation of generations in the plant kingdom and was perhaps the first to point out that the acquisition of a sporophyte must be of immense evolutionary value: in organisms in which the zygote is the only diploid cell, one fertilization is followed by only one meiosis, whereas in organisms with a full diploid generation, one fertilization is followed by numerous meioses, each with its own possibilities of genetic segregations.

Svedelius was not exclusively a phycologist. He also published papers on floral biology and on seed anatomy. His inherent interest in organization, administration, and economics engaged him deeply in the affairs of his university and of several academies and learned societies. In 1935–1950 he was president of the Botanical Section of the International Biological Union.

BIBLIOGRAPHY

I. ORIGINAL WORKS. Svedelius' writings include *Studier öfver Österjöns hafsalgflora* ("Studies of the Marine Algae of the Baltic Sea"; Uppsala, 1901), his dissertation; "Ueber den Generationswechsel bei *Delesseria sanguinea*," in *Svensk botanisk tidskrift*, **5** (1911), 260–324; "Ueber die Tetradenteilung in den vielkernigen Tetrasporangiumanlagen bei *Nitophyllum punctatum*," in *Berichte der Deutschen botanischen Gesellschaft*, **32** (1914), 48–57; "Ueber Sporen an Geschlechtspflanzen von *Nitophyllum punctatum*, ein Beitrag zur Frage des Generationswechsels der Florideen," *ibid.*, 106–116; "Zytologisch-entwickelungsgeschichtliche Studien über *Scinaia furcellata*. Ein Beitrag zur Frage der Reduktionsteilung der nicht tetrasporentragenden Florideen," in *Nova acta Regiae societatis scientiarum upsaliensis*,

4th ser., **4** (1915), 1–55; "Generationsväxlingens biologiska betydelse" ("The Biological Significance of the Alternation of Generations"), in *Svensk botanisk tidskrift,* **12** (1918), 487–490; "Alternation of Generations in Relation to Reduction Division," in *Botanical Gazette,* **83** (1927), 362–384; "The Apomictic Tetrad Division in *Lomentaria rosea* in Comparison With the Normal Development in *Lomentaria clavellosa,*" in *Symbolae botanicae upsalienses,* **2** (1937), 1–54; and "Zytologisch-entwickelungsgeschichtliche Studien über *Galaxaura,* eine diplobiontische Nemalionales-Gattung," in *Nova acta Regiae societatis scientiarum upsaliensis,* 4th ser., **13** (1942), 1–154.

II. Secondary Literature. More detailed biographies are G. F. Papenfuss, "Nils Eberhard Svedelius. A Chapter in the History of Phycology," in *Phycologia,* **1**, no. 4 (1961), 172–182, with a complete bibliography of his phycological papers; and C. Skottsberg, "Nils Eberhard Svedelius 1873–1960," in *Biographical Memoirs of Fellows of the Royal Society,* **7** (1961), 295–312, with a complete bibliography of his works.

J. A. Nannfeldt

SVERDRUP, HARALD ULRIK (*b.* Sogndal, Norway, 15 November 1888; *d.* Oslo, Norway, 21 August 1957), *geophysics.*

Sverdrup was the son of Johan Edvard Sverdrup, a fundamentalist clergyman and teacher, and Maria Vollar, who was related to the Grieg family. The Sverdrup family itself contained a number of prominent educators, industrialists, artists, and politicians, including Johan Sverdrup, prime minister of Norway and an important figure in the introduction of parliamentarianism and social reform in the 1870's and 1880's. Sverdrup was also distantly related to the arctic explorer Otto Sverdrup, a companion of Nansen, for whom the Sverdrup Islands in the Canadian Arctic were named.

Sverdrup received his early education at home. He was much interested in evolution and the natural sciences, but on entering high school in 1901 honored his parents' wishes by studying classical languages. In 1906 he passed the elementary examinations at the University of Norway, then entered the military academy there, graduating as a reserve officer in 1908. He then began studies in the faculty of sciences. At first interested primarily in astronomy, Sverdrup was an enthusiastic and able student, and was soon discovered by Vilhelm Bjerknes, professor of physics and the leading authority on atmospheric circulation. Sverdrup became Bjerknes' assistant in 1911 and was one of several students who followed him when he trans-

ferred to the University of Leipzig two years later. Sverdrup remained in Leipzig for four years, during which he published some twenty papers, either alone or in collaboration. One of these was his doctoral dissertation, "Der nordatlantische Passat," published in 1917. Sverdrup's work of this period was, not surprisingly, strongly influenced by that of Bjerknes, and much of it was concerned with the circulation of the atmosphere. Some of his models and calculations were remarkably exact, and have since been confirmed by more precise measurements.

By 1917 conditions at Leipzig had become intolerable because of World War I, and Bjerknes returned to Norway to become professor of geophysics at the University of Bergen. Sverdrup also returned to Norway, and was soon engaged by the arctic explorer Amundsen to act as chief scientist on an expedition to the North Pole. Sverdrup was eager to go, since the atmospheric conditions that he was studying could be observed more readily in the uniform arctic climate. Since Amundsen's ship, the *Maud,* was small, each crew member had to assume several jobs, and Sverdrup served as navigator and cook, as well as scientist.

The *Maud* expedition left Norway in the summer of 1918. It failed to reach the North Pole, largely because adverse ice and current conditions prevented a regular drift over the polar basin, but Sverdrup was nonetheless able to conduct important research on atmospheric circulation and the magnetic field of the earth. In addition, he became interested in ethnography when the expedition came into contact with some of the tribes, particularly the Chukchi, of northeastern Siberia. This interest, together with an admiration for the culture of primitive peoples, lasted the rest of his life.

In the summer of 1922 the *Maud* was docked for repairs at Seattle and Sverdrup used the occasion to work at the Carnegie Institution of Washington, where he began to interpret the magnetic observations that he had made. He served as sole leader of the expedition when it was resumed in the same year, and continued making oceanographic and meteorological observations until the venture ended three years later. Even though the ship had not actually crossed the pole, Sverdrup was able to unravel the complicated dynamics of the tides in the polar basin. He transcribed part of his results on shipboard, then published them in 1926, the year in which he returned to Norway to succeed Bjerknes as professor of geophysics at the University of Bergen. His complete account of the *Maud* expedition, in which he drew upon observational data to explain the general features of the arctic atmospheric and oceanic circulation and energy distribution, was published in 1933.

In Bergen, Sverdrup also studied the magnetic and oceanographic data obtained by American expeditions in the Pacific and Antarctic oceans. In 1931 he took up an independent research position at the Christian Michelsens Institute and also participated in George Wilkins' adventurous but premature attempt to reach the North Pole by submarine, a voyage that allowed him to make important observations of the deep sea north of Spitsbergen. In 1934 he studied the glaciers of Spitsbergen and, with H. W. Ahlmann, developed the study of the energy balance of glaciers. The following year he went to La Jolla, California, to become director of the Scripps Institute of Oceanography.

At Scripps Sverdrup was primarily concerned with the turbulent processes in the boundary layer between the atmosphere and the sea, although he also found time to work in other areas of geophysics and to write *The Oceans* (1942), a monumental handbook of oceanography that remains an important introduction to the subject. When, during World War II, Scripps became deeply involved in military research, Sverdrup made a number of significant contributions; his precise predictions of tides and the height of waves were particularly valuable in the course of the Pacific war.

In 1948 Sverdrup assumed the directorship of the Norwegian Polar Institute in Oslo. He reorganized the institute, arranged the Norwegian-British-Swedish expedition to Antarctica of 1949–1952, and organized Norwegian participation in the International Geophysical Year 1957–1958. In 1949 he became professor of geophysics at the University of Oslo, then dean of the faculty of science and vice-director of the university. Interested in curriculum reform, he was chairman of a committee for revising the university course of studies somewhat along the lines of those used in the American university system. His demonstrated administrative abilities led to his appointment as chairman of the Norwegian relief program in India. Under his leadership this program was planned to introduce Norwegian technology, particularly as it applied to the fishing industry, to the underdeveloped areas along the Cochin coast without disrupting existing cultural patterns. This plan met with a degree of success that must be attributed to Sverdrup's diplomatic skills and to his profound sympathy for foreign cultures. In the midst of these activities, he died suddenly of a heart attack while attending a meeting.

BIBLIOGRAPHY

I. ORIGINAL WORKS. Sverdrup's most important scientific works are "Der nordatlantische Passat," in *Veröffentlichungen des Geophysikalischen Instituts der Universität Leipzig*, ser. 2, **B 2** (1917); "Dynamic of Tides on the North Siberian Shelf, Results from the Maud Expedition," in *Geofysiske publikasjoner*, **4**, no. 5 (1927); *Scientific Results. The Norwegian North Polar Expedition with the "Maud,"* 3 vols. (Bergen, 1927–1933); *The Oceans*, with M. W. Johnson and R. H. Fleming (New York, 1942).

A complete list of Sverdrup's scientific papers is given in S. Richter, "Bibliografi over H. U. Sverdrups arbeider," in *Det Norske Videnskaps-Akademi i Oslo Årbok 1958* (Oslo, 1959).

II. SECONDARY LITERATURE. The only real biography of Sverdrup is O. Devik, "Minnetale over professor Harald U. Sverdrup," in *Det Norske Videnskaps-Akademi i Oslo Årbok 1958* (Oslo, 1959).

NILS SPJELDNAES

SWAINSON, WILLIAM (*b*. Newington Butts, London, England, 8 October 1789; *d*. Wellington, New Zealand, 7 December 1855), *zoology*.

William Swainson was the eldest surviving son of John Timothy Swainson II, collector of customs at Liverpool and lord of the manor of Hoylake, Cheshire, and his second wife, Frances Stanway.

At the age of fourteen Swainson entered the service of H.M. Customs and Excise but was handicapped by a serious impediment in his speech. His father therefore obtained for him a post in the army commissariat, and in 1807 Swainson was posted first to Malta and then to Sicily. While in Sicily he made extensive collections of botanical and zoological specimens, especially fishes, and became friendly with the eccentric Constantine S. Schmaltz Rafinesque. Swainson visited Greece and Italy, where he was also stationed for a while. In 1815 he retired on half-pay.

Swainson next visited Brazil with Henry Koster, spending part of the years 1817 and 1818 there. Upon his return to England in 1818 Swainson published a brief note on his travels but, disappointed by lack of encouragement, he did not prepare a full account. When his Brazilian material, after long delays, was distributed to specialists for their use, others had forestalled him in describing the new species he had found and his pioneer work was not recognized.

In 1823 Swainson married Mary Parkes of Warwick and thereafter engaged in scientific writing for a living, producing many books and papers during the next seventeen years. He wrote on vertebrates, mollusks, and insects, and he contributed sections on farm and garden pests to Loudon's *Encyclopaedia of Agriculture* and *Encyclopaedia of Gardening*, illustrating all his own work. Unfortunately, Swainson undertook far too much, because of financial pressures, and at times fell seriously behind schedule. Overwork, his wife's death in 1835, and financial losses, as well as a second unsuccessful attempt to obtain a post in the British Museum, caused his decision to emigrate to New Zealand in 1840, and to abandon his scientific writings.

He did, however, publish a few small papers after his emigration, and in 1851–1853 he reported on the timber trees of Victoria, New South Wales, and Tasmania.

William Swainson was a good zoologist, but his unfortunate adherence to the "quinary system" has distorted some of his work. The quinary or circular system, first suggested by William Sharpe Macleay, and eagerly adopted by Swainson, professed that the relationships within any zoological group could be expressed by a series of interlocking circles, and that the "primary circular divisions of any group were three actually, or five apparently." This extraordinary theory was pertinaciously held by Swainson throughout his zoological career and it certainly impaired much of his work. A. Newton and H. Gadow (*A Dictionary of Birds* [1896], p. 35) stated the matter fairly when they wrote that Swainson's indefatigable pursuit of natural history and conscientious labor on its behalf deserve to be remembered as a set-off against the injury he unwittingly caused by his adherence to the absurd quinary system.

Swainson's artistic achievements were of high merit, and he was a pioneer in the use of lithography. His botanical work is unimportant; his claim to remembrance rests upon his zoological work and upon his fine zoological illustrations.

BIBLIOGRAPHY

I. ORIGINAL WORKS. Only separate works are listed here since Swainson's scientific papers are listed in the Royal Society *Catalogue of Scientific Papers*. They are *Instructions for Collecting and Preserving Subjects of Natural History and Botany* (Liverpool, 1808); *Zoological Illustrations*, 3 vols. (London, 1820–1823); 2nd. ser. 3 vols. (London, 1829–1833); *Exotic Conchology* (London, 1821–1822), 2nd ed., S. Hanley, ed. (London, 1841), facs. (with additions), R. T. Abbott, ed. (Princeton, 1968); *The Naturalist's Guide*, 2nd. ed.

(London, 1822); *A Catalogue of the Rare and Valuable Shells of the Late Mrs. Bligh. With an Appendix Containing Scientific Descriptions of many New Species and Two Plates* (London, 1822); *Fauna Boreali-Americana; or the Zoology of the northern parts of British America*, pt. 2. *The Birds* (London, 1831), written with John Richardson; and the following volumes of Lardner's *Cabinet Cyclopaedia* (London); *A Preliminary Discourse on the Study of Natural History* (1834); *Treatise on the Geography and Classification of Animals* (1835); *Natural History and Classification of Quadrupeds* (1835); *Animals in Menageries* (1837); *Natural History and Classification of Birds*, 2 vols. (1836–1837); *Natural History of Fishes, Amphibians and Reptiles*, 2 vols. (1838–1839); *Habits and Instincts of Animals* (1839); *Taxidermy, with the Biography of Zoologists* (1840); *A Treatise on Malacology* (1840); *On the History and Natural Arrangement of Insects* (1840), written with W. E. Shuckard. He also wrote *Elements of Modern Conchology* (London, 1835); *Birds of Western Africa*, 2 vols. (Edinburgh, 1837); and *Flycatchers* (Edinburgh, 1838) for the Naturalist's Library.

Other works to which Swainson contributed include J. C. Loudon, *An Encyclopaedia of Gardening*, new ed. (London, 1834); J. C. Loudon, *An Encyclopaedia of Agriculture*, 4th ed. (London, 1839); and Hugh Murray, *An Encyclopaedia of Geography* (London, 1834).

II. SECONDARY LITERATURE. No full-scale biography of Swainson has yet been published. Biographical notices in various biographical dictionaries are mostly inaccurate. See obituaries in *Proceedings of the Linnean Society of London* (1855–1856), xlix, and in *Gentleman's Magazine* (1856), 532; and Iris M. Winchester, "William Swainson, F.R.S., 1789–1855 and Henry Gabriel Swainson, 1830–1892," in *Turnbull Library Record*, n.s., **1** (1967), 6–19.

NORA F. MCMILLAN

SWAMMERDAM, JAN (*b.* Amsterdam, Netherlands, 12 February 1637; *d.* Amsterdam, 17 February 1680), *biology.*

Swammerdam's father, Jan Jacobszoon Swammerdam, son of a timber merchant, was an apothecary who in 1632 had married Baertje Jans Corvers. The couple's first two children died in early childhood. In 1640 was born Jan's brother, Jacobus, who became an apothecary, and in 1642 a sister, Jannetje. Jan's mother died in 1661. His father had acquired some fame as a collector of curios, including minerals, coins, and animals from all over the world. As a boy, Jan helped care for this collection.

He matriculated in medicine at the University of Leiden on 11 October 1661. Jan's own collection of insects impressed his schoolmates, including Regnier de Graaf, Frederik Ruysch, and Niels Stensen (Steno). Robertus Padtbrugge was a fellow student who later joined the East India Company and sent Swammerdam exotic animals. The eminent professors Franciscus dele Boë Sylvius and Johannes van Horne both refer in their publications to Swammerdam's student researches. He qualified as a candidate in medicine in October 1663, and then spent some time in Saumur, France, staying with Tanaquil Faber, a professor of philology at the Protestant university there.

From about September 1664, Swammerdam lived in Paris as the guest of Melchisédech Thévenot. He was an active member, as was his friend Steno, of Thévenot's scientific academy, an informal club that met to watch experiments and dispute over Cartesian ideas. Returning to Amsterdam about September 1665, Swammerdam joined a group of physicians calling themselves the Private College of Amsterdam, which included Gerhard Blaes (Blasius) and Matthew Slade. The group met irregularly until 1672 and published a description of their dissections. In the winter of 1666–1667, Swammerdam was again in Leiden, where he dissected insects and collaborated with van Horne on the anatomy of the uterus. His medical thesis on respiration, based largely on research carried out in 1663, earned him the M.D. on 22 February 1667. There is no evidence of his ever settling into a medical practice,[1] although in 1670 he was granted the privilege of dissecting bodies in Amsterdam, and he does allude once to being kept from his research by the demands of the seriously ill.[2]

Driven by an inner passion and encouraged by Thévenot and other friends, Swammerdam devoted his life to scientific investigation, but he was interrupted by illness, by his father's insistence that he earn a living, and by periods of depression and religious anxiety. He stayed for a time at The Hague, perhaps as a guest of Maurice, prince of Nassau, who had fishermen bring him specimens, and he occasionally visited Leeuwenhoek in Delft.[3] He lived during the summer of 1670 in the village of Sloten, just outside Amsterdam, where he studied mayflies.

The mystical prophetess Antoinette Bourignon was accompanied in her exile by a friend of Swammerdam's. Jan wrote to her for spiritual comfort on 29 April 1674, and asked her permission before publishing his researches on the mayfly. He visited her in Schleswig-Holstein, between September 1675 and June 1676. On 18 July 1675 Steno sent Swammerdam's drawings of silkworm anatomy to Malpighi, reporting that the author had destroyed the manuscript text and that they should pray for their friend in his search for God.[4] But Swammerdam's rejection of science was not final, for in January 1680 he provided in his will for the publication of his manuscripts, and these give evidence of having been revised in the last year or two of his life. Not until a half century had passed, however, were his wishes carried out; Boerhaave published the *Biblia naturae* in 1737–1738.

Swammerdam's biological researches fall into two distinct categories, although all were characterized by a preference for mechanistic types of explanation supported by great originality of technique and experiment. His studies of insects have a special quality all their own, while most of his other anatomical and physiological work may be called medical. The medical research was conducted within the fabric of currently fashionable theories, often actually in the company of his colleagues. This category includes his thesis on respiration, his book on the anatomy of the uterus, and other scattered notes. His accomplishments in this area were well known to his contemporaries but occasioned several priority disputes. By contrast, his work on insects was in a sense a private quest and remained largely unpublished during his lifetime. The theme of this work was essentially anti-Aristotelian, for he claimed that insects are no less perfect than higher animals and are not really different in their modes of development.

Swammerdam's medical thesis offers a perfectly Cartesian mechanical explanation of the motion of the lungs and the function of breathing, supplemented by the iatrochemistry of Sylvius. Swammerdam struggled to avoid using any attractive powers, whether of the mouth, of the lungs themselves, or of a partial vacuum, to explain the rushing of air into the lungs. Apparently ignorant of Boyle's idea that air has a springiness, Swammerdam argued that the muscular expansion of the chest outward pushes the ambient air down into the lungs. He dramatized this process with a submerged dog that could breathe through a tube. When the dog inhaled, the level of the water's surface rose, but when the tube was stopped up, the lungs would not follow the chest in its expansion. The normal rising and falling of the lungs was simply the result of air having been pushed into them from outside, not of the motion of the thorax. (John Mayow, using Boyle's ideas, easily destroyed Swammerdam's argument in his tract on respiration in 1668.) Swammerdam described a very curious set of experiments, in which he produced bubbling by drawing air out of sealed containers partly filled with water; the experiments seem to be meant to show that the same effects producible by mouth suction can be duplicated with a syringe. Again, his point was that the action of breathing is mechanical.

Swammerdam seems to have believed that when air in a confined space is pushed, the finer particles of air will run out of the container and the remaining air will then consist of heavier parts and will therefore be dense. This idea of the nature of air pressure allowed him to explain what happens in respiration thus: the expanded lungs press on the air contained in the pleural cavity, thus forcing the subtler parts out of this cavity into the heart. He had already demonstrated this process in January 1663, when his professors and fellow students saw him force air into the lungs of a living dog to produce a visible effervescence in the dog's heart. While agreeing with Harvey that the heart does contract of its own power, Swammerdam integrated this with the Cartesian picture of the blood moving by virtue of its increase in volume as well, first in the right side before being cooled by the lungs, and then again when finally perfected on the left side, under the influence of the fine, subtle particles of air. Like Descartes, Swammerdam suggested that emotions like joy, anger, fear, and happiness depend upon the various degrees of motion of the blood in respiration.

Although so many of Swammerdam's ideas about respiration appear misbegotten in the light of modern theory, or even in comparison to those of his contemporaries at Oxford, the assumptions and experimental technique behind them were essentially the same as those used in his classic proof that muscles do not increase in volume upon contraction. Again he was Cartesian in interpreting the old animal spirit, passing from nerves into muscle, as a very subtle but material fluid. Testing the reaction of various muscles of many different animals, Swammerdam learned that the frog was the best subject for this kind of experiment, and it was with this animal that he gave demonstrations to Steno about 1663 and to the Grand Prince Cosimo III in 1669.

The first part of Swammerdam's demonstration was simply an elaboration of the common observation that a muscle can contract when separated from the body. Using both the heart and a long muscle of the frog separated from the body and the blood vessels, he urged that the fact that they would repeatedly respond to the stimulation of the nerve showed that contraction did not depend on an influx of matter from the brain or of blood, both current theories. Simply placing a muscle in a glass tube made the thickening of its belly and the shortening of its length clearly visible. The enlargement of the belly of a muscle had suggested to a number of men that contraction consists of effervescence or some other increase in volume, but Swammerdam devised an elegant experiment to measure the change in volume, using his favorite instrument. Placing a muscle inside a syringe, the mouth of which was blocked by a drop of colored water, he was able to demonstrate that the contraction of the muscle or heart was not accompanied by an outward motion of the drop; if there was motion at all, it was inward, suggesting a slight decrease in volume. Swammerdam did not suggest an alternate mechanism of contraction, nor did he deny the existence of a matter carried through the nerves, but simply noted that this matter must be of insensible volume. His description and drawings of this investigation were first published in 1738, but they were well known to Steno and through him to others, including Croone and Borelli.[5]

It was at Saumur that Swammerdam perfected a technique for displaying the valves of lymphatic vessels, although the existence of these valves was already known. Ruysch, who at Leiden had also been interested in techniques of anatomical preservation, published a description of a similar preparation in 1665. Swammerdam found that his father had shown his drawings to all who were interested, and although Ruysch was probably innocent, Swammerdam expressed annoyance.[6]

During his second stay at Leiden, in the winter of 1666–1667, Swammerdam and van Horne collaborated on the anatomy of human reproductive organs, both male and female. Swammerdam used wax injection to make the vessels distinct. Although van Horne described this anatomical work in 1668, Swammerdam did not publish his drawings of the preparations until de Graaf made public his own investigations on the same subject. Swammerdam then published *Miraculum naturae*, which he sent, along with the preserved specimens themselves (now lost), to the Royal Society asking that his priority be acknowledged. Besides the technique of wax injection, one of the discoveries in dispute was the very nature of human reproduction. According to van Horne, Steno, Swammerdam, and de Graaf, the organs that had been called female testes were really ovaries, like those of egg-laying animals. Swammerdam claimed to have seen eggs in them. Baer in the nineteenth century is more properly credited with this observation, but the important concept that mammals do have ovaries was accepted in the seventeenth century. Although the Royal Society arbitrated the question of priority in favor of Steno, Harvey's pronouncement that all life originates in eggs made their anatomical search a natural one.

In association with the Private College of Amsterdam, Swammerdam dissected the pancreas of fish and analyzed the pancreatic fluid in the context of Sylvius' theory of digestion, and he also described the formation of hernias. The Private College decided to publish as a body, but Swammerdam later noted that certain of their discoveries were entirely his own. He had shown that the spinal marrow consisted of fibers that terminate in the brain and from which nerves proceed out.

Besides these medical studies, Swammerdam pursued a lifelong inquiry into the nature of lower animals. A visitor of 1662 noted that Swammerdam owned a colored copy of Mouffet's entomology.[7] He was actively collecting, observing, and dissecting insects in Saumur, in and around Paris, in Leiden, and to the end of his days in the countryside around Amsterdam. All he managed to publish was the *Historia insectorum generalis*, Part I, and a monograph on the mayfly, which, in the period of his religious crisis, became the occasion for an extended hymn to the Creator. But he left explicit instructions in his will for the publication of the rest of his entomological studies, and Boerhaave was probably accurately carrying out Swammerdam's intentions when he integrated the text of the *Historia* (slightly revised) with the unpublished manuscripts, using it as a framework that further researches filled in.

Swammerdam's thesis about insects was fundamentally new and significant. For his contemporaries, as for Aristotle, there existed three good arguments that not only placed the insects far from higher animals, but even tended to remove them from the realm of subjects open to scientific study. These arguments were: insects lack internal anatomy; they originate by spontaneous generation; and they develop by metamorphosis. Swammerdam believed that all three arguments were false and devoted a wide variety of investigations to refute these ideas.

The 1669 *Historia* was devoted to the overthrow of the idea of metamorphosis, as its title explains: "General Account of the Bloodless Animals, in Which Will be Clearly Set Forward the True Basis of Their Slow Growth of Limbs, the Vulgar Error of the Transformation, Also Called Metamorphosis, Will be Effectually Washed Away, and Comprehended Concisely in Four Distinct Orders of Changes, or Natural Budding Forth of Limbs." The idea of metamorphosis, which Swammerdam was so determined to refute, was that of a sudden and total change from one kind of creature into another, comparable to the alchemical transmutation of a base metal into gold.

William Harvey, calling the starting point of life an egg, defined two distinct modes of development from an egg. The chick grows in a hen's egg by epigenesis, but the butterfly grows in its "egg" (the chrysalis) by metamorphosis, as does an animal appearing in putrid matter. In epigenesis, the embryo is at first tiny and imperfect; it grows in size while acquiring its parts one after another. In metamorphosis the parts come into existence simultaneously and full-sized. Swammerdam consciously and energetically set out to destroy this supposed difference between the epigenetic development of higher animals and the metamorphic origin of lower animals. He used two kinds of evidence: the dissection of larvae and chrysalides before the final emergence of the adult, and a comparison among various types of insects including some that undergo only partial metamorphosis or none at all. It would seem that Swammerdam caught a clue to the nature of metamorphosis from his observations of the aquatic larvae of mayflies (which he first studied in 1661) and dragonflies (watched at Saumur in 1663 or 1664). The wings, which appear in so impressive a manner after the last molt, can be seen in a late larva, folded up in special protuberances on the back. The gradual growth of the insect can be easily seen in the successive larval stages. There is no difficulty in recognizing this process as the life cycle of one animal changing its form as it grows, just as the chick must change in appearance as well as in size before becoming a hen. Believing that the laws of nature are regular and simple, Swammerdam sought to explain all development according to one model. Those changes that seem metamorphic are really no different from the obviously gradual ones, except that they go on invisibly, under the skin.

Curious to find the growth of a butterfly's wings to be as epigenetic as a dragonfly's, Swammerdam searched for the proper dissecting technique. In his thesis of 1667 he had promised that he would soon explain the transformation of a caterpillar into a chrysalis, and by 1669 he had found that if a mature caterpillar, just preparing to become a chrysalis, is treated first with boiling water, then with wine and vinegar, and if the skin is removed, the rudiments of limbs and wings may be discerned. This demonstration was thought to be significant and exciting, both by Swammerdam and by his contemporaries, but there is no evidence for the dramatic scenes portrayed by Boerhaave, Francis J. Cole, and others. An eyewitness account undermines the picture of Swammerdam as a silent auditor at Thévenot's gatherings.[8] The most dramatic moment for Swammerdam himself may have been when he learned that Malpighi had anticipated him, finding rudiments of wings and legs in a silkworm.[9] Swammerdam claimed to have done his dissection in the presence of Magalotti, which would have been in June or July 1669.[10] Swammerdam regarded this demonstration as a great achievement, for the parts of the butterfly are so soft, tender, and folded that they can be recognized in a late caterpillar on the verge of its change only with difficulty. In a slightly younger caterpillar that is active and feeding they can scarcely be distinguished, because they are even more fluid and confused with the other tissue, he said. Swammerdam did not claim to have detected them in an immature caterpillar. They are at first invisible, in his description, not because of any extreme minuteness but because they are too fluid.

The point that Swammerdam considered most important, since it destroyed the previous ideas of metamorphosis, is that the parts of the butterfly do not come into being suddenly in the chrysalis but are already beginning to grow in the caterpillar. They develop by epigenesis, the process that Harvey described for higher animals, not by metamorphosis:

[The limbs] which a worm without legs acquires near the chest after its change are not born in the suddenness of changing, or, to speak more exactly, in the quickness of a budding out or rising up of limbs, but these are growing with the worm at their designated places under the skin, one after another by addition, that is, by *epigenesis* . . .[11] and these parts are not born suddenly, but grow on slowly, the one part after the other . . . and they are increased and born in this swelling, budding forth, rising up, budding, and as if stretching of new limbs, gradually by an addition of parts, *epigenesis*, and by no means by a transformation, *metamorphosis*; therein lies the sole foundation of all the changes of bloodless animals.[12]

Swammerdam's principal concern was with development, not origin. After 1669 he studied the process of development in the chrysalis in more detail. He dissected chrysalides after two days, six

days, twelve days, and sixteen days, reporting that structures at first so fluid and delicate that they cannot be handled gradually acquire form and firmness.

The sole foundation of all the so-called transformations of insects, according to Swammerdam, is the *Popken* or *Nympha*, that is, a pupa. His definition of this new concept is unclear, but he was fairly consistent in using it for the stage where an insect is preparing to molt by growing a new inner skin. Swammerdam's explanation of the nature of the pupa put great emphasis on the idea that the individual animal always remains the same, that is, we are dealing with the life history of one individual, irrespective of moltings and changes in appearance:

. . . a nymph, pupa, or chrysalis is nothing other than such a manner of change from a worm and caterpillar, or, to speak more exactly, such a manner of growing, swelling, budding, or protuberance of parts of a worm or caterpillar, as to bear the specific shape of the future animal itself; or, otherwise, that this growth and so forth of parts in a worm or caterpillar is the animal itself in the form of a pupa. So that the matter being properly considered, a worm or caterpillar does not change into a pupa, but becomes a pupa by the growing of parts; so also this pupa, we may add, afterward does not change into a flying beast, but the same worm or caterpillar, having taken on the form of a pupa by shedding its skin, becomes a flying beast. The above changes are nothing else than those of a chick, which is not changed into a hen, but becomes a hen by the growing of its parts: or also, of the young of a frog which does not change into a frog, but becomes a frog by the swelling of its parts.[13]

After describing the mistaken notion of metamorphosis to be found in Thomas Mouffet, Goedaert, and Harvey, and indicating the pupa as the true basis of all insect development, Swammerdam proposed that all the various modes of insect development fall into one of four groups. The first group comprehends those insects that hatch from the egg in their adult form, afterward undergoing no change save growth. Before hatching, the animal lies inside the eggshell motionless, without food, and occupying the entire volume of the egg. Swammerdam regarded the egg itself as really a kind of pupa. "The animal grew within its mother from invisible but nevertheless real beginnings."[14] The animal's first development having taken place within the parent, what looks like an egg in this class is a formed animal lying hidden under a skin, that is, a pupa. In Swammerdam's view, this mode of development is the most obvious and simple to understand.

In the remaining three orders of development, the animal hatches out of its egg before having reached perfection, so it must become a pupa before appearing in its final shape. In the second kind of development, the animal emerges from its egg without wings, but usually with six legs. It acquires its adult structures by a gradual and visible external process of growth. In some members of the group, such as the earwigs, the difference between the young "worm" and the adult are very slight, consisting only in the addition of wings. In others, such as the mayfly, the changes are greater, involving the loss of larval structures as well as the addition of the adult structures. In all cases the adult structures are acquired by visible external growth, and the animal never completely loses its ability to move. The pupa in this second order is simply the last stage before the final molt from which the winged adult emerges.

Swammerdam understood all remaining modes of development to be fundamentally the same, and to differ from the first two groups in the same respect. He defined them in two more groups, while pointing out that the fourth could justifiably have been included within the third. In both these orders the animal leaves its egg in as yet a very imperfect state, lacking many or most of its adult structures. These it acquires in the course of time, gradually, invisibly, under the skin, where the structures lie folded and soft. The adult parts are all existent and recognizable in the pupa, although in some insects they are very obscure. The pupa in both orders does not feed or move.

Swammerdam divided his third order of development into two subgroups, those whose adult parts are obvious in the pupa because of its thin skin and those whose pupa seems to be without parts externally. The nymphs of ants, bees, and beetles are pupae of the first kind, and the chrysalides or aureliae of butterflies and moths are pupae of the second kind. He believed the difference between them to be merely a matter of the thickness of their skin, and even tried to find a simple mechanical explanation for this difference.

Swammerdam's fourth order of insect development is comprised of insects whose pupa, corresponding exactly to the nymph or chrysalis of the third order, is hidden. This is what happens in most flies; their larvae or maggots form a case called a puparium. Swammerdam insisted that the difference between the third and fourth order is one of appearance only, not of essence. The pupa separates from the larval skin, as in the second and third orders, but the animal does not crawl out of this skin, which hardens to form the puparium. The pupa lies within this case just as the bee's pupa lies sealed in its wax cell. The puparium may retain the shape of the larva, that is, be worm-shaped, or it may round up into the shape of an egg. It is of great importance to recognize, wrote Swammerdam, that this worm- or egg-shaped object is not an egg, as Harvey and others had said, nor a kind of pupa, but that it contains a pupa. Yet Swammerdam himself did see all eggs as pupae in one sense, insofar as they contained and concealed an animal.

Swammerdam emphasized the theme and structure of his insect research by appending to the *Historia* a table designed to show that insects develop in essentially the same fashion as do all other living things. All begin in an egg, grow gradually in size and detail until arriving at adulthood, when they are sexually mature. Swammerdam used the frog to illustrate development in higher animals and the carnation to illustrate development in plants. His table presents insects from each of his orders of development, the louse for the first order, the dragonfly for the second, the ant and the moth for the nymph and chrysalis types of the third order, and the dung fly for the fourth order. Five stages of development from egg to adult are numbered, and the numbers correspond to the figures in his tables, which had evidently been carefully planned with this comparison in mind.

Of the three arguments for the imperfection of insects, Swammerdam's *Historia* was concerned with the refutation of only one, metamorphosis as then understood. Working after 1669, Swammerdam attacked the other two arguments as well. In spite of his famous experiments on maggots in meat, Redi decided that insects found inside plants must have appeared there without parents; the Latin edition of Redi's work, appearing in Amsterdam in 1671, stimulated Swammerdam to collect information about insects that cause plant galls. The idea that insects consisted internally of humors was destroyed by Swammerdam's exceptional skills at microdissection; he refined his technique of injecting fluids, including wax, mercury, air, and alcohol; and he often used very fine scissors instead of knives.[15] He used a single-lens microscope made by Jan Hudde of Amsterdam,[16] and another mounted on flexible arms made by Samuel Musschenbroek.[17]

It is not surprising to find such a skilled microscopist as Swammerdam reporting that a frog embryo consists of globules or that there are oval particles in the blood, but historians should note that he attempted no interpretation of these observations. His dissections of various insects, as well as snails, mussels, cuttlefish, a Portuguese man-of-war, and a hermit crab formed a good portion of the study of all invertebrate anatomy before Cuvier.

Swammerdam's four orders of insect development were transformed by John Ray and Martin Lister into four orders of insects.[18] In the subsequent history of classification, types of development played various roles (Linnaeus did not use them), but clearly Swammerdam's own purpose had not been taxonomic.

Swammerdam is commonly called the founder of the theory of preformation. This is ironic because, Swammerdam, like Malpighi, consciously avoided conjecture. The reciprocal intercourse of snails, pictured in his medical thesis, was in a sense the emblem of all his science, for it represented to him the fact that even the safe assumption that animals are either male or female can be destroyed by an observation. He was loath to let his reasoning run beyond his facts. Still, Swammerdam's work did contribute to the development of the idea of preexistence and even emboîtement. His opposition to sudden metamorphosis could easily be read as an opposition to any change at all, for his own concept of the pupa was obscure, and he had no clear notion of the distinction between growth and differentiation.

Swammerdam opposed both spontaneous generation and metamorphosis on the grounds that they led to atheism by allowing chance and accident to rule instead of law and regularity. The basic law of living things was that they came from parents of the same kind by means of eggs. Nor is their growth in the egg subject to chance, as pangenesis, for example, might suggest, but is simply the increase of parts already present. The actual nature of the egg itself was a very difficult question that Swammerdam realized he had no means of solving. But if growth is conceivable while change in substance is not, inevitably the germs of all living things must have been in existence from the time of Creation. Swammerdam alluded to this idea only briefly. It was probable, said Swammerdam in 1669, that there was no generation of the sort that could leave room for chance processes, but only propagation, that is, the growth of something already in existence.[19] Certainly Swammerdam had no full emboîtement theory clearly in mind, for he located the first principles in the egg produced by the female ovary, yet suggested that this concept might explain the biblical statement that Levi was in his father's loins (Hebrews 7:10). He identified the black spot of a frog's egg as itself a frog with all its parts, without claiming to have seen a miniature, but on the contrary expressing wonder that somehow a tiny black spot really is a frog.[20]

Swammerdam said that he communicated his experiments to a learned man, who suggested that they could even explain how Adam's sin affected all his descendants,[21] and that when Eve's eggs were used up the human race would end,[22] but on all such questions Swammerdam forbore to give an opinion himself. It has always been assumed that it was Malebranche to whom Swammerdam referred. Certainly Malebranche was very quick to incorporate Swammerdam's information into his own philosophy.[23] The manuscripts Swammerdam left in 1680 contain no elaboration of the preformationist paragraphs of 1669 and 1672, but did include a careful description of the complete transformations of anatomy to be seen when a beetle larva becomes an adult, the mere watery humor that is visible in bee eggs, and the beginning of a frog in four globules.

Some biographers describe Swammerdam as a mystic, for he was a follower of a woman who purportedly had spoken with God, and he saw in the short flight of the mayfly an image of man's own brief existence. Yet the word *mystical* certainly does not apply to his scientific work, for his was a mechanistic world, instituted by God and operating like clockwork.

NOTES

1. See Engel, "Records," cited in the bibliography.
2. *Book of Nature*, 117.
3. Antoni van Leeuwenhoek, *The Collected Letters*, I (Amsterdam, 1939), 143, letter to Oldenburg of 7 September 1674.
4. Howard B. Adelmann, *Marcello Malpighi and the Evolution of Embryology*, I (Ithaca, 1966), 399.
5. Leonard G. Wilson, "William Croone's Theory of Muscular Contraction," in *Notes and Records. Royal Society of London*, 16 (1961), 158–178.
6. A. M. Luyendijk-Elshout, Introduction to Frederik Ruysch, *Dilucidatio Valvularum in Vasis et Lacteis* (1665), facsimile (1964).
7. Johan Nordström, "Swammerdamiana: Excerpts From the Travel Journal of Olaus Borrichius and Two Letters from Swammerdam to Thévenot," in *Lychnos* (1954–1955), 21–65.
8. *Ibid.*
9. Swammerdam, *Historia*, 131; *Book of Nature*, II, 2. Adelmann, *Malpighi*, II, 844–845.
10. Anxious to establish his priority over Malpighi, whose *De bombyce* appeared in 1669 (see Adelmann, I, 399), Swammerdam would undoubtedly have mentioned any public demonstration of years before. Instead he refers to a visit from Thévenot and Magalotti, which would have been dur-

ing the tour of the Grand Prince (not yet Duke) of Tuscany, Cosimo III. (He does not claim that the Prince himself witnessed this dissection, though he mentions showing him other discoveries). Careful records of the curiosities seen on the tour of 1667–1668 and references to Thévenot on the summer tour of 1669 are the basis for my dating of the visit with Swammerdam. See G. J. Hoogewerff, *De Twee Reizen van Cosimo de' Medici Prins van Toscane door de Nederlanden (1667–1669): Journalen en Documenten* (Amsterdam, 1919), xlix, 45, 319, 392.

11. My literal translation of the Dutch *Historia*, 26.
12. *Ibid.*, 43.
13. *Ibid.*, 8–9. My interpretation differs from those based on the Flloyd translation, *The Book of Nature*.
14. *Ibid.*, p. 100.
15. Boerhaave, *Book of Nature*, xiv–xvi.
16. Swammerdam, *Historia*, 81. See also Balthasar de Monconys, *Journal des Voyages*, II (Lyons, 1665–1666), 161–162.
17. Boerhaave, *loc cit.*
18. John Ray, *Historia Insectorum* (London, 1710).
19. Swammerdam, *Historia*, 51.
20. Swammerdam, *Miraculum*, 21.
21. *Historia*, 52.
22. Swammerdam, *Miraculum*, 22.
23. Paul Schrecker, "Malebranche et le préformisme biologique," in *Revue internationale de philosophie*, 1 (1938), 77–97.

BIBLIOGRAPHY

I. ORIGINAL WORKS. All of Swammerdam's works appeared in various printings and translations. A complete bibliography, including some other authors who cited him, is given in Schierbeek's biography.

Swammerdam's works include *Tractatus physico-anatomico-medicus de respiratione usuque pulmonum* (Leiden, 1667), reprinted, with Dutch trans., in *Opuscula selecta de arte medica neerlandicorum*, VI (Amsterdam, 1927), 46–181; *Historia insectorum generalis, ofte, Algemeene Verhandeling van de Bloedeloose Dierkens* . . . (Utrecht, 1669), French trans., 1682, repr., 1685, and Latin trans., 1685, repr., 1693. Its text is incorporated into the *Biblia Naturae*.

Other works are *Miraculum naturae sive uteri muliebris fabrica* (Leiden, 1672), repr., 1679, 1680, 1717 (and 1729?); *Ephemeri vita of afbeeldingh van 's Menschen Leven, vertoont in de Wonderbaarelijcke en nooyt gehoorde Historie van het vliegent ende een-dagh-levent Haft of Oever-aas* (Amsterdam, 1675), of which the biological portions, without the hymns to the Creator, were published in English by Edward Tyson as *Ephemeri vita* (London, 1681), and in French in Thévenot's *Recueil des voyages; Bybel der Natuure* (Leiden, 1737–1738), with facing pages in Latin, *Biblia naturae, sive historia insectorum*, 3 vols.; German trans. (Leipzig, 1752); in English as *The Book of Nature*, Thomas Flloyd, trans., with footnotes by John Hill (London, 1758).

II. SECONDARY LITERATURE. In 1727 Boerhaave purchased Swammerdam's manuscripts; he also acquired some papers of biographical interest, including forty-one of Swammerdam's letters to Thévenot. These manuscripts and papers are now in the Universitäts-bibliothek in Göttingen, and a microfilm of them is in Leiden. To this day Boerhaave remains the only scholar to have made use of these papers, so his biography, prefacing the *Biblia naturae* in all its editions, is the chief source for Swammerdam's life. In spite of the fact that parts of it are evidently conjecture, it is on the whole useful and reliable.

Abraham Schierbeek in 1944 combined Boerhaave's biography with later sources and Swammerdam's text when writing his *Jan Swammerdam, zijn Leven en zijn Werken* (N.V. Uitgeversmaatschappij "De Tijdstroom" Lochem [1947]); *Jan Swammerdam (12 February 1637–17 February 1680): His Life and Works* (Amsterdam, 1967).

Sources of information not in Boerhaave, or valuable interpretations, are the following: Francis J. Cole, "The Birthplace of Jan Swammerdam, 1637–1680," in *Isis*, 27 (1937), 452; Hendrik Engel, "Records on Jan Swammerdam in the Amsterdam Archives," in *Centaurus*, 1 (1950), 143–155; and *Observationes anatomicae selectores collegii privat: Amstelodamensi um 1667–1673*, F. J. Cole, ed. (Reading, England, 1938).

On preformation, preexistence, and emboîtement, see Jacques Roger, *Les sciences de la vie dans la pensée française du XVIIIᵉ siècle* (1963), especially pp. 325–384; Howard B. Adelmann, *Marcello Malpighi and the Evolution of Embryology* (Ithaca, N.Y., 1966), 819–886; and Peter J. Bowler, "Preformation and Pre-existence in the Seventeenth Century: A Brief Analysis," in *Journal of the History of Biology*, 4 (1971), 221–244.

MARY P. WINSOR

SWANN, WILLIAM FRANCIS GRAY (*b.* Ironbridge, Shropshire, England, 29 August 1884; *d.* Swarthmore, Pennsylvania, 29 January 1962), *experimental physics, theoretical physics.*

Swann's chief contributions to physics lay in experimental and theoretical studies of cosmic radiation, theoretical research in electromagnetic theory and relativity, and work in the philosophy of physics.

He received his higher education at the Imperial College of Science and Technology, University College, King's College, and the City and Guilds College of London Institute. In 1910 he was awarded the Doctor of Science degree by the University of London. In 1913 Swann went to the United States to become chief of the physics division of the department of terrestrial magnetism at the Carnegie Institution of Washington, where he remained until 1918. For the next nine years he taught physics at the University of Minnesota, the University of Chicago, and at Yale University, where he was director of the Sloane Physics Laboratory from 1924 to 1927. In the latter year Swann became director of the Bartol Research Foundation of the Franklin Institute, the laboratory of which had recently been built on the campus of Swarthmore College. He remained there for the rest of his life, retiring officially in 1959 but staying on as emeritus.

Swann early became interested in geophysics, particularly in regard to the earth's magnetism and atmospheric electricity; and his bibliography shows many papers in the field during the period from 1909 to 1930. The interest in atmospheric electricity naturally led to a growing concern with cosmic radiation, a field he entered vigorously around 1922 and to which he devoted a large part of his research energy. In this area he was equally at home in both theory and experiment, and his frequent summaries of progress were extremely stimulating to all workers in the field. He made the Bartol Research Foundation into one of the world's great centers in cosmic ray studies, a field in which he maintained interest for the rest of his life.

Swann's early fascination with the fundamental problems in physical theory provided by relativity led to many papers on the relation between the latter and electromagnetism and electrodynamics. He was highly critical of most presentations of this subject and was never satisfied until he had probed to the bottom of every difficulty. This attitude induced a concern for the general problems of the philosophy of physics. His lectures in this discipline, always in great demand, led to the preparation of his highly successful book *The Architecture of the Universe* (1934), in which the basic ideas of relativity, thermodynamics, statistical mechanics, and quantum mechanics were set forth with great clarity and charm.

A talented cellist, Swann was a founder and conductor of the Swarthmore Symphony Orchestra. He was a member of the American Philosophical Society and was also prominent in the affairs of the American Physical Society, serving as its president from 1931 to 1933. He received several honorary degrees and was awarded the Elliott Cresson Gold Medal of the Franklin Institute in 1960.

BIBLIOGRAPHY

I. ORIGINAL WORKS. Swann's complete bibliography includes two books and 263 articles. The complete list of papers is available from the Bartol Research Foundation of the Franklin Institute, Swarthmore, Pennsylvania. The following selection is intended to illustrate the breadth of his work.

The books are *The Architecture of the Universe* (New York, 1934) and *Physics* (New York, 1941), written with Ira M. Freeman.

Earlier papers include "The Fitzgerald-Lorentz Contraction, and an Examination of the Method of Determining the Motions of Electrons When Considered Simply as Singularities, Moving so as to Satisfy the Electromagnetic Scheme," in *Philosophical Magazine*, 6th ser., **23** (1912), 86–95; "On the Earth's Magnetic Field," *ibid.*, **24** (1912), 80–100; "The Atmospheric Potential Gradient, and a Theory as to the Cause of Its Connection With Other Phenomena in Atmospheric Electricity, Together With Certain Conclusions as to the Expression for Electric Force Between Two Parallel Charged Plates," in *Terrestrial Magnetism and Atmospheric Electricity*, **18** (1913), 173–184; "On the Origin and Maintenance of the Earth's Charge. Part I," *ibid.*, **20** (1915), 105–126; "The Penetrating Radiation and Its Bearing Upon the Earth's Electric Field," in *Bulletin of the National Research Council. Washington*, no. 17 (1922), 54–77; and "The Fundamentals of Electrodynamics, Part II," in *Bulletin of the National Research Council on Electrodynamics of Moving Media*, no. 24 (1922), 5–74; "The Relation of the Restricted to the General Theory of Relativity and the Significance of the Michelson-Morley Experiment," in *Science*, **62** (1925), 145–148; "The Possibility of Detecting Individual Cosmic Rays," in *Journal of the Franklin Institute*, **206**, no. 6 (Dec. 1928), 771–778; and "Relativity and Electrodynamics," in *Review of Modern Physics*, **2** (July 1930), 243–304.

Later papers are "Electrons as Cosmic Rays," in *Physical Review*, **41**, no. 4 (15 Aug. 1932), 540–542; "On the Nature of the Primary Cosmic Radiation," *ibid.*, **43**, no. 11 (1 June 1933); "The Relation of the Primary Cosmic Radiation to the Phenomena Observed," *ibid.*, **46**, no. 9 (1 Nov. 1934), 828–829; "The Corpuscular Theory of the Primary Cosmic Radiation," *ibid.*, **48** (15 Oct. 1935), 641–648; "Cosmic Ray Observations in the Stratosphere," in *Contributed Technical Papers. Stratosphere Series (National Geographic Society)*, no. 2 (1936), 13–22, written with G. L. Locher, W. E. Danforth, and C. G. and D. D. Montgomery; "The Electrodynamic Force Equation in Its Bearing Upon the Evidence for the Existence of a New Cosmic Ray Particle," in *Physical Review*, **52**, no. 5 (1 Sept. 1937), 387–390; "Showers Produced by Penetrating Rays," in *Physical Review*, **56**, no. 4 (15 Aug. 1939), 378; "The Significance of Scientific Theories," in *Philosophy of Science*, **7**, no. 3 (July 1940), 273–287; "The Relation of Theory to Experiment in Physics," in *Review of Modern Physics*, **13**, no. 3 (July 1941), 190–196; "Mass-Energy Relation in Quantum Theory," in *Physical Review*, **109**, no. 3 (Feb. 1958), 998–1008; and "Certain Matters in Relation to the Restricted Theory of Relativity, With Special Reference to the Clock Paradox and the Paradox of the Identical Twins. I. Fundamentals," in *American Journal of Physics*, **28** no. 1 (Jan. 1960), 55–64.

II. SECONDARY LITERATURE. A biographical sketch

by Martin A. Pomerantz is in *Yearbook. American Philosophical Society* (1962), 178–184. There is also a sketch in *Current Biography, 1960,* 417–419, with photograph.

R. B. Lindsay

SWARTS, FRÉDÉRIC JEAN EDMOND (*b.* Ixelles, Belgium, 2 September 1866; *d.* Ghent, Belgium, 6 September 1940), *chemistry.*

Frédéric Swarts entered the University of Ghent in 1883 and received doctorates in chemistry (1889) and medicine (1891). His father, Théodore Swarts, had succeeded Kekulé as professor of chemistry at the university in 1871. The younger Swarts spent his entire professional career at Ghent, first as *répétiteur* and then, on his father's retirement in 1903, as professor of chemistry. He was a member of the Académie Royale des Sciences des Lettres et des Beaux-Arts de Belgique, which awarded him its Gold Medal, corresponding member of the Institut de France, president of the Institut International de Chimie Solvay, and charter member and vice-president of the International Union of Pure and Applied Chemistry.

After the discovery of fluorine, few of its compounds had been prepared because of the reactivity and toxicity of the element. Swarts was among the first to study organic fluorine compounds. Unable to use methods of direct fluorination because of the violence of the reactions, he developed a double decomposition process using inorganic fluorides, especially antimony trifluoride and mercurous fluoride, and organic polyhalides, where the halogen atoms are on the same carbon atom (the Swarts reaction, 1892). The first synthesis of an organic fluorine compound was trichlorofluoromethane (1891). Swarts synthesized many aliphatic chlorofluoro and bromofluoro derivatives of hydrocarbons, alcohols, and acids. In 1922 he prepared trifluoroacetic acid, the strongest organic acid known.

The aliphatic chlorofluoro compounds became the first fluorochemicals to be used commercially after Thomas Midgley and A. L. Henne in 1930, using a modified Swarts reaction, prepared the group of fluorinated methanes and ethanes known as the Freons.

Swarts made the first extensive investigations of organic-fluorine compounds. He coupled his syntheses of organic fluorine compounds with physicochemical studies and determined their heats of combustion, molecular refractions, and viscosities, proving that fluorinated organic com-

pounds have weaker intermolecular forces than the corresponding nonfluorinated compounds.

BIBLIOGRAPHY

I. Original Works. Important papers include "Sur l'acide fluoracétique," in *Bulletin de l'Académie royale de Belgique. Classe des sciences,* **31** (1896), 675–688; "Sur quelques dérivés fluorés du toluol," *ibid.,* **35** (1898), 375–420; "Contribution à l'étude des combinaisons organiques du fluor," in *Mémoires couronnés et mémoires publiés par l'Académie royal des sciences, des lettres et des beaux-arts de Belgique,* **61** no. 4 (1901–1902); "Investigations thermochimiques des combinaisons organiques du fluor," in *Journal de chimie physique et de physico-chimie biologique,* **17** (1919), 3–70; and "Sur l'acide trifluoracétique," in *Bulletin . . . ,* **8** (1922), 343–370.

II. Secondary Literature. Accounts of the life and work of Swarts are "Frédéric Swarts," in *Bulletin. Société chimique de Belgique,* **49** (1940), 33–35; Marcel Delépine, "Frédéric-Jean Edmond Swarts, 2 Septembre 1866–6 Septembre 1940," in *Comptes rendus hebdomadaires des séances de l'Académie des sciences,* **212** (1941), 1057–1059; Jean Timmermanns, "Frédéric Swarts (1866–1940)," in *Journal of the Chemical Society* (1946), 559–560; and George B. Kauffman, "Frédéric Swarts: Pioneer in Organic Fluorine Chemistry," in *Journal of Chemical Education,* **32** (1955), 301–303.

Albert B. Costa

SWARTZ, OLOF (*b.* Norrköping, Sweden, 21 September 1760; *d.* Stockholm, Sweden, 19 September 1818), *botany.*

Swartz began his studies in the field of medicine at Uppsala University in 1778, the year of Linnaeus' death. He had been interested in botany at an early age, and had already traveled to different parts of Sweden and Finland in order to collect plants and other objects of natural history. His doctoral thesis, written under Linnaeus the younger (who succeeded his father in the chair of botany at Uppsala), and entitled *Methodus muscorum illustrata* (1781), indicated further his scientific devotion. The great adventure in Swartz's life was his journey to the West Indies. He began his trip in 1783, traveling first through eastern North America, stopping at Boston and Philadelphia. Then, during the next two years, he visited Jamaica, Puerto Rico, Haiti, and Cuba. On his way home in 1786 and 1787 he studied the great botanical collections of Linnaeus and Banks in London, comparing his own extensive material with what had already been brought together by botanists of an earlier generation. As a result of studies made during his voyage, Swartz published in 1788 *Nova genera et species plantarum* and other lesser articles and papers. This work was summed up in his magnificent *Flora Indiae Occidentalis I–III* (1797–1806), which included descriptions of all the new genera and species he had found. He described nearly 900 species, most of them new to science.

For several years Swartz lived in Stockholm on a small private income, devoting himself entirely to his botanical research. In 1791 he became Bergian professor and intendant at a newly established school of gardening in Stockholm, owned by the Royal Swedish Academy of Sciences. He received several other appointments in the service of the academy, and finally, in 1811, was elected permanent secretary, the most important position in the academy. He held this office until his death. From 1813 he was professor of botany at the Caroline Institute.

Besides his work on the flora of the West Indies, Swartz is best known for his taxonomic studies of specific plant groups, often in the context of their worldwide distribution. Thus, for example, through his studies of orchids, summarized in *Genera et species Orchidearum* (1805), he was able to improve the systematics of these plants on the basis of the morphological traits of their highly specialized flowers. Swartz's greatest fame, however, rests on his studies of the cryptogams. He broadened greatly the knowledge of Swedish mosses, and he described in his works on the West Indies many new species of lichens and fungi; but, principally, he worked with the ferns of the world. His main works in this field are *Genera et species filicum* (1801) and the monumental *Synopsis filicum* (1806). As in his work on mosses and orchids, Swartz based his fern systematics upon studies of the fructification organs. He tried to deepen the views common in the Linnaean tradition, of which he was a strong adherent, thus opening the way for further study.

Swartz was, along with the much more conservative Thunberg, the most internationally oriented of Swedish botanists. He carried on a huge foreign correspondence and thus had the opportunity to publish his works in Germany, where they found their way to the international scientific community more easily than they would have if published in Sweden. Nevertheless, because of his central position in the Academy of Sciences and because of his universally praised generosity and friendliness, Swartz was the unifying link between the other botanists in his own country.

BIBLIOGRAPHY

I. ORIGINAL WORKS. Swartz's published works in botany are listed in T.O.B.N. Krek, *Bibliotheca botanica suecana* (Uppsala-Stockholm, 1925). Part of his correspondence is in the library of the Royal Academy of Sciences, Stockholm, in the Brinkmanska Arkivet, Trolle-Ljungby, and in the Riksarkivet, Stockholm.

II. SECONDARY LITERATURE. In the posthumous work of Swartz, *Adnotationes botanicae,* J. E. Wikström, ed. (Stockholm, 1829), there are biographies by Wikström, K. Sprengel, and C. A. Agardh. See further S. Lindroth, *Kungl. Svenska Vetenskapsakademiens historia,* II (Stockholm, 1967), 71–75, 229–234, 416–420, and *passim,* and G. Eriksson, *Botanikens historia i Sverige intill år 1800* (Uppsala, 1969), 290–292, 326–328.

GUNNAR ERIKSSON

SWEDENBORG, EMANUEL (*b.* Stockholm, Sweden, 29 January 1688; *d.* London, England, 29 March 1772), *technology, geology, cosmogony, physiology, theology.*

Swedenborg's career is one of the most remarkable in the history of science. In his youth and early manhood he was an enthusiastic scientist and technologist, and published a number of articles in various fields. Almost imperceptibly he turned to religious speculation, which, after a decisive divine revelation, led him to become a visionary and the founder of a religious sect, for which he is best known.

The son of Jesper Swedberg, professor of theology at Uppsala and later bishop of Skara, Swedenborg grew up in Uppsala and studied at its university, specializing in the humanities. He soon turned to the sciences, however, influenced by his brother-in-law, the learned university librarian Erik Benzelius. In the fall of 1710 Swedenborg traveled to England, where he stayed until 1713, mostly in London. During this time he was captivated by what he learned of science. He read Newton. He met Flamsteed, Halley, and John Woodward. He considered the universe to be a problem in mathematics, and, filled with youthful self-confidence, he tried to realize grandiose technical inventions, among them flying machines and submarines. Swedenborg returned to Sweden via Paris and Germany, and in 1716 was appointed extraordinary assessor on the Board of Mines. In this capacity he worked with Christopher Polhem, whom he admired greatly and assisted in far-reaching technical and industrial projects. Many articles in *Daedalus hyperboreus*, Sweden's first, short-lived (1716–1718) scientific journal, which the wealthy Swedenborg published at his own expense, were devoted to Polhem's mechanical inventions. Ennobled in 1719 (until then he signed himself Swedberg), he served for years on the Board of Mines; he was a competent metallurgist and, among other things, experimented with a new process for refining copper ore.

Always manifold in his scientific ambitions Swedenborg during this period wrote many short articles on his observations and theories. They were of varying importance, some indifferent or amateurish in quality, others ingenious and interesting. He was least successful as an astronomer. Swedenborg's attempt to determine longitude at sea by means of the moon (published in 1716 and later several times revised), was submitted in a competition sponsored by the British Parliament. It was rejected by the experts and failed completely. In *Om jordenes och planeternas gång och stånd* ("On the Course and Position of the Earth and the Planets"; Skara, 1718), which was inspired by the Bible, Polhem, and Thomas Burnet's *Telluris theoria sacra*, Swedenborg tried to prove that in earlier times the earth had revolved at a faster rate around the sun. The seasons would have been of similar climate and a paradisiacal spring would have reigned. As the earth slowed down and the length of the year and the seasons increased, the final catastrophe was approaching.

Young Swedenborg was undoubtedly at his best in geology and paleontology. In *Om watnens högd och förra werldens starcka ebb och flod* ("On the Level of the Seas and the Great Tides in Former Times"; Uppsala, 1719) he submitted empirical proof—sedimentary deposits, gravel ridges, fish in landlocked lakes without outlets, and the raising of the land along the Baltic coast—that Scandinavia had once been covered by an ocean from which the land had slowly risen. With the chemist Urban Hiärne, who strongly influenced him, he thus initiated the eighteenth-century debate in Sweden about "water reduction." Swedenborg was very interested in fossils as evidence of a prehistoric flood. He was convinced of their organic origin; and during a journey in 1721–1722, he examined many fossils of plants found near Liège and Aachen. His descriptions of them were published together with other geological papers in his *Miscellanea observata circa res naturales* (Leipzig, 1722).

Swedenborg's plans were to become increasingly grandiose. In his *Principia rerum naturalium* (Leipzig, 1734), probably conceived as a counterpart to Newton's *Principia*, he sought a comprehensive physical explanation of the world based on mathematical and mechanical principles. While remaining faithful to the general principles of Cartesian natural philosophy, which he had learned while studying at Uppsala, Swedenborg elaborated upon them. According to his cosmogony the physical reality has developed from the mathematical point, which was an entity between infinite and finite. Through a vortical movement implanted on the point, a series of material particles developed (the "first finita," the "second finita," and so on) that eventually led to the cosmos in its present state. In contrast to Descartes, Swedenborg believed that the planets had developed from the chaotic solar mass through expansion of its surrounding shell, which finally joined to form a belt along the equatorial plane of the sun. It then exploded, forming the planets and the satellites. Although the basic construction of Swedenborg's thought heralded the later planetary theories of Buffon, Kant, and Laplace, there is nothing to indicate that it exerted any direct influence on posterity.

In the 1730's Swedenborg pursued his materialistic explanation of the universe to its furthest consequence, concluding that the human soul also derived from the movements of the small particles. But at the same time a disturbing feature emerged in his thought. In speculating on paradise and the nature of angels, Swedenborg became increasingly involved—faithful to the Cartesian way of stating the inquiry—in the body-soul problem; and the soul and the mysteries of organic life soon became his main field of research. He planned enormous works in which physiology step by step was transformed into theology: *Oeconomia regni animalis* (2 vols., London–Amsterdam, 1740–1741) and *Regnum animale* (3 vols., The Hague, 1744–1745).

Swedenborg now sought to explain everything in terms of psyche, considering even the body as a manifestation of divine origin: "Everything lives the life of its soul and the soul lives the life of God's spirit." With the help of Malpighi, Swammerdam, and Vieussens he sought to discover the location of the human soul in the brain and its role as intermediary between mortal and divine. In his *Oeconomia* and in certain manuscripts, especially "De cerebro" (first published 1882–1887), he presented for the first time his theory that the activities of the soul, located in specific centers in the cortex of the brain, were built up from the finest "fibers." In this categorical form it was an original and remarkable hypothesis that remained unnoticed by later physiological researchers.

The religious crisis in Swedenborg's life was now approaching. At the beginning of the 1740's he wrestled with the greatest problem in metaphysics. Wishing to find words for the ineffable, he experimented with a logical-mathematical universal language, a *mathesis universalis* on Leibniz's and Wolff's models, but it turned instead into the theory of correspondence. As worked out in its linguistic and philosophical details, this theory taught that existence was made up of three reciprocal levels—the natural, the psychic, and the divine; each word or concept within a certain level corresponded to a word or concept within another.

A financially independent bachelor, Swedenborg journeyed to Holland and England during this period. Restless and excited, he was plagued by dreams and visions that he described in the peculiar *Drömboken* ("Journal of Dreams"; Stockholm, 1859). At the same time he was working on a great narrative of creation, *De cultu et amore Dei*, but abandoned it when the final vision came upon him at London in the spring of 1745: God revealed himself to Swedenborg and ordered him to interpret the meaning of the Bible; on the same night the world of the spirits, Heaven and Hell, were opened to him.

At the age of fifty-seven Swedenborg abandoned his scientific investigations. For the rest of his life he was purely a visionary and prophet. Many thought him mad. In a stream of Latin works, especially the gigantic commentary on the books of Moses, *Arcana coelestia* (8 vols., London, 1749–1756), he developed his theory of the spiritual world, which was to be the beginning of a new universal religion, represented on earth by the Swedenborgian New Church. But despite its bizarre aspects Swedenborg's theology is by no means a chaos of whims and visions. It is characterized by rigorous logic and obviously is rooted in his previous concern with the physical sciences.

BIBLIOGRAPHY

I. ORIGINAL WORKS. Swedenborg's enormous literary production, only part of which was published during his lifetime, is listed by James Hyde, *A Bibliography of the Works of Emanuel Swedenborg* (London, 1906); and by Alfred H. Stroh and Greta Ekelöf, *An Abridged Chronological List of the Works of Emanuel Swedenborg* (Uppsala, 1910). His most important scientific works are mentioned in the text. Most of Swedenborg's early scientific works, including *Principia* (1734) and letters to Erik Benzelius, among others, are in his *Opera quaedam aut inedita aut obsoleta de rebus naturalibus*, 3 vols. (Stockholm, 1907–1911). Swedenborg's work on longitude was published in Latin as *Methodus nova inveniendi longitudinem locorum . . . ope lunae* (Amsterdam, 1721). He also published *Prodromus principiorum rerum naturalium* (Amsterdam, 1721) and monographs on the metallurgy of iron and copper: *Regnum subterraneum sive minerale de ferro* and *Regnum . . . de cupro et orichalco* (Dresden–Leipzig, 1734). together with *Principia rerum naturalium*, are contained in his *Opera philosophica et mineralia*, 3 vols. (Leipzig, 1734).

Swedenborg's MSS on the physiology of the brain was published by R. L. Tafel as *The Brain Considered Anatomically, Physiologically and Philosophically*, 2 vols. (London, 1882–1887), and as *Three Transactions on the Cerebrum*, Alfred Acton, ed., 2 vols. (Philadelphia, 1938–1940). The unfinished *De cultu et amore Dei* was published at London in 1745. Almost all of Swedenborg's scientific works have been translated into English, most of them in the nineteenth century—for instance, *Principia* (London, 1846). His MSS are in the library of the Royal Swedish Academy of Sciences. Many of them, under the title *Autographa*, have been published by R. L. Tafel, 10 vols. (Stockholm, 1863–1870).

II. SECONDARY LITERATURE. The literature is concerned mainly with his theology and spirit theory. Indispensable, although often unreliable, is R. L. Tafel, *Documents Concerning the Life and Character of Emanuel Swedenborg*, 2 vols. (London, 1875–1877). An excellent introduction, especially to his scientific achievement, is Inge Jonsson, *Emanuel Swedenborg* (New York, 1971). A pioneering work in its time was Martin Lamm, *Swedenborg* (Stockholm, 1915), also in German (Leipzig, 1922) and French (Paris, 1936). Later biographies include Ernst Benz, *Emanuel Swedenborg, Naturforscher und Seher* (Munich, 1948); Cyriel Odhner Sigstedt, *The Swedenborg Epic* (New York, 1952); and Signe Toksvig, *Emanuel Swedenborg, Scientist and Mystic* (New Haven, 1948). Inge Jonsson has also written *Swedenborgs skapelsedrama De cultu et amore Dei* (Stockholm, 1961) and *Swedenborgs korrespondenslära* (Stockholm, 1969).

Various aspects of Swedenborg's scientific thought have been investigated by Svante Arrhenius, "Emanuel Swedenborg as a Cosmologist," in Swedenborg's *Opera quaedam* (see above), II (Stockholm, 1908), xxiii–xxxv; Gustaf Eneström, *Emanuel Swedenborg såsom matematiker* (Stockholm, 1890); Tore Frängsmyr, *Geologi och skapelsetro. Föreställningar om jordens historia från Hiärne till Bergman*, Lychnosbibliotek no. 26 (Stockholm, 1969), on Swedenborg as geologist and cosmologist, with an English summary; N. V. E. Nordenmark, "Swedenborg som astronom," in *Arkiv för matematik, astronomi och fysik*, **23**, ser. A, no. 13 (1933); Gerhard Regnéll, "On the Position of Paleontology and Historical Geology in Sweden Before 1800," in *Arkiv för mineralogi och geologi*, **1** (1949–1954), 1–64; and Hans Schlieper, *Emanuel Swedenborgs System der Naturphilosophie* (Berlin, 1901). Martin Ramström has examined Swedenborg's physiology of the brain in important articles, summarized in "Swedenborg on the Cerebral Cortex as the Seat of Psychical Activity," in *Transactions of the International Swedenborg Congress 1910* (London, 1910), 56–70.

STEN LINDROTH

SWIETEN, GERARD VAN (*b*. Leiden, Netherlands, 7 May 1700; *d*. Schönbrunn Palace, Vienna, Austria, 18 June 1772), *medicine*.

Van Swieten was the son of Thomas Franciscus van Swieten, a notary public, and Elisabeth Loo, who were members of the lesser nobility. During the early years of the Dutch Revolutionary War (1568–1648), one branch of the family became Protestant while the other remained Roman Catholic; van Swieten belonged to the latter.[1]

Like many Dutch Catholics, van Swieten studied at Louvain; matriculating in the autumn of 1714 or the winter of 1714–1715, at the "Falcon" liberal arts college. It is not known how long he stayed there, but it is fairly certain that he left without being awarded a degree.[2] On 26 February 1717, van Swieten enrolled as a medical student at the University of Leiden, attracted by the lectures of Boerhaave. After receiving the M.D. degree on 3 July 1725, he established a medical practice in Leiden, which, although it soon became quite sizable, did not prevent him from continuing to attend every lecture of Boerhaave until the latter's death in 1738. Van Swieten had adapted an existing shorthand system to medical language, so his lecture notes, which still exist, reflect Boerhaave's presentation quite closely. Their mutual respect led Boerhaave to show his most interesting private cases to van Swieten and to express a lively interest in those of van Swieten. At various times Boerhaave stated that van Swieten would be the most suitable person to succeed him as a professor.[3]

A few months after receiving the M.D., van Swieten had started a free *privatissimum*. Although it was not associated with the university in any way, the latter, at the instigation of "the eminent van Royen," forbade van Swieten to continue these lessons in 1734.[4] This action made it abundantly clear that despite Boerhaave's favorable opinion, van Swieten, as a Catholic, could not possibly look forward to a professorate at Leiden. Fortunately, he found a post elsewhere. The empress of Austria, Maria Theresa, invited him to become court physician in 1743, at which time van Swieten declined, and again in 1745, after van Swieten had attended her sister Maria Anna in Brussels. This time he accepted, and was put in charge of all court physicians.

Van Swieten soon made himself useful in many other ways. He reorganized the medical faculty of the University of Vienna, taking Leiden as a model, and added a botanical garden and a chemical laboratory, each headed by a professor. Thus he laid the foundation for the Vienna school of medicine, which became world-famous at the turn of the century. Van Swieten became the president of the medical faculty and taught several courses. In addition to his medical services, he reorganized the censorship of books, reserving books on subjects other than theology, law, and politics for himself. He reorganized the court library and was made chief librarian in 1745.

Despite his many obligations, van Swieten still found time to work on his *Commentaria*, of which he had completed the first two volumes (1742, 1745) while in Leiden. This work, which documents Boerhaave's lectures, is not a straightforward transcription but, rather, a series of commentaries on Boerhaave's *Aphorisms*.[5] Therefore, it is not always clear which parts of the text are based on Boerhaave's lectures and which are van Swieten's own. The *Commentaria*, which greatly contributed to the dissemination of Boerhaave's ideas beyond the circle of his pupils, was reprinted many times and was translated into four languages.

Among van Swieten's contributions to medicine was his modification of the traditional treatment of venereal disease with mercurials; his specific, *liquor Swietenii*, which could be taken orally, made the treatment much less painful.[6] He managed to overcome the aversion of the Vienna physicians to inoculation against smallpox, which was introduced to Austria in 1768 by Jan Ingen-Housz. During the Seven Years War (1756–1763) van Swieten wrote a book on the diseases of the army.

Van Swieten's activities were mainly organizational and political; but his role in establishing the great Vienna school of medicine and his dissemination of Boerhaave's ideas by means of his *Commentaria* entitle him to a place in the history of science.

The name *Swietenia* was given to a genus of the Meliaceae family by Nicolas Jacquin. *Swietenia mahogani* is the mahogany tree.

NOTES

1. An ancestor, Adriaen van Swieten (1532–1584), was one of the signers of the Compromise of Breda ("League of Nobles") in 1566, which heralded the Dutch Revolution, and was responsible for dividing the family into two branches of opposing religions. Catholics were not eligible for positions in the government during the Dutch Republic, and the Roman Catholic religion was forbidden in Holland in 1573. The role of the nobility during the Republic was mainly governmental; therefore, unless a Catholic noble family had landed property, as the van Swietens did not, their noble status became meaningless.
In some history books, especially on church history, it is stated that van Swieten was a Jansenist. This is, however, by no means proved.
2. According to Baldinger, there were twelve other students in his class, and van Swieten surpassed all of them at the age of sixteen.
3. According to Baldinger.
4. According to Baumann, this was Adriaan van Royen (1704–1779), from 1729 lecturer on botany and from 1732 professor of medicine and chemistry. Brechka states that it probably was David van Royen (1699–1764), who was secretary to the curators of the university from 1725.
5. *Aphorismi de cognoscendis et curandis morbis* (Leiden, 1709). In the 3rd ed. (Leiden, 1715) the number of aphorisms reached 1,495.
6. *Liquor Swietenii* was a solution of about 0.1 percent by weight of mercurous chloride in alcohol.

BIBLIOGRAPHY

I. ORIGINAL WORKS. Van Swieten's stenographic records of Boerhaave's lectures were inherited by Anton von Störck and are now in the Austrian National Library, Vienna. A copy is in the Rijksmuseum voor de Geschiedenis der Natuurwetenschappen, Leiden, which also has transcriptions made by E. C. van Leersum, who broke the code. Van Swieten's extensive library was bought after his death by Empress Maria Theresa for 18,000 florins (Sandifort, **10**, 887), and is now in the Austrian National Library.

Van Swieten's earliest published work was *De arte fabrica et efficacia in corpore humano* (Leiden, 1725), his dissertation. His major book is *Commentaria in Hermanni Boerhaave Aphorismos de cognoscendis et curandis morbis*, 5 vols. (Leiden, 1742–1772). Vol. I went through 4 eds., II, 3 eds., and III, 2 eds. For the numerous other Latin eds., see Lindeboom (1959), nos. 208–235.

The Dutch trans. is *Verklaaring der korte stellingen van Herman Boerhaave over de kennis en de geneezing der ziektens*, 2 vols. (Leiden, 1760–1763), also 10 vols. (1776–1791). The German trans. is *Erläuterungen der Boerhaavischen Lehrsätze von Erkenntniss und Heilung der Krankheiten*, 5 vols. (Vienna–Frankfurt–Leipzig, 1755–1775). The French trans. *Commentaires des Aphorismes d'Hermann Boerhaave sur la connaissance et la cure des maladies*, 7 vols. (Paris, 1765–1768), also 2 vols. (Avignon, 1766). The English trans. is *The Commentaries Upon the Aphorisms of Dr. Herman Boerhaave, Concerning the Knowledge and Cure of Several Diseases, Incident to Human Bodies*, 18 vols.

(London, 1744–1773), also 11 vols. (1754–1759), 14 vols. (1759–1765, and 1771–1773), and 18 vols. (Edinburgh, 1776).

Some parts of the *Commentaria* on specific subjects were published under separate titles. *Aphorismes de chirurgie*, 5 vols. (Paris, 1753), also 7 vols. (1753–1756) and 5 vols. (1768); *Hermann Boerhaave's kurzgefasste Lehrsätze von Erkenntniss und Heilung der sogenannten chirurgischen Krankheiten*, 2 vols. (Danzig, 1753); *Traité du scorbut, devisé en trois parties*, 2 vols. (Paris, 1756, 1783, 1788, 1837); *Traité des maladies des enfants . . .* (Avignon, 1759); *Traité de la péripneumonie* (Paris, 1760); *Traité de la pleurésie* (Paris, 1763); *Traité des fièvres intermittentes* (Paris, 1766); *Maladies des femmes et des enfans, avec un traité des accouchemens*, 2 vols. (Paris, 1769); *Traité de la petite vérole* (Paris, 1776); and *Erläuterung der Boerhaavischen Lehrsätze der Chirurgie*, 2 vols. (Frankfurt, 1778).

The last work published during his lifetime was *Kurze Beschreibung und Heilungsart der Krankheiten, welche am öftesten in dem Feldlager beobachtet werden* (Vienna, 1758), translated into Dutch as *Korte beschrijving en geneeswijze der ziekten die veelzints in de krijgsheirlegers voorkomen* (Amsterdam, 1760, 1764, 1772, 1780, 1790; Bruges, 1765), into Italian as *Breve descrizione delle malattie che regnano piu communemente nella armate e del metodo di trattarle* (Naples, 1761, 1768), and into French as *Description abrégé des maladies qui regnent le plus communément dans les armées, avec la méthode de les traiter* (Bruges, 1765); an English trans. (1762) also is mentioned.

Posthumous works are *Oratio de morte dubia* (Vienna, 1778); *Considerazione intorno alla pretesa magia postuma per servire alla storia di vampiri* (Naples, 1781); and *Constitutiones epidemicae, et morbi potissimum, Lugduni Batavorum observati, ex ejusdem adversariis* (Vienna–Leipzig, 1782; Geneva, 1783).

II. SECONDARY LITERATURE. See the following, listed chronologically: E. G. Baldinger, *Lobreden auf den Freiherrn Gerhard van Swieten . . .* (Jena, 1772), abbrev. Dutch trans. by E. Sandifort in *Natuur en geneeskundige bibliotheek . . .*, **10** (1773), 205–215; I. Wurz, *Trauerrede auf den hochwohlgeborenen Herrn Gerard van Swieten . . .* (Vienna, 1772); A. Fournier, *G. van Swieten als Zensor, nach archivalischen Quellen* (Vienna, 1877); C. von Wurzbach, "Freiherr Gerhard van Swieten," in *Biographisches Lexicon des Kaiserthums Oesterreich*, XLI (1880), 37–50; W. Müller, *Gerard van Swieten, Biographischer Beitrag zur Geschichte der Aufklärung in Oesterreich* (Vienna, 1883); and E. C. van Leersum: "Gerard van Swieten en qualité de censeur," in *Janus*, **11** (1906), 381–398, 446–469, 501–522, 588–606; "A Couple of Letters of Gerard van Swieten on the *liquor Swietenii* and on the Inoculation of Smallpox," *ibid.*, **15** (1910), 345–371; and "Boerhaave's dictaten, inzonderheid zijne klinische lessen. Met een beschrijving van Gerard van Swieten's stenografische nalatenschap," in *Nederlands tijdschrift voor geneeskunde*, **63** (1919), 50–76.

Also see J. J. van der Kley, "G. van Swieten's *Constitutiones epidemicae et morbi potissimum, Lugduni Batavorum observati*," in *Bijdragen tot de geschiedenis der geneeskunde*, **1** (1921), 286–292; V. Kreutzinger, "Zum 150 Todestage Gerhard von Swieten," in *Janus*, **26** (1922), 177–189; H. Pinkhof, "Een advies van Gerard van Swieten," in *Bijdragen tot de geschiedenis der geneeskunde*, **3** (1923), 189–190; G. van Leeuwen, "Gerard van Swieten," in *Nieuw Nederlandsch biografisch woordenboek*, X (1937), 1005–1006; H. T. van Heuveln, *Gerard van Swieten, Leben, Werk und Kampf* (Veendam, 1942); H. Sandra, "De leer der phthisis bij de oude Nederlandsche schrijvers," in *Bijdragen tot de geschiedenis der geneeskunde*, **23** (1943), 40–46; L. Schönbauer, *Das medizinische Wien* (Vienna, 1947). G. A. Lindeboom, "Gerard van Swieten als hervormer der Weensche medische faculteit," in *Bijdragen tot de geschiedenis der geneeskunde*, **30** (1950), 12–20; E. D. Baumann, *Drie eeuwen Nederlandsche Geneeskunde* (Amsterdam, 1951), 222–225; W. Böhm, *Universitas Vindobonensis* (Vienna, 1952); G. A. Lindeboom, *Bibliographia Boerhaaviana* (Leiden, 1959), 47–54; F. T. Brechka, *Gerard van Swieten and His World, 1700–1772* (The Hague, 1970); D. Willemse, "Gerard van Swieten in zijn brieven aan Antonio Nunes Ribeiro Sanches (1739–1754)," in *Scientiarium historia*, **14** (1972), 113–143; and G. A. Lindeboom, "Het consult van Gerard van Swieten voor aartshertogin Marianne van Oostenrijk, de zuster van Maria Theresia," *ibid.*, 97–111; "Gerard van Swieten, Herr und Landstand Von Tirol," in *"Adler," Zeitschrift für Genealogie und Heraldik*, **9** (1972), 187–188; "Acht brieven van Gerard van Swieten uit zijn Hollandsche jaren (1730–1744)," in *Scientiarum historia*, **15** (1973), 73–89; "De Hollandsche tijd van Gerard van Swieten," in *Nederlandsch tijdschrift voor Geneeskunde*, **117** (1973), 1037–1042; and "Gerard van Swieten und seine Zeit," in *Internationales Symposium veranstaltet von der Universität Wien im Institut für Geschichte der Medizin* (Vienna, 1973), 63–79.

PETER W. VAN DER PAS

SWINDEN, JAN HENDRIK VAN (*b.* The Hague, Netherlands, 8 June 1746; *d.* Amsterdam, Netherlands, 9 March 1823), *electricity, magnetism, meteorology, metrology.*

The son of Philippe van Swinden and Anna Maria Tollosan, van Swinden was a prolific scientific writer; many of his works were written in French, the language of his ancestors, who had been driven from France by the revocation of the Edict of Nantes. Most of his experimental work in electricity, magnetism, and meteorology was conducted before 1795, after which year his time was devoted mainly to scientific committee work. In 1798 he was the leading member of the committee

that introduced the metric system into the Netherlands. He married Sara Ribolleau in 1768 and had one son who died before him.

Van Swinden's father, an eminent barrister, wanted his son to study law. Jan, however, from an early age showed more interest in mathematics and mechanics; and although he entered Leiden University to study law in 1763, he soon changed to natural philosophy and mathematics. He was greatly influenced by Newton's *Principia*, as is shown by his doctoral thesis, *De attractione* (1766). He took every opportunity to popularize Newtonian philosophy, and his inaugural lectures at the universities of Franeker and Amsterdam dealt with this topic.

In 1767 van Swinden obtained the chair of philosophy, logic, and metaphysics at Franeker University. He studied all the popular scientific topics of the period, especially magnetism, electricity, meteorology, and chemistry, and corresponded with many leading scientists, including Bonnet, Euler, Deluc, J. C. Wilcke, Bertholon, and Lalande. His *Tentamen de magnete* (1772) dealt with his mathematical theory of magnetism, and in 1777 he and Coulomb shared the gold medal of the Paris Academy of Sciences for a very detailed prize essay on magnetism, *Recherches sur les aiguilles aimantées.*

Van Swinden's best-known work in this field, *Mémoires sur l'analogie de l'électricité et du magnétisme* (1784), included his prize essay on the analogy between magnetism and electricity, in which he compared Mesmer's animal magnetism with electricity. For this work he was awarded the gold medal of the Bavarian Academy of Sciences in 1778. In 1785 van Swinden and van Marum experimented on the influence of electrical discharges on magnets, using the very large electrostatic generator of the Teylers Stichting at Haarlem. Repeating the experiments of Beccaria and others, they noticed that when soft iron or steel bars were placed perpendicular to the line of discharge, the resulting magnetic strength was greater than when the bars were parallel to the direction of the discharge. This puzzling phenomenon could be explained only after Ampère's work of 1820. Incidentally, Ampère at first thought that the field of force moving around the wire through which the electric current passed was also electrical. In 1822, using his large Offerhaus battery, van Marum demonstrated that it was, in fact, magnetic.

Van Swinden was best-known outside the Netherlands for his extraordinarily accurate meteorological observations. Over a ten-year period, he and some of his pupils at Franeker made hourly observations of the terrestrial magnetism and observed the diurnal variation. His thirteen-year record of barometer, thermometer, and hygrometer readings resulted in the publication of some eighteen papers on meteorological topics in various European journals.

In 1785 van Swinden was appointed professor of philosophy, natural philosophy, mathematics, and astronomy at the University of Amsterdam, where he wrote his mathematical textbook *Theoremata geometrica* (1786; enlarged and translated into Dutch, 1790) and the first two volumes of a general textbook on natural philosophy, *Positiones physicae* (1786). The latter ambitious work was never completed. He was appointed chairman of a committee to correct naval charts, which produced a nautical almanac in 1787. He was assisted in this work by his pupil Pieter Nieuwland, who became a lecturer in mathematics, astronomy, and navigation at the University of Amsterdam. The committee's activities also resulted in the publication of a book on the determination of longitude at sea by lunar observations (1787) and work on nautical instruments (1788). In 1798 van Swinden and Henricus Aeneae were sent to Paris by the Dutch government to attend the congress on the introduction of the metric system. He belonged to the commission (other members were J. G. Tralles, Delambre, Legendre) that recalculated the earth's meridian, one forty-millionth part of which was called the meter.

During the French occupation of the Netherlands, van Swinden served on committees dealing with such diverse topics as currency reform and the restructuring of university education. In 1808 he was appointed the first president of the Royal Institution of the Netherlands (now the Royal Netherlands Academy of Sciences and Letters). In 1813, after the overthrow of the French, William I (made king of the Netherlands in 1815) appointed him a councillor of state in recognition of his efforts on behalf of Dutch science.

BIBLIOGRAPHY

I. ORIGINAL WORKS. Van Swinden's main works are cited in the text. His MS material on the history of the microscope was published posthumously in G. Moll, "On the First Invention of Telescopes, Collected From the Notes and Papers of the Late Professor [J. H.] van Swinden," in *Journal of the Royal Institution of Great Britain*, 1 (1831), 319–332, 483–496. He also wrote a detailed study of Eise Eisinga's planetarium at Franeker,

Beschrijving van een kunstuk, verbeeldende een volledig bewegelijk hemelsgestel, uitgedachten en vervaardigd door Eise Eisinga (Franeker, 1780; repr. 1824, 1831; 3rd ed., enl., 1851). His works are listed in D. Bierens de Haan, *Bibliographie néerlandaise historico-scientifique* (Rome, 1883), 273–277, repr. photographically (Nieuwkoop, 1960, 1965). MSS are in various institutions in the Netherlands: Amsterdam University Library has about 50 letters and many MSS on a variety of topics, including education reform and his trip to Paris in 1798; the Koninklijke Bibliotheek, Amsterdam, has a number of notes dealing with scientific topics: weights, measures, and coinage (KA CCC a–g); magnetism and electricity (KA CCCI a–i); meteorology and the northern lights (KA CCCII a–i); mathematics, probability, and population statistics (KA CCCIII a–b); mechanics, astronomy, chronometry, and technology (KA CCCIV a–d); and science and medicine (KA CCCV a–b).

II. SECONDARY LITERATURE. Only short biographies of van Swinden exist to date: A. J. van der Aa, in *Biographisch woordenboek der Nederlanden*, XVII (Haarlem, 1784), 1124–1132, with a good bibliography; and P. C. Molhuysen and P. J. Blok, *Nieuw Nederlandsch biografisch woordenboek*, IV (Leiden, 1918), 1289–1291, which is slightly more detailed. See also G. C. Gerrits, *Grote Nederlanders by de opbouw der natuurwetenschappen* (Leiden, 1948), 236–241. The best biography in English is G. Moll, "A Biographical Account of J. H. van Swinden," in *Edinburgh Journal of Science*, 1 (1824), 197–208.

WILLEM D. HACKMANN

SWINESHEAD (Swyneshed, Suicet, etc.), RICHARD (*fl. ca.* 1340–1355), *natural philosophy*.

The name Richard Swineshead is best known to the modern historian of science as that of the author of the *Liber calculationum*, a work composed probably about 1340–1350 and famous later for its extensive use of mathematics within physics. Very little is known about this Richard Swineshead, and furthermore it appears almost certain that the little biographical data that are available about any fourteenth-century Swineshead cannot all be apportioned to one man, but that there were at least two or three men named Swineshead who may have left works in manuscript. In the early twentieth century, Pierre Duhem settled this confusion of Swinesheads to his own satisfaction by asserting that there was a John Swineshead who wrote some extant logical works, *De insolubilibus* and *De obligationibus*, and a Roger Swineshead who wrote a work on physics (found in MS Paris, Bibliothèque Nationale lat. 16621)—variously titled

De motibus naturalibus, Descriptiones motuum,
and *De primo motore* (the latter by Duhem). Duhem concluded that the famous "Calculator," as
the author of the *Liber calculationum* was often
called, was not really named Swineshead at all, but
was rather one Richard of "Ghlymi Eshedi," as he
is called in the explicit of the *Liber calculationum*
in MS Paris, Bibliothèque Nationale lat. 6558, f.
70v. Since Duhem's time, historians have rejected
the supposed name "Ghlymi Eshedi" as a scribal
error and have restored the *Liber calculationum* to
Swineshead. They have not, however, completely
unraveled the problem of the existence of two or
three Swinesheads as authors of several logical and
natural philosophical works.

The most satisfactory theory so far proposed
would seem to be that of James Weisheipl, according to whom there were three fourteenth-century
Swinesheads of note. One, named John Swineshead, was a fellow of Merton College from at least
1343 and pursued a career in law; he died in 1372,
leaving no extant works. A second, named Roger
Swineshead, was also at Oxford, but there is
no record of his having been at Merton College.
This Roger Swineshead wrote the logical works
De insolubilibus and *De obligationibus* and the
physical work *De motibus naturalibus*. He may
have been a Benedictine monk and a master in sa-
cred theology and may have died about 1365. The
third Swineshead, Richard Swineshead, was, like
John, associated with Merton College in the 1340's
and was the author of the famous *Liber calculationum*, and possibly also of two extant *opuscula*,
De motu and *De motu locali*, and of at least a partial *De caelo* commentary.

Given the uncertainty of the biographical data, it
seems proper that all the extant physical works
ascribed to any Swineshead should be included in
this article. This includes, most importantly, the
Liber calculationum, but also the *opuscula* ascribed by Weisheipl to Richard Swineshead and
the *De motibus naturalibus* ascribed by Weisheipl
to Roger Swineshead. All of these works can be
said to fall within the "Oxford calculatory tradition," if not with the works of the so-called Merton
school. The *De motibus naturalibus*, as the earliest
work, will be described first (with folio references
to MS Erfurt, Amplonian F 135), followed by the
Liber calculationum (with folio references to the
1520 Venice edition), to be described in much
greater detail, and finally by the fragmentary *opuscula* (with folio references to MS Cambridge,
Gonville and Caius 499/268), which, although they

most probably were written before the *Liber calculationum*, can more easily be described after that
work. Weisheipl's hypothesis will be followed as to
the correct names of the authors of these works.

De motibus naturalibus

The *De motibus naturalibus* was written at Oxford after the *De proportionibus* of Thomas Bradwardine and at about the same time (ca. 1335) as
the *Regule solvendi sophismata* of William Heytesbury. In the material covered, it is similar to the
latter work, and, in fact, both works treat topics
that were to become standard in treatises *de motu*
in the mid- and late fourteenth century. The *De
motibus naturalibus* has eight parts, called *differ-
entiae*: I. Introduction; II. Definitions of Motion
and Time; III. Generation; IV. Alteration; V.
Augmentation; VI. Local Motion; VII. Causes of
Motion; and VIII. Maxima and Minima. In contrast to Heytesbury's work and to later treatises
de motu, however, the *De motibus naturalibus*
includes large sections of traditional natural philosophy as well as the logicomathematical natural
philosophy typical of the later treatises. It contains
many more facts about the natural world (climates,
burning mirrors, tides, comets, milk, apples, frogs,
worms, etc.) and lacks the strong sophismata character of some of the later works. It represents,
therefore, to some extent, a stage halfway between
thirteenth-century cosmological and fourteenth-
century logicomathematical natural philosophy.

This position, halfway between two traditions, is
represented quite strongly in the organization of
the work: the treatise is fairly clearly divided into
metaphysical-physical discussions and logicomathematical treatments. Thus, for example, the three
parts discussing motion in the categories of quality,
quantity, and place (parts IV, V, VI) each contain
two parts, a first dealing with the physics of the
situation and a second dealing with the quantification of motion in that category. Although the logicomathematical topics that Roger discusses are
generally those discussed by the later authors *de
motu*, the order of topics in his work still reflects
an Aristotelian or medical base. Whereas later authors, especially Parisian-trained authors such as
Albert of Saxony, generally discussed the measures of motion with respect to cause first (*penes
quid attenditur motus tanquam penes causam*) and
then discussed the measures of motion with respect to effect (*tanquam penes effectum*), Roger
begins with the effects of motion (as, indeed, does
the Calculator after him). Furthermore, among

effects, he begins with the effects of alteration rather than with the effects of local motion. In accordance with this order of treatment, Roger's basic notions of the measurement of motion come from the category of quality rather than from causes or from locomotion, as was to be the case in seventeenth-century physics. In line with the earlier medical theory of the temperate, Roger places emphasis on mean degrees, and he considers intension at the same time as remission. When he then goes on to talk about possible mean degrees of local motion, and motions being just as fast as they are slow, and so forth, there seems to be no reasonable explanation except that he has taken "measures" which fit with the then current notions of quality and alteration and has applied them by analogy to local motion, even though the result has no apparent basis in the then current notions of local motion. Finally, to all of this, must be added the fact that Roger's basic theoretical terms for his measurements, namely "latitude," "degree," and the like, are earlier found most prominently in medical theory.

From among all the material in the *De motibus naturalibus* concerned with the "measurement" of motion and therefore most closely related to the work of the Calculator perhaps the two points of greatest interest have to do with two idiosyncratic positions which Roger takes, the first having to do with the function relating forces, resistances, and velocities in motion, the second with the relation of latitudes and degrees.

First, in parts VI and VII, Roger rejects the Aristotelian position that velocity is proportional to force and inversely proportional to resistance. Thus in the first chapter of part VI Roger states five conclusions concerning natural local motion which are all aimed at showing that resistance is not required for natural motion (41va–41vb). In part VII, Roger again repeats this view (43vb–44vb). In fact, he says, the equality or inequality of velocities is caused by the equality or inequality of the proportion of proportions of the mover to the moved, where the moved need not resist. Although Roger then accepts the mathematical preliminaries (for example, definitions of the types of proportionalities) that Bradwardine had set down as requisite for investigating velocities, forces, and resistances, he rejects Bradwardine's function relating these variables (see the article on Bradwardine for a description of his logarithmic-type function). Where there is no resistance, Roger asserts, the proportion of velocities is the same as the proportion of moving powers. Where there are resistances, then the proportion of velocities is the same as the proportion of latitudes of resistance between the degrees of resistance equal to the motive powers and the degrees of the media (this conclusion is equivalent in modern terms to stating that velocity is proportional to the difference between the force and resistance). Concerning cases where one motion is resisted and the other is not, Roger says that the proportion of velocities follows no other proportion, or, in modern terms, that he can find no function relating the velocities to forces and resistances. Although there are some obvious resemblances between Roger's position and the position of Ibn Bājja (Avempace) and the young Galileo, it is not a position at all common in the early fourteenth century.

Second, Roger's combinations of latitudes and degrees for measuring motion are also unique to him, so far as is known. Like the latitudes of earlier authors, Roger's latitudes are ranges within which a given quality, motion, or whatever, may be supposed to vary. Thus in part IV he posits the existence of three latitudes for measuring alteration, each distinguishable by reason into two other latitudes (39ra–39rb). In modern terms the first of these latitudes expresses the range within which the intensities of a quality may vary, the second expresses the range within which velocities of alteration may vary, and the third the range within which accelerations and decelerations of alteration may vary. Similarly, in part VI Roger posits five latitudes for measuring locomotion, all of them distinct from one another only in reason (43ra). In modern terms the first three of these latitudes are the ranges within which velocity or speed may vary and the last two are ranges within which accelerations and decelerations, respectively, may vary. All of these are similar to latitudes posited by the other Oxford calculators, although later there was a tendency to dispense with the latitudes of remissness and tardity that Roger posited (see below).

What is different about Roger's system is his postulation of so-called uniform degrees. Thus Roger defines two types of degrees of heat or any other quality (38rb). One type, the "uniformly difform degree," is a component, divisible part of a latitude of quality and is like the degrees hypothesized by later authors including the Calculator. In calling these degrees "uniformly difform," Roger imagines that each such degree will contain within itself a linearly increasing series of degrees above some minimum and below some maximum, as indeed any segment of a latitude would contain. The other type, the "uniform degree," is not a component part of a latitude, but rather is equally intense throughout, whereas in any part of a latitude the intensity varies. Among the Oxford calculators, only Roger makes such a distinction. Uniform degrees appear again when Roger goes on to discuss the measurement of the velocity of alteration. In the motion of intension of a quality, he says, two velocities of intension can have no ratio to one another if one subject gains a single uniform degree more than the other (39ra). Similarly Roger concludes that some local motions are incomparable to others, and that one latitude of local motion can differ from another by a single uniform degree (43va).

Roger's postulation of uniform degrees having no proportion to latitudes does not seem to be the result of intentional atomism. Rather, the case seems to be that as a pioneer in the effort to find mathematical descriptions and comparisons of concrete distributions of qualities and velocities, he could not devise measures applicable to all cases. Earlier authors had made little attempt to deal with nonuniform distributions of qualities. Roger does try to deal with them, but he has one measure for uniform distributions (the uniform degree), and another for uniformly difform (linearly varying) distributions (the latitude), and none at all for difformly difform (nonlinearly varying) distributions. Rather than stating that he is unable to compare motions or distributions of quality that fall into different categories (which would be, from a modern point of view, the justifiable statement), he says that the motions or distributions themselves have no proportion. It seems very likely that it was exactly the kind of effort to "measure" motion represented by the *De motibus naturalibus* that motivated the Calculator to try to straighten things out in his mathematically much more sophisticated work.

Liber calculationum

The *Liber calculationum* is by far the most famous work associated with the name Swineshead. As it appears in the 1520 Venice edition the *Liber calculationum* contains sixteen parts or *tractatus*. Some of these treatises may have been composed later than others, since they are lacking from some of the extant manuscripts. The emphasis in the *Liber calculationum* is on logicomathematical techniques rather than on physical theory. What it provides are techniques for calculating the values of physical variables and their changes, or for solving problems or sophisms about physical changes. Thus, the order of the treatise is one of increasing complexity in the application of techniques rather than an order determined by categories of subject matter, and the criteria for choosing between competing positions on various topics are often logicomathematical criteria. Thus, it is considered important that theory be complete—that it be able to handle all conceivable cases. Similarly, it is considered important that the mathematical measurements of a given physical variable be continuous, so that, for instance, the mathematical measure of an intensity should not jump suddenly from zero to four degrees (unless there is reason to believe that an instantaneous change occurs physically).

As stated above, as late as the beginning of the fourteenth century natural philosophers dealing with the qualities of subjects (for instance, Walter Burley in his treatises on the intension and remission of forms) assumed tacitly that the individual subjects they dealt with were uniformly qualified. Thus, as in the pharmaceutical tradition, they could talk of a subject hot in the second degree or cold in the third degree (and perhaps about what the result of their combination would be) without questioning whether the individual subjects had qualitative variations within themselves. Roger Swineshead in the *De motibus naturalibus* attempted to deal with variations in distribution, but managed only to establish criteria for uniform and for uniformly varying (*uniformiter difformis*) distributions. Richard Swineshead in his *opuscula De motu* and *De motu locali* declared that difform distributions are too diverse to deal with theoretically (212ra, 213rb). In the *Liber calculationum*, however, he manages to deal with a good number of more complicated (*difformiter difformis*) distributions.

The overall outline of the *Liber calculationum* is as follows. It begins with four treatises dealing with the qualitative degrees of simple and mixed subjects insofar as the degrees of the subjects depend on the degrees in their various parts. Treatise I considers measures of intensity (and, conversely, of remissness, that is, of privations of intensity) per se. Treatise II, on difform qualities and difformly qualified bodies, considers the effects of variations in two dimensions—intensity and extension—on the intensity of a subject taken as a whole. Treatise III again considers two variables in examining how the intensities of two qualities, for example, hotness and dryness, are to be combined in determining the intensity of an elemental subject (this, of course, being related to the Aristotelian theory that each of the four terrestrial elements—earth, air, fire, and water—is qualified in some degree by a combination of two of the four basic elemental qualities—hotness, coldness, wetness, and dryness). Treatise IV then combines the types of variation involved in treatises II and III to consider how both the intensity and extension of two qualities are to be combined in determining the intensity of a compound (mixed) subject. Treatises I–IV, then, steadily increase in mathematical complexity.

In treatises V and VI the Calculator introduces a new dimension, that of density and rarity, and determines how density, rarity, and augmentation are to be measured. Density and rarity are mathematically somewhat more complex than qualitative intensity because, even in the simplest cases, they depend on two variables, amount of matter and quantity, rather than on one. Treatises VII and VIII, then, which consider whether reaction is possible and, in order to answer that question, discuss how powers and resistances are to be measured mathematically, involve all of the variables introduced in the preceding six parts. Treatise IX, on the difficulty of action, and treatise X, on maxima and minima, complete the discussion of the measurement of powers by determining that the difficulty of an action is proportional to the power acting and by considering how the limits of a power are determined with respect to the media it can traverse in a limited or unlimited time. Treatise IX is apparently intended to apply to all types of motion, although the examples discussed nearly all have to do with local motion. In treatise X the preoccupation with local motion becomes complete. This direction of attention to local motion is continued in treatise XI, on the place of the elements, where the contributions of the parts of a body to its natural motion are discussed. Up through treatise XI, then, the three usual categories of motion according to the medieval and Aristotelian view—alteration, augmentation, and local motion—are discussed. It is significant and typical of medieval Aristotelianism that alteration is discussed first as, so to speak, the fundamental type of motion. In treatises XII and XIII the field of attention is extended to include light, treatise XII considering the measure of power of a light source and treatise XIII considering the distribution of illumination in media.

Beginning at about treatise X the tone of the *Liber calculationum* seems to change. Whereas in the first six treatises and again in the ninth several positions are compared, in treatises X through XVI, on the whole (except perhaps for treatise

XIII, which is in question form), a single view is expounded. Beginning with treatise XII and continuing at an accelerating pace to the end of the work, the parts consist mostly of long strings of conclusions concerning all the variations on the basic functions of action that can be elicited by Swineshead's mathematical techniques. Treatise XIV consists of conclusions concerning local motion and how its velocity varies depending on the variations of forces and resistances. Treatise XV concerns what will happen if the resistance of the medium varies as the mobile is moving, or if, in a medium with uniformly increasing (*uniformiter difformis*) resistance, an increasing power begins to move. Treatise XVI concerns the various rates at which the maximum degree of a quality will be introduced into a subject depending on its initial state and the varying rate of its alteration, or on the rarefaction of the subject. Why the later treatises of the *Liber calculationum* should differ in tone from the earlier ones is, of course, not explained. It may be simply that the greater complexity involved in the later treatises prevented their being presented in the more usual scholastic question form. But another hypothesis might be that the earlier treatises bear the traces of having been used in university teaching, whereas the later treatises, although in a sense prepared for a similar purpose, never saw actual classroom use. At least the form in which we have them does not seem to reflect that use.

With this sketch of the overall structure of the *Liber calculationum* in hand, a more detailed look at the individual treatises is now in order. Although the *Liber calculationum* is fairly well known to historians of science by title, its contents are to date only very sketchily known, evidently (*a*) because the work is quite difficult and technical and (*b*) because it is not a work known to have influenced Galileo or other figures of the scientific revolution very significantly.

Treatise I: On Intension and Remission. In its structure, treatise I has three basic parts. First, it discusses three positions about the measures of intensity and remissness of qualities; second, it discusses whether and in what way degrees of intensity and remissness of a quality are comparable to each other; and third, it raises and replies to three doubts about rates of variation of quality considered, for instance, as loss of intensity versus increase of remissness or as gain of intensity versus decrease of remissness.

Why should these have been topics of primary interest to Swineshead? Although historians have yet to reveal very much about the connections of the *Liber calculationum* to previous tradition, it is hardly questionable that Richard Swineshead's mathematical inquiries here, like those of Roger Swineshead before him, take place against the background of Aristotelian and medical discussions of qualitative changes, especially changes in hotness, coldness, wetness, and dryness. As in the case of Roger Swineshead, Aristotelian and medical backgrounds may explain why Richard Swineshead starts from the assumption of double measures of quality in terms of intensity and remissness, as related, for instance, to hot and cold, rather than beginning simply from one scale of degrees. And again the medical theory of the temperate, representing health, and of departures from it leading to illness, may similarly explain Richard Swineshead's attention in treatise I to middle or mean degrees of whole latitudes and to degrees which might be said to be "just as intense as they are remiss."

But, furthermore, in the more immediate background of Richard Swineshead's inquiries may have been precisely Roger Swineshead's mathematization of the intensities of qualities, on the one hand, and Richard's own reasoning about the defects of some of Roger's conclusions on the other. Thus, the positions concerning the measures of intensity and remissness that Richard Swineshead considers are (1) that the intensity of any quality depends upon its nearness to the maximum degree of that quality and that remissness depends on distance from that maximum degree; (2) that intensity depends upon the distance from zero degree of a quality and remissness on distance from the maximum degree; and (3) that intensity depends upon the distance from zero degree and remissness upon the nearness to zero degree (2ra–vb). In fact, in the *De motibus naturalibus*, Roger Swineshead had held the second of these positions, and this had led him to various, sometimes peculiar, conclusions comparing the intensity and remissness of degrees (for example, 38va). Thus, Richard Swineshead may well have questioned the wisdom of a position which led to such conclusions and have looked for a better position. Beyond the earlier Aristotelian and medical theories, mathematics might have led him to refer to zero degree and to some small unit as the proper basis for a measurement of intensity. Metaphysics, however, might have led him to refer to the maximum degree of a quality, because any species may be supposed to be defined by its maximum or most perfect exemplar. Mostly on the basis of mathematical consider-

ations, Richard concludes that both intensity and remissness ought to be measured with respect to zero degree (that is, he chooses the third position). (*Tertia positio dicit quod intensio attenditur penes distantiam a non gradu et remissio penes appropinquationem ad non gradum* [2ra].)

A result of Richard's conclusion is that intensity and remissness are no longer symmetrical concepts. Thus, although there can be remission *in infinitum* before zero degree of a quality is reached, there cannot be intension *in infinitum* before the maximum degree of the latitude is reached. This follows as in the case of a finite line (lines often appear in the medieval manuscripts as representations of latitudes), where one can get closer to one extreme *in infinitum* (one can get halfway there, three-fourths of the way there, seven-eighths of the way there, continually halving the distance left), but one cannot get farther and farther from the same end *in infinitum* because one reaches the other end of the line. Consequently, if intensity is measured by distance from zero degree, the maximum degree of a quality must be remiss, which Richard admits (2vb).

In further sections, Swineshead elaborates the concept that remission is a privation with respect to intensity (4rb–4va), and then discusses in more detail the correlations between the latitudes of intensity and remissness and motions of intension and remission. Since remissness is measured by closeness to zero degree, the scale of remissness is an inverse scale (values of remissness are proportional to the inverse of the distance from zero degree) and smaller and smaller distances on the latitude close to zero degree correspond to greater and greater differences in degree of remissness. Swineshead apparently decides in this connection that the easiest solution to the problem of remissness is to label degrees of remissness by the same numbers as the degrees of intensity and merely to say that a degree of two corresponds to twice the remissness of the degree four (5ra). Again, since remission is a privation, if one allowed in imagination intensities beyond the maximum natural degree of the given quality, there would be an infinite latitude between any degree of remission and zero remissness, even though there is only a finite latitude of intensity between any degree of remissness and infinite remissness.

Thus, although it is not stated this way, the net effect of treatise I is to dispense with the need for talking about remissness at all: one can deal with all cases of interest while only considering intensity, and furthermore the intensities one is dealing with will be additive. In this way Richard Swineshead removes what now seems the needless complexity of double measures of quality and at the same time ends up with an additive measure. The treatise by no means provides a complete basis for actual measurements of qualities, but it does help to move in that direction by emphasizing measures of quality that are additive. For the Oxford calculators qualities were not, to use the modern terminology, "intensive magnitudes," but were, even in their intensity, "extensive magnitudes," again to use the modern terminology. In fact, it may be somewhat startling to the modern historian to realize that fourteenth-century authors developed their concept of "dimension" or of additive magnitude in the abstract more often through the discussion of qualitative latitudes than through the discussion of spatial extension, as was to be the case in later science.

It should be noted that treatise I, in addition to determining the proper measures of intensity of qualities, also introduces many of the basic technical terms of the rest of the work. Like the *De motibus naturalibus*, it assumes that any physical variable has a continuous range, called a "latitude," within which it can vary. In the case of qualities, this latitude starts from zero degree (*non gradus*), zero being considered as an exclusive terminus, and goes up to some determinate maximum degree, the exact number of which is usually left vague, but which is commonly assumed to be eight or ten degrees (this number arising out of the previous tradition in which there were, for instance, four degrees of coldness and four degrees of hotness, the two perhaps separated by a mean or temperate mid-degree). Within any latitude there are assumed to be a number of "degrees," these degrees being, so to speak, parts of the latitude rather than indivisibles. Swineshead also makes distinctions between the intensities versus the extensions of qualities. In his use of the terminology of latitudes and degrees, Swineshead was by no means an innovator: he was adopting a familiar set of terms. Among others, Roger Swineshead had talked systematically of the relations of degrees and latitudes before him (although Roger had had his idiosyncratic system of "uniform degrees"). In the thoroughness of his discussion of the pros and cons of various conventions for the measurement of intensity and remissness, Richard Swineshead was, however, outstanding.

Treatises II—IV: On Difformly Qualified Subjects; On the Intension of an Element Possessing Two, Unequally Intense, Qualities; On the Intension and Remission of Mixed Subjects. Directly following the determination of the most appropriate "scale of measure" for intension and remission, in general, in treatise I, treatises II–IV form a single, interrelated whole dealing with the intensity and remissness of simple and mixed subjects insofar as the degrees or "overall measures" of these subjects depend upon the degrees had by their various parts.

Thus, treatise II treats the effects of varying intensities of a single quality as these intensities are distributed over a given subject (and hence considers the two dimensions of intensity and extension) as they bear upon the overall measure of the intensity of the whole, although it only does so for the special cases in which the variation in question is either uniformly difform over the total subject or in which the subject has halves of different, but uniform, intensities. In such cases, Swineshead is in effect asking what measure of intensity is to be assigned the whole. There are, he tells us, two ways (*opiniones* or *positiones*) in which this particular question can be answered: (1) the measure— or as he often calls it, the denomination—of the whole corresponds to the mean degree of the qualified subject (that is, the degree that is equidistant from the initial and final degrees of a uniformly difformly distributed quality or—to take into account the second special case at hand—from the two degrees had by the uniform, but unequally intense, halves of the subject); or (2) the subject should be considered to be just as intense as any of its parts (that is, its overall measure is equivalent to the maximum degree had by the subject [5rb; 6ra]).

Similarly, in treatise III, Swineshead considers how the intensities of two qualities—for example, hotness and dryness—in a given elemental subject (now leaving aside their extension or distribution in this subject) are to be combined in determining the intensity of the whole. We here have to do with three positions: (1) the elemental subject is as intense as the degree equidistant from the degrees of its two qualities, (2) it is as intense as its more remiss quality, or (3) it is as intense as the mean proportional degree between its qualities (9rb).

In treatise IV Swineshead combines the types of variation involved in treatises II and III to consider how both the intensity and the extension of two qualities are to be combined in determining the intensity of a *mixtum* (that is, a compound subject). Four views concerning the measure of such more "complicated" subjects are presented: (1) the intensity of a *mixtum* follows the proportion of the dominant elementary quality to the subdominant elementary quality in it, (2) every *mixtum* is as intense as its dominant elementary quality, (3) every *mixtum* has an intensity in the dominant quality equal to half the difference between its two qualities, (4) the fourth position is presented in two versions: (*a*) The *mixtum* is as intense as the excess of the degree of the dominant quality over the subdominant quality, no account being taken of just what parts of the *mixtum* these qualities are distributed over, or (*b*) it is as intense as the excess between (i) what the dominant quality as extended over such and such a part contributes to the denomination or measure of the whole and (ii) what the subdominant quality as extended over its part of the subject contributes to the denomination of the whole (12va).

However, simply to tabulate the various *positiones* relative to the proper measure of intensity and remissness of the variously qualified simple and mixed subjects that Swineshead presents falls short of representing the substance of treatises II – IV. To begin with, to regard Swineshead's major concern as the unambiguous determination of just which *positio* or theory is the correct one relative to the particular question of measure posed by each treatise is to misrepresent his real interests. At times, Swineshead appears to leave any decision as to the "best theory" an open question. Moreover, even when he does express a preference for a given *positio*, it is seldom without qualifications, and the objections he brings against the opposing, "nonpreferred" *positiones* do not necessarily imply that his primary goal was the "once-and-for-all" rejection of these other *positiones*. His primary concern was rather to show that such and such results follow from this or that *positio*, it being of secondary importance whether these results are, for one reason or another, acceptable or unacceptable (even though they are from time to time so specified); of greater significance was the exhibition of the fact that these results do follow and the explanation of how they follow.

Thus, for example, in treatise III, although Swineshead indicates his preference for the third position (*sustinenda est tertia positio*), it is nonetheless true that the objections or conclusions brought against the second, "less-preferred" position are also relevant to this third position (*sequentur igitur contra istam* [*tertiam*] *positionem inconvenientia sicut contra alias*), with the difference that these same conclusions for the most part are in this instance conceded (11va – 12rb). What is more, when we examine Swineshead's procedure

in presenting the objections to the presumably rejected positions, there emerges a more accurate picture of his objectives. Hence, for example, from the view that the overall degree of an element corresponds to the degree midway between the degrees of its two constituent qualities, Swineshead states that there follows the conclusion that there would occur continuously operating infinite velocities of action. This result should be rejected because then the agent in question would suddenly corrupt the patient upon which it acts. Inadmissible as this consequent of the conclusion might be, far more interesting to Swineshead (and hence more deserving of attention) is the fact that this conclusion does indeed follow (*quod tamen ista conclusio sequatur . . .*) from the *positio* under investigation (9va). If all of this is taken into account, one obtains a much better idea of what these treatises of the *Liber calculationum* are all about and is at the same time less puzzled or surprised at Swineshead's lack of emphasis upon the definitive determination of a single, exclusively correct theory or position.

Something more of the general character of this part of the *Liber calculationum* can be derived from a slightly more detailed example drawn from treatise II. The treatise begins by examining the view that the proper measure of the kind of difformly qualified subjects in question corresponds to the mean degree of the subject. Now one of the proofs supporting this view is that, if we take a subject that is, say, either uniformly difformly hot throughout or difformly hot with each half uniformly hot, and remit the more intense half down to the mean degree while equally rapidly intending the more remiss half up to the mean degree, then, since for every part of the subject that is intended there will be a corresponding part remitted equally and no net gain or loss in intensity, it follows that at the beginning the subject contained an intensity equivalent to the mean degree.

However, this proof of the first position or view will not do according to Swineshead, since when combined with the physical assumption that heating rarefies while cooling condenses, the subject will unavoidably be rarefied in one part and condensed in another when the process of equalizing the halves of the subject is carried out; but the moment this equalization commences, the cooler, more remiss, half will, because of the rarefaction caused by heating, become greater than the more intense half, which means that throughout the whole process intension will be occurring over a greater part than is remission; therefore, Swineshead concludes, at the beginning the whole subject must be more remiss than the mean degree. An objection to this procedure is raised, but it is disposed of through a number of replies establishing that the subject must indeed initially have an overall intensity less than the mean degree (5rb–5vb).

All of this would seem to imply that Swineshead definitely rejected the first "mean degree measure" position, especially if we combine this with the fact that in the following paragraphs he appears to regard the second opposing position (that the subjects in question are just as intense as any of their parts) as acceptable (6ra–6va). However, such a judgment would be premature. Swineshead has argued not directly against the first position as such, but rather against a proof given of it. Furthermore, in the remaining (and one should note, larger and more impressive) part of treatise II, Swineshead returns to this first "mean degree" position and allows its application to difformly qualified subjects each half of which is uniform and, more generally, to "stair-step qualities" in which the intensities differ, but are uniform, over certain determinate parts of the qualified subjects. This applicability is grounded upon the fact that in a difform subject with uniform halves, a quality extended through a half "denominates the whole only half as much as it denominates the half through which it is extended." Swineshead then generalizes this "new rule" and states that if a quality is "extended in a proportionally smaller part of the whole, it denominates the whole with a correspondingly more remiss degree than it does the part through which it is extended" (6va), thus opening the possibility of considering "stair-step" distributions.

After giving proofs for the special and general cases of his new "rule of denomination," Swineshead raises an objection against it: "If the first proportional part of something be intense in such and such a degree, and the second [proportional part] were twice as intense, the third three times, and so on *in infinitum*, then the whole would be just as intense as the second proportional part. However, this does not appear to be true. For it is apparent that the quality is infinite and thus, if it exists without a contrary, it will infinitely denominate its subject" (6va).

Swineshead shows that this latter inference to infinite denomination does not follow and that it arises because one has ignored the proper denomination criterion he has just set forth (6vb–7ra). As a preliminary, he devotes considerable space to the important task of establishing that a subject with a quality distribution as specified by the objection is indeed just as intense as its second proportional part, and he presents in detail just how this is so (6va–6vb). The proportional parts in question are to be taken "according to a double proportion" (that is, the succeeding proportional parts of the subject are its half, fourth, eighth, etc.). Now following the arithmetic increase in intensity over the succeeding proportional parts as stipulated by the objection, it follows that the whole will have the intensity of the second proportional part of the subject. Swineshead proves this by taking two subjects—A and B—and dividing them both according to the required proportional parts. Now take B and "let it be assumed that during the first proportional part of an hour the first [proportional] part of B is intended to its double, and similarly in the second proportional part of the hour the second proportional part of it is intended to its double, and so on *in infinitum* in such a way that at the end [of the hour] B will be uniform in a degree double the degree it now has." Turning then to A, Swineshead asks us to assume that "during the first proportional part of the hour the whole of A except its first proportional part grows more intense by acquiring just as much latitude as the first proportional part of B acquires during that period, while in the second proportional part of the same hour all of A except its first and second proportional parts grows more intense by acquiring just as much latitude as the second proportional part of B then acquires . . . and so on *in infinitum*." Clearly, then, since the whole of A except its first proportional part is equal in extent to its first proportional part, and since the whole of A except its first and second proportional parts is equal to its second proportional part . . . and so on *in infinitum*, it follows that A acquires just as much, and only as much, as B does throughout the hour; therefore, it is overall just as intense as B is at the end of the hour, which is to say that it is doubly intense or has an intensity equivalent to that of its second proportional part [*Q.E.D.*].

In thus determining just how intense A is at the end of its specified intensification, Swineshead has correctly seen that in our terms the infinite geometrical series involved is convergent (if we assume the intensity of the whole of A at the outset to be 1, then $\frac{1}{2} + \frac{2}{4} + \frac{3}{8} + \cdots + \frac{n}{2^n} = 2$). But such an interpretation is misleading. Swineshead gives absolutely no consideration to anything becoming arbitrarily small or tending to zero as we move indefinitely over the specified proportional parts.

Swineshead knows where he is going to end up before he even starts; he has merely redistributed what he already knows to be a given finite increase in the intensity of one subject over another subject, something that is found to be true in most instances of the occurrence of "convergent infinite series" in the late Middle Ages. Yet however Swineshead's accomplishment is interpreted, one should note that his major concern was to show that a subject whose quality was distributed in such a manner *in infinitum* over its parts was in fact consistent with his denomination criterion and did not lead to paradox. It is also notable that, in so increasing the intensity of *A*, he could have specified that the quality in question was heat, arguing, as he had previously argued against the proof of the first position, that on grounds of the physical assumption that heating causes rarefaction, it followed that *A* would not be just as intense as its second proportional part. The fact that he did not do so lends further credence to the view that his major interest was in seeing how many "results" could be drawn out of a given position or assumption, the more complicated and surprising the results the better. One such set of results could be derived by applying a physical assumption to the proof of the first position; another, as in the present instance, by ignoring it.

This interest of Swineshead can be even better illustrated if the present example from treatise II is carried yet one step further. Immediately after answering the objection treated above, another objection is put forth claiming that "from this it follows that *A* is now only finitely intense, yet by means of a merely finite rarefaction will suddenly be made infinitely intense." In Swineshead's reply to the objector's complaint that this is an absurd state of affairs and must be rejected, the important point is again Swineshead's demonstration that this presumably absurd situation can and does obtain (7ra). We can see how this can be so if, Swineshead tells us, we take only every 2^{nth} proportional part of our previously so intensified *A* and then rarefy the second proportional part of *A* by any amount howsoever small, while rarefying each of the succeeding proportional parts twice as slowly as the preceding one. Again, in our terms we have to do with a "divergent series," so the conclusion that *A* is "suddenly made infinitely intense" is a correct one. But to set down the general term of this "series" would be anachronistic and would credit Swineshead with something that was quite outside his thinking. What he should be credited with is ingenious, but much more straightforward. He realized that in selecting only the 2^{nth} propor-

tional parts of *A* he had chosen parts whose intensities were successively double one another. Therefore, in deliberately specifying that the rarefaction over these parts should be successively "twice as slow," it automatically followed that, considering both the extension and intensity of that amount added to each part by rarefaction, the resulting contribution (no matter how small) to the denomination of the whole would be the same in each instance. And since there were an infinite number of such "added parts," the denomination of the whole immediately became infinite. Once again, in our terms, what Swineshead has done amounts to the adding of a constant amount to each term of an "infinite series." It is more profitable, however, to view Swineshead's concern with the infinite in another, much less modern, way. In the two "objections" that have just been cited, Swineshead has first shown that, astonishing as it might seem, a subject whose quality increases *in infinitum* as distributed over its parts is as a matter of fact only finitely intense overall. One can next take this same finitely intense subject, change it by a finite amount as small as you wish, and it immediately becomes infinitely intense. The switch from infinite to finite and then back to infinite again seems more than incidental. Swineshead was partaking of something that was characteristic of the logical — and by then physical — tradition of solving sophisms. In point of fact, at the end of treatise II he even refers to the conclusions he is dealing with (there are fifteen in all) as *sophismata* (9rb).

The foregoing fairly lengthy discussions of the first four treatises of the *Liber calculationum* should give a good impression of the character of the whole work, not forgetting that the later treatises appear to be slightly more expository in form. The descriptions of some of the special features of the treatises that follow assume the continuation of this same basic character without repeatedly asserting it.

Treatises V–VI: On Rarity and Density; On the Velocity of Augmentation. The fifth and sixth treatises again form a logical unit, this time concerning the quantity or rarity and density of subjects and motions with respect to quantity. The relatively long treatise V (16vb–22rb) has three basic parts. It first addresses directly the question of the proper measures of rarity and density, rejecting the position (1) that rarity depends on the proportion of the quantity of the subject to its matter while density depends on the proportion of matter to quantity, and accepting the position (2) that rarity depends on quantity assuming that the amount of matter remains the same (*raritas attenditur penes quantitatem non simpliciter sed in materia proportionata vel in comparatione ad materiam. Et ponit quod proportionabiliter sicut tota quantitas sit maior manente materia eadem, ita raritas est maior* [17ra]).

It is of interest to the modern historian to realize why Swineshead considered the first position to be significantly different from the second position; it may seem, indeed, to be nothing but an improved and more general version of the second position. The explanation of this point turns out to shed important light on the status of Bradwardine's geometric function relating forces, resistances, and velocities, which had been propounded in his *De proportionibus* in 1328. In fact, for Swineshead, if rarity depended upon the proportion (ratio) of quantity to matter, this would have meant that, for instance, when the proportion of quantity to matter was "doubled" (*dupletur* in his terms, but "squared" in modern terms), then the rarity would be doubled, and the resulting function would have been in modern terms logarithmic or exponential in exactly the same way that Bradwardine's function was logarithmic or exponential. It was their understanding of the meaning of the compounding or "addition" and "subtraction" of proportions (equivalent to multiplying and dividing ratios in the modern sense) that essentially forced fourteenth-century thinkers to this function. Finding it difficult, therefore, to propose the dependence of rarity on the ratio of quantity to matter as this would be understood in the simple modern sense, Swineshead was therefore led to his less elegant second position as a substitute emphasizing quantity and assuming the constancy of matter as a subsidiary consideration in order to avoid the intrusion of a proportion per se.

But having proposed the dependence of rarity on quantity assuming the matter constant, Swineshead enters in the second part of the treatise into a long consideration of how rarity should depend upon quantity. This consideration is subsumed under the question whether both rarity and density are positive entities or whether only one of them is positive, and, if so, which (17ra). Here he can rely in an important way upon his discussion in treatise I of positive and privative entities and their interrelations with regard to intensity and remissness. After an involved discussion, he concludes that density is the positive quality (and rarity privative) and that when a subject is rarefied uniformly for a given period of time it acquires quantity difformly, greater and greater quantities corresponding to equal increments of rarity as the subject becomes more rarefied (*densitas se habet positive et ex uniformi rarefactione alicuius per tempus secundum se totum difformiter acquiritur quantitas et si densius et rarius equalis quantitatis equevelociter rarefierent, rarius maiorem quantitatem acquireret quam densius* [18rb]). Thus, the mathematical characteristics of the measures of rarity become similar to those of the measures of remissness in treatise I, and similar conclusions can be reached. It follows, for instance, that the latitude of rarity between any degree of rarity and zero rarity is infinite (18vb), just as a similar conclusion had followed for remissness.

The third and last section of treatise V raises and replies to doubts, many of which are parallel to earlier considerations concerning quality. Swineshead concludes that a uniformly difformly dense body or a body with unequal degrees of uniform density in its two halves is as dense as its mean degree (18vb–20vb). Similarly, he says that bodies are as rare as their mean degrees provided that it is understood that the latitudes of rarity and density are really the same (19vb), and he disposes of a whole series of doubts about how density and rarity are to be compared by saying that the situation is the same in this case as it is in the case of intensity and remissness (*ad que omnia possunt consimiliter argui et responderi sicut arguebatur ubi tanguntur illa de intensione et remissione, mutatis illis terminis intensio et remissio in istis terminis raritas et densitas* [20vb]). Finally, he replies to a doubt about whether, if there were an infinite quantity with a part which was infinitely dense, the whole would be infinitely dense (21rb–22rb) by saying that just as in similar cases concerning qualities, so here a density extended through only a finite part of an infinite subject would not contribute anything to the denomination of the whole subject (21vb–22ra).

When to the above description of treatise V is coupled the observation that nowhere in treatise V does Swineshead directly inquire into the physical significance to be properly correlated with the concepts density and rarity, it should be clear that Swineshead's real interest here must have been in the mathematical functions involved in the various positions, and in the consequences, whether more or less startling, that could be shown to be consistent with these functions. And again, as in earlier treatises, he concludes by saying that many more sophisms could be developed concerning this material, all of which can easily be solved if the material he has presented is well understood (22rb).

In treatise VI, Swineshead then turns from rarity and density as such to motions of augmentation, where augmentation is considered to be the same as increase of rarity. Like Roger Swineshead before him, he begins by rejecting the position espoused in Heytesbury's *Regule solvendi sophismata* that motion of augmentation is to be measured by the proportion of the new quantity to the old quantity (22va–24va). Second, he turns to the position on augmentation held by Roger Swineshead, namely that augmentation is to be measured by quantity acquired irrespective of the quantity doing the acquiring (24va–vb), but he also rejects this position because it does not adequately handle cases in which a quantity is lost at the same time as one is added. Swineshead then replaces Roger Swineshead's position with an improved version which he accepts, saying that augmentation and diminution should be measured by the net change of quantity of the subject (24vb). In reply to an objection concerning what happens according to this position to the concept of uniform augmentation, Swineshead admits in effect that the concepts of uniform velocities of alteration and motion will not then have an easy parallel in the case of the motion of augmentation, although one could speak of equal parts of a subject gaining equal qualities.

The most striking thing about treatise VI is perhaps the fact that the largest section of the treatise is devoted to the refutation of Heytesbury's view concerning the proper measure of augmentation. And here there are two points to be noted about the arguments provided. First of all, a significantly large proportion of them involve what are in effect augmentations from zero quantity. Since the first position is obviously not applicable to augmentations from zero (since this would put a zero into the denominator of the proportion of quantities that it proposes as the proper measure of augmentation), one might argue that these supposed refutations of the position are misguided. And secondly, Swineshead himself eventually concedes several of the refuting arguments although he did consider the first position to be refuted. Yet these arguments are left to stand as if they were strikes against the first position. Thus, Swineshead says that the inferences which can be drawn from the first position are amazing and contrary to one's idea of what the proper measure of a motion should be (23va)—some of these conclusions being ones that involve the unfair augmentation from zero quantity—but he then also concedes that some of these conclusions are simply true no matter how the velocity of augmentation is measured

(23va). So again one might fairly draw the conclusion that Swineshead's major concern is not really the choice between rival measures, but rather the exhibition of mathematical techniques that one might reasonably use in the discussion of any of the positions.

Treatises VII–VIII: On Reaction; On the Powers of Things. As in the works of the other Oxford calculators where reaction is taken up at a fairly early stage, here too the problem of reaction is really the entire problem of how two qualified bodies act on each other and involves all of the variables discussed in the preceding treatises. For those who, like Richard Swineshead, held the so-called addition of part to part theory of qualitative change, the problem was particularly acute. There were numerous well-known cases (*experimenta*) in which reaction seemed to occur (25va). Furthermore, under the addition theory it seemed that the parts of a quality present should be able to act and react with the other qualitative parts nearby. Yet the previously accepted Aristotelian and medical theory of qualitative change had assumed that the qualities of a given subject could be represented by the single degrees of hot, cold, wet, or dry of the whole, so that if two bodies were brought close together such that one could act on the other, only that body with the higher degree, say of heat, would act as the agent or force causing change, and only that body with the lower degree would act as patient and be changed. Clearly the calculators were in a position in which they had to improve upon previous theory by taking account of distributions of quality, and yet the theoretical situation was so complex and mathematically difficult that they faced an almost impossible task.

After preliminary arguments, Swineshead takes, as the foundation of his solution to the problem, the position that the power of a subject is determined by the multitude of form (*multitudo forme*) in it, where multitude of form is determined not only by the intensity of the form and the extension, but also by what might be called the density of form (26vb). He takes density as the most important factor and asserts that if a foot length of fire were condensed to half a foot, it would still contain the same multitude of form even if the intensity were the same as before. Swineshead next turns to the question of whether the whole patient resists the agent or only the part acted on. After considering various positions, he concludes that although the whole patient does not necessarily resist the agent, the whole part of the patient directly opposite the agent resists, and that all parts do not resist equally, parts further from the agent resisting less than those closer. Unfortunately, arguments can be raised to show that no simple proportionality obtains between distance from the agent and lesser resistance. Swineshead asserts, however, that it will be more clearly understood when he deals with illuminations how resistance decreases with distance (27rb – 28rb).

On the basis of these fundamentals Swineshead concludes that reaction cannot occur between uniform bodies such that the reaction is according to the quality contrary to that of the action (28va – 28vb). (By a uniform body Swineshead means uniform not only according to intensity of quality but also according to the amount of form existing in equal parts of the body.) It is possible for the patient to react according to another quality – so that while the agent heats the patient the patient in turn humidifies the agent. Between difform bodies, on the other hand, there can be action with reaction in the contrary quality in another part. Where such reaction occurs the whole agent and whole patient act and resist according to their power insofar as it is applied in the given situation. Thus, Swineshead appears content in his reply to leave the unspoken and rather improbable implication that in all the observed cases of reaction according to the same quality, the qualities of the two bodies must have been difform.

The rest of treatise VII consists of the solution of three *dubia*. The first, also dealt with by John Dumbleton in his *Summa logicae et philosophiae naturalis*, concerns whether an agent will act more slowly if patients are applied to either side of it than it would if it acted on only one of the patients (29va – 30ra). Swineshead is sure that if two actions concur at the same point the action will be faster, but he is not sure of the solution of the doubt if the two patients are far enough apart so that they do not act on each other. In the latter case, he says, the reader may decide for himself whether the patients will assist each other in resisting, since, although some say they do, it is hard to understand how this could be so (30ra). To a second doubt Swineshead concludes that two difform bodies which are similar in those parts nearest each other can nevertheless still act on each other (30ra – 30va), and to a third doubt he concludes that bodies having maximum degrees of contraries can act on each other (30va – 30vb).

It should be clear that in all of treatise VII one of Swineshead's main questions concerns the additivity or summability of the forces and resistances he is dealing with. Indeed, elsewhere additivity was one of the major concerns of the Oxford calculators in their efforts at quantification. With respect to single dimensions such as that of intensity, the calculators were adamant that the measure of intensity should be an additive measure. Following the addition theory of the intension and remission of forms, they assumed that an intensity was equivalent to the sum of its parts. In dealing with actions and reactions of bodies, however, the basis for such additivity was not so easily found. Here, and again in treatise XI concerning local motion, Swineshead appears to concede, perhaps to his own disappointment, that difficulties appear to ensue if one attempts to treat subjects as the sums of their parts in any simple fashion. The difficulties of considering not only the forces and resistances of the parts, but also the varying distances of the parts from each other and the possible interactions of the parts on each other, made a detailed part-by-part quantitative treatment practically impossible. We may admire Swineshead's ingenuity in the face of such odds while agreeing that it is unfortunate that the slant of Aristotelian physics towards alteration rather than local motion caused Swineshead to concentrate on such a difficult problem.

Treatise VIII again takes up the question dealt with in treatise VII concerning how the powers of things are to be measured, and it appears probable that parts of treatises VII and VIII represent Swineshead's successive reworkings of the same basic problem. Despite nine arguments against the view that power is to be measured by multitude of form, Swineshead reaffirms his earlier conclusion that it is. The only thing that he adds here is the remark that the amount of form induced in a subject will depend upon the amount of matter present (31rb). He concedes the nine arguments or conclusions *de imaginatione*, their supposed difficulty being based on the view that, for a given form, intensity and extension are inversely related, which, he says, is only accidentally so (31rb – 31va).

If in the work of Oresme, the concept of the "quantity of quality" was to become fundamental, where quantity of quality was the product of intensity times extension, here we see Swineshead's effort to deal with objections based on a similar concept. Whatever objections there may be to Oresme's concept of "quantity of quality" from a modern point of view, students of medieval science have in recent years become so familiar with the concept that there is a tendency to assume the use of a similar concept in other late medieval authors attempting the quantification of qualities or forms. It deserves emphasizing, therefore, that Richard

Swineshead and the other Oxford calculators of 1330–1350 were familiar with concepts like Oresme's quantity of quality, but rejected them in favor of quantifications in terms of intensities alone or in terms of something like Swineshead's multitude of form. This rejection of "quantity of quality" helps explain, among other things, Swineshead's less than total happiness in treatise II with the "mean degree measure" of difform qualities, a measure that he might otherwise have been expected to favor because of its mathematical attractiveness. Swineshead does not always assume, as Oresme's quantity of quality concept implies, that when the extension of a subject is decreased, the form remaining unchanged, the intensity will increase, and he even goes so far as to assert that a form could be condensed to a point without its intensity increasing (31rb).

Treatises IX–X: On the Difficulty of Action; On Maxima and Minima. The ninth and tenth treatises in a sense carry further Swineshead's treatment of action and the forces causing it. Treatise X has a clear precedent in earlier discussions of maxima and minima, in particular in the discussion found in Heytesbury's *Regule solvendi sophismata*, and treatise IX probably is related, although in a nonobvious way, to Bradwardine's *De proportionibus*. The problem covered in treatise IX (and also in Dumbleton's *Summa*, part VI) seems to have arisen because of the Calculator's acceptance of Bradwardine's function for measuring velocities. For the standard Aristotelian position concerning the relation of forces, resistances, and velocities, there was a simple relationship between forces and the velocities produced with a given resistance, such that each equal part of the force could be interpreted as contributing an equal part of the velocity (and here again arose the question of additivity). For the Bradwardinian position, on the other hand, multiples of a force, with the resistance remaining constant, did not produce equal multiples of the velocity. As a result, one needed some other measure of what a force could do. On this subject, Swineshead first rejects two positions: (1) that the action or difficulty produced depends upon the proportion of greater inequality with which the agent acts, so that an agent acting from a greater proportion produces a greater difficulty (31va); and (2) that the action or difficulty produced depends on a proportion of lesser inequality, because an agent closer in power to the strength of the resistance tires more in acting (31va).

The position that Swineshead adopts is the same as that adopted by Dumbleton, namely that the difficulty produced is proportional to the power acting to its ultimate (31vb). In a given uniform resistance there will be an action of maximum difficulty that cannot be produced in that medium, namely the difficulty equal to the power of the resistance (31vb–32ra). When the power of the agent is doubled, the difficulty it can produce is also doubled. The latitude of difficulty or range of all possible difficulties is infinite (32ra).

The remainder of treatise IX consists of the raising of twelve arguments against Swineshead's preferred position and of his replies to them. In these arguments the connection with Bradwardine's function manifests itself. A common assumption behind the objections is that difficulty (or action) and motion (or velocity) ought to be proportional to each other, so that to move something twice as fast is to produce a double action. As stated above, in the commonly assumed Aristotelian "function," a double force, a double velocity, and presumably a double action or difficulty all seem to be correlated with each other. This is not so in the Bradwardinian function, where a doubling of force does not usually correlate with a doubling of velocity. Swineshead simply asserts here, therefore, that difficulty can be correlated with force or power, and that velocity and difficulty produced do not necessarily correspond to each other (32vb–33rb). The main effect of treatise IX, therefore, is to clear away objections that might be raised about Bradwardine's function by those still thinking in an Aristotelian framework.

Treatise X concerns maxima and minima only with respect to the traversal of space in local motion, and the ground it covers is quite standard. Having stated some familiar definitions and suppositions concerning maxima and minima of active and passive powers, Swineshead states two rules: (1) that both debilitatable and nondebilitatable powers have a minimum uniform resistance that they cannot traverse (in familiar scholastic terminology, a *minimum quod non*); and (2) that with respect to media there is a maximum power that cannot traverse a given medium, namely the power equal to the resistance of the medium (a *maximum quod non* [34rb]). Thus, for a power, say, equal to 3, there will be a minimum resistance it cannot traverse, that is, the resistance 3, and, conversely, for the resistance equal to 3, the power equal to 3 will be the maximum power that cannot traverse it.

The rest of treatise X consists of rules for assigning maxima and minima under a variety of possible conditions, that is, when the medium is uniform and when it is difform, when there is a time limit and when there is not, when the power is constant and when it weakens in acting, and when the medium is infinite and when it is finite. Although they may take a while to decipher, these conclusions are mostly the simple results of the assumption that the force must be greater than the resistance for motion to occur. Swineshead himself seems to feel that he is traversing familiar ground, and the treatise is therefore quite short.

Treatise XI: On the Place of an Element. Swineshead's concern in treatise XI is a single problem relating to the motion of a heavy body in the vicinity of its natural place at the center of the universe: whether in free fall, assuming a void or nonresistant medium, the heavy body will ever reach the center of the universe in the sense that the center of the body will eventually coincide with the center of the universe. If we regard the heavy body in question as a thin rod (*simplex columnare*), the variables that Swineshead has to deal with in resolving the problem become evident: as soon as any part of the rod passes the center of the universe, that part may be considered as acting as a resistance against its continued motion. Now one position that can be taken in resolving the problem is that the body acts as the sum of its parts and that therefore the parts of the rod "beyond the center" actually do resist its motion. Assuming this, lengths or segments of the rod will function both as distances traversed as the rod approaches the center and as the forces and resistances involved in determining such a traversal. If we also assume, with Swineshead, Bradwardine's "function" relating velocities with the forces and resistances determining them, then the task to be carried out is to discover a way to apply this "function" to the "distance-determined" forces and resistances acting upon the falling rod in order to calculate the relevant changes in velocity and thus ascertain whether or not the center of the rod ever will reach the center of the universe.

In what is mathematically perhaps the most complicated and sophisticated section of the *Liber calculationum*, Swineshead accomplishes this task and replies that, on the assumption of the rod acting as the sum of its parts, the two centers will never come to coincide. He presents his argument axiomatically, beginning from a number of strictly mathematical *suppositiones* and *regulae* and then moving to their application to the problem at hand. It will be easier to indicate something of the nature of his accomplishment if the order is, at least in part, reversed. Thus, Swineshead clearly realizes and emphasizes the fact that the distance remain-

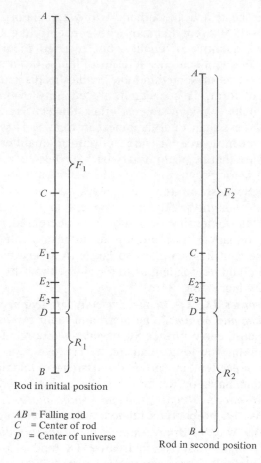

Rod in initial position

AB = Falling rod
C = Center of rod
D = Center of universe

Rod in second position

FIGURE 1

ing between the center of the rod and the center of the universe will always be equal to half the difference between that (greater) part of the rod which is still on this side of the center of the universe and that (lesser) part which is beyond (37ra) (in terms of Figure 1, $CD = (F_1 - R_1)/2$). This obtains no matter what space intervals we consider in the rod's progressive motion toward the center. When this is added to the fact that, with any given motion of the rod, whatever is subtracted from the segment this side of the center of the universe is added to the segment beyond the center, thus determining the "new" forces and resistances obtaining after that motion, Swineshead then has a way to apply Bradwardine's "function" to the whole problem. Divide, for example, the remaining distance (CD) into proportional parts (according to a double proportion); we know the relation of the distance between the centers to the difference between the relevant forces and resistances: $CD = (F_1 - R_1)/2$, but successively following the particular division specified of the remaining distance it is also true that this same half-difference between F_1 and R_1 is equivalent to the excess of F_1 less one-fourth of

$(F_1 - R_1)$ over R_1 plus one-fourth of $(F_1 - R_1)$. But in a strictly mathematical "suppositio" it is stated (and then proved) that the proportion of the thusly decreased F_1 to the thusly increased R_1 will be less than the "sub-double" of the proportion between the original, unaltered F_1 and R_1. (*Si inter aliqua sit proportio maioris inequalitatis, et quarta pars excessus maioris supra minus auferatur a maiori et addatur minori, tunc inter illa in fine erit proportio minor quam subdupla ad proportionem existentem inter ista duo in principio* [35vb].) In modern symbols:

$$\left(F_1 - \frac{F_1 - R_1}{4}\right) : \left(R_1 + \frac{F_1 - R_1}{4}\right) < (F_1 : R_1)^{1/2}.$$

At the same time, the decreased F_1 and the increased R_1 have given us the F_2 and R_2 operative after the rod has moved over the first proportional part of the distance between centers, assuming that its speed is uniform throughout this motion, and, moving over the second proportional part, we can similarly derive F_3 and R_3 and relate them to F_2 and R_2 by means of the same "mathematical supposition," and so on, over succeeding proportional parts and F's and R's. However, the ordering of the force-resistance proportions that is the burden of this mathematical supposition is precisely what is at stake in Bradwardine's "function" claiming that increases and (in the particular problem at hand) decreases in velocity correspond to increases and decreases in the proportion between force and resistance. Bradwardine can therefore be directly applied, yielding resultant velocities over succeeding proportional parts each of which is "more remiss" than half the preceding one ($V_1 > 2V_2 > 4V_3 > \cdots$). Since succeeding proportional parts of the distance decrease by exactly half ($CE_1 = 2E_1E_2 = 4E_2E_3 = \cdots$), it follows that the time intervals for each increment of distance must increase *in infinitum*, which means that the center of the rod will never reach the center of the universe (*maius tempus requireretur ad pertransitionem secunde partis proportionalis quam ad pertransitionem prime . . . et sic in infinitum. Ergo in nullo tempore finito transiret C totam illam distantiam* [37rb]).

Swineshead has reached this result by applying a particular, proportional part division to the distance remaining between the centers, but he provides for the generalization of this division by specifying (and proving) his crucial mathematical supposition in a general form (36va); then we may presumably take any succeeding proportional parts whatsoever in determining the fall of the rod. But

his own use of this more general supposition occurs in a second, different proof of the conclusion that the rod will never reach the center of the universe. In our terms, the first proof summarized above assumes a constant velocity—and hence constant force-resistance proportions—over the relevant distance intervals, thus employing a discontinuous, step function in resolving the problem. In a more compact, and more difficult, proof Swineshead comes more directly to grip with his variables as exhibiting a continuous function. Less tractable, and hence more difficult to represent adequately in modern terms, than the first proof, its substance is tied to the proportional comparison of decreases or losses with what we would term rates of decrease or loss (for example, *motus velocius proportionabiliter remittetur quam excessus; ergo excessus tardius et tardius proportionabiliter remittetur* [37rb]).

In both proofs Swineshead has in effect assumed that the rod or heavy body in question is a *grave simplex*, a limitation that he addresses himself to by considering, in reply to several objections, the body as a *mixtum* (37va). Far more important, however, is another objection. It claims, in effect, that the assumption behind Swineshead's whole procedure up to that point—namely, that the rod does act as the sum of its parts, must be false because it implies that there would exist natural inclinations that would be totally without purpose and vain (*appetitus . . . omnino otiosus . . . vanus*), an inadmissible consequent (37rb).

Swineshead therefore sets forth a second, alternative position, one in which the heavy body in question acts as a whole, where its parts contribute to the natural inclination or desire (*appetitus*) of the whole in a manner that is not given precise mathematical determination (37vb–38ra). As might be expected, Swineshead spends far less time treating, and seems much less interested in, this second position, in spite of the fact that it is apparently the true one. This brevity fits well with the whole tenor of the *Liber calculationum* and with what has been noted above of the greater interest in deriving results than in just what the results are. The treatment based on the first, "false" *positio* of the whole body as the sum of its parts also fits well with much of the rest of the *Liber calculationum*, where the mathematical and logical determination of the contribution of parts to wholes is so often a central issue.

Treatises XII–XIII: On Light; On the Action of Light. These two treatises are concerned with light, first with respect to the power of the light source and second with respect to the illumination produced.

The power of a light source, Swineshead states, is measured in the same way as the power of other agents, namely by the multitude of form (38ra). Equal light sources, then, will be those that are not only equal in intensity but also equal in multitude of form (38rb). Thus, if sources with equal multitudes of form are intended by equal latitudes of intensity, they will gain equally in power, but if sources with unequal multitudes of form are intended by equal latitudes of intensity, the one with more form will increase more in power than the other.

On the basis of these presuppositions, Swineshead then draws a number of conclusions or rules treating what happens when either the quantity of light source is varied (by adding or subtracting matter so that the multitude of form is changed) or the intensity of these sources is varied. He concludes, for instance, that if there are two light sources of different intensity, which at the outset are either equal or unequal in quantity, but which then diminish equally in quantity, then proportionally as one is more intense than the other it will diminish in power more rapidly (38rb–38va). Swineshead does not believe that changing the quantity (extension) of a light source without adding or subtracting matter will change its power, but he says that his conclusions can be proved even better by those who hold such a view (38vb).

It should be noted that in this treatise Swineshead does assume that there is a correlation between intensity and multitude of form, something which he felt it necessary to state as an explicit hypothesis when he dealt with similar problems in treatise II (for example, 8va) and something which he, in effect, ignored in treatise VIII. Had his interests been in determining the one correct physical theory, it is hard to believe that he would not have brought these contexts together and somewhere stated what he felt to be the true physical situation with regard to the connections between the intensity, extension, and "density" of a form. With his attention falling as entirely on the quantitative side as it does, he lets apparent inconsistencies slide, covered by the remark that the connection between the intensities and extensions of a given form are only accidental (31rb).

Treatise XIII consists of the solution of two major doubts and a long string of conclusions. In reply to the first doubt, Swineshead concludes that every light source produces its entire latitude, from its maximum degree down to zero degree, in every

medium in which it suffices to act, but that a source will cast its light to a greater distance in a rarer medium and to a lesser distance in a denser medium (39vb). Light is remitted (is less intense) at more distant points because of the indisposition caused by the medium between the source and the distant point, so since there is no medium between the source and the point next to it there is no remission at that point.

In reply to the second doubt Swineshead concludes that a light source casts a uniformly difform illumination in a uniform medium (40rb–va). Considering the medium between the source and a distant point as an impediment subtracting from the intensity of illumination, Swineshead comes up with a physically reasonable relation leading to a uniformly difform distribution, avoiding the trap of making the intensity inversely proportional to the distance from the light source. This no doubt is the explanation Swineshead had in mind in treatise VII as being helpful in understanding how distant parts combine their actions and resistances (28rb).

These two replies are then followed by a series of fourteen conclusions (numbered 13–26 in sequence with the conclusions of treatise XII) intended to make clearer what has preceded. They appear quite complex, but we may suppose that he arrived at them by a simple visualization of the situation with few if any mathematical calculations. Thus, Swineshead concludes first that if a light source acts in a uniform medium and if a part of the medium next to the agent is made more dense without changing its quantity (extension), then at every point of the rest of the medium farther from the agent the illumination will be remitted with the same velocity as the illumination at the extreme point of the part made denser is remitted (40vb–41ra). Imagining a graph of the original uniformly

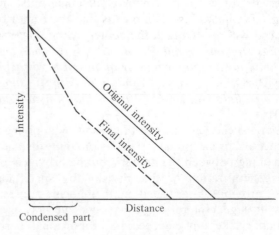

FIGURE 2

difform illumination, we see that this conclusion amounts to saying that when part of the medium is condensed, the slope of decrease of intensity will become steeper in that part, but in the remaining part the slope of decrease will remain the same, being shifted down parallel to itself to connect with the new, more remiss degree at the extreme point of the condensed part (see Figure 2).

Like this first conclusion, Swineshead's other conclusions are easy to understand on the basis of graphs, although he makes no reference to visualizations of the conclusions. In our terms, the variables that he has to work with in the conclusions are that the quantity of the light source determines the rate of decrease of intensity or slope of the distribution of intensities in a given medium, whereas the intensity of the source determines the degree from which that decrease starts. The density of the medium, on the other hand, also determines the slope of the distribution of intensities when the source remains the same. Swineshead can then partially offset changes in the quantity of the light source by changes in the density of the medium, or vice versa, as it suits his purpose (cf. conclusion 19 [41vb]).

It is so natural to us to visualize these conclusions that it is hard to imagine that Swineshead did not do so also. Dumbleton, in the corresponding part of his *Summa*, did make an explicit geometrical analogy, and the tradition of using triangles or cones to represent the dispersal of light in optics would also have prompted mental images of triangles. It is very probable then that the mathematics behind treatise XIII was a simple "visualized geometry."

Treatise XIV: On Local Motion. One of the most exhaustively developed sections of the *Liber calculationum*, treatise XIV begins by stipulating that its contents will be formulated under the assumption "that motion is measured in terms of geometric proportion" (*motum attendi penes proportionem geometricam* [43va]). As immediately becomes obvious, this is Swineshead's elliptical way of informing his readers that he will be accepting Bradwardine's view that variations in velocities correspond directly to variations in the force-resistance proportions determining those velocities (in modern terminology, that arithmetic changes in velocity correspond to geometric changes in the relevant force-resistance ratios). With this as base, what Swineshead accomplishes in setting forth the forty-nine *regulae* that constitute treatise XIV is to give a relatively complete "catalog" of just which *kinds* of changes in velocity correspond to which

kinds of changes in force and resistance and vice versa.

He does this in strict axiomatic fashion, the first three rules presenting what can be regarded as the basic mathematics of proportion which will serve, together with his assumption of Bradwardine's "function," as the key to all that follows. As indicated above, there is no doubt that the medieval tradition of compounding proportions was at the root of Bradwardine's logarithmic-type function, and it is precisely this that Swineshead makes explicit in his initial rules. Thus, the first rule tells us that "whenever a force (*potentia*) increases with respect to a constant resistance (*resistentiae non variatae*), then it will acquire as much proportionally relative to that resistance as it will itself be rendered greater" (43va). That is to say, if some force F_1 acting on a constant resistance R increases to F_2, then the proportional increase in F (the proportion $F_2 : F_1$) is equal to the increase of $F_2 : R$ over $F_1 : R$. As Swineshead makes clear in his proof of this rule, this amounts to a compounding of the proportions involved, that is, when $F_2 : F_1$ is "added to" $F_1 : R$ the result is $F_2 : R$. (Note that following the medieval convention proportions are added to one another [just as are numbers or line segments], when we would say they are multiplied.) In the second and third rules Swineshead establishes corresponding relations for the cases of a decrease in force and an increase or decrease in resistance (the force than being held constant [43va]).

That these rules provide the basis of what Swineshead was attempting to do in treatise XIV can be seen as soon as one introduces the motion or velocities that correspond to or "result from" the force-resistance proportions whose "mathematics of change" he has just established. Thus, to return to the first rule as an example, if we assume that a velocity V_1 corresponds to the proportion $F_1 : R$ and a velocity V_2 to the proportion $F_2 : R$, then, because $F_2 : R$ is greater than $F_1 : R$ by the proportion $F_2 : F_1$ (which is what the compounding of these proportions asserts), it follows that the velocity added is precisely the velocity that results from the proportion $F_2 : F_1$ (and which would result from a proportion $F : R$ equal to $F_2 : F_1$ standing alone). Given this, and the corresponding relations when a resistance is allowed to vary while the force is held constant, Swineshead can determine all that he wishes concerning changes in velocity by paying attention only to the relevant force-force or resistance-resistance proportions representing the changes. When, and only when, these proportions are equal will the corresponding positive or negative increments of velocity be equal.

In deducing his succeeding *regulae* on such a basis, Swineshead does not "calculate" velocity increments from given force-force or resistance-resistance proportions, nor velocities from given force-resistance proportions. In this he was strictly medieval. Rather, he always compares (at least) *pairs* of $F : F$ or $R : R$ proportions. Thus, whenever unequal forces increase or decrease with equal swiftness (*equevelociter*)—which means that $F_2 - F_1 = F_4 - F_3$—then the resultant $F_2 : F_1$, $F_4 : F_3$ proportions will be unequal, whence it follows that the corresponding velocity increments will be unequal. If, on the other hand, the forces increase or decrease proportionally (*eque proportionabiliter*)—which means that $F_2 : F_1 = F_4 : F_3$—then the corresponding velocity increments will be equal. And the same thing holds for increasing or decreasing resistances, the forces being held constant.

Beginning, then, with two rules (4 and 5 [43va]) that apply a change in a *single* force or resistance to, correspondingly, *two* constant resistances or forces (whence the relevant single $F_2 : F_1$ or $R_2 : R_1$ proportions function as pairs since they are applied to pairs of R or F), Swineshead sets forth the implications of his mathematics of force-resistance changes to changes in velocity. In rules 4 and 5, inasmuch as one has a single $F_2 : F_1$ or $R_2 : R_1$ proportion doing double duty, the corresponding velocity increments are naturally the same. (For example, rule 4 reads: "Whenever a force increases or decreases with respect to two equal or unequal, but constant, resistances, it will intend or remit motion with respect to each [of these resistances] with equal swiftness.") Note should be taken of how, throughout treatise XIV, Swineshead handles what we would consider as positive versus negative increments of velocity. Since all determining force and resistance proportions are always of greater inequality (e.g., $F_2 : F_1$ where $F_2 > F_1$ when it is a question of increase in force, $F_1 : F_2$ where $F_1 > F_2$ when decrease is involved), velocity increments are always added, a procedure that follows directly from Swineshead's basic technique of compounding proportions. This means that when it is a question of the remission of motion arising from decreasing forces or increasing resistances, then increments are added to the motion at the end of the change in question, the "sum" of these increments plus the final motion or velocity giving the motion or velocity at the beginning of the change. When the motion is intended, or the velocity increments are positive, the addition is naturally made to the motion obtaining at the beginning of the change.

In rules 6 through 15 (43va–43vb) Swineshead applies the two kinds of force or resistance change, that is, equally swift (*equevelociter*) or equally proportional (*eque proportionabiliter*) increases or decreases, to *pairs* of changing forces or resistances and infers the corresponding changes in velocity. Thus far, the force and resistance changes can be considered as discrete. However, beginning with rule 19 [43vb] Swineshead faces the case of the uniform and the continuous change of a single force or resistance. Now a single uniformly increasing force acting on a constant resistance, for example, will "generate" pairs of proportions $F_2 : F_1$, $F_3 : F_2$, $F_4 : F_3$, etc., where the succeeding proportions have "common terms" because the increase in force is continuous and where $F_2 - F_1 = F_3 - F_2 = F_4 - F_3 = \cdots$ because the increase is uniform. This latter fact entails that $F_2 : F_1 > F_3 : F_2 > F_4 : F_3 > \cdots$, which in turn implies that the increments of velocity will become successively smaller and smaller. Thus, the first half of rule 19 reads: "If a force increases uniformly with respect to a constant resistance, it will intend motion more and more slowly."

It is important, however, to be able to deal with at least certain kinds of nonuniform or difform changes in force and resistance. Hence, in rules 21 and 22 (43vb–44ra), arguing by a *locus a maiori*, Swineshead shows that if (as he has just established) a uniform gain in force or resistance entails a, respectively, slower and slower intension or remission of motion, then a nonuniform, slower and slower gain in force or resistance will necessarily also entail slower and slower intension and remission. Similarly, if a uniform loss in force or resistance entails a, respectively, faster and faster remission or intension of motion, then a nonuniform faster and faster loss in force or resistance also entails faster and faster remission and intension. The difform changes involved in a faster and faster gain, or a slower and slower loss, of force or resistance are not treated, since in such cases no inferences can be made about the resultant $F : F$ and $R : R$ proportions and, hence, about the resultant velocity increments.

However, the types of difform change in force or resistance that Swineshead can and does treat are precisely those needed in much of the remainder of treatise XIV. Up to this point changes in resistance have been independently given. Beginning with rule 23 (44ra) these changes are ascribed to the medium through which a mobile (represented by the force acting upon it) moves. Furthermore, all increase or decrease of resistance has hitherto been considered merely *relative to time* (whether it be *equevelociter* or *eque proportionabiliter*, no matter). But to ascribe variations in resistance to a medium is to speak of increase or decrease *relative to space*. Consequently, the problem facing Swineshead is to connect increments of resistance with respect to space to increments of resistance with respect to time, which is exactly what rule 23 does. Thus, a uniformly difform medium is one in which equal increments of resistance occur over equal spaces or distances. We also know that any body moving through such a medium in the direction of increasing resistance will move continuously more and more slowly (that is, the spaces S_1, S_2, S_3, $\cdots$ traversed in equal times successively decrease). But these two factors imply that, in equal times, the mobile will encounter smaller and smaller increments of resistance. Hence, equal increments of resistance (Swineshead calls them "latitudes of resistance") over space have been connected to decreasing increments of resistance over time. Accordingly, rule 23 reads: "If some force begins to move from the more remiss extreme of a uniformly difform medium and remains constant in strength, then the resistance with respect to it will increase more and more slowly." However, this slower and slower increase in resistance over time is precisely one of those kinds of difform change Swineshead was able to deal with in rules 21 and 22. This allows him to infer in rule 24 (44rb) that the motion of a mobile under a constant force through a uniformly difform medium in the direction of increasing resistance entails that the motion in question will undergo continuously slower and slower remission.

There are media, however, in which the distribution of resistance over equal spaces is difform, but not uniformly difform. What can be said of them? We know what equal changes of velocity are associated with a resistance that changes uniformly proportionally over time (rules 11 and 27 [43va, 44va–44vb]). Thus, if we imagine a medium of uniform resistance which increases in resistance equiproportionally over time as a constant force mobile moves through it, the mobile will remit its motion uniformly, that is, will undergo equal negative increments of velocity in equal times (rule 28 [44vb–45va]). With this rule in hand, Swineshead then imagines another medium with a resistance constant in time but difform with respect to space

and having at each point the resistance which was at the corresponding point of the first medium when the mobile was at that point. The mobile will then have the same motion in the second medium as it had in the first, that is, a uniformly difform motion. This means that (rule 29 [45va–45vb]) there can be a medium with resistance distributed difformly over space in such a way as to cause a mobile moving in it under a constant force to remit its motion uniformly (even though Swineshead could not describe this distribution).

Nevertheless, what Swineshead has established in rule 29 is of considerable importance for much of the remainder of treatise XIV. Rules 30–43 [45vb–48rb] all have to do with what will, or will not, occur when other constant or changing forces move through a medium in which (again rule 29) a given constant force uniformly remitted its motion. Thus, in rule 30 [45vb–46rb], Swineshead proves that two unequal constant forces cannot both uniformly remit their motion in the same medium. It is worthy of note that to prove this rule, Swineshead has to determine where the mobile that does remit its motion uniformly is at the middle instant of its motion. To do this he uses the ratio of space traversed in the first half of the time to the space traversed in the second half of the time and to find this ratio he uses the famous "Merton mean speed theorem," which he proves for the occasion (45vb–46ra). Apart from the fact that Swineshead gives four different proofs of the theorem, it here appears as a fairly routine lemma. He does not assign it any special importance, and does not even give it the honor of labeling it as a separate rule or conclusion.

Holding in mind the constant force specified in rule 29 as able to cause the uniform remission of motion in a given medium, Swineshead concludes treatise XIV by considering what will transpire when constant forces greater or lesser than that constant force are brought into play and when greater or lesser forces that are undergoing continuous intensification or remission are involved (rules 31–43). The last of these rules points out that a constant force greater than that specified in rule 29, but acting in the same medium, will give rise to a faster and faster remission of motion, that is, to a difformly difform motion. This leads to the final rules (44–49 [48rb–48vb]) of the treatise, which together function as a kind of appendix stipulating various facts and relations concerning difformly difform motions. As a whole, treatise XIV is an extremely impressive exhibition of just which cases of the different kinds of variation in force, resistance, and velocity that can be drawn out of Bradwardine's "function" are amenable to determination and treatment. As in the case of many of the other treatises of the *Liber calculationum*, there is a substantial increase in complexity from the beginning to the end of treatise XIV. But perhaps one of Swineshead's most signal accomplishments is his success in the latter part of the treatise in connecting variations in resistance over time with variations in resistance over space. For to the medieval supporter of Bradwardine's function (or of "Aristotle's function" as well for relating forces, resistances, and velocities), motion in a medium that was nonuniform was exceedingly problematic. As soon as the resistance in a medium was allowed to vary, one had to face the difficulty that the degree of resistance of the medium determined the velocity of the motion, while at the same time the velocity determined where in the medium the mobile would be and hence the resistance it would encounter. One seemed caught in a situation involving a double dependency of the relevant variables on each other. But Swineshead's "translation" of spatial increments of resistance into temporal ones automatically rendered the resistance of the medium time dependent and thus circumvented the troublesome double dependency.

Treatises XV–XVI: On a Nonresisting Medium or on the Increase of Power and Resistance; On the Induction of the Highest Degree. Treatises XV and XVI are continuations of treatise XIV and add ever more complications. In treatise XV Swineshead again considers the local motions of constant or changing powers in extended media, but this time he allows the resistance of the medium to vary while the mobile is moving through it or (we would say) takes the increase of power as an independent variable. In the key rule 29 of treatise XIV Swineshead had considered the motion of a mobile through a uniform medium with resistance changing over time, but this was a tool to allow him to deal with spatially difform resistances, the distributions of which he could not otherwise describe. Treatise XV, however, begins by dealing with temporally changing resistances in their own right.

The first conclusion of treatise XV is an example of Swineshead's mathematical ingeniousness, not in that he does complex mathematics, but in that he sees how to avoid complex mathematics. The conclusion concerns a nonresisting medium (or, in modern terms, a fixed space or vacuum) in which a resistance begins to be generated. The resistance first appears at one end of the medium and

moves progressively across the medium in such a way that the resistance increases uniformly from that end up to the point where the resistance ends. In modern terms, then, we might represent the resistance graphically by a straight line that rotates around the origin, starting in a vertical position, rotating at a decreasing rate (so that any point of the line has a constant horizontal velocity), and increasing in length so that the maximum height of the end point is a constant (see Figure 3). If, Swineshead concludes, a mobile begins to move from the same extreme of the medium at which the resistance begins to be generated, then it will move with a constant velocity (always keeping pace with the progress of a given degree of resistance), provided that the maximum resistance moves away from the mobile faster than the mobile could move with that resistance (48vb). Swineshead proves this conclusion first by showing that there could not have been any initial period of time during which the mobile increased or decreased its velocity, and second by showing that the mobile could not later begin to move faster or more slowly than its given resistance. In the later proof he argues, for instance, that if the mobile were supposed to increase its velocity, then it would immediately begin to encounter greater resistances, implying a decrease rather than an increase in velocity and thus a contradiction; and if the mobile were supposed to decrease its velocity, then conversely it would immediately begin to encounter lesser resistances implying an increase rather than a decrease in velocity and thus another contradiction. So, therefore, it must continue with a constant velocity. As stated above, from a modern point of view, any position that connects resistance with velocity as Bradwardine's function does would seem to be very problematic when applied to difform resistances, given that position (and therefore resistance) would determine the velocity of the

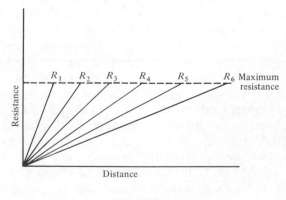

FIGURE 3

mobile, and yet velocity (and initial position) would also determine position, involving a double dependency. We see Swineshead here, however, not only coping with the problems of such a double dependency, but even playing with it and in a sense making sport to come up with ever more intriguing and complicated conclusions. Following the first conclusion, Swineshead proceeds to show that if the motion of the latitude of resistance is accelerated or decelerated the motion of the mobile will accelerate or decelerate also (49ra – 50ra), and he goes on from there to prove nine other conclusions concerned with the generation of a latitude of resistance in a nonresisting medium (50vb – 51rb).

The second main part of treatise XV concerns the motion of powers augmenting from zero degree in uniformly difform resistances. Again, perhaps the first conclusion of this part may serve as an example of the fourteen conclusions proved. If there is a uniformly difform medium terminated at zero degree in which a power begins to move as it augments uniformly from zero degree (always moving according to the proportion of its power to the point of the medium at which it is), then this power will continually move uniformly (51rb – 51va).

The further conclusions of this second part all concern temporally constant uniformly difform resistances, but the powers are allowed to vary in different ways, both uniformly and difformly. These conclusions differ from the conclusions of treatise XIV not only because the resistances involved are uniformly difform rather than difformly difform, but also because the changes of resistance and power are given as the independent variables rather than the velocities, as in treatise XIV.

In this treatise as in the last, the attempt seems to be to give a general description of the possible interrelations of power, resistance, and velocity and their changes. As in the last, too, the main variations of the independent variables considered are uniformly difform variations. This seems to result from the mathematical tractability of such situations rather than from any observational or theoretical context that made such variations likely, as was the case for illumination in treatise XIII, where there was a common belief that the distribution of illumination from a light source was uniformly difform. Within these limitations, Swineshead does, however, manage to build up more and more complex conclusions without doing much explicit mathematics. He rather simply picks those cases, however complex they may appear,

about which something can be said on the basis of the general characteristics of the functions involved.

In the third and last main part of treatise XV Swineshead should then have combined his two variables to allow both resistance and power to vary at the same time and to draw conclusions. The treatise simply ends, however, with the words: "It remains to inquire how both [resistance and power] may simultaneously be acquired." (The 1520 edition adds: "and first are posited rules, etc.") Given the complexity of the conclusions that resulted when only resistance or power was allowed to vary, one could hardly blame Swineshead for failing to push on further.

Treatise XVI is broken down into five chapters, each considering a class of problems concerning the induction of the maximum degree. Chapter 1 considers the alterations of larger and smaller uniformly difform subjects altered either uniformly throughout or by a uniformly difform latitude of alteration. Chapter 2 considers cases where a difformly difform latitude of alteration is extended through the part remaining to be brought to maximum degree in the same way as it was extended through the whole at the start.

Chapters 1 and 2 both consider cases where the alteration is extended at the start through the whole subject. Chapter 3, then, considers cases where the alteration does not extend through the whole subject at the start, but rather begins to be generated at the more intense extreme of the subject. Chapter 4 considers how the induction of the maximum degree is to be measured when the subject is rarefied or condensed during the alteration, deciding that such induction should not be measured by the fixed space outside the subject, but rather, with certain qualifications, by the subject itself. Chapter 5 considers how it may occur, through the successive generation of alteration in a subject, that the subject remains or becomes uniformly difform. Treatise XVI may be the most complex of the *Liber calculationum*, but perhaps enough has been said about the previous treatises so that its character can be imagined without the detailed examination of any of its conclusions.

As in the previous treatises, Swineshead in treatise XVI is preoccupied with uniformly difform alterations and the like, probably because they were well defined, whereas with difformly difform alterations the situation becomes overly complex. It might be remembered that, where alterations are concerned, as in this treatise, there was the common view that all qualitative actions, like light, decrease uniformly difformly (that is, linearly) as one moves away from the agent or source. So here again, as in the treatise on illumination, there might be a physical reason for emphasizing uniformly difform distributions. Nevertheless, if there was such a reason, it is well in the background.

Opuscula

Of the three short *opuscula* that may be assigned to Richard Swineshead, two by explicit ascription to a Swineshead as author, and one by its position between the two others, one is a partial commentary on the *De caelo* and the other two are partially repetitive treatments of motion.

In librum de caelo. Apparently part of a commentary, beginning from text 35 of book I of the *De caelo*, this short fragment is in two main parts, the first dealing with Aristotle's proofs that an infinite body cannot move locally, and the second dealing with the relation of substances to their qualities, in connection with the possibility of action and passion between infinite bodies.

In the first main part, Swineshead considers (1) the proofs that an infinite body cannot rotate, drawing paradoxes concerning the intersections of infinite lines during such rotation; (2) the proofs against translational motion of infinites; and (3) Aristotle's arguments that there cannot be an infinite body so that, *a fortiori*, there cannot be any motion of an infinite body.

In the second main part, Swineshead considers (1) Aristotle's discussion of the possible action and passion of infinites, both with relation to simple subjects and with relation to compounds or mixtures; (2) the question of whether substantial forms can vary within some latitude, apparently with the idea that, if elemental forms can be remitted, then a finite action of an infinite subject might be within the range of possibility; (3) a proof that elements can exist without their qualities; (4) a proof that there cannot be mixed bodies of two or more elements of degrees as remiss as desired (in this part, Swineshead mentions Dumbleton by name and refutes some arguments he makes in part IV of his *Summa*); and (5) arguments concerning the possible perpetuation and duration of compounds. The opinions expressed in this work do not seem to be in conflict with the conclusions of the *Liber calculationum.*

De motu. This second short work (following in Cambridge MS Gonville and Caius 499/268 directly after the *De caelo* fragment) is not explicitly ascribed to Swineshead, but its similarity to the last short work of the manuscript, which is ascribed to Swineshead, is so great that there is every reason to ascribe it also to Swineshead. In the Seville manuscript Colombina 7-7-29 the works (the *De motu* and the following *De motu locali*) appear as one, but this seems hardly plausible since there is a great deal of overlap and repetition between them. It is more likely that they are successive drafts of the same work than that they are both sections of a single larger work.

The *De motu* contains an introduction concerning the material, formal, efficient, and final causes of motion, and two main sections, the first dealing with the measurement of motion with respect to cause and the second with the measurement of motion with respect to effect. Only local motion is considered. The subject matter of both sections is similar to that of treatise XIV of the *Liber calculationum*. Roughly speaking, both the *De motu* and the *De motu locali* seem to occupy an intermediate position between Heytesbury's *Regule* on local motion and the *Calculationes*, a natural supposition being that Swineshead began from Heytesbury's work and went on to develop his ideas from that point.

Concerning the consideration of motion with respect to cause, Swineshead begins by expounding Bradwardine's function relating powers, resistances, and velocities (212ra). This is followed by a number of rules, some of which are the same as, and others similar to, the conclusions of treatise XIV of the *Liber calculationum* (212ra–212va). Swineshead says, for instance, that if a constant power begins to move in the more remiss extreme of a uniformly difform resistance, it will remit its motion more and more slowly (212ra–vb). (Cf. rule 24 of treatise XIV of the *Liber calculationum.*)

In the second section, Swineshead begins with a number of statements concerning the measurement of motion with respect to effect—for instance, that uniform local motion is measured by the line described by the fastest moved point (212vb)—many of which have close analogues in Heytesbury's *Regule.* He states the mean speed rule (213ra) and the rule that in a motion uniformly accelerated from zero or decelerated to zero three times as much is traversed by the more intense half of the motion as by the more remiss half of the motion (213ra), which he derives as a consequence of the mean speed rule.

The second section concludes with five conclusions and a statement concerning the measurement of difform motion. The first three conclusions have to do with the traversal of extended resistances, one of these being the thirtieth rule of treatise XIV of the *Liber calculationum*: if one constant power remits its motion uniformly to zero in a given difform resistance, no other greater or lesser constant power will uniformly intend or remit its motion traversing the same medium (213ra). Concerning velocity in difform motion, Swineshead says that it is not to be measured by the maximum line that is described, but rather by the line that would be described if the velocity were continued for a period of time (213rb).

The *De motu*, then, consists mostly of a series of conclusions along with several stipulations as to how motion is to be measured with respect to cause and with respect to effect. Although the conclusions are so divided, there is little to distinguish them.

De motu locali. This short work receives its title from its explicit, and hence we retain the name despite the fact that this last fragment contains treatments of alteration as well as of local motion. The first two sections of this work correspond to the two main sections of the *De motu*, and many of the rules or conclusions stated are the same.

The work starts with a series of conclusions concerning the effect on velocity of increasing or decreasing the power or resistance in motion (213rb–vb). Many of these conclusions, including eight of the first nine, appear also in the *De motu*, and a similar number, although not always the same ones, appear also in the *Liber calculationum*, treatise XIV. Although these conclusions presuppose Bradwardine's function relating powers, resistances, and velocities, that function is not explicitly stated as it was in the *De motu*.

These rules are followed by a section concerning the measures of resistance, for instance that two resistances of which the most intense degrees are equal must be themselves equal (213vb); and that a motor equal to the maximum degree of a uniformly difform resistance will move in it eternally, never completely traversing it (214ra).

The second section of the *De motu locali* concerns the measures of motion with respect to effect, starting with the stipulation that the velocity of local motion is measured by the line that would be traversed by the fastest moved point (if there is one), provided that it continued its velocity uniformly for a period of time (214rb). Difformly difform motions, Swineshead says, always correspond to some degree within their range of varia-

tion *(ibid.)*, and uniformly difform motions correspond to their middle degrees (214rb–va). On this basis Swineshead mentions four types of sophisms that can arise from the comparison of accelerations to velocities of which some, he says, are possible, that is, not self-contradictory, and some impossible and to be rejected (214va–vb). A mobile can never begin from an infinite part of a magnitude and traverse some part uniformly (215ra), nor can a motion be remitted uniformly from an infinite degree of velocity *(ibid.)*.

If one wants to know how much is traversed by a uniformly difform motion starting and ending at a degree, all one can say in general is that more is traversed than by a mobile moving for the same time with half the maximum degree of the uniformly difform motion (214vb–215ra). All local motions are as fast as any of their parts, and all subjects moved locally are moved as fast as any of their parts, the former being true for all motions but the latter being true only for local motions and not for alterations (215ra).

The third and last section (215ra–215rb) of the *De motu locali* concerns measures of alteration. Like local motion the measure of alteration with respect to cause is the proportion of the power of the altering agent to the power of the altered patient. With respect to effect, the velocity of motion of alteration depends on the maximum latitude of quality that would be acquired by any part of the subject if the velocity were continued for some time period. Irrespective of the measure of velocity of alteration, a subject need not be altered as fast as any of its parts, but often is altered more slowly than a part of it closer to the agent. To determine how fast a subject is altered one has to consider the degree to which it corresponds, calculating the contribution of various degrees to the subject's denomination by the proportion of the subject through which they are extended.

Many sophisms can arise from the comparison of velocities of alteration to the velocities with which subjects are altered. Something may be altered with a faster velocity of alteration and yet be more slowly altered, and hence the two separate measures of alteration must be kept separate. On this basis, it is not contradictory for an agent to alter faster than anything is altered by it. If a uniformly difform alteration is extended throughout a subject, the subject will be altered as the middle degree of that alteration. With brief references to other ways of dealing with alteration the *De motu locali* ends.

Conclusion

As is evident from the discussions of its separate treatises, the *Liber calculationum* places what may seem to be an uncommon emphasis upon the generation of *conclusiones*, *regulae*, *objectiones*, and *sophismata*. This unceasing generation of results occurs in other works of the calculatory tradition, but it reaches a high with Richard Swineshead, so much so as to be nearly the defining characteristic of the *Liber calculationum*. Results are drawn to the very limits of manageability. Swineshead's *opuscula*, *De motu* and *De motu locali*, exhibit the beginnings of this effort to educe results. We, operating with modern mathematics, could generate many more such results, but the subclass that Swineshead himself generates and treats almost completely exhausts the results he could have dealt with, given the techniques at his disposal. And this excogitation of results occurs whether Swineshead is examining two or more *positiones* or *opiniones* relative to a given topic (when, as said above, only slight attention is paid to deciding definitively between *opiniones*) or only one. The major difference between these two cases appears to be that, in the former, Swineshead is more apt to label as *sophismata* the results he is generating. In any event, he makes it quite clear that *conclusiones* can be elicited, objected to, and resolved on both or all sides when a plurality of *opiniones* is at stake (*multe conclusiones possunt elici ex dictis, ad quarum tamen utramque partem probabiles possunt fieri rationes, que per predicta, si bene intelligantur, satis faciliter solvuntur* [34ra]).

Furthermore, there is almost no discussion in the *Liber calculationum* of the contexts in which one might expect the situations represented by these results to occur, nor, indeed, any time spent investigating whether they can occur. Instead, the work proceeds almost entirely *secundum imaginationem*, as Heytesbury's *Regule solvendi sophismata* had before it. In fact, among all other "Mertonian" works, the *Liber calculationum* is most like Heytesbury's *Regule*. Some of the earlier Oxford calculators, like Walter Burley and Roger Swineshead, had fairly frequently considered natural, as well as *de imaginatione*, situations. Richard Swineshead, by contrast, quite consistently imagines situations that will illustrate and draw results out of various theories rather than taking examples from natural occurrence. The emphasis is upon developing and having a set of techniques as complete as one can make it. If we may trust an infer-

ence from the later commentary of Gaetano of Thiene on Heytesbury's *Regule*, one of the reasons for this emphasis was simply the fact that every "calculator" ought to have a system applicable to every conceivable situation (. . . *dicit* [*sc.*, Heytesbury] *quod hoc est tamen impossibile . . . physice loquendo . . . Sed dicit ille magister bene scis hoc, sed quia non implicat contradictionem et est satis imaginabile, ideo calculatores non debent fugere casum* [Venice ed., 1494, 48va]).

The "techniques" that are presented in the *Liber calculationum* may strike the modern reader as basically mathematical. But one must consider such a judgment with care. To begin with, the evidence of the extant manuscripts of the *Liber calculationum* tells us that the medievals themselves did not regard it (or any of the other "calculatory" works, for that matter) as mathematical in the sense of Euclid, Boethius' *Arithmetica*, or Jordanus de Nemore. When the *Liber calculationum* does not take up an entire codex, it or fragments from it invariably appear with other treatises, questions, or notes on natural philosophy or logic. Nevertheless, there is no doubt that, the evidence of medieval codification aside, mathematical functions and considerations pervade Swineshead's major work. They are applied, however, not in order to understand how some phenomenon normally occurs (as was the case in medieval optics, statics, and astronomy), but in a thoroughly *secundum imaginationem* fashion that is totally different from the Greek-based mathematical tradition inherited by the Middle Ages. A good deal of material from the Greek tradition was, of course, utilized by Swineshead, but he utilized it in a most un-Greek way. Mathematical functions are applied in order to determine all conceivable contributions that parts could make to wholes, to distinguish the discontinuous from the continuous, and to encompass situations or results involving infinite intensities, infinite velocities, and other infinite values. It is for these kinds of problems that the *Liber calculationum* contained the required techniques. To the medieval scholar with the patience and ability needed to comprehend this work, the purpose seems to have been that he should learn to operate with the techniques and rules given by Swineshead — just as one was to learn techniques and rules in the tradition of solving sophisms to which the *Liber calculationum* from time to time refers — so expertly as to be able to handle situations and *casus* in every corner of the fourteenth century realm, be it physical, logical, medical, theological, or whatever.

Dissemination and Influence of the
Liber calculationum

Although the work of Swineshead's fellow Mertonians and the English "calculatory" tradition in general is generously represented in later fourteenth-century natural philosophy (very notably so, for example, in the work of Oresme), specific evidence of the *Liber calculationum* during this period is not especially plentiful, although shortly after mid-century the English logician Richard Ferebrich appears to employ parts of treatise XIV in his *Calculationes de motu*. Most of the extant manuscripts of Swineshead's major work are of the fifteenth century, and the records we have of its occurrence in library catalogues for the most part date from 1400 and later. It does appear, however, in at least two "student notebooks" of the later fourteenth century: in one merely in terms of fragmentary traces (MS Bibliothèque Nationale, fonds latin 16621), in the other more substantially (MS Worcester Cathedral, F. 35).

If we ask for evidence of the dissemination and influence not of Mertonian ideas in general or of some particular idea like the so-called Merton mean speed theorem, but rather of parts of the *Liber calculationum* itself, the fifteenth and sixteenth centuries are far richer. The first center of interest is Italy, in the middle and toward the end of the fifteenth century, where Swineshead appears as part of the broader preoccupation with English logic and natural philosophy. He appears, moreover, in terms both *pro* and *contra*. He suffers part of the humanist criticism of the "barbari Britanni" that one finds in the likes of Coluccio Salutati; for Leonardo Bruni he is one of those "quorum etiam nomina perhorresco"; and he even gave his name to the "sophisticas quisquilias et *suisetica* inania" complained about loudly by Ermolao Barbaro and others.

Yet it seems fair to claim that one of the major reasons for these humanist complaints was not Swineshead's works themselves, but rather the fact that they and other English "calculationes" had attracted the attention of a fair number of Italian scholars. Thus, his views are found among those of others treated in works *De reactione* written by Gaietano de Thienis, Giovanni Marliani, Angelus de Fossambruno, Vittore Trincavelli, and Pietro Pomponazzi. He also appears to have been very much in the center of the interest in "calculatory" matters in Padua, and especially Pavia, around the mid-fifteenth century, something that jibes extremely well with the number of times that the *Liber calculationum* was published in these cities. We also know that Nicolletto Vernia, earlier a student of both Paul of Pergola and Gaietano de Thienis, went to Pavia to study the *Calculationes Suisset*, information that fits very well indeed with other things we are able to put together about Vernia's interests. Pomponazzi relates that he engaged in a dispute with Francesco di Nardò armed with *argumentis calculatoriis*; but we have more direct evidence of his concern with Swineshead from the fact that he refers to the "Calculator" in his (unedited) *Questio de anima intellectiva* and from the fact that Vernia owned a copy of the *Liber calculationum* (now Biblioteca Vittorio Emanuele, MS 250).

When one turns to the Italian commentaries or questions on the *Liber calculationum*, the first thing to be noted is that most of this literature is preoccupied only with treatise I: *De intensione et remissione formarum*. It was this part of Swineshead that occupied Pomponazzi in his own treatise of the same title written in 1514, and we have similar sixteenth-century works by Tiberio Baccilieri, Cardinal Domenico Grimani, and Hieronymus Picus. Pomponazzi is critical of Swineshead insofar as the "scale of measure" he proposed in treatise I of the *Liber calculationum* maintains the inverse proportionality of intension and remission and ignores their proper ontological status. Intension and remission should be viewed, Pomponazzi felt, as, respectively, perfection and imperfection; this done, one would not, as Swineshead, "measure" remission by nearness to zero degree, but rather, as an imperfection, in terms of its distance from the maximum degree. Pomponazzi refers to a similar disagreement with Swineshead's "non gradum measure" in his *Super libello de substantia orbis*, where he specifically complains that it runs counter to the *via Aristotelis*. Pomponazzi's criticism can be partially explained by the fact that in his (unedited) lectures on Aristotle's *Physics* he felt that Swineshead and other English "calculators" put too much mathematics (*ille truffe spectant ad mathematicum*) and "geometricalia" into natural philosophy, and (as he complained in his *De intensione et remissione formarum*) constructed a *scientia* that was *media inter physicas et mathematicas*.

Italian *expositiones* or *questiones* on other parts of the *Liber calculationum* are rarer than those on treatise I. Bassanus Politus composed a *Tractatus proportionum* specifically claimed to be *introducto-*

rius ad calculationes Suisset; it sets forth in succinct fashion little more than the standard mathematics of proportion and proportionality drawn from such authors as Euclid and Boethius. More to the content of parts of the *Liber calculationum* is Marliani's *Probatio cuiusdam sentevtie calculatoris de motu locali*. Its concern is with the views of Swineshead on "mean degree measure" in treatise II and his proofs for the "mean speed theorem" in treatise XIV. The two most complete Italian commentaries on the *Liber calculationum* are unedited and unstudied. One is by Christopher de Recaneto, *doctor in artibus* at Padua in 1454, and covers but treatise I and part of treatise II. The other is more extensive, commenting on treatises I–V and VII–VIII, but we know almost nothing of its author, Philippus Aiuta. All we know is that Marliani wrote a *difficultates* sent to Philippus and (as we learn from the incipit of the present commentary) that he was a doctor in arts and medicine. The commentary itself, apparently a compilation of Philippus' view made in 1468 by one Magister Bernardinus Antonius de Spanochiis, relates Swineshead to any number of other mathematicians (especially Euclid) and philosophers, both contemporary, earlier medieval, and ancient. But perhaps its most intriguing aspect is the explicit tendency to render Swineshead more comprehensible by the addition of appropriate figures (*quasdam ymagines in marginibus*).

The second major center of interest in Swineshead was Paris at the beginning of the sixteenth century, where a considerable amount of work was done with the *Liber calculationum*, largely by a group of Spanish and Portuguese scholars. The earliest, and certainly most impressive, among them appears to be Alvaro Thomaz. His *Liber de triplici motu*, published in Paris in 1509, contains an extensive, two-part, preliminary treatise expounding all aspects of the mathematics of proportions, and itself treats all parts of the *Liber calculationum* that deal with *motus*. Alvaro also includes much material drawn from Nicole Oresme, not only explaining, but on occasions expanding what he finds in Swineshead and Oresme. One notable instance of such "expansion" is his treatment of the "infinite series" treated by both of these fourteenth-century authors. Following Alvaro by a few years, both John Dullaert of Ghent (in 1512) and Juan de Celaya (in 1517) include comprehensive expositions of "calculatory" material in their *Questiones* on Aristotle's *Physics*. Celaya treats a good number of *conclusiones* drawn from parts (treatises I, II, IV, VI, XIV, XV) of the *Liber cal-*

culationum and appears to have followed Thomaz in at least the structure of much of what he includes. Another Spanish member of this Paris school was Luis Coronel, who does not, like Celaya, include a lengthy connected exposition of Swineshead material in his *Physice perscrutationes* (published in 1511), but who nevertheless does discuss a fair number of issues and passages from scattered treatises (I, II, V, X, XI) of the *Liber calculationum*. At times he seems to lack a proper understanding of what he is discussing from Swineshead and even complains how *prolixissime et tediose* the reasoning is (in this instance referring to treatise XI). The same kind of complaint and lack of comprehension is probably in part behind the remarks of Diego de Astudillo in his *Questiones* on Aristotle's *Physics* when he excuses his omission of "calculatory disputations" since he would "confound the judgments of beginners . . . ignorant of mathematics." Indeed, if it is a proper appreciation of Swineshead's accomplishments that one has in mind, then none of the "commentators," Italian or Spanish, save Thomaz, qualifies.

Some Renaissance figures continued the fifteenth-century humanist criticism of English "subtilitates" and ridiculed (Luis Vives, for example) Swineshead's work, but others, such as Julius Scaliger and Cardano, praised him as outstandingly acute and ingenious. The most famous later "appreciation" of the Calculator was that of Leibniz. Perhaps initially learning of Swineshead through Scaliger (whom he mentioned in this regard), Leibniz confessed to a certain admiration of Swineshead even before he had had the opportunity to read him. How thoroughly Leibniz finally did read the *Liber calculationum* we do not know; but we do know that he went to the trouble to have the 1520 Venice edition of it transcribed (today Hannover, Niedersächssische Landesbibliothek, MS 615). In Leibniz' eyes, Swineshead's primary accomplishment lay in introducing mathematics into scholastic philosophy, although we should perhaps take "mathematics" to include a certain amount of logic, since at times he coupled Swineshead with Ramon Lull in having accomplished this task. In any event, what Swineshead had done was in his eyes much in harmony with Leibniz' own convictions about the relation of mathematics and "mathematical" logic to philosophy.

Because of the remarks of the likes of Cardano, Scaliger, and Leibniz, Swineshead found his way into eighteenth-century histories of philosophy such as that of Jacob Brucker. After that he was forgotten until Pierre Duhem rediscovered him at the beginning of the twentieth century in his rediscovery of medieval science as a whole.

BIBLIOGRAPHY

I. ORIGINAL WORKS. Manuscripts* of the *Liber calculationum* include Cambridge, Gonville and Caius 499/ 268, 165r–203v (14c.), tr. I–XI, XV, XII–XIII; *Erfurt, Stadtbibl., Amplon. 0.78, 1r–33r (14c.), contains an abbreviated version of tr. I–II, IV–VIII. Ascribed to one "clymiton" (presumably Killington?) by Schum in his catalogue of the Amplonian MSS, apparently drawing his information from Amplonius Ratinck's fifteenth-century catalogue; *Padua, Bibl. Univ. 924, 51r–70r (15c.), tr. I, VII, VIII, IX; *Paris, Bibl. Nat. lat. 6558, 1r–70v (dated 1375), tr. I–XI, XV, XII–XIII; *Paris, Bibl. Nat. lat. 16621 (14c.), *passim*, fragments (often in altered form); e.g., 52r–v, 212v from tr. XIV; *Pavia, Bibl. Univ., Aldini 314, 1r–83r (15c.), tr. I–XI, XV, XII–XIII, XVI, XIV; Perugia, Bibl. Comm. 1062, 1r–82r (15c.); *Rome, Bibl. Angelica 1963, 1r–106v (15c.), tr. I–IX, XI–XVI; *Rome, Bibl. Vitt. Emanuele 250, 1r–82r (15c.), contains all tr. except III in the following order: I, II, V, VI, XIV (incomplete), XV, XIV (complete), XVI, XII, XIII, VII, VIII, IX, IV, X, XI; belonged to Nicoletto Vernia; *Vatican, Vat. lat. 3064, 1r–120v (15c.), tr. I–X, XVI, XI, XV, XIV, XII–XIII, III (again); *Vatican, Vat. lat. 3095, 1r– 119v (15c.), tr. I–X, XVI, XI, XV, XII–XIV; Vatican, Chigi E. IV. 120, 1r–112v (15c.); Venice, Bibl. Naz. San Marco., lat. VI, 226, 1r–98v (15c.). tr. I–II, IV– XII, III (according to L. Thorndike); *Worcester, Cathedral F. 35, 3r, 27r–65v, 70r–75v (14c.), contains, in following order, fragment (Reg. 1–4) of XIV, I–IV, VI–VII, XII–XIII, XVI, V; Cesena, Bibl. Malatest., Plut. IX, sin cod VI.

Editions include Padua *ca.* 1477; Pavia 1498; Venice, 1520. A modern edition of treatise XI has been published in the article of Hoskin and Molland cited below.

The *Opuscula* are *In librum de caelo* (Cambridge, Gonville and Caius 499/268, 204r–211v [15c.]; Worcester, Cathedral F. 35, 65v–69v [14c.], incomplete); *De motu* (Cambridge, Gonville and Caius 499/268, 212r–213r [15c.]; Oxford, Bodl., Digby 154, 42r–44v [14c.]; and Seville, Bibl. Colomb. 7-7-29, 28v–30v [15c.]); and *De motu locali* (Cambridge, Gonville and Caius 499/268, 213r–215r [15c.]; Seville, Bibl. Colomb. 7-7-29, 30v–34r [15c.]).

The *De motibus naturalibus* of Roger Swineshead: Erfurt, Stadtbibl., Amplon. F. 135, 25r–47v (14c.); Paris, Bibl. nat., lat. 16621, 39r, 40v–51v, 54v–62r, 66r–84v (14c.), Fragment of part II, all of parts III– VIII; Venice, Bibl. Naz. San Marco lat. VI, 62, 111r (15c.), definitions of part IV. For MSS of the *De obliga-*

tionibus and *De insolubilibus* ascribed to Roger, see the article by Weisheipl on Roger cited below.

The *Questiones quatuor super physicas magistri Ricardi* (in MSS Vatican, Vat. lat. 2148, 71r–77v; Vat. lat 4429, 64r–70r; Venice, San Marco lat. VI, 72, 81r– 112r, 168r–169v) that have been tentatively ascribed to Swineshead by Anneliese Maier are in all probability not his, but rather most likely the work of Richard Killington (or Kilvington).

II. SECONDARY LITERATURE. The two basic biographical-bibliographical sources are A. B. Emden, *A Biographical Register of the University of Oxford to A.D. 1500* (Oxford, 1957–1959), 1836–1837, which includes material on Roger and John; and James A. Weisheipl, "Roger Swyneshed, O.S.B., Logician, Natural Philosopher, and Theologian," in *Oxford Studies Presented to Daniel Callus* (Oxford, 1964), 231–252. These both replace G. C. Brodrick, *Memorials of Merton College* (Oxford, 1885), 212–213. Emden has a long list of variant spellings of Swineshead such as Swyneshed, which he prefers, Suicet, Suincet, etc.

On Swineshead and the calculatory tradition in general, see Pierre Duhem, *Études sur Léonard de Vinci*, III, "Les précurseurs parisiens de Galilée" (Paris, 1913), 405–480; most of this material is reprinted with some additions, omissions, and changes in Duhem's *Le système du monde*, VII (Paris, 1956), 601–653. See also Marshall Clagett, *The Science of Mechanics in the Middle Ages* (Madison, Wis., 1959), chs. 4–7; Anneliese Maier, *Die Vorläufer Galileis im 14. Jahrhundert* (=*Studien zur Naturphilosophie der Spätscholastik*, I), 2nd ed. (Rome, 1966); *Zwei Grundprobleme der scholastischen Naturphilosophie* (=*Studien*, II), 3rd ed. (Rome, 1968); *An der Grenze von Scholastik und Naturwissenschaft* (=*Studien*, III), 2nd ed. (Rome, 1952); John Murdoch, "*Mathesis in philosophiam scholasticam introducta.* The Rise and Development of the Application of Mathematics in Fourteenth Century Philosophy and Theology," in *Arts libéraux et philosophie au moyen âge* (=Acts du quatrième Congrès International de Philosophie Médiévale), (Montreal–Paris, 1969), 215–254; A. G. Molland, "The Geometrical Background to the 'Merton School,'" in *British Journal for the History of Science*, 4 (1968), 108–125; Edith Sylla, *The Oxford Calculators and the Mathematics of Motion, 1320– 1350: Physics and Measurement by Latitudes* (unpublished diss., Harvard Univ., 1970); "Medieval Quantifications of Qualities: The 'Merton School,'" in *Archive for History of Exact Sciences*, 8 (1971), 9–39; "Medieval Concepts of the Latitude of Forms: The Oxford Calculators," in *Archives d'histoire doctrinale et littéraire du moyen âge*, 40 (1973), 223–283. More particularly on Swineshead see James A. Weisheipl, "Ockham and Some Mertonians," in *Mediaeval Studies*, 30 (1968), 207–213; Lynn Thorndike, *A History of Magic and Experimental Science*, 8 vols. (New York, 1923–1958), III, 370–385.

See the following on particular treatises of the *Liber calculationum* (although much information is also provided on the individual treatises in some of the more

*Many of the MSS do not contain all sixteen *tractatus* of the *Liber calculationum*; the incipits and explicits of each *tractatus* have been checked by the authors for those MSS indicated by an asterisk.

comprehensive literature above): tr. I: Marshall Clagett, "Richard Swineshead and Late Medieval Physics," in *Osiris*, **9** (1950), 131–161; tr. II: John Murdoch, "Philosophy and the Enterprise of Science in the Later Middle Ages," in *The Interaction Between Science and Philosophy*, Y. Elkana, ed. (Atlantic Highlands, N.J., 1974), 67–68; tr. VII: Clagett, *Giovanni Marliani and Late Medieval Physics* (New York, 1941), ch. 2; tr. X: Curtis Wilson, *William Heytesbury: Medieval Logic and the Rise of Mathematical Physics* (Madison, Wis., 1956), ch. 3; tr. XI: M. A. Hoskin and A. G. Molland, "Swineshead on Falling Bodies: An Example of Fourteenth-Century Physics," in *British Journal for the History of Science*, **3** (1966), 150–182; A. G. Molland, "Richard Swineshead on Continuously Varying Quantities," in *Actes du XIIe Congrès International d'Histoire des Sciences*, **4** (Paris, 1968), 127–130; John Murdoch, "Mathesis in philosophiam . . .," 230–231, 250–254; tr. XIV: John Murdoch, *op. cit.*, 228–230; Marshall Clagett, *The Science of Mechanics . . .*, 290–304, for Swineshead's proof of the so-called mean speed theorem.

For functions of *F*, *R*, and *V* similar to Roger Swineshead's, one may consult Ernest Moody, "Galileo and Avempace: The Dynamics of the Leaning Tower Experiment," in *Journal of the History of Ideas*, **12** (1951), 163–193, 375–422. For the "addition" theory of qualitative change mentioned in the discussion of treatise VII, see E. Sylla, "Medieval Concepts of the Latitude of Forms. . . ." This article also contains a more complete discussion of the ideas of Roger Swineshead.

The dissemination and influence of the Liber calculationum. To date, the most adequate treatment of the spread of late-medieval natural philosophy in general is Marshall Clagett's chapter on "English and French Physics, 1350–1600," in *The Science of Mechanics in the Middle Ages* (Madison, Wis. 1959). This chapter contains (630–631) a brief account of a segment of Richard Ferebrich's (Feribrigge) *Calculationes de motu*.

The Italian reception of Swineshead. On the humanist criticism of "Suissetica" and other, equally infamous, "English subtleties," the point of departure is Eugenio Garin, "La cultura fiorentina nella seconda metà del trecento e i 'barbari Britanni,'" as in his *L'età nuova. Ricerche di storia della cultura dal XII al XVI secolo* (Naples, 1969), 139–177; the relevant passages from Coluccio Salutati and Leonardo Bruni Aretino, as well as many other similar sources are cited therein. To this one might add the two anonymous letters of Ermolao Barbaro, edited by V. Branca; *Epistolae* (Florence, 1943), II, 22–23 (on which see the article by Dionisotti below). The various works *De reactione* treating Swineshead's opinion are Angelus de Fossambruno, MS Venice, Bibl. Naz. San Marco, VI, 160, ff. 248–252r; Gaietano de Thienis, *Tractatus perutilis de reactione*, Venice ed., 1491; Giovanni Marliani, *Tractatus de reactione* and *In defensionem tractatus de reactione*, both printed in his *Opera omnia*, II (Pavia, 1482) [on which see Clagett, *Giovanni Marliani and Late Medieval*

Physics, (New York, 1941), ch. 2]; Victorus Trincavellus, *Questio de reactione iuxta doctrinam Aristotelis et Averrois commentatoris*, printed at the end (69r–74r) of the 1520 Venice ed. of the *Liber calculationum*; Pietro Pomponazzi, *Tractatus acutissimi . . . de reactione* (Venice, 1525).

The case for Pavia as the fifteenth-century center of "calculatory," and especially Swineshead, studies is made by Carlo Dionisotti, "Ermolao Barbaro e la Fortuna di Suiseth," in *Medioevo e Rinascimento: Studi in onore di Bruno Nardi* (Florence, 1955), 219–253. Dionisotti briefly treats the evidence for Nicoletto Vernia's studies in Pavia on the Calculator, but see also Eugenio Garin, "Noterelle sulla filosofia del Rinascimento I: A proposito di N. Vernia," in *Rinascimento*, **2** (1951), 57–62. The reference from Vernia's *De anima intellectiva* (MS Venice, Bibl. Naz. San Marco, VI, 105, ff. 156r–160r) was furnished by Edward Mahoney, who is preparing an edition of the text. The relevant bibliography of the Italian commentaries on treatise I, *De intensione et remissione formarum*, of the *Liber calculationum* is Tiberio Baccilieri: Bruno Nardi, *Sigieri di Brabante nel pensiero del Rinascimento italiano* (Rome, 1945), 138–139; Pearl Kibre, "Cardinal Domenico Grimani, 'Questio de intensione et remissione qualitatis': A Commentary on the Tractate of that Title by Richard Suiseth (Calculator)," in *Didascaliae: Studies in Honor of Anselm M. Albareda*, Sesto Prete, ed. (New York, 1961), 149–203; Charles Schmitt, "Hieronymus Picus, Renaissance Platonism and the Calculator," to appear in Anneliese Maier Festschrift; Curtis Wilson, "Pomponazzi's Criticism of Calculator," in *Isis*, **44** (1952), 355–363. Other references to Pomponazzi on Swineshead can be found in Pietro Pomponazzi, *Corsi inediti dell'insegnamento padovano*, I: *Super Libello de substantia orbis, expositio et Quaestiones Quattuor* (1507); *Introduzione e testo a cura di Antonino Poppi* (Padua, 1966); and Bruno Nardi, *Saggi sull' Aristotelismo Padovano dal secolo XIV al XVI* (Florence, 1958).

The relevant sources or literature concerning other parts of the *Liber calculationum* are Bassanus Politus, *Tractatus proportionum introductorius ad calculationes Suiset* (Venice, 1505); Giovanni Marliani, *Probatio cuiusdam sententie calculatoris*, in his *Opera omnia*, II (Pavia, 1482), ff. 19r–25r (on which see Clagett, *Giovanni Marliani and Late Medieval Physics* [New York, 1941], ch. 5); Christopher de Recaneto, *Recolecte super calculationes*, MS Venice, Bibl. Naz. San Marco, Lat. VI, 149, ff. 31r–49v. On Recaneto, see Nardi, *Saggi sull'Aristotelismo Padovano dal secolo XIV al XVI* (Florence, 1958), 117–119, 121–122; Philippus Aiuta, "Pro declaratione Suiset calculatoris," MS Bibl. Vaticana, Chigi E. VI, 197, ff. 132r–149r. Finally, mention should be made of a totally unexamined sixteenth-century work on the same part of the *Liber calculationum* by Raggius of Florence, MS Rome, Bibl. Casan, 1431 (B.VI.7).

The Parisian-Spanish reception of Swineshead. The relevant primary sources are [Alvaro Thomaz], *Liber de triplici motu proportionibus annexis magistri Alvari Thome Ulixbonensis philosophicas Suiseth calculationes ex parte declarans* (Paris, 1509); John Dullaert of Ghent, *Questiones super octo libros phisicorum Aristotelis necnon super libros de celo et mundo* (Lyons, 1512); [Juan de Celaya], *Expositio magistri ioannis de Celaya Valentini in octo libros phisicorum Aristotelis: cum questionibus eiusdem secundum triplicem viam beati Thome, realium et nominalium* (Paris, 1517); Ludovicus Coronel, *Physice perscrutationes* (Paris, 1511); Diego de Astudillo, *Quaestiones super octo libros physicorum et super duos libros de generatione Aristotelis, una cum legitima textus expositione eorundem librorum* (Valladolid, 1532). Of the secondary literature on these – and other related – figures, the two basic articles are by William A. Wallace, "The Concept of Motion in the Sixteenth Century," in *Proceedings of the American Catholic Philosophical Association*, **41** (1967), 184–195; "The 'Calculatores' in Early Sixteenth-Century Physics," in *British Journal for the History of Science*, **4** (1969), 221–232. More detailed bio-bibliographical information on the school of Spanish scholars at Paris in the early sixteenth century can be found in H. Elie, "Quelques maîtres de l'université de Paris vers l'an 1500," in *Archives d'histoire doctrinale et littéraire du moyen âge*, **18** (1950–1951), 193–243; and R. Garcia Villoslada, *La universidad de Paris durante los estudios de Francisco de Vitoria, O.P., 1507–1522, Analecta Gregoriana*, XIV (Rome, 1938). On Alvaro Thomaz' treatment of the "infinite series" in Swineshead (and in Nicole Oresme) see Marshall Clagett, *Nicole Oresme and the Medieval Geometry of Qualities and Motions* (Madison, Wis., 1968), 496–499, 514–516; and H. Wieleitner, "Zur Geschichte der unendlichen Reihen im christlichen Mittelalter," in *Bibliotheca mathematica*, **14** (1913–1914), 150–168. Some biographical details on Alvaro can be found in J. Rey Pastor, *Los matemáticos españoles del siglo XVI* (Toledo, 1926), 82–89.

Later sixteenth- and seventeenth-century appreciation of Swineshead. Appropriate references to Cardano's *De subtilitate* and Julius Scaliger's *Exotericarum exercitationum* are given in Jacob Brucker's *Historia critica philosophiae*, III (Leipzig, 1766), 851. This work contains (849–853) numerous quotations from other authors referring (pro and con) to Swineshead as well as a brief example of the *Liber calculationum* itself. Leibniz' references to Swineshead are too numerous (we know of at least eight of them) to cite completely, but some of the most important of them can be found in L. Couturat's *Opuscules et fragments inédits de Leibniz* (Paris, 1903), 177, 199, 330, 340. Indication of the manuscript copy Leibniz had made of Swineshead can be found in Eduard Bodemann, *Die Handschriften der königlichen offentlichen Bibliothek zu Hannover* (Hannover, 1867), 104–105.

JOHN E. MURDOCH
EDITH DUDLEY SYLLA

SYDENHAM, THOMAS (*b.*, or at least baptized, Wynford Eagle, Dorset, England, 10 September 1624; *d.* London, England, 29 December 1689), *medicine.*

Sydenham was the son of William Sydenham, a Dorset squire, and Mary, daughter of Sir John Geffrey. During the civil war, four or possibly five sons served in the army of Parliament. Two of the sons and the mother lost their lives. After distinguished military service, William, the eldest son, became a close confidant of Cromwell and a prominent figure during the Commonwealth.

Sydenham, himself, saw some military service and eventually attained the rank of captain. It was said that he was left among the dead on the battlefield on one occasion and narrowly escaped death on another. His war service and the prominence of his family in Cromwell's cause gained him political preferences during the Commonwealth period. In what sense their support for Cromwell made Sydenham's family "Puritan" is difficult to say. The major Somerset branches of the family were, by and large, staunchly Anglican and Loyalist; but the Dorset Sydenhams, to whom Thomas belonged, were probably Presbyterian, and his brother William, latterly, Presbyterian-Independent. If a manuscript text entitled "Theologia rationalis" is correctly ascribed to Sydenham, it affords a more precise insight into his particular religious views but nothing on his attitude toward church polity.

The war disrupted Sydenham's earliest education at Oxford soon after his matriculation in Magdalen Hall in 1642. At the end of the first hostilities, he returned to the university, determined to become a physician. Some evidence suggests that he reentered Magdalen Hall and was made master of arts in 1648, possibly so that he could be created bachelor of medicine. In any event, his favor with the parliamentary visitors is clear from his appointment as one of their delegates to Wadham College in 1647 and from his election by them as a fellow of All Souls College in the following year, having been created bachelor of medicine by command of the chancellor of the university a few months before.

Sydenham remained in the academic arena for several years, resigning his fellowship at All Souls in 1655. During this time he may have seen further military service, since Thomas the cornet of the first civil war had become "Captain Sydenham" by 1654. It is known that he received £600 and the promise of employment in view of his financial and military contributions, that he was nominated but not elected to Parliament in 1659, and that on 14

July 1659 he was appointed "comptroller of the pipe."

Within a year or so of his marriage to Mary Gee in 1655, Sydenham began to practice medicine in Westminster, where he remained for the rest of his life. Evidence that he spent some time at Montpellier is no better than, if as good as, evidence that he never left England. It is highly improbable, therefore, that the works of Charles Barbyrac had any influence on him, as has been claimed.

After the Restoration, public political life was likely closed to Sydenham. In any event, he devoted the rest of his career single-mindedly to medicine. He obtained his license to practice from the Royal College of Physicians of London in June 1663. He was admitted member of Pembroke College, Cambridge, on 17 May 1676, and received an M.D. at that time.

In his last years, Sydenham was considerably disabled by gout and renal disease and died at his home in Pall Mall in 1689. He left three sons: William (also a physician), Henry, and James.

Sydenham's depreciation of bookish knowledge and university education for physicians has been linked with the belief that he was himself somewhat untutored and unlettered. But he had ample opportunity for a good education, and a close study of his writings suggests that he was competent in Latin and well versed in contemporary medical thought. Most likely his utilitarian, practical turn of mind owed much to his background, but it would be difficult to say what part was played by native temperament, by religious ethos, by political alignments, or simply by the rural life of a country squire's son. Undoubtedly, this attitude was sustained in later life by the exigencies of an active medical practice. It is much less likely that it can be attributed to a poor education or the diamond-in-the-rough qualities of a cavalry officer, although this image of him has been cultivated. The fragmentary evidence that has survived suggests that his military career during the 1640's and 1650's was a good deal less remarkable than that of his brothers, and his university studies considerably more so. His subsequent career as a noted author, and the associations that he maintained, suggest an intellectual bent, albeit ruggedly individualistic rather than bookishly academic.

Sydenham's associates included Robert Boyle and John Locke. To the former, Sydenham dedicated his first work of 1666, while the latter contributed a commendatory poem to Sydenham in his second edition of 1668. Sydenham's association with Locke was particularly close between 1667 and 1671, when Locke was composing the earliest known drafts of his own *Essay Concerning Human Understanding*. Locke, who eventually qualified himself medically, may have been Sydenham's collaborator, or more likely his student. Certainly Locke served him as an amanuensis, since a number of Sydenham's medical texts are in manuscripts in Locke's handwriting. This fact has raised the question of authorship of the important texts "Anatomia" (1668) and "De arte medica" (1669). Although in Locke's hand, and long thought to be from his head, these texts almost certainly bear the ideas of Sydenham. The two men corresponded through the rest of Sydenham's life, and Locke included him in his *Essay* along with Boyle, Newton, and Huygens as a "master-builder" in the new sciences.

Sydenham, Locke, and Boyle had much in common in their approach to acquiring knowledge of the natural world. They held similar views in epistemology and shared an admiration for Bacon. The question of who might have influenced whom has often been debated, since the results of their respective efforts in medicine, philosophy, and chemistry have been so far-reaching.

Sydenham's philosophy was that of a skeptical physician: skeptical because he thought that human understanding is limited to observing and reasoning about experience and the data of the sensible world; physician because his philosophy was almost exclusively applied to improving medical practice, which made results of treatment the supreme test of the only kind of truth worth having. He was also an optimist, who believed such results to be within human grasp, assured by a nature that is the orderly instrument of a benevolent God.

In his studies of acute diseases, Sydenham began by propounding a method for treating fevers, and he hoped that this method would improve the uncertain and often bad effects of treatment current in his day. The simplicity and naiveté of these early efforts (1666 and 1668) were quickly apparent to him as the Great Plague of London, followed by severe epidemics of smallpox and by puzzling variations in the concurrent continued fevers, demonstrated that the hoped-for reform of therapeutics necessitated closer attention to the differences among diseases confronting him. Therefore, along with notes for a treatise on smallpox, and for a work on medical epistemology, Sydenham kept a notebook (Vaillant Manuscript, Royal College of Physicians, London) of clinical observations from 1669 to 1674. The outcome of this was his *Observationes medicae circa morbor-*

um acutorum historiam et curationem (1676), his magnum opus.

In the preface to this work, Sydenham set forth his premises for more ambitious therapeutic reforms. These premises included his belief in the healing power of nature, nature's orderly production of diseases by species, the need for a more refined delineation of the seasonal and annual variants of these diseases, the unknowability of the insensible causes, the possibility of deriving treatment from the observable phenomena of a disease, and the desirability of making repeated trials of treatment before declaring them effective. In the body of the text, Sydenham exemplified this therapeutic program with respect to acute, epidemic diseases; he paid special attention to one particular factor causing variations in these diseases from epidemic to epidemic. This was the epidemic "constitution," a traditional concept that he had extensively revised.

Sydenham's effort to tie treatment deductively to the observable phenomena, and his concern for epidemic variations, gave an impetus to the more careful bedside observation of disease. Moreover, his insistence that diseases, like plants, have species, was suggestive to eighteenth-century nosographers like Linnaeus, Sauvages, and Cullen. But Sydenham's strong emphasis on the healing power of nature, and methodical treatment designed to modulate that nature, created in his work a systematizing tendency that cast doubt on the need for specific diagnoses. Consequently, almost a century later, he could also be appealed to by such a systematist and vigorous antinosologist as Benjamin Rush, "The Sydenham of America."

For almost two centuries after his death, however, it was particularly as a contributor to therapy that Sydenham acquired his reputation. It was his moderate treatment of smallpox, his use of cinchona, and his invention of liquid laudanum that came to symbolize his contributions to medicine. His renown came chiefly from the fact that he alleviated the suffering of the sick and made ill people well.

In the final decade of his life, Sydenham turned to apply his principles to the chronic diseases and produced a classic description of gout. By this time he had achieved eminence in the world of medical letters, both at home and in continental Europe, having become the "English Hippocrates." Ironically, the only eponymous use of his name that still remains common, "Sydenham's chorea," refers to two paragraphs interjected in one of his treatises, more or less as an aside.

BIBLIOGRAPHY

I. ORIGINAL WORKS. Of the many editions of Sydenham's published works, the best is the *Opera omnia*, William A. Greenhill, ed. (London, 1844; 2nd ed., 1846). It includes a bibliography of the Latin editions of all his writings into the nineteenth century. The standard English trans., *The Works of Thomas Sydenham, M.D.*, 2 vols. (London, 1848), translated from the Latin ed. of Greenhill, with a biography of Sydenham by R. G. Latham, is not always reliable and should be compared with the Latin text, with the nearly contemporary trans. by John Pechey (London, 1696), and with that by John Swan (London, 1742).

A number of Sydenham's MSS and documents relating to his life have been published. The largest collection of these is in Kenneth Dewhurst, *Dr. Thomas Sydenham (1624–1689): His Life and Original Writings* (London, 1966); this includes the controversial "De arte medica" and the "Anatomia," in addition to "Theologia rationalis" and a number of medical fragments. More complete versions of these last works, with other material, are in the unpublished "Medical Observations by Thomas Sydenham," (the so-called Vaillant Manuscript), of various dates, in the library of the Royal College of Physicians, London. This MS is partially in Sydenham's hand, and partially in Locke's. Other literary remains of Sydenham, published and unpublished, are discussed by Dewhurst. See also the appendix to Bates, cited below.

II. SECONDARY LITERATURE. The best known biographies of Sydenham are Joseph F. Payne (London, 1900) and Dewhurst. Payne's biography is not documented, but his article on Sydenham in the *Dictionary of National Biography*, LV (1898), gives extensive references. Payne and Dewhurst differ in a number of details of Sydenham's life, and sometimes both tend to be more assertive than their evidence warrants. L. M. F. Picard, *Thomas Sydenham: Sa vie et ses oeuvres. Thèse pour le doctorat en médecine* (Dijon, 1889), has many details not found in Payne or Dewhurst, and is well documented.

The development and elucidation of Sydenham's concepts of epidemic constitutions, disease species, and methodical treatment can be found in D. G. Bates, "Thomas Sydenham: The Development of His Thought, 1666–1676" (unpublished doctoral diss., The Johns Hopkins University, 1975). A selected bibliography of the secondary literature and an extensive analysis of the Sydenham MSS will also be found there. A full account of the contemporary context for these ideas and Sydenham's influence on eighteenth- and nineteenth-century clinical medicine is still needed.

DONALD G. BATES

SYLOW, PETER LUDVIG MEJDELL (*b.* Christiania [now Oslo], Norway, 12 December 1832; *d.* Christiania, 7 September 1918), *mathematics.*

Sylow was the son of a cavalry captain, Thomas Edvard Sylow, who later became a minister of the government. After graduation from the Christiania Cathedral School in 1850, he studied at the university, where in 1853 he won a mathematics prize contest. He took the high school teacher examination in 1856, and from 1858 to 1898 he taught in the town of Frederikshald (now Halden). Sylow was awarded a scholarship to travel abroad in 1861, and he visited Berlin and Paris. In 1862–1863 he substituted for Ole-Jacob Broch at Christiania University; but until 1898 his only chance for a university chair came in 1869, and he was not appointed. Finally, through Sophus Lie, a special chair was created for him at Christiania University in 1898.

From 1873 to 1881 Sylow and Sophus Lie prepared a new edition of the works of N. H. Abel, and for the first four years Sylow was on leave from his school in order to devote himself to the project. In 1902, with Elling Holst, he published Abel's correspondence. He also published a few papers on elliptic functions, particularly on complex multiplication, and on group theory.

Sylow's name is best-known in connection with certain theorems in group theory and certain subgroups of a given group. In 1845 Cauchy had proved that any finite group G has subgroups of any prime order dividing the order of G. In 1872 Sylow published a 10-page paper containing the first extension of Cauchy's result and perhaps the first profound discovery in abstract group theory after Cauchy. Sylow's main theorem read as follows: First, if p^m is the maximal power of p dividing the order of G, then G has subgroups of order p^i for all i with $0 \leq i \leq m$, and in particular subgroups H of order p^m (called p-Sylow groups); and the index j of the normalizer of H is congruent 1 mod p. Second, the p-Sylow groups of G are conjugate with each other. Sylow's theorems were, and still are, a source of discoveries in group theory and are fundamental to most structural research in finite groups.

BIBLIOGRAPHY

I. ORIGINAL WORKS. Sylow's works are listed in H. B. Kragemo, "Bibliographie der Schriften Ludvig Sylows," in *Norsk matematisk forenings skrifter*, 2nd ser., no. 3 (1933), 25–29. They include "Théorèmes sur les groupes de substitutions," in *Mathematische Annalen*, **5** (1872), 584–594; and "Sur la multiplication complexe des fonctions elliptiques," in *Journal de mathématiques pures et appliquées*, 4th ser., **3** (1887), 109–254.

Sylow's MSS are in the Oslo University Library, U.B. MS, fols. 730–808, and U.B. Brevsamling 7–8.

II. SECONDARY LITERATURE. See T. Skolem, "Ludvig Sylow und seine wissenschaftlichen Arbeiten," in *Norsk matematisk forenings skrifter*, 2nd ser., no. 2 (1933), 14–24; and C. Størmer, "Gedächtnisrede auf Professor Dr. P. L. M. Sylow," *ibid.*, no. 1 (1933), 7–13.

HANS FREUDENTHAL

SYLVESTER, JAMES JOSEPH (*b.* London, England, 3 September 1814; *d.* London, 15 March 1897), *mathematics*.

Although Sylvester is perhaps most widely remembered for his indefatigable work in the theory of invariants, especially that done in conjunction with Arthur Cayley, he wrote extensively on many other topics in the theory of algebraic forms. He left important theorems in connection with Sturm's functions, canonical forms, and determinants; he especially advanced the theory of equations and the theory of partitions.

James Joseph (Joseph then being his surname) was born into a Jewish family originally from Liverpool. The son of Abraham Joseph, who died while the boy was young, James was the sixth and youngest son of nine children, at least four of whom later assumed the name Sylvester for a reason not now apparent.

Until Sylvester was fifteen, he was educated in London, at first in schools for Jewish boys at Highgate and at Islington, and then for five months at the University of London (later University College), where he met Augustus De Morgan. In 1828 he was expelled "for taking a table knife from the refectory with the intention of sticking it into a fellow student who had incurred his displeasure."[1] In 1829 Sylvester went to the school of the Royal Institution, in Liverpool, where he took the first prize in mathematics by an immense margin and won a prize of $500, offered by the Contractors of Lotteries in the United States, for solving a problem in arrangements. At this school he was persecuted for his faith to a point where he ran away to Dublin. There, in the street, he encountered R. Keatinge, a judge and his mother's cousin, who arranged for his return to school.

Sylvester now read mathematics for a short time with Richard Wilson, at one time a fellow of St. John's College, Cambridge, and in October 1831 he himself entered that college, where he stayed until the end of 1833, when he suffered a serious illness that kept him at home until January 1836. After further bouts of illness, Sylvester took the tripos examination in January 1837, placing second. Since he was not prepared to subscribe to the Thirty-Nine Articles of the Church of England, he was not allowed to take the degree or compete for Smith's mathematical prizes—still less secure a fellowship. He went, therefore, to Trinity College, Dublin, where he took the B.A. and M.A. in 1841. (He finally took the equivalent Cambridge degrees in 1872–1873, the enabling legislation having been passed in 1871.)

In 1838 Sylvester went to what is now University College, London, as De Morgan's colleague. He seems to have found the chair in Natural Philosophy uncongenial. In 1839, at the age of twenty-five, he was elected a fellow of the Royal Society on the strength of his earliest papers, written for *Philosophical Magazine* as soon as he had taken his tripos examination. The first four of these concern the analytical development of Fresnel's theory of the optical properties of crystals, and the motion of fluids and rigid bodies. His attention soon turned to more purely mathematical topics, especially the expression of Sturm's functions in terms of the roots of the equation.

From University College, Sylvester moved in 1841 to a post at the University of Virginia. There are many lurid and conflicting reports of the reasons for his having returned to England in the middle of 1843. He apparently differed from his colleagues as to the way an insubordinate student should be treated. He now left the academic world for a time, and in 1844 was appointed Actuary and Secretary to the Equity and Law Life Assurance Company. He apparently gave private tuition in mathematics, for he had Florence Nightingale as a pupil. In 1846, the same year that Cayley entered Lincoln's Inn, Sylvester entered Inner Temple and was finally called to the bar in November 1850. Cayley and Sylvester soon struck up a friendship. At his Oxford inaugural lecture many years later (1885), Sylvester spoke of Cayley, "who though younger than myself, is my spiritual progenitor— who first opened my eyes and purged them of dross so that they could see and accept the higher mysteries of our common mathematical faith." Both men referred on occasion to theorems they had derived separately through the stimulus of their conversations in the intervals between legal business.

In 1854 Sylvester was an unsuccessful candidate both for the chair of mathematics at the Royal Military Academy, Woolwich, and for the professorship in geometry at Gresham College, London. The successful candidate for the former position

soon died, and with the help of Lord Brougham, Sylvester was appointed. He held this post from September 1855 to July 1870. At the same time he became editor, from its first issue in 1855, of the *Quarterly Journal of Pure and Applied Mathematics*, successor to the *Cambridge and Dublin Mathematical Journal*. Assisted as he was by Stokes, Cayley, and Hermite, there was no change in editorship until 1877.

In 1863 Sylvester replaced the geometer Steiner as mathematics correspondent to the French Academy of Sciences. Two years later he delivered a paper on Newton's rule (concerning the number of imaginary roots of an algebraic equation) at King's College, London. A syllabus to the lecture was the first mathematical paper published by De Morgan's newly founded London Mathematical Society, of which Sylvester was president from 1866 to 1868. In 1869 he presided over the Mathematical and Physical Section of the British Association meeting at Exeter. His address was prompted by T. H. Huxley's charge that mathematics was an almost wholly deductive science, knowing nothing of experiment or causation. This led to a controversy carried on in the pages of *Nature*, relating to Kant's doctrine of space and time; Sylvester, however, was not at his best in this kind of discussion. He reprinted an expanded version of his presidential address, together with the correspondence from *Nature*, as an appendix to *The Laws of Verse* (1870). The thoughts of Matthew Arnold, to whom the book was dedicated, are not known. Sylvester had some slight renown throughout his life, especially among his close friends, for his dirigible flights of poetic fancy; and his book was meant to illustrate the quasi-mathematical "principles of phonetic syzygy." Five original verses introduce a long paper on syzygetic relations, and he used his own verse on several other mathematical occasions.

Sylvester translated verse from several languages. For example, under the nom de plume "Syzygeticus," he translated from the German "The Ballad of Sir John de Courcy";[2] and his *Laws of Verse* includes other examples of his work, which is no worse than that of many a nonmathematician. It could be argued, however, that it was worse in a different way. One of his poems had four hundred lines all rhyming with "Rosalind," while another had two hundred rhyming with "Winn." These were products of his later residence in Baltimore. Sylvester had perhaps a better appreciation of music, and took singing lessons from Gounod.

In 1870 Sylvester resigned his post at Woolwich, and after a bitter struggle that involved correspondence in the *Times*, and even a leading article there (17 August 1871), he secured a not unreasonable pension. It was not until 1876, when he was sixty-one, that he again filled any comparable post. When he did so, it was in response to a letter from the American physicist Joseph Henry. The Johns Hopkins University opened in that year, and Sylvester agreed to accept a chair in mathematics in return for his traveling expenses and an annual stipend of $5,000 "paid in gold." "His first pupil, his first class" was G. B. Halsted. A colleague was C. S. Peirce, with whom, indeed, Sylvester became embroiled in controversy on a small point of priority. Peirce nevertheless later said of him that he was "perhaps the mind most exuberant in ideas of pure mathematics of any since Gauss." While at Baltimore, Sylvester founded the *American Journal of Mathematics*, to which he contributed thirty papers. His first was a long and uncharacteristic account of the application of the atomic theory to the graphical representation of the concomitants of binary forms (quadratics). He resigned his position at Johns Hopkins in December 1883, when he was appointed to succeed H. J. S. Smith as Savilian professor of geometry at Oxford.

Sylvester was seventy when he delivered his inaugural "On the Method of Reciprocants" (1 December 1885). By virtue of his chair he became a fellow of New College, where he lived as long as he was in Oxford. He collaborated with James Hammond on the theory of reciprocants (functions of differential coefficients the forms of which are invariant under certain linear transformations of the variables) and also contributed several original papers to mathematical journals before his sight and general health began to fail. In 1892 he was allowed to appoint a deputy, William Esson; and in 1894 he retired, living mainly at London and Tunbridge Wells. For a short period in 1896 and 1897 he wrote more on mathematics (for example, on compound partitions and the Goldbach-Euler conjecture). A little more than a fortnight after a paralytic stroke, he died on 15 March 1897 and is buried in the Jewish cemetery at Ball's Pond, Dalston, London.

Sylvester received many honors in his lifetime, including the Royal Medal (1861) and the Copley Medal (1880). It is of interest that in the receipt of such awards he followed rather than preceded Cayley, who was his junior. Sylvester received honorary degrees from Dublin (1865), Edinburgh (1871), Oxford (1880), and Cambridge (1890).

Sylvester never married. He had been anxious to marry a Miss Marston, whom he met in New York in 1842, on his first visit to America. (She was the godmother of William Matthew Flinders Petrie, from whom the story comes.) It seems that although she had formed a strong attachment for him, she refused him on the ground of religious difference, and neither of them subsequently married.

Sylvester's greatest achievements were in algebra. With Cayley he helped to develop the theory of determinants and their application to nonalgebraic subjects. He was instrumental in helping to turn the attention of algebraists from such studies as the theory of equations—in which he nevertheless did important work—to the theory of forms, invariants, and linear associative algebras generally. His part in this movement is often obscured by his flamboyant style. In 1888 P. G. Tait, in a rather strained correspondence with Cayley over the relations between Tait's solution of a quaternionic equation and Sylvester's solution of a linear matrix equation, wrote with some justice: "I found Sylvester's papers hard to assimilate. A considerable part of each paper seems to be devoted to correction of hasty generalizations in the preceding one!"[3]

A number of Sylvester's early writings concern the reality of the roots of numerical equations, Newton's rule for the number of imaginary roots, and Sturm's theorem. His first published researches into these matters date from 1839, and were followed by a steady stream of special results. In due course he found simple expressions for the Sturmian functions (with the square factors removed) in terms of the roots:

$$f_2(x) = \Sigma (a-b)^2 (x-c) (x-d) \cdots$$
$$f_3(x) = \Sigma (a-b)^2 (a-c)^2 (b-c)^2 (x-d) \cdots.$$

Applying Sturm's process of the greatest algebraic common measure to two independent functions $f(x)$ and $\varphi(x)$, rather than to $f(x)$ and $f'(x)$, he found for the resulting functions expressions involving products of differences between the roots of the equations $f(x) = 0$, $\varphi(x) = 0$. Assuming that the real roots of the two equations are arranged in order of magnitude, the functions are of such a character that the roots of the one equation are intercalated among those of the other.

In connection with Newton's rule, the method of Sturm's proof was applied to a quite different problem. Sylvester supposed x to vary continuously, and investigated the increase and decrease in the changes of sign.[4]

Newton's first statement of his incomplete rule for enumerating imaginary roots dates from 1665–1666.[5] Although valid, the rule was not justified before Sylvester's proofs of the complete rule.

Another problem of great importance investigated in two long memoirs of 1853 and 1864 concerns the nature of the roots of a quintic equation. Sylvester took the functions of the coefficients that serve to decide the reality of the roots, and treated them as the coordinates of a point in n-dimensional space. A point is or is not "facultative" according to whether there corresponds, or fails to correspond, an equation with real coefficients. The character of the roots depends on the bounding surface or surfaces of the facultative regions, and on a single surface depending on the discriminant.[6]

Sylvester showed an early interest in the theory of numbers when he published a beautiful theorem on a product formed from numbers less than and prime to a given number.[7] This he described as "a pendant to the elegant discovery announced by the ever-to-be-lamented and commemorated Horner, with his dying voice"; but unfortunately it was later pointed out to him by Ivory that Gauss had given the theorem in his *Disquisitiones arithmeticae* (1801).[8] It is impossible to do justice in a short space to Sylvester's numerous later contributions to the theory of numbers, especially in the partition of numbers. Sylvester applied Cauchy's theory of residues and originated the concept of a denumerant. He also added several results to Euler's treatment of the "problem of the virgins" (the problem of enumerating positive and integral solutions of indeterminate simultaneous linear equations); but his most novel contributions to the subject are to be found in his use of a graphical method. He represented partitions of numbers by nodes placed in order at the points of a rectangular lattice ("graph"). Thus a partition of 9 (5 + 3 + 1) may be represented by the points of the rows in the lattice. The conjugate partition (3 + 2 + 2 + 1 + 1) is then found by considering the lattice of columns, a fact possibly first appreciated by N. M. Ferrers.[9] This

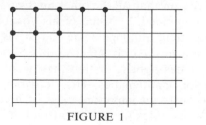

FIGURE 1

representation greatly simplified and showed the way to proofs of many new results in the theory of partitions not only by Sylvester but also by early contributors to his *American Journal of Mathematics*, such as Fabean Franklin.

One of Sylvester's early contributions to the *Journal*, "On Certain Ternary Cubic-Form Equations,"[10] is notable for the geometrical theory of residuation on a cubic curve and the chain rule of rational derivation: From an arbitrary point 1 on the curve it is possible to derive the singly infinite series of points $(1,2,4,5,\cdots 3p \pm 1)$ such that the chord through any two points, m and n, meets the curve again in a point ($m + n$ or $|m - n|$, whichever number is not divisible by 3) of the series. The coordinates of any point m are rational and integral functions of degree m^2 of those of point 1.

Like his friend Cayley, Sylvester was above all an algebraist. As G. Salmon said, the two discussed the algebra of forms for so long that each would often find it hard to say what properly belonged to the other. Sylvester, however, produced the first general theory of contravariants of forms.[11] He was probably the first to recognize that for orthogonal transformations, covariants and contravariants coincide. Moreover, he proved a theorem first given without proof by Cayley, and the truth of which Cayley had begun to doubt. It concerns a certain expression for a number ("Cayley's number") that cannot exceed the number of linearly independent semi-invariants (or invariants) of a certain weight, degree, and extent. Sylvester showed that Cayley's expression for the number of linearly independent ("asyzygetic") semi-invariants of a given type is in fact exact.[12] The result is proved as part of Sylvester's and Cayley's theory of annihilators, which was closely linked to that of generating functions for the tabulation of the partitions of numbers.

Under the influence of Lie's analysis, algebraic invariance was gradually subordinated to a more general theory of invariance under transformation groups. Although Boole had used linear differential operators to generate invariants and covariants, Cayley, Sylvester, and Aronhold were the first to do so systematically. In the calculation of invariants, it may be proved that any invariant I of the binary form (quantic)

$$f = a_0 x^p + p a_1 x^{p-1} y + \cdots + a_p y^p$$

should satisfy the two differential equations

$$\Omega I = 0,$$
$$O I = 0,$$

where Ω and O are linear differential operators:

$$\Omega \equiv a_0 \frac{\partial}{\partial a_1} + 2a_1 \frac{\partial}{\partial a_2} + \cdots + pa_{p-1} \frac{\partial}{\partial a_p},$$

$$O \equiv pa_1 \frac{\partial}{\partial a_0} + (p-1)a_2 \frac{\partial}{\partial a_1} + \cdots + a_p \frac{\partial}{\partial a_{p-1}}.$$

Sylvester called these functions annihilators, built up a rich theory around them, and generalized the method to other forms.[13] With Franklin he exhibited generating functions for all semi-invariants, of any degree, for the forms they studied.[14] Related to these studies is Sylvester's expression, in terms of a linear differential equation, of the condition that a function be an orthogonal covariant or invariant of a binary quantic. Thus the necessary and sufficient condition that F be a covariant for direct orthogonal transformations is that F have as its annihilator

$$y \frac{\partial}{\partial x} - x \frac{\partial}{\partial y} + O - \Omega.$$

Sylvester played an important part in the creation of the theory of canonical forms. What may be his most widely known theorem states that a general binary form of odd order $(2n-1)$ is a sum of n $(2n-1)$-th powers of linear forms. (Thus, for example, a quintic may be reduced to a sum of three fifth powers of linear forms.) Sylvester wrote at length on the canonical reduction of the general $2n$-ic. He showed that even with the ternary quartic, which has fifteen coefficients, the problem was far less simple than it appeared, and that such cannot be simply reduced to a sum of five fourth powers (again with fifteen coefficients). It is here that he introduced the determinant known as the catalecticant, which he showed must vanish if the general $2n$-ic is to be expressed as the sum of n perfect $2n$th powers of linear forms, together with (in general) a term involving the square of the product of these forms.[15]

Early in his study of the effects of linear transformations on real quadratic forms, Sylvester discovered (and named) the law of inertia of quadratic forms.[16] The law was discovered independently by Jacobi.[17] The theorem is that a real quadratic form of rank r may be reduced by means of a real nonsingular linear transformation to the form

$$y_1^2 + \cdots + y_p^2 - y_{p+1}^2 - \cdots - y_r^2,$$

where the index p is uniquely determined. (It follows that two real quadratic forms are equivalent under real and nonsingular transformation if and only if they have the same rank and the same index.)

Another memorable result in the theory of linear transformations and matrices is Sylvester's law of nullity, according to which if r_1 and r_2 are the ranks of two matrices, and if R is the rank of their product,

$$R \leqslant r_1,$$
$$R \leqslant r_2,$$
$$R \geqslant r_1 + r_2 - n,$$

where n is the order of the matrices. For Sylvester the "nullity" of a matrix was the difference between its order and rank, wherefore he wrote his law thus: "The nullity of the product of *two* (and therefore of any number of) matrices cannot be less than the nullity of any factor, nor greater than the sum of the nullities of the *several* factors which make up the product."[18]

Sylvester devised a method (the "dialytic method") for the elimination of one unknown between two equations

$$f(x) \equiv a_0 x^n + a_1 x^{n-1} + \cdots + a_n = 0 \, (a_0 \neq 0),$$
$$\varphi(x) \equiv b_0 x^m + b_1 x^{m-1} + \cdots + b_m = 0 \, (b_0 \neq 0).$$

The method is simpler than Euler's well-known method. Sylvester formed n equations from $f(x)$ by separate and successive multiplication by x^{n-1}, $x^{n-2}, \cdots 1$, and m equations from $\varphi(x)$ by successive multiplication by x^{m-1}, $x^{m-2}, \cdots 1$. From the resulting $m+n$ equations he eliminated the $m+n$ power of x, treating each power as an independent variable. The vanishing of the resulting determinant (E) is a necessary condition for f and φ to have a common root, but the method is deficient to the extent that the condition $E = 0$ is not proved sufficient. This type of approach was superseded in Sylvester's lifetime when Kronecker developed a theory of elimination for systems of polynomials in any number of variables, but elementary texts still quote Sylvester's method alongside Euler's and Bezout's.

Sylvester was inordinately proud of his mathematical vocabulary. He once laid claim to the appellation "Mathematical Adam," asserting that he believed he had "given more names (passed into general circulation) to the creatures of the mathematical reason than all the other mathematicians of the age combined."[19] Much of his vocabulary has been forgotten, although some has survived; but it would be a mistake to suppose that Sylvester bestowed names lightly, or that they were a veneer for inferior mathematics. His "combinants," for example, were an important class of invariants of several q-ary p-ics (q and p constant).[20] His "plagiograph" was less obscure under the title "skew pantograph"; but under either name it was an instrument based on an interesting and unexpected geometrical principle that he was the first to perceive.[21] And in like manner one might run through his works, with their "allotrious" factors, their "zetaic" multiplication, and a luxuriant terminology between.

Sylvester thought his verse to be as important as his mathematics; but he was a poor judge, and the two had little in common beyond an exuberant vocabulary. His mathematics spanned, of course, a far greater range than it is possible to review here. One characteristic of this range is that it was covered without much recourse to the writings of contemporaries. As H. F. Baker has pointed out, in projective geometry Sylvester seems to have been ignorant of Poncelet's circular points at infinity, and not to have been attracted by Staudt's methods of dispensing with the ordinary notion of length. Sylvester's papers simply ignore most problems in the foundations of geometry. Remarkable as some of his writings in the theory of numbers, elliptic integrals, and theta functions are, he would have benefited from a closer reading of Gauss, Kummer, Cauchy, Abel, Riemann, and Weierstrass. Neither Lie's work on the theory of continuous groups nor the algebraic solution of the fifth-degree equation elicited any attention from him, and it is perhaps surprising that Cayley did not persuade him of their value. An illustration of Sylvester's self-reliance is found at the end of one of the last lengthy papers he composed, "On Buffon's Problem of the Needle," a new approach to this well-known problem in probabilities.[22] The paper was the outcome of conversations with Morgan Crofton, when Sylvester was his senior at Woolwich in the 1860's; yet an extension of Barbier's theorem, now proved by Sylvester, had been published in 1868 by Crofton himself. Sylvester's strength lay in the fact that he could acknowledge this sort of inadvertent duplication without significantly diminishing the enormous mathematical capital he had amassed.

NOTES

1. H. H. Bellot, *University College, London, 1826–1926* (London, 1929), 38.
2. *Gentleman's Magazine*, n.s., **6** (Feb. 1871), 38–48.
3. C. G. Knott, *The Life and Scientific Work of Peter Guthrie Tait* (Cambridge, 1911), 159.
4. For this and the preceding doctrines, see especially "On a Theory of the Syzygetic Functions . . ." (1853), repr. in his *Collected Mathematical Papers* (henceforth abbreviated as *CMP*), I, no. 57, 429–586; and "Algebraical Researches, Containing a Disquisition on Newton's Rule

. . .," *ibid.*, II, no. 74 (1864), 376–479. On Newton's rule also see *ibid.*, II, no. 81 (1865), 493–494; no. 84 (1865–1866), 498–513; no. 108 (1871), 704–708; and III, no. 42 (1880), 414–425.
5. See D. T. Whiteside, ed., *The Mathematical Papers of Isaac Newton*, I (Cambridge, 1967), 524.
6. See in particular *CMP*, I, no. 57 (1853), 436.
7. *Ibid.*, no. 5 (1838), 39.
8. *Disquisitiones arithmeticae* (1801), 76.
9. *CMP*, I, no. 59 (1853), 597.
10. *Ibid.*, III, no. 39 (1879–1880), 312–391.
11. *Ibid.*, I, no. 33 (1851), 198–202.
12. *Ibid.*, IV, no. 44 (1886), 515–519; see also no. 42 (1886), 458.
13. See, for example, *ibid.*, III, no. 18 (1878), 117–126; no. 27 (1878), 318–340; IV, no. 41 (1886), 278–302, esp. 288; no. 42 (1886), 305–513, esp. 451.
14. See especially *ibid.*, III, no. 67 (1882), 568–622.
15. See the important memoir in *ibid.*, I, no. 42 (1852), 284–327, with its amusing note to 293: "Meicatalecticizant would more completely express the meaning of that which, for the sake of brevity, I denote catalecticant."
16. *Ibid.*, no. 47 (1852), 378–381; no. 57 (1853), 511; IV, no. 49 (1887), 532.
17. *Journal für Mathematik*, **53** (1857), 275–281.
18. *CMP*, IV, no. 15 (1884), 134.
19. *Ibid.*, no. 53 (1888), 588.
20. For some further details, see P. Gordan, *Vorlesungen über Invariantentheorie*, II (Leipzig, 1887), 70–78.
21. *CMP*, III, no. 3 (1875), 26–34.
22. *Ibid.*, IV, no. 69 (1890–1891), 663–679.

BIBLIOGRAPHY

I. ORIGINAL WORKS. Sylvester published no lengthy volume of mathematics, although his books on versification and its mathematical principles are numerous, and include *The Law of Continuity as Applied to Versification . . . Illustrated by an English Rendering of "Tyrrhena regnum," Hor. 3, 29* . . . (London, 1869); *The Laws of Verse, or Principles of Versification Exemplified in Metrical Translations* (London, 1870); *Fliegende Blätter (Rosalind and Other Poems), a Supplement to the Laws of Verse* (London, 1876); *Spring's Debut. A Town Idyll in Two Centuries of Continuous Rhyme* (Baltimore, 1880); *Retrospect. A Verse Composition by the Savilian Professor of Geometry . . . Tr. Into Latin by Undergraduates of New College* (Oxford, 1884); and *Corolla versuum Cantatrici eximiae . . . a professore Saviliano geometriae apud oxonienses* (Oxford, 1895).

Sylvester's mathematical papers are in *The Collected Mathematical Papers of James Joseph Sylvester*, H. F. Baker, ed., 4 vols. (Cambridge, 1904–1912). Thirty of his 87 known letters from American sources are in R. C. Archibald, "Unpublished Letters of James Joseph Sylvester and Other New Information Concerning His Life and Work," in *Osiris*, **1** (1936), 85–154. Archibald gives full bibliographical information on most of the verse writings. Sylvester wrote a sonnet to the Savilian professor of astronomy, Charles Pritchard, on the occasion of his receiving the gold medal of the Royal Astronomical Society, in *Nature*, **33** (1886), 516. One might have imagined that in his literary flamboyance he was imitating Disraeli, had he not also addressed a sonnet to Gladstone (1890).

Thirty-three of Sylvester's lectures were reported by James Hammond in *Lectures Containing an Exposition of the Fundamental Principles of the New Theory of Reciprocants Delivered During . . . 1886 Before the University of Oxford*, repr. from *American Journal of Mathematics* (Oxford–Baltimore, 1888), Lecture 34 is by Hammond. Sylvester contributed well over 300 different mathematical problems to *Educational Times*. These are calendared in *Collected Papers*, IV, 743–747; and several letters concerning the problems are printed in Archibald, *op. cit.*, 124–128.

II. SECONDARY LITERATURE. H. F. Baker included a personal biography of Sylvester in his ed. of the collected papers. R. C. Archibald, *op. cit.*, 91–95, lists 57 publications dealing with Sylvester's life and works. To these may be added R. C. Archibald, "Material Concerning James Joseph Sylvester," in *Studies and Essays Offered to George Sarton* (New York, 1947), 209–217; and R. C. Yates, "Sylvester at the University of Virginia," in *American Mathematical Monthly*, **44** (1937), 194–201.

The most useful discussions of Sylvester's life and work are A. Cayley, "Scientific Worthies XXV: James Joseph Sylvester," in *Nature*, **39** (1889), 217–219, repr. in *The Collected Mathematical Papers of Arthur Cayley*, XIII (Cambridge, 1897), 43–48; F. Franklin, *People and Problems, a Collection of Addresses and Editorials* (New York, 1908), 11–27, first printed in *Bulletin of the American Mathematical Society*, **3** (1897), 299–309; P. A. MacMahon, obituary in *Nature*, **55** (1897), 492–494; and obituary in *Proceedings of the Royal Society*, **63** (1898), ix–xxv; and M. Noether, obituary in *Mathematische Annalen*, **50** (1898), 133–156. Of these, Noether's article is mathematically the most useful. Cayley wrote much invaluable commentary on Sylvester's work, for which see the index to Cayley's collected papers. The *Johns Hopkins University Circulars* are a convenient source of biography, since the editors often reprinted articles on Sylvester that had first been published elsewhere (such as those cited above by Cayley and Franklin, and the first of MacMahon's).

J. D. NORTH

SYLVESTER II, POPE. See **Gerbert**, also known as **Gerbert d'Aurillac.**

SYLVIUS, FRANCISCUS DELE BOË (*b.* Hanau, Germany, 15 March 1614; *d.* Leiden, Netherlands, 15 November 1672), *medicine.*

Sylvius was of southern Flemish extraction. His grandfather, a merchant and descendant of a noble family, emigrated from Kamerijk (Cambria, now in France) to Frankfurt-am-Main. François was the second son of Isaäc dele Boë and Anna de la Vignette, who was from the same area of southern Flanders. For his primary education he was sent to Sedan, where a Calvinist academy had been established and where he received his first medical instruction. He then went to Leiden, where he studied medicine (1633–1635) under Adolph Vorstius and Otto Heurnius. After visiting the universities of Wittenburg and Jena, he received his degree at Basel on 16 March 1637, defending a thesis on "animal movement and its disorders": *De animali motu ejusque laesionibus*. He already signed his name as Sylvius or, in order to avoid confusion with Jacques Sylvius (1478–1555), as dele Boë, Sylvius.

For a year and a half Sylvius practiced medicine in Hanau, but this seems not to have satisfied him. In any case, after a short study trip through France he returned to Leiden, where he hoped to obtain a post with the university. On 17 March 1638, he matriculated again and at his request received permission to give private lectures on anatomy, which met with great approval. He lectured on the *Anatomicae institutiones* of Caspar Bartholin but soon undertook to give anatomical demonstrations in the gallery of the botanic garden that were extended to physiological experiments. He was, in fact, one of the first to defend Harvey's new theory of the circulation of the blood and demonstrate it on dogs. His vigor was so great that Johannes Walaeus (1604–1649), a sharp critic, became a fervent supporter of Harvey, in return making experiments on the new theory. At these demonstrations Sylvius seems to have met Descartes, who as early as 1637 had accepted Harvey's theory of the circulation, although rejecting his concept of the action of the heart.

Because there seemed to be no prospect of an academic career at Leiden, Sylvius decided in the autumn of 1641 to move to Amsterdam, where he soon established a lucrative practice and earned the general esteem of his colleagues. He was appointed physician of the poor-relief board of the Walloon Church, and in 1657 he became a supervisor of the Amsterdam College of Physicians. His medical colleagues included Nicolaas Tulp, Paulus Barbette, and Hendrik van Roonhuyse; and his interest in chemistry brought him the friendship of Otto Sperling and J. R. Glauber. Despite the demands of his practice and professional commitments, he did not neglect scientific research work, performing postmortem examinations and devoting his spare time to chemical experiments.

In 1658, after extended negotiations, Sylvius was persuaded to accept appointment as professor of medicine at Leiden at the high salary of 1,800 guilders—almost twice the usual amount. On 17 September 1658 he delivered his inaugural oration, on the knowledge of man, *De hominis cognitione*. Devoting himself to his new task with great zeal, he proved to be an outstanding faculty member and his eloquence and gift for teaching attracted students from all parts of Europe. In bedside instruction, which he carried out in the old Caecilia Hospital, he showed himself to be an experienced clinician and a devoted teacher, who attracted many students from foreign countries. Although as a rule bedside teaching was limited to two days a week, Sylvius received permission to take his students daily to the hospital, where he performed the autopsies himself. His own ideas on several medical subjects were defended by his students in public disputations, and in 1669–1670 he was vice-chancellor of the university. The first volume of his main work, *Praxeos medicae idea nova*, was published the following year, but he did not live to see the second volume in print.

In 1647 Sylvius married Anna de Ligne, the daughter of a lawyer, who was thirteen years younger than he. One or two children born of this marriage died at a very early age, and in 1657 his wife died. In December 1666 he married a twenty-two-year-old woman, who died three years later; their only daughter died in 1670.

Sylvius' accomplishments were in anatomy and medical chemistry. Although there is some confusion with Jacobus Sylvius of Paris, a skilled anatomist who also worked on the brain, the Leiden Sylvius was responsible for the description of the *fissura Sylvii* and of the *arteria cerebri media Sylvii*, as well as of the fifth ventricle (pseudo ventricle, ventricle of the septum). The *aquaeductus Sylvii* was known to Galen and had been well described by Jacobus Sylvius. Moreover, Sylvius was the first to describe the tubercles in phthisis. In the history of medicine, however, Sylvius was the most brilliant representative of the iatrochemical school, founded by Paracelsus and continued by J. B. van Helmont, which reached its zenith when Sylvius defended the chemiatric conception from the Leiden chair. He was convinced that all physiological and pathological processes could be conceived perfectly in analogy to the processes and experiments observed in the chemical laboratory and could be explained by fermentation, effervescence, and putrefaction. Acid and alkali were considered as fundamental principles in the animal body.

In his therapeutics Sylvius preferred the new chemical medicines to the Galenic ones, using mercury, antimony, and zinc sulfate, among others. His rather speculative and extravagant theories included the belief that the pancreatic juice was acid and effervesced with the alkaline gall in the duodenum, and that ferments went to the heart, where he thought the blood effervesced. Considering the spleen to be the organ in which the blood is purified, he stressed its function to such an extent that he was called *patronus lienis*. In his last years Sylvius encountered public opposition from Anton Deusing, professor at Groningen, who—to Sylvius' great displeasure—was appointed at Leiden University but died before he could assume his duties.

Although Sylvius, with his exaggeration, may have caused much harm in the medical practice of his students, he can nevertheless be considered a promoter of scientific medical research. His enthusiasm inspired several gifted students to valuable anatomical and physiological work: Jan Swammerdam, Nicolaus Steno, and Regnier de Graaf. Sylvius' ideas on the pancreas induced De Graaf to attempt the experiments in which he obtained the pancreatic juice from a dog by means of a fistula.

BIBLIOGRAPHY

I. Original Works. A more or less complete list of Sylvius' writings is in Baumann's biography (see below). They include *De hominis cognitione*, his inaugural oration (Leiden, 1658; Jena, 1674), reprinted with intro. and Dutch trans. in *Opuscula selecta neerlandicorum de arte medica*, VI (Amsterdam, 1927), 2–45; *Disputationum medicorum decas* (Leiden, 1670, 1674, 1676); and *Praxeos medicae idea nova*, 4 vols. (Leiden, 1671–1674). A collection of his works is *Opera medica* (Amsterdam, 1679).

II. Secondary Literature. See L. Schacht, *Oratio funebris in obitum. Nobilissimi, Clarissimi, Expertissimi, D. Francisci de le Boe, Sylvii* (Leiden, 1673); Frank Baker. "The Two Sylviuses. An Historical Study," in *Johns Hopkins Hospital Bulletin*, 20 (1909), 329–339; E. D. Baumann, *François dele Boë Sylvius* (Leiden, 1949), with portrait; Lester S. King, *The Road to Medical Enlightenment 1650–1695* (London–New York, 1970), 93–112; and E. Ashworth Underwood, "Franciscus Sylvius and his Iatrochemical School," in *Endeavour*, 31 (1972), 73–76.

G. A. Lindeboom

SYLVIUS, JACOBUS. See **Dubois, Jacques.**

SYMMER, ROBERT (*b.* Galloway, Scotland [?], *ca.* 1707; *d.* London, England, 19 June 1763), *electricity.*

Nothing is known of Symmer's life before 1719, when he matriculated at the University of Edinburgh. Among fellow students who became his friends were Andrew Mitchell, Patrick Murdoch, and the poet James Thomson. All took an interest in contemporary natural philosophy, and all, though born and bred in Scotland, made their careers in England. Mitchell, Murdoch, and Symmer became fellows of the Royal Society of London (in 1735, 1745, and 1752, respectively), while their older contemporary Thomson, the best-known of the group, made his reputation with poems celebrating Newtonian science.

In 1735 Symmer took a belated M.A., perhaps to qualify as traveling companion to Francis Greville, Lord Brooke, later earl of Warwick; it was then a common practice for well-educated impecunious Scots to serve as tutors to influential English families, through whose connections they expected to obtain preferment. Symmer followed or conducted Brooke to London and there rejoined Mitchell, Murdoch (who had left Scotland by the tutorial route in 1729), and Thomson, all of whom had begun to prosper. Symmer found preferment in financial administration, for which he may have prepared under Abraham de Moivre, who gave private lessons in practical arithmetic and who, together with two of his students, signed Symmer's certificate for election to the Royal Society. Symmer eventually became head clerk of the office of the Treasurer of the Chamber, which paid the bills of the King's Household. When he lost this position upon a change of ministries in 1757, he preferred retirement to accepting an offer of the governorship of New Jersey.

Symmer devoted his leisure to wooing a young lady (Eleanora Ross of Balkailley, whom he married in 1760), to keeping Mitchell (then plenipotentiary to the court of Frederick the Great) current with English politics, and to experimenting with electricity. He took up this last study in 1758 on discovering that a pair of silk stockings, one black and one white, worn upon the same leg, would strongly attract one another when removed and separated. Symmer wore this peculiar double hosiery to keep mourning (and warm) during winter. Unfortunately for his reputation, he continued to use his stockings to generate the electricity for his experiments—and this, as he wrote to Mitchell, was "enough to disgust the Delicacy of more than one Philosopher."[1]

From the facts that the stockings attracted strongly when separated and weakly when joined, and that the attraction reappeared on every separation, Symmer concluded that the contrary electricities of Franklin derived from two distinct, opposed, positive principles, perhaps materialized as two essentially different, counterbalancing fluids. His conception therefore differed from Dufay's and Nollet's, in which the two electricities were not contrary, and Franklin's, in which one was a privation of the other. Symmer confirmed this insight by studying the condenser, which, when charged and insulated, bore an evident analogy to his superposed stockings. He found that he could charge a Leyden jar with either a black or a white stocking, and he argued that the circumstances of explosion—the shock or the perforation of paper placed in the circuit[2]—suggested that a real fluid sprang from each surface of a discharging condenser. Another, and more important, experiment was suggested by the analogy: since each stocking substitutes for one surface of a Leyden jar, a charged parallel-plate condenser with glass dielectric should cohere if cut longitudinally through its middle. On the other hand, two complete condensers, electrified in series, should not cohere, since at the interface the independent contrary electricities counterbalance. It was essential to Symmer's argument that they counterbalance but not destroy one another, as appears from the fact that the condensers can be exploded separately.

Symmer hoped that his two powers would not only start a revolution in electricity but also "prove to be the genuine Principle of the Newtonian Philosophy."[3] But the English electricians preferred to follow Franklin or Benjamin Wilson. Symmer therefore decided to try his chances abroad, and sent Mitchell copies of his papers for distribution in the Germanies. He himself took charge of converting Nollet, which proved a consequential move. Although Nollet would not accept Symmer's theory, he endorsed the experiments, which he deemed so many proofs of his own views, and which he improved by replacing the stockings with ribbons resting on a plate of glass. He also sent an account of the modified experiments to Giovanni Francesco Cigna in Turin, in the hope that he would use them to destroy the Franklinist theories of Nollet's rival Beccaria.

Cigna in turn improved the experiments, particularly by substituting an insulated lead plate for

Nollet's glass. He observed that if the ribbon were electrified and removed, and the plate discharged, it could be recharged as often as desired by grounding it when the ribbon was returned. Cigna here hit upon the principle of the electrophore. Volta, to whom it is usually ascribed, also came to it inspired indirectly by Symmer: When Cigna announced that Nollet's experiments did not decide between Franklin and Symmer, Beccaria bent theory and experiment to prove his Franklinist views; and in answering Beccaria, Volta invented the electrophore, a device as important as the Leyden jar for the development of electrical theory.

Symmer's expectations were almost realized. Before the end of the eighteenth century, his dualist theory had captured the Continent; and although his countrymen remained singlist, both sides agreed that no experiment known to them could settle whether electricity came in one power or two.

NOTES

1. Symmer to Mitchell, 7 Apr. 1761. British Museum, Add. MS 6839, fols. 220–221.
2. Franklin helped Symmer strike holes in quires of paper; they hoped that the contours of the punctures would show the direction of the discharge, but the results were ambiguous.
3. Symmer to Mitchell, 19 June 1760. British Museum, Add. MS 6839, fol. 183.

BIBLIOGRAPHY

I. ORIGINAL WORKS. Symmer's only published work is "New Experiments and Observations Concerning Electricity," in *Philosophical Transactions of the Royal Society*, **51**, no. 1 (1759), 340–389, comprising four parts read between Feb. and Dec. 1759. His other accessible work is a volume of MS letters addressed to Mitchell: British Museum, Add. MS 6839.

II. SECONDARY LITERATURE. Biographical information about Symmer has been inferred from the Mitchell letters. See J. L. Heilbron, "Robert Symmer, F.R.S. (*c*. 1707–1763) and the Two Electricities," in *Isis*, which includes an estimate of Symmer's work. See also Joseph Priestley, *The History and Present State of Electricity*, 3rd ed. (London, 1775), I, 308–333, and II, 41, 47; and I. B. Cohen, *Franklin and Newton* (Philadelphia, 1956), 543–546.

J. L. HEILBRON

SYNESIUS OF CYRENE (*b.* Cyrene, *ca.* 370; *d. ca.* 414), *astronomy, physics.*

Of Greek ancestry, Synesius was a man of wide interests. He was a gifted pupil of Hypatia, the beautiful Neoplatonic philosopher, mathematician, and astronomer. After a brief period as a soldier, Synesius settled in his homeland as a landed proprietor. His studies were interrupted in 397 by a three-year mission to Constantinople in order to present a gold crown to Arcadius, the new emperor, in a successful attempt to secure alleviation of taxes for his land. On his return to Cyrene, he married a Christian woman from Alexandria. His literary activity was constantly interrupted by his efforts to organize the military defense of his land against barbarian invaders. Although married and not a Christian, Synesius was, despite his great reluctance, pressured to accept baptism and consecration as bishop of Ptolemais (part of the Pentapolis of Cyrenaica) in 410. The remaining years of his life were busy and made difficult by the death of his sons and the barbarian invasions.

Synesius is well-known for his essays, letters, and hymns, which have been carefully studied; but his scientific attainments are also worthy of respect. He was deeply interested in the theoretical aspects of science, but he also sought to make practical applications of his knowledge. Once, apparently while seriously ill, he requested Hypatia to have Alexandrian metalworkers make him a brass "hydroscope" according to his directions. He needed the instrument in order that he might "ascertain the weight of liquids." The exact nature of the notched cylindrical tube is uncertain. Synesius apparently was not the inventor of this hydrometer or areometer; he merely desired an instrument similar to one he had seen.

Synesius apparently invented a "perfected" astrolabe, an instrument at which, he said, Hipparchus had hinted much earlier. He presented this silver astrolabe (really a planisphere) to a friend in Constantinople. The letter accompanying the gift referred to a full description of the astrolabe and its uses, but that work has been lost. The instrument resulted, he explained, from his having "carefully studied the reduction of the sphere to a plane figure." It must, therefore, have been a representation of the heavenly bodies on a flat surface.

Synesius has been considered by some to be the author of an important Greek alchemic work, an obscure and difficult commentary on Pseudo-Democritus. The tract is in the form of a dialogue with Dioskoros, a priest of Serapis at Alexandria. Other than the similar name, there is nothing to indicate that the bishop of Ptolemais composed this work on alchemy, and there is internal evidence that the work was written before he was born.

BIBLIOGRAPHY

I. ORIGINAL WORKS. The first complete ed. of the writings of Synesius was by Dionysius Petavius (Paris, 1612). Most readily available is the collection in J. P. Migne, *Patrologia Graeca*, LXVI (Paris, 1864), 1021–1756. The *Epistolae* were edited by R. Hercher in his *Epistolographi Graeci* (Paris, 1873). A French trans. of the works of Synesius was published by H. Druon (Paris, 1878). Augustine Fitzgerald published English translations in *The Letters of Synesius of Cyrene* (London, 1926) and *The Essays and Hymns of Synesius of Cyrene* (London, 1930).

II. SECONDARY LITERATURE. Detailed bibliographies of special studies on Synesius are in W. S. Crawford, *Synesius the Hellene* (London, 1901); in José C. Pando, *The Life and Times of Synesius of Cyrene as Revealed in His Works* (Washington, D.C., 1940); and in Richard Volkmann, *Synesius von Cyrene* (Berlin, 1869).

The scientific achievements of Synesius are discussed in B. Kolbe, *Der Bishof Synesius von Cyrene als Physiker und Astronom* (Berlin, 1850); and in Paul Tannery, *Recherches sur l'histoire de l'astronomie ancienne* (Paris, 1893), 50–53.

On the supposed authorship of the alchemic tract, see *Bibliotheca chemica*, John Ferguson, ed., II (Glasgow, 1954), 421–422; and especially Edmund O. Lippmann, *Entstehung und Ausbreitung der Alchemie* (Berlin, 1919), 96–98.

KARL H. DANNENFELDT

SZEBELLÉDY, LÁSZLÓ (*b*. Rétság, Hungary, 20 April 1901; *d*. Budapest, Hungary, 23 January 1944), *analytical chemistry*.

Szebellédy was the son of Ferenc Szebellédy, a pharmacist, and Maria Pohl. He earned a degree in pharmacy at the University of Budapest in 1923, but instead of becoming a pharmacist he turned to scientific research. In 1925 he was named assistant to Lajos Winkler at the Inorganic Chemistry Institute of the University of Budapest. An outstanding analytical chemist, Winkler had become famous for his methods of determining the amount of oxygen dissolved in water (1888) and the iodine-bromine number of fats for his work in precision gravimetry, and for his books. Szebellédy collaborated in Winkler's analytical research. His first independent publications (1929) dealt with the classical methods of analysis. He later spent considerable time away from Budapest working with foreign scientists, notably Wilhelm Böttger at Leipzig and William Treadwell at Zurich. In 1934 Szebellédy qualified as a lecturer in analytical chemistry at the University of Budapest, and in 1939 he was appointed professor of inorganic and analytical chemistry. The extensive program of research that he subsequently undertook was prematurely halted by his death from cancer.

Among the topics that Szebellédy investigated was catalytic ultramicroreactions, introduced into analytical chemistry by I. M. Kolthoff and E. B. Sandell for cases in which it is possible to obtain an accurately measurable endpoint (1937). Most catalytic color reactions, however, proceed continuously. Working with Miklós Ajtai, Szebellédy devised the analytical application for this type of reaction (1939). With the assistance of his young co-worker Zoltán Somogyi (whose death during an air raid preceded his own), Szebellédy invented the coulometric titration method (1938), which is widely used in analytical chemistry.

BIBLIOGRAPHY

Szebellédy's paper on coulometric titration is "Die coulometrische Analyse als Präzisionsmethode," in *Zeitschrift für analytische Chemie*, **112** (1938), 313–336, written with Z. Somogyi; and that on catalytic analysis is "Die quantitative Bestimmung von Vanadin mittels aktivierter Katalyse," in *Mikrochemie*, **26** (1939), 87–94, written with M. Ajtai.

A secondary source is F. Szabadváry, *History of Analytical Chemistry* (Oxford, 1966), 190, 316, 317.

F. SZABADVÁRY

SZILARD, LEO (*b*. Budapest, Hungary, 11 February 1898; *d*. La Jolla, California, 30 May 1964), *physics, biology*.

Szilard, one of the most profoundly original minds of this century, contributed significantly to statistical mechanics, nuclear physics, nuclear engineering, genetics, molecular biology, and political science.

The oldest of three children of a successful Jewish architect-engineer, he was a sickly child and received much of his early education at home, from his mother. His electrical engineering studies were interrupted by World War I; drafted into the Austro-Hungarian army, he was still in officers' school at the end of the war. In 1920 he went to Berlin to continue his studies at the Technische Hochschule. The attraction of physics proved too great, however, and he soon transferred to the University of Berlin, where he received the doctorate in 1922. His dissertation, written under the direction of Max von Laue, showed that the second law of thermodynamics not only covers the mean values of thermodynamic quantities but also determines the form of the law governing the fluctuations around the mean values. The continuation of this work led to his famous paper of 1929, which established the connection between entropy and information, and foreshadowed modern cybernetic theory.

During this period in Berlin, as a research worker at the Kaiser Wilhelm Institute and then as *Privatdozent* at the university, Szilard undertook experimental work in X-ray crystallography with Herman Mark. He also began to patent his long series of pioneering discoveries, including devices anticipating most modern nuclear particle accelerators. With Albert Einstein he patented an electromagnetic pump for liquid refrigerants that now serves as the basis for the circulation of liquid metal coolants in nuclear reactors.

Hitler's assumption of power caused Szilard to leave Germany for England in 1933. There he conceived the idea that it might be possible to achieve a nuclear chain reaction. Szilard's search for an appropriate nuclear reaction (he early realized that the neutron was the key), while a guest at St. Bartholomew's Hospital in 1934 and at the Clarendon Laboratory, Oxford, after 1935, led to the establishment of the Szilard-Chalmers reaction and the discovery of the γ-ray-induced emission of neutrons from beryllium. It was only after he came to the United States, in 1938, that he learned of the discovery of fission in Germany by Hahn and Strassmann.

Szilard instantly recognized—as did nuclear physicists in other countries—that fission would be the key to the release of nuclear energy, and he immediately undertook experiments at Columbia University to demonstrate the release of neutrons in the fission process and to measure their number. With Fermi he organized the research there that eventually led to the first controlled nuclear chain reaction, on 2 December 1942, at Chicago. Probably more than any other individual, Szilard was responsible for the establishment of the Manhattan Project; it was he who arranged for the letter from Einstein to President Roosevelt that brought it about. His contributions to the success of its plutonium production branch, both in physics and in engineering, were manifold, especially in the earliest stages. The basic patent for the nuclear fission reactor was awarded jointly to Fermi and Szilard in 1945, but Szilard never realized any financial profit from it.

The last months of the war found Szilard, with James Frank and other Manhattan Project scientists, engaged in a futile effort to convince President Truman to use the first atomic bomb in a nonlethal demonstration to the Japanese of its destructive power.

After the war Szilard turned to biology. With Aaron Novick he invented and constructed a device for studying growing bacteria and viruses in a stationary state by means of a continuous-flow device, called the chemostat, in which the rate of bacteria growth can be changed by altering the concentration of one of the controlling growth factors. He used it for a number of years in fundamental studies of bacterial mutations and various biochemical mechanisms.

In the late 1950's Szilard became increasingly interested in theoretical problems of biology; his 1959 paper "On the Nature of the Aging Process" still stimulates research and controversy. His last paper, "On Memory and Recall," was published posthumously.

Throughout his life Szilard had a profoundly developed social consciousness. On fleeing Nazi Germany to England, one of his first acts was to inspire the organization of the Academic Assistance Council, to help find positions in other countries for refugee scientists. He was one of the leaders of the successful postwar Congressional lobbying effort by Manhattan Project alumni for a bill establishing civilian control over peaceful development of nuclear energy. Szilard was one of the instigators and active early participants in the international Pugwash Conferences on Science and World Affairs, and he wrote extensively on questions of nuclear arms control and the prevention of war. In 1962 he founded the Council for a Livable World, a Washington lobby on nuclear arms control and foreign policy issues.

Szilard was a fellow of the American Physical Society, the American Academy of Arts and Sciences, and the National Academy of Sciences. He received the Einstein Award in 1958 and the Atoms for Peace Award in 1959.

BIBLIOGRAPHY

Many of Szilard's works are being brought together in *Collected Works of Leo Szilard: Scientific Papers*, Bernard T. Feld and Gertrude W. Szilard, eds. (Cambridge, Mass., 1972–   ). His writings include "Über die Ausdehnung der phänomenologischen Thermodynamik auf die Schwankungserscheinungen," in *Zeitschrift für Physik*, **32** (1925), 753–788, his diss.; "Über die Entropieverminderung in einem thermodynamischen System bei Eingriffen intelligenter Wesen," *ibid.*, **53** (1929),

840–856, translated as "On the Decrease of Entropy in a Thermodynamic System by the Intervention of Intelligent Beings," in *Behavioral Science*, **9** (1964), 301–310; "Chemical Separation of the Radioactive Element From Its Bombarded Isotope in the Fermi Effect," in *Nature*, **134** (1934), 462, written with T. A. Chalmers; *The Voice of the Dolphins, and Other Stories* (New York, 1961); a report to the secretary of war (June 1945), written with James Frank, Donald J. Hughes, J. J. Nickson, Eugene Rabinowitch, and Joyce C. Stearns, and a petition to the president of the United States (17 July 1945), in Bulletin of the Atomic Scientists, *The Atomic Age*, M. Grodzins and E. Rabinowitch, eds. (New York, 1963); and reminiscences, in Donald Fleming and Bernard Bailyn, eds., *The Intellectual Migration: Europe and America, 1930–1960* (Cambridge, Mass., 1969).

On his life and work, see the notice by Eugene P. Wigner, in *Biographical Memoirs. National Academy of Sciences*, **40** (1969), 337–341.

BERNARD T. FELD

SZILY, PÁL (*b.* Budapest, Hungary, 16 May 1878; *d.* Mosonmagyaróvár, Hungary, 18 August 1945), *chemistry.*

Szily came from a family of physicians. His father, Adolf Szily, was a doctor and director of a Budapest hospital, and his older brother became a professor of ophthalmology at the University of Budapest. Szily studied medicine at the University of Budapest and after obtaining his medical degree became an assistant at the Institute of Physiology there, where he carried out his fundamental research on the colorimetric determination of hydrogen ion concentration.

Since the time of Robert Boyle various plant juices had been used to determine whether a liquid was acidic or basic. When synthetic substances were introduced as indicators, it was observed that they did not change color at the same level of acidity as the natural juice indicators. On the basis of Arrhenius' theory of ionization (1887), Wilhelm Ostwald introduced the concept of the dissociation constant with a view to ascertaining the strengths of acids and bases as a function of, respectively, hydrogen ion and hydroxyl ion concentration. He also determined the value of the dissociation constant of water. In 1893 Max Le Blanc invented the hydrogen electrode, which made it possible to measure the hydrogen ion concentration electrochemically.

It appears, however, that for a long time chemists were unable to recognize the significance of these developments. They did not comprehend the difference between titrimetrically determinable amounts of acid and the strengths of acids, for most of them dealt only with the former. Physiologists and biologists, however, were more concerned with the strengths of acids, since small changes in acidity play a great role in various life processes. They were therefore the ones to elucidate the concepts underlying the treatment of these questions and to develop appropriate techniques of measurement. The first to do so was Szily, who in 1903 published "Indikátorak alkalmazásáól állati folyadékok vegyhatásának meghatározására" ("Application of Indicators in the Determination of the Reaction of Animal Fluids"), in *Orvosi Hetilap*, **45** (1903), 509–518. After establishing that the reaction of animal fluids—the hydrogen ion concentration of blood serum, for example—cannot be determined titrimetrically, Szily hit upon the idea of using the indicators for this purpose, since each indicator changes color at a specific hydroxyl ion concentration, regardless of the nature of the base. By using various indicators he was able to establish a scale for estimating acidity. In addition, employing seven different indicators, he devised a scale for making an approximate determination of the acidity of the blood serum. In the course of this research he also determined the resistance of blood serum to the effects of acids and bases (its buffer property).

In 1903 Szily lectured on his results before the Physiology Society of Berlin; and Hans Friedenthal, a lecturer at the University of Berlin, arranged for Szily to continue his research there. Friedenthal began investigations in the same area and perfected Szily's method by using a larger number of indicators and by employing standard (buffer) solutions of precisely known hydrogen ion concentration. In 1904 he reported that he had been unsuccessful in his attempt to produce these solutions by successive dilution of acidic or basic solutions. Szily suggested that he prepare stable solutions of reliable hydrogen ion concentrations by mixing primary and secondary phosphates in different proportions. Szily was, consequently, the inventor of artificial buffer solutions. Research in this area was extended by S. P. L. Sørensen, who introduced the concept of pH in 1909.

In 1905 Szily transferred to the surgery clinic of the University of Budapest, and in 1909 he became director of the serological and bacteriological laboratory of the Budapest Jewish Hospital. Henceforth his research was of a purely medical nature. He investigated the therapeutic effects of Salvarsan and communicated his findings to Paul Ehrlich, who followed with interest the results of the introduction of the drug into Hungary. During World War I, Szily directed an army epidemiological unit and was concerned with typhus therapy and the treatment of equine influenza through vaccination. After the war he published studies on protein therapy, but his scientific activity was steadily eclipsed by the demands of his private practice in Budapest. His practice seems to have disappointed him, for in 1928 he went to the small city of Mosonmagyaróvár as urologist with the state health insurance administration.

After the Nazi assumption of power in Hungary, Szily, a diabetic, was taken in 1944 to the concentration camp at Győr. During the last days of the war in Hungary he escaped deportation to Germany through his professional connections. He returned to his post in Mosonmagyaróvár but, unable to secure sufficient medication, died soon afterward.

BIBLIOGRAPHY

I. ORIGINAL WORKS. Szily was author of thirty chemical and medical publications, including the one mentioned above. His medical publications appeared generally in *Wiener Medizinische Wochenschrift* and *Berliner Klinische Wochenschrift* in 1910–1919.

II. SECONDARY LITERATURE. See F. Szabadváry, "Development of the pH concept. A historical survey," in *Journal of Chemical Education*, **41** (1964), 105–107; *History of Analytical Chemistry* (Oxford, 1966), 363, 376–377; and "Szily Pál (1878–1945)," in *Orvostörténeti közlemények* (*Communicationes de historia artis medicinae*), **38** (1966), 121–130, in Hungarian.

Hans Friedenthal's report is "Die Bestimmung der Reaktion einer Flüssigkeit mit Hilfe von Indikatoren," in *Zeitschrift für Elektrochemie*, **10** (1904), 113–119.

F. SZABADVÁRY

AL-ṬABARĪ, ABUꞋL-ḤASAN AḤMAD IBN MU-ḤAMMAD (*b.* Ṭabaristān, Persia, first quarter of the tenth century; *d.* Ṭabaristān, fourth quarter of the tenth century), *philosophy, natural science, medicine.*

Very little is known about al-Ṭabarī's parents or early life. Like his contemporary al-Majūsī (*d.* 994), he studied under the physician Abū Māhir Mūsā ibn Sayyār. After acquiring a good reputation as a physician, al-Ṭabarī became court physician to the Buwayhid king Rukn al-Dawla (reigned 932–976) and his vizier, the literary scholar Abu'l-Faḍl Muḥammad al-Khaṭīb ibn al-ʿAmīd

(*d.* 971). This was a period of great cultural and scientific productivity in Persia and Iraq under the Abbasid caliphate. Several medical authors won wide recognition, not least among them al-Ṭabarī— as is evident from the numerous extant copies of his only known literary contribution, *al-Muꞌālajāt al-Buqrāṭiyya*, which consists of ten treatises on Hippocratic medical treatment.

The text of al-Ṭabarī's work sheds much light on his life. It shows that he was a Muslim, deeply influenced by Neoplatonism and Aristotelianism, who respected other religions in the region: Zoroastrianism, Judaism, and Christianity. Unlike many of his contemporaries, al-Ṭabarī excluded much of the religious and Koranic phraseology and jargon used in similar works. He dealt objectively and open-mindedly with such topics as generation and corruption, life and death, marriage and family, vision and thought, pain and pleasure, matter and soul, time and space, temporal and eternal punishment and reward, and Godhood and resurrection. His approach is entirely free from religious bias and theological limitations, and he seems to have been well-acquainted with the writings of Greek philosophers and natural scientists. His treatment of diseases and their medical therapy also bears witness to his appreciation of and indebtedness to the Hippocratic and Galenic tradition.

Al-Ṭabarī nevertheless contributed original ideas and concepts of historical interest. His medical ingenuity led him to become the first practitioner to describe and recommend effective treatment for the itch mite *Sarcoptes scabiei*, the cause of scabies. His theories on health, deontology, medical therapy, and psychotherapy showed his ability to think independently and to make personal observations unhampered by traditional doctrines.

BIBLIOGRAPHY

Al-Ṭabarī's only known work, *al-Muꞌālajāt al-Buqrāṭiyya*, which exists in several copies, some incomplete, suggests his encyclopedic approach: treatise 1—definitions and interpretations of natural sciences and phenomena, professional deontology, social behavior, metaphysics, and classification of diseases; treatise 2—on skin diseases of the head and face, and their treatment; treatise 3—on diseases of the head; treatise 4—on the anatomy and physiology of the eye, and its diseases; treatise 5—on diseases of the nose and ear; treatise 6—on the diseases of the mouth, teeth, tongue, uvula, larynx, pharynx, and neck (trachea); treatise 7—on skin diseases of the body; treatise 8—on diseases of the chest, lungs, bronchi, all other members of the respiratory system, diaphragm, and the heart, and their treatment; treatise 9 — on the anatomy and physiology, and diseases of the stomach, and their diagnosis and treatment; treatise 10 — on the anatomy and physiology of the liver, spleen, and intestines, their diseases, and the nutritional values of these same organs such as liver, kidneys, brain, and viscera.

Several catalogs of library MSS and bibliographies of literary contributions of this Islamic period list copies of al-Ṭabarī's *al-Muʿ-ālajāt*. They include Joseph Aumer, *Die arabischen Handschriften der K. Hof- und Staatsbibliothek* (Munich, 1866), 357; and Carl Brockelmann, *Geschichte der arabischen Literatur*, I (Leiden, 1943), 272, and *Supplement,* I (Leiden, 1937), 422; and "Firdaus'l-Hikmat of Ali b. Rabban al-Ṭabari," in *Zeitschrift Semitisch*, **8** (1932), 270–288.

Ibn Abī Uṣaybiʿa in his *ʿUyūn al-anbāʾ*, 2 vols. (Cairo, 1882), I, 321, was probably the first of the few Muslim biographers to mention al-Ṭabarī. Brief nineteenth-century biographies of al-Ṭabarī based on Ibn Abī Uṣaybiʿa are L. Leclerc, *Histoire de la médecine arabe*, I (Paris, 1876), 358; and F. Wüstenfeld, *Geschichte der arabischer Ärzte und Naturforscher* (Göttingen, 1840), 56.

Julius Hirschberg, in *Geschichte der Augenheilkunde bei den Arabern* (Leipzig–Berlin, 1905), 107–108, brought out the importance of al-Ṭabarī's work, especially on eye diseases and treatment. Later, Mohammed Rihab, in "Der arabische Arzt aṭ-Ṭabarī," in *Archiv für Geschichte der Medizin*, **19** (1927), 123–168, and **20** (1928), 27–81, stressed the importance of al-Ṭabarī's contribution to medicine, especially his treatise on skin diseases and his discovery of the itch mite. For the latter see also R. Friedman, "The Story of Scabies; at-Tabari, Discoverer of the *Acarus scabiei*," in *Medical Life*, **45** (1936), 163–176.

For further information consult S. Hamarneh, *Catalogue of Arabic Manuscripts on Medicine and Pharmacy at the British Museum* (Cairo, 1975), no. 70; and G. Sarton, *Introduction to the History of Science*, I, 677, and II, 233.

SAMI HAMARNEH

AL-ṬABARĪ, ABU'L-ḤASAN ʿALĪ IBN SAHL RABBĀN (*b.* Marw, Persia, *ca.* 808; *d.* Baghdad, *ca.* 861), *medicine, natural science, theology, government.*

Ṭabarī was born into a prominent and religious Syriac Christian family living in Marw in the region of Khurāsān (near present-day Tehran). His father, Sahl, was a highly placed government official who was learned in medicine, philosophy, theology, and astrology. His scholarship and his religious and philanthropic activities won him the prestigious Syriac title of Rabbān, meaning "teacher." Sahl took a special interest in the upbringing of his son ʿAlī. Besides giving him a good education, Sahl taught him religion, medicine, and philosophy. The fatherly exhortations and advice led young ʿAlī to an appreciation and love of learning. When ʿAlī was ten years old he was taken to Ṭabaristān by his father, who was probably sent there on an assignment for the state. Because of their residence in Ṭabaristān, ʿAlī became known as al-Ṭabarī. There, he devoted his time to the study of medicine, religion, philosophy, and the natural sciences. Because Ṭabarī excelled in learning and as a counselor to the ruler of Ṭabaristān, he was summoned in 840 to the Abbasid capital to serve in the palace of Caliph al-Muʿtaṣim and his successor, Caliph al-Wāthiq (842–847). Under al-Mutawakkil (847–861), Ṭabarī's position was raised to that of companion to the caliph, who "urged and encouraged" him not only to embrace and confess openly his adherence to Islam, but also to defend his new faith against other religions.

In 850 and 855 Ṭabarī wrote his two best-known books, *Firdaws al-ḥikma* and *Al-Dīn wā'l-dawla*, respectively. He dedicated both to his patron and benefactor, al-Mutawakkil.

In *Firdaws* ("Paradise of Wisdom"), Ṭabarī compiled, extracted, and digested information on all aspects of medicine from Greek, Syriac, and Indian medical compendiums. He also added his own observations and interpretations throughout his medical encyclopedia, the first of its kind in Arabic with such scope and comprehensiveness. In addition to medicine, embryology, and surgery, Ṭabarī wrote on toxicology, psychotherapy, cosmogony, and astrology. Ṭabarī also made reference to the outstanding contributions of two of his contemporaries, Yūḥannā ibn Māsawayh (*d.* 857), a pioneer Arabic medical educator and author, and Ḥunayn ibn Isḥāq, the indefatigable translator of medical texts from Syriac and Greek, and one of the foremost Arabic scholars of his time.

Ṭabarī's polemics in *Al-Dīn wā'l-dawla* ("On Religion and Government") shed considerable light on his life, religious beliefs, and philosophy, and reflect on religio-philosophical thought in ninth-century Islam.

It has been erroneously reported that Ṭabarī was a Jew and that he taught the physician Abū Bakr Muḥammad al-Rāzī (865–925). In fact, Ṭabarī must have died in Baghdad before Rāzī was even born. But Rāzī and other medical educators and authors in medieval Islam did benefit from Ṭabarī's works, ingenuity, and ideas, since, through his foresight, industry, and genius, Ṭabarī contributed materially to ninth-century Arabic learning and scholarship.

BIBLIOGRAPHY

I. ORIGINAL WORKS. Muhammad Z. Siddiqi of India, a former student of the late Edward G. Browne, edited Ṭabarī's *Firdaws al-ḥikma* ("Paradise of Wisdom"), with a useful introduction (Berlin, 1928). Since then, other manuscripts—besides those cited in the Berlin and British Museums—have been discovered. Ṭabarī's *Al-Dīn wā'l-dawla* ("On Religion and Government") was edited with an English translation by Alphonse Mingana from a unique manuscript at the John Rylands Library (Cairo–Manchester, 1922–1923).

An Arabic manuscript entitled *Ḥifẓ al-ṣiḥḥa* ("On the Preservation of Health") at the Bodleian Library, Oxford, catalog 1:578, is attributed to Ṭabarī. Other works listed for him by Ibn al-Nadīm in *Al-Fihrist* (completed 987) (Cairo, 1929), p. 426, are *Tuḥfat al-mulūk* and *Kunnāsh al-ḥaḍra* (two medical compendiums dedicated to the Muslim Caliph al-Mutawakkil) and a book on the benefits of solid and liquid diets and drugs.

II. SECONDARY LITERATURE. Several Arabic medieval texts besides *Al-Fihrist* mention Ṭabarī and his works: Ẓahīr al-Dīn ʿAlī al-Bayhaqī (d. 1170), *Tārīkh ḥukamāʾ al-Islām*, Muhammad Kurd ʿAlī edition (Damascus, 1946), 22–23; Yāqūt al-Ḥamawī (d. 1229), *Dictionary of Learned Men*, D. S. Margoliouth, ed., VI (London, 1931), 429, 460. The report by Jamāl al-Dīn al-Qifṭī (d. 1248), *Tārīkh al-ḥukamāʾ*, Julius Lippert, ed. (Leipzig, 1903), 187, errs concerning his religious background and his relation to Rāzī (865–925). Ibn ʿAbī Uṣaybiʿa (d. 1270), *ʿUyūn al-anbāʾ* (Cairo, 1882), 309, quotes both Ibn al-Nadīm and Ibn al-Qifṭī concerning Ṭabarī.

Ṭabarī was mentioned by F. Wüstenfeld, *Geschichte der arabischen Aerzte und Naturforscher* (Göttingen, 1840), 21, and Lucien Leclerc, *Historie de la médecine arabe*, I (Paris, 1876), 292–293. Much attention was paid to Ṭabarī, especially in relation to *Firdaws*, by Edward G. Browne, *Arabian Medicine* (Cambridge, 1921), 37–44; Max Meyerhof, "ʿAlī at-Ṭabarī's Paradise of Wisdom," in *Isis*, **16** (1931), 6–54; and "Ali-at-Ṭabarī, ein persischen Arzt," in *Zeitschrift der deutschen Morgenländischen Gesellschaft*, **10** (1931), 38–68; J. M. Faddegon, "Notice critique sur le Firdausu'l-hikmat de ʿAli b. Rabban al-Tabari," in *Journal Asiatique*, **218** (1931), 327–352; Alfred Siggel, "Gynäkologie, Embryologie und Frauenhygiene aus dem Paradies der Weisheit über die Ali b. Sahl at-Ṭabari," in *Quellen Studien Geschichte der Naturwissenschafte Medizin*, **8**, pts. 1–2 (1941), 216–272; *Die indischen Bücker aus dem Paradies der Weisheit über die Medizin des Ali b. Sahl Rabban al-Ṭabari* (Wiesbaden, 1950); and *Die propädeutischen Kapitel aus dem Paradies der Weisheit* *über die Medizin des Ali b. Sahl Rabban al-Ṭabari* (Wiesbaden, 1953).

See also Carl Brockelmann, *Geschichte der arabischen Literatur* (Leiden, 1943), 265; and supp. I (1937), 414–415; Fuat Sezgin, *Geschichte des arabischen Schrifttums*, III (Leiden, 1970), 236–244, with a valuable bibliography; George Sarton, *Introduction to the History of Science*, I (Baltimore, 1927), 546–549, 574; and S. Hamarneh, "Contributions of Ali al-Tabari to Ninth-Century Arabic Culture," in *Folia Orientalia* (Cracow), **12** (1970), 91–101. On particular subjects, see D. V. Subba Reddy, "Indian Medicine in Firdausu'l-hikmat of ʿAlī b. Rabban al-Ṭabari," in *Bulletin of the Department of the History of Medicine* (Hyderabad), **1** (1963), 26–49; W. Schmucker, *Die pflanzliche und mineralische Materia Medica in Firdaus al-hikma des Ṭabari* (Bonn, 1969); and S. Hamarneh, *Index of Mss. on Medicine and Pharmacy in the Ẓahiriyyah Library* (Damascus, 1969), 77–82 (Arabic text).

SAMI HAMARNEH

TABOR, JOHN (*b.* Faccombe, Hampshire, England, 1667), *medicine.*

Son of the rector of Faccombe parish, Tabor graduated B.A. at Merton College, Oxford, in 1687 and received his medical degree there on 20 March 1694. An adherent of the English iatromathematical school that developed under the aegis of Newtonianism during the early eighteenth century, Tabor attempted to incorporate medical animism into a mathematical framework in his *Exercitationes medicae* (1724). He accepted the rational soul or anima, which presumably induced and controlled the activities of living organisms, as the fundamental cause of physiological processes. Because the anima manifested itself through the movements of bodily parts and fluids according to the established laws of physical motion, however, Tabor held that the primary task of medical theory was the calculation of the size, shape, and movement of organic structures.

Familiar with a wide range of classical and contemporary authors, Tabor owed most to the work of Borelli and employed the computations and mechanical models characteristic of his writings. He devoted considerable attention to detailed, albeit inconclusive, formulations of the shape and elasticity of muscle fibers and offered a comprehensive, if unoriginal, account of the heart's structure and function. While maintaining that the anima was the primary force preserving organic systems against decay, Tabor followed John Freind and James and John Keill in admitting physical attraction as an independent force capable of affecting physiological activity. He construed disease, for example, as the process by which the anima, through muscular spasms, fevers, and similar means, restored bodily equilibrium by counteracting the attractive force of foreign and deleterious particles. Tabor's work had little influence and fell into obscurity with the general demise of iatromathematics in the second half of the eighteenth century. His use of animist hypotheses was intended to emphasize the insufficiency of purely mechanical explanations and reflected Tabor's concern to reconcile reductionist and vitalist traditions in physiological theory.

BIBLIOGRAPHY

I. ORIGINAL WORKS. Tabor's major work was *Exercitationes medicae quae tam morborum quam symptomatum in plerisque morbis rationem illustrant* (London, 1724). An article of antiquarian interest appeared as "An Accurate Account of a Tessellated Pavement, Bath, and Other Roman Antiquities, Lately Discovered Near East Bourne in Sussex," in *Philosophical Transactions of the Royal Society*, 30 (1717–1719), 549–563, 783–802.

II. SECONDARY LITERATURE. The only source for biographical data on Tabor is Joseph Foster, *Alumni Oxonienses*, IV (Oxford, 1892), 1453. A useful account of his medical ideas is Kurt Spengel, *Versuch einer pragmatischen Geschichte der Arzneikunde*, 3rd ed., V (Halle, 1828), 233–234, 349. J. R. Partington, *A History of Chemistry*, II (London, 1961), 623–625, discusses Tabor's opposition to John Mayow's theory of nitro-aerial particles.

MARTIN FICHMAN

TACCHINI, PIETRO (*b.* Modena, Italy, 21 March 1838; *d.* Spilamberto, Modena province, Italy, 24 March 1905), *astronomy, meteorology.*

After obtaining his degree in engineering at the *archiginnasio* of Modena, Tacchini studied astronomy at the observatory of Padua under Giovanni Santini and Virgilio Trettenero. In 1859, following his appointment as deputy director of the observatory of Modena, he established connections with Secchi and Schiaparelli in order to study problems related to the new astrophysics. In 1861 he maintained an active scientific correspondence with Secchi.

Appointed adjunct astronomer at the Palermo observatory in 1863, Tacchini began observations and research on solar physics using the spectroscope. The daily observations of the phenomena on the surface of the sun convinced him of the need for a well-planned national program in order to follow its various phases. He called this effort the study of "solar meteorology," at a time when scientists were just becoming aware that the phenomena of terrestrial meteorology depend upon solar phenomena. The exceptional maximum of the eleven-year sunspot cycle that occurred in 1870, accompanied by the appearance on earth of numerous polar auroras, intensified his observations of the sun at Rome and Palermo.

Secchi and Tacchini decided to found a society to coordinate the work of various Italian observatories and, using standard criteria, to observe solar activity and to promote research on solar physics. Since the spectroscope was virtually the only instrument used for this purpose, the society, founded in 1871, was called the Society of Italian Spectroscopists; its *Memorie,* the first periodical on astrophysics, is still being published by the Italian Astronomical Society, which replaced it in 1920.

A skilled administrator, Tacchini prepared and directed many astronomical expeditions. For the transit of Venus in 1874, Tacchini accompanied his colleagues Alessandro Dorna and Antonio Abetti to Muddapur in Bengal. The principal aim of this expedition was to make extremely accurate observations of the contacts of the disk of Venus with the limb of the sun by using the spectroscope. He traveled to various parts of the world to observe seven total solar eclipses, concentrating his observations especially on the corona and the prominences.

During the eclipse of 1883, which he observed in the Caroline Islands, Tacchini noted white prominences, in contrast with the vivid red ones of hydrogen. Photographic techniques later made it clear that these prominences, which were more extensive than those of hydrogen, are produced by calcium.

In 1879 Tacchini succeeded Secchi as director of the observatory at the Collegio Romano and as director of the Central Meteorological Office, from which he established a vast network of meteorological stations throughout Italy. Fully aware of the advantages of a clear and calm sky, he and Riccò promoted the construction of an observatory on Mt. Etna, at 9,650 feet, for astrophysical and geophysical research. Also with Riccò he enlisted the collaboration of the observatory in Catania for the international project of preparing a chart and a photographic catalog of the sky.

Tacchini was a foreign member of the Royal Astronomical Society and of the Royal Society, and was awarded the Rumford gold medal and the Janssen Prize.

BIBLIOGRAPHY

I. Original Works. Most of Tacchini's numerous publications are in the *Memorie della Società degli spettroscopisti italiani*, in the *Atti dell'Accademia dei Lincei*, and in the publications of the Central Meteorological Office. They include *Il passaggio di Venere sul sole dell' 8 e 9 dicembre 1874 osservato a Muddapur del Bengala* (Palermo, 1875); and "Eclissi totali di sole del dicembre 1870, del maggio 1882, dell'agosto 1886 e 1887," in *Relazioni e note* (Rome, 1888). His correspondence with Secchi is preserved in Italy.

II. Secondary Literature. See G. Abetti, "Celebrazione del primo centenario della nascità di Pietro Tacchini," in *Coelum*, **9** (1939), 81; E. Millosevich, "Necrologia di P. Tacchini," in *Astronomische Nachrichten*, **168**, no. 4009 (1905); and A. Riccò, "Necrologia di P. Tacchini," in *Memorie della Società degli spettroscopisti italiani*, **34** (1905), 85.

G. Abetti

TACCOLA, MARIANO DI JACOMO (*b.* Siena, Italy, 4 February 1381; *d.* Siena, 1453/1458), *mechanics.*

The nickname Taccola, meaning "crow" and referring to a talent for woodcarving, was inherited by Mariano from his father, a winegrower. Taccola's first profession was that of sculptor, and he contributed to the carving of the choir of Siena cathedral in 1408. He was active in civic life from at least 1413 and partially qualified as a notary in 1417. From 1424 to 1431 he was chamberlain of the Casa della Sapienza, a residence for scholars at Siena.

By 1427 Taccola seems to have become intensely interested in mechanical technology, a field to which he devoted most of his time for the rest of his life. His earliest dated sketches of machines are from 1427, when he also conducted practical tests of four of his inventions. The trials included a project for erecting a bridge over the Tiber at Rome and one for harborworks at Genoa.

The visit to Siena in 1432–1433 of the future emperor Sigismund brought Taccola a patron for his mechanical inventions. He was appointed one of Sigismund's *nobiles familiares* (1432) and dedicated an elegant book of drawings of machines and exotic animals to him. In this manuscript (Florence copy) Taccola offered to accompany Sigismund to Hungary to fight the Turks; and it seems that he

did so, for in a later manuscript (New York copy) he remarks that he personally fought against the Turks. Certainly by 1435 Taccola had returned to Siena, where he spent the rest of his life working as a sculptor and finishing his "De machinis libri decem" in 1449. He died sometime between 1453 and 1458.

With Brunelleschi and Giovanni Fontana, Taccola was a founder of the Italian school of Renaissance engineers. Although this school was initially influenced by the preceding generation of German engineers (notably Konrad Kyeser), its main inspiration may well have been the Brunelleschian renaissance of architecture. The members accepted the belief of ancient writers that mechanics was a part of architecture because the architect needed a knowledge of the machines necessary to raise building materials and similar devices. Taccola remarks in his notebook (Munich 197) that he discussed engineering matters with Brunelleschi at Siena.

The literacy of the architect-engineers of the Italian Renaissance school has been greatly underrated. Taccola was not simply a craftsman; he had trained as a notary and had been in close contact with scholars during his years at the Casa della Sapienza. Moreover, passages in his writings and in those of other engineers reveal a knowledge of the natural philosophy taught in the universities.

During the Renaissance mechanical technology was of considerable interest for scholars, including Cardinal Bessarion and the university professor Mariano Sozini. Taccola claims to have shown some of his designs to Sozini; and his acclamation as the "Sienese Archimedes" may well have originated among his humanist friends.

Taccola greatly influenced the Italian engineers of the Renaissance. Many of his designs were subsequently incorporated into the works of Francesco di Giorgio Martini and Roberto Valturio, through whom they reached a wider audience. The originality of Taccola's designs is, however, a difficult question. Certainly many devices and processes made their first recorded appearance in his works. At one time or another he has been credited with the invention of the explosive undermining of city walls, the suction pump, underwater breathing apparatus, the box-caisson method for building bridges, water mains and sluice gates, and vertically axled windmills and water mills. Some of these are now known to have been included in earlier treatises; others may have been set down by Taccola after he had seen them in operation. It may be said that Taccola's importance lies in his encyclopedic account of contemporary machine practice rather than in any original invention.

Two ideas of great later significance did, however, make their first known appearance in Taccola's manuscripts: the chain transmission system and the compound crank with connecting rod. By the latter, rotary motion could be converted to reciprocal motion, a technical concept that has been considered crucial for the postmedieval development of Western technology.

BIBLIOGRAPHY

I. ORIGINAL WORKS. Bayerische Staatsbibliothek, Munich, MS Lat. 197, a notebook containing drawings and texts (1427–1441), is to be published at Wiesbaden. Biblioteca Nazionale Centrale, Florence, MS Palat. 766, is bks. 3 (1430–1432) and 4, dedicated to Sigismund, of a treatise entitled "De ingeneis"; the missing books have been reconstructed by Prager and Scaglia (see below). The MS has been edited by James H. Beck, *Liber tertius de ingeneis ac edifitiis non usitatis* (Milan, 1969).

A second MS at Munich, MS Lat. 28800, comprises Taccola's main treatise, "De machinis libri decem" (1449), formerly known as Codex Wilczek I. Codex Wilczek II, a fifteenth-century copy, is now at the New York Public Library, Spencer Collection, MS 136. It has been edited by G. Scaglia as *De machinis. The Engineering Treatise of 1449*, 2 vols. (Wiesbaden-New York, 1971). A splendidly illustrated plagiary by Paolo Santini is at the Bibliothèque Nationale, Paris, MS Lat. 7239. Later copies of excerpts from Taccola's works are at the Biblioteca Marciana, Venice, MS Lat. VIII 40 (2941) and the Biblioteca Nazionale, Florence, MS Palat. 767. Many drawings from the Venice MS are reproduced in G. Canestrini, *Arte militare meccanica* (Milan, [1946?]). At least three autograph MSS seem to have disappeared.

The MSS are described in P. L. Rose, "The Taccola Manuscripts," in *Physis*, **10** (1968), 337–346. A guide to earlier bibliography is Lynn Thorndike, "Marianus Jacobus Taccola," in *Archives internationales d'histoire des sciences*, **8** (1955), 7–26.

II. SECONDARY LITERATURE. For biographical data see James H. Beck, "The Historical 'Taccola' and Emperor Sigismund in Siena," in *Art Bulletin*, **50** (1968), 309–320. See also Frank D. Prager and Giustina Scaglia, *Mariano Taccola and his Book De ingeneis* (Cambridge, Mass., 1972), and Frank D. Prager, "A Manuscript of Taccola, Quoting Brunelleschi, on Problems of Inventors and Builders," in *Proceedings of the American Philosophical Society*, **112** (1968), 131–149, which also reproduces and transcribes the relevant folios from Munich MS Lat. 197. On Taccola's significance, see Bertrand Gille, *The Renaissance Engineers* (Cambridge, Mass.–London, 1966), 81–87; and Lynn White, Jr., *Medieval Technology and Social Change* (Oxford, 1962), 86, 113.

PAUL LAWRENCE ROSE

TACHENIUS, OTTO (*b.* Herford, Westphalia; *d.* probably Venice, Italy), *medical chemistry, pharmaceutical chemistry.*

The details of Tachenius' life are extremely obscure and are based mainly on statements by his enemies. He is said to have been the son of a miller and to have been apprenticed to an apothecary (which is likely), from whose service he was dismissed for theft. About 1640 he went east to Holstein and Prussia, serving apothecaries in Kiel, Danzig, and Königsberg. In 1644 he went to Italy, acquired an M.D. from Padua in 1652, and settled in Venice, where he sold a "viperine salt" (*sal viperinum*) as a sovereign remedy. While there he wrote a short commentary on J. B. van Helmont's alkahest, in the form of a letter to Duke Frederick of Holstein; he then sent it to Helwig Dieterich, a physician whom he had met in Königsberg, to see through the press. Published as *Epistola de famoso liquore Alkahest*, it is said to have appeared with an appendix criticizing the author's arguments and grammar. (The pamphlet was reportedly published at Venice, but since it now seems to have disappeared, the affair is difficult to disentangle.) Tachenius attacked Dieterich, whom he naturally held responsible, in *Echo . . . de liquore Alcaeist*; it also apparently has disappeared. Dieterich's *Vindiciae adversus Ottonem Techenium* (Hamburg, 1655), however, is extant and gives an account of the whole affair and a scurrilous narrative of Tachenius' youthful career, as well as casting doubt upon the composition of the "viperine salt," which Dieterich claimed was mainly spirit of hartshorn (ammoniacal salt). Tachenius also was attacked by Johann Zwelfer in a new edition of the *Pharmacopoeia Augustana* (1657), on the ground that the viperine salt was no novelty and, in any case, of doubtful efficacy. Tachenius replied in *Hippocrates chemicus*, a defense of the viperine salt that included a discussion of the nature and use of alkalies. In his *Clavis* he further elaborated his theory of alkalies and advanced the theory that acid and alkali are the two principles or elements of all things: acid, hot and dry, provides the masculine principle; alkali, cold and moist, the feminine. According to Tachenius they correspond to the fire and water that Hippocrates found in all things, and hence he claimed to have revived "Hippocratean chemistry"—whatever that may be. His views obviously were derived from the Helmontian theory of acid and alkali as the governing principles of human physiology. Tachenius did not, as historians have claimed, "correctly" define salts as composed of acid and alkali, since to him all matter, animate and inanimate alike, was so composed. *Hippocrates chemicus* is of added interest for its descriptions of industrial methods of the production of soap, sal ammoniac, and corrosive sublimate. The date of his death is unknown; he is variously described as alive in Venice, in either 1669 or 1699, and as having died in 1670.

BIBLIOGRAPHY

I. ORIGINAL WORKS. The first two works published by Tachenius are extremely rare and appear not to have been seen by anyone writing on him since the eighteenth century; their titles were then given as *Epistola de famoso liquore Alkahest Helmontii* (Venice, 1652 [or 1655]) and *Echo ad vindicias chyrosophi de liquore Alcaeist* (Venice, 1656). They were followed by a treatise on diseases of the joints (possibly his M.D. thesis), *Exercitatio de recta acceptatione arthritidis et podagrae* (Padua, 1662). Under the anagrammatic pseudonym Marc Antonio Crassellane chinese [sic] there appeared *Lux obnubilata suapte natura refulgens. Vera de lapide philosophico theorica metro italico descripta . . .* (Venice, 1666; Milan, 1968), ascribed to Tachenius by MSS notes in two copies at the Bibliothèque Nationale—French trans. as *La lumière sortant par soy même des ténèbres* (Paris, 1687, 1693); German trans. as *Das aus der Finsterniss von sich selbst hervorbrechende Light* (Langensalza, 1772).

His most popular works, which went through many eds., often together, were *Hippocrates chemicus, per ignem et aquam methodo inaudita novissimi salis viperini antiquissima fundamenta ostendens* (Venice, 1666, 1678, 1697; Brunswick, 1668; Paris, 1669, 1674; Leiden, 1671); and *Antiquissimae Hippocraticae medicinae clavis manuali experientia in naturae fontibus elaborata* (Brunswick, 1668; Venice, 1669, 1697; Frankfurt, 1669, 1673; Leiden, 1671; Paris, 1671, 1672; Lyons, 1671). An English ed. of both is *Otto Tachenius His Hippocrates Chymicus, Which Discovers the Ancient Foundations of the Late Viperine Salt. And His Clavis Thereunto* (London, 1677, 1690). *Tractorum de morborum principe* was published both with *Hippocrates chemicus* (Venice, 1678) and independently (Osnabrück, 1678, 1679).

II. SECONDARY LITERATURE. Tachenius' acid-alkali theory was first discussed at length in F. Bertrand, *Réflexions nouvelles sur l'acide et sur l'alcalie* (Lyons, 1683). The chief biographical source appears to be J. C. Barchusen, *Historia medicinae* (Amsterdam, 1710), based in turn partly on Dieterich's *Vindiciae*. There are

brief biographies in *Allgemeine deutsche Biographie*, XXXVII (Berlin, 1894, 1971), 340; John Ferguson, *Bibliotheca chemica*, II (London, 1906, 1954), 424–425; and Lynn Thorndike, *A History of Magic and Experimental Science*, VIII, 357–361. For a long summary of *Hippocrates chemicus* and *Clavis*, see J. R. Partington, *A History of Chemistry*, II (London, 1961), 291–296.

MARIE BOAS HALL

TACQUET, ANDREAS (*b.* Antwerp, Belgium, 23 June 1612; *d.* Antwerp, 22 December 1660), *mathematics*.

Tacquet was the son of Pierre Tacquet, a merchant, and Agnes Wandelen of Nuremberg. His father apparently died while the boy was still young but left the family with some means. Tacquet received an excellent education in the Jesuit *collège* of his native town, and a contemporary report describes him as a gifted if somewhat delicate child. In 1629 he entered the Jesuit order as a novice and spent the first two years in Malines and the next four in Louvain, where he studied logic, physics, and mathematics. His mathematics teacher was William Boelmans, a student of and secretary to Gregorius Saint Vincent. After his preliminary training Tacquet taught in various Jesuit *collèges* for five years, notably Greek and poetry at Bruges from 1637 to 1639. From 1640 to 1644 he studied theology in Louvain and in 1644–1645 he taught mathematics there. He took his vows on 1 November 1646 and subsequently taught mathematics in the *collèges* of Louvain (1649–1655) and Antwerp (1645–1649, 1655–1660).

Tacquet's most important mathematical work, *Cylindricorum et annularium*, contained a number of original theorems on cylinders and rings. Its main importance, however, lay in its concern with questions of method. Tacquet rejected all notions that solids are composed of planes, planes of lines, and so on, except as heuristic devices for finding solutions. The approach he adopted was that of Luca Valerio and Gregorius, an essentially Archimedean method. The development of his thought can be seen in the fact that in his *Arithmeticae theoria et praxis* he took the value of ax^n ($x < 1$, $n \to \infty$) to be actually zero. Tacquet's most popular work was *Elementa geometriae*, which went through numerous editions during the seventeenth and eighteenth centuries and was edited and revised by Whiston, Musschenbroek, and Bošković. Although little more than a paraphrase of parts of Euclid and Archimedes, the book was distinguished by its clarity and order. Tacquet's *Opera mathe-*

matica was published posthumously and contained, among other previously printed and unprinted works, his *Astronomia*. In the eighth book of this work he rejected the motion of the earth, first, because there was no proof, physical or philosophical, to prove it; second, because his faith required him to believe in its immobility.

Tacquet's importance was mainly pedagogical and his books taught elementary mathematics to many generations of readers, although his influence on Pascal may have been greater. As a creative mathematician he can hardly be deemed more than minor. He was extremely well-read in mathematics, astronomy, and physics, and seemed to have almost total knowledge of the literature. This makes him appear at times as a typical exponent of the irritatingly erudite eclecticism of seventeenth-century scientific Jesuits. However, most of his works were written as textbooks for the Jesuit *collèges* and had no pretensions to originality. His devotion to his church, his order, and his teaching may explain his relative lack of creativity.

BIBLIOGRAPHY

I. ORIGINAL WORKS. The standard bibliography of Tacquet's works is in C. Sommervogel, *Bibliothèque de la Compagnie de Jésus*, VII (Brussels, 1896), cols. 1806–1811. The most important are *Cylindricorum et annularium* (Antwerp, 1651, 1659), also in the *Opera*; *Elementa geometriae* (Antwerp, 1654, 1665, 1672), which was issued in numerous eds. and revs., including translations into English, Italian and Greek, at least until 1805; and *Arithmeticae theoria et praxis* (Louvain, 1656; Antwerp, 1665, 1682). The *Opera mathematica* (Antwerp, 1669, 1707) contains works on astronomy, spherical trigonometry, practical geometry, and fortification, plus previously published writings on geometry and Aristotle's wheel. Tacquet's correspondence with Huygens is printed in *Oeuvres complètes de Christiaan Huygens, publiées par la Société hollandaise des sciences*, I–III (The Hague, 1888–1890), *passim*.

II. SECONDARY LITERATURE. For biographical information on Tacquet, see H. Bosmans, "Tacquet," in *Biographie nationale*, XXIV (Brussels, 1926–1929), cols. 440–464; and "Le Jésuite mathématicien anversois André Tacquet (1612–1660)," in *Gulden passer*, **3** (1925), 63–87. See also Bosmans' "André Tacquet (S. J.) et son traité d'arithmétique théorique et pratique," in *Isis*, **9** (1927), 66–82. There is no adequate analysis of Tacquet's mathematics and science. For earlier accounts see A. G. Kästner, *Geschichte der Mathematik*, III (Göttingen, 1799), 266–284, 442–449; and J. B. J. Delambre, *Histoire de l'astronomie moderne*, II (Paris, 1821), 531–535. Among modern studies that treat Tac-

quet is C. R. Wallner, "Über die Entstehung des Grenzbegriffes," in *Bibliotheca mathematica*, 3rd ser., **4** (1903), 246–259.

PER STRØMHOLM

IBN ṬAHIR. For a detailed study of his life and work, see **Al-Baghdādī, Abū Manṣūr ᶜAbd al-Qāhir ibn Ṭāhir ibn Muḥammad ibn ᶜAbdallah, al-Tamīnī, al-Shāfiᶜī,** in the Supplement.

TAIT, PETER GUTHRIE (*b.* Dalkeith, Scotland, 28 April 1831; *d.* Edinburgh, Scotland, 4 July 1901), *physics, mathematics.*

Tait was the son of the former Mary Ronaldson and John Tait, who was secretary to the duke of Buccleuch. He was taught first at Dalkeith Grammar School and, after his father's death, at a school in Circus Place and later at the Academy, both in Edinburgh. With his mother and his two sisters Tait lived in Edinburgh with an uncle, John Ronaldson, who introduced the boy to geology, astronomy, and photography. It is interesting to note that the order in the mathematics section of the Edinburgh Academical Club Prize for 1846 was first Tait, then Lewis Campbell, and third J. C. Maxwell. (In the following year Tait was second to Maxwell.) Tait entered Edinburgh University in 1847, and after a session there went in 1848 to Peterhouse, Cambridge, where his tutor was William Hopkins. He graduated as senior wrangler and first Smith's Prizeman in 1852. (Second in the tripos was another student at Peterhouse, W. J. Steele, with whom Tait collaborated on his first book, *Dynamics of a Particle* [1856]. Steele died before completing his portion of the book.)

In 1854 Tait left Cambridge, where he was a fellow of his college, to become professor of mathematics at Queen's College, Belfast. His colleague there was Thomas Andrews, with whom he collaborated in research on the density of ozone and the results of electrical discharge through gases. Other colleagues were Charles Wyville Thomson, who later was scientific leader of the *Challenger* expedition, and James Thomson, brother of William, Lord Kelvin, and discoverer of the effect of pressure on the melting point of ice. Tait's debts to Andrews were undoubtedly great, for the latter introduced him to experimental physics; but he did not, as is occasionally said, introduce Tait to Hamilton's calculus of quaternions, which had occupied Tait while he was at Cambridge.

Tait succeeded J. D. Forbes as professor of natural philosophy at Edinburgh in 1860 and held the chair until shortly before his death. In 1857 he married Margaret Archer Porter, the sister of two Peterhouse friends. One of their four sons, the best amateur golfer of his day, was killed in the Boer War.

At Edinburgh, Tait was confirmed in his recently found liking for experimentation by the duties required of him. In 1862, for example, he wrote a paper jointly with J. A. Wanklyn on electricity developed during evaporation. In 1867, having been greatly taken by Helmholtz's paper on vortex motion, he devised an apparatus for studying vortex smoke rings, thereby giving Kelvin the idea of a vortex atom. His study of vortices was the starting point of a highly important pioneer study of the topology of knots. Tait continued to experiment on thermoelectricity, publishing extensively on the subject and on thermodynamics as a whole. In 1873 he presented a first sketch of his well-known thermoelectric diagram to the Royal Society of Edinburgh. In 1875 he experimented with James Dewar on the behavior of the Crookes radiometer and gave the first satisfactory explanation of it. Between 1876 and 1888, using superb equipment of his own design supplied by the Admiralty, Tait did research on the corrections that it would be necessary to apply to the findings of the *Challeng-er* expedition regarding deep-sea temperatures. This work led to important experimental studies of compressibility and the behavior of materials under impact. In the same connection Tait wrote a classic paper on the trajectory of a golf ball (1896). The fourth in an important series of papers on the kinetic theory of gases (1886–1892) contained, according to Kelvin, the first proof of the Waterston-Maxwell equipartition theorem.

Tait's life was marked by several controversies, two of which reached a wide public. He felt himself committed to quaternions, having promised Hamilton, only a few days before the latter's death, to publish an elementary treatise on the subject. The work appeared in 1867 and was followed by new editions in 1873 and 1890. Tait disliked intensely the vector methods of J. W. Gibbs and Oliver Heaviside, and in a long exchange of polemics tended to have the worst of the argument. In his controversial *Sketch of the History of Thermodynamics* (1868), a highly prejudiced and pro-British account, the reputations of J. R. Mayer and Clausius suffer, while Kelvin and Joule are often praised at their expense.

BIBLIOGRAPHY

C. G. Knott, *Life and Scientific Work of Peter Guthrie Tait* (Cambridge, 1911), lists 365 papers and 22 books written wholly or partly by Tait. The last two books listed are collected volumes of Tait's *Scientific Papers* (Cambridge, 1898–1900). His best-known work was vol. I of *Treatise on Natural Philosophy* (Oxford, 1867; Cambridge, 1878, 1883), written jointly with Sir William Thomson and widely known as "T and T′." A promised vol. II failed to appear. Tait and Thomson also collaborated on an elementary version.

Knott's biography, which refers to all the important obituaries, is itself the fundamental biographical source, although very uncritical. See also J. H. Hamilton Dickson, in *Dictionary of National Biography*, 2nd supp., III (1912), 471–474; and A. Macfarlane, "P.G.T.," in *Bibliotheca mathematica*, 3rd ser., **4** (1903), 185–200. For the controversy over the history of thermodynamics, see D. S. L. Cardwell, *From Watt to Clausius* (London, 1971), 282–289.

J. D. NORTH

TALBOT, WILLIAM HENRY FOX (*b.* Melbury House, Dorsetshire, England, 11 February 1800; *d.* Lacock Abbey, Wiltshire, England, 17 September 1877), *photochemistry, mathematics.*

Talbot was the only child of William Davenport Talbot, an officer of dragoons, and Lady Elisabeth Theresa Fox-Strangways, the eldest daughter of the second earl of Ilchester. Four years after his father's death in July 1800, his mother married Rear Admiral Charles Feilding, who established a warm relationship with his stepson. Talbot grew up with two half sisters in an upper-class family that possessed both social position and culture.

While studying at a boarding school in Rottingdean and later at Harrow, Talbot distinguished himself as a scholar. At age seventeen he entered Trinity College, Cambridge, where he studied classical languages and mathematics, receiving in 1820 the Porson Prize for Greek verse, and graduating in 1821 as twelfth wrangler and second chancellor's medalist. Soon thereafter he published a half dozen papers on mathematics but spent much of the next decade traveling on the Continent, living the life of a gentleman scholar. He established himself in the late 1820's at the family estate, historic Lacock Abbey, ran successfully as a Liberal from Chippenham for the first reform Parliament (1833–1834), and on 20 December 1832 married Constance Mundy of Markeaton, Derbyshire. Talbot was an active member of numerous scholarly and scientific societies, including the Royal Society, the Royal Astronomical Society, and the British Association for the Advancement of Science.

Talbot's formative years were spent under the influence of the dominant Romantic atmosphere of England and Western Europe. He frequented Romantic operas and concerts and avidly read the works of Goethe, Byron, and Scott, naming two of his daughters after characters in Scott's works. His love of nature manifested itself in his lifelong interest in flowers and in his penchant for travel. His fondness for the past was stimulated not only by Scott's historical novels and by his own historic estate, but also by Young and Champollion's deciphering of the hieroglyphics on the Rosetta Stone in the early 1820's and Rawlinson and Hincks's deciphering of the Assyrian cuneiform in the middle 1840's. These stimuli merged with his flair for languages to initiate a lifelong series of translations from Assyrian and other ancient languages and of historical and philological studies. Beginning with a book of Greek verse, *Legendary Tales* (London, 1830), these translations and studies included four other books and at least sixty-two articles in scholarly journals.

After completing his study at Cambridge, Talbot continued his work in mathematics, systematically studying elliptic integrals. Building upon the earlier achievements of Fagnano dei Toschi, Euler, Legendre, Jacobi, and Abel, he addressed himself to the problem of summing the integrals of any function. His early mathematical work led to his election as a fellow of the Royal Society, while his work on elliptic integrals brought him the Royal Medal of the Society for the year 1838 and an appointment to the Royal Society council.

During the same period Talbot's interests in chemistry and optics quickened, and he gradually adopted a unified, dynamic view of physical phenomena. The early nineteenth century witnessed the adoption and modification of new theoretical frameworks in chemistry and optics. The discovery of many new substances stimulated increasing concern with chemical composition and structure, while the wave theory of light posed problems with dispersion, absorption, photochemical reaction, and other forms of light-matter interaction. Although Talbot counted Wheatstone, Brewster, and Babbage among his scientific friends, he most closely followed the ideas of his friend John Herschel on light. Adopting the wave theory of light and a kinetic interpretation of light, heat, and matter, he pursued the problem of light-matter interaction through the study of optics, crystallography, and spectra. Intrigued by the similar optical characteristics of light and radiant heat as demonstrated by Melloni and Forbes, he sought to show the unity of the chemical rays with visible rays and heat rays. He also sought to use light and optical properties as analytical tools in order to determine the nature and structure of matter and to develop methods of chemical identification. Utilizing the vibratory theory of molecular behavior in gases, he suggested in 1835 a connection between spectral lines and chemical composition. In an 1836 paper he employed the polarizing microscope as a tool to explore "the internal structure of transparent bodies, even in their minutest visible particles" (*London and Edinburgh Philosophical Magazine* [1836], p. 288). This paper brought him the honor of being named the Bakerian lecturer of the Royal Society for the year 1836.

It was with the development of photography that Talbot's love of nature and landscapes merged with his interests in optics and photochemistry. His efforts to sketch Italian scenery had met with repeated frustration. When he realized that he lacked artistic talent, he turned in 1823 to the use of a camera obscura as a drawing aid, but without satisfaction. Again in October of 1833, while honeymooning on the shores of Lake Como, he met with failure when he used Wollaston's recently developed boon to nature lovers and amateur artists, the camera lucida. At that time it occurred to Talbot to imprint the image on chemically sensitized paper. Returning to England in January 1834, he and his assistant, Nicholaas Henneman, conducted many experiments; by 1835 they were able to obtain "negatives" by employing tiny camera obscuras and paper sensitized with excess silver nitrate and fixed with excess common salt. Between 1835 and 1839, Talbot and Henneman continued their experiments, motivated by a desire for an analytic tool for research on radiant heat and light, as well as by a desire for reproducing images from nature. Following Arago's announcement to the Académie des Sciences 7 January 1839 of the existence of Daguerre's photographic process, Talbot became concerned over the priority of his work; he frantically sought to improve his process prior to the disclosure of Daguerre's. Nevertheless, Daguerre's process proved to be vastly superior to Talbot's in the quality of the image. In September 1840 Talbot discovered that gallic acid would develop a latent image on paper, and he called this new process the calotype. He patented and then disclosed the process in a paper presented to the Royal Society in June of 1841.

Although Talbot's photographic efforts did not meet with major commercial success and, because of his efforts to enforce his patents, did not win him popular acclaim, his paper on the calotype did bring him the honor of the Rumford Medal of the Royal Society (1842) for the most outstanding piece of research on light during the previous two years. In the middle 1840's he published two of the earliest books illustrated with photographs. Although twenty-eight of his fifty-nine scientific papers were published after 1840, most of these were minor papers on photography and mathematics. In 1852 he patented and published a method of photoengraving called photoglyphy. From the mid-1850's, with the increasing public clamor over his patent suits, Talbot's interests shifted increasingly to philological and historical studies. Despite the significant contribution he made in these scholarly pursuits. It was his development of the first negative-positive process in photography—that union of his naturalistic and artistic inclinations with his unitary photochemical interests—that brought him his greatest recognition both during his lifetime and after his death.

BIBLIOGRAPHY

I. ORIGINAL WORKS. Talbot's published scientific work appears exclusively in the fifty-nine articles listed in the *Royal Society Catalogue of Scientific Papers*. His two books illustrated with calotypes are *The Pencil of Nature*, parts I–VI (London, 1844–1846), and *Sun Pictures in Scotland* (London, 1845); his own remarks are contained in Appendix A of G. Tissandier, *A History and Handbook of Photography* (London, 1878).

Considerable data are contained in the legal records of the Court of Chancery, Public Record Office, London: Talbot *v* Colls (1852), and Talbot *v* Henderson (1854).

Manuscripts and artifacts are located at: Lacock Abbey, Wiltshire, England; Science Museum, London; Royal Society, London; Kodak Museum, Harrow, England; George Eastman House, Rochester, New York; Stark Library, University of Texas, Austin, Texas; and Soviet Academy of Sciences, Moscow. Some of the manuscript materials held in the U.S.S.R. have been published in T. P. Kravets, ed., *Dokumenti po istorii izobretenia fotografi* (Moscow, 1949), in English and Russian. See also Wood and Johnston below.

II. SECONDARY LITERATURE. The only biography of Talbot is Arthur H. Booth's *William Henry Fox Talbot* . . . (London, 1965), which is superficial and unreliable. Even the best sources restrict themselves largely to Talbot's photographic work. These include R. Cull, "Biographical Notice of the Late William Henry Fox Talbot," in *Society of Biblical Archaeology. Transactions*, **6** (1878), 543–549; *Dictionary of National Biography*; H. Gernsheim, "Talbot's and Herschel's Photographic Experiments in 1839," in *Image*, **8** (1959), 132–137; H. and A. Gernsheim, *History of Photography* . . . (New York, 1969); A. Jammes, *William H. Fox Talbot, Inventor of the Negative-Positive Process* (New York, 1973); J. D. Johnston, "William Henry Fox Talbot . . ., Part I," and J. D. Johnston and R. C. Smith, "Part II," in *Photographic Journal*, **87**A (1947), 3–13, and **108**A (1968), 361–371; B. Newhall, "William Henry Fox Talbot," in *Image*, **8** (1959), 60–75; E. Ostroff, "Restoration of Photograph . . .," in *Science*, **154** (7 Oct. 1966), 119–123; M. T. Talbot, "The Life and Personality of Fox Talbot," in *Photographic Journal*, **79** (1939), 546–549; D. B. Thomas, *The First Negatives* (London, 1964); and R. D. Wood, "The Involvement of Sir John Herschel in the Photographic Patent Case, Talbot *v* Henderson, 1854," and "J. B. Reade . . .," in *Annals of Science*, **27** (Sept. 1971), 239–264, and **27** (March 1971), 13–83.

REESE V. JENKINS

TAMM, IGOR EVGENIEVICH (*b.* Vladivostok, Russia, 8 July 1895; *d.* Moscow, U.S.S.R., 12 April 1971), *physics.*

From 1899 Tamm's family lived in the city of Elizavetgrad (now Kirovograd), where his father was a civil engineer. After graduating from the Gymnasium there in 1913, Tamm studied for a year at Edinburgh University; at the beginning of World War I in 1914 he returned to Russia and entered the Faculty of Physics and Mathematics at Moscow University. In 1917 he was a member of the Elizavetgrad City Soviet of Worker and Soldier Deputies and was a delegate to the First Congress of Soviets in Petrograd. The following year Tamm graduated from Moscow University, and in 1921–1922 he worked at the Odessa Polytechnical Institute, where Mandelshtam, who greatly influenced Tamm's later scientific career, was a professor.

From 1922 Tamm worked in Moscow. In 1924 he published his first scientific work, on the electrodynamics of anisotropic media in the special theory of relativity, and became head of the department of theoretical physics at Moscow University, which he directed until 1941. In 1934, after the transfer to Moscow of the Academy of Sciences of the U.S.S.R., Tamm was named director of the theoretical section of its P. N. Lebedev

Physical Institute; and from then on, his activity was concentrated there.

Tamm's first scientific research, begun under the influence of Mandelshtam, was devoted to electrodynamics of anisotropic media, crystal optics in the theory of relativity, quantum theory of paramagnetism, and nonrelativistic quantum mechanics. In a major investigation on the quantum theory of the molecular scattering of light in solid bodies (1930) Tamm conducted the first quantification of elastic (sound) waves in solid bodies and introduced the concept of quanta of sound; later called phonons by Y. I. Frenkel, this concept gained wide acceptance in contemporary physics. In this work he also investigated the Rayleigh scattering of light (the Mandelshtam-Brillouin doublet) and combination scattering (the "Raman effect"), discovered in 1930 by Mandelshtam and G. S. Landsberg in crystals and, at the same time, by C. V. Raman and Krishnan in liquids.

In 1930 Tamm published two works dealing with the phenomenon of relativistic quantum mechanics of the electron, formulated by Dirac: "Über die Wechselwirkung der freien Elektronen . . .," and "Zamechanie dirakovskogo teorii sveta i dispersii" ("A Note on the Dirac Theory of Light and Dispersion"). Dirac's theory received almost general acceptance when it appeared, since it automatically led to the existence of a spin on the electron and allowed a natural interpretation of the fine structure in the spectrum of the hydrogen atom. But the concepts of negative energy states that were involved in the theory appeared unusual until the discovery of the positron and demanded more detailed study of the conclusions from the theory and their experimental verification.

With the aid of a strictly consistent quantum mechanical method, Tamm confirmed the results obtained earlier by Felix Klein and Yoshio Nishina on the basis of the method of correspondence. He also showed that according to Dirac's theory, scattering of even more low-frequency quanta of light from free electrons must occur through intermediate states with the negative electron energies. Thus it was shown that the negative energy states cannot be removed from Dirac's theory. In this work Tamm also proposed a new method of calculation, later developed by H. B. G. Casimir and named for him. Concurrently with Dirac and Oppenheimer, Tamm independently concluded that the fall of the free electron to a negative level was inevitable and determined the probability of annihilation of the electron and "hole."

In 1931–1933 Tamm studied the quantum the-

ory of metals, specifically the external photoeffect in metals and the state levels of the electrons on the surface of the metal. His work with S. P. Shubin was the first to show that the external photoeffect is caused by the presence of a jump in potential on the border of the metal vacuum and is associated with the effect of surface absorption of light, while the optic absorption of light by the metal is associated with the volume effect. In works dating from 1932–1933 Tamm was the first to show, on the basis of quantum mechanics, that, along with the known "zone" electron states inside the crystal, there could also be electron states of a completely different type on the surface of the crystal. Further theoretical and experimental research on semiconductors and dielectrics confirmed that these "Tamm surface levels" of electrons are evident in a great many physical phenomena, particularly in semiconductors, and lead to "barrier" layers.

From 1934 Tamm devoted his research to the atomic nucleus and cosmic rays. Two of the early works were related to the nature of nuclear forces: "Obmennye sily mezhdu neytronami i protonami i teoria Fermi" ("Exchange Forces Between Neutrons and Protons, and Fermi's Theory," 1934) and "β-radioaktivnost i yadernye sili" ("Beta Radioactivity and Nuclear Forces," 1936). Using Fermi's theory of beta radiation, Tamm sought to determine whether the nuclear forces could be caused by an exchange between nucleons, electrons, and neutrinos. In the 1934 work he gave a formula for the potential and evaluated the quantity of force arising in this process, but this kind of exchange interaction proved to be too weak in comparison with the observed nuclear forces and consequently could not serve to explain them. Later it was discovered that the exchange nature of nuclear forces corresponds to the activity; but the exchange is realized not by electrons and neutrinos, as Tamm suggested, but by pi-mesons. All later theories of nuclear forces were constructed according to the theoretical scheme developed in these investigations by Tamm but took into account the role of the pi-meson.

At the same time that he was conducting this research, Tamm and S. A. Altshuler published works on the magnetic moment of the neutron. By analyzing the material he had obtained experimentally, Tamm concluded that although the neutron is a neutral particle, it actually has a magnetic moment. He also correctly estimated the negative sign of this moment. These investigations led Tamm to another important conclusion: that despite current opinion, mesons, which carry an interaction between nucleons, do not have stationary levels in the central Coulomb field. This result led to the work (with L. D. Landau) "O proiskhozhdenii yadernykh sil" ("On the Origin of Nuclear Forces," 1940).

In 1937–1939 Tamm and I. M. Frank developed the theory of radiation of the electron, which moves through a medium with a velocity exceeding the velocity of light in that medium. This theory led to an understanding of the nature of the radiation discovered by S. I. Vavilov and P. A. Cherenkov. For this work Tamm was awarded the Nobel Prize (with I. M. Frank and P. A. Cherenkov) in 1958.

During World War II, Tamm carried out a number of complex practical investigations. In 1945 he returned to the interaction of molecules. In the first of these works he formulated a new method of calculating the interaction not dependent on an expansion in terms of a coupling constant, the large size of which makes perturbation theory inapplicable to quantum meson dynamics. This method, applied by Tamm in 1945 and developed by P. D. Dankov in 1950, is known as the Tamm-Dankov method. It is widely used in the theoretical study of the interaction of mesons with nucleons and of nucleons with each other, particularly in the study of the deuteron.

In 1947 Tamm and V. L. Ginzburg formulated a theory of a molecule that can be found in states with various spins. This work contains the first relativistically invariant wave equations for particles with inner degrees of freedom, described by continuous variables. Tamm's research in the theory of nuclear forces and elementary particles was continued in two directions. One was the construction of a polyphenomenological theory based on the possibility of the existence of isobaric states of nucleons. On this basis Tamm and his colleagues investigated processes of scattering, the photoproduction of pi-mesons by nucleons, and the interaction of nucleons. The other was the development by Tamm, with V. Y. Feynberg and V. P. Silin, of a new form of Tamm's method, proposed by F. J. Dyson and intended particularly for the study of the interaction of pi-mesons with nucleons.

Tamm worked on other questions, including the investigation, according to cascade theory, of cosmic ray showers (with S. Z. Belenky), which were first considered to be ionization losses of particles. Of very great importance was the theory of gas discharge in a powerful magnetic field developed in 1950 by Tamm and A. D. Sakharov. It was the basis of all subsequent Soviet research on guided thermonuclear reactions and led to important results.

An important place among Tamm's investigations was occupied by the work (carried out in 1946 with Mandelshtam) on the meaning of the indeterminacy between time and energy in quantum mechanics. Also worth noting is his work, done in 1948–1949, on several mathematical methods for the theory of particle scattering. During his last years Tamm searched for ways to remove fundamental difficulties in the theory of elementary particles and often presented survey reports at conferences. For example, at the All-Union Conference on Quantum Electrodynamics and the Theory of Elementary Particles (1955), he presented the survey reports "Metod obrezania uravneny po chislu chastits v teorii mezonov" ("Method of Truncating the Equation According to the Number of Particles in the Theory of Mesons"), written with V. P. Silin and V. Y. Feynberg, and "Polufenomenologicheskaya izobarnaya teoria vzaimodeystvia mezonov s nuklonami" ("Semiphenomenological Isobar Theory of Interaction of Mesons With Nucleons"), written with Y. A. Golfand, G. F. Farkov, and others. At the All-Union Conference on the Physics of High-Energy Particles (1956), Tamm, Silin, and Feynberg delivered the survey report "Sravnenie mezonnoy teorii s eksperimentami" ("Comparison of Meson Theory With Experiments").

Tamm's activity was not limited to scientific research. He gave much attention to teaching, to the solution of practical and administrative problems, and to social questions. From 1924 as a docent, and from 1930 as professor and head of the department of theoretical physics at the M. V. Lomonosov Moscow State University, Tamm (in collaboration with Mandelshtam) supervised the orientation and content of all courses in theoretical physics and lectured at the Physics and Mathematics Faculty of the university. During this period he wrote *Osnovy teorii elektrichestva* ("Principles of the Theory of Electricity"), which went through many editions.

The fight for scientific biology, which Tamm led, also is worthy of attention. He maintained the firm conviction that leadership of the natural sciences would pass in the relatively near future from physics to biology. Tamm was active in the Pugwash movement and was awarded the Order of State Prize, First Degree, for his service to science. In 1933 he was elected corresponding member and, in 1953 active member, of the Academy of Sciences of the U.S.S.R.

BIBLIOGRAPHY

I. ORIGINAL WORKS. Tamm's early writings include "Über die Quantentheorie der molekularen Lichtzerstreuung in festen Körpern," in *Zeitschrift für Physik,* **60** (1930), 345–363; "Über die Wechselwirkung der freien Elektronen mit der Strahlung nach der Diracschen Theorie des Elektrons und nach der Quantenelektrodynamik," *ibid.,* **62** (1930), 545–568; "Über eine mögliche Art der Elektronenbindung an Kristalloberflächen," in *Physikalische Zeitschrift der Sowjetunion,* **1** (1932), 733; "Exchange Forces Between Neutrons and Protons, and Fermi's Theory," in *Nature,* **133** (1934), 981; "Nuclear Magnetic Moments and the Properties of the Neutron," *ibid.,* **134** (1934), 380; "Kogerentnoe izluchenie bystrogo elektrona v srede" ("Coherent Radiation of Fast Electrons Passing Through Matter"), in *Doklady Akademii nauk SSSR,* **14,** no. 3 (1937), 107–112; "Svechenie chistykh zhidkostey pod deystviem bystrykh elektronov" ("Luminescence of Pure Liquids Under the Influence of Fast Electrons"); in *Izvestiya Akademii nauk SSSR,* Seria fiz. (1938), nos. 1–2, 29, written with I. M. Frank and P. A. Cherenkov; "The Transmutations of the Cosmic-Ray Electrons and the Nuclear Forces," in *Physical Review,* **53** (1938), 1016–1017; and "Radiation Emitted By Uniformly Moving Electrons," in *Journal of Physics of the U.S.S.R.,* **1,** nos. 5–6 (1939), 439.

Subsequent works are "O proiskhozhdenii yadernykh sil" ("On the Origin of Nuclear Forces"), in *Doklady Akademii nauk SSR,* **29** (1940), 555–556, written with L. D. Landau; "Izluchenie elektrona pri ravnomernom dvizhenii v prelomlyayushchey srede" ("Theory of the Electron in Uniform Motion in a Refracting Medium"), in *Trudy fizicheskago instituta,* **2,** no. 4 (1944), 63, written with I. M. Frank; "The Energy Spectrum of Cascade Electrons," in *Physical Review,* **70** (1946), 660–664, written with S. Z. Belenky; "K teorii spina" ("Toward a Theory of Spin"), in *Zhurnal eksperimentalnogo i teoreticheskogo fizika,* **17,** no. 3 (1947), 227, written with V. L. Ginzburg; and "O nekotorykh matematicheskikh metodakh teorii rasseyania chastits" ("On Certain Mathematical Methods in the Theory of Scattering of Particles"), *ibid.,* **18,** no. 4 (1948), 337–345, and **19,** no. 1 (1949), 74–77.

Later writings include "K relyativistskoy teorii vzaimodeystvia nuklonov" ("Toward a Relativistic Theory of the Mutual Interaction of Nucleons"), *ibid.,* **24,** no. 1 (1954), 3; "Polufenomenologicheskaya teoria vzaimodeystvia π-mezonov s nuklonami. Rasseyanie π-mezonov nuklonami" ("Semiphenomenological Theory of the Mutual Interaction of pi-Mesons With Nucleons. Scattering of pi-Mesons With Nucleons"), *ibid.,* **26,** no. 6 (1954), 649–667, written with Y. A. Golfand and V. Y. Feynberg; "Metod usechennykh uravneny polya i ego primenenie k rasseyaniyu mezonov nuklonami" ("Method of Truncating Field Equations and Its Application to the Scattering of Mesons by Nucleons"), ibid., **29,** no. 1 (1955), 6–19, written with V. P. Silin and

V. Y. Feynberg; "O strukture nuklonov" ("On the Structure of Nucleons"), *ibid.,* **32,** no. 1 (1957), 178–180; "Teoria magnitnykh termoyadernykh reaktsy" ("Theory of Magnetic Thermodynamic Reactions"), in *Fizika plazmy i problemy upravlyaemykh termoyadernykh reaktsy* ("Plasma Physics and Problems of Thermodynamic Reactions"), I (Moscow, 1958), 3–19, 31–41; and *Osnovy teorii elektrichestva,* 7th ed. ("Principles of the Theory of Electricity"; Moscow, 1957).

II. SECONDARY LITERATURE. *Igor Evgenievich Tamm, Materialy k biobibliografii uchenykh SSSR.* Seria fizik, no. 9 (Moscow, 1959), with introductory articles by V. L. Ginzburg and E. L. Feynberg and a bibliography; V. L. Ginzburg and E. L. Feynberg, "Igor Evgenievich Tamm," in *Uspekhi fizicheskikh nauk,* **56,** no. 4 (1955), 469–475, with bibliography of Tamm's most important works; V. L. Ginzburg, A. D. Sakharov, and E. L. Feynberg, "Igor Evgenievich Tamm," *ibid.,* **86,** no. 2 (1965), 353–356; I. M. Lifshits and S. I. Pekar, "Tammovskie svyazannye sostoyania elektronov na poverkhnosti kristalla i poverkhnostynye kolebania atomov reshetki" ("Tamm Connected Electron States on the Surface of a Crystal and Surface Vibration of Atoms in a Lattice"), *ibid.,* **56,** no. 4 (1955), 531–568; S. V. Vonsovsky, A. V. Sokolov, and A. Z. Veksler, "Fotoeffekt v metallakh" ("Photoeffect in Metals"), *ibid.,* 477–530; and V. P. Silin and V. Y. Feynberg, "Metod Tamma-Dankova" ("The Tamm-Dankov Method"), *ibid.,* 569–635.

J. G. DORFMAN

TAMMANN, GUSTAV HEINRICH JOHANN APOLLON (*b.* Yamburg [now Kingisepp, R.S.F.S.R.], St. Petersburg gubernia, Russia, 16/28 May 1861; *d.* Göttingen, Germany, 17 December 1938), *physical chemistry.*

Tammann belonged to the generation of scientists who created the discipline of physical chemistry. He was a founder of metallography and of metallurgy, and he pioneered the study of solid-state chemical reactions.

Tammann was born into a German-speaking, Protestant family from Livonia, the members of which had belonged to the untitled Russian nobility since at least the beginning of the nineteenth century. His father, Heinrich Tammann, was municipal physician in Yamburg and in Gorigoretsk, Mogilev gubernia (now Gorki, Belorussian S.S.R.), and professor of practical medicine at the agricultural college (now Belorussian Agricultural Academy) in Gorigoretsk. He was appointed to the faculty of the University of Moscow but died just before assuming the post. Tammann was then only four years old, and the responsibility for his education fell entirely upon his mother, the former Mathilde Schünmann. She returned to her native Dorpat (now Tartu) and skillfully overcame the considerable financial difficulties facing her. After five years of private tutoring, Tammann entered the Dorpat Gymnasium, where, despite poor grades in languages, he was regularly one of the top students in his class. At the age of fourteen, he was offered a promising military career as a protégé of Friedrich Graf von Berg, a Russian field marshal, but his mother rejected the proposal.

Tammann began to study chemistry at Dorpat in 1879. Even before he wrote his *Kandidatenschrift* (on the vapor pressure of solutions), which he submitted in 1883, he succeeded Wilhelm Ostwald as second assistant to Carl Schmidt, a former student of Justus Liebig and of Friedrich Wöhler. He also taught at the local girl's high school and at the county school. A chemist at Dorpat during this period could expect to find work only in problems related to medicine or agriculture. Consequently, at the urging of Johann Lemberg, Tammann decided to specialize in plant physiology, an area to which he was introduced by Gustav von Bunge. In one of a series of papers in this field (1895) he correctly explained the existence of optimal temperatures for enzyme reactions as the result of two independent processes, each of which is temperature-dependent but responds oppositely to temperature changes: the catalytic reaction and the thermal inactivation of the enzyme. Although Tammann retained a strong interest in fermentation processes, membranes, and osmotic pressure, it soon became apparent that he was destined to work in other fields.

Tammann first studied topics on the boundary between chemistry and physics in the autumn of 1883, when, continuing the work of Adolph Wüllner, he began to determine molecular weights from the lowering of vapor pressure. This research provided the basis for his master's essay, which, when he defended it in 1885, incurred strong criticism from Arthur von Oettingen. The high cost of printing prevented Tammann from broadening this research into a doctoral dissertation. Instead, he submitted a thesis on the metamerism of the metaphosphates; and in the same year (1887) he qualified as a university lecturer. In 1889 he worked in Helmholtz's institute at Charlottenburg and with Ostwald at Leipzig. At Leipzig, Tammann met Arrhenius and Nernst, with whom he maintained close friendships throughout his life. His relations with Ostwald, however, always remained distant. Tammann's promotion to first assistant brought him back to Dorpat, where he advanced with un-usual rapidity. In 1890 he became *Dozent* (refusing, in the same year, an offer of an extraordinary professorship at Giessen). In 1892 he was appointed extraordinary professor and succeeded Schmidt as institute director, and in 1894 he was named full professor.

During his years at Dorpat, Tammann traveled extensively. In 1889–1890 he worked with Nernst at Göttingen on a study of the pressure at which hydrogen is liberated from solutions by the action of metals. He visited Russia several times, partly to learn Russian, on the advice of his friend Mendeleev, who followed his research with great interest. On one of these trips Tammann met Anna Mitscherling, the daughter of a German banker in St. Petersburg. They were married in 1890 and had one son and two daughters. In 1894 Tammann went to the Netherlands, where he made valuable contacts with van't Hoff, Kamerlingh Onnes, Roozeboom, and Jakob van Bemmelen. It was on this occasion that he developed his lifelong interest in heterogeneous equilibria. Also in 1894, during a trip to Nizhni Novgorod, he was stimulated to undertake research on petroleum, during which he discovered several new naphthalenes.[1] In 1897 Tammann traveled to Stockholm, where he saw Berzelius' instruments in such desolate condition that he published an appeal in the *Chemiker-Zeitung*, which prompted the founding of the Berzelius Museum.[2] While visiting the World Exposition at Paris in 1900, he studied the French metallurgical industry and became acquainted with Le Châtelier and his techniques.

At the urging of Nernst, Felix Klein, and the distinguished Prussian minister Friedrich Althoff, a chair of inorganic chemistry (the second in Germany) and a new institute were established at Göttingen in 1903. Tammann was chosen to head the institute, and he remained loyal to Göttingen despite several attractive offers. In 1909 his friend Boris Golitsyn secured his election as full member of the Imperial Academy of St. Petersburg, and, upon his retirement in 1930, he was invited to Riga.

Industry hoped for useful results from the new institute, and Tammann was determined to obtain them by means of a systematic examination of the inorganic materials of daily life. At first he wanted to specialize in silicate chemistry; but a discussion with Arthur Louis Day, who had just received a large grant from the Carnegie Institution for the construction of a geophysical laboratory, convinced him that he should give up this idea and concentrate his attention on metals and glasses.

Tammann continued his program of research when Nernst went to Berlin in 1905, and he succeeded to the latter's professorship at Göttingen in 1907, thus becoming director of the Institute of Physical Chemistry. After his retirement several scientific organizations and metal companies continued to finance Tammann's research, thus enabling him to engage from three to five assistants until 1937.

A giant not only in stature but also in health and capacity for work, Tammann regularly worked in his laboratory for ten hours a day. He was, nevertheless, devoted to his family. Moreover, he possessed an excellent knowledge of Goethe's writings and of Russian history, and he was an ardent swimmer. He restricted his friendships to a few colleagues, with one of whom, Otto Wallach, he would take a walk every Sunday. Tammann was unconventional, avoided all formality, and loved simplicity; yet he inspired respect in all who met him. His relations with co-workers and students, from whom he demanded total commitment, were forthright and often brusque; but basically they were characterized by a deep humanity. Many anecdotes illustrating his unusual sense of humor survive. It served him as an effective weapon when he felt criticism to be in order.

Tammann received many honors, prizes, and awards. He was both a Russian and a Prussian privy councillor. He was awarded four honorary doctorates and was an honorary citizen of the Technische Hochschule of Stuttgart. He belonged to various learned societies, notably the Academies of Berlin, Göttingen, Halle, and Vienna, and was an honorary member of the Russian Academy of Sciences, the Bunsen Society, the German Society for Metallurgy, the Royal Chemical Society, and (with Rutherford and Einstein) the British Institute of Metals.

Tammann's more than five hundred scientific writings extend over a very broad range of subjects and constitute a varied sequence devoted to both fundamental problems and detailed questions. Accordingly, Wilhelm Biltz applied to Tammann a remark of Goethe's: "I have chiseled giants out of marble and cut tiny figurines out of ivory." It is impossible in a few pages to do justice to this rich body of work, which has stimulated research in countless ways.

The theory of dilute solutions proposed by van't Hoff and Arrhenius left an important question unanswered. This deficiency greatly troubled Tammann, who on this question followed the views of Mendeleev. Specifically, in this theory the solutes were considered, by means of a schematic analogy, as ideal gases; however, the reciprocal effects on the solvent were neglected. In order to take these effects into account, Tammann developed the theory of internal pressure in homogeneous systems. According to his theory, the solution behaves like the solvent; the pressure is replaced, in both molecular and ionic solutions, by an attractive force between the solvent and the solute. In experiments begun in 1893 Tammann obtained pressures as high as about 4,000 atmospheres, somewhat greater than those previously reached by Émile Amagat. In 1907 Tammann collected in book form the results of many experiments on various solvents and presented the derivation of his theory. He showed that the temperature-dependence of many properties of solutions (including specific heats, viscosity, surface tension, and optical constants), as well as the pressure-dependence of their conductivity and compressibility, could be understood in the light of his new theory, which has been quite generally confirmed. In a work on compressibility published in 1895, Tammann employed a formula that he attributed to P. G. Tait and that has since been widely known under the latter's name. Only recently has it been pointed out that Tammann's formula is not at all identical with the one given by Tait in 1888.[3]

The field of heterogeneous equilibria—that is, the behavior of matter as a function of pressure, temperature, and chemical composition—was opened by Willard Gibbs's formulation of the phase rule; but it was van der Waals and, above all, Roozeboom who first recognized its outstanding practical significance. When Tammann entered this field in 1895, he treated the problem in its most general form before turning to applications; this allowed him to make substantial contributions to the systematization of inorganic chemistry as well as to the improvement of industrial production methods. The starting point of his research was twofold: the experiments of Thomas Andrews and Louis Cailletet on the equilibrium relationships between the liquid and vapor phases and the theoretical interpretation of the triple point. Many scientists, including Ostwald, believed that a continuous transition exists between the liquid and solid states corresponding to that between the liquid and vapor states. Tammann broke sharply with this conception in 1896. Supporting his argument with experiments and drawing on thermodynamical considerations, he put forward his own views in a monograph published in 1903. He asserted that the melting-point curve cannot end in a critical point; that the pressure-temperature diagram is basically a closed curve; and that, accordingly, all transitions from the crystalline state to other phases must be discontinuous.

Tammann modified his theory in a second monograph (1922), in which he stated that the melting curves must show a maximum (which under certain circumstances might not be a true maximum) and that, as a result, in typical cases the melting temperature ought to decrease again at very high pressures. He confirmed this prediction experimentally in the case of Glauber's salt, but the example was not entirely conclusive. Although several further, unobjectionable examples became known, it was later shown by P. W. Bridgman that up to extremely high pressures, melting-point curve maximums are the exception. This finding meant that Tammann's theory was of little practical significance. Nevertheless, it led him to the insight that the accepted division of matter into three states of aggregation (gas, liquid, and solid) was unsuitable. Anticipating the results of radiography, he postulated instead a twofold division consisting of an isotropic phase (gas, liquid, and amorphic) and an anisotropic phase (crystalline).

Parallel to this research was the series of studies that Tammann began in 1897 on the transition from the isotropic to the anisotropic phase. He showed that crystal growth depends on three independent quantities: the number of nuclei (that is, the number of crystallization centers), the crystallization velocity, and the heat flow. He pursued the study of these fundamental crystallization laws under varied external conditions and on a large number of substances. To a certain extent Tammann's theoretical work in this field culminated in the book *Aggregatzustände* (1922). Starting with notions taken from atomic theory and thermodynamics, he derived a new definition of phase stability; in this undertaking Gibbs's concept of free enthalpy provided the most significant criterion.

Guided by only a few preliminary studies (for example, those of Floris Osmond), Tammann developed a method of determining the chemical composition of a compound from the form of its cooling curve. By 1903 he had perfected the indispensable method of "thermic analysis," which has since been used successfully over a broad range of applications. Tammann employed it to explain systems composed of sulfides and chlorides as well as mixed crystal systems. Most important, however, it provided him with the means of opening up and systematically exploring an important field of inorganic chemistry, the intermetallic compounds.

Until this time it had not been possible to determine whether the fusion of two metals produced compounds of these metals, mixed crystals, or heterogeneous crystal mixtures. When Tammann began his studies of metallic compounds in 1903, little was known about them except what could be found in the works of Le Châtelier, Osmond, Roberts-Austen, C. T. Heycock and F. H. Neville, E. Heyn, F. Wüst, and N. S. Kurnakov, to which he referred. He systematically investigated the field through a combined application of thermic analysis and the microscopic analysis of sections, a technique in use since its development by Schreibers and Widmannstätten. Tammann's goal was to examine the 190 possible series of alloys of twenty common metals taken in mixing proportions that varied in steps of 10 percent by weight. (The total number of alloys was therefore 1,900.) By 1906, with the help of his students the project had progressed to the point that he was able to publish "Ueber die Fähigkeit der Elemente, miteinander Verbindungen zu bilden," which began at the point that Berzelius had reached in his work on the subject. In this article Tammann proved that, in general, the valence relationships and stoichiometric laws of the salts are not valid for metal-compound crystals. He also recognized that the alloys often behave like mixed crystals. World War I was a quiet period for Tammann, who used these years to probe more deeply into the nature of the mixed crystals.

Tammann's research in this area culminated in 1919 in his frequently cited publication on the resistance limits of binary systems as a function of the mixing proportion; in it he set forth the so-called $n/8$ law, which in its most rudimentary form had been used since the Middle Ages in the separation of gold and silver by means of aquafortis (nitric acid). From this law Tammann concluded that the atoms in mixed crystals are not arrayed on a statistical basis but are arranged in accordance with definite mathematical relationships. He realized that his theory of "superlattices" in mixed crystals could be definitively demonstrated only through radiographic inspection. His prediction concerning the superlattices was, in fact, corroborated radiographically for the gold-copper system in 1925 by C. H. Johansson and J. O. Linde. The conjectured relation between resistance limits and superlattices, however, has not proved to be correct; this was first suspected by G. Masing and was later demonstrated, for example, in the gold-silver system.

As Tammann progressed in the interpretation of the chemical properties of alloys, he became increasingly interested in the physical and chemical behavior of metals, in their crystal structure, in their electrical conductivity, and in their mechanical and other properties. Through his study of these topics he opened the field of metal physics. Tammann first addressed himself to two questions that preoccupied him for the rest of his life: What makes it possible for metals in the solid state to be worked? Why do properties of metals change so drastically during the process of cold-working?

Before Tammann began his research in this area, Otto Mügge had shown in the case of salts and transparent minerals that mechanical stresses in crystals produce displacement of their parts along the slip planes. Further, J. A. Ewing and W. Rosenhain had already begun to furnish the first answers concerning the plastic working of metals. Tammann's extended series of works on this subject, which have greatly influenced the techniques of metalworking, began in 1910 with a publication written in collaboration with Otto Faust. Having derived the malleability of metals in the solid state from crystallographic slipping, Tammann, accordingly, saw crystalline rearrangement as the cause of the alterations in the mechanical properties of metals during cold-working, especially the hardening.

It was known that through tempering (heating), the values that certain properties of metals have acquired in the course of being cold-worked return to the levels at which they were before the cold-working began. Tammann explained this phenomenon—which Sorby called recrystallization—as the result of the accumulation of energy during cold-working and of the growth of certain individual crystals at the expense of others. Through repeated recrystallizations Tammann was able to alter the size of crystal grains in metals within broad limits, and under suitable conditions he could even grow single crystals. Such crystals normally do not grow without limit—a fact he attributed to the existence of a *Zwischensubstanz*, a spongelike network consisting of the impurities that always occur along the boundaries of crystal grains. This network, which Tammann isolated in 1921 by elegant etching techniques, could not yet, however, explain other changes that occur during cold-working, such as in the density, color, electrical conductivity, and chemical reactivity of the metals. Tammann conjectured that to account for these changes, it would be necessary to assume the occurrence of alterations within the atoms. Of importance in this connection was his research on the binary-state diagrams of iron and its technically important

alloys, on passivity (especially of the iron-chromium alloys), and on iron carbide.

Tammann's illuminating findings about the physical and chemical bases of the metallurgical production processes first emerged from his research on the equilibria between molten metal and slag during the cooling processes in the interior of the earth. Emil Wiechert, on the basis of observations of earthquakes, had deduced the existence of at least three layers in the earth; and in 1924, Tammann postulated the existence of an intermediary sulfide layer between the outer silicate layer and the earth's iron-nickel core. His application of these conceptions to the techniques of steel production was an innovative and valuable contribution. Tammann also studied meteorites and silicates. In a short series of mineralogical and chemical communications issued by the institute of physical chemistry at Göttingen, he published phase diagrams of silicates and discussed the production and thermochemistry of these compounds. He later made a careful study of nontronite and kaolin. In 1925 he recognized that the concept of the molecule must be modified in dealing with silicates and that a chemical constitutional formula is not meaningful for them.

Since the 1890's the examination of the influence of pressure and temperature on matter had directed Tammann's attention to the phenomenon of allotropy or polymorphism. In *Kristallisieren und Schmelzen* (1903) he summarized his experiments on this subject and showed that the phenomenon is much more common than had been expected. His discovery of new modifications of ice (specifically, ice II and ice III) aroused intense interest; and Tammann himself thought that their discovery, along with that of resistance limits, constituted one of his two most noteworthy single scientific contributions. Tammann described the behavior of compressed liquids in 1911 in an approximate but surprisingly simple equation of state similar to one enunciated by O. Tumlirz. In 1915 he solved the much-disputed problem of the flow of glacial ice by showing that the phenomenon was the result of crystalline slipping. He had previously given an elegant theoretical refutation of the explanation proposed by Ostwald, Poynting, and Niggli, who attributed the flow to a pressure-dependent reduction in the melting point of ice.

Tammann's research on the nature of the states of matter had repeatedly led him to consider the glass state—he used the terms "glass" and "amorphous" synonymously—but he does not seem to have started his long series of studies on the glasses until 1925, when the Society of Glass Technology invited him to write a paper on the subject. In 1933 he published a monograph containing the results of his work, most of which was carried out in collaboration with his students. One of the most surprising findings was that the specific volume of a glass depends on the pressure at which it solidifies—dramatic evidence of the extraordinary complexity of the substances. Tammann was particularly intrigued by the "softening interval," the temperature interval within which glass changes from brittle to viscous. According to Tammann's theory of the states of aggregation, no sudden changes in properties should occur in this temperature region. He also showed that although, under certain conditions, many physical properties do change very considerably in this interval, they always change in a continuous manner.

As early as 1911 Tammann's experiments on diffusion in mixed crystals led him into a new field, the study of reactions of solid bodies with other solids and with gaseous substances. His findings led him to break with the old maxim *corpora non agunt, nisi fluida*. He determined the temperature (later named for him) at which mixtures of crystalline powders sinter and thereby laid the foundation of solid-state chemistry, a field later developed by J. A. Hedvall and W. Jander, among others. Tammann's investigation of the tarnish that forms on metallic surfaces was of the greatest importance for the theory of oxidation. In 1919 he stated that the layer of tarnish grows parabolically with time.[4] (This law was later explained theoretically by Carl Wagner.) In 1922, while examining other cases of oxidation, Tammann and Werner Köster found a logarithmic relation between the thickness of the oxidized layer and the time elapsed. The theoretical significance of this relation was not recognized, however, until forty years later.

Although many of Tammann's works had direct technical applications, his personal goal was the development of pure science, and in the final analysis he was concerned only with the search for the laws of nature. He dismissed verbose and flashy scientific writing with the remark, "It records the artist's earthly pilgrimage, which no one needs to know about." He had a remarkable gift for reducing complex problems to simple questions, which he then solved by means of experiments that often were astonishingly simple. This ability was exemplified in his experiments on resistance limits and on the determination of the thickness of oxidation layers. Two other examples are the "Tammann oven," in which a carbon tube serves as both wall and electrical heating element, and his apparatus for measuring outflowing liquids. Tammann's theoretical work did not always attract the interest of his contemporaries; and since later research has often taken paths that diverged from those he followed, many problems that he isolated remain unsolved. Although not an especially talented lecturer, Tammann was an unusually effective teacher. By having trained more than one hundred doctoral candidates and assistants, he helped to determine the conceptions and working methods of an entire generation of chemical physicists and metallurgists.

NOTES

1. The results are set forth in a patent application.
2. See *Chemiker-Zeitung*, **21** (1897), 654.
3. See A. T. J. Hayward, "Compressibility Equations for Liquids—A Comparative Study," in *Journal of Physics*, sec. D, Applied Physics, **18** (1967), 965.
4. A "Commemorative Symposium on the Oxidation of Metals—50 Years of Research" was organized in 1970 in Atlantic City, N.J., by the Electrochemical Society. The introductory lecture, given by C. Wagner, appeared in German in *Werkstoffe und Korrosion*, **21** (1970), 886–894. DECHEMA (Deutsche Gesellschaft für Chemisches Apparatewesen) organized a colloquium on the same subject, held on 23 Oct. 1970; for the lectures presented there, along with other papers on the subject, see *ibid.*, nos. 11–12.

BIBLIOGRAPHY

I. ORIGINAL WORKS. Tammann's posthumous papers and his autobiographical remarks written for his son, Heinrich, are in the possession of the author. Some autobiographical fragments were published in "Jugenderinnerungen eines Dorpater Chemikers," in *Eesti rohuteadlane* (Tartu), nos. 9–10 (1930), 1029–1034; and in "Die Gründung des Instituts für anorganische Chemie," in *Mitteilungen des Universitätsbundes Göttingen*, **16**, no. 1 (1934), 21–25; see also *ibid.*, **17**, no. 2 (1936), 42–45. For an account of his metallurgical works consult "Ueber die im Göttinger Institut für anorganische Chemie ausgeführten metallographischen Arbeiten," in *Zeitschrift für Elektrochemie*, **14** (1908), 789–804. The correspondence between Arrhenius (51 letters) and Tammann (122 letters) is at the Kungliga Vetenskapsakademien, Stockholm.

Tammann's monographs are *Die Dampftensionen der Lösungen*, which is *Mémoires de l'Académie impériale des sciences de St.-Pétersbourg*, 7th ser., **35**, no. 9 (1887); *Kristallisieren und Schmelzen, ein Beitrag zur Lehre der Aenderungen des Aggregatzustandes*

(Leipzig, 1903); *Ueber die Beziehungen zwischen den inneren Kräften und Eigenschaften der Lösungen* (Hamburg–Leipzig, 1907); *Lehrbuch der Metallographie, Chemie und Physik der Metalle und ihrer Legierungen* (Leipzig–Hamburg, 1914; 2nd ed., 1921; 3rd ed., Leipzig, 1923), the 4th ed. of which, *Lehrbuch der Metallkunde* (Leipzig, 1932), was translated from the 3rd ed. into English by R. S. Dean and L. G. Swenson as *A Textbook of Metallography* (New York, 1925) and into Russian (Moscow–Leningrad, 1935); *Die chemischen und galvanischen Eigenschaften von Mischkristallreihen und ihre Atomverteilung, zum Gedächtnis der Entdeckung des Isomorphismus vor 100 Jahren*, a special issue of *Zeitschrift für anorganische und allgemeine Chemie* (Leipzig, 1919); *Aggregatzustände, die Änderung der Materie in Abhängigkeit von Druck und Temperatur* (Leipzig, 1922; 2nd ed., 1923), translated into English by R. F. Mehl as *The States of Aggregation* (Princeton, 1925); *Der Glaszustand* (Leipzig, 1933), translated into Russian (Moscow, 1935); and *Lehrbuch der heterogenen Gleichgewichte* (Brunswick, 1934), translated into Russian (Moscow, 1935).

Tammann prepared a bibliography of his works up to 1901 that was published in G. V. Levitsky, ed., *Biografichesky slovar professorov i prepodavateley Imperatorskago yurievskago, byvshago Dertpskago, universiteta*, I (Yur'ev, 1902), 257–259. An almost complete list of Tammann's journal articles can be found in Poggendorff, IV, 1474; V, 1240–1241; VI, 2610–2612; VIIa, 623–625.

The articles can be grouped into the following main categories: (1) physiology (more than 10 papers); (2) inorganic chemistry (nearly 10 papers, one of which gives for the first time the correct constitutional formula of H_2O_2); (3) solutions, vapor tensions, and osmosis (almost 50 papers); (4) phase rule and state of aggregation (over 70 papers); (5) metallography and metallurgy (a series of 123 [incorrectly numbered 1–121] "Metallographische Mitteilung" were published by him and his co-workers in *Zeitschrift für anorganische Chemie* [1904–1925], plus about 80 additional papers); (6) glasses (about 40 papers); (7) chemical reactions in solids and the oxidation on surfaces (over 20 papers); and (8) geochemistry, silicates, and meteorites (about 15 papers).

From 1904 to 1939 Tammann was coeditor of 200 vols. of *Zeitschrift für anorganische und allgemeine Chemie*.

II. SECONDARY LITERATURE. On the history of Tammann's family see *Deutsches Geschlechterbuch*, CXLII (Marburg, 1967), 373–391. The "Festschrift zum 65. Geburtstag von Gustav Tammann" constitutes all of *Zeitschrift für anorganische und allgemeine Chemie*, **154** (1926). The two best evaluations of Tammann's work as a whole are W. Biltz, "Gustav Tammann zum siebzigsten Geburtstag," *ibid.*, **198** (1931), 1–31; and W. E. Garner, "The Tammann Memorial Lecture," in *Journal of the Chemical Society* (1952), 1961–1973. For discussions of individual aspects

of Tammann's work see A. Portevin, "La méthode d'analyse thermique et les travaux sur les alliages au laboratoire du Professeur Tammann," in *Revue de Métallurgie* (*Mémoires*), **4** (1907)–**6** (1909); W. Fraenkel, "Die neuen Forschungen G. Tammanns über Mischkristalle," in *Naturwissenschaften*, **8** (1920), 161–166; F. Körber, "Kristallisieren und Schmelzen," in *Zeitschrift für Metallkunde*, **23** (1931), 134–137; G. Grube, "Die Forschungen G. Tammanns über die Konstitution der Legierungen," *ibid.*, 137–138; G. Masing, "Tammanns Untersuchungen über Kaltreckung, Verfestigung und Rekristallisation," *ibid.*, 139–142; and W. Köster, "Arbeiten von G. Tammann über die chemischen Eigenschaften von Metallen und Legierungen," *ibid.*, 142–146.

The most useful obituaries of Tammann are G. Masing, "Gustav Tammann 1861–1938," in *Berichte der Deutschen chemischen Gesellschaft*, sec. A, **73** (1940), 25–30; and "Gustav Tammann†," in *Zeitschrift für Elektrochemie*, **45** (1939), 121–124, also in *Metall und Erz*, **37** (1940), 189–192; H. O. von Samson-Himmelstjerna, "Gustav Tammann," in *Umschau in Wissenschaft und Technik*, **43** (1939), 88–90; and an unsigned article in *Nachrichten von der Gesellschaft der Wissenschaften zu Göttingen*, *Jahresbericht* for 1938–1939 (1939), 54–66. The satirical remarks on the Third Reich in W. Biltz's obituary, "Gustav Tammann†," in *Zeitschrift für anorganische und allgemeine Chemie*, **240** (Jan. 1939), 114–115, reveal Biltz's political position – which was also Tammann's – and contributed to Biltz's early retirement. Other articles are cited in Poggendorff, VI, 2610, and VIIa, 623.

See also W. Köster, "Zum 100. Geburtstag von Gustav Tammann," in *Metall*, **15** (1961), 704–706, also in *Zeitschrift für Metallkunde*, **52** (1961), 379–381. Several authentic anecdotes about Tammann are reported in J. Hausen, *Was nicht in den Annalen steht*, 2nd ed. (Weinheim, 1958). S. Boström's article "Gustav Tammann," in *Baltische Hefte*, **10** (1964), 139–150, is unreliable and useful, at best, for several anecdotes.

G. A. TAMMANN

TANFILEV, GAVRIIL IVANOVICH (*b.* Tallinn, Russia, 6 March 1857; *d.* Odessa, U.S.S.R., 4 September 1928), *geography, phytogeography, soil science.*

Tanfilev began to study the flora of the chernozem steppes as a student at the Faculty of Physics and Mathematics of St. Petersburg University. After graduating in 1883, he worked in the Department of Agriculture of the Ministry of State Lands (1884–1892), on an expedition to study methods of forest and water management on the Russian steppes (1893–1894), in the St. Petersburg Botanical Garden (1895–1904), and on the Soil

Commission of the Free Economic Society (1888–1905). These activities were accompanied by field investigations of soil and vegetation in European Russia and in western Siberia. Tanfilev participated in the compilation of the soil map of European Russia and was awarded the Great Gold Medal at the Paris World Exhibition in 1900.

In his master's thesis, *Predely lesov na yuge Rossii* ("The Boundaries of the Forest in Southern Russia," 1894), Tanfilev concluded that the absence of forest on the steppe is a result of increased soil alkalinity and bedrock, both due to the dry climate. The lack of forest in the tundra was explained by the marshiness of its soils, the low temperature, and the permafrost, which destroys the roots of trees. In the forest-tundra and forest-steppe border regions, Tanfilev held, there is a constant struggle that results in the dislocation of the zonal boundaries. His conclusions on the battle between forest and steppe and between tundra and forest provoked a heated discussion among geographers, phytogeographers, and soil scientists that has continued unresolved to the present time.

Developing Dokuchaev's ideas on the zonal structure of the Russian landscape, Tanfilev studied the physicogeographical regionalization of European Russia (1897) and five years later published his classic work *Glavneyshie cherty rastitelnosti Rossii* ("Main Features of the Vegetation of Russia"), with a brilliant analysis of the broad zones of plant cover on the plains and the vertical belts in the mountains of the Crimea, Caucasus, and Turkistan. The most important feature of this work is the historical approach to the formation of vegetation zones in post-Tertiary time.

For more than twenty years, Tanfilev studied the cultural geography of plants. His research in this area culminated in *Ocherk geografii i istorii glavneyshikh kulturnykh vastenii* ("Sketch of the Geography and History of the Main Cultivated Plants," 1923).

The breadth of his geographical outlook and his knowledge of natural history based on personal research resulted in a major work on the physical geography of Russia. Four volumes appeared during his lifetime (1916–1924) and the fifth was published posthumously (1931). With its exhaustive bibliography, it was the most detailed and complete collection of information on the natural history of Russia until the early 1930's.

In addition to his research, Tanfilev taught at the universities of St. Petersburg (1895–1903) and Novorossysk, in Odessa (1904–1928).

BIBLIOGRAPHY

I. ORIGINAL WORKS. Tanfilev's *Geograficheskie raboty* ("Geographical Works"; Moscow, 1953) includes a bibliography of his writings.

II. SECONDARY LITERATURE. See S. T. Belozerov, *Gavriil Ivanovich Tanfilev* (Moscow, 1951), which includes a bibliography of his writings and of secondary literature; and "Gavriil Ivanovich Tanfilev," in *Otechestvennye fiziko-geografy i puteshestvenniki* ("Native Physical Geographers and Travelers"; Moscow, 1959); L. S. Berg, "Gavriil Ivanovich Tanfilev," in *Priroda*, 17, no. 10 (1928); and A. A. Borzov, "Professor Gavriil Ivanovich Tanfilev," in *Zemlevedenie*, 30, no. 4 (1928).

A. I. SOLOVIEV

TANNERY, JULES (*b.* Mantes-sur-Seine, France, 24 March 1848; *d.* Paris, France, 11 November 1910), *mathematics*.

Tannery was the youngest of the three children of Delphin Tannery, an engineer with the Compagnie des Chemins de Fer de l'Ouest. The eldest child was a daughter and the second was the engineer and historian of science Paul Tannery. The family moved first to Redon, in Ille-et-Vilaine, where his father supervised the construction of a railroad line, and then to Mondeville near Caen.

At the *lycée* in Caen, he was an excellent student, and he won several prizes in the *concours général*. His brother, who was passionately interested in philosophy and Greek antiquity, gave him a taste for these subjects. In 1866 Tannery was admitted with highest standing to the science section of the École Normale Supérieure and, simultaneously, to the École Polytechnique. He decided to enter the École Normale, and in 1869 placed first in the *agrégation*. He was then assigned to teach mathematics at the *lycée* in Rennes, and in 1871 he was named to a post at the *lycée* in Caen, where his former classmate Émile Boutroux was also teaching.

During this period Tannery underwent a religious crisis caused by his profound desire to admire without remorse pagan antiquity, the cult of reason, and the ideas of Lucretius.

Tannery returned to Paris in 1872 as *agrégé-préparateur* of mathematics at the École Normale. Encouraged by Hermite, he began work on a thesis inspired by the works of Fuchs ("Propriétés des intégrales des équations différentielles linéaires à coefficients variables"), which he defended in 1874. Two years later he became editor of the *Bulletin des sciences mathématiques*, on which he collaborated with Darboux, Hoüel, and Picard until his death. He wrote a great number of book reviews for the journal—more than 200 for the years 1905–1910 alone. Characterized by rigorous criticism and an excellent style, the reviews are models of their kind in both form and content.

Tannery taught higher mathematics at the Lycée Saint-Louis and substituted for the professor of physical and experimental mechanics at the Sorbonne. In 1881 he was named *maître de conférences* at the École Normale and, shortly afterward, at the École Normale for women located in Sèvres. From 1884 until his death Tannery served as assistant director of scientific studies at the École Normale; in this post he displayed the full measure of his abilities. At the same time, from 1903, he was professor of differential and integral calculus at the Faculty of Sciences of Paris.

A member of several educational commissions and of the Conseil Supérieur de l'Instruction Publique, Tannery played an important role in the pedagogical reforms in France at the beginning of the twentieth century. Through his lectures and supervisory duties at the École Normale this gifted teacher gave valuable guidance to many students and inspired a number of them to seek careers in science (for example, Paul Painlevé, Jules Drach, and Émile Borel). Tannery was elected *membre libre* of the Académie des Sciences on 11 March 1907, replacing Paul Brouardel.

Tannery possessed considerable gifts as a writer. The pure and elegant style of the poems he composed in his free hours clearly bears the stamp of a classic sensibility. His vast culture, nobility of character, and innate sense of a rationally grounded morality are reflected in each of his *Pensées*, a collection of his thoughts on friendship, the arts, and beauty. Often they exhibit a very refined sense of humor.

Among his scientific publications, the *Introduction à la théorie des fonctions d'une variable* exercised an especially great influence on younger generations of mathematicians. Émile Borel stated that it was a profound, vigorous, and elegant work that taught him how to think. In another book, written with Jules Molk, Tannery presented the results of applying Fuchs's theorems to the linear differential equation that defines the periods of an elliptic function. Tannery also gave a new expansion of the Euler equation. In algebra, following the path opened by Hermite, Tannery studied the similar transformations of the quadratic forms, the invariants of the cubic forms, and the symmetric functions. In geometry, he concentrated his research on the osculating plane of skewed cubic equations and on a fourth degree surface of which the geodesic lines are algebraic. Poincaré highly esteemed Tannery and commented very favorably on his writings. Tannery's work was known abroad, especially in Germany, where a translation of his book *Notions de mathématiques* was published in 1909.

In 1880 Weierstrass published "Zur Funktionenlehre," in which he dealt with the convergence of a series whose terms are rational functions of one variable. Upon reading it, Tannery sent Weierstrass solutions he obtained in a simpler manner, utilizing elementary theorems of function theory. Weierstrass translated Tannery's letter into German and published it in *Monatsberichte der königlich-preussischen Akademie der Wissenschaften zu Berlin* (1881, 228–230).

Tannery reflected a great deal on the role of number in science, and he sought to show how the entire subject of analysis could be built up on the basis merely of the notion of whole number. In his speculations on the notion of infinity, he arrived at the conclusion that it is equivalent to the simple possibility of indefinite addition. Finally, his interest in the history of science—undoubtedly inspired by his brother—led him to publish Galois's unpublished manuscripts and the correspondence between Liouville and Dirichlet.

Galois had entrusted his manuscripts to his friend Auguste Chevalier, who gave them to Liouville. The latter bequeathed his library to one of his sons-in-law, Célestin de Blignières (1823–1905), a former student at the École Polytechnique and a disciple of Auguste Comte. Mme de Blignières, Liouville's daughter, in turn, gave Galois's papers to Tannery, along with her father's correspondence with Dirichlet.

In his *Éloges et discours académiques* (p. 101), Émile Picard drew the following parallel between Jules and Paul Tannery:

> They were extremely close all their lives. Of very different natures, the two brothers complement each other. Paul derived a certain tranquillity from his positivist convictions. A philologist and scholar of extraordinary erudition, he sought to follow, in innumerable notes and articles, the historical evolution of science from Greek antiquity until the end of the seventeenth century. Jules's philosophy, on the other hand, did not free him from intellectual anxiety. His outlook was less universal than his brother's, but also more profound. He had both the subtle mind of the metaphysician and the penetrating insight of the disillusioned moralist.

BIBLIOGRAPHY

I. ORIGINAL WORKS. Tannery's books include *Introduction à la théorie des fonctions d'une variable* (Paris, 1886), 2nd ed., 2 vols. (1904–1910); *Eléments de la théorie des fonctions elliptiques*, 4 vols. (Paris, 1893–1902, with Jules Molk); *Leçons d'arithmétique théorique et pratique* (Paris, 1894; 7th ed., 1917); *Introduction à l'étude de la théorie des nombres et de l'algèbre supérieure*, Émile Borel and Jules Drach, eds. (Paris, 1895), taken from Tannery's lectures at the École Normale Superieure; *Notice sur les travaux scientifiques de M Jules Tannery* (Paris, 1901); *Notions de mathématiques* (Paris, 1903), German trans. (Leipzig, 1909), with historical notes by Paul Tannery; *Leçons d'algèbre et d'analyse à l'usage des classes de mathématiques spéciales*, 2 vols. (Paris, 1906), with Paul Tannery; *Liste des travaux de Paul Tannery* (Bordeaux, 1908), prepared by P. Duhem and preceded by obituaries written by Duhem and J. Tannery; and *Science et philosophie* (Paris, 1912), with a brief article by Émile Borel.

Tannery's articles include "Sur l'équation différentielle linéaire qui relie au module la fonction complète de première espèce," in *Comptes rendus hebdomadaires des séances de l'Académie des sciences*, **86** (1878), 811–812; "Sur quelques propriétés des fonctions complètes de première espèce," *ibid.*, 950–953; "Sur les intégrales eulériennes," *ibid.*, **94** (1882), 1698–1701; and "Sur les fonctions symétriques des différences des racines d'une équation," *ibid.*, **98** (1884), 1420–1422; "Les Mathématiques dans l'Enseignement secondaire," in *La revue de Paris*, **4** (1900), 619–641; "Principes fondamentaux de l'arithmétique," with J. Molk, in *Encyclopédie des sciences mathématiques*, pt. 1, I (Paris, 1904), 1–62; "Sur l'aire du parallélogramme des périodes pour une fonction pu donnée," in *Bulletin des sciences mathématiques*, **28** (1904), 108–117; "Paul Tannery," in *Comptes rendus du IIe Congrès international de philosophie* (Geneva, 1905), 775–797; "Manuscrits et papiers inédits de Galois," in *Bulletin des sciences mathématiques*, **30** (1906), 226–248, 255–263, and **31** (1907), 275–308; "Correspondance entre Liouville et Dirichlet," *ibid.*, **32** (1908), 47–62, 88–95, and **33** (1909), 47–64; "Discours prononcé à Bourg-la-Reine" (at the inauguration of a plaque placed on the house in which Galois was born), *ibid.*, **33** (1909), 158–164; "Pour la science livresque," in *Revue de métaphysique et de morale*, **17** (1909), 161–171; and "Pensées," in *La revue du mois*, **11** (1911), 257–278, 399–435.

II. SECONDARY LITERATURE. The first obituaries of Tannery are the addresses given by P. Painlevé and É. Picard on 13 and 14 November 1910, in *Bulletin des sciences mathématiques*, **34** (1910), 194–197. These were followed by É. Borel, "Jules Tannery, 24 mars 1848–11 novembre 1910," in *La revue du mois*, **11** (1911), 5–16; Émile Hovelaque, "Jules Tannery," in *La revue de Paris*, **1** (1911), 305–322; and A. Châtelet, "Jules Tannery," in *Enseignement mathématique*, **13** (1911), 56–58.

A small book of 140 pages entitled *En souvenir de Jules Tannery MCMXII* was published by subscription by Tannery's friends in 1912; it contains an address by Ernest Lavisse, director of the École Normale, a biographical article by Émile Boutroux, and a selection of Tannery's "Pensées." See also Émile Picard, "La vie et l'oeuvre de Jules Tannery membre de l'Académie," in *Mémoires de l'Académie des sciences de l'Institut de France*, **58** (1926), i–xxxii; the same article, with a few revisions, appeared as "Un géomètre philosophe: Jules Tannery," in *La revue des deux mondes*, **31** (1926), 858–884, and in Picard's *Éloges et discours académiques* (Paris, 1931), 51–104.

See also Poggendorff, III, 1324; IV, 1476; V, 1242; and G. Sarton, "Paul, Jules et Marie Tannery," in *Isis*, **38** (1947–1948), 33–51, which in addition contains a list of Jules Tannery's works on pp. 47–48.

PIERRE SPEZIALI

TANNERY, PAUL (*b.* Mantes-la-Jolie, Yvelines, France, 20 December 1843; *d.* Pantin, Seine–St. Denis, France, 27 November 1904), *history of science, history of mathematics.*

An engineer and administrator by profession, Tannery could devote only his leisure hours to scholarship. Despite this limitation, however, he accomplished a vast amount of penetrating and wide-ranging research and became one of the most influential figures in the rapidly developing study of the history of science at the beginning of the twentieth century. Like his younger brother, Jules, who later became a mathematician, Tannery early received a deeply Christian education from his parents, S. Delphin Tannery, an engineer who worked for railroad companies, and the former E. Opportune Perrier. After proving to be a brilliant pupil at a private school in Mantes, Tannery attended the *lycées* of Le Mans and Caen, where he showed great enthusiasm for the classics, although he had enrolled as a science student. His philosophy teacher, Jules Lachelier, communicated to Tannery a passion for the subject and strengthened his interest in classical antiquity. In 1860 Tannery fulfilled his father's hopes by obtaining one of the highest scores on the competitive entrance examination for the École Polytechnique, where he acquired a solid education in science and technology but devoted much time to other subjects as well. In particular he began to learn Hebrew and developed a strong interest in the teaching of mathematics.

Upon graduating from the École Polytechnique in 1863, Tannery entered the École d'Application des Tabacs as an apprentice engineer. At this time he read Auguste Comte's *Cours de philosophie positive*, an initiation into positivist philosophy that so profoundly influenced him that years later he approached the study of the history of science as a spiritual disciple of Comte.

After working for two years as an assistant engineer at the state tobacco factory in Lille, Tannery was transferred in 1867 to an administrative post at the headquarters of the state tobacco administration in Paris, where he enjoyed a more active intellectual and artistic life. He served in the Franco-Prussian War as an artillery captain and was present during the siege of Paris. An ardent patriot, he was deeply affected by the defeat and never consented to acknowledge the terms of the peace treaty as definitive. Upon demobilization Tannery resumed his former duties. At the same time he eagerly studied philosophy and mathematics, subjects that he discussed with his brother, Jules, who taught at Caen and later at the École Normale Supérieure of Paris, and with such young philosophers as É. Boutroux. In 1872 the tobacco administration sent Tannery to supervise the construction of several buildings in the Périgord region. While there he became seriously ill and was obliged to convalesce for a long period. He used this time to further his knowledge of ancient languages, acquiring a mastery of this field that was evident in his very first publications.

In March 1874 Tannery began to direct an extensive construction project at the state tobacco factory of Bordeaux. This university city had a very active intellectual life, and he soon decided to spend his leisure time investigating various topics in the history of the exact sciences in antiquity, as well as a number of philosophical and philological questions. From 1876 Tannery participated in the work of the Société des Sciences Physiques et Naturelles de Bordeaux and published many studies in its *Mémoires* and in the *Revue philosophique de la France et de l'étranger*, which had recently been founded at Paris. He gradually began to send material to other journals, eventually becoming a fairly regular contributor to about fifteen French and foreign periodicals. He published hundreds of memoirs, articles, notes, and reviews while pursuing a brilliant career in the state tobacco administration. Although many other historians of science have been obliged to conduct their research concurrently with their professional activities, none of them seems to have produced a body of work comparable to Tannery's in scope and importance.

Although his stay at Bordeaux had proved enriching and fruitful, Tannery soon ended it. In 1877, at his own request, he was appointed engineer at the tobacco factory of Le Havre, a city with intellectual resources far inferior to those of Bordeaux but near the region of Caen, where Tannery's parents lived. He continued, however, to take a lively interest in Greek science; and his survey of mathematics at the time of Plato ("L'éducation platonicienne"), published in the *Revue philosophique de la France et de l'étranger*, was enthusiastically received and was translated into English and German. Meanwhile, his professional obligations, already considerable, become still greater in 1880, when he became acting director of the tobacco factory.

In June 1881 Tannery married Marie-Alexandrine Prisset (1856–1945), daughter of a well-to-do notary in Poitiers. Although she had received only a modest education, his young wife encouraged Tannery to pursue his scholarly research. Several trips abroad during this period enabled Tannery to meet leading scholars, notably J. L. Heiberg, H.-G. Zeuthen, G. Eneström, and M. Cantor, with whom he maintained close and fruitful relationships. Since his situation at Le Havre provided little encouragement for ,his research, however, Tannery soon sought a transfer to Paris.

His request was granted, and in July 1883 he was named appraiser-engineer in a Paris tobacco factory. Once again he was able to devote all his leisure time to scholarship. Although relatively brief, this Paris period was extremely productive. Tannery's principal area of interest was the history of mathematics; he gave a private course on the subject at the Faculty of Sciences in 1884–1885 and published an important series of articles on Greek geometry in the *Bulletin des sciences mathématiques*. He also pursued studies already under way on the origins of Greek science and on various philological questions. In addition he printed previously unpublished Greek texts, as well as original studies on a wide range of topics. Research at the Bibliothèque Nationale and a scholarly visit to Italy enabled him to begin work on two important editorial projects: an edition of the manuscripts of Diophantus, which was entrusted to him in 1883, and one of Fermat's works, for which he received a joint commission with Charles Henry in 1885.

At the end of 1886 Tannery had to leave Paris, in order to direct the tobacco factory at Tonneins

(Lot-et-Garonne). Deprived of the resources of the Bibliothèque Nationale, he was limited to editorial work and to perfecting his manuscripts. He revised and completed a series of articles that had been appearing in the *Revue philosophique de la France et de l'étranger* since 1880 and presented them in book form as *Pour l'histoire de la science hellène. De Thalès à Empédocle*, his first separately printed publication. Tannery also regrouped and completed another series of articles, which had been appearing since 1884 in *Bulletin des sciences mathématiques*, into a second, shorter book, *La géométrie grecque, comment son histoire nous est parvenue et ce que nous en savons*, I. *Histoire générale de la géométrie élémentaire* (the only part to be published). In addition, he continued to prepare the edition of Fermat's works.

Promoted to director of the Bordeaux tobacco factory in January 1888, Tannery spent two years in the city in which he had first become aware of his vocation for history. Renewing contact with intellectual circles there, he became friendly with an amateur scholar, Polydore Hochart, who assisted him in collecting material on the Bordeaux correspondents of Mersenne—the first step in a great project that Tannery was not able to complete. He also worked on a study of Greek astronomy, in which he sought, through a very detailed analysis of the *Almagest*, to gain insight into the different theories outlined by Ptolemy. (The study was published in the *Mémoires de la Société des sciences physiques et naturelles de Bordeaux* in 1893.)

At the beginning of 1890 Tannery returned to the Paris headquarters of the state tobacco authority in order to organize the manufacture of matches and to give instruction in the relevant techniques to the apprentice engineers at the École d'Application des Tabacs. In 1893 he was appointed director of the factory at Pantin, near Paris, a post that he held until his death in 1904. Although this appointment entailed heavy administrative and social responsibilities, Tannery did a remarkable amount of research during this final period of his life. He regularly contributed articles, memoirs, notes, and book reviews to about fifteen journals and completed his editions of the works of Diophantus and of Fermat. Tannery also undertook vast new projects, such as collaborating on the *Histoire générale du IVe siècle à nos jours* of Ernest Lavisse and A. N. Rambaud, teaching at the Collège de France for several years, and preparing a new critical edition of the works and correspondence of Descartes. Through his regular correspondence with French and foreign colleagues and through his activities at several congresses, he laid the foundations for international collaboration in the history of science.

A rapid survey of the various aspects of Tannery's work provides some idea of the scope and importance of his accomplishments during these final years. He wrote some 250 articles, notes, and other communications on the most varied issues in the history of the exact sciences, the history of philosophy, and philology, most of them concerning antiquity, Byzantine civilization, and Western civilization from the Middle Ages to the seventeenth century; they occupy five volumes of his collected *Mémoires scientifiques*.

In the years immediately after 1893, however, Tannery concentrated most of his effort on completing his two major editorial projects. The two volumes of Diophantus' *Opera omnia* appeared in 1893 and 1895. (Tannery also began work on a French translation, but he did not complete it.) The three volumes of the *Oeuvres de Fermat*, which Tannery edited with Charles Henry, were published between 1891 and 1896. The first volume contains mathematical works and "Observations sur Diophante"; the second (1894) contains Fermat's correspondence; and the third consists of French translations of the writings and of Latin fragments by Fermat as well as of several texts by J. de Billy and J. Wallis. Tannery, who played the principal role in editing these volumes, also assembled material for a fourth (*Compléments* . . .), which was completed by Henry and published in 1912. A fifth volume, containing further supplementary material, was published by C. de Waard in 1922.

In 1892 Tannery agreed to substitute for Charles Lévêque in the chair of Greek and Latin philosophy at the Collège de France. Without fundamentally altering the character of the chair, Tannery sought to place greater emphasis on the history of ancient scientific thought and to illustrate its influence on the formation of modern science. Unfortunately, he did not publish any of his courses, and we have a record only of the main subjects he treated. These included Aristotle's *Physics* and *De caelo*, an interpretation of Plato, ancient theories of matter, the commentaries of Simplicius, and atomistic doctrines, as well as various currents of ancient philosophy and even fragments of Orphic poetry. At the end of the academic year 1896–1897, however, a new project began to occupy almost all Tannery's time: an edition of the works of Descartes. Accordingly, he gave up teaching and thereby renounced the possibility of succeeding Lévêque.

Tannery was interested in Descartes during his first stay in Bordeaux, though only in principle, since all his research during that period pertained to ancient thought. But from 1890 on the preparation of his edition of Fermat's work led him to make a thorough study of Descartes's correspondence and to publish a number of items that had remained in manuscript. The rigor of his editorial work and his deep knowledge of seventeenth-century science brought him, in 1894, the co-editorship (with the historian of modern philosophy Charles Adam) of a new critical edition of the works and correspondence of Descartes that was destined to replace the very dated, eleven-volume edition by Victor Cousin (1824–1826). In the last ten years of Tannery's life this undertaking, the scope and importance of which are obvious, absorbed a growing portion of his leisure. His first—and most difficult—task was the preparation of volumes I–V, devoted to Descartes's correspondence (published 1897–1903). He also participated in editing volumes VI (*Discours de la méthode* and *Essais* [1902]), VII (*Meditationes de prima philosophia* [1904]), and IX (*Méditations* and *Principes* [1904]), and left valuable notes for the other volumes published by Henry. This edition, called the "Adam-Tannery" Descartes, is too well-known to require detailed description here. A major contribution to the history of ideas, and especially to the history of science in the seventeenth century, it sparked a renewal of interest in Cartesian philosophy. By its rigor and precision, and the wealth of its documentation, it far surpassed the earlier editions and marked an important step in the elaboration of modern methods of producing critical editions. Only recently has it been necessary to publish a revised and enlarged edition that takes into account the documentary discoveries made since the beginning of the twentieth century.

Although during the final decade of his career Tannery devoted an ever increasing amount of time to this editorial effort, he still managed to publish a large number of studies, chiefly on ancient science and medieval and Byzantine mathematics. Moreover, his vast erudition enabled him to reply to numerous questions posed in the *Intermédiaire des mathématiciens* and to contribute valuable notes to several fascicles of the *Encyclopédie des sciences mathématiques*. Along with his highly specialized works, he wished to produce a more general account of the history of science, the initial outlines of which he had sketched in his chapters

of Lavisse and Rambaud's *Histoire générale*. At the beginning of 1903 it appeared that Tannery would have an especially favorable opportunity to carry out this project. The death of Pierre Laffitte had left vacant the chair of the history of science at the Collège de France, which had been created for him in 1892, and the Assembly of professors at the Collège had voted to maintain the chair. The two consultative bodies, the Assembly and the Académie des Sciences, informed the minister of education that Tannery was their first choice among several candidates. His nomination seemed so certain that he began to write the inaugural lecture of his course. But, for obscure political and philosophical reasons the minister chose the candidate who was second on the list submitted to him: the crystallographer Grégoire Wyrouboff, a positivist philosopher with little competence in the history of science. Strictly speaking the minister was within his rights. Tannery was deeply disappointed by this unjust decision, however, which was vainly opposed by the many French and foreign scholars who considered Tannery one of the leaders in the field. Although the case is not clear, Sarton and Louis have revealed some of Chaumié's motives. First of all it is certain that a militant positivist and freethinker like Wyrouboff fitted more easily into the anticlericalism of Émile Combes's government than a fervid Catholic like Tannery. But it appears also that the minister preferred a course of studies that was oriented toward contemporary science, as Wyrouboff proposed, to the program of general scientific history proposed by Tannery. But there is no doubt that the "scandal of 1903" did great damage to the development of the history of science in France.

Tannery was convinced of the necessity of an international effort to catalog documentary sources and to eliminate the nationalistic interpretations of the history of science that were all too common at that time. The four volumes of his *Mélanges scientifiques* that are devoted to correspondence reveal the extent of his relations with the leading historians of science in France, Germany, Scandinavia, Italy, and elsewhere. Tannery also was active at the international congresses of historical studies (Paris, 1900; Rome, 1903), philosophy (Paris, 1900; Geneva, 1904), and mathematicians (Heidelberg, 1904). Conscious of the interdisciplinary role of the history of science, Tannery wanted the subject to be recognized as a field in its own right by historians and philosophers, as well as by scientists. He also hoped that students of the field would become aware of the distinctive contribution it could make and that close contacts would be established between historians of science in all countries.

This effort was suddenly interrupted a few weeks after Tannery returned from the Geneva congress of 1904. Suffering from cancer of the pancreas, he died at the end of November in that year. A considerable portion of his work was dispersed in various specialized—and sometimes hard-to-find—journals. His widow soon undertook to collect the publications and regroup them according to major subjects: exact sciences in antiquity, in the Middle Ages, and in the Byzantine world; modern science; history of philosophy; philology; and so on. To these she added the book reviews and the correspondence. A number of distinguished historians of science, including Heiberg, Zeuthen, and Loria, assisted her in this project. Through their devotion and hers, the seventeen volumes of Tannery's *Mémoires scientifiques* now include all his works, except for his three books on ancient science and his editions of Diophantus, Fermat, and Descartes. With the aid of C. de Waard, Marie Tannery also began work on the edition of the *Correspondance du P. Marin Mersenne* that her husband had hoped to undertake.

It would be impossible in an article of this length to convey the importance of a body of work as extensive and varied as Tannery's. Perhaps its most notable characteristic is an unwavering concern for rigor and precision. The detailed studies that constituted the bulk of his output were, in Tannery's view, only a necessary stage in the elaboration of much broader syntheses that would ultimately lead to a comprehensive history of science that he himself could only initiate. While some of the results that he published during thirty years of scholarly activity have been brought into question by documentary discoveries or by new interpretations, a large number of his studies retain their value. Even more important, however, is the fruitful influence that Tannery's work has exerted on historians of science in the twentieth century.

BIBLIOGRAPHY

I. ORIGINAL WORKS. Lists of Tannery's works were published by Marie Tannery in *Mémoires de la Société des sciences physiques et naturelles de Bordeaux*, 6th ser., **4** (1908), 299–382; and by P. Louis in Tannery's *Mémoires scientifiques*, XVII (Toulouse–Paris, 1950), 61–117. G. Eneström presented "Liste des travaux de Paul Tannery sur les mathématiques et la philosophie des mathématiques," in *Bibliotheca mathematica*, 3rd ser., **6** (1905), 292–304. Shorter bibliographies have been offered by G. Sarton in *Osiris*, **4** (1938), 703–705; and by R. Taton in *Revue d'histoire des sciences et de leurs applications*, **7** (1954), 369–371. And on the occasion of his candidacy at the Collège de France in Apr. 1903, Tannery drew up "Titres scientifiques de Paul Tannery," reproduced in *Mémoires*, X, 125–136.

Tannery's published work consists of several books, major editions of scientific writings, and a very large number of articles. The three principal books are devoted to ancient science: *Pour l'histoire de la science hellène. De Thalès à Empédocle* (Paris, 1887); 2nd ed. prepared by A. Diès with a pref. by F. Enriques (Paris, 1930); *La géométrie grecque . . .*, I, *Histoire générale de la géométrie élémentaire* (Paris, 1887), the only part to be published; and *Recherches sur l'histoire de l'astronomie ancienne* (Paris, 1893). A fourth, briefer publication concerned the preparation of the ed. of Descartes: *La correspondance de Descartes dans les inédits du fonds Libri* (Paris, 1893).

His major eds. of scientific works are *Oeuvres de Fermat*, 3 vols. (Paris, 1891–1896), edited with C. Henry, plus IV (*Compléments*), published by C. Henry (1912), and V (*Suppléments*) (1922), published by C. de Waard; *Diophanti Alexandrini opera omnia*, 2 vols. (Leipzig, 1893–1895); and *Oeuvres de Descartes*, 12 vols. and supp. (Paris, 1897–1913), with C. Adam—Tannery participated in the editing of vols. I–VII and IX. He also began work on eds. that were continued at the urging of Mme Tannery: *Correspondance du P. Marin Mersenne*, C. de Waard, R. Pintard, and B. Rochot, eds. (Paris, 1932–   ); and Georgius Pachymeres, *Quadrivium*, E. Stéphanou, ed. (Vatican City, 1940).

Most of Tannery's articles, as well as his correspondence, were collected in the *Mémoires scientifiques*, published by Mme Tannery with the aid of several historians of science. The material is grouped as follows: I–III, *Sciences exactes dans l'antiquité* (Toulouse–Paris, 1912–1915); IV, *Sciences exactes chez les Byzantins* (1920); V, *Sciences exactes au Moyen Âge* (1922); VI, *Sciences modernes* (1926); VII, *Philosophie ancienne* (1925); VIII, *Philosophie moderne* (1927); IX, *Philologie* (1929); X, *Supplément au tome VI. Sciences modernes. Généralités historiques* (1930); XI–XII, *Comptes-rendus et analyses* (1931–1933); XIII–XVI, *Correspondance* (1934–1943); and XVII, *Biographie, bibliographie, compléments et tables* (1950).

The bibliography given by P. Louis in *Mémoires scientifiques*, XVII, 61–117, which indicates the vol. and first pg. of the works reproduced in this ed., also lists articles not in the *Mémoires*, including the 200 articles Tannery wrote for the *Grand encyclopédie* and his notes to certain chapters of the *Encyclopédie des sciences mathématiques*. Vol. XVII of the *Mémoires* also contains a "Table analytique des mémoires scientifiques," 449–494, which considerably facilitates working with this rich and varied collection of studies, as well as an index of Greek words, 495–506.

II. SECONDARY LITERATURE. See the following, listed chronologically: Charles Adam, "Paul Tannery et l'édition de Descartes," in *Oeuvres de Descartes*, C. Adam and P. Tannery, eds., VIII, v–xviii; H. Bosmans, "Notice sur les travaux de Paul Tannery," in *Revue des questions scientifiques*, 3rd ser., **8** (1905), 544–574; *Discours prononcés aux obsèques de M. Paul Tannery* . . . (Toulouse, 1905); P. Duhem, "Paul Tannery (1843–1904)," in *Revue de philosophie*, **5**, no. 1 (1905), 216–230; F. Picavet, "Paul Tannery, historien de la philosophie," in *Archiv für Geschichte der Philosophie*, 3rd ser., **18** (1905), 293–302; J. Tannery, "Notice sur Paul Tannery," in *Rapports et compte-rendus du IIe Congrès international de philosophie* (Geneva, 1905), 775–797, also in *Mémoires de la Société des sciences physiques et naturelles de Bordeaux*, 6th ser., **4** (1908), 269–293; H.-G. Zeuthen, "L'oeuvre de Paul Tannery comme historien des mathématiques," in *Bibliotheca mathematica*, 3rd ser., **6** (1905), 260–292; G. Milhaud, "Paul Tannery," in *Revue des idées*, **3** (1906), 28–39, also in *Nouvelles études sur l'histoire de la pensée scientifique* (Paris, 1911), 1–20; P. Duhem, "Paul Tannery et la Société des sciences physiques et naturelles de Bordeaux," in *Mémoires de la Société des sciences physiques et naturelles de Bordeaux*, 6th ser., **4** (1908), 295–298; and A. Rivaud, "Paul Tannery, historien de la science antique," in *Revue de métaphysique et de morale*, **11** (1913), 177–210.

Later works are G. Loria, "Paul Tannery et son oeuvre d'historien," in *Archeion* (Rome), **11** (1929), lxxx–xcii; J. Nussbaum, *Paul Tannery et l'histoire des physiologues milésiens* (Lausanne, 1929); F. Enriques, "La signification et l'importance de l'histoire de la science et l'oeuvre de Paul Tannery," in Paul Tannery, *Pour l'histoire de la science hellène*, 2nd ed. (Paris, 1930), xi–xxi; Marie Tannery, P. Boutroux, and G. Sarton, "Paul Tannery," "L'oeuvre de Paul Tannery," and "Bibliographie des travaux de Paul Tannery," in *Osiris*, **4** (1938), 633–705; G. Sarton, "Paul, Jules and Marie Tannery," in *Isis*, **38** (1947), 33–51; and P. Louis, "Biographie de Paul Tannery," in Tannery's *Mémoires scientifiques*, XVII, 1–49. The last two articles contain an account of the Wyrouboff affair. See also a group of articles by H. Berr, S. Delorme, J. Itard, R. Lenoble, P.-H. Michel, G. Sarton, P. Sergescu, J. Tannery, and R. Taton in *Revue d'histoire des sciences et de leurs applications*, **7** (1954), 297–368.

There are accounts of the life and work of Marie Tannery by P. Ducassé, in *Osiris*, **4** (1938), 706–709; P. Louis, in Tannery's *Mémoires scientifiques*, XVII, 51–59; G. Sarton, in *Isis*, **38** (1947), 44–47, 50; and C. de Waard, in *Revue d'histoire des sciences et de leurs applications*, **2** (1948), 90–94.

RENÉ TATON

TARDE, JEAN (*b.* La Roque-Gageac, France, 1561 or 1562; *d.* Sarlat, France, 1636), *astronomy, geography.*

After receiving a doctorate in law from the University of Cahors, Tarde continued his studies at the Sorbonne. Ordained a priest, he was assigned to the parish of Carves, near Belvès, and later rose to be the canon theologian of the cathedral church of Sarlat. In 1594, when the bishop wished to determine the effects of the religious wars in France on the diocese of Sarlat, he designated Tarde vicar-general and commissioned him to make a map of the bishopric.

Tarde charted the neighboring diocese for the bishop of Cahors in 1606. In this topographical survey he used a small quadrant equipped with a compass needle and attached to a sundial. In compliance with the bishop's request that he publish an explanation of this instrument, Tarde wrote and dedicated to the bishop *Les usages du quadrant à l'esguille aymantée* (1621), for which the royal privilege was dated 8 June 1620. On the same day Tarde obtained privileges for the two other works published during his lifetime: *Borbonia sidera* (1620) and his translation of this Latin treatise into French, *Les astres de Borbon* (1622). These works were based on Tarde's conversations with Galileo, whom he had visited in Florence on 12–15 November 1614. Among the numerous subjects they discussed were the recently discovered sunspots. After returning to France, Tarde observed the spots for five years and reached the erroneous conclusion that they were planets, which he proceeded to name in honor of the French royal house, as Galileo had done with the satellites of Jupiter and the Medici family.

Tarde's interpretation of the sunspots was demolished by Gassendi in a letter to Galileo dated 20 July 1625. In that communication he pointed out that despite an assiduous program of observations, Tarde had been unable to identify any sunspot that exhibited the periodic returns characteristic of the true planets, as Tarde himself acknowledged.

BIBLIOGRAPHY

I. ORIGINAL WORKS. Tarde's published works are *Borbonia sidera* (Paris, 1620), translated by Tarde as *Les astres de Borbon* (Paris, 1622, 1623, 1627); *Les usages du quadrant à l'esguille aymantée* (Paris, 1621, 1623, 1627, 1638); and *Les chroniques de Jean Tarde*, Gaston de Gérard and Gabriel Tarde, eds. (Paris, 1887). Unpublished is "Voyage de Jean Tarde dans le midi et en Italie," listed by Philippe Lauer in Bibliothèque Nationale (Paris), *Collections manuscrites sur l'histoire des provinces de France, inventaire*, II (Paris, 1911), p. 60, no. 106, fols. 26–38. For the various eds. of his map of the bishopric of Sarlat, see pp. 395–396 in Dujarric-Descombes, who enumerated Tarde's other geographical works.

II. SECONDARY LITERATURE. See Albert Dujarric-Descombes, "Recherches sur les historiens du Périgord au XVIIe siècle," in *Bulletin de la Société historique et archéologique du Périgord*, **9** (1882), 371–412, 489–497; Antonio Favaro, "Di Giovanni Tarde e di una sua visita a Galileo dal 12 al 15 novembre 1614," in *Bullettino di bibliografia e storia delle scienze matematiche e fisiche*, **20** (1887), 345–371, 374; "Lettre de Claude Aspremont à M. Pichard, chanoine théologal de l'église cathédrale de Périgueux, au sujet du 'docte escrit du télescope de M. Tarde' " (1630), listed in Lauer, *op cit.*, II, p. 51, no. 92, fol. 53; and Gabriel Tarde, "Observations au sujet des astres de Borbon du chanoine Tarde," in *Bulletin de la Société historique et archéologique du Périgord*, **4** (1877), 169–173. Gassendi's letter to Galileo is in Galileo Galilei, *Le opere*, A. Favaro, ed., XIII (Florence, 1903; repr. 1935), no. 1729, lines 56–64; and Gassendi, *Opera omnia* (Stuttgart, 1964; repr. of Lyons, 1658 ed.), VI, 5.

EDWARD ROSEN

TARGIONI TOZZETTI, GIOVANNI (*b*. Florence, Italy, 11 September 1712; *d*. Florence, 7 January 1783), *natural history*.

Targioni's father, Benedetto, was a doctor; his mother, Cecilia, was the daughter of Gerolamo Tozzetti, a jurist. He added her maiden name to his paternal surname, Targioni. In 1734 Targioni Tozzetti received his degree in medicine at Pisa; for the rest of his life he practiced medicine in Florence, where, among other things, he promoted prophylactic inoculation against smallpox. In 1739 he was appointed director of the Magliabechi Library, a position which required his cataloging thousands of books and manuscripts. Targioni Tozzetti was strongly inclined toward natural history. His father, a passionate student of botany, understood and appreciated this interest, and encouraged it by entrusting his son, in 1731, to the botanist Pier Antonio Micheli. For six years Targioni Tozzetti was Micheli's shadow, the latter's pleasure in teaching being matched by the former's in learning. After Micheli's death in 1737 Targioni Tozzetti was deemed worthy to be director of Florence's botanical garden and to teach botany.

A scientific journey from Florence to Cortona, with Micheli in 1732, served to emphasize Targioni Tozzetti's true vocation, that of traveling naturalist. Long journeys undertaken between 1742 and 1745 enabled him to observe natural phenomena and the ancient monuments of consid-

erable sections of Tuscany. The harvest gathered in the field of natural science was truly outstanding, encompassing the three kingdoms of nature.

In his study on the relations between normal hydrography and landform, Targioni Tozzetti made wide-reaching synthetic observations, starting with the most minute analytic observations. Some of the major scientists of his time believed that the erosive action of currents, even though increased by time, was entirely insufficient to account for wide valleys and deep gorges. Assuming a decisive position against the most famous of them all, Buffon, who believed it essential in explaining these phenomena to posit the action of marine currents prior to the emergence of land, Targioni Tozzetti maintained that all the valleys and gorges he had observed were the result of erosion caused by currents. He also noted the enormous quantity of materials altered by the waters themselves in the course of time. On the basis of these observations Targioni Tozzetti was able to outline, for the first time in the history of science, the morphological evolution of certain landscapes, such as that of the hills of the Tuscan ante-Apennines, formed by Pliocene marine sediments. Going back to "very remote times, unknown to us," Targioni Tozzetti said that the hills appeared to have been formed by current-caused erosion on the marine platform that emerged after the sea had receded. He reconstructed the movement of this platform by identifying it with the plane that connects the summits of the existing hills. Considering the future, he stated that these hills would also be "broken up and destroyed" by erosion.

Targioni Tozzetti's interest was also aroused by the disappearance of early Pleistocene lakes, where we find today the characteristic intermountain basins of the Apennines. In the Upper Valdarno he demonstrated the existence of a large lake in antiquity; he then studied the disappearance of the waters as a result of the complete alluvial refilling of the basin. Last, he investigated the regressive erosion that the waters cause on the lacustrine deposits. He also explained with great clarity the origin of the gorges in the wide Arno Valley by the presence of very hard rocky masses which were buried by the lacustrine sediments lacking cohesion. It is in these sediments that one not infrequently finds the bones of elephants and other large mammals. Targioni Tozzetti demonstrated that these fossils are not the remains of elephants that accompanied Hannibal's army during the Second Punic War, as scholars of the period believed; rather, they were a part of the fauna of

Tuscany before the appearance of man in the region.

Throughout his life Targioni Tozzetti hoped to write a full description of Tuscany from both the general synthetic and the regional analytic points of view. The work was never carried out; but his *Prodromo*, published in 1754, is of great interest, for it outlines in minute detail the plan of his work—a plan amazing for the modernity of its conception. The general description would have been developed in much the same manner as would be used today: examination of the relief, hydrography, climate, flora, fauna, and finally human manifestations. Targioni Tozzetti's great understanding of the relations between nature and man extended to such diverse topics as the changes introduced by man in the courses of rivers or at their mouths; the changes in malarial marshlands (a very important economic and social problem in Tuscany in the eighteenth century); the location of population centers in relation to relief or to water; the construction of roads or ports; and the better exploitation by man of all the natural resources. In brief, he saw man as an indefatigable and efficient modifier of terrestrial surfaces: "It would not be useless to consider Tuscany as it indeed was before it was inhabited my man . . . to understand the great changes that have followed successively from industry and later from human negligence." Today Targioni Tozzetti is recognized as one of the precursors of modern human geography.

Targioni Tozzetti was unable to devote much time to scientific research, since he was fully occupied with his duties as a physician and a librarian. He himself felt "condemned to waste his life in studies opposed to his inclination." But the results he achieved, even though limited, justify his being considered, after Lazzaro Spallanzani, as the most active Italian naturalist of the eighteenth century. His scientific passion was transmitted to later generations: his son Ottaviano, his nephew Antonio, and his grandnephew Adolfo were doctors and naturalists of note.

BIBLIOGRAPHY

I. ORIGINAL WORKS. Targioni Tozzetti's writings include *Relazione d'alcuni viaggi fatti in diverse parti della Toscana, per osservare le produzioni naturali, e gli antichi monumenti di essa*, 6 vols. (Florence, 1751–1754; 2nd ed., 12 vols., 1768–1779); *Prodromo della corografia e della topografia fisica della Toscana* (Florence, 1754), and two works valuable for the history of science, which he was one of the first to cultivate, *Notizie sugli aggrandimenti delle scienze fisiche accaduti in Toscana nel corso di anni LX del secolo XVII* (Florence, 1780), and *Notizie della vita e delle opere di Pier' Antonio Micheli* (Florence, 1858). Some of his more interesting scientific material is in the anthology of F. Rodolico, *La Toscana descritta dai naturalisti del settecento* (Florence, 1945), *passim*.

II. SECONDARY LITERATURE. Biographical and bibliographical information is in *Novelle letterarie*, **14** (1783), col. 97. On Targioni Tozzetti's work, see the following (listed chronologically): O. Marinelli, "Giovanni Targioni Tozzetti e la illustrazione geografica della Toscana;" in *Rivista geografica italiana*, **11** (1904), 1–12, 136–145, 226–236; R. Concari, "La geografia umana nei 'Viaggi' di Giovanni Targioni Tozzetti," *ibid.*, **41** (1934), 28–41; and F. Rodolico, "La collezione mineralogica di Giovanni Targioni Tozzetti," in *Catalogo del Museo di storia della scienza* (Florence, 1954), 274–280; and "Lo studio 'fisico' della città di Firenze impostato da Giovanni Targioni Tozzetti nel 1754," in *Rivista geografica italiana*, **64** (1967), 110–113. A detailed description of his journeys, accompanied by itinerary maps, is in F. Rodolico, *L'esplorazione naturalistica dell'Appennino* (Florence, 1963), 133–137, 152–160, 366–369.

FRANCESCO RODOLICO

IBN ṬĀRIQ. See **Yaᶜqūb ibn Ṭāriq**.

TARTAGLIA (also **Tartalea** or **Tartaia**), **NICCOLÒ** (*b*. Brescia, Italy, 1499 or 1500; *d*. Venice, Italy, 13 December 1557), *mathematics*, *mechanics*, *topography*, *military science*.

The surname Tartaglia, which Niccolò always used, was a nickname given to him in his boyhood because of a speech impediment resulting from a wound in the mouth (*tartagliare* means "to stammer"). According to his will, dated 10 December 1557 and now in the Venice State Archives, he had a brother surnamed Fontana, and some historians have attributed that surname to Niccolò as well.

Tartaglia's father, Michele, a postal courier, died about 1506, leaving his widow and children in poverty. Six years later, during the sack of Brescia, Niccolò, while taking shelter in the cathedral, received five serious head wounds. It was only through the loving care of his mother that he recovered. At the age of about fourteen, he went to a Master Francesco to learn to write the alphabet; but by the time he reached "k," he was no longer able to pay the teacher. "From that day," he later wrote in a moving autobiographical sketch, "I never returned to a tutor, but continued to labor by myself over the works of dead men, accompanied only by the daughter of poverty that is called industry" (*Quesiti*, bk. VI, question 8).

Tartaglia began his mathematical studies at an early age and progressed quickly. He moved to Verona, probably sometime between 1516 and 1518, where he was employed as "teacher of the abacus." Certain documents dating from 1529–1533, preserved in the Verona section of the State Archives, testify that he had a family, that he was in reduced financial circumstances, and that he was in charge of a school in the Palazzo Mazzanti. In 1534 he moved to Venice, where he was "professor of mathematics." Tartaglia also gave public lessons in the Church of San Zanipolo (Santi Giovanni e Paolo). Nearly all his works were printed in Venice, where he remained for the rest of his life except for a return to Brescia for about eighteen months in 1548–1549. During this time he taught at Sant'Afra, San Barnaba, San Lorenzo, and at the academy of the nearby village of Rezzato. He died in Venice, poor and alone, in his dwelling in the Calle del Sturion near the Rialto Bridge.

The most important mathematical subject with which Tartaglia's name is linked is the solution of third-degree equations. The rule for solving them had been obtained by Scipione Ferro in the first or second decade of the sixteenth century but was not published at the time. It was rediscovered by Tartaglia in 1535, on the occasion of a mathematical contest with Antonio Maria Fiore, a pupil of Ferro; but Tartaglia did not publish it either. On 25 March 1539, Tartaglia told Girolamo Cardano about it at the latter's house in Milan. Although Cardano had persistently requested the rule and swore not to divulge it, he included it in his *Ars magna* (1545), crediting Ferro and Tartaglia. This breach of promise angered Tartaglia; and in the *Quesiti* (bk. IX), he presented his own research on third-degree equations and his relations with Cardano, whom he discussed in offensive language.

Lodovico Ferrari, who devised the solution of fourth-degree equations, rose to Cardano's defense and sent a notice (*cartello*) of mathematical challenge to Tartaglia. Between 10 February 1547 and 24 July 1548 they exchanged twelve printed brochures (Ferrari's six *Cartelli* and Tartaglia's six *Risposte*, all usually known as *Cartelli*), which are important for their scientific content and are notable for both polemical liveliness and bibliographical rarity. The exchange was followed by a debate between Tartaglia and Ferrari in the Church of Santa Maria del Giardino, in Milan, on 10 August 1548. The scientific portion of the dispute consisted of the solution of sixty-two problems that the two contestants had posed to each other. Although centering mainly on arithmetic, algebra, and geometry, the questions also dealt with geography, astronomy, architecture, gnomonics, and optics. They offer a vivid picture of the state of the exact sciences in mid-sixteenth-century Italy.

Tartaglia's other mathematical contributions concern fundamentals of arithmetic, numerical calculations, extraction of roots, rationalization of denominators, combinatorial analysis, and various other problems that are now considered quaint and amusing. "Tartaglia's triangle," the triangular array of binomial coefficients also known as "Pascal's triangle," is found in the *General trattato* (pt. II [1556]) but also appears in earlier works by other authors, although in a different configuration.

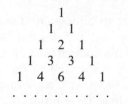

The *Cartelli* also contain an extreme-value problem proposed by Ferrari that Tartaglia solved without including the relevant demonstration.

In geometry Tartaglia was a pioneer in calculating the volume of a tetrahedron from the lengths of its sides and in inscribing within a triangle three circles tangent to one another (now called Malfatti's problem). In the *Cartelli* Ferrari and Tartaglia contributed to the theory of division of areas and especially to the geometry of the compass with fixed opening—subjects to which Tartaglia returned in the *General trattato*. Of special importance to geometry, as well as to other fields, was Tartaglia's Italian translation, with commentary, of Euclid's *Elements* (1543), the first printed translation of the work into any modern language.

Tartaglia's contribution to the diffusion of the works of the great classical scientists was not confined to this translation, however. One of the first publishers of Archimedes, he produced an edition (1543) of William of Moerbeke's thirteenth-century Latin version of some of Archimedes' works. Tartaglia returned to Archimedes in 1551, publishing an Italian translation, with commentary, of part of Book I of *De insidentibus aquae* that was included in the *Ragionamento primo* on the *Travagliata inventione*. Material left by Tartaglia provided the basis for Curtius Troianus' publication in

1565 of *De insidentibus aquae* (books I and II) and of Jordanus de Nemore's *Opusculum de ponderositate*. The latter work, entitled *Liber Jordani de ratione ponderis* in various thirteenth-century manuscripts, is important in the history of mechanics because it contains the first correct solution of the problem of the equilibrium of a heavy body on an inclined plane. (Tartaglia had also published such a solution in the *Quesiti.*)

Yet, despite these contributions to the dissemination of knowledge, Tartaglia drew criticism—sharp at times—by apparently presenting William of Moerbeke's translation as his own, by not crediting Jordanus with the solution of the inclined-plane problem, and by proposing in the *Travagliata inventione* a procedure mentioned by others for raising submerged ships. Any unbiased judgment must take into consideration that an extremely easygoing attitude then obtained with regard to literary property.

Tartaglia's contributions to the art of warfare aroused widespread and lasting interest, and the broad range of his competence in nonmathematical areas is also demonstrated in the *Quesiti*. In this work Tartaglia dealt with algebraic and geometric material (including the solution of the cubic equation), and such varied subjects as the firing of artillery, cannonballs, gunpowder, the disposition of infantry, topographical surveying, equilibrium in balances, and statics. His various proposals on fortifications were praised by Carlo Promis. In his attempts at a theoretical study of the motion of a projectile—a study in which he was a pioneer—Tartaglia reached the following notable conclusions: the trajectory is a curved line everywhere; and the maximum range, for any given value of the initial speed of the projectile, is obtained with a firing elevation of 45°. The latter result was obtained through an erroneous argument, but the proposition is correct (in a vacuum) and might well be called Tartaglia's theorem. In ballistics Tartaglia also proposed new ideas, methods, and instruments, important among which are "firing tables."

Problems of gunnery led Tartaglia, in *Nova scientia*, to suggest two instruments for determining inaccessible heights and distances. The historian Pietro Riccardi considered them "the first telemeters" and cited their related theories as "the first attempts at modern tachymetry." In the *Quesiti*, Tartaglia showed how to apply the compass to surveying, and in the *General trattato* he presented the first theory of the surveyor's cross. Hence Riccardi also asserted that he was responsible for "the major advances in practical geometry of the first half of the sixteenth century."

Tartaglia's attitude toward military matters is shown in his letter dedicating *Nova scientia* to Francesco Maria della Rovere, duke of Urbino; the letter eloquently demonstrates his discreet reticence and effectively reflects his ethical qualities.

The short work *Travagliata inventione* deals not only with raising sunken ships but also with diving suits, weather forecasting, and specific weights. Tartaglia's experiments on the latter are described in Jordanus de Nemore's *De ponderositate*.

Tartaglia's pupils included the English gentleman Richard Wentworth, who was probably the author of an Italian manuscript now at Oxford (Bodleian Library, MS 584), in which Tartaglia is mentioned several times; Giovanni Antonio Rusconi, author of a book on architecture (Venice, 1540); Maffeo Poveiano, author of a work on arithmetic (Bergamo, 1582); and the mathematician and philosopher Giovanni Battista Benedetti, who in his noted work on the geometry of the compass with fixed opening (Venice, 1553) stated that he began the study of Euclid with Tartaglia.

BIBLIOGRAPHY

I. ORIGINAL WORKS. Tartaglia's works are *Nova scientia* (Venice, 1537); *Euclide Megarense* (Venice, 1543); *Opera Archimedis* (Venice, 1543); *Quesiti et inventioni diverse* (Venice, 1546); *Risposte* to Lodovico Ferrari, 6 pts. (1–4, Venice, 1547; 5–6, Brescia, 1548); *Travagliata inventione* (Venice, 1551), with *Ragionamenti* and *Supplimento*; *General trattato di numeri et misure*, 6 pts. (Venice, 1556–1560); *Archimedis De insidentibus aquae* (Venice, 1565); and *Iordani Opusculum de ponderositate* (Venice, 1565). For further information on the various editions see Pietro Riccardi, *Biblioteca matematica italiana* (Modena, 1870–1928; repr. Milan, 1952), I₂, 496–507, with supplements in the series of *Aggiunte*.

The original copies of the *Cartelli* are very rare, as is the autographed ed. (212 copies) by Enrico Giordani, *I sei cartelli di matematica disfida . . . di Lodovico Ferrari, coi sei contro-cartelli in risposta di Niccolò Tartaglia* (Milan, 1876). Facs. eds. of the *Quesiti* (Brescia, 1959) and the *Cartelli* (Brescia, 1974) have been published with commentaries by Arnaldo Masotti.

Some of Tartaglia's works on the art of warfare were translated during his lifetime into German (1547) and French (1556). Modern eds. include the following:

1. The new. ed. with English trans. and commentary by E. A. Moody, of Jordanus de Nemore's *De ponderositate*, based on thirteenth–fifteenth-century MSS with Tartaglia's ed. as guide, and prepared with the as-

sistance of R. Clements, A. Ditzel, and J. L. Saunders. It is included in E. A. Moody and Marshall Clagett, *The Medieval Science of Weights* (*Scientia de ponderibus*) (Madison, Wis., 1952; 2nd ed., 1960), 167–227, 330–336, 388–413.

2. The new eds. of Thomas Salusbury's seventeenth-century versions of *Travagliata inventione* with *Ragionamenti* and *Supplimento*, and *Archimedis De insidentibus aquae*, in *Mathematical Collections and Translations. In Two Tomes by Thomas Salusbury. London 1661 and 1665* in facs., with analytical and biobibliographical intro. by Stillman Drake (London–Los Angeles, 1967), II, 331–402, 479–516.

3. The English versions, by Stillman Drake, of long excerpts concerning mechanics, from *Nova scientia* and the *Quesiti*, in *Mechanics in Sixteenth-Century Italy*, selections from Tartaglia *et al.*, translated and annotated by S. Drake and I. E. Drabkin (Madison, Wis., 1969), 61–143.

Tartaglia's correspondence (or extracts from it) are in the *Quesiti* and in the *Terzo ragionamento* on the *Travagliata inventione*. Two letters dealing with fortifications were exchanged in 1549 with the military engineer Jacopo Fusto Castriotto: copies, perhaps from the writers' own time, are at the old city archives, at the University of Urbino. They were published by Vincenzo Tonni-Bazza, "Di una lettera inedita di N. Tartaglia," in *Atti dell'Accademia nazionale dei Lincei. Rendiconti*, 5th ser., **10** (1901), 39–42; and "Frammenti di nuove ricerche intorno a N. Tartaglia," in *Atti del Congresso internazionale di scienze storiche, Roma, 1903*, XII (Rome, 1907), 293–307. Facsimiles of the letters are in Masotti, *Studi su N. Tartaglia* (see below), pls. xxiii, xxiv.

II. SECONDARY LITERATURE. Works within each section are listed chronologically.

On Tartaglia's life and works, see Baldassarre Boncompagni, "Intorno ad un testamento inedito di N. Tartaglia," in *In memoriam Dominici Chelini–Collectanea mathematica* (Milan, 1881), 363–412, with full-page facs. of his will; Antonio Favaro, "Intorno al testamento inedito di N. Tartaglia pubblicato da Don B. Boncompagni," in *Rivista periodica dei lavori dell' Accademia di Padova*, **32** (1881–1882), 71–108; Vincenzo Tonni-Bazza, "N. Tartaglia nel quarto centenario natalizio," in *Commentari dell'Ateneo di Brescia* (1900), 160–179; Antonio Favaro, "Per la biografia di N. Tartaglia," in *Archivio storico italiano*, **71** (1913), 335–372; and "Di N. Tartaglia e della stampa di alcune sue opere con particolare riguardo alla 'Travagliata inventione,'" in *Isis*, **1** (1913), 329–340; *Ateneo di Brescia–Scoprendosi il monumento a N. Tartaglia* (Brescia, 1918); *Commentari dell'Ateneo di Brescia* (1918), 77–151; Arnaldo Masotti, "Commemorazione di N. Tartaglia," *ibid.* (1957), 25–48; "Sui 'Cartelli di matematica disfida' scambiati fra L. Ferrari e N. Tartaglia," in *Rendiconti dell'Istituto lombardo di scienze e lettere*, Classe di scienze, sec. A, **94** (1960), 31–41; "Su alcuni possibili autografi di N. Tartaglia," *ibid.*, 42–46; and "N. Tar-

taglia," in *Storia di Brescia*, II (Brescia, 1963), 597–617, with 4 full-page plates. Masotti's *Studi su N. Tartaglia* (see below) contains many bibliographical details.

On Tartaglia's works, their translations, and certain MSS by Tartaglia or related to him, see "N. Tartaglia e i suoi 'Quesiti' " and "Rarità tartagliane," in *Atti del Convegno di storia delle matematiche, promosso dall'Ateneo di Brescia nel 1959 in commemorazione del quarto centenario della morte del Tartaglia* (Brescia, 1962), 17–56, 119–160, with 37 full-page plates, which are also in A. Masotti, *Studi su N. Tartaglia* (Brescia, 1962).

Tartaglia's algebra is treated in Pietro Cossali, *Origine, trasporto in Italia, primi progressi in essa dell'algebra*, II (Parma, 1799), 96–158; Silvestro Gherardi, "Di alcuni materiali per la storia della Facoltà matematica nell'antica Università di Bologna," in *Nuovi annali delle scienze naturali* (Bologna), 2nd ser., **5** (1846), 161–187, 241–268, 321–356, 401–436, with additions translated into German by Maximilian Curtze in *Archiv der Mathematik und Physik*, **52** (1870–1871), 65–205; Ettore Bortolotti, "I contributi del Tartaglia, del Cardano, del Ferrari, e della scuola matematica bolognese alla teoria algebrica delle equazioni cubiche," in *Studi e memorie per la storia dell'Università di Bologna*, **10** (1926), 55–108; and *The Great Art or The Rules of Algebra, by Girolamo Cardano*, translated and edited by T. Richard Witmer, with foreword by Oystein Ore (Cambridge, Mass., 1968), 8, 9, 52, 96, 239, as well as the foreword and preface, *passim*.

On his contributions to geometry, see Antonio Favaro, "Notizie storico-critiche sulla divisione delle aree," in *Memorie del R. Istituto veneto di scienze, lettere ed arti*, **22** (1883), 151–152; J. S. Mackay, "Solutions of Euclid's Problems, With a Ruler and One Fixed Aperture of the Compasses, by the Italian Geometers of the Sixteenth Century," in *Proceedings of the Edinburgh Mathematical Society*, **5** (1887), 2–22; W. M. Kutta, "Zur Geschichte der Geometrie mit constanter Zirkelöffnung," in *Nova acta Academiae Caesareae Leopoldino Carolinae germanicae naturae curiosorum*, **71** (1896), 80–91; Giovanni Sansone, "Sulle espressioni del volume del tetraedro," in *Periodico di matematiche*, 4th ser., **3** (1923), 26–27; Harald Geppert, "Sulle costruzioni geometriche che si eseguiscono colla riga ed un compasso di apertura fissa," *ibid.*, **9** (1929), 303–309, 313–317; and Giuseppina Biggiogero, "La geometrica del tetraedro," in *Enciclopedia delle matematiche elementari*, II, pt. 1 (Milan, 1936), 220, 245.

Statics and dynamics are discussed in Raffaello Caverni, *Storia del metodo sperimentale in Italia*, 5 vols. (Florence, 1891–1900), I, 53–54; IV, 190–198; Pierre Duhem, *Les origines de la statique*, I (Paris, 1905), 111–112, 119–120, 199; Alexandre Koyré, "La dynamique de N. Tartaglia," in *La science au seizième siècle–Colloque international de Royaumont 1957* (Paris, 1960), 91–116; and S. Drake, "Introduction" to *Mechanics in Sixteenth-Century Italy* (see above), 16–26, which also includes Tartaglia's links with Archimedes and Euclid as well as with Jordanus de Nemore.

Tartaglia's contributions to the military sciences are treated in Max Jähns, *Geschichte der Kriegswissenschaften*, 3 vols. (Munich–Leipzig, 1889–1891; facs. repr. New York, 1965), xix, 507, 596–605, 626, 707–712, 718, 797–802, 850, 985, 1008.

On fortifications, see Carlo Promis, "Della vita e delle opere degl' italiani scrittori di artiglieria, architettura e meccanica militare da Egidio Colonna a Francesco Marchi 1285–1560," in Francesco di Giorgio Martini, *Trattato di architettura civile e militare*, pt. 2 (Turin, 1841), 69–71, 78; H. Wauvermans, "La fortification de N. Tartaglia," in *Revue belge d'art, de sciences et de technologie militaires*, 1, IV (1876), 1–42; and Antonio Cassi Ramelli, *Dalle caverne ai rifugi blindati—Trenta secoli di architettura militare* (Milan, 1964), 320, 326, 346, 354, 360.

Tartaglia's ballistics is discussed in P. Charbonnier, *Essais sur l'histoire de la balistique* (Paris, 1928), 3, 6, 8–38, 41, 54, 66, 75, 87, 266; A. R. Hall, *Ballistics in the Seventeenth Century* (Cambridge, 1952), 33, 36–43, 45–52, 55, 61, 68–70, 81, 83, 95, 105; and E. G. R. Taylor, *The Mathematical Practitioners of Tudor and Stuart England 1485–1714* (Cambridge, 1954,), which mentions Tartaglia especially in connection with William Bourne and Cyprian Lucar, who translated Tartaglia's writings on ballistics into English—see 17, 30–31, 33, 42, 176, 321, 323, 328, 370.

On Tartaglia's topography, see Giovanni Rossi, *Groma e squadro ovvero storia dell'agrimensura italiana dai tempi antichi al secolo XVII°* (Turin, 1877), 7–8, 115–116, 122–138, 140, 142, 156, 157, 161, 166, 169–171, 213; P. Riccardi, "Cenni sulla storia della geodesia in Italia dalle prime epoche fin oltre la metà del secolo XIX," pt. 1, in *Memorie dell'Accademia delle scienze dell'Istituto di Bologna*, 3rd ser., 10 (1879), 474–478; R. T. Gunther, *Early Science in Oxford*, I (Oxford, 1920; repr. London, 1967), 310, 339, 368; and E. G. R. Taylor, "Cartography, Survey and Navigation," in C. Singer *et al.*, *A History of Technology*, III (Oxford, 1957), 539.

ARNALDO MASOTTI

TASHIRO, SHIRO (in Japanese sources called **Tashiro Shirosuke**) (*b.* Kagoshima prefecture, Japan, 12 February 1883; *d.* Cincinnati, Ohio, 12 June 1963), *biochemistry*.

Tashiro, the son of Shirobe and A. Tashiro, immigrated to the United States in 1901. After graduating B.S. from the University of Chicago in 1909, he served as fellow and assistant in physiological chemistry at Chicago from 1910 until he received the Ph.D. in 1912 at Chicago. In 1913–1914 he was an associate in physiological chemistry, in 1914–1918 instructor, and in 1918 an assistant

professor at Chicago. Tashiro was appointed to the University of Cincinnati College of Medicine in 1919 as associate professor of biochemistry and assistant director of the Biochemistry Service, Cincinnati General Hospital. He returned to Japan for study, and on 26 July 1923 Kyoto University granted him the doctor of medical science degree for a dissertation entitled "Carbon Dioxide Production From Nerve Fibres When Resting and When Stimulated; A Contribution to the Chemical Basis of Irritability; A New Method and Apparatus for the Estimation of Exceedingly Minute Quantities of Carbon Dioxide." Tashiro was appointed full professor at the University of Cincinnati in 1925. He retired in 1952.

Tashiro's career was founded on his invention of the biometer, prior to which no method of analysis was available for minute quantities of carbon dioxide. In conjunction with H. N. McCoy, Tashiro devised an apparatus that could detect carbon dioxide in quantities as small as one ten-millionth of a gram. The fundamental principle of the biometer depended upon the possibility of precipitating exceedingly minute quantities of carbon dioxide as barium carbonate on the surface of a small drop of barium hydroxide solution. When the drop of barium hydroxide is exposed to any sample of a gas free from carbon dioxide, it remains clear; but when more than a definite amount of carbon dioxide is introduced, a precipitate of carbonate appears that is detectable through a lens. Tashiro found that the minimum amount of carbon dioxide that gives a precipitate is 1.0×10^{-7}g. Through the use of the biometer Tashiro was able to conclude that injured living tissue (nerve tissue and dry seeds) had a greater output of carbon dioxide than uninjured tissue, while dead tissue did not emit any carbon dioxide. If injured tissue gave off carbon dioxide, it was still alive.

Tashiro's contributions covered many fields: metabolism in nerves; metabolism gradation in the nerve considered as an organism; metabolism in the growth of tissues; anesthetics; biochemical and physiological factors in the production of a gastric ulcer; dacryohemorrhea; and cholinergics.

Tashiro married Shizuka Kawasaki of Honolulu on 9 November 1915. He contributed to numerous scientific journals, and was a president of the Cincinnati section of Sigma Xi, national honor research society, and the Daniel Drake Society. He received the Crown Prince Memorial Prize from the Imperial Academy of Japan and was a member of many chemical and biological societies in the United States, France, and in the United Kingdom. In 1953 Tashiro became the first Japanese to be admitted to American citizenship at the Cincinnati Immigration and Naturalization office.

In almost all of his undertakings Tashiro's observations were fundamental. His work on the nature of the nerve impulse and its propagation was intimately linked to his invention of the biometer. His studies on bile salts ranged from questioning whether there were bile salts in normal blood to a possible role for these compounds in formation of a gastric ulcer. With N. C. Foot, also of the University of Cincinnati, Tashiro translated an important treatise by Rinya Kawamura on tsutsugamushi disease, scrub typhus (1926).

BIBLIOGRAPHY

I. ORIGINAL WORKS. Tashiro's published writings are *A Chemical Sign of Life* (Chicago, 1917) and numerous papers published in biochemical and physiological journals between 1914 and 1952, including *American Journal of Physiology, Biological Bulletin, Internationale Zeitschrift für physikalisch-chemische Biologie, Journal of Biological Chemistry, Journal of Infectious Diseases, Medical Bulletin of the University of Cincinnati, Proceedings of the American Society of Biological Chemists, Proceedings of the National Academy,* and *Proceedings of the Society for Experimental Biology and Medicine.*

He and N. C. Foot translated *Studies on Tsutsugamushi Fever,* which is *Medical Bulletin, College of Medicine, University of Cincinnati,* **4**, spec. nos. 1 and 2 (1926).

II. SECONDARY LITERATURE. Biographical literature appears to be very scanty. Extremely brief references are made to Tashiro in *Nihon Igakuhakase-Roku,* Munetoshi Konuma, ed. (1954); and *Kyoto Daigaku Gakui-Roku, 1921–1951* ("Directory of Doctorates Granted by Kyoto University"; Kyoto, 1952). He is listed in *American Men of Science,* 10th ed. (1962) and *World Who's Who in Science,* 1949.

Some information on his life and work appeared in newspapers (1927–1963) and are on file at the Public Library of Cincinnati and Hamilton County, Cincinnati, Ohio (Cincinnati *Enquirer,* 1927, 1943, 1953, 1963; New York *Times,* 1932, 1941, 1953; Cincinnati *Post,* 1945, 1953, 1963).

STACEY B. DAY

TAUBER, ALFRED (*b.* Pressburg, Slovakia [now Bratislava, Czechoslovakia], 5 November 1866; *d.* Theresienstadt, Germany [now Terezin, Czechoslovakia], 1942 [?]), *mathematics.*

Tauber entered the University of Vienna in 1884, concentrating on mathematics, physics, philosophy, and political economy. His doctoral dissertation, "Über einige Sätze der Gruppentheorie" (1888), was written under Gustav von Escherich and was intended for publication, although it never appeared in print. In 1891 Tauber qualified as *Privatdozent* with the *Habilitationsschrift* "Über den Zusammenhang des reellen und imaginären Teiles einer Potenzreihe" and subsequently lectured on the theory of series, trigonometric series, and potential theory. From 1895 he also lectured on the mathematics of insurance, a subject of little interest to him. He was subsequently awarded a monthly salary for this work, and from 1899 he also lectured on the subject at the Technical University of Vienna, where he was appointed *Honorardozent* in 1901. Financial responsibilities obliged Tauber to accept the post of head of the mathematics department of the Phönix insurance company in Vienna (1892–1908). After obtaining an assistant professorship at the university in 1908 he remained adviser to the company until 1912. He had an important role in investigations of mortality tables carried out by a group of insurance companies (1903–1907) and was consultant on insurance to the chamber of commerce and legal adviser to the commerce court of Vienna.

Tauber never assumed the duties of a full professor at the University of Vienna, and the title was not formally conferred upon him until 1919. The reasons for his difficulties are not known, but he was apparently not on good terms with some of the professors there. Almost all of his lectures were given at the Technical University. He retired in 1933 but remained as *Privatdozent* at both universities until 1938. Nothing is known about his last days. The central information office of the Vienna police headquarters contains only one entry, dated 28 June 1942: "Departure to Theresienstadt [concentration camp]."

Tauber's scientific work can be divided into three areas. The first comprises papers on function theory and potential theory; those in the latter area, although overshadowed by the work of Lyapunov, are still important. His most important memoir was "Ein Satz aus der Theorie der unendlichen Reihen" (1897). In 1826 Abel had proved a limit theorem on power series (Abel's limit theorem), the converse of which is true, as Tauber demonstrated, only if an additional condition is stipulated; such conditions are now called Tauberian conditions. These theorems are of fundamental importance in analysis, as was shown especially by G. H. Hardy and J. E. Littlewood, who coined the term "Tauberian theorems," and by N. Wiener. Tauber apparently did not follow subsequent developments of this theorem and, remarkably, did not seem to have considered his memoir of particular importance.

The second group includes papers on linear differential equations and the gamma functions. Although of interest, they did not achieve the importance of his other works.

The third group contains papers and reports on the mathematics of insurance. In "Über die Hypothekenversicherung" (1897) and "Gutachten für die sechste internationale Tagung der Versicherungswissenschaften" (1909) he formulated his Risiko equation.

BIBLIOGRAPHY

I. Original Works. A bibliography of Tauber's works may be found in the article by Pinl and Dick (see below). His outstanding work was "Ein Satz aus der Theorie der unendlichen Reihen," in *Monatshefte für Mathematik und Physik*, **8** (1897), 273–277. See also "Über den Zusammenhang des reellen und imaginären Teiles einer Potenzreihe," *ibid.*, **2** (1891), 79–118, his *Habilitationsschrift*; "Über einige Sätze der Potentialtheorie," *ibid.*, **9** (1898), 74–88; and "Über die Hypothekenversicherung," in *Österreichische Revue*, **22** (1897), 203–205.

II. Secondary Literature. On Tauber and his work, see obituaries by E. Bukovics and J. Rybarz in *Festschrift der technischen Hochschule Wien* (Vienna, 1965–1966), I, 344–346; II, 130–132; and Maximilian Pinl and Auguste Dick, "Kollegen in einer dunkeln Zeit: Schluss," in *Jahresbericht der Deutschen Mathematikervereinigung*, **75** (1974), 166–208, especially 202–208, which includes a bibliography.

E. Hlawka

TAURINUS, FRANZ ADOLPH (*b.* Bad König, Odenwald, Germany, 15 November 1794; *d.* Cologne, Germany, 13 February 1874), *mathematics*.

In F. Engel and P. Stäckel's *Die Theorie der Parallellinien von Euklid bis Gauss* two writings of Taurinus are mentioned as contributions to the subject. Since their book is a collection of documents in the prehistory of non-Euclidean geometry, they reproduce the most important passages of the original works, including extracts from those of Taurinus, which in 1895 were available in only a few copies.

According to the information given by Engel and Stäckel, Taurinus was the son of a court official of the counts of Erbach-Schöneberg; his mother was the former Luise Juliane Schweikart. He studied law at Heidelberg, Giessen, and Göttingen, and from 1822 lived in Cologne as a man of independent means; he thus had the leisure to pursue various scientific interests.

Taurinus presented the results of his mathematical investigations in *Die Theorie der Parallellinien* (1825) and *Geometriae prima elementa* (1826). He received the stimulus for these studies from his uncle F. K. Schweikart (1780–1857), who from 1820 was professor of law at the University of Königsberg, and with whom he corresponded concerning his work. Taurinus also communicated several of his results and demonstrations to Gauss, whose replies are printed in Gauss's *Werke* (VII, 186).

According to Engel and Stäckel, Taurinus' investigations on the theory of parallel lines sought to demonstrate that the sole admissible geometry is Euclidean. As the basis for his argumentation Taurinus used the axiom of the straight line, which postulates that through two points there could be exactly one straight line. In this regard, however, he had no choice but to accept the "internal consistency" of the "third system of geometry," in which the sum of the angles of a triangle amounts to less than two right angles.

His remarks in *Geometriae prima elementa* show that by 1826 Taurinus had clearly recognized the lack of contradiction of this "third system," "logarithmic-spherical geometry," as he called it; had even developed the suitable trigonometry; and had successfully applied trigonometry to a series of elementary problems.

Taurinus' works on the problem of parallel lines, like those of his uncle, Schweikart, represent a middle stage in the historical development of this problem between the efforts of Saccheri and Lambert, on the one hand, and those of Gauss, Lobachevsky, and Bolyai, on the other. Although he sought to preserve the hegemony of Euclidean geometry by reference to the infinite number of non-Euclidean geometries; nonetheless, through an idea that was very close to Lambert's, he moved on to non-Euclidean trigonometry as it was later developed by Bolyai and Lobachevsky.

Moreover, Taurinus presented the idea that elliptical geometry can be "realized" on the sphere. This concept was first taken up again by Bernhard Riemann.

BIBLIOGRAPHY

Taurinus' major works are *Die Theorie der Parallellinien* (Cologne, 1825) and *Geometriae prima elementa* (Cologne, 1826).

F. Engel and P. Stäckel, *Die Theorie der Parallellinien von Euklid bis Gauss* (Leipzig, 1895), contains selections from Taurinus' works.

KARLHEINZ HAAS

TAYLOR, BROOK (*b.* Edmonton, Middlesex, England, 18 August 1685; *d.* London, England, 29 December 1731), *mathematics.*

Brook Taylor was the son of John Taylor of Bifrons House, Kent, and Olivia, daughter of Sir Nicholas Tempest, Bart. The family was fairly well-to-do, and was connected with the minor nobility. Brook's grandfather, Nathaniel, had supported Oliver Cromwell. John Taylor was a stern parent from whom Brook became estranged in 1721 when he married a woman said to have been of good family but of no fortune. In 1723 Brook returned home after his wife's death in childbirth. He married again in 1725 with his father's approval, but his second wife died in childbirth in 1730. The daughter born at that time survived.

Taylor's home life seems to have influenced his work in several ways. Two of his major scientific contributions deal with the vibrating string and with perspective drawing. His father was interested in music and art, and entertained many musicians in his home. The family archives were said to contain paintings by Brook, and there is an unpublished manuscript entitled *On Musick* among the Taylor materials at St. John's College, Cambridge. This is not the paper said to have been presented to the Royal Society prior to 1713, but a portion of a projected joint work by Taylor, Sir Isaac Newton, and Dr. Pepusch, who apparently was to write on the nonscientific aspects of music.

Taylor was tutored at home before entering St. John's College in 1701, where the chief mathematicians were John Machin and John Keill. Taylor received the LL.B. degree in 1709, was elected to the Royal Society in 1712, and was awarded the LL.D. degree in 1714. He was elected secretary to the Royal Society in January 1714, but he resigned in October 1718 because of ill health and perhaps because of a loss of interest in this rather confining task. He visited France several times both for the sake of his health and for social reasons. Out of these trips grew a scientific correspondence with Pierre Rémond de Montmort dealing with infinite series and Montmort's work in probability. In this Taylor served on some occasions as an intermediary between Montmort and Abraham De Moivre. W. W. Rouse Ball reports that the problem of the knight's tour was first solved by Montmort and De Moivre after it had been suggested by Taylor.[1]

Taylor published his first important paper in the *Philosophical Transactions of the Royal Society* in 1714, but he had actually written it by 1708, according to his correspondence with Keill. The paper dealt with the determination of the center of oscillation of a body, and was typical both of Taylor's work and of the times, in that it dealt with a problem in mechanics, used Newtonian dot notation, and led to a dispute with Johann I Bernoulli.

The period of 1714–1719 was Taylor's most productive, mathematically. The first editions of both his mathematical books, *Methodus incrementorum directa et inversa* and *Linear Perspective*, appeared in 1715. Their second editions appeared in 1717 and 1719 respectively. He also published thirteen articles, some of them letters and reviews, in the *Philosophical Transactions* during the years 1712–1724. These include accounts of experiments with capillarity, magnetism, and the thermometer. In his later years Taylor turned to religious and philosophical writings. His third book, *Comtemplatio philosophica*, was printed posthumously by his grandson in 1793.

Taylor is best known for the theorem or process for expanding functions into infinite series that commonly bears his name. Since it is an important theorem, and since there is disagreement as to the amount of credit that should be given to him for its development, an outline of his derivation of the theorem will be given here. The discussion of Proposition VII, Theorem III of the *Methodus incrementorum* includes the statement:

If z grows to be $z + n\dot{z}$ then x equals

$$x + \frac{n}{1}\dot{x} + \frac{n}{1}\cdot\frac{n-1}{2}\ddot{x} + \frac{n}{1}\cdot\frac{n-1}{2}\cdot\frac{n-2}{3}\dddot{x}, \text{ etc.}$$

Taylor used dots below the variables to represent increments or finite differences, and dots above to represent Newton's fluxions.

The above statement is a notationally improved version of Newton's interpolation formula as given in Lemma 5 of Book III of his *Principia*. This formula had first appeared in a letter from James Gregory to John Collins in 1670.[2] Taylor had derived this formula inductively from a difference table written in terms of x and its successive differences.

Next, Taylor made the substitutions

$$v = n\dot{z}, \ \dot{v} = v - \dot{z} = (n-1)\dot{z}, \ \ddot{v} = \dot{v} - \dot{z}, \text{ etc.,}$$

to derive the statement: "as z growing becomes $z + v$, x likewise growing becomes

$$x + \dot{x}\frac{v}{1 \cdot \dot{z}} + \ddot{x}\frac{v\dot{v}}{1 \cdot 2\dot{z}^2} + \dddot{x}\frac{v\dot{v}\ddot{v}}{1 \cdot 2 \cdot 3 \cdot \dot{z}^3} + \cdots \text{ etc."}$$

The final step in the derivation and Taylor's original statement of the theorem, which in modern notation is

$$f(x+h) = f(x) + \frac{f'(x)}{1!}h + \frac{f''(x)}{2!}h^2 + \frac{f'''(x)}{3!}h^3$$

$$+ \cdots \frac{f^{(n)}(x)}{n!}h^n + \cdots,$$

is finally derived in Corollary II to Theorem III as follows: "for evanescent increments [write] the fluxions which are proportional to them and make all of $\ddot{v}$, $\dot{v}$, v, $\dot{y}$, y equal, then as with time flowing uniformly z becomes $z + v$, so will x become

$$x + \dot{x}\frac{v}{1\dot{z}} + \ddot{x}\frac{v^2}{1 \cdot 2\dot{z}^2} + \dddot{x}\frac{v^3}{1 \cdot 2 \cdot 3\dot{z}^3} + \cdots \text{ etc."}$$

This becomes the modern form of Taylor's series when we realize that with "time flowing uniformly" $\dot{z}$ is a constant, $\frac{\dot{x}}{\dot{z}} = \frac{dx}{dz}$, and v is the increment in the independent variable.

Taylor's first statement of this theorem had been given in a letter of 26 July 1712 to John Machin, which has been reprinted by H. Bateman. In it Taylor remarked that this discovery grew out of a hint from Machin given in a conversation in Child's Coffeehouse about the use of "Sir Isaac Newton's series" to solve Kepler's problem, and "Dr. Halley's method of extracting roots" of polynomial equations, which had been published in the *Transactions* for 1694.

This shows Taylor's fairness, care, and familiarity with the literature. He used his formula to expand functions in series and to solve differential equations, but he seemed to have no foreshadowing of the fundamental role later assigned to it by Lagrange nor to have any qualms about the lack of rigor in its derivation. Colin Maclaurin noted that the special case of Taylor's series now known as Maclaurin's theorem or series was discussed by Taylor on page 27 of the 1717 edition of the *Methodus*. The term "Taylor's series" was probably first used by L'Huillier in 1786, although Condorcet used both the names of Taylor and d'Alembert in 1784.[3]

Although infinite series were in the air at the time, and Taylor himself noted several sources and motivations for his development, it seems that he developed his formula independently and was the first to state it explicitly and in a general form. Peano based his claim for Johann I Bernoulli's priority on an integration in which Bernoulli used an infinite series in 1694.[4] Pringsheim showed that it is possible to derive Taylor's theorem from Bernoulli's formula by some changes of variable. However, there seems to be no indication that Taylor did this, nor that Bernoulli appreciated the final form or generality of the Taylor theorem. Taylor's Proposition XI, Theorem IV, on the other hand, is directly equivalent to Bernoulli's integration formula. However, Taylor's derivation differs from Bernoulli's in such a way as to entitle him to priority for the process of integration by parts.

Taylor was one of the few English mathematicians who could hold their own in disputes with Continental rivals, although even so he did not always prevail. Bernoulli pointed out that an integration problem issued by Taylor as a challenge to "non-English mathematicians" had already been completed by Leibniz in *Acta eruditorum*. Their debates in the journals occasionally included rather heated phrases and, at one time, a wager of fifty guineas. When Bernoulli suggested in a private letter that they couch their debate in more gentlemanly terms, Taylor replied that he meant to sound sharp and "to show an indignation."

The *Methodus* contained several additional firsts, the importance of which could not have been realized at the time. These include the recognition and determination of a singular solution for a differential equation,[5] a formula involving a change in variables and relating the derivatives of a function to those of its inverse function, the determination of centers of oscillation and percussion, curvature, and the vibrating string problem. The last three problems had been published earlier in the *Philosophical Transactions*, as had been a continued fraction for computing logarithms.

Newton approached curvature by way of the determination of the center of curvature as the limit point of the intersection of two normals. Although this was not published until 1736, Taylor was familiar with Newton's work, since, after applying his own formula, Taylor remarked that the results agreed with those given by Newton for conic sections. Taylor, however, conceived of the radius of curvature as the radius of the limiting circle through three points of a curve, and associated curvature with the problem of the angle of contact dating back to Euclid. He then used curvature and the radius of curvature in giving the first solution for the normal vibrations of the simplest case of the plucked string. In propositions XXII and XXIII he showed that under his conditions each point will vibrate in the manner of a cycloidal pendulum, and he determined the period in terms of the length and weight of the string and a weight supported by the string. There is little doubt that Taylor's work influenced later writers since, for example, Bernoulli cited Taylor in letters to his son Daniel on this topic.

The *Methodus* qualifies Taylor as one of the founders of the calculus of finite differences, and as one of the first to use it in interpolation and in summation of series.

Taylor contributed to the history of the barometer by explaining a derivation of the variation of atmospheric pressure as a logarithmic function of the altitude, and he also contributed to the study of the refraction of light.

Like all of Taylor's writing, his book on linear perspective was so concise that Bernoulli characterized it as "abstruse to all and unintelligible to artists for whom it was more especially written."[6] Even the second edition, which nearly doubled the forty-two pages of the first, showed little improvement in this matter. Its effect, nevertheless, was very substantial, since it passed through four editions, three translations, and twelve authors who prepared twenty-two editions of extended expositions based on Taylor's concepts. He developed his theory of perspective in a formal and rigorous fashion in a sequence of theorems and proofs. The most outstanding and original of his ideas in this field were his definition and use of vanishing points and vanishing lines for all lines and planes, and his development of a theory and practice for the inverse problem of perspective that later served as a basis for work by Lambert and for the development of photogrammetry. Taylor also made free use of the idea of associating infinitely distant points of intersection with parallel lines, and he sought to devise methods for doing geometric constructions directly in perspective.

A study of Brook Taylor's life and work reveals that his contribution to the development of mathematics was substantially greater than the attachment of his name to one theorem would suggest. His work was concise and hard to follow. The surprising number of major concepts that he touched upon, initially developed, but failed to elaborate further leads one to regret that health, family concerns and sadness, or other unassessable factors, including wealth and parental dominance, restricted the mathematically productive portion of his relatively short life.

NOTES

1. W. W. Rouse Ball, *Mathematical Recreations and Essays* (London, 1912), p. 175.
2. H. W. Turnbull, *James Gregory Tercentenary Memorial Volume* (London, 1939), pp. 119–120.
3. Gino Loria, *Storia delle matematiche*, 2nd ed. (Milan, 1950), p. 649.
4. G. Peano, *Formulario matematico*, 5th ed. (Turin, 1906–1908), pp. 303–304.
5. E. L. Ince, *Ordinary Differential Equations* (New York, 1944), p. 87.
6. *Contemplatio philosophica*, p. 29, quoted from *Acta eruditorum*.

BIBLIOGRAPHY

I. ORIGINAL WORKS. The major source of biographical data as well as the only publication of his philosophical book is *Contemplatio philosophica: A Posthumous Work of the late Brook Taylor, L.L.D. F.R.S. Some Time Secretary of the Royal Society to Which Is Prefixed a Life of the Author by his Grandson, Sir William Young, Bart., F.R.S. A.S.S. with an appendix containing Sundry Original Papers, Letters from the Count Raymond de Montmort, Lord Bolingbroke, Mercilly de Villette, Bernoulli, & c.* (London, 1793).

This book and the mathematical letters appended to it are reproduced in Heinrich Auchter, *Brook Taylor der Mathematiker und Philosoph* (Würzburg, 1937). Both of these books have a picture of Taylor as secretary of the Royal Society (1714) as a frontispiece. This picture may be derived from a plaque, since it is signed "R. Earlem, Sculp." It is labeled "From an Original Picture in the Possession of Lady Young." A nearly identical picture labeled "J. Dudley, Sculp." is reproduced in *The Mathematics Teacher*, **27** (January 1927), 4. It is also labeled "London, Published March 26, 1811 by J. Taylor, High Holborn."

Charles Richard Wild, in *A History of the Royal Society* (London, 1848), lists a portrait of Taylor painted by Amiconi among the portraits in possession of the Royal Society, but *The Record of the Royal Society*, 3rd ed. (London, 1912), records in its "List of Portraits in Oil in Possession of the Society" "Brook Taylor L.L.D. F.R.S. (1685–1731). Presented by Sir W. Young, Bart., F.R.S. Painter Unknown."

The two editions of Taylor's *Methodus* cited above were both published in London, as were the editions of his *Linear Perspective*. Complete data on the editions and extensions of this book are contained in P. S. Jones, "Brook Taylor and the Mathematical Theory of Linear Perspective," in *The American Mathematical Monthly*, **58** (Nov. 1951), 597–606.

Additional data on Taylor's correspondence is to be found in H. Bateman, "The Correspondence of Brook Taylor," in *Bibliotheca Mathematica*, 3rd ser., **7** (1906–1907), 367–371; Edward M. Langley, "An Interesting Find," in *The Mathematical Gazette*, **IV** (July 1907), 97–98; Ivo Schneider, "Der Mathematiker Abraham de Moivre," in *Archive for History of Exact Sciences*, **5** (1968/1969), 177–317.

II. SECONDARY LITERATURE. For details of one of Taylor's disputes see Luigi Conte, "Giovanni Bernoulli e le sfida di Brook Taylor," in *Archives de l'histoire des sciences*, **27** (or **1** of new series), 611–622.

The most extensive history of Taylor's theorem is Alfred Pringsheim, "Zur Geschichte des Taylorschen Lehrsatzes," in *Bibliotheca mathematica*, 3rd ser., I (Leipzig, 1900), 433–479.

PHILLIP S. JONES

TAYLOR, CHARLES VINCENT (*b*. near Whitesville, Missouri, 8 February 1885; *d*. Stanford, California, 22 February 1946), *biology*.

Charles Vincent Taylor, the youngest of ten children, was born to Isaac Newton Taylor and Christina Bashor Taylor, on a farm near Whitesville, Missouri. He was a descendant of a family whose members included eminent lawyers, Baptist clergymen, a general, a senator, and a governor. Because his father's farm was not very productive, young Taylor had to work his way through Mount Morris College, Illinois. In college he was prominent in student affairs and, because of his fine singing voice, in musical groups as well. After receiving his B.A. he became principal of a high school in Valley City, North Dakota. His deep interest in biology led him to enroll in 1914 as a graduate student at the University of California, in Berkeley, where he took the M.A. under the supervision of Joseph A. Long, based upon a study of fertilization in the mouse, and the Ph.D. in 1917 under Charles A. Kofoid, based upon a study of the neuromotor apparatus of the ciliate *Euplotes*. He was an instructor of zoology at the university (1917–1918), then Johnston scholar at the Johns Hopkins University (1918–1920). Taylor returned to the University of California, where he taught as assistant professor (1920–1923). In 1921, he married one of his students, Lola Lucille Felder. Spirited and interested in the arts, she brought to the family a measure of gaiety and fun that served as a balance to her husband's more serious nature. Four children resulted from the marriage: Jeanne, Elouise, Lenore, and Isaac Newton.

During the years that he was associated with the University of California, Taylor spent some of his summers at the Marine Biological Laboratory, in Woods Hole, Massachusetts, where he collaborated with Robert Chambers on micromanipulative studies. His microsurgical experiments on the function of motor organelles and of the micronucleus in *Euplotes*, published in 1920 and 1924, are classics. In the summers of 1922 and 1923 he was on the staff at Johns Hopkins Marine Station. Taylor was assistant professor at the University of Michigan (1923–1924), and research associate at the Tortugas laboratory of the Carnegie Institution in the summers of 1924 and 1926. During these years he studied the organization and early development of marine eggs.

In 1925 Taylor was appointed to the staff of the biology department at Stanford University and quickly advanced to full professor. In 1930 he received a particularly attractive offer from the University of Michigan, but decided that biology had a more promising future at Stanford. He took leave that year, however, to teach at the University of Chicago. Upon his return to Stanford, he was made Herzstein professor of biology and chairman of the biology department (both 1931), and then dean of the School of Biological Sciences (1934).

The series of papers that Taylor and his collaborators published on the encystment and excystment of the ciliate *Colpoda duodenaria* has not been superseded or surpassed. From his first experiments published with H. Albert Barker in 1930 to the last papers published shortly before his death in 1946, he demonstrated his progressively more effective control of the physical conditions and state of the experimental organism, a control that necessitated a study of the structure and cytological details of reorganization in order to make certain of the taxonomic position of the experimental animal. Taylor also saw the need for an axenic culture of the organism and made efforts to see this accomplished. As a consequence, one of his collaborators, Laura Garnjobst, finally showed that encystment resulted from the lack of any one of five of the known nutritional factors in the diet. Taylor also suggested a study of stromatogenesis as the basis for resolving the taxonomic position of that most celebrated genus of protozoans, *Tetrahymena*, which was then in a confused state. His earlier interests, in fibrillar systems in protozoans, in solgel transformations in the protoplasm of protozoans, and in the organization of marine eggs and their early development, were essential to his deep interest in reorganization, differentiation, and redifferentiation in protoplasm. The micromanipulator known by his name was an instrument designed to enable him to complete studies on these subjects.

As administrator in the Stanford biology department, Taylor held strong views; he believed that too many scientists emphasized the differences between organisms and their functions, burrowing deeper and deeper into their specialties until they lost sight of what he called the "common denominators" in life. He looked for and emphasized these basic concepts and reorganized the department of biological sciences at Stanford so that such concepts would become the guiding principles. With the help of a sympathetic faculty that he had attracted to the department, he introduced a series of foundation courses to achieve his purpose. Many generations of students benefited from the broad background in basic biology that they received at Stanford. His idealism was misunderstood as a power play by some, however, who resented the engulfment of smaller departments into a larger unit.

In recognition of his many achievements Taylor was elected to the National Academy of Sciences in 1943. Two members of the department, Beadle and Tatum, won the Nobel Prize for work done in the department during Taylor's headship.

Taylor organized a symposium for the celebration of the hundredth anniversary of the cell theory (of Schleiden and Schwann) in 1939. He obtained funds that enabled him to attract an international assembly of eminent scientists. The symposium resulted in the monograph "The Cell and Protoplasm," edited by Forest R. Moulton, and published in 1940.

BIBLIOGRAPHY

I. ORIGINAL WORKS. Taylor's writings include "Demonstration of the Function of the Neuromotor Apparatus in *Euplotes* by the Method of Microdissection," in *University of California Publications in Zoology*, **19** (1920), 403–470; "Fatal Effects of the Removal of the Micronucleus in *Euplotes*," with W. P. Farber, *ibid.*, **26** (1924), 131–144; "Improved Micromanipulation Apparatus," *ibid.*, **26** (1925), 443–454; "An Investigation on Organization of a Sea Urchin Egg," with D. H. Tennant and Douglas M. Whitaker, in *Carnegie Institution of Washington. Publications*, **391** (1929), 1–104; "A Study of the Conditions of Encystment of *Colpoda cucullus*," with H. Albert Barker, in *Physiological Zoology*, **4** (1931), 620–634; "Effects of a Given X-Ray Dose on Cysts of *Colpoda steini* at Successive Stages in their Induced Excystment," with Morden G. Brown and Ar-

thur G. R. Strickland, in *Journal of Cellular and Comparative Physiology*, **9** (1936), 105–116; "Structural Analysis of *Colpoda duodenaria*," with Waldo H. Furgason, in *Archiv für Protistenkunde*, **90** (1938), 320–339; "Growth Studies of *Colpoda duodenaria* in the Absence of Other Living Organisms," with Willem J. Van Wagtendonk, in *Journal of Cellular and Comparative Physiology*, **17** (1941), 349–353.

II. SECONDARY LITERATURE. On Taylor and his work, see Charles H. Danforth, "Biographical Memoir of Charles Vincent Taylor," in *Biographical Memoirs. National Academy of Sciences*, **25** (1948), 205–225; Waldo H. Furgason, "The Significant Cytostomal Pattern of the 'Glaucoma-Colpidium Group' and a Proposed New Genus and Species, *Tetrahymena geleii*," in *Archiv für Protistenkunde*, **94** (1940), 224–266; Laura Garnjobst, "The Effects of Certain Deficient Media on Resting Cyst Formation in *Colpoda duodenaria*," in *Physiological Zoology*, **20** (1947), 5–14; Forest R. Moulton, ed., *The Cell and Protoplasm* (Washington, D.C., 1940); Victor C. Twitty, "Charles Vincent Taylor," in *Anatomical Record*, **98** (1947), 242–243.

ARTHUR C. GIESE

TAYLOR, FRANK BURSLEY (*b.* Fort Wayne, Indiana, 23 November 1860; *d.* Fort Wayne, 12 June 1938), *geology.*

Taylor was the only child of Fanny Wright and Robert Stewart Taylor. His father, a judge and Republican politician, became wealthy from his practice of patent law, specializing in the new electrical and telephone industries. Judge Taylor's business and his interest in flood control on the Mississippi River led him to a considerable mastery of science. Frank Taylor graduated from Fort Wayne High School in 1881 and entered Harvard in 1882. He took courses in geology and astronomy as a special student until ill health forced him to drop out in 1886. Accompanied by F. Savary Pearce, a Philadelphia physician, Taylor traveled through the Great Lakes region for the next several years, studying its postglacial geological history. He married Minnetta Amelia Ketchum of Mackinac Island on 24 April 1899. She accompanied him on field trips, driving the horses and, later, their automobile.

Taylor's father paid his son's field and publishing expenses until May 1900, when Frank obtained his first job, as assistant to Alfred C. Lane at the Michigan Geological Survey. He then became an assistant in the glacial division of the U.S. Geological Survey from June 1900 to 1916, first under the direction of Thomas Chrowder Chamberlin and then of Frank Leverett. His field assignments were in New England and in the Great Lakes area. In 1908, 1909, and 1911 he mapped the moraines of southern Ontario for the Canadian Geological Survey. The American Association for the Advancement of Science awarded Taylor a research grant in 1920 and 1921 to study the New York moraines. Apart from this grant Taylor was again supported by his father's estate from 1916 to 1938. He was an active member of the Geological Society of America, the Michigan Academy of Sciences, and the AAAS.

Before he joined the U.S. Geological Survey in 1900, Taylor had formulated a history for the Great Lakes region from the period of the fullest extension of the Wisconsinian glaciation through the ice sheet's retreat to the present time. Between 1892 and 1896 he argued that old beachlines indicated that a marine submergence of the area had followed the disappearance of the glacier, an idea he dropped when his fieldwork of 1895 on the succession of terminal moraines convinced him that the lakes were formed by ice dams instead. Grove Karl Gilbert had encouraged Taylor to study moraines as the crucial test of his submergence theory. Once he accepted the ice dam theory, his reconstruction of Great Lakes history matched current views on this part of the geological record.

Taylor's studies of beachlines and moraines suggested that retreat of the Wisconsinian glacial field was not steady. Rather, the ice sheet had melted back and then partially readvanced, perhaps dozens of times. Inspired by Chamberlin's reports from the Greenland expeditions of 1896, Taylor decided that Great Lakes topography had controlled the ice sheet, not the other way around. Once local features in the old Midwest were taken into account, the pattern of retreat and partial readvance was a regular series. Taylor's work on glacial history culminated in U.S. Geological Survey monograph 53, *The Pleistocene of Indiana and Michigan and the History of the Great Lakes* (Washington, D.C., 1915), which he wrote with Frank Leverett. This book and Taylor's articles after 1900 show that his federal government experience led him to use the sophisticated geological terminology that marked a professional scientist.

Taylor's scheme included a complicated series of drainage systems to remove glacial meltwater. He paid special attention to the time when the main channel was a strait across what is now Lake Nipissing and its related rivers. During the Nipissing episode, he observed, the flow of Niagara Falls was much less than that over the modern ledge, a hypothesis he supported with studies of the narrower gorge of the past. Gilbert had suggested a lesser flow during some part of the postglacial era; Taylor worked on the details and supplied the reason. One important implication of this diminished flow was that the retreat of the falls could no longer be a reliable geochronological indicator.

Taylor was influenced in his glacial work by the publications of Gerhard de Geer as well as by Gilbert and Chamberlin. He adopted de Geer's concept of an isobase of deformation to describe the uplift of land to the northeast during glacial retreat. Below the isobase no uplift had occurred. Taylor calculated the amount and direction of deformation from the tilting of originally horizontal beachlines of postglacial lakes.

Taylor's courses in astronomy at Harvard inspired some of his later scientific work. He later recalled that on 13 December 1884, it occurred to him that the moon had once been a comet and had been captured by the earth during its last pass through the solar system. In 1898 he elaborated this idea into a theory for the origin of the whole planetary system. Taylor credited Daniel Kirkwood, then an astronomer at Indiana University, with first publishing a similar theory in connection with the origin of the asteroids. According to Taylor, as comets passed close to the sun, they were captured as planets that spun in the orbit of Mercury. Upon each new capture, the planets shifted out one orbit toward Neptune's. His fullest explanation of cosmogony appeared in his privately published book (1903) on the subject, in which he spelled out some of the mathematics and physics of the theory. Taylor felt compelled to challenge Isaac Newton's explanation for the orbit of the moon, because Newton's system did not rigidly determine the moon's course. Taylor believed that the orbits of the moons and planets must be determinate, but the mathematics of the situation seems to have been beyond his grasp. It is doubtful that determinate satellite orbits were required for Taylor's theory.

Taylor's 1898 work on the planetary system, published as a forty-page pamphlet (now extremely rare), also contained his first articulation of a theory of the history of continents. When the moon was captured by the earth, Taylor argued, it created a tidal force on the planet and increased the earth's speed of rotation. These two forces pulled the continents away from the poles toward the equator. He did not return to this point in 1903, but in 1910 published his first detailed arguments for a theory of continental drift in a paper on the origin and arcuate shape of Tertiary mountain ranges. He explicitly acknowledged his debt to Eduard Suess's work on the Asian ranges as a source for much of his theory. Taylor said that as the continents slid toward the equator, they encountered obstructions that created loops of mountian ranges, just as the Wisconsinian glacial sheet had formed lobes as it met local topographical features. Taylor's theory of 1910 also involved movement of crustal material away from the mid-Atlantic ridge.

Taylor published no papers from 1917 through 1920. He spent those years reading and thinking about ways to defend, expand, and clarify his theory of continental drift and mountain creation. His later papers connected geological phenomena, such as earthquakes, to his theory; added studies of other arcuate Tertiary ranges; and argued that the uplift following the Wisconsinian glaciation could be accounted for by crustal creep. These papers also spelled out the differences of Taylor's views from those of Alfred Wegener, whose theory of continental drift was first published in 1912. Taylor rejected isostatic adjustment as a mechanism for crustal movement because he believed its working required a fluid interior for the earth. Wegener's theory used movements toward isostasy on a fluid subcrust to shift continents, while Taylor's slid continents along a narrow shear zone of a fairly rigid earth. Taylor's theory did not fully anticipate the features of plate tectonics, however. The most notable difference is that plate tectonics does not require capture of the moon or other astronomical events to account for earth movements; terrestrial forces are considered adequate.

BIBLIOGRAPHY

I. ORIGINAL WORKS. Leverett (see below) lists Taylor's publications but occasionally omits abstracts of articles published in full elsewhere and, in at least two instances, cites pages incorrectly. Two articles should be added to his compilation: "A Short History of the Great Lakes," in Inland Educator, 2 (Mar., Apr., May 1896), 101–103, 138–145, 216–223, respectively; and "Geological History of the Great Lakes," in Scientific Monthly, 49 (July 1939), 49–56. According to the National Union Catalog at the Library of Congress, only two copies of Taylor's An Endogenous Planetary System. A Study in Astronomy (Fort Wayne, 1898) are in public libraries, one at the John Crerar Library in Chicago and one at the U.S. Geological Survey Library, Reston, Virginia. The Planetary System; A Study of Its Structure (Fort Wayne–London, 1903) is a more accessible account of Taylor's astronomical theory; and "Bearing of the Tertiary Mountain Belt on the Origin of the Earth's Plan," in Bulletin of the Geological Society of America, 21 (1910), 179–226, is a more available statement on the history of continents than the 1898 pamphlet.

II. SECONDARY LITERATURE. Richard Flint, Glacial and Quaternary Geology (New York, 1971), chs. 2, 13, 21, 30, provides helpful background for assessing Taylor's work on recent geological history. For useful critiques of Taylor's theory of continental drift, see Anthony Hallam, A Revolution in the Earth Sciences: From Continental Drift to Plate Tectonics (Oxford, 1973), 3–6, and Ursula Marvin, Continental Drift: The Evolution of a Concept (Washington, D.C., 1973), 63–64.

Biographical details about Taylor are available in Frank Leverett, "Memorial to Frank Bursley Taylor," in Proceedings of the Geological Society of America for 1938 (1939), 191–200. Shorter sketches are by J. H. Bretz, in Dictionary of American Biography, supp. 2, 653–654; American Men of Science, 5th ed. (1933); Who's Who in America, 1936–1937, 2387; by A. C. Lane, in Proceedings of the American Academy of Arts and Sciences, 75 (1944), 176–178; by Frank Leverett, in Science, n.s. 88 (5 August 1938), 121–122; and Harvard University, Class of 1886, Secretary's Report, 7 (1911), 305–307, and 12 (1936), 416–419.

MICHELE L. ALDRICH

TAYLOR, FREDERICK WINSLOW (b. Germantown [part of Philadelphia], Pennsylvania, 20 March 1856; d. Philadelphia, 21 March 1915), engineering.

The scion of an aristocratic Philadelphia family, Taylor seemed destined to follow his father, Franklin, along a well-worn groove to a genteel law practice. But after graduating from Phillips Exeter Academy in 1874 he showed the independence of his strong-minded mother, Emily Annette Winslow, and chose instead to become a mechanical engineer. After serving his apprenticeship as a machinist and pattern maker, Taylor went to work at the Midvale Steel Company in Philadelphia, where he rose from laborer to chief engineer in six years. He obtained the M.E. degree by correspondence from Stevens Institute of Technology in 1883. He married Louise M. Spooner of Philadelphia in 1884.

Taylor was one of a number of engineers who were attempting to convert engineering into a science. He assumed that there were laws (or rational principles) underlying all areas of engineering practice, including management. Beginning at Midvale and continuing through his career as a consultant, Taylor conducted a series of painstaking investigations of metal cutting, tool steel, belting, reinforced concrete, management, and other subjects. These works were highly empirical and owed little to theory, for which Taylor had neither understanding nor sympathy. It was by such a process of cut-and-try experiment that Taylor and J. Maunsel White discovered the process, named for them, for the heat treatment of tool steel (1898). Under the name "high-speed steel" this invention revolutionized machine shop practice by permitting the speed of metal-cutting machinery to be more than doubled.

The achievement for which Taylor is most remembered was his development of "scientific management." He wanted to reduce all aspects of management to "exact science"; and his approach, sometimes termed "task management," was to determine exactly how much each worker should accomplish in a given time. This entailed the discovery of a new measure of human work. At first Taylor attempted to find a correlation between fatigue and foot-pounds of work, but such a direct solution eluded him. Instead, he found what he considered to be the atomistic units of work: "elementary motions." Taylor first broke down a set of operations into these motions and timed them with a stopwatch. He then analyzed the sequence of motions, eliminated the unnecessary ones, and combined the remainder into an optimum series. After adding percentages to cover necessary rest and unavoidable delays, Taylor thought he could calculate the time required for any task.

Time-and-motion study was only the first of a series of managerial innovations. To set times, to assign daily tasks, and to prepare written instructions for each worker required a planning department, which became the nerve center of management under Taylor's system. Precisely determined tasks entailed the complete standardization of tools, operations, and routing. Taylor also devised methods of cost accounting, inventory control, records keeping, and a functional organization of authority that facilitated rational management

Taylor thought that his system of management provided the basis of a scientific ethics. Through it he hoped to end class conflict and establish social justice. Although these larger goals were not achieved, Taylor's system had a profound influence on modern management thought.

BIBLIOGRAPHY

I. ORIGINAL WORKS. The Taylor papers are in the library of Stevens Institute of Technology, Hoboken, N.J.

They include MSS of unpublished addresses as well as correspondence. There is an interesting autobiographical fragment in a letter from Taylor to Morris L. Cooke, 2 Dec. 1910. A printed guide to the papers is available at the repository.

A convenient assemblage of Taylor's most important publications is in Frederick W. Taylor, *Scientific Management: Comprising Shop Management, The Principles of Scientific Management, and Taylor's Testimony Before the Special House Committee* (New York, 1947). Taylor's various papers presented to the American Society of Mechanical Engineers are listed in its *Seventy-Seven Year Index* (New York, 1951). The greatest of these was also published as a book, *On the Art of Cutting Metals* (New York, 1907). In addition he wrote two works with Sanford E. Thompson: *A Treatise on Concrete* (New York, 1905) and *Concrete Costs* (New York, 1912).

II. SECONDARY LITERATURE. The standard biography is Frank B. Copley, *Frederick W. Taylor* (New York, 1923). Memoirs include H. K. Hathaway, ed., "Tributes to Frederick W. Taylor," in *Transactions of the American Society of Mechanical Engineers*, 37 (1915), 1459–1496; "Frederick Winslow Taylor," *ibid.*, 1527–1529; and The Taylor Society, *Frederick Winslow Taylor, A Memorial Volume* (New York [*ca.* 1920]). See also Carl W. Mitman, "Frederick Winslow Taylor," in *Dictionary of American Biography*, XVIII, 323–324.

Modern evaluations of Taylor and his system are in Hugh G. J. Aitken, *Taylorism at the Watertown Arsenal* (Cambridge, Mass., 1960), 13–48; Samuel Haber, *Efficiency and Uplift* (Chicago–London, 1964), 1–30; Edwin Layton, *The Revolt of the Engineers* (Cleveland, 1970), 134–139; Milton J. Nadworny, *Scientific Management and the Unions* (Cambridge, Mass., 1955), 1–33; and Sudhir Kakar, *Frederick Taylor: A Study in Personality and Innovation* (Cambridge, Mass., 1970).

EDWIN LAYTON

TEALL, JETHRO JUSTINIAN HARRIS (*b.* Northleach, England, 5 January 1849; *d.* Dulwich, England, 2 July 1924), *petrography, geology.*

The son of Jethro Teall, a landowner of Sandwich, Kent, and Mary Hathaway of Northleach, Teall was born after the death of his father. He was educated at Northleach Grammar School, at Cheltenham, and at St. John's College, Cambridge, taking the natural sciences tripos in 1872 and receiving the M.A. in 1876. He was inspired to choose geology instead of mathematics at Cambridge by his tutor, T. G. Bonney, and attended Adam Sedgwick's geology course as Woodwardian professor. Teall was the first recipient of the Sedgwick Prize, in 1874, for an essay dealing with the phosphatic deposits near Cambridge. Election to a fellowship of his college followed in 1875, and he retained this post until his marriage to Harriet Cowen of Nottingham, in 1879. The years between 1872 and 1888 were divided between lecturing under the University Extension Scheme in the Midlands, in the north and west of England, and in London, and petrographical research at Cambridge. His lectures attracted large audiences; and his association with the early days of University College, Nottingham, is particularly remembered.

The field of petrography was almost new at this time. The polarizing microscope had been developed by W. H. Fox Talbot in 1834 by making use of William Nicol's single-vision calcite prism (1829). Thin sections were made by H. C. Sorby in the 1850's and J. Clifton Ward had applied the technique to Lake District lavas during the ensuing decade, but a great avenue of research was opening up. Through his work on the pitchstone of Eigg, the whin sill and dikes of northern England, the Cheviot lavas, the Cornish granites, and Lizard gabbros, Teall gave major impetus to the subject. From 1886 to 1888 he was engaged in publishing the definitive work on British petrography with which his name will always be associated. The encouragement given by Bonney and the influence of Rosenbusch, leading petrographical systematist of the time in Europe, had borne good fruit; and Teall had added many new ideas of his own to both igneous and metamorphic petrography.

In 1888 Sir Archibald Geikie invited Teall to join the Geological Survey of Great Britain as a geologist, to take charge of the petrographical work. The primary geological survey of the northwestern Highlands of Scotland had begun in 1885, and its spectacular results demanded close petrographical study. This Teall provided, for the Highlands and for other parts of the United Kingdom, in a series of contributions to official memoirs and a number of important private papers appearing between 1888 and 1903. In 1901 he was chosen to succeed Geikie as director of the Geological Survey. He was at the same time president of the Geological Society of London; and his influential addresses to the Society on the evolution of petrological ideas (1901, 1902) were considered sufficiently important by the Smithsonian Institution to reproduce in its *Report of the Board of Regents.* . . .

During his eleven years as director of the Geological Survey, Teall's output of original work was necessarily curtailed by the demands of administration; but he had the satisfaction of leading the official British geological effort during a productive period. His contributions to science were

recognized by his election to the Royal Society in 1890 and by the award of the Bigsby Medal of the Geological Society in 1889 and its highest award, the Wollaston Medal, in 1905. The Paris Academy presented him with its Delesse Prize in 1907; and his official work was recognized with a knighthood in 1916.

BIBLIOGRAPHY

I. ORIGINAL WORKS. A full list of Teall's writings is given in the *Geological Magazine* article cited below. They include "On the Chemical and Microscopical Characters of the Whin Sill," in *Quarterly Journal of the Geological Society of London*, **40** (1884), 640–657; "The Metamorphosis of Dolerite into Hornblende-Schist," *ibid.*, **41** (1885), 133–144; *British Petrography, With Special Reference to the Igneous Rocks* (London, 1888); and "The Evolution of Petrological Ideas," in *Quarterly Journal of the Geological Society of London*, **57** (1901), lxii–lxxxvi, and **58** (1902), lxiii–lxxviii.

II. SECONDARY LITERATURE. Biographies are H. H. Thomas, "Sir Jethro Justinian Harris Teall," in *Dictionary of National Biography* for 1922–1930 (1937), 826–827; and H. Woodward, "Eminent Living Geologists. Jethro Justinian Harris Teall," in *Geological Magazine*, 5th ser., **6** (1909), 1–8. Obituaries are in E. B. Bailey, *Geological Survey of Great Britain* (London, 1952), 144–170; J. S. Flett, *The First Hundred Years of the Geological Survey of Great Britain* (London, 1937), 143–160; *Proceedings of the Royal Society*, **B 97** (1925), xv–xvii; *Quarterly Journal of the Geological Society of London*, **81** (1925), lxiii–lxv.

K. C. DUNHAM

TEICHMANN, LUDWIK KAROL (*b.* Lublin, Poland, 16 September 1823; *d.* Cracow, Poland, 24 November 1895), *anatomy.*

Teichmann's name is associated mainly with his discovery of a simple chemical test for the presence of blood that was widely used. His parents died when Teichmann was six, and his two aunts helped him to complete his secondary education. In 1847 he enrolled at Protestant Theological Faculty at Dorpat, but soon became interested in natural science. In 1850 he was one of the seconds in a duel that ended with the death of a colleague, a circumstance that forced him to flee the country. From Hamburg he went to Heidelberg, where he entered the Faculty of Medicine in November 1850. Working as an anatomical preparator in the department headed by Jacob Henle, he also studied chemistry, physics, and technology. In 1852 he followed Henle to Göttingen, where he graduated M.D. on 18 December 1855 with the dissertation "Zur Lehre der Ganglien." In 1853, while still a student, he published a paper on the crystallization of certain organic compounds of the blood, describing the preparation of the microscopic crystals of hemin (heme chloride). This was the first, and for some ten years the only, test for the presence of blood in suspect stains on clothes, furniture, or other objects. Because of its simplicity and specificity, it became one of the accepted tests in forensic medicine. During the same period he mastered time-consuming anatomical preparations to supply Henle with illustrations for his *Handbuch der systematischen Anatomie*. Henle's failure to acknowledge Teichmann's contributions led to a conflict.

After graduation Teichmann became provisional prosector of anatomy and was granted the Blumenbach fellowship, which allowed him to visit other European anatomical departments and meet prominent anatomists: Koelliker, Johannes Müller, Gegenbaur, A. Retzius, M. P. C. Sappey, Richard Quain, Sharpey. He was particularly well received by Joseph Hyrtl in Vienna, who helped him during an illness and encouraged him to continue his career in anatomy. Hyrtl remained Teichmann's good friend in later years. In 1859 Teichmann obtained the *venia legendi* at Göttingen and in 1861 went to Cracow, where he was offered the chair of pathological anatomy. In 1868 he became professor of descriptive anatomy and retained that post until his retirement in 1894. In 1873 he opened a new anatomical theater and provided many specimens for its museum.

Teichmann's main scientific interest was in the lymphatic vessels and their origin, which he studied by means of an original injection method. He maintained that no direct communication exists between blood capillaries and lymphatics, and discovered the obstruction of lymphatic vessels in elephantiasis.

BIBLIOGRAPHY

I. Original Works. Teichmann's most important papers are "Über die Krystallisation der organischen Bestandteile des Bluts," in *Zeitschrift für rationelle Medicin*, n.s. **3** (1853), 375–388; and "Über das Haematin," *ibid.*, n.s. **8** (1857), 141–148, in which the method of preparing hemin (heme chloride) crystals is described. *Das Saugadersystem vom anatomischen Standpunkte* (Leipzig, 1861) is his main publication on the lymphatic system. In later years Teichmann is reported to have published 30 papers (in Polish and German) on the lymphatics and others on anatomical techniques. No bibliography of his works seems to have been published.

II. Secondary Literature. A biographical sketch based on Teichmann's handwritten autobiography is Leon Wachholz, "Ludwik Teichmann, szkic biograficzno-historyczny," in *Archiwum historji i filozofji medycyny*, **10** (1930), 34–62, summarized in English by A. Laskiewicz, "Professor Ludwik Karol Teichmann, M.D. 1823–1895," in *Bulletin of Polish Medical Science and History*, **8** (1965), 91–92. See also F. Lejars, "Un grand anatomiste polonais Ludwig Teichmann," in *Revue scientifique* (*Revue rose*), 4th ser., **5** (1896), 481–487.

Vladislav Kruta

TEILHARD DE CHARDIN, PIERRE (*b.* near Orcines, Puy-de-Dôme, France, 1 May 1881; *d.* New York, N.Y., 10 April 1955), *paleontology, geology.*

Teilhard was born into an aristocratic family at Sarcenat, the familial home. In 1898 he entered the Jesuit order and, after initial studies at Aix-en-Provence and the Isle of Jersey, was assigned to a Jesuit school in Cairo, where he taught physics and chemistry from 1905 to 1908. In Egypt he acquired his first extensive experience in fieldwork, which awakened his interest in the geology of the Tertiary. Although he published a monograph on Eocene strata in Egypt, Teilhard did not acquire true professional competence until he was transferred to the Jesuit house at Hastings, England, where between 1908 and 1912 he studied not only theology but also vertebrate paleontology. Ordained a priest, he returned to Paris in 1912 to study geology and paleontology with Marcellin Boule at the Museum of Natural History; these researches, interrupted by wartime duty as a stretcher-bearer, led to his Sorbonne thesis (1922) on the mammals of the Lower Eocene in France.

From 1920 to 1923 Teilhard taught geology at the Catholic Institute in Paris. In the latter year he made his first journey to China to participate in a paleontological mission with Émile Licent. By the time he returned to Paris, his habit of interpreting such theological questions as original sin in the light of evolutionary ideas had attracted opposition, with the result that he was forbidden to continue lecturing at the Catholic Institute. In April 1926 he departed for virtual exile in China.

The years 1908–1912 had been ones of critical intellectual formation. At Hastings he became acquainted with the evolutionary philosophy of Henri Bergson, whose book *L'évolution créatrice* proved to be the most important source of Teilhard's emerging world view, although Teilhard's notion of a converging cosmos was antithetical to that of Bergson. By 1916 (in his essay "La vie cosmique") the main lines of Teilhard's idea of a cosmic and directed evolutionary force had already developed. In Paris, before his definitive departure for China, Teilhard further developed his philosophical ideas in conjunction with the Bergsonian philosopher Édouard Le Roy and the Russian geologist V. I. Vernadsky. Le Roy and Teilhard attended Vernadsky's 1922–1923 Sorbonne lectures on geochemistry, in which the Russian explicated his concept of the biosphere. It was this stimulus that led Teilhard, in a series of lectures on evolution in 1925–1926, to develop the concept of the noosphere, or thinking layer of the earth, representing a higher stage of evolutionary development. During his first months in China he set down his ideas in *Le milieu divin*, in which the theme of man as the culmination of the evolutionary impulse emerges in full relief.

The next few years, spent largely in collaboration with Licent, were productive ones for Teilhard. He continued work on Quaternary and Tertiary mammals, participating in 1928 in a joint study with Boule, Licent, and Henri Breuil on the Chinese Paleolithic, his contribution being studies on geology and his specialty, mammalian fauna, which he found to be quite similar to the mammals of the European Pleistocene. In 1929 he was scientific adviser to the Chinese Geological Survey and, in his own words, "heading the geological advance in China." By the end of the decade he had terminated his relationship with Licent and had shifted his scholarly connections from French to Sino-American institutions; it was against this background that the discoveries at Chou-k'ou-tien were made. There, in 1929, a human cranium, that of the celebrated *Sinanthropus*, was unearthed by Pei Wen-chung. Teilhard, as the research team's geologist (as well as coordinator of operations), was able to demonstrate the earliness of the skull, which later proved to be a close relation of the *Pithecanthropus* of Java.

The next phase of Teilhard's career was devoted largely to geological research as he sought to synthesize the continental geology of Asia. In 1929 he began a series of expeditions, including the Roy Chapman Andrews Central Asia expedition (summer 1930) and the Croisière Jaune expedition of 1931–1932 (which Teilhard regarded as a pseudo-scientific venture but one that nevertheless enabled him to complete syntheses of the tectonics of northern China and of the Pleistocene geology of Central Asia).

By 1934 Teilhard was acting director of the Geological Survey and an active participant in the Cenozoic Research Laboratory in Peking. He next sought to connect the Tertiary and Quaternary geologic structure of northern China with that of the south, following the lines of fissure, a project that led to a trip to India with Helmut de Terra to connect the geology of the subcontinent with that of China. From 1931 to 1938 Teilhard produced a series of essays contributing to his synthesis of Asian geology and paleontology.

After 1938, with the exception of two trips to Africa, Teilhard's fieldwork was over. During the Japanese occupation he wrote several important monographs on human paleontology and fossil mammals in China. It was during this same period that his major philosophical works were conceived, beginning with the first chapter of *Le phénomène humain* in 1938.

The Teilhardian thesis is not a scientific theory but, rather, a philosophical world view based on certain themes drawn from the evolutionary synthesis and expressed in mystical, often poetic, terms. Teilhard discerned in the historical development of the cosmos a law of "complexity-consciousness," a notion reminiscent of Haeckel's views on the psychic unity of the organic world, only extended on a cosmic scale to include the inorganic world. According to Teilhard's law, each successive stage in the evolutionary process is marked, first, by an increasing degree of complexity in organization and, second, by a corresponding increase in degree of consciousness. Evolution thus proceeds in orderly fashion from the inorganic to the organic, from less complex to more highly organized forms of life, through the process of hominization and beyond to "planetization," whereby all the peoples of *Homo sapiens* are to achieve collectively an ultrahuman convergence, seen symbolically as a final "Point Omega."

As a rationale for his view of an anthropocentric universe, Teilhard invoked Heisenberg's uncertainty principle to demonstrate that man is the center of all perspective in the natural world. He then applied the second law of thermodynamics to explain the complexification of the universe over time. Energy, instead of being lost through entropy, is converted into what Teilhard termed "radial energy," a metaphysical construct standing for the evolutionary forces productive of increasing cultural complexity.

In terms of evolutionary process, Teilhard has

been typically interpreted as a neo-Lamarckian exponent of orthogenesis: a process of accretion of changes tending in the same direction, toward a divinely inspired mankind. As T. Dobzhansky has noted, Teilhard's notion of orthogenesis was an eccentric one, the teleological implications of which have been overstressed by religionists to the point of distorting Teilhard's conception of the evolutionary process. That he was a finalist in the philosophical sense cannot be denied; but his finalism was applied to the evolutionary process only in a retrospective way, as a commentary on the cosmic past. His real understanding of evolution was considerably closer to scientific orthodoxy than has generally been supposed, and toward the end of his life it drew closer to the neo-Darwinian synthesis. He saw evolution functioning through a series of purposeful "gropings" (*tâtonnements*) that are random until the "purpose" is achieved. The *hasard dirigé* that governs the process need not be understood in a theologically teleological sense, however, but as a process of response to environmental challenges.

After the war Teilhard returned to Paris, where he labored in vain to publish *Le phénomène humain*. In 1947 he was ordered to refrain from philosophical writing and in 1949 was denied permission by his order to succeed to Breuil's chair of paleontology at the Collège de France. The result of these reverses was a second "exile"—to New York (1951–1955) and a research appointment at the Wenner-Gren Foundation for Anthropological Research. He resumed fieldwork on two trips to South Africa to inform himself of the research on *Australopithecus*. The African experience made it possible for him to complete his scientific synthesis of hominization, in which he characterized anthropogenesis as a bipolar process having an abortive Asian center and another in Africa that led directly to *Homo sapiens*. At the same time Teilhard continued to relate human origins to general geological development. In his final essays he again articulated his view of man as the primary focus of recent evolutionary development.

The diffusion of Teilhardian evolutionism is not a spurious phenomenon, but a further phase in the popularization of the theory of evolution, whereby entire sectors of society previously hostile to Darwinism have been brought into the evolutionary consensus. The primary diffusion began with the publication of *Le phénomène humain* in 1955, peaked around 1967, and, by 1970, had encompassed all the cultures of the Catholic West. In 1957 the Holy Office ordered the works of Teilhard removed from the libraries of Catholic institutions and forbade their sale in Catholic bookstores. This move was a prelude to the *monitum* of 30 June 1962 advising the faithful of errors and ambiguities in Teilhard's philosophical and theological writings. At the same time, however, the Jesuit order relaxed its former stance and now produced the leading ecclesiastical defenders of Teilhard. That the *monitum* proved a dead letter can be seen from the feverish Teilhardian literary activity in France, Spain, and (with stronger opposition) Italy, which has had the effect of depolemicizing evolution in most intellectual and many educational sectors of the Catholic world.

A different phenomenon has been the reception of Teilhardism by European Marxists, especially in the Soviet Union. There, Teilhard's teleological interpretation of evolution has been seen as convergent with dominant concerns of Marxist ideology. The future evolution of the noosphere is to be effected on the basis of the socialization of mankind into ever larger collectivities. Although economic and technological development are indispensable to this movement, both Teilhard and the Marxists believe that "spiritual" (=ideological) factors play a decisive role, particularly a belief in the supreme value of evolution (progress).

BIBLIOGRAPHY

I. ORIGINAL WORKS. The complete scientific works of Teilhard are collected in *Pierre Teilhard de Chardin: L'oeuvre scientifique*, Nicole and Karl Schmitz-Moormann, eds., 10 vols. (Munich, 1971). Of the collected works in the series published in Paris, only vol. II, *L'apparition de l'homme* (1956), translated as *The Appearance of Man* (New York, 1966), contains essays that are, properly speaking, scientific. See also vol. I, *Le phénomène humain* (1955), translated as *The Phenomenon of Man* (New York, 1959); vol. III, *La vision du passé* (1957), translated as *The Vision of the Past* (New York, 1966), and vol. VIII, *Le groupe zoologique humain* (1963), translated as *Man's Place in Nature* (New York, 1966). His fieldwork in China and Africa can be followed in *Lettres de voyages* (Paris, 1956), translated as *Letters From a Traveller* (New York, 1962).

II. SECONDARY LITERATURE. The burgeoning literature on Teilhard and Teilhardism has been cataloged in several bibliographical guides: Joan E. Jarque, *Bibliographie générale des oeuvres et articles sur Pierre Teilhard de Chardin* (Fribourg, 1970); Ladislaus Polgar, *Internationale Teilhard-Bibliographie, 1955–1965* (Munich, 1965); and Daniel Poulin, *Teilhard de Chardin. Essai de bibliographie (1955–1966)* (Quebec, 1966). Selected works on Teilhard are listed yearly in

Archivum historicum Societatis Jesu (Rome). See also Alfred P. Stiernotte, "An Interpretation of Teilhard as Reflected in Recent Literature," in *Zygon*, **3** (1968), 377–425. Useful as critical apparatus are Claude Cuénot, *Nouveau lexique Teilhard de Chardin* (Paris, 1968); and Paul l'Àrchevêque, *Teilhard de Chardin. Index analytique* (Quebec, 1967), a composite index to the first 9 vols. of Teilhard's *Oeuvres*.

Among the periodicals published by societies devoted to the thought of Teilhard, see Société Teilhard de Chardin (Brussels), *Revue* (1960–   ) and *Univers* 1964–   ); Société Pierre Teilhard de Chardin (Paris), *Carnets Teilhard* (1962–   ); Association des Amis de Pierre Teilhard de Chardin (Paris), *Cahiers* (1958–1965) and *Bulletin* (1966–   ); the Teilhard Center for the Future of Man, *Teilhard Review* (1966–   ); and Gesellschaft Teilhard de Chardin (Munich), *Acta Teilhardiana* (1964–   ).

The standard biography of Teilhard is Claude Cuénot, *Pierre Teilhard de Chardin, les grandes étapes de son évolution* (Paris, 1958), also in English (Baltimore, 1965). Works dealing primarily with Teilhard's scientific career are George B. Barbour, *In the Field With Teilhard de Chardin* (New York, 1965); Louis Barjon and Pierre Leroy, *La carrière scientifique de Pierre Teilhard de Chardin* (Monaco, 1964); Henri Breuil, "Les enquêtes du géologue et du préhistorien," in *Table ronde*, no. 90 (June 1955), 19–24; Paul Chauchard, *La pensée scientifique de Teilhard* (Paris, 1965); George Magloire, *Teilhard et le sinanthrope* (Paris, 1964); Henry Fairfield Osborn, "Explorations, Researches and Publications of Pierre Teilhard de Chardin, 1911–1931," *American Museum Novitates*, no. 485 (25 Aug. 1931); Jean Piveteau, *Le Père Teilhard de Chardin savant* (Paris, 1964); and Helmut de Terra, *Mein Weg mit P. Teilhard de Chardin* (Munich, 1962), also in English (London, 1964).

General works on Teilhard's philosophy are Henri de Lubac, *La pensée religieuse du Père Teilhard de Chardin* (Paris, 1962), also in English (New York, 1967); Émile Rideau, *La pensée du Père Teilhard de Chardin* (Paris, 1965), also in English (New York, 1967); and Bernard Towers, *Teilhard de Chardin* (London, 1966). For the "prehistory" of Teilhard's Catholic evolutionism in France, see Henri Begouen, *Quelques souvenirs sur le mouvement des idées transformistes dans les milieux catholiques* (Paris, 1945). Among the explications of Teilhardian evolutionism, see Bernard Delfgaauw, *Teilhard de Chardin* (Baarn, Netherlands, 1961), translated as *Evolution: The Theory of Teilhard de Chardin* (New York, 1969); and Fernando Riaza, *Teilhard de Chardin y la evolución biológica* (Madrid, 1968). Commentary by scientists, from favorable to hostile, includes essays by Theodosius Dobzhansky in *The Biology of Ultimate Concern* (New York, 1969), 213–233, and George Gaylord Simpson in *This View of Life* (New York, 1964), 108–137; and P. B. Medawar's famous critique in *Mind* (Oxford), **70** (1961), 99–106. See also Stephen Toulmin's analysis, "On Teilhard de Chardin," in *Commentary*, **39**, no. 3 (Mar. 1965), 50–55.

Studies of Teilhard's sources are underrepresented in the literature. For his dependence on Bergson, see Madeleine Barthélemy-Madaule, *Bergson et Teilhard de Chardin* (Paris, 1963); on the fleeting, but critical, relationship with Vernadsky, see I. I. Mochalov, *V. I. Vernadsky: Chelovek i myslitel* (Moscow, 1970) 136–138. On Teilhard and Marxist thought, there are numerous articles by Roger Garaudy, including "The Meaning of Life and History in Marx and Teilhard de Chardin: Teilhard's Contribution to the Dialogue Between Christians and Marxists," in *Marxism and Christianity: Studies in the Teilhardian Synthesis* (London, 1967), 58–72; and "Freedom and Creativity: Marxist and Christian," in *Teilhard Review*, **2** (1968–1969), 42–49.

The *monitum* and Catholic opposition to Teilhard are discussed by René d'Ouince, *Un prophète en procès: Teilhard de Chardin dans l'église de son temps*, 2 vols. (Paris, 1970); and by Philippe de la Trinité, *Rome et Teilhard de Chardin* (Paris, 1964) and *Pour et contre Teilhard de Chardin* (Paris, 1970).

The diffusion of Teilhardism has yet to be studied systematically. Representative national studies and bibliographies are (France) J. Hassenforder, *Étude de la diffusion d'un succès de libraire (Le phénomène humain)* (Paris, 1957); (England) Bernard Towers, "The Teilhard Movement in Britain," in *Month*, **36** (1966), 188–196; (Germany) Helmut de Terra, *Bibliographie des deutschsprachigen Schrifttums von und über Pierre Teilhard de Chardin, 1955–1964* (Frankfurt, 1965); (Italy) Elio Gentili, "Pierre Teilhard de Chardin in Italia. Bibliografia," in *Scuola cattolica*, **93** (1965), supp. biblio. 1, 247–334, and **95** (1967), supp. biblio. 2, 138–181; and Marcello Vigli, "Fortuna e funzioni del teilhardismo in Italia," in *Questitalia*, **11** (1968), 352–370; (Soviet Union and eastern Europe) Ladis K. D. Kristof, "Teilhard de Chardin and the Communist Quest for a Space Age World View," in *Russian Review*, **28** (1969), 277–288; and V. Pasika, "Teiiar de Sharden," in *Filosofskaya entsiklopedia*, V (Moscow, 1970), 192–193; (Spain) Miguel Crusafont Pairó, "Teilhard de Chardin en España," in *Acta Teilhardiana*, **5** (1968), 53–63. For a quantitative overview, see José Rubio Carracedo, "Quince años después: Del teilhardismo a Teilhard," in *Arbor* (Madrid), **76** (1970–1971), 43–46.

THOMAS F. GLICK

TELESIO, BERNARDINO (*b.* Cosenza, Italy; 1509; *d.* Cosenza, 1588), *natural philosophy.*

Telesio was one of the group of sixteenth-century Italian speculators known to scholars as "nature philosophers," somewhat to the disparagement of other thinkers who dealt with natural philosophy as then understood but who taught in universities. Telesio's life was relatively uneventful, except for a brief period when he was taken prisoner during the sack of Rome. He was born in Cosenza, near the toe of the Italian boot; and, after schooling elsewhere in Italy, he returned to spend most of his life there. His first training was obtained from his uncle, a capable scholar who taught him Greek as well as Latin. This at once put Telesio into the special category of men who were able to read philosophical or scientific texts from antiquity in the original language and were not forced to depend upon medieval translations or exegesis.

When Telesio arrived at Padua, then, he was able to compare the interpretations of Aristotle or Galen given in his courses with the Greek texts. The Averroist tradition of Aristotelian interpretation did not appeal to him because it was based on Arab sources. Moreover, there is no trace in his writings of any interest in terminist logic or Mertonian physics, as exemplified in the works of "The Calculator" and other Oxford writers, even though these writings had been widely studied in universities of northern Italy during the previous century. Telesio left Padua profoundly dissatisfied with the Aristotelian doctrines presented there. He does not spell out his indictment in detail: in fact, he seldom makes more than passing allusions to contemporary doctrines. When he speaks of "the followers of Aristotle," he is more often referring to ancient Peripatetics than to his contemporaries.

After leaving Padua, Telesio spent some time in a Benedictine monastery developing his own system. He began to write while staying at Naples under the patronage of the Carafa family (Telesio was himself a nobleman, although an impoverished one). He developed his thought in opposition to that of Aristotle and the Greek medical writers, with some use of the Greek commentators. He is considered an arch anti-Aristotelian, yet his own style of thinking is so much like that of Aristotle that he might almost be thought of as an Aristotelian revisionist. Why, otherwise, should Telesio have thought it necessary to make a pilgrimage in 1563 to Brescia in order to explain his views to Vincenzo Maggi, a teacher renowned for his knowledge of Aristotle in the Greek? Maggi listened attentively to his views for several days, then confessed that he could not find anything contradictory about them. This was presumably a tribute to the thoroughness of Telesio's grasp of Aristotle—a grasp so firm that even those most conversant with Aristotle in the Greek were not able to challenge his interpretations or his counterarguments.

Reassured by his interview with Maggi, Telesio published the first version of his major work in 1565, under the title *De rerum natura iuxta propria principia*. The first part of this title, at this late date in the Renaissance, might lead one to expect a presentation of Epicurean physics as found in Lucretius' great poem of the same title, which had been discovered in the previous century. The expectation would be disappointed, however, for Telesio was not an atomist or a corpuscularian at all. This crucial fact must be kept constantly in mind, for it separates Telesio from other so-called "new philosophers" with whom he was later associated (for instance, by Descartes and Leibniz), who were mainly atomists. The subtitle was intended to repudiate principles imposed upon nature and thus expressed Telesio's rejection of what in a later century would have been called a priori theorizing.

In the preface Telesio immediately states that sense is the only valid starting point for speculation on nature. This pronouncement has been taken by most scholars as an empiricist manifesto, but such a view is misleading if one does not recognize that Telesio was not essentially interested in methodology: he never commented on the *Organon* or other logical works. Such epistemology as can be found in his writings occurs in his discussion of the *De anima* and other biological works. Since he was conversant with Galen, Telesio must have encountered that writer's logical empiricism, with its insistence upon the equal roles of sense and reason in science. But there is no stress on reasoning in Telesio's thought: indeed, reasoning is reduced to the detection of similarities among the deliverances of the senses. For this one-sided reliance upon sense alone Telesio was taken to task by another "nature philosopher," Francesco Patrizzi. (Patrizzi's criticisms, with Telesio's rather unconvincing rejoinders, are printed as an appendix in Fiorentino's book, listed in the bibliography).

At any rate Telesio, to judge from his writings, was certainly no more, and probably far less, of a practicing empiricist than his favorite philosophical target, Aristotle. He did not have a theory of experiment such as some scholars claim to find in the works of his contemporary Zabarella, nor did he make any controlled observations like those of Patrizzi. Nor did Telesio have a sophisticated conception of the importance of measurement. Nor, finally, was he a mechanist, in spite of the fact that he rejected action at a distance as being the result of an "occult" quality and in spite of his insistence upon the role of matter as a principle of nature.

Having learned all this, surely the reader must be asking, "Why, then, should Telesio be of any interest whatever to the historian of modern science?" The answer lies in the way in which he deployed certain Aristotelian concepts so as to achieve a new system of physical explanation, rejecting metaphysical entities that had no explanatory role in physics. Telesio's arguments are just about as plausible (or implausible, as the case may be) as Aristotle's, yet they differ drastically in their results. Surely nothing could have been more disturbing to Aristotelians than this!

What, then, are the chief features of Telesio's scheme? His basic explanatory arsenal consists of two opposing factors, heat and cold, to which must be added a third principle termed *materia* but not to be identified with Aristotle's potentiality, at least not officially. "Heat" and "cold" have taken the place of Aristotelian forms. Telesio is quite explicit on this point: He regards "forms" as "snoring"—that is, as otiose and hence dispensable (this may be viewed as one of the earlier attacks on "substantial forms"). Just as "matter" and "form" cannot really be separated in Aristotelian metaphysics, so "heat" and "cold" and "matter" are physically inseparable for Telesio. In general, heat is associated with motion, expansion, light, and life, while cold is associated with immobility, contraction, darkness, and death—although there is considerable wavering as to the precise relationships between these entities.

The following passage (from *De rerum natura* [1586 edition], I, 5) sums up Telesio's scheme: "Three principles [*principia*] of things altogether must be posited: two active natures [*agentes naturae*], heat and cold, and a bodily bulk [*corporea moles*]. . . ." This "bulk" or "matter" is described as being "inert" and "dead," all actions or operations being foreign to it. Aristotle had given a somewhat similar account of heat and cold in *De generatione et corruptione* (at 329b23), where he identifies "the hot" and "the cold," "the wet" and "the dry" as primary (tangible) qualities. In keeping with Aristotelian texts such as this, heat and cold were called *primae activae qualitates* by such contemporary Aristotelians as Zabarella. But for Aristotle the active and the passive qualities make up the four elements (fire being a combination of the hot and the dry, and so on), whereas for Telesio wetness and dryness are not primary but derivative. New explanations are thus required for the traditional "media," water and air.

All of this Telesian doctrine is supposed to rest, as we have seen, on sense—that is, upon observable features of the cosmological landscape. Thus we feel the warmth of the sun and the coldness of the earth. We feel the immobility of the earth (Telesio was no Copernican and, indeed, seems not even to have been acquainted with the heliocentric hypothesis) while we see the sun moving in the sky. As a first crude hypothesis this is perhaps not unpromising—or, any rate, not much less promising than Aristotle's cosmology. But obviously Telesio will have his hands full to explain, on the basis of his two active principles alone, all sorts of changes shown to us by sense. We might note that in making the sun fiery or "igneous," Telesio was, unwittingly, helping to contribute to the breakdown of the barrier that Aristotle had set up between celestial and sublunary physics, the breakdown triumphantly announced by Galileo in his *Dialogue Concerning the Two Chief World Systems*.

Telesio also introduced concepts of space and time that anticipated the absolute space and time of Newtonian physics:

> And thus clearly space can be conceded to be different from the bulk of entities . . . and all entities are located in it. . . . Any given thing is in that portion of space in which it is located, and of which it is the place, and which is completely incorporeal, foreign to all action and all operation, being only a certain aptitude for sustaining bodies and nothing else, ... thus completely different from everything [*De rerum natura*, I, 25].

Thus there can be a void (*vacuum*). Telesio also held that time would continue to flow on even though no motion were observed by man or even existed. He thus broke away from Aristotle's conception of place as the surface of the containing body and of time as the measure of motion.

In keeping with his general approach, Telesio regarded the soul (or *spiritus*) as corporeal—having dispensed with "forms" altogether, he obviously could not accept Aristotle's definition of the soul as "the form of an organic body." This spirit "derived from the seed," for which the body's integument is a container, is distinguished, not very clearly, by Telesio from the soul introduced by God. Sensation, which cannot be the "reception of forms without matter," as defined by Aristotle, is the "perception of the actions of things and impulsions of air and [the soul's] own passions and immutations and motions" (*De rerum natura*, VII, 2). A thoroughly naturalistic ethics is then developed, with virtues being faculties that ensure the conservation and perfection of spirit (*ibid.*, IX, 4). As we have seen, reasoning is subsidiary to sensation, the deficiencies of which it supplies in situations in which the whole of a thing's qualities are not directly observable (*ibid.*, VIII, 3). Telesio's discussions of virtues and vices, as they are displayed by a self-interested creature pursuing its own conservation, anticipate similar treatments in the seventeenth century (Descartes, Hobbes, Spinoza). All in all, perhaps the most judicious verdict on Telesio's thought is that it represented "a robust re-thinking of pre-Socratic naturalism" (Eugenio Garin, *Storia della filosofia italiana*, II [Turin, 1966], 711).

BIBLIOGRAPHY

I. ORIGINAL WORKS. During Telesio's lifetime three eds. of his major work appeared, all under the basic title *De rerum natura iuxta propria principia* but with contents progressively augmented (Rome, 1565; 2nd ed., Naples, 1570; 3rd ed., Naples, 1586). There is a modern ed., by V. Spampanato, 3 vols. (I, Modena, 1910; II, Genoa, 1913; III, Rome, 1923). No one has as yet made a thorough study of Telesio's changes from the earlier to the later eds., even though there are copies of the 1570 ed. with corrections in Telesio's own hand (Naples, Bibl. Naz. XVI E 68), as well as an autograph commentary on the work (Vatican, Cod. Ottob. Lat. 1292). A new and definitive ed. is being prepared by Luigi De Franco (I, Cosenza, 1965). Shorter treatises also exist in MS (for instance, Naples, Bibl. Naz. VIII C 29); some were published by Telesio's disciple Antonio Persio under the title *Varii de naturalibus rebus libelli* (Venice, 1590). A treatise on lightning has been published by Carlo Delcorno, "Il commentario 'De fulmine' di Bernardino Telesio," in *Aevum*, **41** (1967), 474–506.

II. SECONDARY LITERATURE. Still the basic secondary work is Francesco Fiorentino, *Bernardino Telesio*, 2 vols. (Florence, 1872–1874), with an appendix containing previously unpublished material. A bibliography of Telesian scholarship up to 1937 is given in Giovanni Gentile, *Il pensiero italiano del Rinascimento*, 4th ed. (Florence, 1968), 507–522. Of particular interest are the following: Roberto Almagià, "Le dottrine geofisiche di Bernardino Telesio," in his *Scritti geografici (1905–1957)* (Rome, 1961), 151–178; Ernst Cassirer, *Das Erkenntnisproblem* (Berlin, 1906), 212–218; A. Corsano, "La psicologia del Telesio," in *Giornale critico della filosofia italiana*, **21** (1940), 5–12; and Luigi Firpo, "Filosofia italiana e controriforma. IV. La proibizione di Telesio," in *Rivista di filosofia*, **42** (1951), 30–47, which gives the text of a condemnation of Telesio's writings at Padua in 1600.

On Telesio's biology, the most detailed account is Edoardo Zavattari, *La visione della vita nel Rinascimento* (Turin, 1923). On the relation of physics to metaphysics, see Giacomo Soleri, "La metafisica di Bernardino Telesio," in *Rivista di filosofia Neoscolastica*, **34** (1942), 338–356. The most complete work in English is Neil

van Deusen, *Telesio, the First of the Moderns* (New York, 1932).

NEAL W. GILBERT

TENNANT, SMITHSON (*b.* Selby, Yorkshire, England, 30 November 1761; *d.* Boulogne, France, 22 February 1815), *chemistry*.

Tennant's father was the Reverend Calvert Tennant, a fellow of St. John's College, Cambridge, and later vicar of Selby; his mother, Mary Daunt Tennant, was the daughter of an apothecary. Both parents had died by the time he was twenty, leaving him an inheritance of land. During 1781 he was a medical student at Edinburgh, where he attended Joseph Black's lectures. In October 1782, he moved to Christ's College, Cambridge, from which he received the M.B. in 1788 and the M.D. in 1796. He was elected fellow of the Royal Society in January 1785 and received the Copley Medal in 1804. In 1799 he was a founding member of the Askesian Society, which soon became the Geological Society. In 1813 he was appointed professor of chemistry at Cambridge. Tennant's travels included a visit to Sweden in 1784, where he met Scheele and Gahn, and a journey to France in 1814–1815 that ended in a fatal riding accident.

Tennant wrote little and consequently was accused of indolence. In 1796 he communicated to the Royal Society his study of the combustion of the diamond. Lavoisier had carried out a series of similar experiments and observed that the gaseous product turned limewater cloudy, as in the burning of charcoal. However, he maintained that this common result merely showed that both charcoal and diamond were in the class of combustibles. Reluctant to stress the analogy further, Lavoisier even wrote that the nature of diamond might never be known. But Tennant insisted that since equal quantities of charcoal and diamond were entirely converted in combustion to equal quantities of fixed air, then both substances must be chemically identical. Certain scientists, notably Humphry Davy, continued to suspect that there were minute chemical differences between these forms of carbon; but Davy soon returned to the interpretation first given by Tennant.

Tennant's most important work, the discovery of two new elements in platinum ore, was described in a paper to the Royal Society in 1804. The extraction of pure, malleable platinum from its crude ore was a problem that taxed eighteenth-century chemists. A notebook preserved at Cambridge on Tennant's travels shows that he had discussed the problem with Gahn and Crell in 1784. At that time the standard procedure was to digest the crude ore in aqua regia; this technique left an insoluble black residue that Proust mistook for graphite. At about the same time Collet-Descotils, Fourcroy, Vauquelin, and Tennant realized that this residue contained something new. Collet-Descotils inferred the existence of a new metal from the red color it gave to platinum precipitates; Fourcroy and Vauquelin called the new metal *ptène* but soon admitted that they had confused two different metals. Tennant alone recognized that the black powder contained two new metals, which he proceeded to isolate and characterize. He called one iridium on account of the variety of colors it produced; the other he named osmium because of the distinctive odor of its volatile compounds.

Tennant had interested William Wollaston in platinum while they were students at Cambridge. By 1800 they had became business partners, selling platinum boilers for the concentration of sulfuric acid and other products made of platinum.

BIBLIOGRAPHY

See Donald McDonald, "Smithson Tennant, F.R.S. (1761–1815)," in *Notes and Records. Royal Society of London*, **17** (1962), 77–94. On Tennant's MSS, see L. F. Gilbert, "W. H. Wollaston MSS. at Cambridge," *ibid.*, **9** (1952), 311–332. His memoirs are listed in the Royal Society *Catalogue of Scientific Papers*.

D. C. GOODMAN

TENNENT, DAVID HILT (*b.* Janesville, Wisconsin, 28 May 1873; *d.* Bryn Mawr, Pennsylvania, 14 January 1941), *biology*.

Tennent was one of four children born to Thomas Tennent, a contractor, and his second wife, Mary Hilt. Thomas also had two children by his first wife. Young David thus grew up in a large family, and lived a rather rigorous and austere life as a child. He became interested in science early and hoped to study medicine, but he was prevented from doing so by the accidental death of his father in 1893. He first became a licensed pharmacist, then in 1895 entered Olivet College in Michigan, where he received the B.S. in 1900. In 1904 he

received the Ph.D. from the Johns Hopkins University, where he had studied under W. K. Brooks.

While a graduate student, Tennent spent one year as a substitute instructor at Randolph-Macon College. In 1904 he became instructor in biology at Bryn Mawr College, where he taught for thirty-four years. After his retirement he was a research professor there until his death. In 1909 Tennent married Esther Maddux; their only child, David Maddux, born in 1914, became a research biochemist.

The major part of Tennent's work was in marine biology, and consisted principally of experiments on marine eggs. While a graduate student, he spent several summers at the U.S. Fisheries laboratories in Beaufort, North Carolina; later he spent a number of summers in the Dry Tortugas at the biological laboratory of the Carnegie Institution. He worked also at a number of other marine laboratories in the United States and abroad, and spent two sabbatical leaves in Japan.

Tennent concentrated most of his efforts on the study of echinoderm development. His particular interest was in the role of the nucleus, which he studied both as an embryologist and as a cytologist. His most important investigations dealt with the study of echinoderm hybridization.

Tennent performed cross fertilizations between species, genera, orders, and classes within the Echinodermata. He found that after exposing the eggs of some species (such as *Lytechinus*) to monovalent cations, they could be more easily fertilized by foreign sperm than by sperm of their own species. It was known that chromosomes are often eliminated from the mitotic spindles in hybrids. Tennent, a skilled cytologist, developed an intimate knowledge of the configurations of the chromosome sets and thereby established that it was the paternal chromosomes that were eliminated, presumably as a result of incompatibility between maternal cytoplasm and paternal chromatin. He also showed that, depending on the number of paternal chromosomes eliminated, the embryo develops more or less, sometimes solely, under the influence of the maternal chromosomes. Tennent distinguished for the first time between the autosomes and the sex chromosomes of a number of echinoderms; and by hybridizing two forms that differ in the shape of their sex chromosomes, he established for the first time that the male is the digametic sex in sea urchins.

Like Boveri and Driesch before him, Tennent wished to determine the time at which the influence of the paternal chromosomes first manifests itself in development. Boveri had performed only preliminary experiments, and Driesch only crude ones, to elucidate this point. By crossing species that differed clearly in several features, Tennent confirmed the conclusions of Boveri and Driesch that maternal factors control the earliest phases of development, and that the paternal factors are expressed later in development. Another important contribution to the study of echinoderm hybrids was his demonstration that the direction of development toward the character of the maternal or the paternal species could be altered by changing the hydrogen ion concentration of the seawater in which the hybrids were maintained.

Although he was never a complete innovator in his investigations, the skill, caution, objectivity, and patience with which Tennent worked enabled him to establish on a firm foundation cytological and developmental truths that had merely been intimated by some of his more original predecessors.

BIBLIOGRAPHY

The most detailed biography of Tennent, with a complete bibliography of his articles, is M. S. Gardiner, "Biographical Memoir of David Hilt Tennent 1873– 1941," in *Biographical Memoirs. National Academy of Sciences*, **26** (1951), 99–119.

JANE OPPENHEIMER

TEN RHYNE, WILLEM (*b*. Deventer, Netherlands, 1647; *d*. Batavia, Netherlands Indies [now Djakarta, Indonesia], 1 June 1700), *medicine, botany.*

Little is known of the early life of ten Rhyne. After attending the Illustre School in Deventer, he studied medicine from about 1664 to 1666 at the University of Franeker. Then, in 1668, he went to the University of Leiden, where he studied under Sylvius and became an adherent of his iatrochemical school. In 1668 he received his medical degree with the dissertation *De dolore intestinorum a flatu*. In 1669 he published an essay on gout, *Dissertatio de arthritide*, and a treatise on a text of Hippocrates in which he also discussed a number of salts.

In June 1673 ten Rhyne left for Batavia to serve as physician to the Dutch East India Company. During a twenty-six-day stay at the Cape of Good Hope (October–November 1673), he studied the flora and fauna of the area and also the Hottentots.

He published his findings in *Schediasma de promontorio Bonae Speï, ejusque tractus incolis Hottentottis* (1686).

Ten Rhyne arrived in Batavia in January 1674 and in addition to his medical duties he gave anatomy lessons to the local surgeons. He was soon sent by the company to the trading station on Decima in the harbor at Nagasaki. There was a surgeon at Decima, but the emperor had requested that the Dutch East India Company also bring out a qualified physician. Ten Rhyne served in Japan from 1674 until 1676, when he returned to Batavia. In 1677 he was appointed governor of the leper colony. From 1679 until 1681 he was physician on the west coast of Sumatra and from 1681 until his death he was a member of the judicature in Batavia.

During the two years in Japan, ten Rhyne studied tea culture, describing the tea plant, the manufacture and use of tea, and the influence of the stimulant on the body. His findings were published in Jacob Breyn's *Exoticarum plantarum centuria prima* (1678). In this same work of Breyn's, ten Rhyne also gave complete descriptions of the Japanese camphor tree and the plants he had collected at the Cape of Good Hope.

As a result of his work on tropical flora, Hendrik Adriaan van Reede tot Drakestein asked ten Rhyne to collaborate with him on the *Hortus Malabaricus*, which appeared in Amsterdam in twelve volumes between 1679 and 1703.

In 1687 ten Rhyne published his classic work on leprosy: *Verhandelingen van de Asiatise melaatsheid* ("Treatise on Asiatic Leprosy"). He presented an excellent description of the disease and gave an account of its etiology, prophylaxis, and therapy, which is still valid.

Ten Rhyne also published a work (1683) on the practice of acupuncture in Japan.

BIBLIOGRAPHY

I. ORIGINAL WORKS. Ten Rhyne's major works are *Dissertatio de dolore intestinorum a flatu* (Leiden, 1668); *Dissertatio de arthritide* (Leiden, 1669); *Meditationes in Hippocratis textum vigesimum quartum de veteri medicina, cum laciniis de salium figuris* (Leiden, 1669, 2nd ed., 1672); "Excerpta ex observationibus Japonicis de fructice thee, cum fasciculo rariorum plantarum ab ipso inpromontorio Bonae Speï et Sardanha sinu anno 1673 collectarum, atque demum ex India anno 1677 in Europam ad Jacobum Breynium transmissarum," in Jacob Breyn, *Exoticarum plantarum centuria prima* (Danzig, 1678); *Dissertatio de arthritide, mantissa schematica de acupunctura, orationes tres de chymiae et botanicae antiquitate et dignitate, de physiognomia, et de monstris* (London–The Hague, 1683; 2nd ed., Leipzig, 1690); *Schediasma de promontorio Bonae Speï, ejusque tractus incolis Hottentottis* (Schaffhausen, 1686); and *Verhandelingen van de Asiatise melaatsheid* (Amsterdam, 1687), reprinted with English translation in *Opuscula Selecta Neerlandicorum de arte medica*, **14** (1937), 34–113.

II. SECONDARY LITERATURE. On ten Rhyne and his work, see A. J. van der Aa, *Biographisch Woordenboek der Nederlanden*, X (Haarlem, 1874), 96; H. Kronenberg, *Nieuw Nederlandsch Biographisch Woordenboek*, VI (Leiden, 1924), 1213; L. S. von Römer, *ibid.*, IX (Leiden, 1933), 861–863; and J. M. H. van Dorssen, "Willem ten Rhyne," in *Geneeskundig tijdschrift voor Nederlandsch-Indië*, **51** (1911), 134–228.

H. A. M. SNELDERS

TERMIER, PIERRE (*b.* Lyons, France, 3 July 1859; *d.* Grenoble, France, 23 October 1930), *metamorphic petrology, structural geology, geotectonics.*

Termier's grandiose synthesis of the geological structure of the Alps (1903) made him the founder of modern tectonics and geodynamics. His works are numerous and stylistically unsurpassed. His vivid essays and biographies of his great teachers are collected in *À la gloire de la terre, La joie de connaître*, and *La vocation de savant*; a fourth volume, *Mélanges*, was published posthumously by his daughter, Jeanne Boussac-Termier.

Termier's interest in literature developed at an early age. His father, Francisque Termier, was often away from the family home in Lyons, and his mother, Jeanne, guided him through his early years. Termier proudly recalled having read poems to his mother at the age of five. A brother, Joseph, was born when Pierre was thirteen.

In 1868 Termier was sent to the Collège des Maristes in Saint-Chamond (Loire), where he developed a passion for mathematics, in addition to his favorite subjects, literature and philosophy. After graduating in 1876 he continued his education in Paris at the École Sainte-Geneviève and, from 1878 to 1880, at the École Polytechnique. On a mountaineering trip to the Belledonne Massif in the western Alps, Termier discovered his vocation for geology. In 1880 he entered the École des Mines in Paris, where he attended the mineralogy course of Ernest Mallard. His thesis was based on a field study of igneous rocks in the Harz Mountains.

In 1883 he married Alice Beylier, and they made their first home in Nice, where Termier was ap-

pointed inspector of mines (*ingénieur ordinaire*). Administrative duties took him as far as Corsica. But since he preferred teaching, he applied for the vacant chair at the École des Mines in Saint-Étienne. In 1885 Termier was appointed professor of physics and electricity and later of mineralogy and geology. Under the auspices of the Service de la Carte Géologique de la France he began geologic mapping of the Massif Central (Plateau Central). Although he was attracted by the Tertiary volcanoes of Mont-Mézenc, his work soon focused on the metamorphic Paleozoic basement in the area of Saint-Étienne, especially Mont-Pilat. Termier was greatly stimulated by his colleague Urbain Le Verrier, professor of metallurgy and chemistry, who had also become involved in geologic mapping through his close friendship with August Michel-Lévy, director of the geological survey. Le Verrier concentrated on the problem of granite formation, particularly the process of feldspathization. Termier's field research on the Massif Central was incorporated in five sheets of the *Carte géologique détaillée de la France* (1:80,000).

For thirty years Charles Lory had been the only geologist to carry out field mapping in the French Alps. It was only after Lory's death in 1888 that Marcel-Alexandre Bertrand, who had introduced the nappe theory into Alpine geology, transferred his field research from the Provençal thrust belt to the Alps. For this project, Bertrand assembled a team of geologists. Lory's successor at the University of Grenoble, Wilfrid Kilian, was entrusted with the mapping of the High Calcareous Alps of Savoy. Just at this time the Termier brothers, who were climbing their favorite mountains in the Haute Vanoise, suffered an accident. Receiving word of this and intrigued by Pierre Termier's reputation, Bertrand recognized in him the ideal collaborator for the work in the massifs and the metamorphic zone of Savoy. An extremely fruitful cooperation began, and Termier soon regarded Bertrand as his great mentor and friend. Together they explored the Vanoise in the summer of 1890. Termier went on to complete the mapping of the Haute Vanoise for the 1:80,000 map series. His initial report of 1891 was an epoch-making contribution to Alpine geology, since for the first time the progressive stages of the regional metamorphism were mapped over a considerable distance. The metamorphic grade, transgressive across the stratigraphic sequence, was found to be controlled by the Alpine structure alone. This discovery, in turn, confirmed Lory's early assumption that the axial belt of crystalline schists (*schistes lustrés*) represented a transformed Mesozoic sedimentary sequence. In his report of 1894 on the Grandes Rousses Massif, Termier was able to distinguish also between Hercynian and superimposed Alpine fold structures.

In 1894 Ernest Mallard died suddenly, and Termier was appointed to succeed him as professor of mineralogy and petrology at the École des Mines in Paris. With some regret the Termiers, with their son and five daughters, left the countryside of southern France for Paris, where a second son was born. They maintained a second home at Varces-Allières-et-Risset, near Grenoble. Although the ensuing years brought further triumphs to Termier's successful career, he was spared neither grief nor sorrow. It soon became apparent that his wife suffered from parkinsonism. In 1906 his elder son died in an accident at the age of thirteen, and the following year Bertrand died. Termier found some comfort in a new friendship with the writer Léon Bloy.

After the death of Auguste Michel-Lévy in 1911, Termier was elected director of the Service de la Carte Géologique de la France. The following year his teaching responsibility was increased to include the main course in physical geology at the École des Mines in Paris. Termier attracted many students, for no one could speak of the beauty of the mountains with greater skill and affection. He stressed also his belief in the philosophic and religious values of science, looking upon faith and science as coming from the same source.

In 1914 Termier was elected inspector general of mines. During World War I he served as colonel with the French artillery. In 1916 his wife died in Varces-Allières-et-Risset. Shortly afterward, his son-in-law Jean Boussac died from an injury received near Verdun; Boussac was noted for his works on the Eocene Alpine flysch. Termier suffered yet another bereavement with the death of his younger son from meningitis in 1924.

In 1909 Termier was elected member of the Académie des Sciences. He was made an officer of the Legion of Honor in 1914 and a commander in 1927. He had three terms as president respectively of the Société Minéralogique and the Société Géologique of France, and was vice-president of the Académie des Sciences; at the time of his death, Termier was president elect of the Academy. The Geological Society of London elected him foreign correspondent in 1923 and foreign member in 1929. At the centennial of the Geological Society of France in 1930, he received the degree of doctor *honoris causa* from the University of Innsbruck.

Termier's love of travel enabled him to make the expeditions necessary to unravel the tectonics of Alpine Europe. Research and consulting work took him to Scandinavia, the Urals, Siberia, Mexico, the Colorado Plateau, the Canadian Rockies, and Quebec, as well as to North Africa and Spain. In 1930, on his last trip to Morocco, he fell ill and died shortly after his return to Grenoble.

Termier's field research was apparently directed toward the metamorphic rather than the structural history of the areas he had selected for study. In the Franco-Italian Alps he searched for the causes of regional metamorphism. At first he tried to organize his results so that they would fit into the framework of the widely accepted theory of dynamic metamorphism, in which heat was attributed to the mechanical energy produced during folding and thrusting. By 1903, however, Termier had become a bitter opponent of the theory. Dynamic action deformed but did not transform, and mylonitic rocks were its only product, he argued at the Ninth International Geological Congress in Vienna (1903). He saw the cause of regional metamorphism related, somehow, to the depth of burial in the geosyncline. But geologic depth alone would not be sufficient to cause metamorphism. He assumed the causative factor to be the influx of juvenile liquids and vapors, the *colonnes filtrantes*, which brought with them alkali silicates. Extending the ideas of Le Verrier, he compared the process of feldspathization with the spreading of a grease spot (the *tâche d'huile* mechanism). Termier concluded that the progressive stages of regional metamorphism would ultimately result in massive granitic rocks. The negligible role that he attributed to penetrative movements was subsequently challenged, mainly by the Austrian school, which initiated the study of petrofabrics in support of its case.

Termier's contributions to regional tectonics effected revolutionary changes in the perception of global dynamics, at first only among Alpine geologists. In the dramatic dispute on the structure of the eastern Alps, Termier, as Bertrand's disciple, emerged as the new leader of the French structural geologists, all of whom adhered to the concepts of Eduard Suess as set forth in his *Das Antlitz der Erde*. Suess elucidated for the first time the global grouping of mountain belts in space and time. He argued that the structure of the Alpine-Carpathian mountains could best be explained as the product of a one-sided tectonic drive that thrust the sedimentary fill of the *Tethys* sea onto the old European *Vorland*. Termier first visited Suess late in 1899 for advice concerning French explorative drillings in the Carpathians. The results confirmed Suess's prediction that the Upper Silesian coalfield would extend southward beneath the Carpathian thrust sheets. The French were the first to translate Suess's classic; their elaborate edition (1897–1918) appropriately opens with a preface by Bertrand and concludes with a eulogy by Termier.

Large-scale nappe structures (Bertrand's *nappes de recouvrement*) had been incontestably demonstrated in the Swiss Alps by Hans Schardt (1893) and Maurice Lugeon (1902), and in the Franco-Italian Alps mainly by Termier himself (1899, 1902). It was the metamorphic petrology of the Vanoise that enabled Termier to decipher the tectonics of that region. The key to the structure of the Briançonnais zone in particular was seen in the interpretation of the "thrust slice number four" (*quatrième écaille*); thus the crystalline capping of a few mountaintops west of Briançon became also the cradle of a tectonic principle: that of the "squashing thrust plate" (the *traîneau écraseur*). A rigid mass of schists had been shoved westward over folded flysch and older sediments, which built up the fanlike structure of the Briançonnais. The fold crests of the overridden fan were thrown into tucks and flattened out under the advancing plate. In general, nappe structures were formed either by recumbent folding, gravity sliding, or overthrusting. The *traîneau écraseur*, however, is a thrust plate actively pushed over the top of another block; its width is a measure of the shortening of the crust.

Although the nappe interpretation of the Swiss Alps necessitated corresponding structures in Austria, the constitution of the eastern Alps, some 500 kilometers in length, still remained obscure until, after the International Geological Congress in Vienna (1903), Friedrich Becke led a field trip to Ziller Valley and the Hohe Tauern. On the summit of Amtshorspitze, Termier boldly declared the eastern Alps to be a pile of nappes and the Hohe Tauern in particular to be a window exposing the geosynclinal fill of *schistes lustrés*; he could not help seeing lithological and structural similarities to the western Alps, including the *traîneau écraseur*, which here assumed much larger dimensions. Shortly afterward Termier proved his claim by verifying the window structure of the Hohe Tauern as well as the Lower Engadine in Switzerland. The

Hohe Tauern window implied a thrust plate, 120 kilometers in width, similar in size to overthrusts that had already been inferred in Scandinavia. To Termier, the entire structure of the Alps seemed to require a total crustal shortening of 500 kilometers or more. He himself did not fail to consider the geotectonic aspects of this conclusion, and although he did not accept Alfred Wegener's notion of continental drift, he insisted that considerable lateral motion of the crustal blocks had occurred.

Termier's classic perception of the structure of the Alps underwent much modification, but its basic implication of large-scale plate motion was reaffirmed in the later works of Émile Argand, Rudolf Staub, Leopold Kober, and others.

BIBLIOGRAPHY

I. ORIGINAL WORKS. Among Termier's publications are: "Étude sur le massif cristallin du Mont-Pilat, sur la bordure orientale du Plateau Central entre Vienne et Saint-Vallier . . .," in *Bulletin des Services de la carte géologique de France et des topographies souterraines*, no. 1, I (1889), 1–58; "Étude sur la constitution géologique du massif de la Vanoise (Alpes de Savoie)," *ibid.*, no. 20, II (1891), 367–514; "Le massif des Grandes-Rousses (Dauphiné et Savoie)," *ibid.*, no. 40, VI (1894), 169–288; "Les nappes de recouvrement du Briançonnais," in *Bulletin de la Société géologique de France*, 3rd ser., **27** (1899), 47–84; "Quatre coupes à travers les Alpes franco-italiennes," *ibid.*, 4th ser., **2** (1902), 411–433; "Les schistes cristallins des Alpes occidentales," in *International Geological Congress, comptes-rendus 9th, Vienna, 1903* (Vienna, 1904), 571–586, repr. in *La joie de connaître, suite de À la gloire de la terre* (Paris, 1926); "Les montagnes entre Briançon et Vallouise," in *Mémoires pour servir à l'explication de la Carte géologique détaillée de la France* (Paris, 1903); "Sur la structure des Hohe Tauern (Alpes du Tyrol)," in *Comptes rendus hebdomadaires des séances de l'Académie des sciences*, **137** (1903), 875–876; "Les nappes des Alpes orientales et la synthèse des Alpes," in *Bulletin de la Société géologique de France*, 4th ser., **3** (1903), 712–765; "Sur la fenêtre de la Basse-Engadine," in *Comptes rendus hebdomadaires des séances de l'Académie des sciences*, **139** (1904), 648–650; "Roches à lawsonite et à glaucophane et roches à riébeckite de Saint-Véran (Hautes-Alpes)," in *Bulletin de la Société française de minéralogie*, **27** (1904), 265–269; "Les alpes entre le Brenner et la Valteline," in *Bulletin de la Société géologique de France*, 4th ser., **5** (1905), 209–289; *La synthèse géologique des Alpes* (Liège, 1906), repr. in *À la gloire de la terre, souvenirs d'un géologue* (Paris, 1922); "Sur la genèse des terrains cristallophylliens," in *International Geological Congress, comptes rendus 11th, Stockholm, 1910* (Stockholm, 1912), I, 587–595; "Les problèmes de la géologie tectonique dans la Méditerranée occidentale," in *Revue générale des sciences,* **22** (1911), 225–234, repr. in *À la gloire de la terre . . .*; "La dérive des continents," *Bulletin de l'Institut océanographique de Monaco,* no. 443 (15 Apr. 1924), repr. in *La joie de connaître . . .*, translated as "The Drifting of the Continents," in *Smithsonian Report for 1924* (1925), 219–236; *La vocation de savant, suite de À la gloire de la terre et de La joie de connaître* (Paris, 1929); *Mélanges,* pref. by Jeanne Boussac-Termier (Paris, 1932).

II. SECONDARY LITERATURE. The most complete biographies are A. George, *Pierre Termier* (Paris, 1933), and E. Raguin's *éloge* in *Bulletin de la Société géologique de France,* 5th ser., **1** (1931), 429–495, including a complete bibliography. Other notices are by L. Lecornu, in *Comptes rendus hebdomadaires des séances de l'Académie des sciences,* **191** (1930), 685–687; G. Aichino, in *Bollettino. R. Ufficio geologico d'Italia,* **55**, no. 12 (1930), 1–4; E. J. Garwood, in *Proceedings of the Geological Society of London,* **87** (1930–1931), 1x–1xii; L. J. Spencer, in *Mineralogical Magazine,* **23** (1933), 359–360; and the pref. by Jeanne Boussac-Termier in *Mélanges* (Paris, 1932).

E. B. Bailey, in *Tectonic Essays, Mainly Alpine* (Oxford, 1935), sets Termier's structural synthesis of the Alps in historical perspective; and H. H. Read evaluates his contribution to metamorphic petrology in *The Granite Controversy* (London, 1957).

JOHN HALLER

TESLA, NIKOLA (*b.* Smiljan, Croatia [now Yugoslavia], 10 July 1856; *d.* New York, N.Y., 7 January 1943), *physics, electrical engineering.*

Tesla was born of Serbian parents in a mountain village that was then part of Austria-Hungary. His father, Milutin Tesla, was a clergyman of the Serbian Orthodox church, while his mother, Djuka Mandić, although illiterate, was a skillful inventor of home and farm implements. Tesla himself was intended for the clergy, but early developed a taste for mathematics and science. When he was seven, the family moved to Gospić, where he finished grammar school and graduated from the Real-Gymnasium. He then attended the Higher Real-Gymnasium in Karlovac and, upon graduation, persuaded his father to let him enter the Joanneum, the polytechnical college of Graz, Austria.

It was while he was a student in Graz that Tesla's attention was first drawn to problems of the induction motor. His observation that a Gramme dynamo that was being run as a motor in a classroom demonstration sparked badly between its commutator and brushes led him to suggest that a motor without a commutator might be devised—an idea that his professor ridiculed. Nothing daunted, Tesla continued to develop the idea. In 1879 he left Graz to enroll at the University of Prague, but left without taking a degree when his father died. He then held a number of jobs; in 1881 he went to Budapest to work for the new telephone company there. During his year there he thought of the principle of the rotating magnetic field, upon which all polyphase induction motors are based. The discovery, by his own account, was instantaneous, complete, and intuitive. Walking in a park with a friend, Antony Szigety, Tesla was moved to recite a passage from Goethe's *Faust* (of which he had the whole by heart) when " . . . the idea came like a lightning flash. In an instant I saw it all, and drew with a stick on the sand the diagrams which were illustrated in my fundamental patents of May, 1888, and which Szigety understood perfectly." It was, however, some time before he was able to exploit his invention commercially.

In 1882 Tesla went to Paris as an engineer with the Continental Edison Company. The following year he was sent to Strasbourg to repair an electric plant, and while there built a crude prototype of his motor. He thus experienced "the supreme satisfaction of seeing for the first time rotation effected by alternating currents without commutator." In 1884 he went to the United States to promote his new alternating-current motor. He arrived in New York with a working knowledge of a dozen languages, a book of poetry, four cents, and an introduction to Thomas Edison. Although Edison was totally committed to direct current, he gave Tesla a job, and for a year Tesla supported himself redesigning direct-current dynamos for the Edison Machine Works. By 1885 he had left Edison and had gone into business developing and promoting an industrial arc lamp. He was forced out of the company when production began, however, and for a time lived precariously, doing odd jobs and day labor. Within two years he was back on his feet, and had formed his own laboratory for the development of his alternating-current motor.

By 1888 Tesla had obtained patents on a whole polyphase system of alternating-current dynamos, transformers, and motors; the rights to these were bought in that year by George Westinghouse, and the "battle of the currents" was begun. Although Edison continued to espouse direct current, Tesla's system triumphed to make possible the first large-scale harnessing of Niagara Falls and to provide the basis for the whole modern electric-power industry. In 1889 Tesla became an American citizen.

During the next few years Tesla worked in his New York laboratories on a wide variety of projects. He was very successful, particularly in his invention of the Tesla coil, an air-core transformer, and in his further research on high-frequency currents. In 1891 he lectured on his high-frequency devices to the American Institute of Electrical Engineers, and this lecture, coupled with a spectacular demonstration of these apparatuses, made him famous. He repeated his performance in Europe, to great acclaim, and enjoyed international celebrity.

In 1893 the Chicago World Columbian Exposition was lighted by means of Tesla's system and work was begun on the installation of power machinery at Niagara Falls. In a lecture-demonstration given in St. Louis in the same year—two years before Marconi's first experiments—Tesla also predicted wireless communication; the apparatus that he employed contained all the elements of spark and continuous wave that were incorporated into radio transmitters before the advent of the vacuum tube. Engrossed as he was with the transmission of substantial amounts of power, however, he almost perversely rejected the notion of transmission by Hertzian waves, which he considered to be wasteful of energy. He thus proposed wireless communication by actual conduction of electricity through natural media, and, working in Colorado Springs, Colorado, in 1899–1900, proved the earth to be a conductor. In a further series of experiments, Tesla produced artificial lightning in flashes of millions of volts that were up to 135 feet long—a feat that has never been equaled. It was at his Colorado laboratory, too, that Tesla, who had become increasingly withdrawn and eccentric ever since the death of his mother in 1892, announced that he had received signals from foreign planets, a statement that was greeted with some skepticism.

Tesla's vision always embraced the widest applications of his discoveries. Of his wireless system, he wrote in 1900: "I have no doubt that it will prove very efficient in enlightening the masses, particularly in still uncivilized countries and less accessible regions, and that it will add materially to general safety, comfort and convenience, and maintenance of peaceful relations." With the financial backing of J. P. Morgan, he began work on a worldwide communications system, and a 200-foot transmission tower was constructed at Shoreham,

on Long Island. By 1905, however, Morgan had withdrawn his support, and the project came to an end. The tower was destroyed by dynamite, under mysterious circumstances, in 1914.

Although he continued to enjoy a measure of fame, Tesla made little money from his inventions, and became increasingly poor during the last decades of his life. His name continued to flourish before the public, however, since he was a reliable source for scientific prophecy, and exploited as such in the popular press. While he gave demonstrations of some of his earlier marvels—his exhibition of a radio-guided teleautomatic boat filled Madison Square Garden in 1898—he became oracular in his later years and, for example, offered no proof of the potent "death-ray" that he announced in 1934, on his seventy-eighth birthday. Nonetheless, Tesla continued to invent devices of commercial and scientific worth, from which, since he seldom bothered to seek a patent, he received little profit.

Tesla was a complete recluse in his last years, living in a series of New York hotel rooms with only pigeons for company. At his death his papers and notes were seized by the Alien Property office; they are now housed in the Nikola Tesla Museum in Belgrade, Yugoslavia, a country in which he is revered as a national hero.

BIBLIOGRAPHY

I. ORIGINAL WORKS. The greatest part of Tesla's notes and correspondence is in the Nikola Tesla Museum, Belgrade, Yugoslavia. That institution has published a selection of source materials, in English, as Leland I. Anderson, ed., *Nikola Tesla, 1856–1943: Lectures, Patents, Articles* (Belgrade, 1956), which includes an autobiographical sketch; another autobiographical segment is "Some Personal Recollections," in *Scientific American* (June, 1915).

II. SECONDARY LITERATURE. A commemorative volume of speeches made on the occasion of the centenary of Tesla's birth is *A Tribute to Nikola Tesla: Presented in Articles, Letters, Documents* (Belgrade, 1961). Full biographies are Inez Hunt and Wanetta W. Draper, *Lightning in His Hand: The Life Story of Nikola Tesla* (Denver, 1964); and John J. O'Neill, *Prodigal Genius: The Life of Nikola Tesla* (New York, 1944). Shorter treatments include Haraden Pratt, "Nikola Tesla, 1856–1943," in *Proceedings of the Institute of Radio Engineers*, **44** (1956), 1106–1108; and Kenneth M. Swezey, "Nikola Tesla, Pathfinder of the Electrical Age," in *Electrical Engineering*, **75** (1956), 786–790; and "Nikola Tesla," in *Science*, **127** (1958), 1147–1159.

KENNETH M. SWEZEY

TESTUT, JEAN LÉO (*b.* Saint-Avit Sénieur, Dordogne, France, 22 March 1849; *d.* Caudéran, near Bordeaux, France, 16 January 1925), *anatomy, anthropology.*

The son of Jean Testut and the former Marie Deynat, Léo Testut began his medical studies at Bordeaux, where he was successively *interne des hôpitaux, préparateur* in physiology, and *chef de travaux* in anatomy (1877). He completed his studies at Paris and in 1877 defended a doctoral dissertation entitled "De la symétrie dans les affections de la peau." As a result of his work in the laboratories of Pierre Paul Broca, Louis Ranvier, Étienne-Jules Marey, Jean-Louis de Quatrefages, and Félix Pouchet, he was able to consolidate his threefold training in anatomy, physiology, and anthropology. In 1880 Testut became *agrégé* in anatomy and physiology in the medical faculty at Bordeaux. He was appointed professor of anatomy at Lille in 1884 and transferred to a similar post at Lyons in 1886. In 1919 he retired and moved to Beaumont. During the Franco-Prussian War Testut won the *médaille militaire*, and he died a commander of the Legion of Honor. He married Jeanne Clissey, whose death preceded his own.

Testut's chief professional activity was the teaching of anatomy through lectures and books. His most important work, the three-volume *Traité d'anatomie humaine* (1889–1892), went through six editions in his lifetime; it was translated into Italian and Spanish and was used throughout the world. Testut also published a *Précis d'anatomie descriptive* (1901) and a two-volume *Traité d'anatomie topographique* (1905–1909; with Octave Jacob). Further, he was the editor of a popular series of condensed medical textbooks. In addition to medicine, Testut wrote on comparative anthropology, paleopathology, archaeology, and local history.

BIBLIOGRAPHY

I. ORIGINAL WORKS. *Recherches sur quelques muscles surnuméraires de la région scapulaire antéro-interne* (Paris, 1883); *Les anomalies musculaires chez l'homme expliquées par l'anatomie comparée, leur importance en anthropologie* (Paris, 1884); *Anatomie anthropologique. Qu'est-ce que l'homme pour un anthropologiste?* (opening lesson of the anatomy course, given at the Faculté de Médecine of Lyons, 15 November 1886), (Paris, 1887); *Recherches anthropologiques sur le squelette quaternaire de Chancelade (Dordogne)* (Lyons, 1889); *Traité d'anatomie humaine: anatomie descriptive, histologie, développement,* 3 vols. (Paris, 1889–1892; 9th ed., 1949); *Précis d'anatomie descriptive, aide-mémoire à l'usage des candidats au premier examen de doctorat* (Paris, 1901; 15th ed., 1944); *Traité d'anatomie topographique, avec applications médicochirurgicales,* 2 vols. (Paris, 1905–1909; 4th ed., 1921), written with Octave Jacob.

II. SECONDARY LITERATURE. A. Latarjet, "Léo Testut," in *Paris médical,* **56** (1925), 199–200; A. Policard, "Léo Testut," in *Presse médicale,* **10** (1925), 157.

See also the editorial "Le professeur Testut, de Lyon," in *Chanteclair,* **107** (1912), 7.

CHARLES COURY

THĀBIT IBN QURRA, AL-ṢĀBIʾ AL-ḤARRĀNĪ (*b.* Ḥarrān, Mesopotamia [now Turkey], 836; *d.* Baghdad, 18 February 901), *mathematics, astronomy, mechanics, medicine, philosophy.*

Life. Thābit ibn Qurra belonged to the Sabian (Mandaean) sect, descended from the Babylonian star worshippers. Because the Sabians' religion was related to the stars they produced many astronomers and mathematicians. During the Hellenistic era they spoke Greek and took Greek names; and after the Arab conquest they spoke Arabic and began to assume Arabic names, although for a long time they remained true to their religion. Thābit, whose native language was Syriac, also knew Greek and Arabic. Most of his scientific works were written in Arabic, but some were in Syriac; he translated many Greek works into Arabic.

In his youth Thābit was a money changer in Ḥarrān. The mathematician Muḥammad ibn Mūsā ibn Shākir, one of three sons of Mūsā ibn Shākir, who was traveling through Ḥarrān, was impressed by his knowledge of languages and invited him to Baghdad; there, under the guidance of the brothers, Thābit became a great scholar in mathematics and astronomy. His mathematical writings, the most studied of his works, played an important role in preparing the way for such important mathematical discoveries as the extension of the concept of number to (positive) real numbers, integral calculus, theorems in spherical trigonometry, analytic geometry, and non-Euclidean geometry. In astronomy Thābit was one of the first reformers of the Ptolemaic system, and in mechanics he was a founder of statics. He was also a distinguished physician and the leader of a Sabian community in Iraq, where he substantially strengthened the sect's influence. During his last years Thābit was in the retinue of the Abbasid Caliph al-Muʿtaḍid (892–902). His son Sinān and his grandsons Ibrāhīm and Thābit were well-known scholars.

Mathematics. Thābit worked in almost all areas of mathematics. He translated many ancient mathematical works from the Greek, particularly all the works of Archimedes that have not been preserved in the original language, including *Lemmata*, *On Touching Circles*, and *On Triangles*, and Apollonius' *Conics*. He also wrote commentaries on Euclid's *Elements* and Ptolemy's *Almagest*.

Thābit's *Kitāb al-Mafrūḍāt* ("Book of Data") was very popular during the Middle Ages and was included by Naṣīr al-Dīn al-Ṭūsī in his edition of the "Intermediate Books" between Euclid's *Elements* and the *Almagest*. It contains thirty-six propositions in elementary geometry and geometrical algebra, including twelve problems in construction and a geometric problem equivalent to solution of a quadratic equation $(a + x)x = b$. *Maqāla fī istikhrāj al-aʿdād al-mutaḥābba bi-suhūlat al-maslak ilā dhālika* ("Book on the Determination of Amicable Numbers") contains ten propositions in number theory, including ones on the constructions of perfect numbers (equal to the sum of their divisors), coinciding with Euclid's *Elements* IX, 36, on the construction of surplus and "defective" numbers (respectively, those greater and less than the sum of their divisors) and the problem, first solved by Thābit, of the construction of "amicable" numbers (pairs of numbers the sum of the divisors of each of which is equal to the other). Thābit's rule is the following: If $p = 3 \cdot 2^n - 1$, $q = 3 \cdot 2^{n-1} - 1$, and $r = 9 \cdot 2^{2n-1} - 1$, are prime numbers, then $M = 2^n \cdot pq$ and $N = 2^n \cdot r$ are amicable numbers.

Kitāb fī Taʾlīf al-nisab ("Book on the Composition of Ratios") is devoted to "composite ratios" (ratios of geometrical quantities), which are presented in the form of products of ratios. The ancient Greeks, who considered only the natural numbers as numbers, avoided applying arithmetical terminology to geometrical quantities, and thus they named the multiplication of ratios by "composition." Composition of ratios is used in the *Elements* (VI, 23), but is not defined in the original text; instead, only particular cases of composite ratios are defined (*Definitions* V, 9–10). An addition by a later commentator (evidently Theon of Alexandria, in VI, 5) on composite ratios is done in a completely non-Euclidean manner.

Thābit criticizes *Elements* VI, 5, and proposes a definition in the spirit of Euclid: for three quantities A, B, and C, the ratio A/B is composed of the ratios A/C and C/B, and for six quantities A, B, C, D, E, F the ratio A/B is composed of the ratios C/D and E/F, if there are also three quantities L, M, N, such that $A/B = L/M$, $C/D = L/N$, $E/F = N/M$. He later defines the "multiplication of quantities by a quantity" and systematically applies arithmetical terminology to geometrical quantities. He also proves a number of theorems on the composition of ratios and solves certain problems concerning them. This treatise was important in preparing the extension of the concept of number to positive real numbers, produced in a clear form in the eleventh century by al-Bīrūnī (*al-Qānūn al-Masʿūdī*) and al-Khayyāmī (*Sharḥ mā ashkhāla min muṣādarāt Kitāb Uqlīdis*).

In *Risāla fī Shakl al-qiṭāʿ* ("Treatise on the Secant Figure") Thābit gives a new and very elegant proof of Menelaus' theorem of the complete spherical quadrilateral, which Ptolemy had used to solve problems in spherical astronomy; to obtain various forms of this theorem Thābit used his own theory of composite ratios. In *Kitāb fī Misāḥat qaṭʿ al-makhrūṭ alladhī yusammā al-mukāfiʾ* ("Book on the Measurement of the Conic Section Called Parabolic") Thābit computed the area of the segment of a parabola. First he proved several theorems on the summation of a numerical sequence from

$$\sum_{k=1}^{n} (2k-1) = n^2 \text{ to } \sum_{k=1}^{n} (2k-1)^2 + \frac{n}{3}$$

$$= \frac{2}{3} \cdot 2n \sum_{k=1}^{n} (2k-1).$$

He then transferred the last result to segments $a_k = (2k-1)a$, $b_k = 2k \cdot b$ and proved the theorem that for any ratio α/β, however small, there can always be found a natural n for which

$$\frac{n}{2n \cdot \sum_{k=1}^{n} (2k-1)} < \alpha/\beta,$$

which is equivalent to the relation $\lim_{n \to \infty} \frac{1}{n^2} = 0$.

Thābit also applied this result to the segments and divides the diameter of the parabola into segments proportional to odd numbers; through the points of division he then takes chords conjugate with the diameter and inscribes in the segment of the parabola a polygon the apexes of which are the ends of these chords. The area of this polygon is valued by upper and lower limits, on the basis of which it is shown that the area of the segment is equal to 2/3 the product of the base by the height. A. P. Youschkevitch has shown that Thābit's computation is equivalent to that of the integral $\int_0^a \sqrt{x}\, dx$ and not $\int_0^b x^2 dx$, as is done in the computation of the area in Archimedes' *Quadrature of the Parabola*. The computation is based essentially on the application of upper and lower integral sums, and the proof is done by the method of exhaustion; there, for the first time, the segment of integration is divided into unequal parts.

In *Maqāla fī Misāḥat al-mujassamāt al-mukāfiya* ("Book on the Measurement of Parabolic Bodies") Thābit introduces a class of bodies obtained by rotating a segment of a parabola around a diameter: "parabolic cupolas" with smooth, projecting, or squeezed vertex and, around the bases, "parabolic spheres," named cupolas and spheres. As in *Kitāb . . . al-mukāfi'* he also proved theorems on the summing of a number sequence; a theorem equivalent to $\lim_{n\to\infty} \alpha^n = 0$ for any α, $0 < \alpha < 1$; and a theorem that the volume of the "parabolic cupola" is equal to half the volume of a cylinder, the base of which is the base of the cupola, and the height is the axis of the cupola: the result is equivalent to the computation of the integral $\int_0^a x\,dx$.

Kitāb fī Misāḥat al-ashkāl al-musaṭṭaḥa wa'l-mujassama ("Book on the Measurement of Plane and Solid Figures") contains rules for computing the areas of plane figures and the surfaces and volumes of solids. Besides the rules known earlier there is the rule proved by Thābit in "another book," which has not survived, for computing the volumes of solids with "various bases" (truncated pyramids and cones): if S_1 and S_2 are the areas of the bases and h is the height, then the volume is equal to $V = 1/3 h (S_1 + \sqrt{S_1 S_2} + S_2)$.

Kitāb fi'l-ta'attī li-istikhrāj ʿamal al-masā'il al-handasiyya ("Book on the Method of Solving Geometrical Problems") examines the succession of operations in three forms of geometrical problems: construction, measurement, and proof (in contrast with Euclid, who examined only problems in construction ["problems"] and in proof ["theorems"]. In *Risāla fi'l-ḥujja al-mansūba ilā Suqrāṭ fi'l-murabbaʿ wa quṭrihi* ("Treatise on the Proof Attributed to Socrates on the Square and Its Diagonals"), Thābit examines the proof, described by Plato in *Meno*, of Pythagoras' theorem for an isosceles right triangle and gives three new proofs for the general case of this theorem. In the first, from a square constructed on the hypotenuse, two triangles congruent to the given triangle and constructed on two adjacent sides of the square are taken out and are added to the two other sides of the square, and the figure obtained thus consists of squares constructed on the legs of the right triangle. The second proof also is based on the division of squares that are constructed on the legs of a right triangle into parts that form the square constructed on the hypotenuse. The third proof is the generalization of Euclid's *Elements* VI, 31. There is also a generalization of the Pythagorean theorem: If in triangle ABC two straight lines are drawn from the vertex B so as to cut off the similar triangles ABE and BCD, then $AB^2 + BC^2 = AC$ $(AE + CD)$.

In *Kitāb fī ʿamal shakl mujassam dhī arbaʿ ʿashrat qāʿida tuḥīṭu bihi kura maʿlūma* ("Book on the Construction of a Solid Figure . . .") Thābit constructs a fourteen-sided polyhedron inscribed in a given sphere. He next makes two attempts to prove Euclid's fifth postulate: *Maqāla fī burhān al-muṣādara 'l-mashhūra min Uqlīdis* ("Book of the Proof of the Well-Known Postulate of Euclid") and *Maqāla fī anna 'l-khaṭṭayn idhā ukhrijā ʿalā zawiyatayn aqal min qā'imatayn iltaqayā* ("Book on the Fact That Two Lines Drawn [From a Transversal] at Angles Less Than Two Right Angles Will Meet"). The first attempt is based on the unclear assumption that if two straight lines intersected by a third move closer together or farther apart on one side of it, then they must, correspondingly, move farther apart or closer together on the other side. The "proof" consists of five propositions, the most important of which is the third, in which Thābit proves the existence of a parallelogram, by means of which Euclid's fifth postulate is proved in the fifth proposition. The second attempt is based on kinematic considerations. In the introduction to the treatise Thābit criticizes the approach of Euclid, who tries to use motion as little as possible in geometry, asserting the necessity of its use. Further on, he postulates that in "one simple motion" (parallel translation) of a body, all its points describe straight lines. The "proof" consists of seven propositions, in the first of which, from the necessity of using motion, he concludes that equidistant straight lines exist; in the fourth proposition he proves the existence of a rectangle that is used in the seventh proposition to prove Euclid's fifth postulate. These two treatises were an important influence on subsequent attempts to prove the fifth postulate (the latter in particular influenced Ibn al-Haytham's commentaries on Euclid). Similar attempts later led to the creation of non-Euclidean geometry.

Kitāb fī Quṭūʿ al-usṭu wāna wa-basīṭihā ("Book on the Sections of the Cylinder and Its Surface") examines plane sections of an inclined circular cylinder and computes the area of the lateral surfaces of such a cylinder between the two plane sections. The treatise contains thirty-seven propositions. Having shown in the thirteenth that an ellipse is obtained through right-angled compression of the circle, in the next Thābit proves that the area of an ellipse with semiaxes a and b is equal to the area of the circle of radius $\sqrt{ab}$; and in the propositions 15–17 he examines the equiaffine transformation, making the ellipse into a circle equal to it.

Thābit proves that in this case the areas of the segments of the ellipse are equal to the areas of the segments of the circle corresponding to it. In the thirty-seventh proposition he demonstrates that the area of the lateral surface of the cylinder between two plane segments is equal to the product of the length of the periphery of the ellipse that is the least section of the cylinder by the length of the segment of the axis of the cylinder between the sections. This proposition is equivalent to the formula that expresses the elliptical integral of the more general type by means of the simplest type, which gives the length of the periphery of the ellipse.

The algebraic treatise *Qawl fī Taṣḥīḥ masāʾil al-jabr bi 'l-barāhī al-handasiyya* ("Discourse on the Establishment of the Correctness of Algebra Problems . . .") establishes the rules for solving the quadratic equations $x^2 + ax = b$, $x^2 + b = ax$, $x^2 = ax + b$, using *Elements* II, 5–6. (In giving the geometrical proofs of these rules earlier, Al-Khwārizmī did not refer to Euclid.) In *Masʾala fī sʿamal al-mutawassiṭayn waqisma zāwiya maʿlū ma bi-thalāth aqsām mutasāwiya* ("Problem of Constructing Two Means and the Division of a Given Angle Into Three Equal Parts"), Thābit solves classical problems of the trisection of an angle and the construction of two mean proportionals that amount to cubic equations. Here these problems are solved by a method equivalent to Archimedes' method of "insertion" which basically involves finding points of intersection of a hyperbola and a circumference. (In his algebraic treatise al-Khayyāmī later used an analogous method to solve all forms of cubic equations that are not equivalent to linear and quadratic ones and that assume positive roots.)

Thābit studied the uneven apparent motion of the sun according to Ptolemy's eccentricity hypothesis in *Kitāb fī Ibṭāʾ al-ḥaraka fī falak al-burūj wa surʿatihā bi-ḥasab al-mawāḍiʿ allatī yakūnu fīhi min al-falak al-khārij al-markaz*("Book on the Deceleration and Acceleration of the Motion on the Ecliptic . . ."), which contains points of maximum and minimum velocity of apparent motion and points at which the true velocity of apparent motion is equal to the mean velocity of motion. Actually these points contain the instantaneous velocity of the unequal apparent motion of the sun.

A treatise on the sundial, *Kitāb fī ālāt al-sāʿ āt allatī tusammā rukhāmāt*, is very interesting for the history of mathematics. In it the definition of height h of the sun and its azimuth A according to its declination δ, the latitude ϕ of the city and the hour angle t leads to the rules $\sin h = \text{dos}(\phi - \delta) - \text{versed}$ $\sin t \cdot \cos \delta \cdot \cos \phi$ and $\sin A = \dfrac{\sin t \cdot \cos \delta}{\cos h}$, which are equivalent to the spherical theorems of cosines and sines for spherical triangles of general forms, the vertexes of which are the sun, the zenith, and the pole of the universe. The rules were formulated by Thābit only for solving concrete problems in spherical astronomy; as a general theorem of spherical trigonometry, the theorem of sines appeared only at the end of the tenth century (Manṣūr ibn ʿIrāq), while the theorem of cosines did not appear until the fifteenth century (Regiomontanus). In the same treatise Thābit examines the transition from the length of the shadow of the gnomon l on the plane of the sundial and the azimuth A of this shadow, which in essence represent the polar coordinates of the point, to "parts of longitude" x and "parts of latitude" y, which represent rectangular coordinates of the same point according to the rule $x = l \sin A$, $y = l \cos A$.

In another treatise on the sundial, *Maqāla fī sifat al-ashkāl allatī tahduthu bi-mamarr ṭaraf ẓill al-miqyās fī saṭh al-ufug fī kull yawm wa fī kull balad*, Thābit examines conic sections described by the end of a shadow of the gnomon on the horizontal plane and determines the diameters and centers of these sections for various positions of the sun. In the philosophical treatise *Masāʾil suʾila ʿanhā Thābit ibn Qurra al-Ḥarrānī* ("Questions Posed to Thābit . . ."), he emphasizes the abstract character of number (*ʿadad*), as distinct from the concrete "counted thing" (*maʿdūd*), and postulates "the existence of things that are actually infinite in contrast with Aristotle, who recognized only potential infinity. Actual infinity is also used by

Thābit in *Kitāb fi'l qarasṭūn* ("Book on Beam Balance").

Astronomy. Thābit wrote many astronomical works. We have already noted his treatise on the investigation of the apparent motion of the sun; his *Kitāb fī Sanat al-shams* ("Book on the Solar Year") is on the same subject. *Qawl fī īḍāḥ al-wajh alladhī dhakara Baṭlamyūs* . . . concerns the apparent motion of the moon, and *Fī ḥisāb ru'yat al-ahilla*, the visibility of the new moon. In what has been transmitted as *De motu octave spere* and *Risāla ilā Isḥāq ibn Ḥunayn* ("Letter to . . .") Thābit states his kinematic hypothesis, which explains the phenomenon of precession with the aid of the "eighth celestial sphere" (that of the fixed stars); the first seven are those of the sun, moon, and five planets. Thābit explains the "trepidation" of the equinoxes with the help of a ninth sphere. The theory of trepidation first appeared in Islam in connection with Thābit's name.

Mechanics and Physics. Two of Thābit's treatises on weights, *Kitāb fī Ṣifat al-wazn wa-ikhtilāfihi* ("Book on the Properties of Weight and Non-equilibrium") and *Kitāb fi'l-Qarasṭūn* ("Book on Beam Balance"), are devoted to mechanics. In the first he formulates Aristotle's dynamic principle, as well as the conditions of equilibrium of a beam, hung or supported in the middle and weighted on the ends. In the second treatise, starting from the same principle, Thābit proves the principle of equilibrium of levers and demonstrates that two equal loads, balancing a third, can be replaced by their sum at a midpoint without destroying the equilibrium. After further generalizing the latter proposition for the case in which "as many [equal] loads as desired and even infinitely many" are hung at equal distances, Thābit considers the case of equally distributed continuous loads. Here, through the method of exhaustion and examination of upper and lower integral sums, a calculation equivalent

to computation of the integral $\int_a^b xndx$. The result

obtained is used to determine the conditions of equilibrium for a heavy beam.

Thābit's work in natural sciences includes *Qawl fi'l-Sabab alladhī ju'ilat lahu miyāh al-baḥr māliḥa* ("Discourse on the Reason Why Seawater Is Salted"), extant in manuscript, and writings on the reason for the formation of mountains and on the striking of fire from stones. He also wrote two treatises on music.

Medicine. Thābit was one of the best-known physicians of the medieval East. Ibn al-Qifṭī, in *Ta'rikh al-ḥukamā*, tells of Thābit's curing a butcher who was given up for dead. Thābit wrote many works on Galen and medicinal treatises, which are almost completely unstudied. Among these treatises are general guides to medicine—al-Dhakhīra fī 'ilm al-ṭibb ("A Treasury of Medicine"), *Kitāb al-Rawḍa fi 'l-ṭibb* ("Book of the Garden of Medicine"), *al-Kunnash* ("Collection")—and works on the circulation of the blood, embryology, the cure of various illnesses—*Kitāb fī 'ilm al-'ayn* . . . ("Book on the Science of the Eye . . ."), *Kitāb fi'l-jadarī wa'l-ḥaṣbā* ("Book on Smallpox and Measles"), *Risāla fī tawallud al-ḥaṣāt* ("Treatise on the Origin of Gallstones"), *Risāla fi'l-bayāḍ alladhī yaẓharu fi'l-badan* ("Treatise on Whiteness . . . in the Body")—and on medicines. Thābit also wrote on the anatomy of birds and on veterinary medicine (*Kitāb al-bayṭara*), and commented on *De plantis*, ascribed to Aristotle.

Philosophy and Humanistic Sciences. Thābit's philosophical treatise *Masā'il su'ila 'anhā Thābit ibn Qurra al-Ḥarrānī* comprises his answers to questions posed by his student Abū Mūsā ibn Usayd, a Christian from Iraq. In another extant philosophical treatise, *Maqāla fī talkhīṣ mā aṭā bihi Arisṭūṭālīs fī kitābihi fī Mā ba'd al-ṭabī'a*, Thābit criticizes the views of Plato and Aristotle on the motionlessness of essence, which is undoubtedly related to his opposition to the ancient tradition of not using motion in mathematics. Ibn al-Qifṭī (*op. cit.*, 120) says that Thābit commented on Aristotle's *Categories*, *De interpretatione*, and *Analytics*. He also wrote on logic, psychology, ethics, the classification of sciences, the grammar of the Syriac language, politics, and the symbolism in Plato's *Republic*. Ibn al-Qifṭī also states that Thābit produced many works in Syriac on religion and the customs of the Sabians.

BIBLIOGRAPHY

I. ORIGINAL WORKS. Thābit's MSS are listed in C. Brockelmann, *Geschichte . . . Literatur*, 2nd ed., I (Leiden, 1943), 241–244, and supp. I (Leiden, 1937), 384–386; Fuat Sezgin, *Geschichte des arabischen Schrifttums*, III (Leiden, 1970), 260–263, and V (Leiden, 1974), 264–272; and H. Suter, *Die Mathematiker und Astronomen der Araber und ihre Werke* (Leipzig, 1900), 34–38, and *Nachträge* (1902), 162–163. Many of his works that are no longer extant are cited by Ibn al-Qifṭī in his *Ta'rīkh al-ḥukamā'*, J. Lippert, ed. (Leipzig, 1903), 115–122.

His published writings include *Kitāb al-Mafrūḍāt*

("Book of Data"), in Naṣīr al-Dīn al-Ṭūsī, *Majmūʿ al-rasāʾil*, II (Hyderabad, 1940), pt. 2; *Maqāla fī istikhrāj al-aʿdād al-mutaḥābba bi-suhūlat al-maslak ilā dhālikâ* ("Book on the Determination of Amicable Numbers by an Easy Method"), Russian trans. by G. P. Matvievskaya in *Materialy k istorii . . .*, 90–116; *Kitāb fī taʾlīf al-nisab* ("Book on the Composition of Ratios"), Russian trans. by B. A. Rosenfeld and L. M. Karpova in the *Fiziko-matematicheskie Nauki v Stranakh Vostoka* ("Physical-Mathematical Sciences in the Countries of the East"; Moscow, 1966), 9–41; *Risāla fī Shakl al-qiṭāʿ* ("Treatise on the Secant Figure"), in Latin trans. by Gerard of Cremona, with notes and German trans.; *Risāla fiʾl-ḥujja al-mansūba ilā Suqrāṭ fiʾl-murabbaʿ wa quṭrih* ("Treatise on the Proof Attributed to Socrates on the Square and Its Diagonals"), Arabic text with Turkish trans. in A. Sayili, "Sābit ibn Kurranin Pitagor teoremini temini," and in English in Sayili's "Thābit ibn Qurra's Generalization of the Pythagorean Theorem"; and *Kitāb fī ʿamal shakl mujassam dhī arbaʿ ʿashrat qāʿida tuḥīṭu bihi kura maʿlūma* ("Book on the Construction of a Solid Figure With Fourteen Sides About Which a Known Sphere Is Described"), ed. with German trans. in E. Bessel-Hagen and O. Spies, "Tābit b. Qurra's Abhandlung über einen halbregelmässigen Vierzehnflächner."

Additional works are *Maqāla fī burhān al-muṣādara ʾl-mashhūra min Uqlīdis* ("Book of the Proof of the Well-Known Postulate of Euclid"), Russian trans. in B. A. Rosenfeld and A. P. Youschkevitch, *Dokazatelstva pyatogo postulata Evklida . . .*, and English trans. in A. I. Sabra, "Thābit ibn Qurra on Euclid's Parallels Postulate"; *Maqāla fī anna ʾl-khaṭṭayn idhā ukhrijā ʿalā zāwiyatayn aqall min qāʾimatayn iltaqayā* ("Book on the Fact That Two Lines Drawn [From a Transversal] at Angles Less Than Two Right Angles Will Meet"), Russian trans. by B. A. Rosenfeld in "Sabit ibn Korra. Kniga o tom, chto dve linii, provedennye pod uglami, menshimi dvukh pryamykh, vstretyatsya," *Istoriko-matematicheskie issledovania*, **15** (1962), 363–380, and English trans. in Sabra, *op. cit.*; and *Qawl fī tashīḥ masāʾil al-jabr biʾl-barahīn al-handasiyya* ("Discourse on the Establishment of the Correctness of Algebra Problems With the Aid of Geometrical Proofs"), ed. and German trans. in P. Luckey, "Tābit b. Qurra über die geometrischen Richtigkeitsnachweis der Auflösung der quadratischen Gleichungen."

Further works are *Qawl fī īḍāḥ al-wajh alladhī dhakara Baṭlamyūs anna bihi istakhraja man taqaddamahu masīrat al-qamar al-dawriyya wa-hiya al-mustawiya* ("Discourse on the Explanation of the Method Noted by Ptolemy That His Predecessors Used for Computation of the Periodic [Mean] Motion of the Moon"), German trans. of the intro. in Hessel-Hagen and Spies, *op. cit.*; *Kitāb fī sanat al-shams* ("Book on the Solar Year"), medieval Latin trans. in F. J. Carmody, *The Astronomical Works of Thabit b. Qurra*, 41–79, and English trans., with commentary, by O. Neugebauer in "Thābit ben Qurra. On the Solar Year and On the Motion of the

Eighth Sphere," in *Proceedings of the American Philosophical Society*, **106** (1962), 267–299; medieval Latin trans. of work on the eighth sphere, "De motu octave spere," in Carmody, *op. cit.*, 84–113, and English trans. in Neugebauer, *op. cit.*, 291–299; *Risāla ilā Isḥāq ibn Ḥunayn* ("A Letter to . . ."), included by Ibn Yūnus in his "Great Ḥakimite *zīj*," Arabic text and French trans. by J. J. Caussin de Parceval, "Le livre de la grande table Hakémite observée par . . . Ebn Younis," 114–118; and *Kitāb fī ālāt al-sāʿāt allatī tusammā rukhāmāt* ("Book on the Timekeeping Instruments Called Sundials"), ed. with German trans. by K. Garbers, ". . . Ein Werk über ebene Sonnenuhren . . .," in *Quellen und Studien zur Geschichte der Mathematik, Astronomie und Physik*, Abt. A, **4** (1936).

Thābit also wrote *Maqāla fī ṣifat al-ashkāl allatī taḥduthu bi-mamarr ṭaraf ẓill al-miqyās fī saṭḥ al-ufuq fī kull yawm wa fī kull balad* ("Book on the Description of Figures Obtained by the Passage of the End of a Shadow of a Gnomon in the Horizontal Plane on Any Day and in Any City"), German trans. in E. Wiedemann and J. Frank, "Über die Konstruktion der Schattenlinien von Thābit ibn Qurra"; *Kitāb fī ṣifat al-wazn wa-ikhtilāfihi* ("Book on the Properties of Weight and Nonequilibrium"), included by ʿAbd al-Raḥman al-Khāzinī in his *Kitāb mīzān al-ḥikma* ("Book of the Balance of Wisdom"), 33–38; *Kitāb fiʾl-qarasṭūn* ("Book on Beam Balances"), medieval Latin trans. in F. Buchner, "Die Schrift über der Qarastūn von Thābit b. Qurra," and in E. A. Moody and M. Clagett, *The Medieval Science of Weights*, 77–117 (with English trans.), also German trans. from Arabic MSS in E. Wiedemann, "Die Schrift über den Qarasṭūn"; and *al-Dhakhīra fī ʿilm al-ṭibb* ("A Treasury of Medicine"), ed. by G. Ṣubḥī (Cairo, 1928).

Recensions of ancient works are Euclid's *Elements*, ed. with additions by Naṣīr al-Dīn al-Ṭūsī, *Taḥrīr Uqlīdis fī ʿilm al-handasa* (Teheran, 1881); Archimedes' *Lemmata*, Latin trans. with additions by al-Nasawī, in *Archimedis Opera omnia*, J. L. Heiberg, ed., 2nd ed., II (Leipzig, 1912), 510–525; Archimedes' *On Touching Circles* and *Triangles* in *Rasāʾil ibn Qurra* (Hyderabad, 1940); Apollonius' *Conics*, bks. 5–7, Latin trans. in *Apollonii Pergaei Conicorum libri VII* (Florence, 1661), German trans. in L. Nix, *Das fünfte Buch der Conica des Apollonius von Perga in der arabischen Uebersetzung des Thabit ibn Corrah; De plantis*, ascribed to Aristotle, ed. in A. J. Arberry, "An Early Arabic Translation From the Greek"; and Galen's medical treatises, in F. Sezgin, *Geschichte des arabischen Schrifttums*, III, 68–140.

II. SECONDARY LITERATURE. See A. J. Arberry, "An Early Arabic Translation From the Greek," in *Bulletin of the Faculty of Arts, Cairo*, **1** (1933), 48–76, 219–257, and **2** (1934), 71–105; E. Bessel-Hagen and O. Spies, "Tābit b. Qurra's Abhandlung über einen halbregelmässigen Vierzehnflächner," in *Quellen und Studien zur Geschichte der Mathematik, Astronomie und Physik*, Abt. B, **2** (1933), 186–198; A. Björnbo, "Thābits Werk über den Transversalensatz . . .," in *Abhandlun-*

gen zur Geschichte der Naturwissenschaften und der Medizin, **7** (1924); F. Buchner, "Die Schrift über der Qarastūn von Thābit b. Qurra," in Sitzungsberichte der Physikalisch-medizinischen Sozietät in Erlangen, **52–53** (1922), 171–188; F. J. Carmody, The Astronomical Works of Thabit b. Qurra (Berkeley–Los Angeles, 1960); J. J. Caussin de Parceval, "Le livre de la grande table Hakémite observée par . . . Ebn Iounis," in Notices et extraits des manuscrits de la Bibliothèque nationale, **7**, pt. 1 (1803–1804), 16–240; D. Chvolson, Die Ssabier und Ssabismus, I (St. Petersburg, 1856), 546–567; and P. Duhem, Les origines de la statique, I (Paris, 1905), 79–92; and Le système du monde, II (Paris, 1914), 117–119, 238–246.

Also see Ibn Abi Uṣaybiʿa, ʿUyūn al-anbāʾfi tabaqāt al-aṭibbāʾ, A. Müller, ed., I (Königsberg, 1884), 115–122; A. G. Kapp, "Arabische Übersetzer und Kommentatoren Euklids . . .," in Isis, **23** (1935), 58–66; L. M. Karpova, "Traktat Sabita ibn Korry o secheniakh tsilindra i ego poverkhnosti" ("Treatise of Thābit ibn Qurra on the Sections of the Cylinder and Its Surface"), in Trudy XIII Mezhdunarodnogo kongressa po istorii nauki (Papers of the XIII International Congress on the History of Science), sec. 3–4 (Moscow, 1974), 103–105; E. S. Kennedy, "The Crescent Visibility Theory of Thābit ibn Qurra," in Proceedings of the Mathematical and Physical Society of the UAR, **24** (1961), 71–74; ʿAbd al-Raḥmān al-Khāzinī, Kitāb mīzān al-ḥikma (Hyderabad, 1940); L. Leclerc, Histoire de la médecine arabe, I (Paris, 1876), 168–172; P. Luckey, "Tābit b. Qurra's Buch über die ebenen Sonnenuhren," in Quellen und Studien zur Geschichte der Mathematik, Astronomie und Physik, Abt. B, **4** (1938), 95–148; and "Tābit b. Qurra über die geometrischen Richtigkeitsnachweis der Auflösung der quadratischen Gleichungen," in Berichte de Sächsischen Akademie der Wissenschaften, Math.-nat. Kl., **13** (1941), 93–114; and G. P. Matvievskaya, Uchenie o chisle na srednevekovom Blizhnem i Srednem Vostoke ("Number Theory in the Medieval Near East and Central Asia"; Tashkent, 1967); and "Materialy k istorii ucheniya o chisle na srednevekovom Blizhnem i Srednem Vostoke" ("Materials for a History of Number Theory in the Medieval Near and Middle East"), in Iz istorii tochnykh nauk na srednevekovom Blizhnem i Srednem Vostoke ("History of the Exact Sciences in the Medieval Near and Middle East"; Tashkent, 1972), 76–169.

Additional works are M. Meyerhof, "The 'Book of Treasure,' an Early Arabic Treatise on Medicine," in Isis, **14** (1930), 55–76; E. A. Moody and M. Clagett, The Medieval Science of Weights (Madison, Wis., 1952); L. Nix, Das fünfte Buch der Conica des Apollonius von Perga in der arabischen Uebersetzung des Thabit ibn Corrah . . . (Leipzig, 1889); S. Pines, "Thabit b. Qurra's Conception of Number and Theory of the Mathematical Infinite," in Actes du XIᵉ Congrès international d'histoire des sciences, III (Wrocław–Warsaw–Cracow), 160–166; B. A. Rosenfeld and L. M.

Karpova, "Traktat Sabita ibn Korry o sostavnykh otnosheniakh" ("Treatise of Thābit ibn Qurra on the Composition of Ratios"), in Fiziko-matematicheskie nauki v stranakh Vostoka ("Physical-Mathematical Sciences in the Countries of the East"), I (Moscow, 1966), 5–8; B. A. Rosenfeld and A. P. Youschkevitch, "Dokazatelstva pyatogo postulata Evklida . . ." ("Proofs of Euclid's Fifth Postulate . . ."), in Istoriko-matematicheskie issledovania, **14** (1961), 587–592; A. I. Sabra, "Thābit ibn Qurra on Euclid's Parallels Postulate," in Journal of the Warburg and Courtauld Institutes, **31** (1968), 12–32; A. Y. Sansur, Matematicheskie trudy Sabita ibn Korry ("Mathematical Works of Thābit ibn Qurra"; Moscow, 1971); G. Sarton, Introduction to the History of Science, I (Baltimore, 1927), 599–600; A. Sayili, "Sābit ibn Kurranin Pitagor teoremini temini," in Türk Tarih Kurumu. Belleten, **22**, no. 88 (1958), 527–549; and "Thabit ibn Qurra's Generalization of the Pythagorean Theorem," in Isis, **51** (1960), 35–37; and O. Schirmer, "Studien zur Astronomie der Araber," in Sitzungsberichte der Physikalisch-medizinischen Sozietät in Erlangen, **58** (1927), 33–88.

See also F. Sezgin, Geschichte des arabischen Schrifttums, III (Leiden, 1970), 260–263; T. D. Stolyarova, "Traktat Sabita ibn Korry 'Kniga o karastune'" ("Thābit ibn Qurra's Treatise 'Book of Qarastūn'"), in Iz istorii tochnykh nauk na srednevekovom Blizhnem i Srednem Vostoke ("History of the Exact Sciences in the Medieval Near East and Central Asia"; Tashkent, 1972), 206–210; and Statika v stranakh Blizhnego i Srednego Vostoka v IX–XI vekakh ("Statics in the . . . Near East and Central Asia in the Ninth-Eleventh Centuries"; Moscow, 1973); H. Suter, "Die Mathematiker und Astronomen der Araber und ihre Werke," in Abhandlungen für Geschichte der mathematischen Wissenschaften, **10** (1900); "Uber die Ausmessung der Parabel von Thābit ben Kurra al-Harrani," in Sitzungsberichte der Physikalisch-medizinischen Societät in Erlangen, **48–49** (1918), 65–86; and "Die Abhandlungen Thābit ben Kurras und Abū Sahl al-Kūhīs über die Ausmessung der Paraboloide," ibid., 186–227; J. Vernet and M. A. Catalá, "Dos tratados de Arquimedes arabe: Tratado de los círculos tangentes y Libro de los triángulos," Publicaciones del Seminario de historia de la ciencia, **2** (1972); E. Wiedemann, "Die Schrift über den Qarastūn," in Bibliotheca mathematica, 3rd ser., **12**, no. 1 (1912), 21–39; and "Über Thābit, sein Leben und Wirken," in Sitzungsberichte der Physikalisch-medizinischen Sozietät in Erlangen, **52** (1922), 189–219; E. Wiedemann and J. Frank, "Über die Konstruktion der Schattenlinien auf horizontalen Sonnenuhren von Thābit ibn Qurra," in Kongelige Danske Videnskabernes Selskabs Skrifter, Math.-fys. meddel., **4** (1922), 7–30; F. Woepcke, "Notice sur une théorie ajoutée par Thābit ben Korrah à l'arithmétique spéculative des grecs," in Journal asiatique, 4th ser., **20** (1852), 420–429; F. Wüstenfeld, Geschichte der arabischen Ärzte (Leipzig, 1840), 34–36; and A. P. Youschkevitch, "Note sur les déterminations infinitésimales chez Thabit ibn Qurra," in *Archives internationales d'histoire des sciences*, no. 66 (1964), 37–45; and (as editor), *Istoria matematiki s drevneyshikh vremen do nachala XIX stoletiya* ("History of Mathematics From Ancient Times to the Beginning of the Nineteenth Century"), I (Moscow, 1970), 221–224, 239–244.

B. A. ROSENFELD
A. T. GRIGORIAN

THADDAEUS FLORENTINUS. See **Alderotti, Taddeo.**

THALES (*b.* Miletus, Ionia, 625 B.C. [?]; *d.* 547 B.C. [?]), *natural philosophy.*

Thales is considered by Aristotle to be the "founder" ($\dot{\alpha}\rho\chi\eta\gamma\acute{o}\varsigma$) of Ionian natural philosophy.[1] He was the son of Examyes and Cleobuline, who were, according to some authorities, of Phoenician origin. But the majority opinion considered him a true Milesian by descent ($\iota\vartheta\alpha\gamma\epsilon\nu\acute{\eta}\varsigma$ $M\iota\lambda\acute{\eta}\sigma\iota\sigma\varsigma$), and of a distinguished family. This latter view is probably the correct one since his father's name seems to be Carian rather than Semitic, and the Carians had at this time been almost completely assimilated by the Ionians. According to Diogenes Laërtius, Apollodorus put Thales' birth in Olympiad 35.1 (640 B.C.) and his death at the age of 78 in Olympiad 58 (548–545 B.C.). There is a discrepancy in the figures here: probably 35.1 is a mistake for 39.1 (624), since the confusion of $\bar{\epsilon}$ and $\bar{\vartheta}$ is a very common one. Apollodorus would in that case characteristically have made Thales' death correspond with the date of the fall of Sardis, his *floruit* coincide with the eclipse of the sun dated at 585 B.C.—which he is alleged to have predicted—and assumed his birth to be the conventional forty years before his prime.[2]

Even in antiquity there was considerable doubt concerning Thales' written works. It seems clear that Aristotle did not have access to any book by him, at least none on cosmological matters. Some authorities declare categorically that he left no book behind. Others, however, credit him with the authorship of a work on navigation entitled "The Nautical Star Guide," but in spite of a tradition suggesting that Thales defined the Little Bear and recommended its navigational usefulness to Milesian sailors,[3] it is extremely doubtful that he was the actual author of this work, since Diogenes Laërtius informs us that this book was also attributed to a certain Phokos of Samos. It is most un-

likely that a work of Thales would have been ascribed to someone of comparative obscurity, but not the converse.

Much evidence of practical activities associated with Thales has survived, testifying to his versatility as statesman, tycoon, engineer, mathematician, and astronomer. In the century after his death he became an epitome of practical ingenuity.[4] Herodotus records the stories that Thales advised the Ionians to establish a single deliberative chamber at Teos and that he diverted the river Halys so that Croesus' army might be able to cross. (Herodotus is skeptical about the latter explanation.)[5] Aristotle preserves another anecdote that credits Thales with considerable practical knowledge. According to this account, Thales, when reproached for his impracticality, used his skill in astronomy to forecast a glut in the olive crop, went out and cornered the market in the presses, and thereby made a large profit. Aristotle disbelieves the story and comments that this was a common commercial procedure that men attributed to Thales on account of his wisdom.[6] Plato, on the other hand, whose purpose is to show that philosophy is above mere utilitarian considerations, tells the conflicting anecdote that Thales, while stargazing, fell into a well and was mocked by a pretty Thracian servant girl for trying to find out what was going on in the heavens when he could not even see what was at his feet.[7] It is clear that these stories stem from separate traditions—the one seeking to represent the philosopher as an eminently practical man of affairs and the other as an unworldly dreamer.

Thales achieved his fame as a scientist for having predicted an eclipse of the sun. Herodotus, who is our oldest source for this story, tells us that the eclipse (which must have been total or very nearly so) occurred in the sixth year of the war between the Lydians under Alyattes and the Medes under Cyaxares, and that Thales predicted it to the Ionians, fixing as its term the year in which it actually took place.[8] This eclipse is now generally agreed to have occurred on 28 May 585 B.C. (−584 by astronomical reckoning). It has been widely accepted that Thales was able to perform this striking astronomical feat by using the so-called "Babylonian saros," a cycle of 223 lunar months (18 years, 10 days, 8 hours), after which eclipses both of the sun and moon repeat themselves with very little change. Neugebauer, however, has convincingly demonstrated that the "Babylonian saros" was, in fact, the invention of the English astronomer Edmond Halley in rather a weak moment.[9] The Babylonians did not use cycles to predict solar eclipses but computed them from observations of the latitude of the moon made shortly before the expected syzygy. As Neugebauer says,

. . . there exists no cycle for solar eclipses visible at a given place; all modern cycles concern the earth as a whole. No Babylonian theory for predicting a solar eclipse existed at 600 B.C., as one can see from the very unsatisfactory situation 400 years later, nor did the Babylonians ever develop any theory which took the influence of geographical latitude into account.[10]

Accordingly, it must be assumed that if Thales did predict the eclipse he made an extremely lucky guess and did not do so upon a scientific basis, since he had no conception of geographical latitude and no means of determining whether a solar eclipse would be visible in a particular locality. He could only have said that an eclipse was possible somewhere at some time in the (chronological) year that ended in 585 B.C. But a more likely explanation seems to be simply that Thales happened to be the *savant* around at the time when this striking astronomical phenomenon occurred and the assumption was made that as a savant he *must* have been able to predict it. There is a situation closely parallel to this one in the next century. In 468–467 B.C. a huge meteorite fell at Aegospotami. This event made a considerable impact, and two sources preserve the absurd report that the fall was predicted by Anaxagoras, who was the Ionian *savant* around at that time.[11]

The Greeks themselves claim to have derived their mathematics from Egypt.[12] Eudemus, the author of the history of mathematics written as part of the systematization of knowledge that went on in the Lyceum, is more explicit. He tells us that it was "Thales who, after a visit to Egypt, first brought this study to Greece" and adds "not only did he make numerous discoveries himself, but he laid the foundations for many other discoveries on the part of his successors, attacking some problems with greater generality and others more empirically." Proclus preserves for us some of the discoveries that Eudemus ascribed to Thales, namely, that the circle is bisected by its diameter,[13] that the base angles of an isosceles triangle are equal,[14] and that vertically opposed angles are equal.[15] In addition he informs us that the theorem that two triangles are equal in every respect if they have two angles and one side respectively equal was referred by Eudemus to Thales with the comment that the latter's measuring the distance of

ships out at sea necessarily involved the use of this theorem.[16]

From the above it can be seen that Eudemus credited Thales with full knowledge of the theory behind his discoveries. He also held that Thales introduced geometry into Greece from Egypt. Our surviving sources of information about the nature of Egyptian mathematics, however, give us no evidence to suggest that Egyptian geometry had advanced beyond certain rule-of-thumb techniques of practical mensuration. Nowhere do we find any attempt to discover why these techniques worked, nor anything resembling a general and theoretical mathematics. It seems most unlikely, then, that the Greeks derived their mathematics from the Egyptians. But could Thales have been the founder of theoretical mathematics in Greece, as Eudemus claimed? Here again the answer must be negative. The first three discoveries attributed to him by the Peripatetic most probably represent "just the neatest abstract solutions of particular problems associated with Thales."[17] Heath points out that the first of these propositions is not even proved in Euclid.[18] As for the last of them, Thales could very easily have made use of a primitive angle-measurer and solved the problem in one of several ways without necessarily formulating an explicit theory about the principles involved.

Van der Waerden, on the other hand, believes that Thales did develop a logical structure for geometry and introduced into this study the idea of proof.[19] He also seeks to derive Greek mathematics from Babylon. This is a very doubtful standpoint. Although Babylonian mathematics, with its sexagesimal place-value system, had certainly developed beyond the primitive level reached by the Egyptians, here too we find nowhere any attempt at proof. Our evidence suggests that the Greeks were influenced by Babylonian mathematics, but that this influence occurred at a date considerably later than the sixth century B.C. If the Greeks had derived their mathematics from Babylonian sources, one would have expected them to have adopted the much more highly developed place-value system. Moreover, the Greeks themselves, who are extremely generous, indeed overgenerous, in acknowledging their scientific debts to other peoples, give no hint of a Babylonian source for their mathematics.

Our knowledge of Thales' cosmology is virtually dependent on two passages in Aristotle. In the *Metaphysics* (A3, 983b6) Aristotle, who patently has no more information beyond what is given here, is of the opinion that Thales considered water to be the material constituent of things, and in the *De caelo* (B13, 294a28), where Aristotle expressly declares his information to be indirect, we are told that Thales held that the earth floats on water. Seneca provides the additional information (*Naturales quaestiones*, III, 14) that Thales used the idea of a floating earth to explain earthquakes. If we can trust this evidence, which seems to stem ultimately from Theophrastus via a Posidonian source, the implication is that Thales displays an attitude of mind strikingly different from anything that had gone before. Homer and Hesiod had explained that earthquakes were due to the activity of the god Poseidon, who frequently bears the epic epithet "Earth Shaker." Thales, by contrast, instead of invoking any such supernatural agency, employs a simple, natural explanation to account for this phenomenon. Cherniss, however, has claimed that Aristotle's knowledge of Thales' belief that the earth floats on water would have been sufficient to induce him to infer that Thales also held water to be his material substrate.[20] But it is impossible to believe that Aristotle could have been so disingenuous as to make this inference and then make explicit conjectures as to why Thales held water to be his ἀρχή. Aristotle's conjectured reasons for the importance attached by Thales to water as the ultimate constituent of things are mainly physiological. He suggests that Thales might have been led to this conception by the observation that nutriment and semen are always moist and that the very warmth of life is a damp warmth. Burnet has rejected these conjectures by Aristotle on the ground that in the sixth century interests were meteorological rather than physiological.[21] But, as Baldry has pointed out, an interest in birth and other phenomena connected with sex is a regular feature even of primitive societies long before other aspects of biology are thought of.[22] However this may be, it is noteworthy that, in view of the parallels to be found between Thales' cosmology and certain Near Eastern mythological cosmogonies,[23] there exists the possibility that Thales' emphasis upon water and his theory that the earth floats on water were derived from some such source, and that he conceived of water as a "remote ancestor" rather than as a persistent substrate. But even if Thales was influenced by mythological precedents[24] and failed to approximate to anything like the Aristotelian material cause, our evidence, sparse and controversial though it is, nevertheless seems sufficient to justify the claim that Thales was the first philosopher. This evidence suggests that Thales' thought shared certain basic characteristics with that of his Ionian successors. These Milesian philosophers, abandoning mythopoeic forms of thought, sought to explain the world about them in terms of its visible constituents. Natural explanations were introduced by them, which took the place of supernatural and mystical ones.[25] Like their mythopoeic predecessors, the Milesians firmly believed that there was an orderliness inherent in the world around them. Again like their predecessors, they attempted to explain the world by showing how it had come to be what it is. But, instead of invoking the agency of supernatural powers, they sought for a unifying hypothesis to account for this order and, to a greater or lesser extent, proceeded to deduce their natural explanations of the various phenomena from it. Two elements, then, characterize early Greek philosophy, the search for natural as opposed to supernatural and mystical explanations, and secondly, the search for a unifying hypothesis. Both of these elements proved influential in paving the way for the development of the sciences, and it is in the light of this innovation that Thales' true importance in the history of science must be assessed.

NOTES

1. *Metaphysics*, A3, 983b17 ff. (DK, 11A12).
2. These datings are now approximately in accordance with the figures given by Demetrius of Phalerum, who placed the canonization of the Seven Sages (of whom Thales was universally regarded as a member) in the archonship of Damasias at Athens (582–581 B.C.).
3. Callimachus, *Iambus*, 1, 52 f. 191 Pfeiffer (DK, 11A3a).
4. See Aristophanes, *Birds* 1009; *Clouds* 180.
5. Herodotus, I, 170; I, 75 (DK, 11A4, 11A6).
6. *Politics*, A11, 1259a6 (DK, 11A10).
7. *Theaetetus*, 174A (DK, 11A9). It is odd that Plato should have applied this story to someone as notoriously practical in his interests as Thales. It makes one think that there may be at least a grain of truth in the story. See my review of Moraux's Budé edition of the *De caelo*, in *Classical Review*, n.s., **20** (1970), 174, and M. Landmann and J. O. Fleckenstein, "Tagesbeobachtung von Sternen in Altertum," in *Vierteljahrsschrift der Naturforschenden Gesellschaft in Zürich*, **88** (1943), 98, notwithstanding Dicks' scornful dismissal of their suggestion. Certainly the motive for this story is clear, but it could have been Thales' practice that determined its form. In general Dicks is far too skeptical in his treatment of the stories told of Thales and relegates them to the status of "the famous story of the First World War about the Russians marching through England with 'snow on their boots.'" But on this latter story see Margo Lawrence, *Shadow of Swords* (London, 1971), in which she reveals that soldiers from Russia, wearing Russian uniform, carrying balalaikas, and singing Slavonic songs, did in fact disembark in 1916 at Newcastle upon Tyne. Admittedly the snow on their boots must be left to folklore.
8. I, 74 (DK, 11A5).
9. O. Neugebauer, *The Exact Sciences in Antiquity*, 141.
10. *Ibid.*, 142.

11. See Diogenes Laërtius, II, 10 (DK, 59A1), and Pliny, *Historia naturalis*, II, 149 (DK, 59A11). See also Cicero, *De divinatione*, I.50.112 (DK, 12A5a), and Pliny, *ibid.*, II, 191, for a sixth-century parallel, where Anaximander is alleged to have predicted an earthquake.

12. See Herodotus, II, 109, who believes that geometry originated from the recurrent need to remeasure land periodically flooded by the Nile; Aristotle, *Metaphysics*, A3, 981b20–25, who believes that mathematics evolved in a highly theoretical way as the invention of a leisured class of Egyptian priests; and Eudemus, who, in spite of being a Peripatetic, sides with Herodotus rather than with Aristotle (see Proclus, *Commentary on Euclid's Elements*, I, 64.16 [Friedlein]).

13. *Commentary on Euclid's Elements*, 157.10 (DK, 11A20).

14. *Ibid.*, 250.20.

15. *Ibid.*, 299.1.

16. *Ibid.*, 352.14.

17. G. S. Kirk, *The Presocratic Philosophers*, 84.

18. T. L. Heath, *Greek Mathematics*, I, 131.

19. B. L. van der Waerden, *Science Awakening*, 89.

20. H. Cherniss, "The Characteristics and Effects of Presocratic Philosophy," in *Journal of the History of Ideas*, **12** (1951), 321.

21. J. Burnet, *Early Greek Philosophy*, 48.

22. H. C. Baldry, "Embryological Analogies in Early Greek Philosophy," in *Classical Quarterly*, **26** (1932), 28.

23. For an excellent account of Egyptian and Mesopotamian cosmogonies, see H. Frankfort, ed., *Before Philosophy* (Penguin Books, London, 1949), pub. orig. as *The Intellectual Adventure of Ancient Man* (Chicago, 1946).

24. Aristotle, it may be noted, cites the parallel in Greek mythology of Oceanus and Tethys, the parents of generation (*Metaphysics*, A3, 983b27ff. [DK,1B10]). But the Greek myth may itself be derived from an oriental source.

25. The gods of whom Thales thought everything was full (see Aristotle, *De anima*, A5, 411a7 [DK, 11A22]) are manifestly different from the personal divinities of traditional mythology.

BIBLIOGRAPHY

For a collection of sources see H. Diels and W. Kranz, *Die Fragmente der Vorsokratiker*, 6th ed., 3 vols. (Berlin, 1951–1952), I, 67–79 (abbreviated as DK above).

See also H. C. Baldry, "Embryological Analogies in Presocratic Cosmogony," in *Classical Quarterly*, **26** (1932), 27–34; J. Burnet, *Greek Philosophy: Part I, Thales to Plato* (London, 1914); and *Early Greek Philosophy*, 4th ed. (London, 1930); H. Cherniss, "The Characteristics and Effects of Presocratic Philosophy," in *Journal of the History of Ideas*, **12** (1951), 319–345; D. R. Dicks, "Thales," in *Classical Quarterly*, n.s. **9** (1959), 294–309; and "Solstices, Equinoxes and the Presocratics," in *Journal of Hellenic Studies*, **86** (1966), 26–40; J. L. E. Dreyer, *A History of the Planetary Systems from Thales to Kepler* (Cambridge, 1906), repr. as *A History of Astronomy from Thales to Kepler* (New York, 1953); W. K. C. Guthrie, *A History of Greek Philosophy*, I (Cambridge, 1962); T. L. Heath, *Aristarchus of Samos* (Oxford, 1913); and *Greek Mathematics*, I (Oxford, 1921); U. Hölscher, "Anaximander und die Anfänge der Philosophie," in *Hermes*, **81** (1953), 257–277, 385–417; repr. in English in Allen and Furley, *Studies in Presocratic Philosophy*, I (New York, 1970), 281–322; C. H. Kahn, "On Early Greek Astronomy," in *Journal of Hellenic Studies*, **90** (1970), 99–116; G. S. Kirk and J. E. Raven, *The Presocratic Philosophers* (Cambridge, 1957); O. Neugebauer, "The History of Ancient Astronomy, Problems and Methods," in *Journal of Near Eastern Studies*, **4** (1945), 1–38; *The Exact Sciences in Antiquity* (Princeton, 1952; 2nd ed., Providence, R.I., 1957); and "The Survival of Babylonian Methods in the Exact Sciences of Antiquity and Middle Ages," in *Proceedings of the American Philosophical Society*, **107** (1963), 528–535; and B. L. van der Waerden, *Science Awakening*, Arnold Dresden, trans. (Groningen, 1954).

JAMES LONGRIGG

THAN, KÁROLY (*b.* Óbecse, Hungary [now Bečej, Yugoslavia], 20 December 1834; *d.* Budapest, Hungary, 5 July 1908), *chemistry.*

Than was the third son of János Than, an estate manager, and Ottilia Petény; his elder brother, Mór Than, became a well-known painter. He attended several secondary schools, but interrupted his education in 1849, when he was fifteen, to enlist in the Hungarian army during the Hungarian war of independence. At the end of the war, later that same year, he returned home to find his family ruined financially; he therefore worked in a number of pharmacies while completing his secondary studies. A scholarship permitted him to study pharmacy at the University of Vienna, where he took the doctorate in 1858 under Redtenbacher, who engaged him as his personal assistant. Than then received a government subsidy which allowed him to undertake a long educational trip, during which he studied with Bunsen in Heidelberg and with Wurtz in Paris. In 1859 he returned to Vienna to work in Redtenbacher's laboratory.

By 1860 the political situation within the Austrian empire had changed to a degree that Hungarian could be reintroduced as the language of instruction in Hungarian universities. The incumbent professor of chemistry at the University of Budapest, the Austrian Theodor Wertheim, did not have full command of the language, and left to teach at Graz; in 1860 Than was called to replace him. Than also served as director of the chemistry laboratory, and built it into a significant institution. He was active in all the Hungarian scientific organizations, and was vice-president of the Hungarian Academy of Sciences.

Than's own research embraced many fields of chemistry. He introduced the use of potassium bicarbonate (1860) and potassium biiodate (Than's salt, 1890) as standard titrimetric substances in volumetric analysis, and suggested, even before the publication of Arrhenius' ionic theory, that analytical results be reported as carefully determined atom groupings, rather than according to their salts. He discovered carbonyl sulfide (1867), determined the precise vapor density of hydrochloric acid, defined the concept of the molecular volume of a gas (1887), and demonstrated that the anomalous vapor density of ammonium chloride is the result of the thermal dissociation of that compound. His two-volume textbook on general chemistry, *A kisérleti chemia elemei* (1897–1906), was one of the first works to be based on the concepts of physical chemistry.

In 1872 Than married Ervina Kleinschmidt; they had five children. He was created a baron in 1908, shortly before his death.

BIBLIOGRAPHY

I. ORIGINAL WORKS. *A kisérleti chemia elemei* ("Detailed Experimental Chemistry"), 2 vols. (Budapest, 1897–1906). For other publications, see Poggendorff, III, pt. 2, 1333; IV, pt. 2, 1487; V, 1248.

II. SECONDARY LITERATURE. The most complete biography is F. Szabadváry, *Than Károly* (Budapest, 1971), with complete list of Than's writings and a portrait. For discussions of Than and his work, see J. R. Partington, *A Textbook of Inorganic Chemistry*, 6th ed. (London, 1950), 115, 634; F. Szabadváry, *History of Analytical Chemistry* (Oxford, 1966), 252–254; Z. Szökefalvi-Nagy and F. Szabadváry, "Ein Vorschlag zur Darstellung der Analyseergebnisse in 'Ionenform' schon vor der Ausarbeitung der Ionentheorie," in *Talanta*, **13** (1966), 503–506.

F. SZABADVÁRY

THAXTER, ROLAND (*b.* Newtonville [part of Newton], Massachusetts, 28 August 1858; *d.* Cambridge, Massachusetts, 22 April 1932), *cryptogamic botany.*

Thaxter was the son of Levi Lincoln Thaxter and Celia Laighton. On his father's side he was descended from Thomas Thaxter, an Englishman who settled at Hingham, Massachusetts, in 1638. His mother established a considerable reputation in the field of literature by her poems; and his father also was active in literary studies, being an authority on the life and works of Browning. Thaxter attended Boston Latin School and entered Harvard in 1878, graduating with the A.B. in 1882 and the A.M. and Ph.D. in 1888. His chosen field of study was natural history. At the Harvard Graduate School of Arts and Sciences he was able to concentrate on cryptogamic botany under the direction of W. G. Farlow, and from 1886 to 1888 he served as the latter's assistant.

From 1888 to 1891 Thaxter was mycologist at the Connecticut Agricultural Experiment Station; but since his inclination was strongly toward pure, as opposed to applied, research, he was happy to return to Harvard in 1891, at Farlow's invitation, as assistant professor of cryptogamic botany. He became full professor in 1901 and assumed complete responsibility for teaching and research in that field. In 1919, on the death of Farlow, he was nominated professor emeritus and honorary curator of the cryptogamic herbarium, positions which he held until his death.

A Unitarian, Thaxter was married in 1887 to Mabel Gray Freeman of Springfield, Massachusetts, by whom he had four children. Despite poor health, he made several extended study journeys to the West Indies and southernmost South America. He was a member or fellow of numerous learned societies, both American and foreign, and was president of the Botanical Society of America in 1909.

Thaxter's published contributions in mycology were characterized by meticulous accuracy and are classics in their field. His name is associated chiefly with research on the little-known group of entomogenous fungi, which culminated in the publication of a five-volume monograph on the Laboulbeniaceae, a unique and isolated family of fungi that occur as minute parasites on the integuments of various insects; the numerous plates illustrating this treatise, exquisite in their execution, were all by Thaxter. He also published extensively on other groups of fungi, notably the Phycomycetes, and on the hitherto unrecognized assemblage of bacterialike organisms known as the Myxobacteriaceae.

Thaxter's work has had a profound and lasting influence on the development of mycology and of cryptogamic botany generally.

BIBLIOGRAPHY

Thaxter's principal work, *Contribution Towards a Monograph of the Laboulbeniaceae*, was published in 5 pts. by the American Academy of Arts and Sciences (1896–1931).

On his life and work, see the notice by G. P. Clinton, in *Biographical Memoirs. National Academy of Sci-*

ences, **17** (1937), 55–64, with comprehensive bibliography of Thaxter's publications between 1875 and 1931.

I. M. LAMB

THAYER, WILLIAM SYDNEY (*b.* Milton, Massachusetts, 23 June 1864; *d.* Washington, D.C., 10 December 1932), *medicine.*

Thayer, known as "Billy" to his friends and medical colleagues, was the eldest of four children of a prominent New England family. His father, James B. Thayer, was professor of law at Harvard; his mother, Sophia Ripley, was a granddaughter of Gamaliel Bradford and cousin of Ralph Waldo Emerson. His younger brother, Ezra, became dean of the Harvard Law School.

Thayer entered Harvard University at age sixteen, graduated with the B.A. and Phi Beta Kappa honors in 1885, and began medical studies at the Harvard Medical School the same fall. While there, he was particularly stimulated by the professor of pathology, Reginald Heber Fitz, the author of a classic study of appendicitis, who combined clinical and laboratory work, a model Thayer followed in his own career. After receiving his medical degree in 1889, Thayer continued his studies at the principal pathological laboratories of Berlin and Vienna. He returned to Boston in 1890; engaged in private practice very briefly; and later that year accepted a position as resident physician at the Johns Hopkins Hospital, opened the year before. Thayer was recommended for this position by a Harvard classmate, the surgeon J. M. T. Finney, who had preceded him to Baltimore.

At Hopkins, where Thayer spent his entire medical career except for wartime service, he immediately came under the influence and tutelage of William Osler, one of the most impressive and forceful medical teachers of his era. Thayer's solid grounding in the laboratory study of disease fitted well into the Hopkins system, for Osler himself had been a pathologist before turning to clinical medicine. Thayer did most of his important investigative work early in his Baltimore years. Using techniques such as blood staining, which he had learned from Paul Ehrlich in Germany, Thayer investigated a number of diseases and the blood cell's response to them.

The two most prevalent diseases that Thayer encountered in the wards of the Johns Hopkins Hospital when he began his duties were malaria and typhoid fever. Since Civil War days, diagnoses had been confused by the supposed existence of typhomalarial fever. Thayer, fresh from the German laboratories where Virchow, Ehrlich, and others stressed the importance of microscopic study of stained tissues, put these new techniques to good use in an extensive study of malaria in Baltimore. With a colleague from the medical clinic, John Hewetson, Thayer published *The Malarial Fevers of Baltimore* (1895), an analysis of 616 cases of proven malaria seen at the Hopkins in the first five years of the hospital's existence. Besides being an extensive review of the literature and a historical summary of the existing knowledge of malaria, the work clearly differentiated the characteristic fever cycles associated with the distinct species of malaria parasites. Two years later Thayer published *Lectures on the Malarial Fevers*, which quickly became one of the standard works on the subject. He chided his fellow American physicians for being "lamentably backward" in appreciating the advances that had been made since Laveran's discovery of the malaria parasite in 1880.

Under Osler's influence, Thayer slowly changed the emphasis of his work from the science of medicine to its art, from the laboratory to the bedside.

Upon Osler's departure for Oxford in 1905, Thayer was advanced to the position of professor of clinical medicine; but L. F. Barker was chosen to succeed Osler. Both men continued to work together amicably, however; and when Harvard offered Thayer a chair in 1912, he declined. He was a superb diagnostician and clinical teacher, always urging his students to make full use of their senses but not to neglect the laboratory aids to diagnosis. In the first two decades of the twentieth century, he wrote a number of important papers on aspects of cardiology, such as heart blocks, arteriosclerosis, cardiac murmurs, and the third heart sound. He also inspired a number of students and house officers in their work; many later became famous in their own right. For many years Thayer and the professor of pathology, W. G. MacCallum, conducted the clinicopathologic conference attended by most students and house officers.

In 1917, Thayer participated in the Red Cross mission to Russia to study health conditions and to determine what aid was necessary. The task was the more arduous because Thayer had to leave behind his ailing wife, Susan C. Thayer, who died while he was away. They had been married in 1902, and their only child had died in early infancy. Despite his personal anguish, Thayer continued to respond to what he felt was his duty. General Pershing made him director of general medicine for the A.E.F. in 1918. Thayer returned to Hopkins the following year, becoming professor of medicine and physician-in-chief to the Johns Hopkins Hospital. He was named professor emeritus in 1921, but continued his large consulting practice in the Baltimore-Washington area.

Thayer was known as a clinician's clinician, widely sought out for difficult diagnoses, and much respected for his teaching abilities. He was adept in the use of language, his own as well as French, German, and Russian, and urged his students to learn foreign languages. He was a literary man, widely read, and published a volume of poetry. He was known for his dapper dress and the ever-present flower in his lapel. Thayer's greatest influence, like that of Osler before him, was experienced by the many students who learned the art of medicine from him at the bedside. He received numerous foreign medals and citations and honorary degrees. He was also a member of the Board of Overseers of Harvard University.

BIBLIOGRAPHY

I. ORIGINAL WORKS. Thayer's bibliography includes nearly 180 articles on a great variety of clinical subjects. His three books on medical subjects deserve special notice: *The Malarial Fevers of Baltimore* (Baltimore, 1895), written with John Hewetson; *Lectures on Malarial Fevers* (New York, 1897); and *Osler and Other Papers* (Baltimore, 1931).

II. SECONDARY LITERATURE. The only book-length biography is Edith G. Reid, *The Life and Convictions of William Sydney Thayer* (London, 1936), a somewhat gushing portrayal but useful for Thayer the man. For Thayer the physician see especially "The Thayer Memorial Exercises . . .," in *Johns Hopkins Hospital Bulletin*, **55** (1934), 201–219. See also L. F. Barker, "William Sydney Thayer," in *Science*, **76** (1932), 617–619; and Henry M. Thomas, Jr., "Dr. Thayer," in *Johns Hopkins Hospital Bulletin*, **54** (1934), 211–215; and "William Sydney Thayer, Distinguished Physician and Teacher," *ibid.*, **109** (1961), 61–65. Three books not specifically about Thayer are nevertheless important sources: Alan Chesney, *The Johns Hopkins Hospital and the Johns Hopkins University School of Medicine*, I *1867–1893* (Baltimore, 1943), pp. 170–172; Harvey Cushing, *The Life of Sir William Osler*, 2 vols. (London, 1925), *passim*; and J. M. T. Finney, *A Surgeon's Life* (New York, 1940), 309–315.

GERT H. BRIEGER

THEAETETUS (*b.* Athens, *ca.* 417 B.C.; *d.* Athens, 369 B.C.), *mathematics*.

The son of Euphronius of Sunium, Theaetetus studied under Theodorus of Cyrene and at the Academy with Plato. Although no writing of his has survived, Theaetetus had a major influence in the development of Greek mathematics. His contributions to the theory of irrational quantities and the construction of the regular solids are particularly recorded; and he probably devised a general theory of proportion—applicable to incommensurable and to commensurable magnitudes—before the theory developed by Eudoxus and set out in book V of Euclid's *Elements*.

The *Suda* lexicon has two entries[1] under the name Theaetetus:

"Theaetetus, of Athens, astronomer, philosopher, disciple of Socrates, taught at Heraclea. He was the first to write on (or construct) the so-called five solids. He lived after the Peloponnesian war."

"Theaetetus, of Heraclea in Pontus, philosopher, a pupil of Plato."

Some have supposed that these notices refer to the same person, but it is more probable, as G. J. Allman[2] conjectures, that the second Theaetetus was a son or other relative of the first sent by him while teaching at Heraclea to study at the Academy in his native city.

Plato clearly regarded Theaetetus with a respect and admiration second only to that which he felt for Socrates. He made him a principal character in two dialogues, the eponymous *Theaetetus* and the *Sophist*; and it is from the former dialogue that what we know about the life of Theaetetus is chiefly derived.[3] In the dialogue Euclid of Megara gets a servant boy to read to his friend Terpsion a discussion between Socrates, Theodorus, and Theaetetus that Plato recorded soon after it took place on the day that Socrates faced his accusers, that is, in 399 B.C. Since Theaetetus is there referred to as a μειράκιον ("a youth"), it is implied that he was an adolescent, say eighteen years old, that is, he was born about 417 B.C.[4] His father, we are told, left a large fortune, which was squandered by trustees; but this did not prevent Theaetetus from being a liberal giver. Although Theaetetus was given the rare Greek compliment of being καλος τε καὶ ἀγαθός ("a thorough gentleman"), it was the beauty of his mind rather than of his body that impressed his compatriots; for, like Socrates, he had a snub nose and protruding eyes. Among the many young men with whom Theodorus had been acquainted, he had never found one so marvelously gifted; the lad's researches were like a stream of oil flowing without sound. Socrates predicted that Theaetetus would become notable if he came to full years. In the preface to the dialogue Euclid relates how he had just seen Theaetetus being carried in a dying condition from the camp at Corinth to Athens; not only had he been wounded in action, after acquitting himself gallantly, but he had contracted dysentery. This would be in the year 369 B.C., for the only other year in that century in which Athens and Corinth were at war, 394 B.C., would hardly allow time for Theaetetus' manifold accomplishments.[5]

The *Theaetetus* is devoted to the problem of knowledge; and the *Sophist*, apart from a method of definition, to the meaning of nonbeing. Although Theaetetus plays a major part in both discussions, there is no reason to think that he was a philosopher in the usual sense of the word. Plato merely used him as a vehicle for thoughts that he wanted expressed. That the two *Suda* passages use the term "philosopher" proves nothing, since the lexicon regularly calls mathematicians philosophers.[6]

In the summary of the early history of Greek geometry given by Proclus, and probably taken from Eudemus, Theaetetus is mentioned along with Leodamas of Thasos and Archytas of Tarentum as having increased theorems and made an advance toward a more scientific grouping,[7] the zeal for which is well shown in the mathematical passage that Plato introduces into the *Theaetetus*.[8] In this passage Theaetetus first relates how Theodorus demonstrated to him and the younger Socrates (a namesake of the philosopher) in each separate case that $\sqrt{3}, \sqrt{5} \cdots \sqrt{17}$ is a surd. He adds: "Since the number of roots[9] seemed to be infinite, it occurred to us to try to gather them together under one name by which we could call all the roots." Accordingly Theaetetus and the younger Socrates divided all numbers into two classes. A number that could be formed by multiplying equal factors they likened to a square and called "square and equilateral." The other numbers—which could not be formed by multiplying equal factors, but only a greater by a less, or a less by a greater—they likened to an oblong and called "oblong numbers." The lines forming the sides of equilateral numbers they called "lengths," and the lines forming oblong numbers they called "roots." "And similarly," concluded the Theaetetus of the dialogue, "for solids," which can only mean that they attempted a similar classification of cube roots.

The classification may now seem trivial, but the discovery of the irrational was a fairly recent matter[10] and involved a complete recasting of Greek mathematics; and Theaetetus was still only a young man. His more mature work on the sub-

ject is recorded in a commentary on the tenth book of Euclid's *Elements*, which has survived only in Arabic and is generally identified with the commentary that Pappus is known to have written. In the introduction to this commentary it is stated:[11]

> The aim of Book X of Euclid's treatise on the Elements is to investigate the commensurable and the incommensurable, the rational and irrational continuous quantities. This science had its origin in the school of Pythagoras, but underwent an important development at the hands of the Athenian, Theaetetus, who is justly admired for his natural aptitude in this as in other branches of mathematics. One of the most gifted of men, he patiently pursued the investigation of the truth contained in these branches of science, as Plato bears witness in the book which he called after him, and was in my opinion the chief means of establishing exact distinctions and irrefutable proofs with respect to the above-mentioned quantities. For although later the great Apollonius, whose genius for mathematics was of the highest possible order, added some remarkable species of these after much laborious application, it was nevertheless Theaetetus who distinguished the roots which are commensurable in length from those which are incommensurable, and who divided the more generally known irrational lines according to the different means, assigning the medial line to geometry, the binomial to arithmetic, and the apotome to harmony, as is stated by Eudemus the Peripatetic.

The last sentence gives the key to the achievement of Theaetetus in this field. He laid the foundation of the elaborate classification of irrationals, which is found in Euclid's tenth book; and in particular Theaetetus discovered, and presumably named, the medial, binomial, and apotome. The medial is formed by the product of two magnitudes, the binomial ("of two names") by the sum of two magnitudes, and the apotome (implying that something has been cut off) by the difference of two magnitudes. It is easy to see the correlation between the medial and the geometric mean, for the geometric mean between two irrational magnitudes,[12] a, b, is $\sqrt{ab}$ and is medial. It is also easy to see the correlation between the binomial and the arithmetic mean, for the arithmetic mean between a, b, is $(\frac{1}{2}a + \frac{1}{2}b)$; and this is a binomial. It is not so easy to see the connection between the apotome and the harmonic mean; but a clue is given in the second part of the work, where the commentator returns to the achievement of Theaetetus and observes that if the rectangle contained by two lines is a medial, and one of the sides is a binomial, the other side is an apotome. This in turn recalls Euclid,

Elements X.112, and amounts to saying that the harmonic mean between *a, b*, that is, $2ab/(a + b)$, can be expressed as

$$\frac{2ab}{a^2 - b^2} \cdot (a - b).$$

This leads to the question how much of Euclid's tenth book is due to Theaetetus. After a close examination, B. L. van der Waerden concluded that "The entire book is the work of Theaetetus."[13] There are several reasons, however, for preferring to believe that Theaetetus merely identified the medial, binomial, and apotome lines, correlating them with the three means, as the Arabic commentary says, and that the addition of ten other species of irrationals, making thirteen in all, or twenty-five when the binomials and apotomes are further subdivided, is the work of Euclid himself. A scholium to the fundamental proposition X.9 ("the squares on straight lines commensurable in length have to one another the ratio which a square number has to a square number . . .") runs as follows: "This theorem is the discovery of Theaetetus, and Plato recalls it in the *Theaetetus*, but there it is related to particular cases, here treated generally."[14] This would be a pointless remark if Theaetetus were the author of the whole book.

The careful distinction made in the "Eudemian summary" between Euclid's treatment of Eudoxus and Theaetetus is also relevant. Euclid, says the author, "put together the elements, arranging in order many of Eudoxus' theorems, perfecting many of Theaetetus', and bringing to irrefutable demonstration the things which had been only loosely proved by his predecessors."[15] The implication would seem to be that book V is almost entirely the discovery of Eudoxus save in its arrangement, but book X is partly due to Theaetetus and partly to Euclid himself. The strongest argument for believing that Theaetetus had an almost complete knowledge of the Euclidean theory of irrationals is that the correlation of the apotome with the harmonic mean implies a knowledge of book X.112; but it is relevant that the genuine text of Euclid probably stops at book X.111 with the list of the thirteen irrational straight lines.[16]

A related question is the extent to which the influence of Theaetetus can be seen in the arithmetical books of Euclid's *Elements*, VII–IX. Euclid X.9 depends on VIII.11 ("Between two square numbers there is one mean proportional number . . ."), and VIII.11 depends on VII.17 and VII.18 (in modern notation, $ab : ac = b : c$, and $a : b = ac : bc$). H. G. Zeuthen has argued[17] that these propositions are an inseparable part of a whole theory established in book VII and in the early part of book VIII, and that this theory must be due to Theaetetus with the object of laying a sound basis for his treatment of irrationals. It is clear, however, as T. L. Heath has pointed out,[18] that before Theaetetus both Hippocrates and Archytas must have known propositions and definitions corresponding to these in books VII and VIII; and there is no reason to abandon the traditional view that the Pythagoreans had a numerical theory of proportion that was taken over by Euclid in his arithmetical books. Theaetetus merely made use of an existing body of knowledge.

Theaetetus' work on irrationals is closely related to the two other main contributions to mathematics attributed to him. The only use made of book X in the subsequent books of Euclid's *Elements* is to express the sides of the regular solids inscribed in a sphere in terms of the diameter. In the case of the pyramid, the octahedron, and the cube, the length of the side is actually determined; in the case of the icosahedron, it is shown to be a minor; and in the case of the dodecahedron, to be an apotome. It is therefore significant that in the passage from the *Suda* lexicon (cited above) Theaetetus is credited as the first to "write upon" or "construct" the so-called five solids ($\pi\rho\hat{\omega}\tau o\varsigma$ $\delta\grave{\epsilon}$ $\tau\grave{\alpha}$ $\pi\acute{\epsilon}\nu\tau\epsilon$ $\kappa\alpha$-$\lambda o\acute{\nu}\mu\epsilon\nu\alpha$ $\sigma\tau\epsilon\rho\epsilon\grave{\alpha}$ $\acute{\epsilon}\gamma\rho\alpha\psi\epsilon$). It is also significant that at the end of the mathematical passage in the *Theaetetus* he says that he and his companion proceeded to deal with solids in the same way as with squares and oblongs in the plane. Probably on the authority of Theophrastus, Aëtius[19] attributed the discovery of the five regular solids to the Pythagoreans; and Proclus[20] actually attributes to Pythagoras himself the "putting together" ($\sigma\acute{\nu}\sigma\tau\alpha\sigma\iota\varsigma$) of the "cosmic figures." They are called "cosmic" because of Plato's use of them in the *Timaeus* to build the universe;[21] and no doubt the $\sigma\acute{\nu}\sigma\tau\alpha\sigma\iota\varsigma$ is to be understood as a "putting together" of triangles, squares, and pentagons in order to make solid angles as in that dialogue rather than in the sense of a formal construction. Theaetetus was probably the first to give a theoretical construction for all the five regular solids and to show how to inscribe them in a sphere. A scholium to Euclid, *Elements* XIII, actually attributes to Theaetetus rather than to the Pythagoreans the discovery of the octahedron and icosahedron.[22] On the surface this is puzzling, since the octahedron is a more elementary figure than the dodecahedron, which requires a knowledge of the pentagon; but many objects of dodecahedral form have been found from days much earlier than Pythagoras,[23] and the Pythagorean Hippasus is known to have written on "the construction of the sphere from the twelve pentagons."[24] (It would be in this work, if not earlier, that he would have encountered the irrational, and for his impiety in revealing it, he was drowned at sea.) If the Pythagoreans knew the dodecahedron, almost certainly they knew also the octahedron and probably the icosahedron; and the scholium quoted above may be discounted. The achievement of Theaetetus was to give a complete theoretical construction of all five regular solids such as we find in Euclid, *Elements* XIII; and Theaetetus must be regarded as the main source of the book, although Euclid no doubt arranged the materials in his own impeccable way and put the finishing touches.[25]

The theory of irrationals is also linked with that of proportionals. When the irrational was discovered, it involved a recasting of the Pythagorean theory of proportion, which depended on taking aliquot parts, and which consequently was applicable only to rational numbers, in a more general form applicable also to incommensurable magnitudes. Such a general theory was found by Eudoxus and is embodied in Euclid, *Elements* V. But in 1933[26] Oskar Becker gave a new interpretation of an obscure passage in Aristotle's *Topics*.[27] He suggested that the theory of proportion had already been recast in a highly ingenious form; and if so, the indication is that it was so recast by Eudoxus' older contemporary Theaetetus.

In the passage under discussion Aristotle observes that in mathematics some things are not easily proved for lack of a definition—for example, that a straight line parallel to two of the sides of a parallelogram divides the other two sides and the area in the same ratio; but if the definition is given, it becomes immediately clear, "for the areas have the same ἀνταναίρεσις as the sides, and this is the definition of the same ratio." What does the Greek word mean? The basic meaning is "a taking away," and the older commentators up to Heath

and the Oxford translation supposed that it meant "a taking away of the same fraction." In the figure *EF* is the straight line parallel to the sides *AB*, *DC* of the parallelogram *ABCD*, and *AE*, *BF* are the same parts of *AD*, *BC* respectively as the parallelogram *ABFE* is of the parallelogram *ABCD*. This would be in accordance with the Pythagorean theory of proportion, and the passage would contain nothing significant. But Becker drew attention to the comment by Alexander of Aphrodisia[28] on this passage; he uses the word ἀνθυφαίρεσις and observes that this is what Aristotle means by ἀνταναίρεσις. This might not in itself prove very much—the meaning could still be much the same—if it were not, as Becker also noted, that Euclid, although he does not employ the noun ἀνθυφαίρεσις, does in four places[29] use the verb, ἀνθυφαιρεῖν, and—this is the really significant fact—uses it to describe the process of finding the greatest common measure between two magnitudes. In this process the lesser magnitude is subtracted from the greater as many times as possible until a magnitude smaller than itself is left, and then the difference is subtracted as many times as possible from the lesser until a difference smaller than itself is left, and so on continually (ἀνθυφαιρουμένου δὲ ἀεὶ τοῦ ἐλάσσονος ἀπὸ τοῦ μείζονος). In the case of commensurable magnitudes the process comes to an end after a finite number of steps, but in the case of incommensurable magnitudes the process never comes to an end. A mathematician as acute as Theaetetus would realize that this could be made a test of commensurability (as it is in Euclid, *Elements* X.2) and that by adopting a definition of proportion based on this test he could have a theory of proportion applicable to commensurable no less than incommensurable magnitudes.[30]

It is possible that such a general theory was evolved before Eudoxus by some person other than Theaetetus, but in view of Theaetetus' known competence and his interest in irrationals, he is the most likely author. The attribution becomes even more credible if Zeuthen's explanation of how Theodorus proved the square roots of $\sqrt{3}$, $\sqrt{5}$ . . . $\sqrt{17}$ to be irrational is accepted (see the article on Theodorus of Cyrene); for according to his conjecture Theodorus used this method in each particular case, and Theodorus was the teacher of Theaetetus. Although there is no direct evidence that Theaetetus worked out such a pre-Eudoxan theory of proportion, the presumption in favor is strong; and it has convinced all recent commentators.

It is not known whether Theaetetus made any

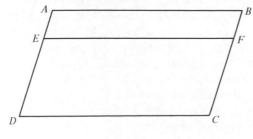

FIGURE 1

discoveries outside these three fields. In the "Eudemian summary" Proclus says:[31] "Hermotimus of Colophon advanced farther the investigations begun by Eudoxus and Theaetetus; he discovered many propositions in the elements and compiled some portion of the theory of loci." While it is clear that Theaetetus studied mathematics under Theodorus, it is uncertain whether he did so at Cyrene or at Athens. It may be accepted that at some time he taught in Heraclea, and he may have been the teacher of Heraclides Ponticus.[32]

NOTES

1. *Suda Lexicon*, Ada Adler, ed., I, pt. 2 (Leipzig, 1931), Θ 93 and 94, p. 689.6–9.
2. G. J. Allman, "Theaetetus," in *Hermathena*, 6 (1887), 269–278, repr. in *Greek Geometry From Thales to Euclid* (London–Dublin, 1889), 206–215.
3. Plato, *Theaetetus*, *Platonis opera*, J. Burnet, ed., I (Oxford, 1899), 142a–148b; Plato, Loeb Classical Library, H. N. Fowler, ed., VII (London–Cambridge, Mass., 1921; repr. 1967), 6.1–27.24.
4. The birth of Theaetetus has usually been placed in 415 B.C., or even as late as 413, which would make him not more than sixteen years old in 399; but the instances given in H. G. Liddell, R. Scott, and H. Stuart Jones, *A Greek-English Lexicon* (Oxford, 1940), *s.vv.* μειράκιον and ἔφηβος, show clearly that a μειράκιον would not be younger than eighteen and might be nearly as old as twenty-one. A sentence in the *Chronicle* of Eusebius–preserved in the Armenian and in Jerome's Latin version–*Sancti Hieronymi interpretatio chronicae Eusebii Pamphili*, in *Patrologia Latina*, J.-P. Migne, ed., vol. XXVII = S. Hieronymi, vol. VIII (Paris, 1846), cols. 453–454–which would place the central point of Theaetetus' activity in the third year of the 85th Olympiad (438 B.C.)–must be dismissed as an error. Eusebius' statement is repeated by George Syncellus, *Corpus scriptorum historiae Byzantinae*, B. G. Niebuhr, ed., pt. 7.1; *Georgius Syncellus et Nicephorus*, G. Dindorff, ed., I (Bonn, 1829), p. 471.9.
5. It is one of Eva Sachs's principal achievements in her pioneering inaugural dissertation, *De Theaeteto Atheniensi mathematico* (Berlin, 1914), 16–40, to have established this point irrefutably against E. Zeller and others.
6. But Malcolm S. Brown, "Theaetetus: Knowledge as Continued Learning," in *Journal of the History of Philosophy*, 7 (1969), 359, maintains that Theaetetus "influenced both the course of mathematics and that of philosophy." Brown quotes Sachs, *op. cit.*, p. 69, in support: "Ille re vera philosophus fuit perfectus"; but it is doubtful if Sachs meant the Latin word to imply that Theaetetus was a metaphysician. Brown seizes on the statement of Theaetetus at the beginning of his conversation with Socrates: "When I make a mistake you will correct me" (*Theaetetus*, 146c.). Brown sees in the mathematical work of Theaetetus a process of successive approximations, which can be construed as "containing errors which are being corrected." He holds also that there is an epistemological analogue, "a well-directed discussion of opinions which, even if unsuccessful in arriving at a final answer, would nevertheless permit of an improvement (even an indefinite improvement) of opinion"; and he believes that in this dialogue at least Plato yielded somewhat to the suggestion of Theaetetus that "knowledge is continued learning" (p. 379).
7. Proclus, *In primum Euclidis*, G. Friedlein, ed. (Leipzig, 1873; repr., Hildesheim, 1967), p. 66.14–18; English trans., Glenn R. Morrow, *Proclus: A Commentary on the First Book of Euclid's Elements* (Princeton, 1970), p. 54.11–14.
8. Plato, *Theaetetus*, *Platonis opera*, J. Burnet, ed., I (Oxford, 1899), 147c–148b; Plato, Loeb Classical Library, H. N. Fowler, ed., VII (London–Cambridge, Mass., 1921; repr., 1967), pp. 24.9–27.24.
9. The Greek word is δυνάμεις, which at a latter date could only mean "squares"; but here its meaning would appear to be "roots," and we can only suppose that at this early stage in Greek mathematics the terminology had not become fixed. It is not necessary with Paul Tannery ("Sur la langue mathématique de Platon," in *Annales de la Faculté des lettres de Bordeaux*, 1 [1884], 96, repr. in *Mémoires scientifiques*, 2 [1912], 92) to alter δύναμις without any MS authority to δυναμένη, the later technical expression for a square root. For a very full discussion of a different interpretation, See Árpád Szabó, *Anfänge der griechischen Mathematik* (Munich–Vienna, 1969), 14–22, 43–57. Szabó holds that δύναμις means *Quadratwert eines Rechtecks* ("square value of a rectangle"), that is, the square equivalent in area to a rectangle. This interpretation has attractions, for the fact that Plato categorically describes δυνάμεις as γραμμαί, "lines," and sets δύναμις in opposition to μῆκος, a rational length, seems fatal to it. But Szabó establishes that δύναμις cannot be power in general.
10. But not so recently as the time of Plato himself. Even if the Athenian stranger in the *Laws* is identified with Plato, it is reading too much into his words αὐτὸς ἀκούσας ὀψέ ποτε τὸ περὶ ταῦτα ἡμῶν πάθος (819d 5–6) to suppose that the irrational was not discovered until the fourth century B.C. Likewise the statement in the "Eudemian summary," in Proclus, *op. cit.*, p. 65.19–21, that Pythagoras "discovered the matter of the irrationals" (τὴν τῶν ἀλόγων πραγματείαν . . . ἀνεῦρεν) must be wrong, and there is almost certainly a textual error–ἀλόγων for ἀναλόγων ("proportionals"). The existence of irrational magnitudes was almost certainly discovered, as Greek tradition asserted, by Hippasus of Metapontum in the middle of the fifth century B.C. The best discussion of the date is Kurt von Fritz, "The Discovery of Incommensurability by Hippasus of Metapontum," in *Studies in Presocratic Philosophy*, David J. Furley and R. E. Allen, eds., I (London–New York, 1970), 382–412. For an attempt to show that the discovery was made in the closing years of the fifth century, see Eric Frank, *Platon und die sogennanten Pythagoreer* (Halle, 1923). Árpád Szabó, *op. cit.*, pp. 60–69, 111–118, 238, seeks to show that the irrational was discovered in the study of mean proportionals as opposed to the prevailing theory that it arose from the study of diagonals of squares after the discovery of "Pythagoras' theorem."
11. The translation is based in the main on that of William Thomson, in William Thomson and Gustav Junge, *The Commentary of Pappus on Book X of Euclid's Elements* (Cambridge, Mass., 1930; repr., New York, 1968), 63; but his "powers" (that is, the squares), although a faithful rendering of the Arabic, has been modified, since "roots" appears to be the meaning. The ambiguity of the Greek δύναμις, before the terminology became fixed, is reflected in the Arabic.
12. It would be going beyond the evidence to attribute to Theaetetus the Euclidean notion (X, *Definition* 3) that a straight line may be rational but commensurable only in square with a rational straight line; that is, that if r is a rational straight line and m, n integers with m/n in its lowest terms not a square, then $\sqrt{m/n} \cdot r$ is rational. T. L. Heath observes, "It would appear that Euclid's terminology here differed as much from that of his predecessors as it does from ours," and he aptly cites the expression of Plato (following the Pythagoreans), in the *Republic* 546c 4–5: ἄρρητος διάμετρος τοῦ πεμπάδος ("the irrational diameter of five") for the diagonal of a square of side five units; that is,

for Plato, and presumably for Theaetetus, as for us, $\sqrt{50}$ is irrational, whereas Euclid would have called it "rational but commensurable in square only." Eva Sachs takes a contrary view, *Die fünf platonischen Körper*, p. 105, but without satisfactory reasons.

13. B. L. van der Waerden, *Science Awakening*, 2nd ed. (Groningen, 1956[?]), p. 172. In full, he writes: "Has the same Theaetetus who studied the medial, the binomial and the apotome, also defined and investigated the ten other irrationalities, or were those introduced later on? It seems to me that all of this is the work of one mathematician. For, the study of the 13 irrationalities is a unit. The same fundamental idea prevails throughout the book, the same methods of proof are applied in all cases. Propositions X.17 and 18 concerning the measurability of the roots of a quadratic equation precede the introduction of binomial and apotome, but these are not used until the higher irrationalities appear on the scene. The theory of the binomial and the apotome is almost inextricably interwoven with that of the 10 higher irrationals. Hence—the entire book is the work of Theaetetus." The conclusion does not follow. The unity may be due to Euclid himself, using some propositions already proved, adding refinements of his own, and welding the whole into one, as Proclus testifies. The division of irrationals into medial, binomial, and apotome can perfectly well be separated from the subdivisions into more complex irrationals. If it were true that X.17 and 18 are not used until after the introduction of the binomial and the apotome, this would prove nothing since they are in their correct logical position; and for that matter, the whole of book X is not used again until book XIII; but, in fact, X.18 is used in X.33, whereas the binomial is not introduced until X.36 and the apotome until X.73.

14. *Euclidis opera omnia*, J. L. Heiberg and H. Menge, eds., V (Leipzig, 1888), Scholium 62 in Elementorum Librum X, p. 450.16–18. There is good reason to believe that the scholiast is Proclus. See H. Knoche, *Untersuchungen über die neu aufgefundenen Scholien des Proklus Diadochus zu Euclids Elementen* (Herford, 1865), p. 24; and J. L. Heiberg, "Paralipomena zu Euclid," in *Hermes*, **38** (1903), p. 341.

15. Proclus, *op. cit.*, p. 68.7–10; Eng. trans. *op. cit.*, p. 56.19–23.

16. J. L. Heiberg gives conclusive reasons for bracketing propositions 112–115, in *Euclidis opera omnia*, J. L. Heiberg and H. Menge, eds., V, p. lxxxv, and concludes: "non dubito, quin hae quoque propositiones 112–115 e doctrina Apollonii promptae sint; nam antiquae sunt et bonae, hoc saltim constare putaverim, eas ab Euclide scriptas non esse."

17. H. G. Zeuthen, "Sur la constitution des livres arithmétiques des Eléments d'Euclide et leur rapport à la question de l'irrationalité," in *Oversigt over det Kongelige Danske Videnskabernes Selskabs Forhandlinger* (1910), 395–435.

18. Thomas Heath, *A History of Greek Mathematics*, I (Oxford, 1921), 211.

19. Aëtius, *Placita*, II, 6, 5, in H. Diels, *Doxographi Graeci* (Berlin, 1879), p. 334; and *Die Fragmente der Vorsokratiker*, H. Diels and W. Kranz, eds., 6th ed., I (Dublin–Zurich, 1951; repr., 1969), p. 403.8–12.

20. Proclus, *op. cit.*, p. 65.20–21; Eng. trans., *op. cit.*, p. 53.5. Morrow translates the Greek word as "structure."

21. Plato, *Timaeus* 53c–55c; *Platonis opera*, J. Burnet, ed., IV (Oxford, 1915); Loeb Classical Library, *Plato, Timaeus etc.*, R. G. Bury, ed. (London–Cambridge, Mass., 1929; repr., 1966), pp. 126.16–134.4.

22. *Euclidis opera omnia*, J. L. Heiberg and H. Menge, eds., V (Leipzig, 1888), Scholium 1 in Elementorum Librum XIII, p. 654.1–10.

23. One, discovered in 1885 at Monte Loffa in the Colli Euganei near Padua, of Etruscan origin, is dated between 1000 and 500 B.C. (F. Lindemann, "Zur Geschichte der Polyeder

24. und der Zahlzeichen," in *Sitzungsberichte der Bayerischen Akademie der Wissenschaften zu München*, **26** (1897), 725.

24. Iamblichus, *De communi mathematica scientia* 25, N. Festa, ed. (Leipzig, 1891), 77.18–21; *De vita Pythagorica* 18.88, A. Nauck, ed. (Leipzig, 1884; repr., 1965).

25. In the course of a full discussion Eva Sachs, in *Die fünf platonischen Körper* (Berlin, 1917), asserts (p. 105) that the construction of the five solids in Euclid, *Elements*, XIII, 13–17, springs from Theaetetus. She approves H. Vogt, in *Bibliotheca mathematica*, **9**, 3rd ser. (1908–1909), p. 47, for controverting Paul Tannery, *La géométrie Grecque* (Paris, 1887), p. 101, who would ascribe the construction of the five solids to the Pythagoreans while leaving to Theaetetus the calculation of the relation of the sides to the radius of the circumscribing sphere: for how, she and Vogt ask, can the exact construction be accomplished without a prior knowledge of this relation? The question how much of Euclid's book XIII is due to Theaetetus is bound up with the difficult question how much, if any, is due to the Aristaeus who is mentioned by Hypsicles in the so-called *Elements*, Book XIV, J. L. Heiberg and H. Menge, eds., vol. V, p. 6.22–23, as the author of a book entitled *Comparison of the Five Figures*, and whether this Aristaeus is to be identified with Aristaeus the Elder, author of a formative book on solid loci, that is, conics. T. L. Heath, in *The Thirteen Books of Euclid's Elements*, III (Cambridge, 1908; 2nd ed., 1925; repr., New York, 1956), p. 439, following C. A. Bretschneider, *Die Geometrie und die Geometer vor Eukleides* (Leipzig, 1870), p. 171, took the view that "as Aristaeus's work was the newest and latest in which, before Euclid's time, this subject was treated, we have in Euclid XIII at least a partial recapitulation of the contents of the treatise of Aristaeus"; but Eva Sachs, *op. cit.*, p. 107, denies this conclusion.

26. Oskar Becker, "Eudoxos Studien I: Eine voreudoxische Proportionenlehre und ihre Spuren bei Aristoteles und Euklid," in *Quellen und Studien zur Geschichte der Mathematik, Astronomie und Physik*, **2B** (1933), 311–333. To some extent the theory had already been adumbrated independently by H. G. Zeuthen, "Hvorledes Mathematiken i Tiden fra Platon til Euklid," in *Kongelige Danske VidenskaberNes Selskabs Skrifter*, **5** (1915), 108, and E. J. Dijksterhuis, *De Elementen van Euclides, I* (Groningen, 1929), 71, as Becker himself recognizes in *Das mathematischen Denken der Antike* (Göttingen, 1957), p. 103, n. 25. Becker failed to convince T. L. Heath, *Mathematics in Aristotle* (Oxford, 1949; repr., 1970), 80–83, who in the absence of confirmatory evidence could "only regard Becker's article as a highly interesting speculation" (p. 83). It has also been criticized by K. Reidemeister, *Das exakte Denken der Griechen* (Hamburg, 1949), p. 22, and by Árpád Szabó, "Ein Beleg fur die voreudoxische Proportionlehre?" in *Archiv für Begriffsgeschichte*, **9** (1964), 151–171, and in his *Anfänge der griechischen Mathematik* (Munich–Vienna), 134–135, 180–181. The theory received support, however, from a Leiden dissertation by E. B. Plooij, *Euclid's Conception of Ratio as Criticized by Arabian Commentators* (Rotterdam, 1950). Becker rejected the criticisms in *Archiv für Begriffsgeschichte*, **4** (1959), p. 223, and adhered to his theory in his book *Grundlagen der Mathematik in geschichtlicher Entwicklung* (Bonn, 1954; 2nd ed., 1964). His theory has been wholeheartedly endorsed by B. L. van der Waerden, *Science Awakening*, 2nd ed. (Groningen, 1956 [?]), 175–179; by Kurt von Fritz in "The Discovery of Incommensurability by Hippasus of Metapontum," in *Studies in Presocratic Philosophy*, David J. Furley and R. E. Allen, eds., I (London–New York, 1970), 408–410, esp. note 87; but his statement that Heath "still called the definition 'metaphysical' " is unfair, since Heath said it was " 'metaphysical' (as Barrow would say)," and in any case this was in *The Thirteen Books of Euclid's Elements*, II (Cambridge, 1908; 2nd ed., 1925; repr., New

York, 1956), p. 121, written before Becker's theory was enunciated; by Malcolm S. Brown, *op. cit.*, pp. 363–364; and by Wilbur Knorr, *The Evolution of the Euclidean Elements* (Dordrecht, 1975).

27. Aristotle, *Topics* VIII.3, 158B 29–159A 1.

28. Alexander of Aphrodisias, *Commentarium in Topica*, Strache and Wallies, eds., in *Commentaria in Aristotelem Graeca*, II (Berlin, 1891), 545.12–17.

29. Euclid, *Elements*, VII.1, VII.2, X.2, and X.3, J. L. Heiberg. ed., II (Leipzig, 1884), 188.13–15, 192.6–7; III (Leipzig, 1886), 12–14, 10.4–5; E. S. Stamatis, ed. (post J. L. Heiberg), II (Leipzig, 1970), 105.8–9, 107.3–4; III (Leipzig, 1972), 3.19–20, 5.8–9.

30. The Arabian commentator al-Māhānī (*fl. ca.* 860), followed by al-Nayrīzī (*fl. ca.* 897), dissatisfied with Euclid's definition, worked out for himself an "anthyphairetic" definition, as was recognized by E. B. Plooij, *op. cit.* For al-Nayrīzī, see *Anaritii in decem libros priores Elementorum Euclidis ex interpretatione Gherardi Cremonensis*, M. Curtze, ed., in *Euclidis opera omnia*, J. L. Heiberg and H. Menge, eds., *Supplementum*, pp. 157–160.

31. Proclus, *op. cit.*, p. 67.20–23; English trans., *op. cit.*, p. 56.9–12.

32. Eva Sachs, *De Theaeteto Atheniensi Mathematico*, p. 64, following Ulrich von Wilamowitz-Moellendorf.

BIBLIOGRAPHY

No original writing by Theaetetus has survived, even in quotation, although his work is undoubtedly embedded in Euclid, *Elements*, X and XIII.

Secondary literature includes G. J. Allman, "Theaetetus," in *Hermathena*, 6 (1887), 269–278, repr. in *Greek Geometry From Thales to Euclid* (London–Dublin, 1889), 206–215; Oskar Becker, "Eudoxos Studien I: Eine voreudoxische Proportionenlehre und ihre Spuren bei Aristoteles und Euklid," in *Quellen und Studien zur Geschichte der Mathematik, Astronomie und Physik*, **2B** (1933), 311–333; *ibid.*, **3B** (1934), 533–553, repr. in O. Becker, ed., *Zur Geschichte der griechischen Mathematik* (Darmstadt, 1965); in *Archiv für Begriffsgeschichte*, **4** (1959), 223; and in *Grundlagen der Mathematik in geschichtlicher Entwicklung* (Bonn, 1954; 2nd ed., 1964), 78–87; Malcolm S. Brown, "Theaetetus: Knowledge as Continued Learning," in *Journal of the History of Philosophy*, **7** (1969), 359–379; Kurt von Fritz, "The Discovery of Incommensurability by Hippasus of Metapontum," in *Annals of Mathematics*, **46** (1945), 242–264; "Platon, Theaet und die antike Mathematik," in *Philologus*, **87** (1932), 40–62, 136–178; and David J. Furley and R. E. Allen, eds., "The Discovery of Incommensurability by Hippasus of Metapontum," in *Studies in Presocratic Philosophy* I (London–New York, 1970), 382–412.

See also Thomas Heath, *A History of Greek Mathematics*, I (Oxford, 1921), 203–204, 209–212; Pauly-Wissowa, *Real-Encyclopädie der classischen Altertumswissenschaft*, 2nd ser., V, cols. 1351–1372; Eva Sachs, *De Theaeteto Atheniensi mathematico* (Inaugural diss., Berlin, 1914): *Die fünf platonischen Körper* (Berlin, 1917), 88–119; Árpád Szabó, "Ein Beleg für die voreudoxische Proportionenlehre?" in *Archiv für Begriffsgeschichte*, **9** (1964), 151–171; "Die Fruhge-

schichte der Theorie der Irrationalitaten," in *Anfänge der griechischen Mathematik*, pt. 1 (Munich–Vienna, 1969), 38–130; "Die voreuklidische Proportionlehre," *ibid.*, pt. 2, pp. 131–242; Heinrich Vogt, "Die Entdeckungsgeschichte des Irrationalen nach Plato und anderen Quellen des 4. Jahrhunderts," in *Bibliotheca mathematica*, 3 ser., **10** (1909–1910), 97–155; "Zur Entdeckungsgeschichte des Irrationalen," *ibid.*, **14** (1913–1914), 9–29; B. L. van der Waerden, *Ontwakende Wetenschap* (Groningen, 1950), also in English, Arnold Dresden, trans., *Science Awakening* (Groningen, 1954; 2nd ed., [?], 1956), 165–179; A. Wasserstein, "Theaetetus and the History of the Theory of Numbers," in *Classical Quarterly*, n.s. **8** (1958), 165–179; H. G. Zeuthen, "Notes sur l'histoire des mathématiques VIII; Sur la constitution des livres arithmétiques des Eléments d'Euclide et leur rapport à la question de l'irrationalité," in *Oversigt over det Kongelige Danske Videnskabernes Selskabs Forhandlinger* (1910), 395–435; "Sur les connaissances géométriques des Grecs avant la reforme platonicienne de la géométrie," *ibid.* (1913), 431–473; and "Sur l'origine historique de la connaissance des quantités irrationelles," *ibid.* (1915), 333–362; and Wilbur Knorr, *The Evolution of the Euclidean Elements* (Dordrecht, 1975), chs. 7, 8.

See also the Bibliography of the article on Theodorus of Cyrene.

IVOR BULMER-THOMAS

THEGE, MIKLÓS VON KONKOLY. See **Konkoly Thege, Miklós von.**

THEMISTIUS (*b.* Paphlagonia, A.D. 317 [?]; *d.* Constantinople, *ca.* 388), *philosophy, politics.*

Themistius is one of the most interesting representatives of the late Peripatetic school, being at the same time an outstanding Aristotelian scholar, a teacher of philosophy, an eloquent speaker, and an influential politician and diplomat. Some of his ideas are still vital, especially his doctrine of toleration and universal philanthropy. He was born about 320 (presumably in 317) in Paphlagonia, the country of his parents.[1] His father, Eugenius, was a teacher of philosophy, concerned mainly with Aristotle but also with Pythagoras, Plato, Zeno of Citium, and Epicurus. Themistius attended his father's lectures, probably at Constantinople.[2] He himself began teaching philosophy in 345.

As a philosopher Themistius followed in the footsteps of his father, adhering mainly to Aristotle without disregarding Plato. His definition of philosophy as a constant attempt to imitate God, so far as it is possible for man to do so, comes primarily from Plato's *Theaetetus*. His chief philosophical concern was not with logic or metaphysics but with ethics. The teaching of Themistius was very influential,[3] and many students came to Constantinople to attend his lectures. Aiming at the complete education of his students, he provided not only theoretical instruction but also practical preparation for the moral life. He wanted to make Aristotle understandable to everyone, not by an ordinary commentary, but by paraphrasing the texts of the Stagirite and summarizing the philosophical content. In connection with his lecturing, Themistius arranged meetings with the students and discussed particular problems with them. Presumably his paraphrases of Aristotle, as well as his commentaries on Plato, were written between 345 and 355. The paraphrases include the following: that of the *Posterior Analytics*, translated from Arabic into Latin by Gerard of Cremona; of the *Prior Analytics*, not preserved; of the *Physics*; of the *De anima*, translated into Latin by William of Moerbeke (22 November 1267); of the *De caelo* and the twelfth book of the *Metaphysics*, both preserved only in a Hebrew translation; and of the *Categories, Topics, De sensu, De generatione et corruptione*, and possibly of the *Nicomachean Ethics*, none of which has been preserved. The paraphrase of the *Parva naturalia*, attributed to Themistius, was written by Sophonias. None of the commentaries on Plato has been preserved. Many of the paraphrases were translated into Arabic: Themistius was frequently used and quoted by medieval Arabic philosophers. He also wrote some philosophical treatises: Περὶ ἀρετῆς, which has been preserved in a Syrian translation only, and Περὶ ψυχῆς, which is known through some fragments quoted by Stobaeus.[4] The Περὶ γήρως attributed to him is not authentic.

Themistius' political career started in 355, when he was appointed senator on 1 September. The Emperor Valens entrusted him with the education of his son; and Themistius was also appointed the tutor of Arcadius, the son of Theodosius I. He had close relations with the Emperor Julian, who with his help endeavored to revive the ancient Hellenic religion, although he intended to be tolerant toward the Christians. In 383–384 Themistius was *praefectus urbis* and *princeps senatus*. His speeches are closely connected with his political career: thirty-one of them have been completely preserved, two almost completely (*Orationes* XXIII, XXXIII), four are known only through fragments, and the content of three may be reconstructed— the Περὶ ἀρετῆς, his speech on toleration, and his "Epistula ad Julianum." The favorite topics of his speeches are philanthropy, liberty of conscience, the relation between politics and philosophy, the duties of the state, and the ideal of the statesman. The text of *Oratio* XII, entitled "De religionibus" and addressed to the Emperor Valens, is not authentic in the Dindorf edition: it was written by Andreas Dudith (1533–1589) of Breslau. As for *Oratio* XXVI, H. Kesters maintains that it was borrowed entirely from Antisthenes with only minor stylistic modifications.[5] Gregory of Nazianzus called Themistius his friend and praised him as the king of eloquence. Yet Themistius made no effort in his writings to be original, clinging always to classical thought and ancient wisdom, and remaining faithful to the traditional Hellenic religion.

NOTES

1. *Orationes*, Dindorf ed., II.33.28.
2. *Ibid.*, XX.295.3 ff.; XXXIV.460.18; XVII, 261.11–14.
3. See *ibid.*, "Oratio Constantii," 23.31–24.4.
4. Stobaeus, Wachmuth and Hense, eds., III, 468, IV, 530, and V, 1032, 1086–1092.
5. H. Kesters, *Plaidoyer d'un Socratique contre le Phèdre de Platon* (Louvain–Paris, 1959).

BIBLIOGRAPHY

I. ORIGINAL WORKS. Themistius' paraphrases are in *Commentaria in Aristotelem Graeca*, as follows: *In libros Aristotelis De anima paraphrasis*, R. Heinze, ed., V, pt. 3 (Berlin, 1899); *Analyticorum posteriorum paraphrasis*, M. Wallies, ed., V. pt. 1 (Berlin, 1900); *In Aristotelis Physica paraphrasis*, H. Schenkl, ed., V, pt. 2 (Berlin, 1900); *In libros Aristotelis De caelo paraphrasis hebraice et latine*, S. Landauer, ed., V, pt. 4 (Berlin, 1902); and *In Aristotelis Metaphysicorum librum* Λ *paraphrasis hebraice et latine*, S. Landauer, ed., V, pt. 5 (Berlin, 1903).

The *Orationes* have been edited by W. Dindorf (Leipzig, 1832; repr. Hildesheim, 1961) and by H. Schenkl, completed by G. Downey (Leipzig, 1965–   ).

Medieval versions in Latin are *Commentaire sur le traité de l'âme d'Aristote, traduction de Guillaume de Moerbeke*, critical ed. by G. Verbeke (Louvain–Paris, 1957; repr., Leiden, 1973); and "Paraphrasis of the *Posterior Analytics* in Gerard of Cremona's Translation," J. R. O'Donnell, ed., in *Mediaeval Studies* (Toronto), **20** (1958), 239–315.

II. SECONDARY LITERATURE. See G. Downey, "Education and Public Problems as Seen by Themistius," in *Transactions and Proceedings of the American Philological Association*, **86** (1955), 291–307; "Education in the Christian Roman Empire. Christian and Pagan Theories Under Constantine and His Successors," in *Speculum*, **32** (1957), 48–61; and "Themistius and the Defence of Hellenism in the Fourth Century," in *Harvard Theological Review*, **50** (1957), 259–274; W. Stegemann, "Themistios," in Pauly-Wissowa, *Real-Ency-*

clopädie der classischen Altertumswissenschaft, 2nd ser., V, pt. 2 (1934), cols. 1642–1680; and G. Verbeke, "Themistius et le *De unitate intellectus* de saint Thomas," in *Revue philosophique de Louvain*, **53** (1955), 141–164.

G. VERBEKE

THENARD, LOUIS JACQUES (*b.* La Louptière [now Louptière-Thenard], Aube, France, 4 May 1777; *d.* Paris, France, 20 or 21 June 1857), *chemistry*.

Thenard was the second son of Étienne Amable Thenard and Cécile Savourat, peasant farmers, who had seven children. He received an elementary education from a local priest, and his obvious intelligence marked him out, so that at the age of eleven he was sent to the *collège* at Sens. He soon had the ambition to become a pharmacist and went to Paris with two friends to take advantage of the educational resources of the capital. Thenard attended the public courses of Vauquelin and Fourcroy and was taken into the Vauquelin household as a bottle washer and scullery boy. Vauquelin eventually allowed him to deputize for him in his lecture course; Thenard's first official appointment came in December 1798, when he was named demonstrator at the École Polytechnique.

When Vauquelin retired from his chair at the Collège de France, Thenard was nominated to succeed him (13 April 1804). Upon the founding in 1808 of the faculties of sciences, Thenard was appointed professor of chemistry at the Paris Faculty. With a secure income and a place in the new scientific-teaching community, he could think of marriage; and in 1814, after four years of negotiating with the family, he married the daughter of Arnould Humblot-Conté. Fourcroy's death in 1809 left a vacancy in the chemistry section of the First Class of the Institute, to which Thenard was elected (29 January 1810). He was a member of the Society of Arcueil and his work in this period (*ca.* 1807–1814) reveals the influence of his colleagues in that group, not least the physical approach of its leader, Berthollet.

Thenard was a lifelong member of the Société d'Encouragement pour l'Industrie Nationale; and when its founder, Chaptal, died in 1832, he was elected president. His interest in applied chemistry also meant that he played a prominent part in judging the national industrial exhibitions held in 1818 and at five-year intervals thereafter. He was also a member of the governing body of the Conservatoire National des Arts et Métiers.

Thenard was appointed dean of the Paris Faculty of Sciences in 1822. In 1830 he was nominated to the Royal Council of Public Instruction, on which he was especially concerned with the teaching of the physical sciences at the university level. From 1845 to 1852 he was chancellor of the University of France—the highest post in the French educational system.

Thenard was made successively a knight (1814), officer (1828), commander (1837), and grand officer (1842) of the Legion of Honor. In 1825 he was given the title of baron. In 1827 and in 1830 Thenard was elected to the Chamber of Deputies, his politics being to the right of center. On 11 October 1832 he was nominated as a peer; and in the upper chamber, as in the lower, his contributions to debates were usually on technical and scientific matters. He was particularly influential in his support of the sugar beet industry, which had begun in Napoleonic times and under the Restoration was threatened by the importation of cane sugar.

Thenard's early scientific work, particularly his interest in plant and animal chemistry, betrays the influence of his first patrons, Vauquelin and Fourcroy. In 1801 he obtained a new acid by distilling tallow. He called it sebacic acid and showed that what Guyton de Morveau had called sebacic acid was only impure acetic acid. Three years later he showed that the acid that Berthollet had named "zoonic acid" (obtained by distilling meat) was, again, really impure acetic acid. In his analysis of bile Thenard obtained a resin and another substance that he named "picromel," which was found to be a good solvent of fats.

His most important organic work was on the esters, then called "ethers." The name "ether" was given to any neutral product formed by the reaction of an acid with alcohol. The only "ether" that had been prepared and studied with any success prior to this time was "sulfuric ether"; but since it was what is now known as diethyl ether and not a true ester, knowledge of this compound tended to hinder rather than help the investigation of other "ethers." It was part of Thenard's achievement to distinguish "sulfuric ether" from the true esters. He made a careful study of the action of nitric, hydrochloric, acetic, benzoic, oxalic, citric, malic, and tartaric acids on ethyl alcohol and prepared the respective esters, many for the first time. His preparation of "nitric ether" (ethyl nitrite) is of value for his concern to obtain a pure product and to determine the yield.

Unknown to Thenard, "muriatic ether" (ethyl chloride) had been prepared slightly earlier by

Gehlen; but Thenard's memoir on this ester is notable for its study of the influence of time on chemical reactions involving organic compounds. He studied the reaction at room temperature between ethyl chloride and a concentrated solution of caustic potash over a period of three months, testing for the decomposition of the ester with silver nitrate solution.

Thenard's quantitative study of "acetic ether" (ethyl acetate) may be regarded as a model for its time. He studied both its preparation (in the presence of concentrated sulfuric acid) and its hydrolysis, always referring quantities of acid to equivalent weights of potash. By distilling the ester with an aqueous solution of caustic potash, he obtained alcohol and potassium acetate. Thenard thus proved conclusively by both analysis and synthesis that the "acetic ether" was a simple compound of acetic acid and alcohol, a valuable datum for organic chemistry. Thenard made the important statement that when alcohol combines with vegetable or mineral acid, the alcohol acts as a "true salifiable base."[1] Thus he drew an extremely useful analogy between the action of acids on bases to form salts in inorganic chemistry and the action of acids on alcohols to form esters in organic chemistry. This analogy was later extended by Chevreul in his study of saponification.

That Thenard was a worthy heir to the analytical skill of Vauquelin is shown by his early study of nickel (1802). He took particular care to obtain nickel free from traces of cobalt, iron, and arsenic. Typically, he announced the discovery of a new, higher oxide of nickel. It was, however, his study of certain cobalt compounds, published in 1804, that brought him greater fame. There was a particular need in France under the Consulate for a new blue pigment; and Thenard was commissioned by the minister of the interior, Chaptal, to obtain one. At one time lapis lazuli had been used, but it had become extremely rare and expensive. Prussian blue was not an effective substitute, and so Thenard experimented with cobalt arsenate, used in the coloration of Sèvres porcelain. He found that alumina heated in certain proportions with the arsenate or phosphate of cobalt produced the most permanent pigment. His final trials on the pigment included exposure to bright light for two months and exposure to acids, alkalies, and hydrogen sulfide. It became known as "Thenard's blue," although a similar color had been obtained earlier by K. F. Wenzel and Gahn. Thenard was helped in his research by the professor of drawing at the École Polytechnique, Léonor Mérimée, who later de-

veloped the use of hydrogen peroxide for restoring paintings.

An appreciable part of Thenard's research was concerned with the combining proportions of elements in certain compounds, particularly metal oxides. One of his earliest pieces of work was a report on the existence of six different oxides of antimony, which Proust reduced to two; the correct number (three) was determined later by Berzelius. Thenard announced the existence of four different oxides of cobalt and investigated the oxides and salts of mercury. He did research on the two sulfides of arsenic, realgar and orpiment, and showed that they contain no oxygen. In 1805 he published a memoir on the oxidation of metals in general. Thenard could not agree with Berthollet that oxidation of metals might take place in an indefinite number of stages, yet he believed that there were more different oxides of each metal than most chemists of the time were prepared to admit. He considered the solubility of different oxides in acids, making a particular study of iron and examining the oxidation of freshly precipitated ferrous hydroxide. Thenard established the existence of the unstable white ferrous oxide and thus helped to throw light on the chemistry of iron salts. He investigated phosphates of soda and ammonia, and analyzed phosphorous acid. His analysis of alloys of antimony and tin are a further reminder of his interest in combining proportions (he considered these alloys as compounds).

In 1812 Thenard obtained crystals of ammonium hydrosulfide by mixing ammonia gas and hydrogen sulfide. The proportions of the elements in another sulfide, hydrogen persulfide, had been studied by Berthollet; and Thenard later reexamined this problem. Believing that oxygen and sulfur were analogous elements and having discovered hydrogen peroxide, he considered that hydrogen persulfide was its analogue. He concluded that it varied in composition between extremes of "four atoms of sulfur and one atom of hydrogen sulfide" and "eight atoms of sulfur and one atom of hydrogen sulfide." The apparently variable composition helped to convince Thenard that it was a compound with a variable amount of physically dissolved sulfur. In the later editions of his *Traité* he presented both hydrogen peroxide and hydrogen persulfide as "compounds the elements of which obey forces other than affinity."

Thenard soon acquired a reputation as an analyst and thereby met Biot. In 1803 Biot was nominated by the First Class of the Institute to examine reports of meteorites; samples were brought back to Paris and a chemical analysis was carried out by Thenard. His most important collaboration with Biot was on a comparison of calcite and aragonite, since the two substances presented one of the earliest examples of dimorphism. Thenard's chemical analysis showed no difference between the two minerals despite their different crystalline forms. He and Biot concluded: "The same chemical principles combined in the same proportions can give rise to compounds that differ in their physical properties."[2]

A considerable amount of research was carried out by Thenard in collaboration with Gay-Lussac in 1808–1811, during which period they published about twenty papers. Thenard probably first met Gay-Lussac either when the latter was a student at the École Polytechnique or when they were both on the junior staff of that institution. The earliest record of their collaboration was on the occasion of Gay-Lussac's solo balloon ascent on 16 September 1804. Gay-Lussac took the flask of air he had collected at a high altitude to the laboratory of the École Polytechnique and with Thenard analyzed that air in comparison with ordinary Paris air. It was, however, the news of Davy's isolation of potassium, which reached Paris in the winter of 1807–1808, that prompted them to undertake a sustained collaboration largely in emulation of the English chemist. On 7 March 1808 they announced to the First Class of the Institute that they had prepared potassium by purely chemical means. The method, which involved fusing potash with iron filings in a gun barrel, had the advantage of producing potassium (and similarly sodium) in reasonable quantities, whereas Davy had been able to produce only tiny quantities of the substances. A controversy arose over the nature of potassium and sodium, Davy claiming that they were elements while Gay-Lussac and Thenard gave undue attention to experimental evidence suggesting that they were metal hydrides.

When funds were made available to construct a giant voltaic pile at the École Polytechnique (larger than that used by Davy at the Royal Institution), Gay-Lussac and Thenard were put in charge of the apparatus. Their results, reported in full in their *Recherches physico-chimiques*, are rather disappointing; Davy had effectively creamed the field. The superiority of the French chemists emerges in their investigations of the reactions of potassium metal. By strongly heating it in hydrogen, they prepared potassium hydride; and by heating the hydride in carefully dried ammonia, they obtained the olive-green solid KNH_2. When the solid was heated, it decomposed and ammonia, hydrogen, and nitrogen were released. The action of water on the solid produced potash and ammonia. Thenard and Gay-Lussac went on to use potassium to decompose boric acid and announced the isolation of a new element, boron, in November 1808. They obtained nearly anhydrous hydrofluoric acid by distilling calcium fluoride with concentrated sulfuric acid in a lead retort; and by heating calcium fluoride with boron trioxide, they obtained the gas boron fluoride, which they collected over mercury.

In their work on chlorine Gay-Lussac and Thenard were surprised to find that when the gas was passed over red-hot charcoal, it was not decomposed. This cast doubt on whether the gas then called "oxymuriatic acid gas" really was a compound containing oxygen. The authority of Berthollet persuaded them that this conclusion was not fully justified, and accordingly they mentioned it as only a possibility. It was left to Davy in 1810, after he had read their memoir, to announce that chlorine was in fact an element. Thenard and Gay-Lussac, however, deserve full credit for their pioneering contributions to photochemistry. They investigated the effect of light on mixtures of chlorine and hydrogen and chlorine and ethylene. The extent of the reaction in darkness or in a diffused light was judged by the change in the greenish-yellow color of the chlorine gas. Bright sunlight was found to bring about combination with explosive violence.

Another fruitful collaboration by Gay-Lussac and Thenard was that carried out in 1810 on the combustion analysis of vegetable and animal substances. Lavoisier's published organic analysis had made use of oxygen gas; but the two young chemists greatly extended the generality of this method by using an oxidizing agent, potassium chlorate. On the basis of their analysis they divided vegetable compounds into three classes according to the proportion of hydrogen and oxygen they contained. The class (containing starch and sugar) in which hydrogen and oxygen were in the same proportions as in water corresponds to the carbohydrates. Although in this joint research it is impossible to separate the contributions of Thenard from those of Gay-Lussac, one has the impression that Thenard usually came second to his friend in the quality, originality, and precision of his research.

Inspired by the fundamental work of Lavoisier on alcoholic fermentation, the Institute in 1800 and 1802 offered a prize on the subject. Thenard submitted a memoir and, according to a standard source, it "provided many of the facts upon which

Liebig subsequently based his views."[3] He pointed out that all fermenting liquids deposit a material similar to brewer's yeast and he demonstrated that it contained nitrogen. His study of yeast used to ferment pure sugar showed that it underwent a gradual change and was finally reduced to a white material that contained no nitrogen and produced no reaction with sugar. Thenard had begun by asking, "How is sugary matter changed into alcohol and carbonic acid by means of an intermediate body? What is the nature of this body? How does it act on sugar?"[4] The young chemist was not able to solve these complex problems, which a generation later became a subject of vigorous dispute between biological microscopists and chemists. Berzelius, for example, opposed biological explanations with the theory that fermentation was merely an example of contact catalysis due to a nonliving catalyst—a view that may be traced back to Thenard's work. In 1820, when he was studying the effect of finely divided metals on hydrogen peroxide, Thenard compared this phenomenon to the action of yeast in alcoholic fermentation.[5]

Thenard's greatest single discovery was that of hydrogen peroxide. He read his first paper on the subject to the Académie des Sciences on 27 July 1818, and successive volumes of the *Annales de chimie* contain his researches. The work had its origins in his earlier collaboration with Gay-Lussac, in which they had shown that when potassium or sodium is heated in dry oxygen, a higher oxide is obtained. Heating baryta strongly in oxygen also produced a new higher oxide. In the presence of water all these peroxides decomposed, liberating oxygen. The discovery of hydrogen peroxide seems to have been related to Lavoisier's theory of chemistry, according to which metals combined with acids to form salts only after an initial oxidation reaction; thus it was the metal oxide rather than the metal that dissolved in the acid. The metal should not be too highly oxidized, however, because it would then have little affinity for acids (acids were considered as extreme products of oxidation). Thenard wished to test this idea by seeing whether barium peroxide would dissolve in acids.

Thenard's first paper on hydrogen peroxide announced that he had prepared new oxygenated acids by treatment of barium peroxide with mineral acids. Thus, for instance, barium peroxide dissolved in dilute nitric acid to produce a neutral solution. The barium nitrate was precipitated as barium sulfate, leaving what we recognize as hydrogen peroxide. Unfortunately Thenard used

sulfuric acid to remove the barium salt and therefore had an acid product. Using this process, he prepared an "oxygenated acid" containing up to eleven times its own volume of oxygen. Since heating caused decomposition, his method of concentration was to use a vacuum pump at room temperature. By September 1818 Thenard had employed this method in preparing a product containing thirty-two times its own volume of oxygen. He recognized that its decomposition was accelerated by light and found that when the concentrated product came into contact with silver oxide, the oxygen was liberated in a violent reaction. By 23 November he had prepared "oxygenated water" and had begun to doubt whether his "oxygenated acids" were true compounds. Thenard had now, therefore, prepared a second compound of hydrogen and oxygen. It was neutral and could be distilled in a vacuum without decomposition. He found that the decomposition occurring when, for example, manganese dioxide was added, was exothermic. He went on to prepare a very concentrated product containing more than four hundred times its own volume of oxygen and found that it attacked the skin.

A major problem throughout this research had been to discover whether oxygen could combine with acids or water indefinitely, thus supporting the largely discredited ideas of Berthollet. This had been one of Thenard's motives for preparing an increasingly concentrated product. Finally he announced that he had succeeded in reaching the saturation point. This pure "oxygenated water" had a density of 1.455 (modern 1.465) and reacted explosively with various metal oxides. Usually the oxygen evolved consisted of both the "excess" oxygen of the hydrogen peroxide and the oxygen of the metal oxide. In some cases, however, the peroxide acted as an oxidizing agent (for instance, with arsenious oxide). He made the important observation that acids render hydrogen peroxide more stable.

Thenard completed his work on hydrogen peroxide by giving a detailed description of its preparation, starting from pure barium nitrate, which was heated to decompose it; oxygen was passed over the product to convert it into barium peroxide. The latter was then made into a paste in an ice-cooled vessel and just enough sulfuric acid added to precipitate all the barium, which was separated by filtration. Further purification was described to remove alumina, iron, and silica impurities. Thenard's complete work on hydrogen peroxide was summarized in a long article published in 1820 in the *Mémoires* of the Academy. In it he concluded that hydrogen peroxide is a true peroxide (*peroxide d'hydrogène*) and contains twice as much oxygen as water does. He used it to prepare new peroxides and noted its oxidizing action on sulfides. Mérimée, his colleague at the École Polytechnique, suggested applying this reaction to restoration of old paintings.

In Thenard's final and comprehensive paper on hydrogen peroxide (1820), he devoted several pages to the effect of finely divided metals on hydrogen peroxide, distinguishing, for example, between silver in an extreme state of division, finely divided, filings, and massive. Platinum, gold, osmium, palladium, rhodium, and other metals also were listed according to their state of division. Thenard was particularly concerned how these metals could take part in chemical reactions without apparently being affected.

This earlier work will help to explain Thenard's particular interest in catalysis in 1823. Indeed, as early as 1813 he had investigated the effect of the presence of metals in promoting the decomposition of ammonia gas passed through a red-hot glazed porcelain tube.[6] In August 1823 news reached Paris that Döbereiner had shown that spongy platinum at room temperature could bring about the combination of hydrogen and oxygen and that the heat from this reaction was sufficient to make the metal incandescent. Thenard collaborated with Dulong in experiments to confirm this finding. They extended the research by varying the physical state of the metal and by substituting other metals and other gaseous reactions. They demonstrated that the temperatures at which metals showed such effects depended on their state of division. Thenard and Dulong found that palladium, rhodium, and iridium had the same effect as platinum; and they went on to investigate the surface effects of other solids and the conditions under which substances lose their catalytic effect. Thenard, therefore, made significant contributions to knowledge of surface catalysis, although the term "catalyst" was not introduced by Berzelius until 1834.

Thenard was the author of a large and important chemistry textbook that went through six editions and was translated into German, Italian, and Spanish (the section on analysis was translated into English). Through this book he helped restore France to its traditional role as supplier of chemistry textbooks to the rest of the world; his only serious rival was the British chemist Thomas Thomson, who during the first two decades of the nine-

teenth century produced successive editions of his own textbook. The first edition of Thenard's *Traité de chimie élémentaire* was published in four volumes in 1813–1816. The first two volumes dealt with inorganic chemistry, the third with organic chemistry (divided into vegetable and animal), and the fourth with analytical chemistry. Similar substances were grouped together and discussed in general terms before consideration of their individual properties. In the Lavoisier tradition, oxygen was still considered as a unique element. Besides drawing on previous textbooks—such as those of Lavoisier, Fourcroy, and Thomson—Thenard incorporated the most recent research of his contemporaries. Plates and detailed descriptions of apparatus were provided, and in later editions were published as a separate volume. The detailed index included in each volume makes Thenard's book a particularly useful reference work for the chemistry of its period.

Thenard took great pains to bring successive editions of his textbook up to date. In the sixth and final edition (1834–1836) there is a major rearrangement of the material. Particularly important is the addition of a fourth part that he described as an "Essai de philosophie chimique," in which he dealt with the general principles of chemical combination and classification. He continued, however, to show the same reserve about Dalton's atomic theory that he had expressed in earlier editions.

NOTES

1. *Mémoires de la Société d'Arcueil*, **2** (1809), 24.
2. *Ibid.*, 206.
3. A. Harden, *Alcoholic Fermentation*, 4th ed. (London, 1934), 4.
4. *Annales de chimie*, **46** (1802), 206–207.
5. *Mémoires de l'Académie royale des sciences de l'Institut de France*, 2nd ser., **3**, *année* 1818 (1820), 487.
6. *Annales de chimie*, **85** (1813), 61.

BIBLIOGRAPHY

I. ORIGINAL WORKS. Thenard's chemistry textbook went through six eds., all published at Paris: *Traité de chimie élémentaire, théorique et pratique*, 4 vols. (1813–1816; 2nd ed., 1817–1818; 3rd ed., 1821; 4th ed., 5 vols., 1824; 5th ed., 1827; 6th ed., 1834–1836). With Gay-Lussac he wrote *Recherches physico-chimiques*, 2 vols. (Paris, 1811).

A selection from Thenard's research papers is presented below. The order follows that of the text.

"Sur l'acide sébacique," in *Annales de chimie*, **39** (1801), 193–202; "Observations sur l'acide zoonique," *ibid.*, **43** (1802), 176–184; "Mémoire sur la bile," in *Mémoires de la Société d'Arcueil*, **1** (1807), 23–45; "Mémoire sur les éthers," *ibid.*, 73–114; "Deuxième mémoire sur les éthers . . .," *ibid.*, 115–134; "Troisième mémoire sur les éthers . . .," *ibid.*, 140–160; "De l'action des acides végétaux sur l'alcool . . .," *ibid.*, **2** (1809), 5–22; "Essai sur la combinaison des acides avec les substances végétales et animales," *ibid.*, 23–41.

"Sur le nickel" (1802), in *Annales de chimie*, **50** (1804), 117–133; "Considérations générales sur les couleurs, suivies d'un procédé pour préparer une couleur bleue aussi belle que l'outremer," in *Journal des mines*, **15** (1804), 128–136; "Différents états de l'oxide d'antimoine . . .," in *Annales de chimie*, **32** (1799), 257–269; "Sur l'oxidation des métaux en général et en particulier du fer," *ibid.*, **56** (1805), 59–85; "Observations sur les hydro-sulfures," *ibid.*, **83** (1812), 132–138; "Mémoire sur le soufre hydrogéné ou l'hydrure de soufre," *ibid.*, 2nd ser., **48** (1831), 79–87; "Mémoire sur l'analyse comparée de l'aragonite et du carbonate de chaux rhomboidal," in *Mémoires de la Société d'Arcueil*, **2** (1809), 176–206, written with Biot.

Five memoirs written with Gay-Lussac: "Sur les métaux de la potasse et de la soude," in *Annales de chimie*, **66** (1808), 205–217; "Sur la décomposition et la recomposition de l'acide boracique," *ibid.*, **68** (1808), 169–174; "Sur l'acide fluorique," *ibid.*, **69** (1809), 204–220; "De la nature et des propriétés de l'acide muriatique et de l'acide muriatique oxigéné," in *Mémoires de la Société d'Arcueil*, **2** (1809), 339–358; and "Sur l'analyse végétale et animale," in *Annales de chimie*, **74** (1810), 47–64.

"Sur la fermentation vineuse," in *Annales de chimie*, **46** (1803), 294–320; "Observations sur des nouvelles combinaisons entre l'oxigène et divers acides," in *Annales de chimie et de physique*, 2nd ser., **8** (1818), 306–312; "Nouvelles observations sur les acides et les oxides oxigénés," *ibid.*, **9** (1818), 51–56, 94–98; "Observations sur l'influence de l'eau dans la formation des acides oxigénés," *ibid.*, 314–317; "Nouvelles recherches sur l'eau oxigénée," *ibid.*, 441–443; "Suite des expériences sur l'eau oxigénée," *ibid.*, **10** (1819), 114–115, 335; "Nouvelles observations sur l'eau oxigénée," *ibid.*, **11** (1819), 85–87, 208–216; "Mémoire sur la combinaison de l'oxygène avec l'eau, et sur les propriétés extraordinaires que possède l'eau oxigénée," in *Mémoires de l'Académie royale des sciences de l'Instiut de France, année 1818*, **3** (1820), 385–488.

With Dulong he wrote "Note sur la propriété que possèdent quelques métaux de faciliter la combinaison des fluides élastiques," in *Annales de chimie et de physique*, 2nd ser., **23** (1823), 440–444; and "Nouvelles observations sur la propriété dont jouissent certains corps de favoriser la combinaison des fluides élastiques," *ibid.*, **24** (1823), 380–387.

II. SECONDARY LITERATURE. See M. P. Crosland, *The Society of Arcueil. A View of French Science at the Time of Napoleon*, I (London, 1967), *passim;* F. Du-

bois, *Éloge de M. Thenard, prononcé dans la séance publique annuelle de l'Académie impériale de médecine du 9 Décembre 1862* (Paris, 1863); P. Flourens, "Éloge historique de Louis-Jacques Thenard," in *Éloges historiques*, 3rd ser. (Paris, 1862), 201–248; L. R. Le Canu, *Souvenirs de M. Thenard* (Paris, 1857); J. R. Partington, *A History of Chemistry*, IV (London, 1964), esp. 90–96; and P. Thenard, *Un grand français. Le chimiste Thenard, 1777–1857 par son fils; avec introduction et notes de Georges Bouchard* (Dijon, 1950).

M. P. CROSLAND

THEODORIC BORGOGNONI OF LUCCA. See **Borgognoni of Lucca, Theodoric.**

THEODORIC OF FREIBERG. See **Dietrich von Freiberg.**

THEODORUS OF CYRENE (*b.* Cyrene, North Africa, *ca.* 465 B.C.; *d.* Cyrene [?], after 399 B.C.), *mathematics.*

Theodorus was the mathematical tutor of Plato and Theaetetus and is known for his contribution to the early development of the theory of irrational quantities. Iamblichus includes him in his catalog of Pythagoreans.[1] According to the account of Eudemus as preserved by Proclus,[2] he was a contemporary of Hippocrates of Chios, and they both came after Anaxagoras and Oenopides of Chios. Diogenes Laërtius[3] states that he was the teacher of Plato; and Plato represents him as an old man in the *Theaetetus*, which is set in 399 B.C. Since Anaxagoras was born *ca.* 500 and Plato in 428 or 427, it is reasonable to suppose that Theodorus was born about 465. This would make him sixty-six years old in the fictive year of the *Theaetetus*. According to the dialogue he had been a disciple of Protagoras but had turned at an early age from abstract speculation to geometry.[4] He was in Athens at the time of the death of Socrates.[5] He is also made a character by Plato in the *Sophist* and the *Politicus*. Plato may have sat at his feet in Athens just before the death of Socrates or at Cyrene during his travels after that event. In the dialogue Theaetetus tells Socrates that he learned geometry, astronomy, harmony, and arithmetic from Theodorus.[6] As with Plato, this could have been at Athens or Cyrene.

In the dialogue[7] Theaetetus is made to relate how Theodorus demonstrated to him and to the younger Socrates, a namesake of the philosopher, that the square roots of 3, 5, and so on up to 17 (excluding 9 and 16, it being understood) are incommensurable with the unit; and Theaetetus goes on to say how he and Socrates tried to find a general formula that would comprehend all square roots. Plato clearly purports to be giving a historical account[8] and to be distinguishing the achievement of Theodorus from that of Theaetetus; and it would appear that Theodorus was the first to demonstrate the irrationality of $\sqrt{3}$, $\sqrt{5}$, $\cdots$, $\sqrt{17}$. Two questions immediately arise. Why did he start at $\sqrt{3}$? Why did he stop at $\sqrt{17}$? The answer to the former question must be that the irrationality of $\sqrt{2}$ was already known. It was, indeed, known to the earlier Pythagoreans; and there is a high probability that it was the discovery of the incommensurability of $\sqrt{2}$ with the unit that revealed to the Greeks the existence of the irrational and made necessary a recasting of Greek mathematical theory.[9] After this discovery it would be natural for Theodorus and others to look for further examples of irrationality.

The answer to the second question depends on how Theodorus proved the irrationality of the numbers under examination, and is not so easy. We may rule out at once the suggestion of F. Hultsch that Theodorus tried the method of successively closer approximation, because it would never *prove* irrationality.[10] The answer is dependent also on the meaning given to the words πως ἐνέσχετο. They usually have been translated "for some reason he stopped."[11] A glance at the uses of ἐνέχειν given in the lexicons, however, shows, as R. Hackforth first appreciated, that the Greek must mean "somehow he got into difficulties."[12]

This rules out the possibility that Theodorus stopped at 17 merely because he had to stop somewhere and felt he had proved enough.[13] It also rules out the possibility, despite the contention of A. Wasserstein, that Theodorus merely applied to 3, 5, $\cdots$, 17 the proof of the irrationality of $\sqrt{2}$.[14] This was known to Aristotle and is interpolated in the text of Euclid's *Elements*[15]; it may have been the way in which the irrationality of $\sqrt{2}$ was originally demonstrated. In this proof it is shown that, if the diagonal of a square is commensurable with its side, the same number will be both odd and even.[16] This proof can be generalized for all square roots, and indeed for all roots, in the form "$\sqrt[m]{N}$ is irrational unless N is the m-th power of an integer n."[17] Theodorus would soon have recognized the generality and would have run into no difficulties after 17.

It has been suggested that the Pythagorean de-

votion to the decad may have led Theodorus to stop where he did.[18] For $\sqrt{3}$ can be represented as $\sqrt{2^2 - 1^2}$, and so on for all the odd numbers up to $\sqrt{17} = \sqrt{9^2 - 8^2}$, at which point all the numerals from 1 to 9 would have been exhausted; Theodorus, however, would not have run into any difficulty in proceeding farther by this method, nor does it afford any proof of irrationality.

The above hypothesis is similar to one propounded by an anonymous commentator on the *Theaetetus*.[19] He first says that Plato made Theaetetus start with $\sqrt{3}$ because he had already shown in the *Meno* that the square on the diagonal of a square is double that on the side. He then proceeded to point out that Theaetetus was both a geometer and a student of musical theory. The tone interval has the ratio 9:8. If we double the two numbers we have 18:16; and between these two numbers the arithmetic mean is 17, dividing the extremes into unequal ratios, "as is shown in the commentaries on the *Timaeus*." The comment of Proclus on Plato, *Timaeus* 35B (*Commentarium in Timaeum*, 195A), is relevant, but we need not pursue it because it is clearly a rather farfetched hypothesis to explain why Theodorus stopped at 17.

An ingenious theory has been put forward by J. H. Anderhub.[20] If a right-angled isosceles triangle with unit sides is set out as in Figure 1, its

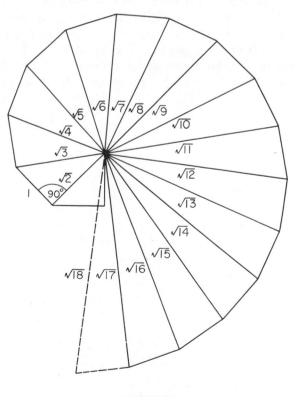

FIGURE 1

hypotenuse is $\sqrt{2}$. If at one extremity of the hypotenuse a perpendicular of unit length is erected, we have a second triangle with hypotenuse $= \sqrt{3}$. The process can be continued with all the hypotenuses $\sqrt{2}, \sqrt{3} \cdots$ radiating from a common point, and the angles at the common point can be shown to be 45°, 35°15', and so on. The total of all the angles up to hypotenuse $= \sqrt{17}$ is approximately 351°10', and the total up to $\sqrt{18}$ is approximately 364°48'—that is, after $\sqrt{17}$ the circle has been completed and the triangles begin to overlap. But although this would have given Theodorus a reason for stopping, he would have had no difficulty in going on; and the method does not prove the irrationality of any hypotenuse.

There is one theory, put forward by H. G. Zeuthen, that satisfies the requirements that there shall be a separate proof for each number $\sqrt{3}, \sqrt{5}, \cdots$ as Plato's text suggests, and that after $\sqrt{17}$ the proof will encounter difficulties.[21] Zeuthen's suggestion is that Theodorus used the process of finding the greatest common measure of two magnitudes as set out in Euclid's *Elements*, X.2, and actually made a test of incommensurability by Euclid: "If when the lesser of two unequal magnitudes is continually subtracted from the greater, the remainder never measures the one before it, the magnitudes will be incommensurable."[22] The method may conveniently be illustrated from $\sqrt{17}$ itself. Let ABC be a right-angled triangle in which $AB = 1$, $BC = 4$, so that $CA = \sqrt{17}$. Let CD be cut off from CA equal to CB so that $AD = \sqrt{17} - 4$, and let DE be drawn at right angles to CA. The triangles CDE, CBE are equal and therefore

$DE = EB$. The triangles ADE, ABC are similar and $DE = 4AD$. We therefore have $DE = 4AD = 4(\sqrt{17} - 4)$. Now from EA let EF be cut off equal to ED and at F let the perpendicular FG be drawn. Then by parity of reasoning

$$AF = AB - BF = AB - 2DE$$
$$= 1 - 8(\sqrt{17} - 4)$$
$$= (\sqrt{17} - 4)(\sqrt{17} + 4)$$
$$- 8(\sqrt{17} - 4)$$
$$= (\sqrt{17} - 4)^2.$$

Obviously, the process can be continued indefinitely, so that $ABC, ADE, AFG, \cdots$ is a diminishing series of triangles such that

$$AB : AD : AF \cdots = 1 : (\sqrt{17} - 4) : (\sqrt{17} - 4)^2 \cdots$$

and we shall never be left with a magnitude that exactly measures CA, which is accordingly incommensurable.

Theodorus would certainly have used a geometrical proof, but the point can be made as shown below in modern arithmetical notation. The process of finding the greatest common measure of 1 and $\sqrt{17}$ (if any) may be set out as follows:

1) $\sqrt{17}$ (4

$$\frac{4}{\sqrt{17}} - 4$$

$(\sqrt{17} - 4))1(8$

$$\frac{8(\sqrt{17} - 4)}{1 - 8(\sqrt{17} - 4)}$$
$$= (\sqrt{17} - 4)(\sqrt{17} + 4) - 8(\sqrt{17} - 4)$$
$$= (\sqrt{17} - 4)(\sqrt{17} + 4 - 8)$$
$$= (\sqrt{17} - 4)^2.$$

The next stage in the process would be to divide $(\sqrt{17} - 4)^2$ into $(\sqrt{17} - 4)$, but this is the same as dividing $(\sqrt{17} - 4)$ into 1, which was the previous step. The process is therefore periodic and will never end, so that 1 and $\sqrt{17}$ do not have a greatest common measure. It will be recognized as the same process as that for finding a continued fraction equal to $\sqrt{17}$.

It is a powerful argument in favor of this theory that Plato, in the passage of the *Theaetetus* under discussion, for the first time in Greek literature uses the term οὐ σύμμετρος ("incommensurable") for what had previously been described as ἄρρητος ("inexpressible"). This strongly reinforces the conviction that he was doing something new, and that

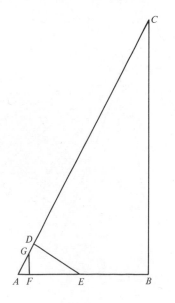

FIGURE 2

the novelty consisted in using the test of incommensurability later found in Euclid.

These proofs, geometrical and arithmetical, are simple; and the former would certainly have been within the grasp of Theodorus. So would the earlier proofs for $\sqrt{3}$, $\sqrt{5}$, and so on.[23] The next case, $\sqrt{18}$, would not call for investigation since $\sqrt{18} = 3\sqrt{2}$; but $\sqrt{19}$ presents difficulties at which even a modern mathematician may quail. Recurrence does not take place until after six stages, which, on the basis of the exposition of B. L. van der Waerden, may be set out as follows.[24] We start by subtracting the appropriate multiple of 1 from $\sqrt{19}$ and get a remainder $\sqrt{19} - 4$. We now divide $\sqrt{19} - 4$ into 1. But

$$\frac{1}{\sqrt{19}-4} = \frac{\sqrt{19}+4}{3}.$$

We treat ($\sqrt{19} + 4$) and 3 in exactly the same way, subtracting $2 \cdot 3$ from $\sqrt{19} + 4$ and getting $\sqrt{19} - 2$. Now.

$$\frac{3}{\sqrt{19}-2} = \frac{\sqrt{19}+2}{5};$$

and we subtract the 5 from $\sqrt{19} + 2$, getting $\sqrt{19} - 3$, and divide this into 5. But

$$\frac{5}{\sqrt{19}-3} = \frac{\sqrt{19}+3}{2};$$

and after subtracting $3 \cdot 2$ from $\sqrt{19} + 3$, we get $\sqrt{19} - 3$ again. But

$$\frac{2}{\sqrt{19}-3} = \frac{\sqrt{19}+3}{5},$$

and subtracting 5 from $\sqrt{19} + 3$ yields $\sqrt{19} - 2$. Now

$$\frac{5}{\sqrt{19}-2} = \frac{\sqrt{19}+2}{3};$$

and by subtracting $2 \cdot 3$ from $\sqrt{19} + 2$ we obtain $\sqrt{19} - 4$. But

$$\frac{3}{\sqrt{19}-4} = \frac{\sqrt{19}+4}{1};$$

subtracting $4 \cdot 1$ from $\sqrt{19} + 4$ leaves us with $\sqrt{19}$, and dividing 1 into $\sqrt{19}$ brings us back where we started. The process is therefore periodic and will never end, so that $\sqrt{19}$ is incommensurable with 1.

This is formidable enough in modern notation, and impossible to set out in a drawing, particularly a drawing in sand. If this is the method that Theodorus used, it is therefore fully understandable why he stopped at $\sqrt{17}$.

Although this is only a hypothesis, there is no other that fits the facts so well; and if his pupil Theaetetus developed a theory of proportion based on the method of finding the greatest common measure, as is argued in the article devoted to him in this *Dictionary*, it becomes virtually certain that this is the method employed by Theodorus.

Proclus, in analyzing curves in the manner of Geminus, criticizes "Theodorus the mathematician" for speaking of "blending" in lines.[25] He is probably to be identified with Theodorus of Cyrene, since in his only other reference Proclus describes the subject of this article. He may also be identified with the Theodorus whom Xenophon held up as a model of a good mathematician.[26]

NOTES

1. Iamblichus, *De vita Pythagorica*, 267; L. Deubner, ed. (Leipzig, 1937), p. 146.8–9.
2. Proclus, *In primum Euclidis*, G. Friedlein, ed. (Leipzig, 1873; repr. Hildesheim, 1967), 65.21–66.7.
3. Diogenes Laërtius, *Vitae philosophorum*, II.103, III.6; H. S. Long, ed., I (Oxford, 1964), 100.9–13, 123.18.
4. Plato, *Theaetetus* 164E–165A, in *Platonis opera*, J. Burnet, ed., I (Oxford, 1899; frequently repr.).
5. It is not obvious why James Gow, *A Short History of Greek Mathematics* (Cambridge, 1884), 164, should flatly contradict the evidence of Plato's dialogue and say, "He does not seem to have visited Athens."
6. Plato, *Theaetetus*, 145C–D.
7. *Ibid.*, 147D–148B.
8. Jean Itard, *Les livres arithmétiques d'Euclide*, Histoire de la Pensée, X (Paris, 1961), is exceptional in regarding as tenable the view that Theodorus and Theaetetus may not be historical persons but "personnages composites nés dans l'esprit même de Platon."
9. The fullest account of this subject is in Kurt von Fritz, "The Discovery of Incommensurability by Hippasus of Metapontium," in *Studies in Presocratic Philosophy*, David J. Furley and R. E. Allen, eds., I (London–New York, 1970), 382–412. But in his earlier paper with the same title in *Annals of Mathematics*, **46** (1945), 242–264, Fritz exposed himself to some strictures, of which he has not taken notice, from A. Wasserstein, "Theaetetus and the Theory of Numbers," 165, n. 3.
10. F. Hultsch, "Die Näherungswerthe irrationaler Quadratwurzeln bei Archimedes," in *Nachrichten von der königlich Gesellschaft der Wissenschaften zu Göttingen*, **22** (1893), 368–428. Hultsch received some support from T. L. Heath in his early work, *The Works of Archimedes* (Cambridge, 1897), lxxix–lxxx, in which he regarded it as "pretty certain" that Theodorus, like Archimedes after him, represented $\sqrt{3}$ geometrically as the perpendicular from an angular point of an equilateral triangle to the opposite side. He also presumed that Theodorus would start from the identity $3 = 48/16 = (49-1)/16$, so that

$$\sqrt{3} < \sqrt{\frac{48+1}{16}} = \frac{7}{4};$$

but in his later work, *A History of Greek Mathematics*, I (Oxford, 1921), 204, he realized that this "would leave Theodorus as far as ever from *proving* that $\sqrt{3}$ is incommensurable." These approximations may, of course, have played a part in Theodorus' researches until he found a demonstrative proof.

11. "There he stopped" (B. Jowett); "here he somehow came to a pause" (B. J. Kennedy); "il s'était, je ne sais pourquoi, arrêté là" (A. Diès); "there, for some reason, he stopped" (F. M. Cornford); "at that he stopped" (H. N. Fowler); "qui, non so come, si fermò" (M. Timpanaro Cardini). But the latest translator, J. McDowell (Oxford, 1973), has the sense right—"at that point he somehow got tied up."

12. *A Greek-English Lexicon*, H. G. Liddell and R. Scott, eds., new ed. by H. Stuart Jones (Oxford, 1940), see ἐνέχω, II, 565. The general meaning of the passive and middle is "to be held, caught, entangled in"; and a particularly relevant example is given in II.2, [κῦρος] ἐνείχετο ἀπορίηισι; Herodotus 1.190. *Theatetus* 147D is the only passage quoted for the meaning "come to a standstill" (II.5), and therefore it can hardly determine the meaning of that passage.

R. Hackforth, "Notes on Plato's *Theaetetus*," 128. It is significant that Hackforth's interest is purely literary, and his interpretation is therefore free from any bias in favor of some particular mathematical solution. He is supported by Malcolm S. Brown, "*Theaetetus*: Knowledge as Continued Learning," in *Journal of the History of Philosophy*, **7** (1969), 367.

13. Wasserstein, *op. cit.*, 165, makes this suggestion without necessarily endorsing it. G. H. Hardy and E. M. Wright, *An Introduction to the Theory of Numbers*, 4th ed. (Oxford, 1960), 43, in the light of their views about the difficulty of generalizing the Pythagorean proof for $\sqrt{2}$ (see note 14), regard the suggestion as credible.

14. It is the main burden of Wasserstein's paper (cited above) that this is precisely what Theodorus did. He argues that the difficulties of effecting a valid generalization are such as would have been perceived by Theodorus and that "it was precisely this refusal of the rigorous mathematician to enumerate a general theory based on doubtful foundations that led his pupil Theaetetus to investigate not only the problem of irrationality but also the more fundamental arithmetical questions." Although it may be conceded that Theodorus was an acute mathematician, it is most unlikely that he, or any other ancient mathematician, would have thought about this problem in the manner of G. H. Hardy and E. M. Wright. (See note 16.) Wasserstein's thesis is controverted in detail by Brown, *op cit.*, 366–367, but in part for an irrelevant reason. Brown accepts van der Waerden's view that bk. VII of Euclid's *Elements* was already in "apple-pie order" before the end of the fifth century, whereas Wasserstein, like Zeuthen, regards it as the work of Theaetetus; but Wasserstein's contention that Theodorus applied the traditional proof for $\sqrt{2}$ can be detached from this belief.

15. Aristotle, *Prior Analytics* 1.23.41a23–30; W. D. Ross, ed. (Oxford, 1949, corr. repr. 1965), English trans. by A. J. Jenkinson as *Analytica priora*, in *The Works of Aristotle*, W. D. Ross, ed., I (Oxford, 1928; repr. 1968). Euclid, *Elements*, X, app. 27; *Euclidis opera omnia*, J. L. Heiberg and H. Menge, eds., III (Leipzig, 1886), 408.1–410.16; E. S. Stamatis, ed., in *Euclidis Elementa* post J. L. Heiberg, III (Leipzig, 1972), 231.10–233.13. An alternative proof is also given. In earlier eds. the proof was printed as Euclid, *Elements*, X.117, but it is now recognized as an interpolation.

16. T. L. Heath, *A History of Greek Mathematics*, I (Oxford, 1921), 205, purports to give a fairly easy generalization; but it is logically defective in that he assumes that "if $m^2 = N \cdot n^2$, therefore m^2 is divisible by N, so that m also is a multiple of N," which is true only if N is not itself the multiple of a square number. Wasserstein, *op cit.*, 168–169, corrects Heath. Hardy and Wright, *op. cit.*, 40, show that the generalization is not so simple as Heath represented it to be and "requires a good deal more than a 'trivial' variation of the Pythagorean proof." This is true; but Hardy and Wright are working to standards of logical rigor far beyond what

any mathematician of the fifth century B.C. would have demanded, and Theodorus could fairly easily have found a generalization that would have satisfied his own standards.

17. Hardy and Wright, *op cit.*, 41. The authors discuss Theodorus' work helpfully in the light of modern mathematics on 42–45.

18. See Brown, *op cit.*, 367–368, and his n. 26.

19. *Anonymer Kommentar zu Platons Theaetet*, H. Diels and W. Schubart, eds., Berliner Klassikertexte, II (Berlin, 1905). The passage is reproduced and translated, as is Proclus' commentary on the relevant passage in the *Timaeus*, with illuminating notes, in Wasserstein, *op cit.*, 172–179. The commentator does not appear to accept his own suggestion, saying that Theodorus stopped at 17 because that is the first number after 16, and 16 is the only square in which the number denoting the sum of the sides is equal to the number denoting the area ($4 + 4 + 4 + 4 = 4 \times 4$).

20. Both B. L. van der Waerden, *Science Awakening*, English trans. by Arnold Dresden of *Ontwakende Wetenschap*, 2nd ed., I (Groningen, n.d.), 143; and Árpád Szabó, *Anfänge der griechischen Mathematik* (Munich–Vienna, 1969), 70, attribute this interesting construction to J. H. Anderhub, *Joco-Seria: Aus den Papieren eines reisenden Kaufmannes*, but I have not been able to obtain a copy.

21. H. G. Zeuthen, "Sur la constitution des livres arithmétiques des *Éléments* d'Euclide et leur rapport à la question de l'irrationalité," in *Oversigt over det K. Danske Videnskabernes Selskabs Forhandlinger* for 1910 (1910–1911), 422–426. The theory is taken up again in articles in the same periodical in the volumes for 1913 and 1915. Zeuthen's thesis is supported by O. Toeplitz, 28–29; and by Brown, *op cit.*

22. *Euclidis opera omnia*, J. L. Heiberg and H. Menge, eds., III (Leipzig, 1886), 6.12–8.13; E. C. Stamatis, ed., in *Euclidis Elementa post J. L. Heiberg*, III (Leipzig, 1972), 3.19–4.19.

23. The cases of $\sqrt{5}$ and $\sqrt{10}$ are similar to $\sqrt{17}$. The case of $\sqrt{3}$ is a little more difficult, involving one more step before recurrence takes place. The case of $\sqrt{13}$ is difficult, as may be seen from the process of expressing it as a continued fraction given by G. Chrystal, *Algebra*, II (Edinburgh, 1889), 401–402, where it is shown that recurrence occurs only after five partial quotients:

$$\sqrt{13} = 3 + \frac{1}{1+} \frac{1}{1+} \frac{1}{1+} \frac{1}{1+} \frac{1}{6+} \frac{1}{1+} \cdots,$$

Perhaps it was Theodorus' experience with $\sqrt{13}$ that made him unwilling to embark on $\sqrt{19}$. The same method can be applied to $\sqrt{2}$, although it is probable that $\sqrt{2}$ was originally proved irrational not by this method but by that referred to by Aristotle (see note 15). Zeuthen, *loc. cit.*, and Heath, *loc. cit.*, give the proofs for $\sqrt{5}$ and $\sqrt{3}$; and Heath adds a geometrical proof for $\sqrt{2}$; Hardy and Wright, *op. cit.*, give proofs for $\sqrt{5}$ and $\sqrt{2}$. The method is used by Kurt von Fritz in *Studies in Presocratic Philosophy*, I, 401–406, to prove the incommensurability of the diagonal of a regular pentagon in relation to its side.

24. Van der Waerden, *op. cit.*, 144–146. The method is a simplification of the process of finding the greatest common measure as used in the text for $\sqrt{17}$ by taking new ratios equal to the actual ratios of the process; but van der Waerden's exposition is rather elliptical, and it may more clearly be set out as here.

25. Proclus, *In primum Euclidis*, G. Friedlein, ed., 118.7–9. (The reference in Friedlein's index is incorrect.) In favor of identifying him with Theodorus of Cyrene is the fact that Plato in one place (*Theaetetus* 143B) calls the Cyrenaic "Theodorus the geometer"; and Diogenes Laërtius, *op. cit.*, also calls him "the Cyrenaic geometer" and "the mathematician." Van der Waerden, *op. cit.*, 146, accepts the identification, but it is rejected (by implication) by H. Diels and

W. Kranz, eds., *Die Fragmente der Vorsokratiker*, 6th ed. (Dublin–Zurich, 1954; repr. 1969) and most writers; Glenn R. Morrow, *Proclus: A Commentary on the First Book of Euclid's Elements* (Princeton, 1970), 95, n. 70, thinks the reference is to Theodorus of Soli, who is cited by Plutarch on certain mathematical difficulties in the *Timaeus*. Diogenes Laërtius, *loc. cit.*, refers to twenty persons with the name Theodorus, and Pauly-Wissowa lists no fewer than 203. There was even a second Theodorus of Cyrene, a philosopher of some repute, who flourished at the end of the fourth century B.C. In the passage under discussion Proclus is reproducing Geminus' classification of curves; and in treating mixed curves he says the mixing can come about through "composition," "fusing," or "blending." According to Geminus and Proclus, but not Theodorus, planes can be blended but lines cannot.

26. Xenophon, *Memorabilia*, which is *Commentarii* IV.2, 10; *Xenophontis opera omnia*, E. C. Marchant, ed., II (Oxford, 1901; 2nd ed., 1921; repr. 1942), ll. 25–26.

BIBLIOGRAPHY

The works listed in the bibliography of the article on Theaetetus will serve also for Theodorus. In addition, the following, listed chronologically, may be consulted: T. Bonnesen, in *Periodico di mathematiche*, 4th ser., **1** (1921), 16; H. Hasse and H. Scholz, *Die Grundlagenkrisis der griechisch Mathematik* (Berlin, 1928), 28; K. von Fritz, "Theodorus 31," in Pauly-Wissowa, *Real-Encyclopädie der classischen Altertumswissenschaft*, 2nd ser., V (Stuttgart, 1934), cols. 1811–1825; J. H. Anderhub, *Joco-Seria: Aus den Papieren eines reisenden Kaufmannes* (Wiesbaden, 1941); R. Hackforth, "Notes on Plato's *Theaetetus*," in *Mnemosyne*, 4th ser., **10** (1957), 128; A. Wasserstein, "*Theaetetus* and the History of the Theory of Numbers," in *Classical Quarterly*, n.s. **8** (1958), 165–179; O. Toeplitz, *Kantstudien*, **33**, 28–29; M. Timpanaro Cardini, *Pitagorici, testimonianze e frammenti*, fasc. 2; Bibliotheca di Studi Superiori, **41** (Florence, 1962), 74–81.

IVOR BULMER-THOMAS

THEODOSIUS OF BITHYNIA

THEODOSIUS OF BITHYNIA (*b*. Bithynia, second half of the second century B.C.), *mathematics, astronomy.*

Theodosius was the author of *Sphaerics*, a textbook on the geometry of the sphere, and minor astronomical and astrological works. Strabo, in giving a list of Bithynians worthy of note in various fields, mentions "Hipparchus, Theodosius and his sons, mathematicians."[1] Vitruvius mentions Theodosius as the inventor of a sundial suitable for any region.[2] Strabo's references are usually in chronological order in their respective categories; and since Hipparchus was at the height of his career in 127 B.C., while Strabo and Vitruvius both flourished about the beginning of the Christian era, these statements could refer to the same person

and probably do. They harmonize with the fact that Theodosius is quoted by name as the author of the *Sphaerics* by Menelaus (fl. A.D. 100). To allow sufficient time for his sons to be recognized as mathematicians in their own right before Strabo, Theodosius may best be regarded as a younger contemporary of Hipparchus, born in the second half of the second century B.C. and perhaps surviving into the first century; indeed, it is unlikely that such a work as the *Sphaerics* would have been written long after the development of spherical trigonometry by Hipparchus, for this development makes it look old-fashioned.

Confusion has been created, however, by the notice or notices in the notoriously unreliable *Suda Lexicon*. The passage reads:

> Theodosius, philosopher, wrote *Sphaerics* in three books, a commentary on the chapter of Theudas, two books *On Days and Nights*, a commentary on the *Method* of Archimedes, *Descriptions of Houses* in three books, *Skeptical Chapters*, astrological works, *On Habitations*. Theodosius wrote verses on the spring and other types of works. He was from Tripolis.[3]

It seems probable that the first sentence in this passage confuses the author of the *Sphaerics* with a later skeptical philosopher, for Theudas flourished in the second century of the Christian era;[4] and it also is probable that the second and third sentences should be regarded as a separate notice about a third Theodosius. This would be unimportant if the third sentence had not given rise to the belief that the author of the *Sphaerics* was born at Tripolis in Phoenicia, and in almost all editions until recently he has been described as Theodosius of Tripolis.[5]

Spherics, the geometry of the sphere, was needed for astronomy and was regarded by the ancient Greeks as a branch of astronomy rather than of geometry. Indeed, the Pythagoreans called astronomy "spherics"; and the stereometrical books XII and XIII of Euclid's *Elements*, which lead up to the inscription of the regular solids in a sphere, contain nothing about the geometry of the sphere beyond the proof that the volumes of spheres are in the triplicate ratio of their diameters. Euclid treated this subject in his *Phaenomena*, and just before him Autolycus had dealt with it in his book *On the Moving Sphere*. From a comparison of propositions quoted or assumed by Euclid and Autolycus, it may be inferred that much of Theodosius' *Sphaerics* is derived from some pre-Euclidean textbook, of which some have conjectured that Eudoxus was the author.[6] There is nothing in it that can strictly be called trigonometry, although in III.11 Theodosius proves the equivalent of the formula $\tan a = \sin b \tan A$ for a spherical triangle right-angled at C.

Two of the other works mentioned by the *Suda* have survived. *On Habitations* treats the phenomena caused by the rotation of the earth, particularly what portions of the heavens are visible to the inhabitants of different zones. *On Days and Nights* studies the arc of the ecliptic traversed by the sun each day. Its object is to determine what conditions have to be satisfied in order that the solstice may occur in the meridian at a given place and in order that day and night may really be equal at the equinoxes.

One reason why these three works have survived must be that they were included in the collection that Pappus called "The Little Astronomy"[7]—in contrast with "The Great Astronomy" or *Almagest* of Ptolemy. Pappus also annotated the *Sphaerics* and *On Days and Nights* in some detail.[8] All three works were translated into Arabic toward the end of the ninth century.[9] The translation of the *Sphaerics* up to II.5 is by Qusṭā ibn Lūqā and thereafter by Thābit ibn Qurra. The *Sphaerics* was translated from Arabic into Latin in the twelfth century by Plato of Tivoli and Gerard of Cremona.

There is no reason to doubt that the Theodosius who wrote the *Sphaerics* was also the author of the commentary on the *Method* of Archimedes mentioned by the *Suda*, for the subject matter would be similar. It may be accepted also that he wrote astrological works. It is tempting to think that the Διαγραφαὶ οἰκιῶν, *Descriptions of Houses*, mentioned in the *Suda*, dealt with the "houses of the planets"; but the latter term is always οἰκοι, not οἰκίαι. It must be considered an architectural work, which could, however, be by the author of the *Sphaerics*. The other works mentioned in the *Suda* must be regarded as by another person of the same name. Theodosius' discovery of a sundial suitable for all regions—πρὸς πᾶν κλίμα—may have been recorded in a book, but nothing is known about it.

NOTES

1. Strabo, *Geography* XII.4, 9 c 566, A. Meineke, ed. (Leipzig, 1853), II, 795.13–14.
2. Vitruvius, *De architectura* IX.8,1, F. Krohn, ed. (Leipzig, 1912), p. 218.7.
3. *Suda Lexicon*, under Θεοδόσιος, Ada Adler, ed., II (Leipzig, 1931), Θ 142 and 143, p. 693.
4. Diogenes Laërtius, *Vitae philosophorum* IX.116, H. S.

Long, ed. (Oxford, 1964), II, 493.14. He was, according to Diogenes, the fifth skeptical philosopher in succession to Aenesidemus, who flourished at the time of Cicero.
5. Even the definitive ed. by J. L. Heiberg (1927) is entitled "Theodosius Tripolites Sphaerica" but the first entry in the corrigenda (p. xvi) is "Tripolites deleatur ubique."
6. The following propositions in the *Sphaerics* are certainly pre-Euclidean: bk. I, props. 1, 6, 7, 8, 11, 12, 13, 15, 20; bk. II, props. 1, 2, 3, 5, 8, 9, 10, 13, 15, 17, 18, 19, 20; bk. III, prop. 2.
7. Ὁ μικρὸς ἀστρονομουμενος (*sc.* τόπος). Pappus, *Collection* VI *titulus*, F. Hultsch, ed., *Pappi Alexandrini Collectionis quae supersunt*, II (Berlin, 1877), 475.
8. *Sphaerics, ibid.,* VI.1–33, props. 1–26, F. Hultsch, ed., 475–519; *On Days and Nights, ibid.,* VI.48–68, props. 30–36, F. Hultsch, ed., II, 530–555.
9. H. Wenrich, *De auctorum Graecorum versionibus et commentariis Syriacis Arabicis etc.* (Leipzig, 1842), 206; H. Suter, *Die Mathematiker und Astronomen der Araber und ihre Werke* (Leipzig, 1900), 41.

BIBLIOGRAPHY

I. ORIGINAL WORKS. The three surviving works of Theodosius are in many MSS, of which the most important is Codex Vaticanus Graecus 204 (10th cent.). The *Sphaerics* was first printed in a Latin ed. translated from the Arabic (Venice, 1518), which was followed by Voegelin's Latin ed. (Vienna, 1529), also taken from the Arabic. The *editio princeps* of the Greek text (with Latin trans.) is J. Pena, *Theodosii Tripolitae Sphaericorum libri tres* (Paris, 1558). Subsequent eds. are F. Maurolico (Messina, 1558; Latin trans. only); C. Dasypodius (Strasbourg, 1572; enunciations only in Greek and Latin); C. Clavius (Rome, 1586; Latin trans. only, with works of his own); J. Auria (Rome, 1587); M. Mersenne (Paris, 1644); C. Dechales (Lyons, 1674); I. Barrow (London, 1675); J. Hunt (Oxford, 1707); E. Nizze (Berlin, 1852). The definitive ed. is J. L. Heiberg, "Theodosius Tripolites Sphaerica," in *Abhandlungen der Gesellschaft der Wissenschaften zu Göttingen*, phil.-hist. Kl., n.s. **19**, no. 3 (1927), which contains notes on the MSS (i–xv), text with Latin trans. (1–165), and scholia (166–199).

The Greek enunciations of *On Habitations* and *On Days and Nights* were included by Dasypodius in his ed. (Strasbourg, 1572) and Latin translations of the two texts were published by J. Auria (Rome, 1587 and 1591, respectively), but the Greek texts were not printed until the definitive ed. by R. Fecht, "Theodosii De habitationibus liber De diebus et noctibus libri duo," in *Abhandlungen der Gesellschaft der Wissenschaften zu Göttingen*, phil.-hist. Kl. n.s. **19**, no. 4 (1927), which contains notes (1–12), text and Latin trans. of *On Habitations* (13–43), scholia on *Habitations* (44–52), text and Latin trans. of *On Days and Nights* (53–155), and scholia on *Days and Nights* (156–176). The scholia were first edited by F. Hultsch, "Scholien zur Sphärik des Theodosios," in *Abhandlungen des philosophisch-historische Classe der K. Sächsischen Gesellschaft der Wissenschaften*, **10**, no. 5 (1887).

There is a German trans. of the *Sphaerics* by E. Nizze, *Die Sphärik des Theodosios* (Stralsund, 1826). There are French translations by D. Henrion (Paris, 1615); J. B. du Hamel (Paris, 1660); and Paul ver Eecke, *Théodose de Tripoli: Les sphériques* (Paris–Bruges, 1927).

II. SECONDARY LITERATURE. The most useful material on Theodosius is Thomas Heath, *A History of Greek Mathematics* (Oxford, 1921), II, 245–252; the Latin intro. to R. Fecht's ed. (see above), 1–12; and K. Ziegler, "Theodosius 5," in Pauly-Wissowa, *Real-Encyclopädie der classischen Altertumswissenschaft*, n.s. V, cols. 1930–1935. Other sources, listed chronologically, are A. Nokk, *Über die Sphärik des Theodosios* (Karlsruhe, 1847); F. Hultsch, "Die *Sphärik* des Theodosios und einige unedierte Texte," in *Berichte der Sächsischen Gesellschaft der Wissenschaften* (1885); R. Carra de Vaux, "Remaniement des *Sphériques* de Théodose par Jahia ibn Muhammed ibn Abī Schukr al-Maghrabī al Andalusī," in *Journal asiatique*, 17 (1891), 287–295; P. Tannery, *Recherches sur l'histoire de l'astronomie ancienne* (Paris, 1893), 36–37; and A. A. Björnbo, "Studien über Menelaos' *Sphärik*: Beiträge zur Geschichte des Sphärik und Trigonometrie der Griechen," in *Abhandlungen zur Geschichte der mathematischen Wissenschaften*, 14 (1902), 64–65; and "Über zwei mathematische Handschriften," in *Bibliotheca mathematica*, n.s. 3 (1902), 63–75.

IVOR BULMER-THOMAS

THEON OF ALEXANDRIA (*fl.* Alexandria, second half of fourth century), *mathematics, astronomy.*

Theon's scholarly activity is firmly dated by his reports of two eclipses that he observed at Alexandria in 364: the solar eclipse of 16 June and the lunar eclipse of 26 November.[1] Other chronological references in his works all point to the 360's and 370's. The solar eclipse of 364 is used as an example of calculation in both the greater and the lesser commentaries on Ptolemy's *Handy Tables*, the lesser commentary providing examples of calculations that correspond to the dates 15 June 360 and 17 November 377.[2] Also, a list of Roman consuls preserved in one manuscript of Theon's edition of the *Handy Tables* stops with the consuls of the year 372.[3] There is only one ancient biographical notice on Theon, and that very brief.[4] It states that Theon lived under the emperor Theodosius I (reigned 379–395), a date consistent with the above evidence. Theon's daughter, Hypatia, who was famous in her own right as a mathematician (she is credited, among other things, with a revision of book 3 of her father's commentary on the *Almagest*) and as a Neoplatonic philosopher, was torn to pieces by a mob of fanatic Christians at Alexandria in 415. Since there is no mention of Theon in the circumstantial account we have of this event, it is likely that he was already dead. Like his daughter, Theon was certainly a pagan. Whether he, too, favored Neoplatonism cannot be determined.

The ancient biographical notice also informs us that Theon was a member of the "Museum." This was an institution for the support of advanced learning, established at Alexandria about 300 B.C. by Ptolemy I, which had nourished many famous scholars but by Theon's time had declined sadly — if, indeed, it still existed (Theon is the last attested member). Whether he was connected with the Museum or not, Theon was certainly actively engaged in higher education. In the preface to his commentary on the *Almagest*, he says that he has composed the work at the urging of those who attended his lectures on the subject.[5] Indeed, all his extant works are the outcome of his "professorial" activity, being either commentaries on or editions of recognized classics of mathematics and astronomy, intended for the use of students. I will deal with the commentaries in the order in which Theon wrote them, which is established by internal references from one to the other.

Theon's most extensive work is his commentary on Ptolemy's *Almagest*. This was originally in thirteen books, corresponding to the number of books of the *Almagest*; but book 11 is lost, only a fragment of book 5 survives, and there are probably lacunae in other books. The passage in the preface mentioned above suggests that the commentary is a redaction of Theon's lectures, and that is how it reads. It is for the most part a trivial exposition of Ptolemy's text, explaining obvious points at excessive length. Despite Theon's promise to improve over previous commentators on the *Almagest*, "who claim that they will only omit the more obvious points, but in fact prove to have omitted the most difficult,"[6] the commentary is open to precisely this criticism. It is never critical, merely exegetic. To the modern reader it is almost useless for understanding Ptolemy; but it is of value for the occasional information it provides on now-lost mathematical and astronomical works, notably Zenodorus' treatise "On Isoperimetric Figures" in book 1. This passage probably is taken from the earlier commentary on the *Almagest* by Pappus (*fl.* 320), of which only books 5 and 6 survive. Comparison of the two commentaries for book 6 (the only area where they overlap) shows that while Theon borrows much from Pappus, his work is not a mere rewriting of his predecessor's but contains extensive contributions of his own.

Theon also published two commentaries on the *Handy Tables*. The latter, issued by Ptolemy after he had completed the *Almagest*, were meant to provide a convenient means of computing the positions of the heavenly bodies and other astronomical phenomena. In the preface to the larger commentary Theon claims that whereas he had predecessors who commented on the *Almagest*, he is the first to write a commentary on the *Handy Tables*. The earlier of the two commentaries is an extensive one, in five books, addressed to Eulalius and Origenes, whom Theon calls his "companions" (in the Museum ?). In it Theon explains not only how to use the tables but also the reasons for the operations and the basis of the tables' construction, and provides geometrical demonstrations. Thus it frequently covers the same ground as the commentary on the *Almagest*. The second, much smaller, commentary is addressed, like the commentary on the *Almagest*, to Epiphanius, presumably a pupil of Theon's. In the preface Theon refers to the larger commentary as "the more reasoned (λογικωτέρα) introduction to computation with the *Handy Tables*," and explains that he has written this new work for that majority of his pupils in the subject who are unable to follow geometrical proofs.[7] The smaller commentary, then, merely sets out the rules for computation with the tables, adding occasional worked examples but no reasons. Theon's remark indicating the low mathematical caliber of his students is corroborated by what we should surmise from the nature of his works in general.

All other extant works by Theon are editions of previous authors. "Edition" here does not mean an attempt to establish the authentic text but, rather, a reworking of the original in a form considered more suitable for students. The most notable of Theon's editions is that of Euclid's *Elements*, which was so influential that it consigned the original text to near oblivion. Theon himself attests his work in his commentary on the *Almagest*, book 1, chapter 10, where he says: "That sectors of equal circles are in the ratio of the angles [at the centers] we have proved in our edition of the *Elements* at the end of the sixth book."[8] Indeed, nearly all extant manuscripts of the *Elements* have a proposition to that effect attached to book 6, proposition 33; and many of the manuscripts have titles indicating that they are "from the edition of Theon" or even "from the lectures (συνουσίαι) of Theon."

It was not until the early nineteenth century, however, when Peyrard discovered that the manuscript Vaticanus Graecus 190, which lacks that proposition and is significantly different from the vulgate in other respects, must be an example of the pre-Theonic text, that it became possible to determine the nature of Theon's alterations of Euclid. They are many but mostly trivial, leaving the essential content of the *Elements* almost unchanged. In many places the wording has been altered or expanded to achieve consistency or perspicuity of expression. Of the occasional changes of mathematical substance, a very few are corrections of real mistakes in Euclid's text. More are due to Theon's misunderstanding the original. In some cases he apparently omits what he considers wrong. He makes frequent additions to fill what he considers gaps in Euclid's reasoning, even interpolating whole propositions, as in the above example. On the whole, his edition can hardly be said to improve on the original, although it may well have fulfilled its purpose of being easier for his students to use.

Other works by Euclid of which Theon produced editions are the *Data* (a treatise on what elements of a geometrical figure must be given to determine it) and the *Optics*, both of which exist in Theonic and pre-Theonic versions. The first of these obviously was intended for more advanced students but shows the same general characteristics as the edition of the *Elements*, except that in it Theon is more inclined to abbreviate Euclid's exposition. The Theonic version of the *Optics*, on the other hand, is so different from the original, not only in its language (which is characteristic of the later *koine*) but also in the form of the proofs, that Heiberg conjectured that the text we have consists of Theon's lectures on the subject as taken down by one of his students. This view is supported by the introduction to the Theonic version, which is an exposition of the principles of optics, mostly in indirect speech, occasionally introduced by "he said" or the like. "He" is not identified in the text; but this part clearly has been taken down from a lecture, and it is a plausible guess that "he" is Theon. There is no direct evidence, however, that Theon was responsible for this version, although he is the most likely candidate.

The same may be said of a treatise on catoptrics (theory of visual reflection) that in the manuscripts is attributed to Euclid but must be judged spurious on stylistic grounds alone. Analysis of the contents shows that it is a late compilation containing a mixture of Euclidean and post-Euclidean optical theory. The style and nature of the treatise would be appropriate for Theon, but that does not prove his authorship. Both the *Optics* and the *Catoptrics* are elementary, and are on a far lower scientific level than Ptolemy's *Optics*, which was, however, neglected in later antiquity and has survived only through the Arabic tradition. If, then, it is correct to associate Theon with these "Euclidean" optical works, we have an example in yet another branch of mathematics of his pedagogical activity, directed toward beginning students.

Theon also produced the version in which Ptolemy's *Handy Tables* have come down to us, according to the superscriptions in the manuscripts. The only evidence we have for the original version is Ptolemy's own introduction giving instructions for their use. From this it appears that the changes introduced by Theon were slight, and confined mostly to the arrangement of the tables and updating the chronological list. No one, however, has yet investigated the problem thoroughly.

Among lost works attributed to Theon by the ancient biographical source is a "Treatise on the Small Astrolabe."[9] Arabic bibliographical works also attribute to him a work entitled "On Operation With the Astrolabe."[10] The term "small astrolabe" evidently is used to distinguish this instrument from the "armillary sphere" (which is always the meaning of $\dot{\alpha}\sigma\tau\rho o\lambda\dot{\alpha}\beta o\nu$ in the *Almagest*). Thus it must refer to the "astrolabe" in the medieval and modern sense, that is, an instrument used to solve problems in spherical astronomy by means of projection of the celestial sphere onto a plane. This interpretation is confirmed by the Arabic sources, which use *asṭurlāb* only in this sense.

No work on the astrolabe predating the sixth century survives, but we do have the treatise of John Philoponus (*fl.* 520) in Greek, and that of Severus Sebokht (written before 660) in Syriac. The latter draws on a previous treatise, the author of which he calls "the philosopher." The historian al-Yaʿqūbī, writing in Arabic about 875, lists the contents of a treatise on the astrolabe that he ascribes to Ptolemy.[11] Neugebauer has shown that Sebokht's treatise corresponds closely to that described by al-Yaʿqūbī. Since Sebokht distinguishes "the philosopher" from Ptolemy (whose tables he quotes by name), and since al-Yaʿqūbī attributes to Ptolemy works (such as "On the Armillary Sphere") that other Arabic bibliographical sources attribute to Theon,[12] Neugebauer concludes, plausibly, that Theon is the author of the astrolabe treatise described by al-Yaʿqūbī and used by Sebokht. It is most unlikely, however, that Theon invented the astrolabe. The essential mathematical theory (of mapping circles of the celestial sphere onto a plane by stereographic projection) is treated by Ptolemy in his *Planisphaerium*, and the instrument may well predate Ptolemy.

Other lost works attributed to Theon in the Greek biographical source are "On Omens [for weather?] and Examination of Birds and the Cry of Ravens," "On the Rising of the Dog Star," and "On the Rising of the Nile." Nothing is known of these; and some or all should perhaps be attributed to the grammarian Theon of the first century of the Christian era, as should certainly the commentary by "Theon" on Aratus' astronomical poem *Phaenomena*. A slight work on the composition of an astronomical ephemeris found in one manuscript of Theon's commentary on the *Handy Tables* and ascribed to Theon by Delambre[13] certainly belongs to a later period.

Theon was a competent mathematician for his time, but completely unoriginal. He typifies the scholastic of later antiquity who was content to expound recognized classics in his field without ever attempting to go beyond them. The parts of his works that are of most interest for the modern reader, apart from the occasional pieces of historical information, are the worked examples of computations in his commentaries. It is of no small interest to see how the Greeks carried out calculations using their form of the sexagesimal place-value system (Theon provided worked examples of extraction of a square root, as well as multiplication and division). The detailed calculation of the solar eclipse of 364 (which Theon demonstrated both according to the *Almagest* tables and according to the *Handy Tables*) is also most instructive.

For a man of such mediocrity Theon was uncommonly influential. As we have seen, it was his version of Euclid's *Elements* that gained most currency. It was in his edition that the *Handy Tables* passed to Islamic astronomers (among whom it went under his name), and thence (via al-Battānī's work and the Toledan Tables) to Latin Europe in the twelfth century. His commentaries on the *Almagest* and the *Handy Tables* continued to be studied in the Greek-speaking Eastern Empire, and are the basis of at least one Byzantine commentary, that of Stephen of Alexandria on the *Handy Tables*. The work on the astrolabe was probably the main, if not the sole, source of transmission of the theory of that instrument to Islamic astronomy, whence it came to medieval Europe.

One short passage in Theon's shorter commentary on the *Handy Tables* had a remarkable history. He states that "certain ancient astrologers" believed that the tropical and solstitial points had a vibrating back-and-forth motion over eight degrees of the ecliptic. Although not accepting this theory, he explains how to compute the resultant correction to be applied to the positions of the heavenly bodies.[14] According to Theon, the tropical points of "the astrologers" are eight degrees in advance of (to the east of) those of Ptolemy in 158 B.C., and move westward with respect to the latter at a rate of one degree in eighty years. (Thus they would coincide in 483, at which point they would begin to move eastward again.) There is perhaps one other trace of this theory in antiquity, but it was not until Theon's description reached the Islamic astronomers that it bore fruit.

When observational astronomy began to be seriously practiced, under the caliph al-Maʾmūn (early ninth century), it was soon realized that the rate of precession (motion of the tropical points with respect to the fixed stars) as determined by Ptolemy (one degree in one hundred years) was not valid, and that 1.5 degrees in one hundred years was closer to the truth. Rather than impute error to the admired Ptolemy, many preferred to believe that the rate of precession was not a constant, but varied cyclically; the idea undoubtedly came from this passage of Theon's, as is shown by the earliest reference we have, in which the astronomer Ḥabash al-Ḥāsib (ca. 850) is said to have introduced into one set of his astronomical tables "the back-and-forth motion of the ecliptic according to the opinion of Theon."[15] Soon afterward Thābit ibn Qurra (ca. 870) wrote a treatise expounding the theory and proposing a physical model to account for it. This was translated into Latin in the twelfth century under the title "De motu octave spere," and proved enormously influential in western Europe. The theory, usually known as "trepidation," was adopted by the makers of the Alfonsine Tables, and appears in various forms in the works of Peurbach, Johann Werner, and Copernicus. It was still seriously discussed in the late sixteenth century.

NOTES

1. Both in bk. 6 of his commentary on the *Almagest*, Basel ed., 332 and 319, respectively.
2. *Tables manuelles astronomiques*, N. Halma, ed., I, 77–87; examples are on 31 and 74. In the second passage the "90th" year of Diocletian was corrected by H. Usener in his *Kleine Schriften*, III, 22, n. 20, to "94th" on the basis of MS readings. The correction is confirmed by my computations. This passage, however, is probably an interpolation.
3. "Fasti Theonis Alexandrini," H. Usener, ed., 367–368, 381.
4. *Suda Lexicon*, Ada Adler, ed., II, 702.
5. *Commentaires . . . de Théon . . .*, A. Rome, ed., II, 317.
6. *Ibid.*, 318.
7. *Tables manuelles astronomiques*, I, 27.
8. *Commentaires . . . de Théon . . .*, A. Rome, ed., II, 492.
9. *Suda Lexicon*, loc. cit.
10. For instance, *Fihrist*, G. Flügel, ed., I, 268.
11. Translated by M. Klamroth in *Zeitschrift der Deutschen morgenländischen Gesellschaft*, **42** (1888), 23–25.
12. *Ibid.*, 20–23; compare *Fihrist*, loc cit.
13. *Histoire de l'astronomie ancienne*, II, 635.
14. *Tables manuelles astronomiques*, I, 53.
15. Ibn al-Qifṭī, J. Lippert, ed., 170.

BIBLIOGRAPHY

I. ORIGINAL WORKS. Bks. 1–4 of the commentary on the *Almagest* were edited by A. Rome as *Commentaires de Pappus et de Théon d'Alexandrie sur l'Almageste*, II and III (Vatican City, 1936–1943), the commentary by Pappus being vol. I (1931)—they are Studi e Testi, nos. 72, 106, and 54, respectively. For the remaining books one must still consult the text in the Greek *Almagest*, *Claudii Ptolemaei magnae constructionis . . . lib. xiii. Theonis Alexandrini in eosdem commentariorum lib. xi* (Basel, 1538). On the relationship of Theon's commentary to that by Pappus, see Rome, *op. cit.*, II, lxxxii–lxxxvi; on Hypatia's supposed revision of bk. 3, *ibid.*, III, cxvi–cxxi.

The longer commentary on the *Handy Tables* has never been printed, except for two short passages published by Usener on pp. 360 and 372–373 of his ed. of Theon's list of consuls, "Fasti Theonis Alexandrini," pp. 359–381 in T. Mommsen, ed., *Chronica minora saeculorum IV. V. VI. VII.* (Berlin, 1898), which is *Monumenta Germaniae historica, auctores antiquissimi*, **13**, pt. 3. I have consulted the longer commentary in MS Nuremberg, Stadtbibliothek Cent. Gr. V, 8, fols. 215r–237v. The shorter commentary is printed in the very bad ed. of the *Handy Tables* by N. Halma, *Tables manuelles astronomiques de Ptolémée et de Théon*, I (Paris, 1822), 27–105. Ptolemy's own intro. to the *Handy Tables* is published by J. L. Heiberg in *Claudii Ptolemaei Opera quae exstant omnia*, II, *Opera astronomica minora* (Leipzig, 1907), 159–185.

On Theon's ed. of Euclid's *Elements*, see J. L. Heiberg, *Litterargeschichtliche Studien uber Euklid* (Leipzig, 1882), 174–180; and esp. Heiberg's prolegomena to his critical ed. of the *Elements*, *Euclidis Opera omnia*, V (Leipzig, 1888), li–lxxvi; for the *Data* see H. Menge, *ibid.*, VI (*Euclidis Data cum commentario Marini*), xxxii–xlix; for the *Optics*, Heiberg, *Litterargeschichtliche Studien*, 138–148; for the *Catoptrics, ibid.*, 148–153, and *Euclidis Opera omnia*, VII (*Optica et Catoptrica*), xlix–l.

II. SECONDARY LITERATURE. A good account is Konrat Ziegler, "Theon 15," in Pauly-Wissowa, *Real-Encyclopädie der classischen Altertumswissenschaft*, 2nd ser., X, cols. 2075–2080. The evidence for Theon's period of activity was collected by H. Usener, "Vergessenes," in his *Kleine Schriften*, III (Leipzig–Berlin,

1914), 21–23. The ancient biographical source is *Suda Lexicon*, Ada Adler, ed., II (Leipzig, 1931), 702, ll. 10–16. On Hypatia, see Socrates Scholasticus, *Historia ecclesiastica*, bk. 7, ch. 15, in J.-P. Migne, ed., *Patrologiae cursus completus*, series Graeca, LXVII, 767–770.

On the sources of the *Catoptrics* see A. Lejeune, "Recherches sur la catoptrique grecque," in *Mémoires de l'Académie royale de Belgique, Classe des lettres*, **52**, no. 2 (1957), 112–151. On Theon and the astrolabe see O. Neugebauer, "The Early History of the Astrolabe," in *Isis*, **40** (1949), 240–256. The treatise of Philoponus was published by H. H. Hase as "Joannis Alexandrini de usu astrolabii . . . libellus," in *Rheinisches Museum für Philologie*, **6** (1839), 127–171; that by Severus Sebokht by F. Nau, "Le traité sur l'asfrolabe plan de Sévère Sabokht," in *Journal asiatique*, 9th ser., **13** (1899), 56–101, 238–303.

The passages in al-Yaʿqūbī's work referring to the astrolabe and armillary sphere were translated by M. Klamroth as "Ueber die Auszüge aus griechischen Schriftstellern bei al-Jaʿqûbî IV," in *Zeitschrift der Deutschen morgenländischen Gesellschaft*, **42** (1888), 1–44. What purports to be the Arabic translation of the work on the armillary sphere is extant in the MS Bombay, Mollā Fīrūz 86. See Fuat Sezgin, *Geschichte des arabischen Schrifttums*, V (Leiden, 1974), 401. Bibliographical works in Arabic mentioning Theon include Ibn al-Nadīm, *Kitāb al-Fihrist*, G. Flügel, ed., I (Leipzig, 1871), 268; and Ibn al-Qiftī, *Taʾrīkh al-ḥukamāʾ*, J. Lippert, ed. (Leipzig, 1903), 108. Ptolemy's *Planisphaerium*, which exists only in the Arabic tradition, is printed (in the medieval Latin trans. from the Arabic) in his *Opera astronomica minora*, 227–259.

The work on the construction of an ephemeris is in Halma, *op. cit.*, III, 38–42, and described by J.-B. J. Delambre in his *Histoire de l'astronomie ancienne*, II (Paris, 1817), 635–638. Examples of division and extraction of a square root in the sexagesimal system, taken from Theon's commentary on the *Almagest*, are reproduced by T. L. Heath in his *A History of Greek Mathematics*, I (Oxford, 1921), 58–62. On Theon's calculation of the solar eclipse of 364 see A. Rome, "The Calculation of an Eclipse of the Sun According to Theon of Alexandria," in *Proceedings of the International Congress of Mathematicians, Cambridge, Mass., 1950*, I (Providence, R.I., 1952), 209–219. On Stephen of Alexandria's commentary on the *Handy Tables*, see H. Usener, "De Stephano Alexandrino," in his *Kleine Schriften*, III, 247–322.

For a possible use in a fourth-century papyrus of the "trepidation" described by Theon, see J. J. Burckhardt, "Zwei griechische Ephemeriden," in *Osiris*, **13** (1958), 79–92. The reference to Ḥabash's use of trepidation is in Ibn al-Qiftī, *op. cit.*, 170. The Latin text of Thābit's *De motu octave spere* has been printed many times; it is best consulted in J. M. Millás Vallicrosa, *Estudios sobre Azarquiel* (Madrid–Granada, 1943–1950), 496–509, trans. and commentary by O. Neugebauer, "Thabit ben Qurra 'On the Solar Year' and 'On the Motion of the

Eighth Sphere,' " in *Proceedings of the American Philosophical Society*, **106** (1962), 264–299. The best discussion of the history of the theory of trepidation in the Latin West is Jerzy Dobrzycki, "Teoria precesji w astronomii średniowiecznej" ("The Theory of Precession in Medieval Astronomy"), with Russian and English summaries, in *Studia i materiały z dziejów nauki polskiej*, ser. C, **11** (1965), 3–47. See also J. L. E. Dreyer, *History of the Planetary Systems From Thales to Kepler* (Cambridge, 1906), index under "Trepidation."

G. J. Toomer

THEON OF SMYRNA (*fl.* early second century A.D.), *mathematics, astronomy.*

Theon is known chiefly for his handbook, usually called *Expositio rerum mathematicarum ad legendum Platonem utilium*. He may well have been the person called "the old Theon" by Theon of Alexandria in his commentary on the *Almagest*. Ptolemy referred to "Theon the mathematician," who is almost certainly the Theon discussed here, and ascribed to him observations of the planets Venus and Mercury made in 127, 129, 130, and 132 (*Almagest* 9.9, 10.1, 10.2). The latest writers named by Theon were Thrasyllus, who was active under Tiberius, and Adrastus, the Peripatetic and Aristotelian scholar, who flourished not earlier than A.D. 100. A contemporary bust of Theon from Smyrna has an inscription calling him *Platonikos*: he was thus also known as a philosopher, and his philosophical interests are evident in the *Expositio*.

The treatise is valuable for its wide range of citation from earlier sources. There is little evidence of mathematical originality. Despite the title, the book has little to offer the specialist student of Plato's mathematics. It is, rather, a handbook for philosophy students, written to illustrate how arithmetic, geometry, stereometry, music, and astronomy are interrelated. Geometry and stereometry are cursorily treated, however, perhaps because Theon assumed his readers to be adequately acquainted with them. A promise to provide a lengthy treatment of the harmony of the cosmos (p. 17, l. 24, Hiller edition) is not kept in the extant manuscripts; if that part of the treatise was ever written, it may have been lost early.

The arithmetical section treats the types of numbers in the Pythagorean manner; Theon dealt, for example, with primes, geometrical numbers (such as squares), "side" and "diameter" numbers, and progressions.

Music is divided into three kinds: instrumental, musical intervals expressed numerically (theoretical music), and the harmony of the universe. Theon stated clearly that he is not claiming to have discovered any musical principles himself; his aim is to expand the findings of his predecessors. He therefore quoted amply from his authorities—Thrasyllus, Adrastus, Aristoxenus, Hippasus, Eudoxus, and, of course, Plato. In the account of proportions and ratios the discussion concerns the treatment in Eratosthenes' *Platonikos* of the difference between interval and ratio ($\delta\iota\acute{\alpha}\sigma\tau\eta\mu\alpha$ and $\lambda\acute{o}\gamma o\varsigma$). Eratosthenes is also followed in the exposition of the different kinds of means. Some of the musical part descends into mere number mysticism; it is perhaps the least satisfactory feature of the work. A typical remark (p. 106, Hiller ed.) is that "the decad determines number in all respects. It embraces nature entire within itself, even and odd, moving and unmoved, good and bad."

In contrast, the astronomical section, which also depends much on Adrastus, is of great merit. The earth is a sphere; mountains are minute when compared with the earth, which lies at the center of the universe. The several circles of the heavens are explained, as are the assumed deviations in latitude of the sun, moon, and planets. The various views concerning the order of the heavenly bodies are noted; those of the (neo)Pythagoreans are contrasted with the systems of Eratosthenes and "the mathematicians." Some interesting hexameter verses quoted (pp. 138–140, Hiller ed.) on this topic are said to be by Alexander of Aetolia, but are perhaps by Alexander of Ephesus, a contemporary of Cicero; to the other planets, the earth, the sun, the moon, and the sphere of the fixed stars, Alexander gives a tone, so that all are set in an octave by arrangement of the intervals. Eratosthenes did not count the stationary earth, so in his verses he gave a note each to all seven moving bodies and an eighth to the sphere of the fixed stars. This is as close as Theon came to delivering the promised exposition of the harmony of the cosmos.

Theon explained the progressions, stations, and retrogradations of the planets. He described the eccentric and epicyclic hypotheses, and their equivalence. He seemed to consider Hipparchus as the inventor of the epicyclic hypothesis (p. 188, l. 16, Hiller ed.) that "Hipparchos praised as his own"; but there is a misunderstanding, because Apollonius clearly understood the principle of the epicycle before Hipparchus. Apollonius is not among the authorities cited by Theon.

Estimates of the greatest arcs of Mercury and Venus from the sun are given as 20° and 50° (p.

187, ll. 10–13, Hiller ed.). After an extensive account of the systems of rotating spheres worked out by Eudoxus, Callippus and Aristotle (pp. 178 ff., Hiller ed.), Theon turned to conjunctions, transits, occultations, eclipses, and the axis through the poles and the center of the zodiac.

Historically the most valuable part of the concluding pages is the brief fragment from Eudemus on pre-Socratic astronomy, which is full of problems. For example, the extant archetype manuscript here states that according to Anaximander, the earth is "on high" ($\mu\epsilon\tau\acute{\epsilon}\omega\rho o\varsigma$) and "moves" ($\kappa\iota\nu\epsilon\hat{\iota}\tau\alpha\iota$) about the center of the cosmos. Montucla's emendation of $\kappa\iota\nu\epsilon\hat{\iota}\tau\alpha\iota$ to $\kappa\epsilon\hat{\iota}\tau\alpha\iota$ ("rests") (see p. 198, l. 19, Hiller ed.) is attractive but by no means certain, since we do not know what Eudemus wrote, whatever Anaximander's view of the matter may have been. Anaximenes, not Anaxagoras, is here said to have declared that the moon "has her light from the sun."

Other works by Theon are lost. He himself referred to a commentary on Plato's *Republic* (*Expositio* p. 146, l. 4, Hiller ed.). Ibn al-Nadīm's *Fihrist* mentioned a treatise by him on the titles of Plato's writings and the order in which they should be read. He wrote on the ancestry of Plato, but not certainly in a separate treatise; the study may have formed part of the *Republic* commentary (see Hiller ed., p. 146, on Proclus, *On Timaeus*, p. 26A).

BIBLIOGRAPHY

The text of the *Expositio* depends almost entirely on two MSS in Venice: the number theory and the music are in Venet. Marc. 307 (11th–2th cent.), and the astronomy in Venet. Marc. 303 (13th–14th cent.). The first part (pp. 1–119, Hiller ed.) was edited by Ismael Boulliau (Paris, 1644); the other (pp. 120–205, Hiller ed.) by T. H. Martin (Paris, 1849; repr. Groningen, 1971). Both were edited together by E. Hiller in the Teubner version (Leipzig, 1878).

For further discussion, see K. von Fritz, in Pauly-Wissowa, *Real-Encyclopädie der classischen Altertumswissenschaft*, 2nd ser., X (1934), 2067–2075, *s.v.* Theon (14), with bibliography; and T. L. Heath, *A History of Greek Mathematics*, II (Oxford, 1921), 238–244. On the hexameter verses, see E. Hiller, in *Rheinisches Museum für Philologie*, **26** (1871), 586–587; and A. Meineke, *Analecta Alexandrina* (Berlin, 1843; repr. Hildesheim, 1964), 372–374.

G. L. HUXLEY

THEOPHILUS (**Theophilus Presbyter,** also called **Rugerus**) (*fl.* Helmarshausen, Germany [?], early twelfth century), *metallurgy, chemistry.*

The pseudonymous author of *De diversis artibus*, an instructive treatise on practical arts for the adornment of the church, Theophilus wrote in the first quarter of the twelfth century—perhaps, as Lynn White has suggested, in 1122–1123 in answer to Bernard of Clairvaux's animadversions on ecclesiastical luxury. On the basis of a note "qui et Rugerus," written in the seventeenth century on the title page of the Vienna manuscript, Albert Ilg identified Theophilus with the Benedictine monk Roger, who was active as a goldsmith in Helmarshausen around 1100 and slightly after. Although this identification was not accepted by two subsequent editors, Degering and Theobald, the most recent studies support it. Helmarshausen was an important center in northwestern Germany for all of the arts described by Theophilus, and some surviving pieces of ecclesiastical metalwork made by the historic Roger are of a style that almost seems designed to illustrate the metalworking techniques described in the manuscript.

The work is often called *Diversarum artium schedula*, following Lessing, who adopted a phrase from the preface to book I in two manuscripts that lacked titles. The title *De diversis artibus* was found by Dodwell on both the Vienna and the Cambridge manuscripts, and has been used by him and subsequent writers.

There are three parts to the work—book I, on the art of the painter; book II, on the art of the worker in glass; and book III, on the art of the metalworker. The last is most detailed. Art historians have made much use of book I; but the sections on glass and metalwork are of more importance in the history of science and technology, for they constitute the earliest firsthand accounts of many pyrotechnological processes that later bore fruit in chemical science and engineering, as well as in the entire modern materials industry.

With no theoretical speculation whatever, Theophilus recorded intimate practical details of the preparation of pigments, dyes, stained glass, brass, and bronze; the alloying and working of gold and silver; the heat treatment of steel; and the casting of metal objects ranging from small silver chalice handles made by the lost-wax process to huge bronze bells cast in clay molds shaped on a lathe. He described the separation of gold and silver by cementation and by sulfide reaction, as well as the removal of impurities by cupellation. His solder compositions were close to the minimum-melting-point alloys in the series copper-silver and lead-tin as known today. Theophilus gave details for the manufacture on a fairly large scale, for use as pigments, of mercury sulfide, basic copper acetate (verdigris), lead oxides (both PbO and Pb_3O_4), and lead carbonate. Silver sulfide was made and used as niello; linseed oil appeared as a varnish; gold leaf and powder were prepared for manuscript illumination; and vegetable colors sensitive to pH were properly employed. Glass was made by melting a fritted mixture of sand and beechwood ashes in wide-mouthed pots set in a relatively large furnace with a separate fritting hearth. This is the first written reference to the use of wood ashes to produce potassium glass, which two centuries earlier had begun to replace the ancient sodium glass based on natron. The color of Theophilus' glass changed with melting conditions and seems to have depended on the state of oxidation of iron and manganese present as impurities in the raw materials, although coloring through intentional additions of metallic oxides had been well established centuries earlier.

Mechanically, Theophilus made no use of the wind and water power sources that were just being introduced; but he described smaller devices, such as the rotary grindstone, the lathe (in several modifications), an elaborate organ, and a device for crosshatching iron surfaces to receive silver and gold overlay. He described in detail all the metalworker's tools, including the wire-drawing plate. There is little quantitative measurement and no philosophical speculation on the nature of materials; but Theophilus admirably reflects the practical environment and the mental attitude that characterized prescientific technology, and that led to many discoveries of the properties of different kinds of substances, the effects of heat upon them, and the nature of chemical reactions in general. Theophilus was not, of course, the inventor or discoverer of the processes he records, which had existed as practical tradition—in some cases for many centuries—without being reflected in the written record. Virtually everything he says is clear and is confirmed by the evidence of surviving contemporary objects.

Theophilus was an original writer—the first to describe clearly, from personal experience, the practical arts for the purpose of instruction and inspiration. His *De diversis artibus* is an incomparably better source of information on medieval technology than are the compilations of ancient and corrupt recipes, such as the *Mappae clavicula* and the *Compositiones variae* and their derivatives, which were in existence at the same time and were more a product of the acquisitiveness of librarians than of the practical labors of technical men.

BIBLIOGRAPHY

I. Original Works. The earliest MSS of the *De diversis artibus* are two of the 12th century, one at Wolfenbüttel (Herzog-August Bibliothek 4373) and one at Vienna (Nationalbibliothek 2527). The 13th-century MS in the British Museum (Harley 3915) is the most complete. For a listing of later MSS, see Johnson, Dodwell, and Hawthorne and Smith (below).

The best Latin text, with critical apparatus and English trans., is C. R. Dodwell, *Theophilus, De diversis artibus . . . . Theophilus, The Various Arts . . . .* (London, 1961). The first complete printed ed., based mainly on the Wolfenbüttel MS, was published by G. E. Lessing in his *Zur Geschichte und Literatur aus den Schützen der herzoglichen Bibliothek zu Wolfenbüttel,* VI (Brunswick, 1781), frequently repr. throughout the 19th century in Lessing's *Sämmtliche Schriften.* A critical text and French trans. by Charles de l'Escalopier (Paris, 1843) was soon followed by Robert Hendrie's text (mainly based on the British Museum MS) and English trans., *Theophili, qui et Rugerus, presbyteri et monachi libri III. De diversis artibus: Seu diversarum artium schedula . . .,* with a second title page, *An Essay Upon Various Arts . . . by Theophilus, Called Also Rugerus, Priest and Monk, Forming an Encyclopedia of Christian Art of the Eleventh Century* (London, 1847). A frequently cited, though carelessly edited, text and German trans. is by Albert Ilg: *Theophilus Presbyter Schedula diversarum artium. . . . Revidierter Text, Übersetzung und Appendix,* no. 7 in the series Quellenschriften für Kunstgeschichte und Kunsttechnik des Mittelalters und der Renaissance (Vienna, 1874).

All the above eds. were mainly art-historical or philological in purpose. The first to be edited primarily for its technical content was the text, and German trans., of bks. II and III by Wilhelm Theobald, *Technik des Kunsthandwerks im zehnten* [sic] *Jahrhundert des Theophilus Presbyter Diversarum artium schedula, in auswahl neu herausgegeben, übersetzt und erläutert. . . .* (Berlin, 1933). Then, after over a century of neglect in English, two independent eds. appeared within two years—Dodwell (see above) and J. G. Hawthorne and C. S. Smith, *On Divers Arts. The Treatise of Theophilus. Translated From the Medieval Latin With Introduction and Notes* (Chicago, 1963). There are several other 19th-century eds.

II. Secondary Literature. Discussions of Theophilus' treatise and its influence are in the intro. to the printed eds. listed above. The German 1933 and English 1963 translations have extensive technical notes on glass and metalwork. For pigments, see especially H. Rosen-Runge, "Die Buchmalereirezepte des Theophilus," in *Münchner Jahrbuch der bildenden Kunst,* 3rd ser., **3–4** (1952–1953), 159–171; and *Farbgebung und Technik frümittelalterliche Buchmalerei. Studien zu den Traktaten Mappae Clavicula und Heraclius,* 2 vols. (Munich, 1967).

On the MSS and background, see Hermann Degering, "Theophilus Presbiter qui et Rugerus," in *Westfälische Studien . . . Alois Bömer gewidmet* (Leipzig, 1928), 248–262; R. P. Johnson, "Note on Some Manuscripts of the *Mappae Clavicula,*" in *Speculum,* **10** (1935), 72–81; "The Manuscripts of the *Schedula* of Theophilus Presbyter," *ibid.,* **13** (1938), 86–103; and *Compositiones variae . . . An Introductory Study,* XXIII, no. 3 in Illinois Studies in Language and Literature (Urbana, 1939); D. V. Thompson, "The *Schedula* of Theophilus Presbyter," in *Speculum,* **7** (1932), 199–220; "Theophilus Presbyter . . .," *ibid.,* **42** (1967), 313–339; Lynn White, Jr., "Theophilus Redivivus," in *Technology and Culture,* **5** (1964), 224–233; and C. S. Smith and J. G. Hawthorne, "Mappae Clavicula, a Little Key to the World of Medieval Techniques," in *Transactions of the American Philosophical Society,* **64,** pt. 4 (1974).

Cyril Stanley Smith

THEOPHRASTUS (*b.* Eresus, Lesbos, *ca.* 371 B.C.; *d.* Athens, *ca.* 287 B.C.), *botany, mineralogy, philosophy.*

Theophrastus was associated with Aristotle for more than two decades and succeeded him as head of what came to be known as the Peripatetic school. According to one report (Diogenes Laërtius V, 36), he studied under Plato before joining Aristotle. It is likely that he met Aristotle in Asia Minor (347) or on Lesbos (344–342), went with him to Macedonia (342–335), and then to Athens when Aristotle returned and began to teach in the Lyceum (335). When Aristotle retired to Chalcis shortly before he died (322), Theophrastus became the leader of the scholars and students who had met with Aristotle at the Lyceum.

During his tenure of thirty-five years Theophrastus had two thousand students, among them the physician Erasistratus and the philosopher Arcesilaus. So well was he regarded by the Athenians that an attempt to prosecute him for impiety failed and a restrictive law against him and other philosophers was repealed. On his death he bequeathed the school's property jointly to ten relatives and associates. To one of these, Neleus, he left the library, which would have included not only his own writings and those of Aristotle but also, presumably, the collection of others' writings made by Aristotle and himself. The provisions in his will for repairs to the property, for the use of it by a few friends, and for the disposition of the books suggest that the school had suffered in the tumult through which Athens had passed in the years before his death and that he regarded its future as uncertain. (On the transmission of the Peripatetic texts, see "Aristotle: Tradition and Influence.")

The Hellenistic lists of Theophrastus' writings contain over two hundred titles that cover not only the various branches of science and philosophy but also history, law, literature, music, poetics, and politics. Even if there is duplication in the lists, if some titles belong to parts of longer works, and if some are incorrectly ascribed, it is nevertheless evident that Theophrastus was a man of remarkable learning and industry. From his writings there remain only two longer works on botany, a few short treatises on science, an essay on metaphysics, the *Characters*, and fragmentary excerpts and paraphrases in the works of later writers. In length the two botanical works are about double the remainder.

From such meager and unbalanced evidence a uniform account and just assessment of Theophrastus' scientific accomplishments are impossible. He has generally been considered a botanist whose contributions in other fields were secondary to those of his teacher. His dependence on Aristotle may have been distorted by the transmission of the texts; several of the shorter treatises, notably the *Metaphysics* and *De sensibus*, are found in manuscripts with the longer works of Aristotle on the same subjects, and many of the fragments of lost works are in later Greek commentaries to Aristotle, thus giving the impression that his work was little more than an appendix.

Recent scholarship (Regenbogen and Steinmetz) has done much to correct this impression, but it is doubtful that an exact line can be drawn between the contributions of the two men. Their fundamental agreement is evident from their writing, but it does not follow that their long association was that of teacher and student. That, even when disagreeing, Theophrastus does not mention Aristotle by name is probably a sign not merely of respect but also of his assumption of responsibility for their work as a whole. The books that Neleus inherited from Theophrastus were a Peripatetic corpus. Apparently there was no systematic attempt to divide the works by author until catalogs were made toward the end of the third century B.C.; and even after the editions of Andronicus of Rhodes in the first century B.C., doubt remained. Within the works attributed to Aristotle in antiquity, modern scholars have not only discerned the influence of Theophrastus but also have identified some treatises as partly or wholly his. Questions of authorship are beyond the scope of this article. If in what follows differences are stressed, they should be regarded as due to a continuing process rather than to a radical change in attitude or method.

A further problem in an account of Theophrastus is the state of the preserved evidence. The latest general edition of his work (Wimmer) is based on incomplete knowledge of the manuscripts and fragments, and few of the individual works have received detailed study. It seems best to confine this article to a few works that are accessible in more recent editions with commentary and scholarly translation.

The general trend of Theophrastus' thought is shown by the *Metaphysics*. In the main he does not deviate from Aristotle's assumptions but, rather, points out the difficulties in their application. Thus he agrees that reality is divided into the intelligible and the sensible and that the intelligible cause of the sensible world is an unmoved first mover that causes motion by being the object of desire. But, he asks, if there is only one such mover, why do all the heavenly bodies not have the same motion? Why does desire not presuppose soul and, therefore, a psychical motion better than rotation? Why is rotation limited to the heavenly bodies and shared only incidentally by the sublunar region? If motion is as essential to the heavenly bodies as life is to living things, does it need any explanation (7–11, 27–28)?

With regard to teleology, too, Theophrastus has doubts. He accepts the general principle that nature does nothing in vain, but he questions its applicability. In the heavens, and still more in the terrestrial region, some things seem to be due to coincidence or necessity. What purpose is served by the incursions and refluxes of the sea or by the birth and nutrition of animals—let alone by such superfluous things as the breasts of males or such positively harmful things as the horns of deer? If, he says, nature does desire what is best, most things are recalcitrant; even among animate things, which are a small part of the universe, there are few for which existence is better than nonexistence (15, 28–32).

In the *Metaphysics*, Theophrastus offers no new or conclusive answers to the problems raised—nor is there evidence that he ever did. He does, however, suggest a way of dealing with the phenomena alone. We should perhaps conceive the unity of the universe to be that of a system the various parts of which are fitted together in the greatest possible harmony but differ in the degree to which they possess order, the heavenly bodies possessing more and the sublunar region less (16, 34). Hence there must be different kinds of knowledge, and each kind must use a method appropriate to its object: there must be different methods for the objects of reason; for primary natural objects; and for secondary natural objects, such as animals, plants, and inanimate things (22). When we advance to first principles, we contemplate them with the mind; but the starting point in our search for causes is sense perception, which observes differences among its objects and supplies material for thought (19, 24–25). This emphasis on the differences among objects and methods of knowledge, and on the need to start from observation of the particular, is characteristic of Theophrastus' scientific works as a whole.

On the nature of the primary material substances, Theophrastus accepted Aristotle's theory of four qualitatively distinguished simple bodies. In the introductory sections of his *De igne*, however, he gives a penetrating criticism of the theory. Comparing fire with the other simple bodies, he makes several observations that cast doubt on its status as an elementary substance: the other simple bodies change into one another but cannot generate themselves, but fire both generates and destroys itself; the ways in which fire is generated are for the most part violent; fire is generated in many different ways, but the other simple bodies are generated only by natural change into one another; moreover, these other simple bodies exist by themselves, but fire requires fuel as a substrate and is destroyed when the fuel has been exhausted (1–3).

The last objection is the most serious; if fire cannot exist without fuel, it cannot rightly be called a primary substance or principle, since it is neither simple nor prior to its substrate (4). Theophrastus considers several possibilities: that the first sphere is pure and unmixed heat, that celestial and terrestrial fires are different in kind, and that the sun is a kind of fire. He appears inclined to view heat rather than fire as a principle, for, he says, heat is more widely distributed than fire and is more influential in natural processes. He comes to no conclusion but instead notes further difficulties. If heat is always bound up in a substrate, it appears to be an affection of something else and not a principle. If it is objected that fire cannot exist independently, the same may be said of all the simple bodies, since they are all compounds and are reciprocally involved (8). As he recognizes, his discussion of fire has led to larger questions about the nature of first causes.

Theophrastus declines to attempt answers to the larger questions, and in the main part of *De igne* he concerns himself with terrestrial phenomena of fire. His topics include not only such central matters as the generation, preservation, and extinction of fire but also such farfetched examples as the quenching of fire by salamanders, the melting of coins in the belly, and the jumping of grain on Babylonian threshing floors. In short, he excludes nothing that seems, or is said, to be connected with fire and heat.

In some explanations he relies on two Aristotelian concepts, the interaction of opposites and antiperistasis (the concentration of one thing by another). By the former he explains the generation and destruction of fire: fire is nourished by moist fuel but is destroyed by an excess of moisture or cold, or by a greater fire (10–11, 20, 26–27). By the latter he explains why, in cold weather, fires burn more rapidly, baths are warmer, and our bodies are stronger (12–13, see also 14–18), and why fires are extinguished by excessive compression (11, 58). The difference between the two concepts is that the latter assumes that the qualitative opposites are stable and that the greater does not assimilate the lesser, as it does in combustion. This assumption runs through much of the treatise. He speaks of fire, heat, and flame as if they were composed of discrete particles having different degrees of fineness; and he explains interaction by the symmetry or asymmetry between the particles of one substance and the pores of another (for instance, 42). In so doing he appears to abandon the theory of qualitative elements and return to the pre-Socratic effluence-pore theory. It is clear, however, that the particles are not Democritean atoms, for interaction requires both the appropriate size of particles and pores and the qualitative difference between the substances. Theophrastus has not arrived at a new theory about the essential nature of fire as an element. He has, rather, demonstrated that, as Aristotle had said (*Meteorologica*, 340b21–23), the fire of our experience is different from elemental fire and that the various phenomena associated with it do not have a single explanation. It remained for his successor Strato to formulate a Peripatetic atomism.

Among the extant writings Theophrastus' monograph on petrology, *De lapidibus*, best illustrates his investigation into inanimate compounds of the elements. In this, along with several other works known only from fragments and references, he carries forward the detailed investigation proposed by Aristotle at the end of *Meteorologica* III. His theoretical basis is the classification already made by Plato and adapted by Aristotle: metals are composed of water, and stones and mineral earths are composed of earth (1). On this basis he gives a brief description of the processes by which stones and mineral earths are formed (2–3): their matter is earth that has been purified and made uniform through conflux or filtering or some other kind of separation; the purity and uniformity of the matter determines such qualities as smoothness, density, luster, and transparency; solidification of the matter is due in some cases to heat and in others to cold—although it might seem that all things composed of earth are solidified by heat, since solidification and dissolution are contrary processes.

By thus admitting that heat and cold may have the same effect, Theophrastus recognizes that the classification, as simply stated, is not adequate to account for the diversity of the phenomena. Just as metals are solidified by cold and dissolved by heat, stones and earths ought to be solidified by heat and dissolved by cold; but in fact some stones, such as metal-bearing ores, are dissolved by heat (9). It is noteworthy, too, that although he apparently intends conflux and filtering to account for some distinctive differences between formations (deposits and veins have been suggested by Eichholz), he makes only two inconclusive references to them when he turns to specific instances (50, 61).

The body of the work is a systematic discussion of stones (3–47) and mineral earths (48–69) found around the Mediterranean and in the farther regions traversed by Alexander's army. Substances are distinguished by visual and tactile qualities and by their behavior, particularly in reaction to fire (9–19). Included are the earliest known Greek references to the use of mineral fuel (16), the pearl (36), the touchstone in testing alloys (45–47), and the manufacture of white lead (56). Of particular interest for the history of technology are the accounts of the preparation of pigments (50–60) and the uses of earths dug from pits (61–69).

Theophrastus' purpose is not to give an exhaustive treatment of the subject but to illustrate differences between types and to record unusual cases for further investigation. His descriptions are for the most part brief and restricted to what is readily observable, and he omits many substances that must have been familiar (his list is only one-tenth that of Pliny). How much Theophrastus knew from his own observation is questionable. He probably did not collect specimens systematically or conduct experiments. He frequently makes it clear that he is relying on written documents or hearsay; he has not always observed what he reports as fact, as is shown by his statement that the pearl is transparent. His reliance on the reports of others leads him to treat seriously what might seem too fantastic even for mention, such as stones formed by the urine of the lynx (28) and pumice formed by sea-foam (19,22). Such instances underscore the factual limitations of Theophrastus' work, but they do not detract from its historical significance. It is the first methodical study of mineralogy and the only one before Agricola's in the sixteenth century that considers mineral substances for themselves rather than for their curative or magical properties.

Theophrastus' works on botany correspond to Aristotle's *Historia animalium* and *De partibus animalium*; in *Historia plantarum* he is concerned with description, classification, and analysis, and in *De causis plantarum* with etiology. In the first book of *Historia plantarum*, taking the tree as his standard, he deals with general matters: permanent and annual parts and their composition; classification into tree, shrub, undershrub, and herb; general and special differences in the plants as wholes and in their parts. From this Theophrastus proceeds to particulars: book II, domesticated trees, their propagation, and their care; book III, wild trees; book VI, undershrubs; books VII and VIII, herbaceous plants. Included are three books on special topics: book IV, trees and plants peculiar to certain regions; book V, woods and their uses; book IX, plant juices and medicinal herbs. The main subjects of *De causis plantarum* are the following: book I, generation and propagation, sprouting and fruiting; book II, effects of natural factors; book III, effects of cultivation; book IV, seeds; book V, alteration, degeneration, and death; book VI, plant juices. (The treatise *De odoribus* and the lost treatise on wine and olive oil may originally have followed book VI.)

Within this framework Theophrastus describes and discusses some 550 species and varieties, extending geographically from the Atlantic through the Mediterranean littoral and as far east as India. Among his literary sources he cites poets, philosophers, and scientists from Homer to Plato (notably Empedocles, Menestor, and Democritus among the pre-Socratics who had written on plants). He makes frequent references to the beliefs and practices of farmers, physicians, root cutters, and other groups, as well as to the inhabitants of various regions (especially Macedonia, Arcadia, and the vicinity of Mt. Ida). His anonymous sources undoubtedly include not only oral reports but also technical writings, such as those by Diocles of Carystus on roots and poisons, and nontechnical writings, such as those by men who accompanied Alexander and noted vegetation of military importance or special interest along the way. (On the last see, for example, *Historia*, bk. IV.)

In his typological procedure Theophrastus makes no fundamental innovations; Aristotle had already used the same procedure in many other subjects, including zoology. Nor does he differ from Aristotle in his physiological theory. He regards plants as living things with a life dependent on the proportion of their innate heat and moisture and on the harmonious relation between them and their environment (*Historia*, I, 1, 1; 2,4 f.; 11, 1; *De causis*, I, 4,6; 10,5; 21,3; 22,2–3). His chief difference is, rather, in perspective. Aristotle regards plants as the lowest members of a system that culminates in man, as sharing with animals the nutritive faculty of the soul, and as illustrating similarities and dissimilarities within the system as a whole. Theophrastus, on the other hand, concentrates on the plants themselves and avoids systematization beyond his immediate subject. He does not speak of the plant's soul; and, although he does use analogy between plants and animals, he emphasizes its limits and says that to strive after comparison where none is possible is a waste of effort and may cause us to abandon the method that is appropriate to the investigation (*Historia*, I,1,4–5).

Theophrastus' insistence on appropriate method follows from his recognition of the differences between plants and animals (*Historia*, I,3,4) and of the manifold nature of plants. Generalization about plants as a whole is difficult because no part is common to them all as the mouth and stomach are common to all animals; they do not all have root, stem, branch, twig, leaf, flower, fruit, bark, core, fibers, and veins, although these and such parts belong to the plant's essential nature (*Historia*, I,1,10 f.). This diversity also makes it difficult to generalize about major classes and even about individual kinds; there is overlapping between classes, some plants seem to depart from their essential nature when they are cultivated (*Historia*, I,3,2), and each kind embraces several different forms (*Historia*, I,14,3). It is now clear why in the *Metaphysics* Theophrastus speaks of a method appropriate to plants as distinct from inanimate substances and even animals. In the study of such diverse material our object is not the universal but the particular, and our instrument is not reason but sense perception (*De causis*, II,4,8); we must pursue the unknown through what is manifest to the senses (*Historia*, I,2,3); and in offering explanations we must use causal principles that are in accord with the particular natures of the plants, for our accounts must agree with our observations (*De causis*, I,1,1).

Consistent with this methodological principle, Theophrastus treats received theory and opinion with respect and skepticism, and seldom commits himself outright on one side or the other. Thus he quotes Aristotle's dictum that nature does nothing in vain, but he does so only in support of what is already evident to perception (*De causis*, I,1,1). He explains the pericarp by anthropocentric teleology as being for man's nourishment, but he goes on to explain it in relation to the seed (*De causis*, I, 16,1; compare I,21,1). The reported infertility of cypress seeds makes him doubt that Aristotle's dictum is true, but he does not renounce it (*De causis*, IV,4,2). So, too, Theophrastus speaks of spontaneous generation and transmutation as if they were simple facts; but again he offers explanations that might have led him to reject these notions, and in the end he leaves the question open (*Historia*, III,1,4–6; VIII,8,3–4). The same noncommittal attitude is evident in his treatment of particular reports. Along with the credible, he includes nonsensical tales, such as that the scorpion is killed by the application of wolfsbane but revived by white hellebore. His comment on this last is significant for his use of all the theories and evidence received from others: "Fabulous tales are not made up without reason" (*Historia*, IX,18,2).

By assembling his data impartially, classifying and discussing them within an elastic system, and withholding judgment when it was not secured by facts, Theophrastus created what he called an appropriate method and laid the groundwork for modern botany. Many of his observations and explanations were necessarily incomplete or erroneous; use of the simplest magnifying lens would have resolved many of his doubts. Among his contributions of lasting interest, his accounts of the following may be mentioned: the "pericarpion," used for the first time as a technical term (*Historia*, I,2,1); parenchymatous and prosenchymatous tissues (*Historia*, I,2,5, f.); petalous and apetalous flowers (*Historia*, I,13,1); hypogynous, perigynous, and epigynous insertions of the corolla (*Historia*, I,13,3); centripetal and centrifugal inflorescences (*Historia*, VII,14,2); angiosperms and gymnosperms (*Historia*, I,11,2); monocotyledons and dicotyledons (*Historia*, VIII, 2,1–4). All except the first of these terms are modern, but there is no doubt that Theophrastus correctly distinguished the features to which they are applied. In the last passage he gives the clearest and most accurate description of germinating seeds before Malpighi in the seventeenth century.

Theophrastus' achievement in botany is all the

more remarkable when we bear in mind that these two works were a small part of his writings. Their preservation does not allow us to suppose that botany was his primary interest; the loss of his works on other subjects may have been due not to their lesser importance but to the chances of manuscript transmission or to the tastes of later antiquity. Nothing in his writing indicates that he thought himself to be—as he has since been called—a professional botanist or that he considered his work comprehensive in detail or in theory. Of the plants that Theophrastus mentions only a third are not attested from other sources, and domesticated and familiar wild varieties are predominant (he says that most of the wild are nameless and little-known; *Historia*, I,14,4); he also omits many plants that he must have known.

Although some of his accounts (such as that of germinating seeds) indicate personal observation, they do not warrant the belief that Theophrastus had an experimental garden or made extensive field trips in Greece, let alone abroad. Nor is there any reason to think that he had collaborators or trained informants either in the Greek part of the Mediterranean or with Alexander's army; if he had, there could hardly be so many gaps and uncertainties in his information. Some of his second-hand information he could not test himself; but, even when he could easily have done so, in some cases he did not (see, for example, *Historia*, VII,1,3–5). It may be asked what Theophrastus' intention was in writing at such length about incomplete and unverified evidence. The answer is probably to be found in his frequent reminders to himself and his readers that there must be further investigation. He was aware that what he wrote was merely the beginning, that more and better data were needed, and that his explanations might need revision. His hopes apparently came to nothing. Later Greek and Roman authors enlarged the stock of useful knowledge and Pliny compiled it, but scientific botany progressed no further until the Renaissance.

Theophrastus was no less influential as a historian and critic of science than as a scientist. Besides several studies of individual pre-Socratics, he wrote a general history in sixteen or eighteen books known as the *Physicorum opiniones*. As Diels has shown, this work was the direct or indirect source of many of the summaries made by the doxographers. The most extensive of these summaries, a handbook known as *Placita philosophorum*, was compiled by Aëtius in the second century from an earlier Stoic summary that in turn was based on Theophrastus' history, with additions of later Stoic and Epicurean material. Through these and related summaries Theophrastus provided not only many of the details of pre-Aristotelian theories but also their selection and schematic arrangement.

It has been supposed that Theophrastus' aim was to write an objective history, but this supposition may be questioned. The extracts on material causes that have been preserved from the first book, although they indicate firsthand knowledge of the pre-Socratic texts, closely follow the summary of causal theories given by Aristotle in *Metaphysics* I; and on other topics there are many similarities between the doxographers and the summary accounts of Aristotle. It would seem that the *Physicorum opiniones* was a compilation of Aristotle's accounts, supplemented by quotations, biographical data, and other information omitted by Aristotle, and arranged under the main topics discussed by Aristotle. Aristotle's purpose in discussing earlier theories is to put them in relation to his own—that is, to show to what extent they anticipated or approximated his and where they were inadequate; hence he reports only what is relevant to his theory and states it in terms of his theory. It may be that Theophrastus intended no more, that his history was a handbook to be used as background for his own exposition of Peripatetic theories. The use to which he might put such a handbook is suggested by his *De sensibus*, in which he reviews and criticizes earlier physiological psychology. Throughout he bases his criticism on Aristotle's doctrine that sense perception involves qualitative change; and, even when he cites the texts of the writers whom he discusses (such as Plato's *Timaeus*), he reformulates the theories so that they may be judged by Peripatetic standards.

BIBLIOGRAPHY

I. ORIGINAL WORKS. Editions of Theophrastus' writings are J. G. Schneider, 5 vols. (Leipzig, 1818–1821); F. Wimmer, 3 vols. (Leipzig, 1854–1862), also one vol. with Latin trans. (Paris, 1866); and H. Diels, *De sensibus* and fragments of *Physicorum opiniones*, in *Doxographi Graeci* (Berlin, 1879).

Editions with commentary and translation are *Historia plantarum* (with *De odoribus* and *De signis tempestatum*), A. Hort, ed., 2 vols. (London, 1916); *De causis plantarum*, bk. I, R. E. Dengler, ed. (Ph.D. diss., Univ. of Pa., 1927); *De sensibus*, G. M. Stratton, ed. (New York, 1927); *Metaphysics*, W. D. Ross and F. H. Fobes, eds. (Oxford, 1929); *De lapidibus*, E. R. Caley and J. C. Richards, eds. (Columbus, Ohio, 1956), and

D. E. Eichholz, ed. (Oxford, 1965); and *De igne*, V. Coutant, ed. (Assen, Netherlands, 1971).

II. SECONDARY LITERATURE. See O. Regenbogen, "Theophrastos von Eresos," in Pauly-Wissowa, *Real-Encyclopädie der classischen Altertumswissenschaft*, supp. VII, 1353–1562. Studies that have appeared since Regenbogen's survey include J. B. McDiarmid, "Theophrastus on the Presocratic Causes," in *Harvard Studies in Classical Philology*, **61** (1953), 85–156, and P. Steinmetz, *Die Physik des Theophrast* (Bad Homburg, 1964).

J. B. McDIARMID

THEUDIUS OF MAGNESIA (*fl.* fourth century B.C.), *mathematics.*

Theudius, an early member of the Academy, is known only from a passage in Proclus' commentary on Euclid's *Elements* (*In primum Euclidis Elementorum librum commentarii*, G. Friedlein, ed. [Leipzig, 1883; repr. 1967], I, pp. 67–68). After mentioning Leo (who made an improved collection of the elements of geometry and invented *diorismi*, means of determining when a problem is soluble and when not) and Eudoxus, Proclus says:

> Amyclas [or, better, Amyntas] of Heraclea, one of Plato's friends, Menaechmus, a pupil of Eudoxus who had also studied with Plato, and Dinostratus his brother, made the whole of geometry still more perfect. Theudius the Magnesian had a reputation for excellence in mathematics and in the rest of philosophy; for he ordered . . . the elements carefully and made many of the limiting [or partial] theorems more general.

Proclus then states that another geometer, Athenaeus of Cyzicus, lived at about the same time. "These men associated . . . in the Academy and undertook investigations jointly." Next are mentioned Hermotimus of Colophon, who added to the *Elements*, and Philippus of Medma (or Opus), who is said to have revised and published Plato's *Laws*. All these statements by Proclus may well have originated with an excellent authority, the historian of mathematics Eudemus of Rhodes. Theudius may be placed between Eudoxus and Philippus; that is, he was a contemporary of Aristotle. Indeed, T. L. Heath made the reasonable suggestion that the propositions in elementary geometry that are quoted by Aristotle were taken from Theudius' *Elements*. We have, however, no means of knowing which propositions and theorems were his discoveries; nor are we told which Magnesia was his home.

BIBLIOGRAPHY

See K. von Fritz, in Pauly-Wissowa, *Real-Encyclopädie der classischen Altertumswissenschaft*, XI, pt. 2 (1936), 244–246; T. L. Heath, *A History of Greek Mathematics*, I (Oxford, 1921), 319–321; and *The Thirteen Books of Euclid's Elements* (repr. New York, 1956), 116–117; Glenn R. Morrow, *Proclus: A Commentary on the First Book of Euclid's Elements* (Princeton, 1970), 56, n. 45; and F. Wehrli, *Die Schule des Aristoteles*, VII *Eudemos von Rhodos* (Basel, 1955).

G. L. HUXLEY

THÉVENOT, MELCHISÉDECH (*b.* Paris, France, 1620 or 1621; *d.* Issy [now Issy-les-Moulineaux], France, 29 October 1692), *scientific correspondence and translation, natural philosophy.*

Thévenot was one of the important correspondents linking Paris to the rest of the European scientific world. He influenced the organization and founding of the French Academy of Sciences and was an intimate of Christiaan Huygens, Henry Oldenburg, Adrien Auzout, and numerous other mid-seventeenth-century personages. He was appointed keeper of the royal library in 1684 and admitted as a member of the Academy of Sciences in 1685.

Little is known of Thévenot's personal life. After his formal education he traveled about Europe and made several voyages later in his life, including two diplomatic missions to Italy, but did not leave the Continent ("Thévenot's" voyages to the eastern Mediterranean and to northern Africa were those of his nephew Jean). Thévenot was a bibliophile and man of letters with a personal library of thousands of works, including a rich collection of books and manuscripts in foreign languages. One of the relatively few French scientists who read English, Thévenot also knew Greek, Latin, Hebrew, and several oriental languages, including Arabic and Turkish. His manuscript collection passed to the royal library in 1712.

Groups of savants and amateurs in mid-seventeenth-century Paris met occasionally in private houses to discourse on philosophy and nature. From about 1654, and for a decade thereafter, Henri Louis Habert de Montmor held such meetings with enough regularity and sense of purpose that his group has been called the "Montmor Academy." Thévenot attended Montmor's meetings at least as early as 1658, and regularly for the next several years. Perhaps he began attending as early as 1655, for he met Huygens then, at a time when Huygens is known to have visited often with

Montmor and with Pierre Gassendi, who was then living in Montmor's house. Thévenot's associates at the Montmor meetings included Auzout, Pierre Petit, Ismael Boulliau, Bernard Frenicle de Bessy, Jacques Rohault, and Girard Desargues, as well as most of the important scientific figures who passed through Paris. In these early years the Montmor Academy considered clocks and other mechanical devices, astronomical discoveries, questions of spontaneous generation and other biological matters, recent English and Italian studies on the void, and capillarity. These two latter phenomena especially interested Thévenot as early as 1658, and this interest contributed to his later development of a bubble level. Although there were those at the Montmor meetings, such as Thévenot, who emphasized experiment and observation, other members preferred rhetoric to experiment and the Montmor Academy gained a reputation for disputation and displays of temper.

After about 1662, partly because of these squabbles, Thévenot provided occasions for additional meetings and experimentation in his country house at Issy, several miles south of Paris. There he supported the mathematician Frenicle de Bessy, the Danish anatomist Nils Stensen, and a chemical demonstrator. Also at Issy, Thévenot pursued his studies of the void and made various astronomical and magnetic studies, aided by Petit, Auzout, Frenicle de Bessy, and Huygens. Various problems, including the continuing bickering over the proper emphasis to be placed upon experiment, led to the demise of the Montmor Academy in 1664. Thévenot held his meetings for another year or so, but lack of sufficient funds for apparatus and experimentation hampered his work.

About this time efforts were made to reorganize the Montmor Academy. Samuel-Joseph Sorbière, its permanent secretary, approached the leading minister of Louis XIV, Jean-Baptiste Colbert, and presented him with the draft of a revised constitution and a letter asking for royal protection. At about the same time another plan was proposed for a new academy of scientists. The latter plan, a document of some twenty-six clauses and two thousand words, exists as an unsigned, undated manuscript.[1] Evidence indicates that the plan, entitled "Project de la Compagnie des sciences et des arts," was written about 1663 or 1664 by a group that included Thévenot, Auzout, and Petit. The proposed *compagnie* would perform experiments and make observations to disabuse the world of its "vulgar errors," seek to invent new machines, work especially at discovering the causes of ill health, make lists and tables of practical arts and machines, seek to improve navigation and commerce, publish the memoirs of those who voyaged to foreign lands, and write a universal natural history. It would be composed of

. . . the most knowledgeable in all the true sciences that one can find, as in geometry, in mechanics, optics, astronomy, geography &c., in physics, medicine, chemistry, anatomy, &c., or in the applied arts, as architecture, fortifications, sculpture, painting, and design, the conduct and elevation of waters [hydraulics], metallurgy, agriculture, navigation &c.[2]

Religion and politics would be excluded. This Baconian program promised to form the *compagnie* for the "perfection of the sciences and the arts and, in general, to search for all that can bring utility or convenience to the human race, and particularly to France."[3] Thévenot's utilitarian project for a *compagnie des sciences et des arts* was quite different from one proposed by Charles Perrault, who envisioned an academy that was less practical and more philosophical and cultural, the pure sciences being allied with belles lettres rather than with engineering.

The Academy of Sciences that emerged in 1666 was more in Perrault's design than in Thévenot's. The amateurs among the Montmor group, including Thévenot, were not members of the new academy. Brown implies that Thévenot, as an amateur, was omitted from consideration.[4] Maury claims that Thévenot, although the "father" of the new academy, was not included among the original members because of "infirmities" that kept him at Issy.[5] This does not accord with the *éloge* in the *Journal des sçavans*, evidently written by a personal friend (possibly Jean Gallois), which states that Thévenot, "being of a robust constitution, . . . enjoyed excellent health" until the month of his death, when, attacked by a fever, he initiated a continuing fast that served further to weaken his health and brought on his death. Recent evidence published by McKeon quotes Thévenot, in a letter to Prince Leopold, as saying he had been invited to become a member.[6] In any case, Thévenot finally became a member of the Academy of Sciences in 1685, filling the place of Pierre de Carcavi, who had died in 1684.

Throughout the 1660's and 1670's Thévenot maintained a wide correspondence with numerous persons. Much of it related to his celebrated translation and publication of voyages of discovery, *Relations de divers voyages . . . ..* His only notable direct contribution to science was in instrumentation: a bubble level, later improved by Robert Hooke and by Huygens. Thévenot's work on the level was probably connected with his experiments on capillarity and the siphon, undertaken in 1658–1661. He mentioned his level in 1661 and 1662 in letters to Vincenzo Viviani and to Huygens, and it was publicized in an unsigned pamphlet in 1666.[7] Thévenot's original design probably began to evolve in 1661 and was publicly mentioned at various times between 1666 and 1681, when he described it in his essay "Discours sur l'art de la navigation," published in his *Recueil de voyages* . . .. The original bubble level seemed to lack convexity in the glass tube, a fact remarked upon by Huygens.

Thévenot described and illustrated his level in 1681, still without discussing convexity in the tube, although he did mention the possibility of utilizing Auzout's idea of metal cross hairs with a lens for accurate measurement. The level tube, he said, was about the diameter of one's little finger and its length was seven or eight times its diameter. The level was filled with alcohol and mounted on a stone ruler fitted with a viewing lens. Glass fabrication methods made it difficult to obtain tubes of constant cross section, and Thévenot's design initially was used by others simply to align a plane surface parallel to the horizon. Thévenot's claims that his level would be useful in finding magnetic declination at sea and determining a plane parallel to the horizon at sea seem rather exaggerated. Daumas states that Thévenot's design did not come into common use until the mid-eighteenth century with the development of improved construction techniques.[8]

One other incident made Thévenot a subject of discussion in the scientific salons: his presentation and development of a theory concerning the cause of human and animal respiration. Sometime during 1660 an unnamed person at the Montmor Academy had suggested that a constant atmospheric pulsation caused the "movements of the heart, of the *punctum saliens* of the egg, that of the brain, the diaphragm, or of respiration."[9] Thévenot said that the idea, if not true, at least had some merit; and he proceeded to attempt to demonstrate the atmospheric pulsation experimentally. He claimed that if one put water into a flask with a capillary neck and then tipped the flask so that the water filled part of the neck, one could observe the water pulsating in sympathy with the atmospheric pulsation. After a slight warming, one could observe the "diastolic and systolic [motions] with all the circumstances that one finds in the parts of animals that have this movement," the rate of motion depending on the amount of heat applied.[10]

Thévenot spread this news through Oldenburg and Huygens, and it was widely discussed for a time. This incident is quite typical of the sort of experiment performed and the type of tales told in seventeenth-century science, and Thévenot is not to be imagined a fool. His scientific contributions, however, should be seen as limited to his general encouragement of scientific enterprise through his letters, his personal efforts, and his published translations. In the period after 1685, when he was a member of the Academy of Sciences, he occasionally discussed items at its meetings: for example, a buffalo-like creature in North America, lemon juice as a medicinal cure, the excision and subsequent regeneration of a lizard's tail, and ipecac as useful in treating dysentery.

NOTES

1. See Huygens, *Oeuvres complètes*, IV, 325–329, for the text of this document.
2. *Ibid.*, 328.
3. *Ibid.*, 325.
4. Harcourt Brown, *Scientific Organizations* . . ., 117.
5. L.-F. A. Maury, *L'ancienne Académie des sciences*, 12–13.
6. McKeon, "Une lettre de Melchisédech Thévenot . . .," 2–3.
7. Huygens, *Oeuvres complètes*, XXI, 105–108, presents Huygens' description of Thévenot's level.
8. Maurice Daumas, *Les instruments scientifiques aux XVIIe et XVIIIe siècles*, 77.
9. Thévenot to Huygens, in Huygens, *Oeuvres complètes*, III, 405.
10. *Ibid.*, 406.

BIBLIOGRAPHY

I. ORIGINAL WORKS. Consult the *Catalogue général des livres imprimés de la Bibliothèque nationale*, CLXXXVI, or Michaud's *Biographie universelle*, 2nd ed., XLI, for detailed listing of Thévenot's works. Discussions of the publishing history of Thévenot's *Voyages* appear in Armand Gaston Camus, *Mémoire sur la collection des grands et petits voyages* . . . (Paris, 1802), 279 ff.; and James Lenox, *The Voyages of Thévenot* (New York, 1879).

Thévenot's most famous work was his collection of translations of voyages of discovery, *Relations de divers voyages curieux* . . ., 4 vols. (Paris, 1663–1672); and a small supplement, *Recueil de voyages de Mr Thévenot* (Paris, 1681). The latter contains Thévenot's description of his level in "Discours sur l'art de la navigation." The *Catalogue de la bibliothèque de Thévenot* (Paris, 1694) contains a short autobiographical preface by Thévenot. (I have not examined the latter work.) Drawing on previous books by Everard Digby the elder and by Nicholas Winman, Thévenot wrote a primer on swimming that was published after his death as *L'art de nager* (Paris, 1696) and went through numerous illustrated French and English eds. over the next century.

Coincident with his interests in hydrostatics and mechanics, Thévenot began an ed. of works by Hero and others but died during the preparation. The task was completed by Jean Boivin and Philippe de La Hire: *Veterum mathematicorum, Athenaei, Bitonis, Apollodori, Heronis, Philonis et aliorum opera . . .* (Paris, 1693).

Letters written by and concerning Thévenot are in Christiaan Huygens, *Oeuvres complètes*, 22 vols. (The Hague, 1888–1950), III–VII, IX–X, XVII, XX, XXII; *The Correspondence of Henry Oldenburg*, edited and translated by A. Rupert Hall and Marie Boas Hall, (Madison, Wis., 1965–), I–III, VI. Robert M. McKeon published a letter from Thévenot to Prince Leopold in Florence, "Une lettre de Melchisédech Thévenot sur les débuts de l'Académie royale des sciences," in *Revue d'histoire des sciences et de leurs applications*, **18** (1965), 1–6. On Thévenot's influence on the founding of the Academy of Sciences, see also T. McClaughlin, "Une lettre de Melchisédech Thévenot," in *Revue d'histoire des sciences*, **27** (1974), 123–126. Harcourt Brown published an unsigned letter concerning Swammerdam's investigations and properly attributes this to Thévenot in his *Scientific Organizations in Seventeenth Century France (1620–1680)* (Baltimore, 1934), 280–281. Thévenot's comments and reports at the Academy of Sciences for the years 1685–1689 are mentioned in *Histoire de l'Académie royale des sciences depuis 1666 jusqu'à 1699*, I, II (Paris, 1733).

II. SECONDARY LITERATURE. The best general introduction to scientific societies in Thévenot's era, as well as to his career, is Brown, *op cit.* A contemporary *éloge* of Thévenot is in *Journal des sçavans*, **20** (17 Nov. 1692), 646–649 (pub. 1693). A brief biography is in Louis Moréri, *Le grand dictionnaire historique de Moréri*, X (Paris, 1759), 138–139. Subsequent biographical sketches of Thévenot add nothing to these. A brief history of the level and of the acceptance of Thévenot's bubble level is in Maurice Daumas, *Les instruments scientifiques aux XVIIᵉ et XVIIIᵉ siècles* (Paris, 1953), 76–78. For additional discussion of this, see Gilbert Govi, "Recherches historiques sur l'invention du niveau à bulle d'air," in *Bullettino di bibliografia e di storia delle scienze matematiche e fisiche*, **3** (1870), 282–296. McKeon's article (cited above) contains a discussion of events at the time of the founding of the Academy of Sciences in 1666; see also Brown, *op cit.*; Guillaume Bigourdan, "Les premières sociétés savantes de Paris . . .," in *Comptes rendus . . . de l'Académie des sciences*, **163** (1916), 937–943; **164** (1917), 129–134, 159–162, 216–220—also published separately as a pamphlet (Paris, 1919). In addition, consult L.-F. Alfred Maury, *L'ancienne Académie des sciences* (Paris, 1864), 10–13, 31, 37–38; and Roger Hahn, *The Anatomy of a Scientific Institution, the Paris Academy of Sciences,*

1666–1803 (Berkeley, 1971), 6–8. For information concerning Thévenot and his interests in astronomy and scientific instrumentation, see Robert M. McKeon, "Établissement de l'astronomie de précision et oeuvre d'Adrien Auzout" (unpub. diss., University of Paris, 1965).

C. STEWART GILLMOR

THIELE, F. K. JOHANNES (*b.* Ratibor, Upper Silesia, Germany [now Raciborz, Poland], 13 May 1865; *d.* Strasbourg, Germany [now France], 17 April 1918), *chemistry.*

Thiele, a major contributor to our knowledge of nitrogen compounds and to the theory of unsaturated organic molecules, was the second of six children of Friedrich August Thiele, a leading citizen of Ratibor and owner of a publishing house and bookstore. His mother, the former Elfriede Koppe, died when he was six. Thiele studied at the University of Breslau (1883–1884) and then at Halle under Jacob Volhard, obtained his doctorate there in 1890, and taught analytical and organic chemistry. His studies on the nitrogen compounds guanidine and hydrazine and their derivatives, some of them explosive, interested both industry and government.

In 1893 Thiele became associate professor under Adolf von Baeyer at Munich, where he continued his work on nitrogen derivatives and developed his most important research, which dealt with conjugated unsaturated systems—structures involving alternate single and double bonds along a chain of atoms. In 1902 he was appointed professor at Strasbourg, where he expanded and modernized the chemical institute and in 1910 became rector of the university. During World War I, Thiele served for a time as a censor of telegrams and developed a gas mask against carbon monoxide. On Volhard's death in 1910, he became editor of *Justus Liebig's Annalen der Chemie.* In the same year he was elected to the Munich Academy of Sciences. He died, unmarried, of a heart ailment at age fifty-three.

Organic chemistry seemed divided, in the latter nineteenth century, into two parts—the derivatives of benzene, C_6H_6, and the rest, including unsaturated compounds. The latter, containing double or triple bonds, $\diagdown C = C \diagup$ and $-C \equiv C-$, added bromine (and other reagents) readily, forming $\diagdown CBr - CBr \diagup$ and $-CBr_2 - CBr_2-$. Benzene, to which Kekulé in 1865 had assigned a structure with three double bonds

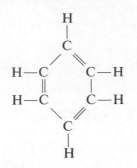

was quite unreactive, however, adding bromine only in the presence of light.

Thiele constructed a bridge between the two realms. Building on Fittig's and A. von Baeyer's discovery that structures C=C—C=C added hydrogen, H_2, not as expected, at a double bond, but at the ends of the chain, thereby yielding CH—C=C—CH, with a new double bond in the center, Thiele proposed that "double bond" is a misnomer because the atoms are not bound twice as strongly as when singly bound. Rather, doubly bound carbon atoms retain a "partial valence" that explains their reactivity. In a system of alternating single and double bonds, which Thiele called a "conjugated system," the inner partial valences neutralize each other, leaving the end atoms reactive.

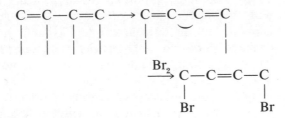

Since benzene has a closed conjugated system

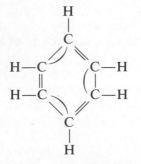

its lack of reactivity is explained.[1] Thiele's theory stimulated extensive research by himself and others, and was a direct precursor of electronic theories of organic reaction mechanisms.[2]

Thiele's extensive research on nitrogen chemistry, particularly on derivatives of hydrazine [H_2NNH_2], and guanidine [$HN=C(NH_2)_2$], led to the discovery of numerous new compounds and new synthetic processes. He prepared nitramide (NH_2NO_2), which is isomeric with hyponitrous acid ($H_2N_2O_2$); these were the first examples in inorganic chemistry of compounds having identical molecular formulas but different properties. He also achieved the synthesis of five- and seven-membered ring compounds containing nitrogen.

NOTES

1. J. Thiele, "Zur Kenntnis der ungesättigten Verbindungen," in *Justus Liebig's Annalen der Chemie*, **306** (1899), 87–266; **319** (1901), 129–143.
2. C. K. Ingold, *Structure and Mechanism in Organic Chemistry*, 2nd ed., p. 76.

BIBLIOGRAPHY

I. ORIGINAL WORKS. A full bibliography, listing over 130 articles and the titles of dissertations by Thiele's students, is included in the obituary by F. Straus (see below). A section of Thiele's paper on conjugated systems (*Annalen der Chemie*, **306** [1899], 89–90) is translated in H. M. Leicester and H. S. Klickstein, eds., *A Sourcebook in Chemistry* (New York, 1952), 510–511.

II. SECONDARY LITERATURE. Fritz Straus, "Johannes Thiele," in *Berichte der Deutschen chemischen Gesellschaft*, **60** (1927), 75A–132A, consists of an obituary, extensive discussion of his chemical work, and full bibliography. Poggendorff, IV, 1489–1490, and V, 1249–1250, presents biographical notes and bibliography. J. R. Partington, *A History of Chemistry*, IV (London, 1964), 847–848, summarizes Thiele's chemical contributions and includes important references. Thiele's theory of partial valences is discussed in F. Henrich, *Theorien der organischen Chemie* (Brunswick, 1912), 34–82; in E. Hjelt, *Geschichte der organischen Chemie* (Brunswick, 1916), 459–460, 467–469; and, more recently, in C. K. Ingold, *Structure and Mechanism in Organic Chemistry*, 2nd ed. (Ithaca, N.Y., 1969), 75–77, 184, 957–958.

Thiele's contributions to the chemistry of organic nitrogen compounds are referred to in N. V. Sidgwick, T. W. J. Taylor, and W. Baker, *The Organic Chemistry of Nitrogen* (Oxford, 1937), 274, 286, 287, 297, 348, 361, 378, 384, 446.

OTTO THEODOR BENFEY

THIELE, THORVALD NICOLAI (*b.* Copenhagen, Denmark, 24 December 1838; *d.* Copenhagen, 26 September 1910), *astronomy, mathematics, actuarial mathematics.*

Thiele was the son of Just Mathias Thiele, a well-known Danish folklorist and art historian. While studying at the University of Copenhagen, young Thiele was awarded a gold medal for a paper on the geometry of the apparent course of a solar eclipse. In 1866 he took his doctorate, and from 1875 to 1906 he was professor of astronomy at the university and director of the university observatory.

Thiele's scientific work has been characterized by C. Burran as "a treatment of numerical values derived from observations." If the word "observation" is taken in its widest sense, and if the word "treatment" is taken to mean a penetrating and original mathematical analysis, then this description must be regarded as apt. The topic of Thiele's dissertation was the determination of the orbit of the visual double star γ Virginis. He developed a new method of orbit determination, now known as the Thiele-Innes method (with some of the formulas later arranged for mechanical computation by Robert Innes). Thiele discussed the systematic errors in the observational material for this star and later for other double stars, using in particular the series of observations published in 1878–1879 by Otto W. Struve.

For many years Thiele continued and intensified his studies of the systematic and accidental errors of observation, thus approaching the field of actuarial mathematics. Indeed, for nearly forty years he was the manager of a life insurance company; in this work he satisfied his interest in the practical use of mathematics and numerical computations. In his scientific work, Thiele tried to discover, by means of numerical calculations, the laws for the distribution of the spectral lines of certain elements; and he was an early pioneer in the numerical search for solutions to the three-body problem, developing the Thiele (or Thiele-Burrau) transformation for this purpose.

The mathematical background of his work is given in his books *Theory of Observations* (1903) and *Interpolationsrechnung* (1909). Because of an eye disease, Thiele was unable to do any practical astronomical observation during much of his career, but he took an early part in the development of photography for astronomical purposes.

BIBLIOGRAPHY

I. ORIGINAL WORKS. Thiele's books include *Undersøgelse af Omløbsbevaegelsen i Dobbeltstjernesystemet Gamma Virginis* (Copenhagen, 1866); *Almindelig Iagttagelseslaere: Sandsynlighedsregning og mindste Kvadraters Methode* (Copenhagen, 1889); *Elementaer Iagttagelseslaere* (Copenhagen, 1897); *Theory of Observations* (London, 1903); and *Interpolationsrechnung* (Leipzig, 1909).

His articles include "Castor, calcul du mouvement relatif et critique des observations de cette étoile double," in *Festskrift, Copenhagen University* (1879); review and discussion of Otto W. Struve's measurements of double stars, in *Vierteljahrsschrift der Astronomischen Gesellschaft*, **15** (1880), 314–348; "Note on the Application of Photography to the Micrometric Measurements of Stars," in *Washington Observations for 1885*, appendix I (1889), 58–67; "Om Nutidens Reform af den iagttagende Astronomie," in *Festskrift, Copenhagen University* (1893); "On the Law of Spectral Series," in *Astrophysical Journal*, **6** (1897), 65–76; "Resolution into Series of the Third Band of the Carbon Band Spectrum," *ibid.*, **8** (1898), 1–27; "Tal og Symboler som Bestemmelser mellem Numeraler," in *Festskrift, Copenhagen University* (1901).

Papers are in *Tidsskrift for Matematik* (Copenhagen, 1859–1903); *Royal Danish Academy*, Oversigter and Skrifter (Copenhagen, 1880–1908); and in *Astronomische Nachrichten*, **48–138** (1858–1895). See also Poggendorff, IV, 1488–1489; V, 1250.

II. SECONDARY LITERATURE. Articles on Thiele are in *Dansk Biografisk Leksikon*, XXIII (1942), 503–506; and C. Burrau, in *Vierteljahrsschrift der Astronomischen Gesellschaft*, **46** (1911), 208–210; J. P. Gram, in *Nyt Tidsskrift for Mathematik*, **21B** (1910), 73–78; N. E. Nørlund, in *Fysisk Tidsskrift*, **9** (1910), 1–7; J. P. Gram, "Professor Thiele som Aktuar," in *Dansk Forsikringsaarbog*, **7** (1910), 26–37.

AXEL V. NIELSEN

THIERRY OF CHARTRES, also known as **Magister Theodoricus Carnotensis** (*b.* Brittany, France, last quarter of the eleventh century; *d. ca.* 1155), *philosophy, theology.*

As early as 1121 Thierry is believed to have taught at the cathedral school of Chartres, together with his brother Bernard, who was acting as chancellor (1119–1126). In 1127 he is recorded as archdeacon of Dreux, near Chartres, and before 1134 he is known to have taught in Paris, where Adalbert, later archbishop of Mainz (1137–1141), studied rhetoric, grammar, and logic under him. Among his students in Paris were also Master Bernard the Breton, later bishop of Quimper (1159–1167), the grammarian Master Peter Helias of Poitiers, Master Ivo of Chartres, Archbishop William of Tyre (1175–1185), John of Salisbury, later bishop of Chartres (1176–1180), and Master Clarembald, archdeacon of Arras.

Although Thierry's fame was based mainly on his courses on the trivium (grammar, logic, rhetoric), he is believed to have taught mathematics with great success. In fact, he is considered to have introduced the use of the *rota* or zero into European mathematics. A *Tractatus de rebus universalibus*, now lost, was dedicated to "Master Thierry." Bernard Silvestre dedicated his *Cosmographia* "to the most famous teacher, Thierry." A translation from Arabic into Latin of Ptolemy's *Planisphaerium*, made in Toulouse in 1144, is dedicated to "Thierry, the Platonist." An epitaph edited by A. Vernet, which celebrates Thierry as "a worthy successor of Aristotle," reveals that he was the first Latin scholar to comment on Aristotle's *Prior Analytics* and *Sophistici Elenchi*.

In the 1130's Thierry began to teach in Paris. He was among the masters who attended the papal consistory at Reims in 1148, where the orthodoxy of Gilbert, bishop of Poitiers, was examined. About the same time, Thierry and Master Gerland of Besançon were guests of Archbishop Albero of Trier. At a later date Thierry seems to have returned to Chartres, for the death roll of Chartres cathedral calls him "chancellor and archdeacon of Notre-Dame [of Chartres]." He bequeathed to the cathedral his Library of the Seven Liberal Arts, called *Eptatheucon* (destroyed by fire in 1944, preserved on film), Justinian's *Institutes, Novellae,* and *Digest*, and forty-five other books. A. Vernet maintains that Thierry retired (*ca.* 1155) to a Cistercian monastery to die and be buried in a monk's habit.

Today Thierry is probably best known for his short commentary on the introductory chapters of Genesis, the *Tractatus de sex dierum operibus*, in the first part of which he explains the unfolding of the universe on the basis of physical laws and provides an analysis of the Biblical text. In the second part he calls upon the quadrivium (arithmetic, music, geometry, astronomy) to lead him to the knowledge of the creator of the universe.

According to Thierry, there are four causes that account for the existence of the universe: (1) God as efficient, (2) His wisdom as formal, (3) His goodness as final, and (4) the four elements (fire, air, water, earth) as material cause created by God "at the beginning" out of nothing. The first three causes reflect the Trinity, for the efficient cause is the Father, the formal cause the Son, and the final cause the Holy Spirit. The four elements were created in a single moment. When Scripture speaks of six days for the creation, we may interpret a natural day as the time in which one whole rotation of the sky, from sunrise to sunrise, is completed or as the period required for the illumination of the air all across the sky.

Thierry held that, once created, the heaven could not stand still because of its extreme lightness. Enveloping all things, it could not move forward from place to place but was bound to rotate in a circular motion. The highest and lightest element, fire, produced both light and heat. The second element, air, conveyed the heat to the third element, water, and by warming it suspended a mass of waters, called firmament, above the air as high as the region of the moon. As a result of this removal of water, the fourth element, earth, appeared in the form of islands. Because of the heat, the earth then conceived the power of producing plants and trees. Acting on the mass of waters suspended in the sky, the heat caused the stellar bodies to be formed, for all stars are made of water and are still nourished on moisture. Because of the greater intensity of heat caused by the stars, the water on earth began to produce such things as water animals and birds. Then earth, too, conceived the power of generating animals—among which was man, made in the image and likeness of God.

All this took place in successive steps during the first six rotations of the heaven. To regulate the orderly succession of time, the various seasons and climates, and the normal process of procreation, the Creator implanted "seminal causes" in the elements. Thierry held that, in addition, a divine power, called the world soul, presides and rules over all matter so as to give it form and order.

BIBLIOGRAPHY

I. ORIGINAL WORKS. Thierry's *Eptatheucon* is still unpublished. A fragment of his commentary on Cicero's *De inventione* has been edited by W. H. D. Suringar in *Historia critica scholiastarum Ratinorum*, I (Leiden, 1834), 213–252. The latest edition of Thierry's *Tractatus de sex dierum operibus* is found in Nikolaus M. Häring, ed., *Commentaries on Boethius by Thierry of Chartres and His School* (Toronto, 1971), 555–575. An analysis is given in N. M. Häring, "The Creation and Creator of the World According to Thierry of Chartres and Clarembald of Arras," in *Archives d'histoire doctrinale et littéraire du moyen âge*, **22** (1955), 137–216, with text edition. Commentaries by Thierry and his school on the *Theological Tractates* of Boethius have been edited by N. M. Häring, *Commentaries on Boethius*, 57–528.

II. SECONDARY LITERATURE. A. Vernet, "Une épitaphe inédite de Thierry de Chartres," in *Recueil de travaux offerts à M. Clovis Brunel*, **2** (1955), 660–670;

E. Jeauneau, "Simples notes sur la cosmologie de Thierry de Chartres," in *Sophia*, **23** (1955), 172–183; and "Mathématiques et trinité chez Thierry de Chartres," in Paul Wilpert, *Miscellanea mediaevalia*, **2** (Berlin, 1963), 289–295; and "Note sur l'école de Chartres," in *Studi medievali*, 3rd ser., V, 2 (1964), 1–45; F. Brunner, "Creatio numerorum, rerum est creatio," in *Mélanges offerts à René Crozet* (Poitiers, 1966), 719–725.

NIKOLAUS M. HÄRING

THIRY, PAUL HENRI. See **Holbach, Paul Henri Thiry, Baron d'.**

THISELTON-DYER, WILLIAM TURNER (*b.* Westminster, England, 28 July 1843; *d.* Witcombe, Gloucestershire, England, 23 December 1928), *botany.*

Although he made no really signal contribution to scientific knowledge, Thiselton-Dyer played a central role in the botanical life of late Victorian England. Through his participation in T. H. Huxley's famous summer course in elementary biology, given at South Kensington for school teachers in the science and art department of the government, he helped extend to botanical circles Huxley's emphasis on evolutionary principles and pioneering efforts in laboratory teaching. As assistant director (1875–1885) and then director (1885–1905) of the Royal Botanic Gardens at Kew, he engineered and oversaw the immense expansion of economic botany throughout the British Empire.

Thiselton-Dyer was the elder son of Catherine Jane Firminger, an accomplished field botanist who introduced him to William Hooker's *British Flora*,[1] and her husband William George Thiselton-Dyer, a physician from Westminster who established a successful practice in Berkeley Street, London. Young Thiselton-Dyer's maternal uncle, T. A. C. Firminger, was a chaplain in Bengal and author of a standard manual of gardening for Bengal and Upper India. His maternal grandfather, Thomas Firminger, served as assistant astronomer royal at Greenwich Observatory from 1799 to 1808. Thiselton-Dyer, who was often addressed as "Dyer" and is sometimes so listed in indexes, derived his name from his paternal grandfather, William Matthew Thiselton, a printer and barrister who took the additional name Dyer by royal license in 1840.

Until 1863, Thiselton-Dyer was educated entirely in London, initially at St. Peter's School in Ea-

ton Square, then at King's College School, and finally at King's College itself, which he entered in 1861 as a medical student. In 1863 he transferred to Christ Church, Oxford, where he read mathematics under Henry J. S. Smith and chemistry under Benjamin Collins Brodie, Jr. After taking his Oxford bachelor of arts with honors in 1865, Thiselton-Dyer turned to natural history under the influence of George Rolleston, Henry N. Moseley, and E. Ray Lankester. In 1867 he won first-class honors in the final Natural Sciences School at Oxford.

By 1870, when he graduated as a bachelor of science from the University of London, Thiselton-Dyer had already served for two years as professor of natural history at the Royal Agricultural College, Cirencester. In 1869 he published (with his friend Henry Trimen) *Flora of Middlesex* and (with Arthur H. Church, a colleague at Cirencester) an English adaptation of Samuel W. Johnson's popular American work, *How Plants Grow*. From 1870 to 1872 he was professor of botany in the Royal College of Science, Dublin. While there he entered into correspondence with Joseph Dalton Hooker, director of the Royal Botanic Gardens at Kew. In 1872, on Hooker's recommendation, he was appointed professor of botany at the Royal Horticultural Society at South Kensington and Chiswick. During the same year he became private secretary and editorial assistant to Hooker.[2]

In the summer of 1873, when T. H. Huxley was abroad because of illness, Thiselton-Dyer assumed general direction of the South Kensington course. With the help of M. A. Lawson of Oxford, he particularly developed the botanical side of the teaching and became the leader of the campaign to bring laboratory training and the new physiological approach into British botany. In the summer of 1874, when Huxley resumed the course, Thiselton-Dyer acted as his botanical demonstrator with assistance from Sydney H. Vines, later professor of botany at Oxford. In the summers of 1875 and 1876 Thiselton-Dyer again offered a series of botanical lectures, with Vines again assisting him in the associated laboratory teaching. His direct participation in the course then effectively ceased, although he did give a final series of botanical lectures in 1880.[3] As the major botanical force behind the course during its early years, he did much to ensure its immense influence and success and to give a new direction to British botany. Toward the same end, he assisted Alfred W. Bennett in an annotated English translation of Sachs's pathbreaking *Textbook of Botany* (1875). He was a natural choice to take charge of the Jodrell Laboratory at Kew upon its completion in 1876. There, under his watchful eye, worked many of the rising stars of the new school of British botany, including Bower, Walter Gardiner, Dukinfield H. Scott, and Marshall Ward.

Overseeing the Jodrell Laboratory was, however, only one aspect of Thiselton-Dyer's new responsibilities at Kew, for he had been named assistant director of the Royal Botanic Gardens in 1875. Hooker had persuaded the government to reactivate this position, vacant since he had succeeded his father, William Jackson Hooker, as director in 1865, chiefly to handle the growing demands on Kew from the colonial office and individual planters throughout the empire. Thiselton-Dyer resigned his professorship at the Royal Horticultural Society and threw himself into his new duties with enormous energy and immediate success. During his first year in office, for example, he sent some Brazilian hevea plants to Ceylon, where they ultimately gave rise to the immense rubber plantations of Ceylon and the Malay Peninsula. Almost equally spectacular results followed his 1880 dispatch of some West Indian cacao plants to his old friend Henry Trimen, who had become director of the botanical gardens at Peradeniya, Ceylon.

In 1877 Thiselton-Dyer married Hooker's eldest daughter, Harriet Ann, who survived him and by whom he had one son and one daughter. In 1885 he succeeded his father-in-law as director of the Royal Botanic Gardens. For the next twenty years his individual contributions were often submerged in and indistinguishable from those of the institution over which he kept so tight a rein. Decisive, direct, methodical, and well-organized, as well as more than a little stubborn, insensitive, and autocratic, he intervened in matters as parochial as the uniforms to be worn by the Kew guards and as expansive as colonial economic development. During his directorship, the Jodrell Laboratory enhanced its reputation as a leading center of botanical research, while the gardens, library, herbarium, and several other buildings at Kew were enlarged and improved. He also paid close attention to the landscaping of the gardens, being particularly concerned with creating a sense of open vistas in the sometimes oppressively luxuriant foliage of Kew.

As director of Kew Gardens, Thiselton-Dyer pursued and expanded the efforts he had made as assistant director to develop economic botany and colonial agriculture. He adapted to the purpose a plan used for more than a century by the East India Company. Officers trained at Kew were placed in charge of botanic stations established throughout the empire. These officers then directed the development of local economic botany with guidance from Kew. To facilitate communication with these officers and other colonial botanists and planters, Thiselton-Dyer founded the *Kew Bulletin* in 1887. In West Africa, by his own account, such efforts increased the value of the rubber export from nothing in 1882 to £500,000 in 1898, while the value of the cocoa export rose from £4 in 1892 to £200,000 in 1904.[4] Partly for the contributions he thus made to the British and colonial economies, Thiselton-Dyer was created Companion of the Order of St. Michael and St. George in 1882, Companion of the Order of the Indian Empire in 1892, and Knight Commander of the Order of St. Michael and St. George in 1899. He served as botanical adviser to the secretary of state for the colonies from 1902 to 1906.

Thiselton-Dyer inherited the onerous task of supervising the great botanical surveys of British colonial territories that had been launched under the two Hookers who preceded him as director of Kew Gardens. In fact, he had been contributing to these surveys since 1872, when he served as editorial assistant to J. D. Hooker, then just beginning the *Flora of British India*. In 1873, in connection with this work, Thiselton-Dyer described the Indian species of six families of flowering plants. When he became director, he and his staff devoted much of their time and energy to the Indian *Flora*, which Hooker continued to edit in retirement and of which the seventh and final volume appeared in 1897. With this project behind them, Thiselton-Dyer and his staff turned to two other major surveys—the flora of South Africa (*Flora capensis*), begun in 1859 and suspended in 1865, and that of tropical Africa (*Flora of Tropical Africa*), begun in 1868 and suspended in 1877. Thiselton-Dyer edited the reports of these surveys throughout the period of his directorship and into retirement, turning the *Flora capensis* over to Sir David Prain in 1913 and completing the *Flora of Tropical Africa* in 1925. From 1895 to 1906 he also took over from Hooker the editorship of the *Icones plantarum* and the *Index Kewensis*, a massive index of the names and bibliographies of all known plants. Eighteen volumes of the *Kew Bulletin* appeared during his directorship. During 1905–1906 he also edited *Curtis's Botanical Magazine*.

Despite the weight of his duties at Kew, Thiselton-Dyer found time to participate in the activities of several botanical and scientific societies. Elected to fellowship in the Linnean Society in 1872, he

THISELTON-DYER

served on its council from 1874 to 1876 and again from 1884 to 1887, being vice-president from 1885 to 1887. He was also vice-president of the Horticultural Society from 1887 to 1889. At the 1888 meeting of the British Association for the Advancement of Science, he was president of section D (biology), while at the 1895 meeting he presided over the new section K (botany), in the founding of which he played a leading role. From 1886 to 1888 he served on the council and during 1896–1897 as vice-president of the Royal Society, to which he had been elected fellow in 1880.

In 1905 Thiselton-Dyer resigned as director of the Royal Botanic Gardens and retired to Witcombe in Gloucestershire, where he took an active part in county affairs and indulged his passion for ancient botany, his favorite sources being Virgil, Pliny, Theophrastus, Galen, and Dioscorides. He revised the vocabulary of Greek plant names for Liddell and Scott's *Greek-English Lexicon*; contributed the botanical chapters to *A Companion to Greek Studies*, edited by Leonard Whibley (1905), and to *A Companion to Latin Studies*, edited by John E. Sandys (1910); published three articles covering some thirty especially difficult and obscure ancient plant names for the *Journal of Philology*; and assisted Sir Arthur Holt in his two-volume edition of Theophrastus' *Historia plantarum* (1916).

Thiselton-Dyer's heavy editorial and administrative responsibilities sharply restricted his opportunities for original research. His detailed study of the cycads, perhaps his most ambitious work, was incorporated into the *Flora capensis* as a supplement to the fifth volume (1933). His more general scientific papers and addresses reveal him to have been a fervent Darwinian who repeatedly insisted on the utility of specific characters and who defended the principle of natural selection at a time when its sufficiency as an explanation of evolution was under widespread attack.[5] Despite his role in the creation of the new physiological school of British botany, he often deplored the growing disdain for the old natural history method of systematic botany. He particularly emphasized the value of studying geographical distribution, to which he traced Darwin's discovery of the theory of descent, and which was for him still its main support.

NOTES

1. W. T. Thiselton-Dyer, "Plant Biology in the 'Seventies,' " in *Nature*, **115** (1925), 70.
2. Mea Allan, *The Hookers of Kew, 1785–1911* (London, 1967), 224.
3. See Thiselton-Dyer, *op. cit.* More generally on the South Kensington course and Thiselton-Dyer's part in it, see J. Reynolds Green, *A History of Botany in the United Kingdom from the Earliest Times to the End of the 19th Century* (London, 1914), 528–537; S. H. Vines, "The Beginnings of Instruction in General Biology," in *Nature*, **115** (1925), 714–715; and F. O. Bower, *Sixty Years of Botany in Britain (1875–1935): Impressions of an Eyewitness* (London, 1938), *passim*.
4. See *Kew Bulletin*, (1929), 74.
5. See, e.g., W. T. Thiselton-Dyer, "The Utility of Specific Characters," in *Nature*, **54** (1896), 293–294, 435–436, 522; and Ethel Romanes, *The Life and Letters of George John Romanes* (London, 1896), *passim*. On the more general contemporary debate over natural selection, see John E. Lesch, "The Role of Isolation in Evolution: George J. Romanes and John T. Gulick," in *Isis* (in press).

BIBLIOGRAPHY

I. Original Works. No complete bibliography of Thiselton-Dyer's works exists in print. For the period up to 1900, see the Royal Society *Catalogue of Scientific Papers*, VII, 588; IX, 767–768; XII, 728; and XIX, 79–80, which lists 86 papers by him alone and five coauthored with others. Among the more interesting of these are "On Spontaneous Generation and Evolution," in *Quarterly Journal of Microscopical Science*, **10** (1870), 333–354; "The Duke of Argyll and the Neo-Darwinians," in *Nature*, **41** (1890), 247–248; "Acquired Characters and Congenital Variation," *ibid.*, 315–316; "Historical Account of Kew to 1841," in *Kew Bulletin* (1891), 279–327; "Variation and Specific Stability," in *Nature*, **51** (1895), 459–461; and those cited in note 5 above.

For Thiselton-Dyer's more general views on Darwinism, the state of British botany, and the value of studying systematic botany and geographical distribution, see *Report of the British Association for the Advancement of Science*, **58** (1888), 686–701; and *ibid.*, **65** (1895), 836–850. See also the forty-eight-page brochure, Alfred Russel Wallace and Thiselton-Dyer, *The Distribution of Life* (New York, 1885); and Thiselton-Dyer, "The Geographical Distribution of Plants," in *Darwin and Modern Science*, Albert C. Seward, ed. (Cambridge, 1909), 298–318. For access to other works by Thiselton-Dyer, especially several prefaces and introductions, see *British Museum Catalogue of Printed Books*, LVIII, 354–355.

A wealth of manuscript material relating to Thiselton-Dyer is deposited in the herbarium and library of the Royal Botanic Gardens, Kew. Among other items there are a number of his diaries, notebooks, reports, and abstracts of lectures; three bound volumes of letters written by him between 1906 and 1922 (nearly all of them to Sir David Prain); four bound volumes of letters to him; and one bound volume of letters to Lady Thiselton-Dyer in connection with a projected memoir of him, together with her notes on the project and the following draft chapters: F. O. Bower, "The Influence of Sir William Thiselton-Dyer Upon the Teaching of Botany in Britain";

Sir J. Farmer, "The Chelsea Physic Garden"; D. Prain on Thiselton-Dyer's service to Indian botany; H. W. Ridley on his contribution to the Indian rubber industry; A. C. Seward, "Sir William Thiselton-Dyer's Contributions to the Study of Fossil Plants"; S. H. Vines, "Some Account of My Relations With the Late Sir W. Thiselton-Dyer"; and W. Dallimore, "Recollections of Sir William Thiselton-Dyer as Director of the Royal Botanic Gardens, Kew." Seventeen letters between Thiselton-Dyer and T. H. Huxley are preserved in the Huxley Papers at Imperial College, London. For published versions of several letters from G. J. Romanes to Thiselton-Dyer, see Ethel Romanes (note 5 above).

II. SECONDARY LITERATURE. Despite the rich manuscript material described above, and despite Thiselton-Dyer's pertinence to topics as important as the introduction of laboratory teaching into English biology or the relationship between botany and imperialism, no adequate study of him exists. For obituary notices, see *Kew Bulletin* (1929), 67–75; *Nature*, **123** (1929), 212–215; and *Proceedings of the Royal Society*, **106B** (1930), xxiii–xxix. See also D'Arcy Wentworth Thompson, "Sir William Thiselton-Dyer," in *Dictionary of National Biography, 1922–1930*, 830–832; and the sources cited in note 3 above.

GERALD L. GEISON

THÖLDE, JOHANN. See **Valentine, Basil.**

THOLLON, LOUIS (*b*. Ambronay, Ain, France, 2 May 1829; *d*. Nice, France, 8 April 1887), *solar physics.*

Thollon's scientific career began in 1878, when Raphaël Bischoffsheim, the founder of the Nice observatory, requested his assistance in setting up the spectroscopic equipment for the observatory. Thollon designed a high dispersion light spectroscope containing four dispersive prisms, two of which were made with carbon disulfide. Each prism was traversed twice by the ray of light, and the measurement of the position of the lines was effected with the aid of a micrometer. In order to eliminate thermal effects, the apparatus was frequently tested on several solar lines selected as reference points. Work on the spectroscope was completed in 1883.

At the start of his own research, in 1879, Thollon carried out an experiment that has become classic. He demonstrated the Doppler-Fizeau effect in a concrete manner. If one alternately projects on the slit of a spectroscope the eastern and western sides of the sun, the spectral lines exhibit a displacement representing the difference of 4 km

per second between the radial velocities of the two sources. The telluric lines that originate in the terrestrial atmosphere remain fixed. This method of using the telluric lines for reference was employed by N. Dunnèr in 1890 to measure the rotational velocity of the sun.

Thollon established a great chart of the solar spectrum, which was published posthumously, in 1890. The spectrum extends from the visible red to the middle green (from 7,600 Å to 5,100 Å); it contains 3,448 lines, of which 2,336 are solar and 1,112 are telluric, with 246 lines being common. In addition to the position of the lines, the chart gives their intensities at a solar height of 10° and 30° above the horizon, for dry air and saturated air, and also, by extrapolation, for the case of observations made outside the earth's atmosphere. This chart is the last and most important of the documents for which broad data were gathered about the solar spectrum by means of a spectroscope. Such information was subsequently obtained by spectrography.

Thollon was awarded a prize by the Académie des Sciences in 1885.

BIBLIOGRAPHY

I. ORIGINAL WORKS. Thollon published eight notes on spectroscopic technique to the *Comtes rendus hebdomadaires des séances de l'Académie des sciences*, **86–96** (1878–1883); and nine notes on spectroscopic observations of comets, eclipses, and novae, *ibid.*, **92–102** (1881–1886).

Thollon's most important works on solar spectroscopy are "Déplacement de raies spectrales, dû au mouvement de rotation du soleil," *ibid.*, **88** (1879), 169–171; "Constitution et origine du groupe B du spectre solaire," in *Bulletin astronomique*, **1** (1884), 223–230; "Nouveau dessin du spectre solaire," *ibid.*, **3** (1886), 330–343; "Spectroscopie solaire," in *Annales de l'Observatoire de Nice*, **2** (1886), D1–D28; and "Nouveau dessin du spectre solaire," *ibid.*, **3** (1890), A1–A112, with 17 plates in the atlas.

II. SECONDARY LITERATURE. See J. Janssen, "Allocution . . . à l'occasion de la mort de M. Thollon," in *Comptes rendus hebdomadaires des séances de l'Académie des sciences*, **104** (1887), 1047–1048; "Dr. L. Thollon," in *Observatory*, **10** (1887), 207; and E. W. Maunder, "M. Thollon's Atlas of the Solar Spectrum," in *Monthly Notices of the Royal Astronomical Society*, **51** (1891), 260–261. See also A. Cornu, "Sur la méthode Döppler-Fizeau," in *Annuaire publié par le Bureau des longitudes* (1891), D25–D26.

JACQUES R. LÉVY

THOMAS, HUGH HAMSHAW (*b.* Wrexham, Denbighshire, Wales, 29 May 1885; *d.* Cambridge, England, 30 June 1962), *paleobotany.*

Born and brought up in Wales, Thomas spent all of his adult life in Cambridge, apart from service in the two world wars. He was the son of William Hamshaw Thomas and Elizabeth Lloyd. His father, a men's outfitter, was active in the public service of his community. Hugh Hamshaw, the second son, was educated at a private school, Grove Park, until he won a scholarship to Downing College, Cambridge, in 1904. His early interest in fossils, which he collected in the local coalpits, continued at Cambridge, where he read for the natural sciences tripos and took part I but changed to history for part II, although continuing to keep up his interest in botany. He was particularly influenced by A. C. Seward, the professor of botany, and in 1908, the year he graduated, his first scientific paper was published in the *Philosophical Transactions of the Royal Society.*

Intended for the civil service, Thomas took the examination but rejected the post he was offered and remained in Cambridge. He supported himself by elementary tutoring while continuing his research, mainly with E. A. N. Arber of the Sedgwick Museum of Geology. In 1909 he was appointed curator of the Botany School Museum, a post that he held until 1923; during this time he gradually shifted his teaching to botany. In 1911 he worked for a few months with Nathorst in the Stockholm Museum, and he appears to have also visited Russia about the same time. His election as a fellow of Downing College in 1914 gave him financial security.

Thomas spent most of World War I with the Royal Flying Corps in the Near East developing new techniques of mapping from aerial photographs, which were of considerable strategic importance. He continued his work in this field when he returned to Cambridge and kept in touch with research there. His work is still cited today. His interest in aerial photography also brought about his only work on ecology; he wrote on the flora of the Libyan desert and on the aerial survey of vegetation.

In 1923 Thomas was appointed to a university lectureship, and he married Edith Gertrude Torrance from Cape Town, who encouraged him to collect fossils in South Africa. They had one daughter and one son, who studied aircraft engineering and continued some of his father's work.

Thomas spent World War II with the RAF in England, where he was in charge of a specialist unit on photographic interpretation for Intelligence.

Thomas' scientific work was important because of the comprehensiveness of his collecting and fieldwork, his techniques of interpretation, and his detailed work on the systematics of fossil plant groups. Paleontology was mainly carried out in museums at that time, but Thomas collected extensively in England and in many areas abroad. Seward encouraged him to reexamine the Jurassic flora of Yorkshire, which resulted in Thomas' series of papers published between 1911 and 1925.

Work with Nathorst and with Thore Gustaf Halle, whom he also met in Stockholm, showed him the importance of a detailed examination of impressions of the epidermis from fossil plants. He extended this approach to attempts to examine even the compressed internal structures, which was a feature of his most important paper on the Caytoniales in 1925. In this paper he examined the leaves, particularly the petioles, the ovaries, and the pollen organs of hundreds of specimens before concluding that the family, which he named, was closely related to the angiosperms, although not in the direct line of descent. Thomas' paper on Triassic pteridosperms from South Africa, published in 1933, was also important because the pteridosperms were at one time a dominant group in the Southern hemisphere. The publication of this paper was followed by his election in 1934 as a fellow of the Royal Society.

Although Thomas had no formal training in geology, he did some work for the Geological Survey. His later publications on comparative morphology of plants were received with reservations by some of his colleagues. He also wrote on the history and philosophy of science.

BIBLIOGRAPHY

I. ORIGINAL WORKS. The two major papers are "The Caytoniales, a New Group of Angiospermous Plants from the Jurassic Rocks of Yorkshire," in *Philosophical Transactions of the Royal Society*, **213B** (1925), 299–363; and "On Some Pteridospermous Plants from the Mesozoic Rocks of South Africa," *ibid.*, **222** (1933), 193–265.

Thomas appears to have written no books, but there are several monographs listed by Thomas M. Harris, published by the British Museum (Natural History) and the Russian Geological Committee. His work for the Geological Survey is not listed by Harris and comprises

"Refractory materials . . . ," in *Geological Survey Special Reports on the Mineral Resources of Great Britain*, **16** (1920); and "The Geology of the South Wales Coalfield," in *Geological Survey Topographical Memoirs*, **10–12** (1909–1916).

II. SECONDARY LITERATURE. Most comprehensive is the obituary by Thomas M. Harris, in *Biographical Memoirs of Fellows of the Royal Society*, **9** (1963), 287–299, which includes a bibliography of his major works.

DIANA M. SIMPKINS

THOMAS, SIDNEY GILCHRIST (*b.* London, England, 16 April 1850; *d.* Paris, France, 1 February 1885), *metallurgy.*

Thomas invented and commercialized the basic process for dephosphorizing pig iron in the making of wrought iron and steel. As a result of his work, vast deposits of phosphoric iron ores that were previously unsuitable could be converted into steel by either the Bessemer or open-hearth methods. By the early years of the twentieth century most steel was being made by the basic process.

Thomas' father, William Thomas, was a Welshman employed in the civil service. Between the ages of ten and sixteen Thomas was educated at Dulwich College (equivalent to a high school or preparatory school), where he prepared for the matriculation examinations at London University. He intended to study medicine. When his father died in 1867 he abandoned these plans, and after a brief tenure as a teacher of classics at an Essex school he accepted a junior clerkship at a London police court. The following year (1868) he voluntarily transferred to the Thames police court in Stepney, the lower depths of London society, and he remained there for eleven years until the success of his invention enabled him to devote himself completely to metallurgy.

In a full account of his life, his sister Lilian Gilchrist Thompson reported that their mother was a "keen Liberal" and Thomas a "militant Radical" as an adolescent. He was strongly sympathetic to the North in the American Civil War, and he aspired to earn a fortune through applied science and to use it to assist the unfortunate and the neglected. Upon his early death, at the age of thirty-four, he left a sizable estate to his sister with instructions that it be used for "doing good discriminatingly." Lilian Thompson outlived her brother by more than half a century and executed his will scrupulously, largely by sponsoring various efforts to improve the conditions of workers, especially women.

Although Thomas never married, his letters reveal a spirited appreciation of feminine companionship.

During his early years as a police-court clerk, Thomas pursued his interests in metallurgy and applied chemistry by attending courses at the Royal School of Mines and the Birkbeck Literary and Scientific Institution (now Birkbeck College). At the School of Mines he passed all of the examinations, but could not matriculate because he was unable to meet the requirement of regular attendance at the metallurgy lectures. It was in response to a chance remark by a Birkbeck lecturer that Thomas resolved to find a method for producing Bessemer steel from phosphoric ores, a challenge that had been confounding the foremost metallurgists since the introduction of Bessemer's process. (In the older puddling process the phosphorus was readily removed.) By the end of 1875 Thomas had formulated the theory that, in order to remove the phosphorus, it was necessary to provide a strong base so that the phosphoric acid produced in the converter could combine with the base and form a slag. At first he experimented with basic linings for the converter formed chiefly of lime or limestone, but it was found that to preserve the linings from rapid deterioration and to produce a highly basic slag it was necessary to add substantial amounts of basic substances to the molten iron. In the commercial process it was mainly the additives rather than the linings that produced the phosphorus-bearing slag.

To overcome the constraints of both the demands of his clerkship and his lack of adequate experimental facilities, Thomas enlisted the collaboration of his cousin, Percy Carlyle Gilchrist, who was employed as a chemist in a Welsh ironworks. The collaboration proved fruitful and in 1877 the first of many patents was taken out. Although Thomas announced his achievement the following year at a meeting of the Iron and Steel Institute, it was not until 1879 that success was achieved on a commercial scale. At the spring meeting of the Iron and Steel Institute the Thomas-Gilchrist process was fully acknowledged.

So successfully did Thomas manage his patents, and so knowledgeable was he of the intricacies of international patent law, that he was able to defend his rights against formidable challenges. One challenge was, however, irresistible. Unknown to Thomas, the British metallurgist George James Snelus had patented the use of basic linings for the Bessemer converter in 1872. Although Snelus had failed to perfect the process, or even to produce usable linings, Thomas chose to avoid litigation, and a settlement was reached through the arbitration of William Thomson (later Lord Kelvin). Snelus received a share of the profits of the British and American (but not the Continental) rights and in 1883 both men received a Bessemer Gold Medal from the Iron and Steel Institute.

During the final years of his life, Thomas took out several patents on the preparation of the phosphate-rich basic slag for use as fertilizer, a technique that achieved considerable importance after his death.

These later years were also spent in a vain search for health as Thomas traveled extensively, hoping to benefit from climates more congenial than that of Great Britain. He died after a lingering illness diagnosed as emphysema, an ailment disproportionately common among employees of the poorly ventilated London police courts.

BIBLIOGRAPHY

I. ORIGINAL WORKS. Thomas and Gilchrist jointly authored "On the Elimination of Phosphorus," in *Journal of the Iron and Steel Institute*, **14–15** (1879), 120–134; "A Note on Current Dephosphorising Practice," *ibid.*, **19** (1881), 407–412; "The Manufacture of Steel and Ingot-iron from Phosphoric Pig-iron," in *Journal of the Society of Arts*, **30** (1882), 648–660. For a list of Thomas' lesser publications, see Lilian Gilchrist (Thomas) Thompson, *Sidney Gilchrist Thomas: An Invention and Its Consequences* (London, 1940), 56–57.

II. SECONDARY LITERATURE. Two full biographies are R. W. Burnie, *Memoir and Letters of Sidney Gilchrist Thomas* (London, 1891); and Lilian Gilchrist Thompson, *op. cit.* The latter is based heavily on the former but contains additional material on the adoption of the basic process and on his sister's use of the fortune he left. For biographical essays on Thomas and Snelus, see William T. Jeans, *The Creators of the Age of Steel* (New York, 1884).

HAROLD DORN

THOMAS OF CANTIMPRÉ, also known as **Thomas Brabantinus (Brabançon)** (*b.* Leeuw–Saint Pierre, Brabant, Belgium, *ca.* 1186–1210; *d.* Louvain, between 1276 and 1294), *theology, natural history, encyclopedism.*

Thomas of Cantimpré was descended from a noble family named De Monte or Du Mont, residing at Hellenghem (present-day Bellingen) near Leeuw–Saint Pierre, hence his further designation as Thomas van Hellenghem. He entered the abbey of Cantimpré near Cambrai as a novice and re-

mained there for some fifteen years. In 1232 he entered the Dominican Order in Louvain. Thomas was educated in the schools of Liège, Cologne, and Paris (Collège St. Jacques). He presumably was a pupil of Albertus Magnus at Cologne and Paris between 1245 and 1248. The date of his death, as of his birth, is uncertain. He was apparently alive in 1276 but was no longer living in 1294 (Thorndike, II, 374).

The content of Thomas' writings fitted well into the dominant precepts exemplified in the encyclopedic works of his contemporaries, Bartholomaeus Anglicus, Thomas Aquinas, Vincent of Beauvais, and others who adhered to a belief in the essential unity of the natural and the supernatural worlds. Hence, while primarily a theologian who studiously composed biographies of ecclesiastics and saints, Thomas also wrote on natural and pseudo science with the avowed intention of furthering knowledge of theological rather than of scientific truths. His work on bees, *Bonum universale de apibus*, deals with the orders of bees as they compare with the orders or hierarchy of prelates; and his major work on natural phenomena, *De naturis rerum*, on which he toiled for some fourteen or fifteen years and completed between 1228 and 1244, was intended, he informs us, to provide illustrative materials for use in sermons and arguments to bolster the faith. (The title *De naturis rerum* has been utilized, instead of *De natura rerum*, since it has the authority of thirteenth-century manuscripts of the work and most of the later manuscripts. See Thorndike, II, 397–398; and in *Isis*, **54** [1963], 269–277, for lists of MSS with the title *De naturis rerum*.)

Nevertheless, despite his avowed theological bent, Thomas of Cantimpré revealed in the *De naturis rerum* a lively interest in the real and natural world. The subjects treated in the twenty books into which the work is usually divided are largely those of the natural sciences. There are three books on man: one on the parts of the human body, containing a chapter on each part and its ills and their cures (with considerable information on gynecology and obstetrics); another book on the soul; and a third book on strange and monstrous races of men. Then there are seven books on animals: quadrupeds, birds, marine monsters, fish, serpents, and worms; and two books on the vegetable kingdom, including aromatic and medicinal trees and herbs. Finally, there are individual books on fountains and other bodies of water, precious metals, the seven regions of the air, the spheres and planets, meteorology, and the universe and the four elements, with an additional (or twentieth) book on the heavens and eclipses of the sun and moon added in some manuscripts.

Throughout the *De naturis rerum*, Thomas gives evidence of his adherence to the beliefs regarding natural phenomena current in his time, as well as of an undue reliance upon the credibility of his authorities. He also shared with many of his contemporaries a modified belief in astrology. In considering the effects of each of the planets when it was in the ascendant, he noted the moon's influence on the rise and fall of humors and infirmities of the human body; Mercury's purification of the mind of man; the effect of Venus in the generation of all earthly things; the numerous attributes of the sun relating particularly to natural phenomena, such as rain, snow, and the growth and decay of plants; the influence of Mars in causing anger to rise in men, heating the heart and liver, and undermining the health; Jupiter, through its hotness and dryness, causing all living things to spring forth; and Saturn, which causes seeds when planted in the earth to be mortified so that they will bring forth fruit. Throughout his account of the planets Thomas cited supporting passages from Scripture, and he concluded: that "except for human free will and special manifestations of divine will, all nature is placed by God under the rule of the stars. The influence of the Sun and Moon is manifest and 'why should we not with entire reason believe the same of the other planets?' " (Thorndike, II, 393–394).

Thomas also adhered to other beliefs in the occult. He indicated in the book on precious stones his belief in the marvelous powers and occult virtues of stones and gems and in the additional virtues imparted by sculptured gems. Thomas evinced an interest in alchemy; in the book on the seven metals, he alluded to the transmutation of metals (speaking of copper) and cited the *Lumen luminum*, a work on alchemy, which he attributed to Aristotle.

In addition to the instances related to the occult sciences, Thomas also provided interesting items regarding technological improvements. He thus gives, in the book on precious stones (in the discussion of adamant), a description of the mariner's compass, already described by Thomas' earlier contemporary Alexander Neckam (Thorndike, II, 387–388). In the book on the seven metals (in the discussion of tin), Thomas appears to have made one of the first mentions of modern plumbing in his account of the use of molten lead to fuse the pipes of aqueducts. According to Thomas, the pipes "used to be joined with tin, but in 'modern times' human art has thought out a method of uniting them with hot molten lead." Thomas also mentioned steel (Thorndike, II, 392).

As a theologian and encyclopedist, Thomas of Cantimpré did not add to the sum of the scientific knowledge of his time, but he did, in *De naturis rerum*, make clear what the current notions were concerning natural phenomena. He also reported on significant technological developments known to his contemporaries, and thus performed the service of disseminating knowledge that he had culled from his authorities as well as from his own observation.

BIBLIOGRAPHY

I. ORIGINAL WORKS. Information regarding the biographies of churchmen and saints and also the *Bonum universale de apibus* (on prelates) is in W. E. van der Vet, *Het Biënboec van Thomas Van Cantimpré en zijn exempelen* (The Hague, 1902), 29. Book I of the *Bonum universale de apibus* in Middle High German was edited by Nils Otto Heinertz, *Die mittelniederdeutsche Versien des Bienenbuches von Thomas von Chantimpré. Das erste Buch* (Lund, 1906).

The *De naturis rerum* is extant in some 151 MSS. Of these 144 have been enumerated by G. J. J. Walstra, "Thomas de Cantimpré, De naturis rerum. État de la question," in *Vivarium*, **5**, pt. 2 (1967), 146–171; **6**, pt. 2 (1968), 46–61, in preparation for a critical edition of the text. H. Boese, "Zur Textüberlieferung von Thomas Cantimpratensis' Liber de natura rerum," in *Archivum F. F. Praed.*, **39** (1969), 53–68, lists 44 MSS, seven of which, dated in the fourteenth and fifteenth centuries, were not included in Walstra's list. Boese has also published a first volume containing the text: Thomas Cantimpratensis, *Liber de natura rerum. Editio princeps secundum codices manuscriptos*, I, *Text* (Berlin, 1973). Unfortunately this volume contains no critical apparatus, which will apparently follow in a second volume. Earlier both the text and a considerable number of the manuscripts were described by Lynn Thorndike, *History of Magic and Experimental Science*, II (New York, 1923), 396–398; "More Manuscripts of Thomas of Cantimpré, De naturis rerum," in *Isis*, **54**, pt. 2 (1963), 269–277. Both Thorndike and Walstra indicated that the work frequently appears in the manuscripts as anonymous or ascribed to authors other than Thomas of Cantimpré. Also the number of books varies from nineteen to twenty; and there is a difference in their sequence. For example, in some manuscripts, instead of beginning with the book on the parts of the human body (book I), the text begins with the book usually numbered XVI, on the seven regions of the air, and ends with the book on the seven metals (usually book XV). Translations of the work into Flemish are by Jacob van Maerlant, in J. H.

Bormans, *Der naturen bloeme van Jacob van Maerlant*, books I–IV (Brussels, 1857), and E. Verwijs, *Jacob van Maerlant's naturen bloeme* (Groningen, 1878), into Dutch by Broeder Gheraert, in J. Clarisse, *Sterte-en-natuur-kundig* (Leiden, 1847); and into Middle High German by Konrad von Megenberg, in Fr. Pfeiffer, *Dar Buch der Natur* (Stuttgart, 1867).

Portions of the text of Thomas of Cantimpré have also been published separately. Sections from book I have been edited by Christ. Ferckel, *Die Gynäkologie des Thomas von Brabant. Ausgewählte Kapitel aus Buch I de naturis rerum beendet . . . 1240, zum ersten Male herausgegeben* (G. Klein, Alte Meister der Medizin, No. 5) (Munich, 1912), and Alfons Hilka, "Eine altfranzösische moralisierende Bearbeitung des Liber de Monstruosis Hominibus Orientis aus Thomas von Cantimpré, De naturis rerum nach der einzigen Handschrift (Paris, Bibl. Nat. fr. 15106)," in *Abhandlungen der Gesellschaft der Wissenschaften zu Göttingen Philologisch-Historische Klasse*, 3rd ser., no. 7 (1933), 1–73.

II. SECONDARY LITERATURE. Lynn Thorndike, *op. cit.*, has reviewed the principal biographical details, together with previous biographical literature, and has given an analysis of the content of the *De naturis rerum* as contained in the manuscripts. G. J. J. Walstra, *op. cit.*, has similarly analyzed the contents and brought together the listings of some 144 manuscripts so far identified, compiling as well a bibliography of all the previous works treating both the author and *De naturis rerum*. See also a review of the text in H. Boese, "Sur Textüberlieferung . . .," cited above.

PEARL KIBRE

THOMAZ, ALVARO (also known as **Alvaro Tómas** or **Alvarus Thomas**) (*b.* Lisbon, second half of the fifteenth century; place and date of death unknown), *physics, mathematics.*

Biographical data on Thomaz are lacking, save that he was regent of the Collège de Coqueret at Paris on 11 February 1509, as indicated in the colophon of his principal work, and that he is mentioned in the archives of the University of Paris as a master of arts at the same college in 1513. Thomaz is noteworthy for his *Liber de triplici motu proportionibus annexis . . . philosophicas Suiseth calculationes ex parte declarans* ("Book on the Three [Kinds of] Movement, With Ratios Added, Explaining in Part Swineshead's Philosophical [i.e., Physical] Calculations"), printed at Paris in 1509. This work shows Thomaz to be a mathematician and physicist of considerable ability who understood and organized the teachings of fourteenth-century English calculators and Parisian terminists, such as Oresme, making them available

to a wide audience of European scholars in the sixteenth century.

Thomaz' work is divided into three parts, the first and second of which are compact expositions of ratios and proportions respectively, while the third is a lengthy application to problems concerning motion. This last part treats, in turn, local motion, augmentation, and alteration. Although designed as a guide to the thought of Richard Swineshead, Thomaz' treatise is not patterned after Swineshead's *Liber calculationum* ("Book of Calculations"), but follows instead an ordering suggested jointly by Thomas Bradwardine's *Tractatus de proportionibus* ("Treatise on Ratios") and by William Heytesbury's *Tractatus de tribus praedicamentis* ("Treatise on the Three Categories"). The first two parts seem to have been inspired by the inferior work of a certain Bassanus Politus, *Tractatus proportionum introductorius ad calculationes Suisset* ("Treatise on Ratios, an Introduction to Swineshead's Calculations"), printed in Venice in 1505, a work that Thomaz effectively castigated as worthless.

Thomaz' citation of authorities was extensive. His mathematics was drawn mainly from Nicomachus, Boethius, Johannes Campanus, and Jordanus de Nemore, while for Euclid he cited "the new translation of Bartholomeus Zambertus." Among the Schoolmen he referred to Thomas Aquinas (and his commentator, Capreolus), Robert Holkot, Duns Scotus, Albert of Saxony, Marsilius of Inghen, Gregory of Rimini, and John Maior. He knew too of the work of Paul of Venice, James of Forli, Cajetan of Thiene, John de Casali, Andrew de Novo Castro, Peter of Mantua, and a writer whom he identified as the Conciliator (Pietro d'Abano). Above all he was conversant with the complex details of Bradwardine's, Heytesbury's, and Swineshead's writings, and also with the little-understood *De proportionibus proportionum* ("On the Ratios of Ratios") of Oresme. Edward Grant states in his edition of the latter work: "Alvarus is the only author known to me who shows an extensive acquaintance with, and understanding of, Oresme's treatise" (p. 71).

Thomaz manifested some originality and considerable independence of judgment, as witness his rejection and reformulation of many of Swineshead's and Oresme's propositions. His treatment of falling bodies was highly imaginative in terms of the types of motive forces and resistive media discussed, but unfortunately was diffuse and inconclusive; contrary to what some scholars have suggested, it contains no explicit adumbration of Galileo's law of uniform acceleration. Thomaz showed facility in the summation of series, generally indicating when they converge and when they do not and, in cases where he cannot determine a precise value, providing limits between which this value must lie.

The influence of Thomaz' work is difficult to assess. Through his colleague at Coqueret, Juan de Celaya, he seems to have assisted in the formation of Celaya's later disciple, Domingo de Soto, who was the first to apply unequivocally the Mertonian "mean-speed theorem" to the case of falling bodies. Thomaz' treatise was cited by many Spaniards, favorably by the Salamancan masters Pedro Margallo and Pedro de Espinosa and by the Dominican Diego de Astudillo, and unfavorably by the Augustinian Alonso de la Veracruz, who blamed Thomaz' "calculatory sophisms" for much wasted time (and midnight oil) on the part of students in arts. At Paris, however, there can be little doubt that Thomaz was the calculator par excellence at the beginning of the sixteenth century, and the principal stimulus for the revival of interest there in the Mertonian approach to mathematical physics.

BIBLIOGRAPHY

I. ORIGINAL WORK. Thomaz' *Liber de triplici motu . . .*, is unavailable in translation; a copy of the original is in the library of the University of Michigan.

II. SECONDARY LITERATURE. For discussions of Thomaz and his work, see Pierre Duhem, *Études sur Léonard de Vinci*, III (Paris, 1913), 531–555, 557, 561; J. Rey Pastor, *Los matemáticos españoles del siglo XVI*, Biblioteca scientia no. 2 (Toledo, 1926), 82–89; Edward Grant, ed. and trans., *Nicole Oresme: De proportionibus proportionum and Ad pauca respicientes* (Madison, 1966), index; and William A. Wallace, "The 'Calculatores' in Early Sixteenth-Century Physics," in *British Journal for the History of Science*, **4** (1969), 221–232.

WILLIAM A. WALLACE, O.P.

THOMPSON, BENJAMIN (COUNT RUMFORD) (*b.* Woburn, Massachusetts, 26 March 1753; *d.* Auteuil, France, 21 August 1814), *physics*.

Thompson's father, Benjamin Thompson, and his mother, Ruth Simonds, were small village farmers in New England. He had little formal schooling, educating himself by self-study with the help of friends and local clergymen. Taking up schoolteaching, he moved to Concord, New Hampshire, where almost immediately (1772) he made an ad-

vantageous marriage with a wealthy widow, Sarah Walker Rolfe, fourteen years his senior. They had one child, Sarah, and permanently separated in 1775. Thompson soon came to the attention of the royal governor of New Hampshire, who commissioned him a major. He became an active Tory in the early part of the American Revolution. He fled to London after the fall of Boston and progressed rapidly in British government circles to become undersecretary of state for the colonies.

After a brief military career in South Carolina and on Long Island in New York, Thompson retired from the British army at the age of thirty-one with the rank of colonel. Knighted by George III, he joined the court of the elector of Bavaria, where he rose to become head of the Bavarian army. Thompson was made a count of the Holy Roman Empire by the Bavarian duke in 1793, taking the name of Count Rumford, after the old name of Concord, New Hampshire.

In 1796 Thompson established the largest prizes that had yet been given for scientific research, singling out the American Academy of Arts and Sciences in Boston and the Royal Society of London as the organizations that would award biennial Rumford premiums for work in heat and light. The prizes are still given. He returned briefly to London around 1800 but settled a few years later in Paris, where he married the widow of Antoine Lavoisier. The marriage was unsuccessful, and he separated from his wife and retired to Auteuil, near Paris, to write and work vigorously on science and technology.

Thompson was an active fellow of the Royal Society of London; he founded the Royal Institution of Great Britain; and in later years he was active in the Institut de France. He was a recipient of many honors and a member of many other scientific societies, including the American Philosophical Society in Philadelphia, the American Academy of Arts and Sciences in Boston, and the Bavarian Academy in Mannheim. He left the residue of his estate to Harvard University to establish a Rumford professorship, which still exists.

Professionally, Thompson was a soldier of fortune. His first serious scientific study was to determine the optimal position of firing vents in cannon and to measure the velocity of the shot as a function of the composition of gunpowder. He used a ballistic pendulum method first introduced by Benjamin Robins. Thompson's long paper on this subject, published in 1781, won him fellowship in the Royal Society of London. Throughout his life he intermittently pursued his studies on the force of gunpowder. In 1797 he published the description of a device for proving gunpowder, which was generally accepted as the standard method by both the British and the Bavarian armies. It was during his investigations of cannon that he was impressed by the large amount of heat generated in cannon barrels by the explosion of gunpowder even when no ball was being fired. He was thus led to accept the vibratory theory of heat, which he championed actively all his life. Thompson's most famous experiment in this area was his demonstration of the process of boring cannon with a dull drill, which he carried out in the arsenal at Munich. Because the heat generated in this process seemed limitless, he reasoned that a fluid caloric did not exist. Thompson carried out many other experiments to demonstrate the reasons for his disbelief in the caloric theory. He unsuccessfully attempted to determine whether heat had weight, which would be an attribute of a fluid; he weighed, at different temperatures, fluids that had markedly different specific heats and heats of fusion. He studied the anomalous expansion of water between 4°C and 0°C to show that the concept that thermal expansion is caused by fluid caloric taking up space was false. He never realized the connection between heat and energy, although he did carry on experiments to demonstrate spontaneous interdiffusion of different density liquids at constant temperature, and he postulated that fluids are in constant random motion.

In his role as military commander for the elector of Bavaria, Thompson demonstrated a genius for technological improvement that was widely recognized at the time, and many of his innovations are still used. In an effort to economize in the military establishment, he made careful studies of the insulating properties of cloth and fur, showing that the principal loss of heat was by convection, and that by inhibiting convection currents greater insulation could be achieved. He also demonstrated that heat passes with great difficulty through vacuums.

Thompson increased the labor force for making military clothing by sweeping Munich clear of beggars and setting them to work in military workhouses. Faced with the problem of feeding this labor force as well as feeding soldiers in the army, he studied the science of nutrition. He developed a theory of the nutritional value of water and introduced soup as a staple diet. He experimented with many cheap foods for mass feeding of the poor, introduced the potato into Central Europe, and published a long essay containing many recipes for the preparation of hearty meals. He searched for a

substitute for alcoholic beverages for the common man and wrote extensively on the advantages of drinking coffee, analyzed the brewing of coffee, and designed a large number of drip-type coffee makers. In order to increase the efficiency of cooking devices he studied the insulation properties of solids and invented the concept of enclosing a fire in an insulated box, designing what is now called a kitchen range. His interest in the efficiency of heat transfer led him to design a double boiler and special pots and pans for use on his stoves. He also championed the use of the pressure cooker, invented by Papin. His studies of convection currents led to the design of a roaster for meat and the invention of a calorimeter for measuring the heats of combustion of various fuels to be used in his stoves. To help lower the cost of feeding the Bavarian army, he introduced military gardens where the soldiers could grow their own foods. He provided a demonstration museum for the general Bavarian populace by laying out the large park in the center of Munich known as the English Gardens.

In connection with his military workhouses, Thompson studied the efficiency of illumination, inventing the shadow photometer that bears his name. He also introduced the concept of a standard candle, defining the details of what was the international unit of luminous intensity until the twentieth century. In connection with his studies of illumination, Thompson designed oil lamps, the so-called Rumford lamps. He studied the transmission of light through glass and various translucent substances, including cloth; he also measured the diffusion of light passing through ground glass, silk, and other lamp shade material. As a result of his shadow photometer measurements, he became interested in the phenomena associated with colored shadows and wrote extensively not only about this subject but also about the psychological effects of complementary colors. Thompson's theoretical work on the theory of light centered around its relationship with heat, and its effect on chemical reactions and photosynthesis.

As his international fame for technological innovation grew during his lifetime, Thompson turned his attention to the popularization of technology as a useful endeavor. He established the Royal Institution of Great Britain in London as a museum of technology primarily for the education of artisans and the poor. He hoped to provide them with knowledge and skills in the construction of devices using heat and light. To support this institution financially Rumford initiated scientific lectures and courses of instruction by public subscription for the wealthy London aristocracy, hiring men of the stature of Humphry Davy and Thomas Young as full-time research scientists and lecturers. This effort was so successful that the original purpose of the Institution gradually disappeared and Rumford lost interest although he maintained contact with Davy and his assistant Michael Faraday throughout his life. The Royal Institution has continued as a leading British scientific society.

Thompson was much bothered by the evils of a smoky fireplace. He studied air currents in open fireplaces and introduced the smoke shelf, the throat, and the damper characteristic of the modern chimney. By giving attention to the proper relationship between the size of the fireplace opening and the size of the throat, he increased the efficiency of the fireplace. He also set up equipment for measuring the fundamental properties of heat radiation and demonstrated at the same time as did John Leslie that mat surfaces radiate heat better than shiny ones. His studies led him to design fireplaces with beveled sides and backs to throw more heat into the room. Thompson's studies of the flow of heated fluids allowed him to design steam-heating systems with the proper separation of steam and water. He introduced them not only into private houses but also into the large auditoriums of the Royal Institution in London and the Institut de France in Paris. In addition, Thompson designed commercial distribution systems for steam in the manufacture of soap and in brewing and dyeing.

BIBLIOGRAPHY

I. ORIGINAL WORKS. Thompson published sixty-four papers and essays, and these have been reprinted in five volumes, edited by Sanborn C. Brown and published in Cambridge, Mass.: *The Nature of Heat* (1968); *Practical Applications of Heat* (1969); *Devices and Techniques* (1969); *Light and Armament* (1970); and *Public Institutions* (1970).

II. SECONDARY LITERATURE. The standard biography of Benjamin Thompson is George E. Ellis, *Memoir of Sir Benjamin Thompson, Count Rumford, With Notices of His Daughter* (Boston, 1871), published in connection with *The Complete Works of Count Rumford*, 4 vols. (Boston, 1870–1875).

SANBORN C. BROWN

THOMPSON, D'ARCY WENTWORTH (*b.* Edinburgh, Scotland, 2 May 1860; *d.* St. Andrews, Scotland, 21 June 1948), *natural history, classics, mathematics, oceanography.*

Thompson was the son of D'Arcy Wentworth Thompson, classical master at the Edinburgh Academy and, later, professor of classics at Queen's College, Galway. His mother was Fanny Gamgee, daughter of Joseph Gamgee, a veterinary surgeon. Her brother was Arthur Gamgee, "the first biochemist." Thompson was educated at the Edinburgh Academy and the University of Edinburgh (1877–1880), where he studied anatomy under Turner, chemistry under Crum Brown, and zoology under Wyville Thomson, recently returned from the *Challenger* expedition. He then studied at Trinity College, Cambridge (1880–1883), where he was subsizar and later scholar, and where he read zoology under Francis M. Balfour and physiology under Michael Foster. While there he published his first work, a translation of H. Müller's *Fertilisation of Flowers*, for which Charles Darwin wrote the preface. He gained first-class honors in parts I and II of the natural sciences tripos and for a year taught physiology under Foster. In 1884 Thompson was elected professor of biology at University College, Dundee, and in 1917 was transferred to the chair of natural history at St. Andrews.

Thompson's first marine investigation, that of the fur-seal fisheries, took place in 1896, when he was sent by the British government to the Bering Sea. After representing Great Britain at Washington, D.C., at the Anglo-American commission of inquiry into the Bering Sea seal fishery in 1897, Thompson was made Companion of the Order of the Bath in 1898, in recognition of the success of his mission. A foundation member of the Conseil Permanent International pour l'Exploration de la Mer, he served on the Council from 1902 to 1947, was chairman of the Statistical Committee, and editor of the *Bulletin statistique* (1902–1947).

In 1901 Thompson married Maureen Drury; they had three daughters. In 1916 he was elected fellow of the Royal Society, in 1928 president of the Classical Association (of England and Wales), from 1934–1939 president of the Royal Society of Edinburgh, and in 1936 president of the Scottish Classical Association. He was awarded a knighthood during the coronation honors in 1937.

Thompson did not fit into any particular category; he was equally a scholar, scientist, naturalist, classicist, mathematician, and philosopher. Inheriting a love of the classics from his father and brought up by his scientific grandfather, he straddled two worlds and dominated both.

Thompson's paper "On the Shapes of Eggs and the Causes Which Determine Them," published in

Nature, 1908, shows the direction in which his thought was taking him. In his 1911 presidential address to section D of the British Association, "Magnalia Naturae; or the Greater Problems of Biology," he discussed, for the first time, what he called "the exploration of the borderline of morphology and physics." This was preparatory to the 1917 *On Growth and Form*, his great contribution to scientific literature. In this work Thompson departed from contemporary zoology, which was occupied with orthodox questions of comparative anatomy and evolution, and treated morphological problems by mathematics. The theme was original, unorthodox, and revolutionary. The chapter "On the Comparison of Related Forms" is a demonstration of the orderly deformation of related organic forms mapped out in accordance with Descartes's method of coordinates. The diagrams of transformation have contributed to other work on problems of growth and have influenced research in embryology, taxonomy, paleontology, and ecology.

Thompson initiated no school of research and was followed by no band of disciples. But the indirect influence of *On Growth and Form* is so wide and so important that it is hard to calculate. Scientists, engineers, architects, painters, and poets have acknowledged their indebtedness to this essay that ranges over a wide field of scientific discovery, thought, and history.

BIBLIOGRAPHY

I. ORIGINAL WORKS. For a list of the published writings of D'Arcy Wentworth Thompson, see *Essays on Growth and Form* (cited below), 386–400.

Major works include H. Müller, *The Fertilisation of Flowers*, Thompson, trans. and ed., with a preface by Charles Darwin (London, 1893); *A Bibliography of Protozoa, Sponges, Coelenterata, and Worms for the Years 1861–1883* (Cambridge, 1885); "John Ray," in *Encyclopaedia Britannica*, 9th ed., XX (1886); *A Glossary of Greek Birds* (Oxford, 1895); "On the Shapes of Eggs, and the Causes Which Determine Them," in *Nature*, **78** (1908), 111–113; Aristotle, *Historia animalium*, Thompson, trans. and ed. (Oxford, 1910); "Magnalia Naturae; or the Greater Problems of Biology," in *Nature*, **87** (1911), 325–328; reprinted in *Smithsonian Institution Annual Report* (1911); *On Aristotle as a Biologist*, with an introduction on Herbert Spencer (Oxford, 1911); "Morphology and Mathematics," in *Transactions of the Royal Society of Edinburgh*, **50** (1915), 857–895; *On Growth and Form* (Cambridge, 1917); "Natural Science: Aristotle," in *The Legacy of Greece*, R. W. Livingstone, ed. (Oxford, 1921); *Science and the*

Classics (Oxford, 1940); and *A Glossary of Greek Fishes* (Oxford, 1947).

II. SECONDARY LITERATURE. Important writings on Thompson and his works include Ruth D'Arcy Thompson, *D'Arcy Wentworth Thompson, The Scholar Naturalist, 1860–1948*, with a postscript by P. B. Medawar, "D'Arcy Thompson and Growth and Form" (Oxford, 1958); W. Le Gros Clark and P. B. Medawar, eds., *Essays on Growth and Form* (Oxford, 1945); and Ruth D'Arcy Thompson, *The Remarkable Gamgees* (Edinburgh, 1974).

Brief discussions and obituaries include Clifford Dobell, "D'Arcy Wentworth Thompson," in *Obituary Notices of Fellows of the Royal Society*, **6** (1949), 599–617; W. T. Calman, "Sir D'Arcy Thompson, C.B., LL.D., F.R.S.," in *Royal Society of Edinburgh Year Book* (1946–1948), 44–48; Douglas Young, "Sir D'Arcy Thompson as Classical Scholar," *ibid.*; R. S. Clark, "D'Arcy Wentworth Thompson," in *Journal du Conseil. Conseil permanent international pour l'exploration de la mer*, **16**, no. 1 (1949), 9–13; G. E. Hutchinson, "In Memoriam, D'Arcy Wentworth Thompson," in *American Scientist*, **36** (1948), 577; Lancelot Law Whyte, ed., *Aspects of Form* (London, 1951; 2nd ed., 1968); S. Brody, *Bioenergetics and Growth* (New York, 1945); J. S. Huxley, *Problems of Relative Growth* (London, 1932); and Jack Burnham, *Beyond Modern Sculpture* (Harmondsworth, Middlesex, 1968).

RUTH D'ARCY THOMPSON

THOMPSON, JOHN VAUGHAN (*b.* Berwick-upon-Tweed, England [?], 19 November 1779; *d.* Sydney, New South Wales, Australia, 21 January 1847), *natural history*.

Little is known of Thompson's early life beyond the fact that he spent part of it in the vicinity of Berwick-upon-Tweed, in northern England, where he studied medicine and surgery. In March 1799 he was appointed assistant surgeon to the Prince of Wales Own Fencible Regiment, which had been raised by Sir William Johnston in 1798. Thompson was promoted, after his transfer as assistant surgeon in the 37th Regiment of Foot, on 3 July 1800, to surgeon in June 1803, staff surgeon in December 1812, and then to deputy inspector general of army hospitals in July 1830. In 1835 he was posted as medical officer to the convict settlements in New South Wales, a post he held until February 1844, when he retired on half-pay.

Thompson's early service with the medical department of the British army coincided with the Napoleonic Wars. In December 1799 he went with his regiment to Gibraltar. Early in 1800 he was posted to Guiana and the West Indies, at that time a theater in the war between England, and France and the Netherlands. Thompson's stay gave him the opportunity to familiarize himself with the local fauna and flora. He is said to have returned to England in 1809 (although one of his letters in the archives of the Linnean Society is headed London April 7, 1807, thus suggesting that his service in the West Indies was interrupted by a trip to England).

Three years later Thompson was sent to the Mascarene Islands, where it is claimed one of his duties was to introduce the use of vaccine into Madagascar, although in official correspondence of this period he is styled "Government Agent for Madagascar," which suggests that he was also charged with diplomatic duties. From 1816 to 1835 he was stationed at Cork (often referred to as Cove of Cork) in Ireland, where he undertook much of his research on marine invertebrates. Indeed, this period proved to be the most fruitful of his life. His later post in New South Wales was not distinguished by work in natural history, although he returned to an earlier interest in the introduction of useful plants to the colony.

Thompson's personal life remains largely an enigma. It is not recorded whether he married, and no personal accounts from friends or acquaintances appear to exist. This was perhaps the result of his official duties, which kept him in relatively remote stations, away from the main centers of intellectual and scientific development in the British Isles. He was elected a fellow of the Linnean Society of London on 6 February 1810, and he corresponded—and evidently was on familiar terms—with Alexander MacLeay, a former secretary of the society, who was later appointed colonial secretary to the government of New South Wales. Thompson's work on marine invertebrates was to lead him to a number of revolutionary new concepts in fundamental systematics, which brought him into acrimonious conflict with the zoological establishment in London. His correspondence and published writings of that time suggest a man impatient with the conservatism of his opponents, and eventually embittered by their opposition.

Thompson's biological publications fall into three categories: his earliest writings on botany, a subject to which he returned in later life; his writings of a general nature on zoology; and his absorbing and most valuable contributions in marine zoology. He made little contribution to medical science, although he published in 1832 a pamphlet entitled *The Pestilential Cholera Unmasked . . .,*

a work devoted to diagnosis and treatment of cholera, but exhibiting little understanding of the causative factors involved in the disease. The pamphlet was topical, however, because cholera had been spreading westward from Asia during the previous decade, and the year 1832 saw the first major outbreak in the British Isles.

Thompson's early preoccupation with botany is shown by the publication in 1807 of *A Catalogue of Plants Growing in the Vicinity of Berwick-upon-Tweed*, a competent local flora. That same year two of his botanical communications were read to the Linnean Society in London. The first, "On the Genus *Kaempferia*," was primarily concerned with the systematic arrangement of the genus. The second, "An Account of Some New Species of Piper [pepper], With a Few Cursory Observations on the Genus," was published in 1808. This paper is interesting in that it gives incidentally a list of his travels in the West Indies, and his observations on the genus being made in Trinidad, Saint Vincent, and Grenada. His stay in Trinidad also resulted in an unpublished paper entitled "Description of a New Genus of the Natural Order of Myrti," which was read on 3 March 1812 to the Linnean Society.

During Thompson's stay in Mauritius, he continued his botanical studies and compiled *Catalogue of the Exotic Plants Cultivated in the Mauritius . . .,* which was published anonymously, but according to Thompson's claim after the suppression of the title page bearing his name (presumably someone wanted to deprive Thompson of the credit), in November 1816, soon after he left the island. The catalogue was the first work on the plants of the island to be published locally, and is useful in listing the dates of introduction of many of the exotic forms grown in the Botanic Gardens and elsewhere. It also shows Thompson's interest in the importation of useful plants, an interest he shared with many other colonists of the time. Thompson's last botanical studies, which he wrote after he had settled in New South Wales, dealt with the importation and cultivation of cotton and sugarcane.

Thompson's miscellaneous zoological publications began with his "Description of a New Species of the Genus Mus, Belonging to the Section of Pouched Rats," written in Jamaica; the paper was read in 1812 and published in 1815. In 1829 he published an account of his study of bones of the extinct Mascarene bird fauna made during his stay on the islands; the paper is entitled "Contributions Towards the Natural History of the Dodo . . . a Bird Which Appears to Have Become Extinct

Towards the End of the Seventeenth or Beginning of the Eighteenth Century."

It was apparently while returning from Mauritius in 1816 that Thompson made his first study of marine invertebrates. South of Madagascar he observed a puzzling luminosity in the sea. He trailed a muslin hoop net over the stern of the ship and caught a profusion of small marine animals hitherto invisible in the water. Thompson has been credited with being the first person to use a plankton net, and there is little doubt that his use of it in July or August 1816 was his own idea entirely; but he was anticipated by John Cranch, who used a similar tow net on James Kingston Tuckey's expedition to the River Zaire (or Congo) in April 1816. Thompson, unlike Cranch, lived to use his muslin net to catch marine plankton for many years.

In 1827 Thompson published *Memoir on the Pentacrinus europaeus*, in which he announced the discovery of a shallow-water European species of crinoid echinoderm in Cove harbor. The crinoids, especially the feather stars and sea lilies, were known only from dried specimens found in the West Indies, and their affinities were little known. His note added considerably to what was already known from the work of J. S. Miller. Thompson returned to the subject of *Pentacrinus* in 1836, when he showed that it was the young stage of the European *Comatula*; at the same time he described the then almost unknown polychaete *Myzostomum costatum*, commensal on the feather star, although he referred to it as a "complete zoological puzzle!"

One of Thompson's principal contributions to zoology was the discovery that certain planktonic forms of crustacean, then known by the genus name *Zoea*, undergo metamorphoses until recognizable as the young of the European edible crab (*Cancer pagurus*). He published his findings as the first of his memoirs in the *Zoological Researches . . .*, but he failed to prove the complete metamorphic cycle because his zoea died in the process of change; it was only by comparing them with ova from a berried female crab that he was able to deduce the relationship. Thompson's announcement was accompanied by a second memoir "On the genus *Mysis*," however, in which he showed that the mysidacean crustaceans hatch in a form very similar to that of the adult. Both memoirs appeared only months before Rathke's work on the development of the crayfish (*Potamobius*, formerly *Astacus*), which demonstrated that the young hatch at a late stage of development. It is not sur-

prising then that many established zoologists treated Thompson's claim of metamorphosis in the Crustacea with distinct and often derisory doubt. The issue was a serious one, for the taxonomy in use at the time, as expounded by William Leach and Georges Cuvier, distinguished the Crustacea from the Insecta on the grounds that the development of the former proceeded directly and without metamorphosis. Nevertheless, Thompson was soon able to prove his hypothesis. In his third memoir in the *Zoological Researches . . .* (1829), he described a successful experiment of 1827 in which he kept an ovigerous crab in captivity and examined the newly hatched larvae. In 1830 he claimed to have observed newly hatched larvae of eight genera of brachyuran Crustacea to be zoea; in 1835 he published notes on the natural history of the pea crab *Pinnotheres* (a commensal of the mussel, *Mytilus*), in which he again observed the larvae hatched as zoea; and in 1836 he published a report on his experimental hatching of the eggs of the spider crab *Macropodia rostrata*, as well as other papers on the development of Crustacea. Certain zoologists, notably John O. Westwood, refused to be convinced of the truth of Thompson's observations, even denying altogether the evidence that he presented, and the controversy became heated. Eventually others took up the problem and confirmed Thompson's findings.

Thompson's second important achievement in marine biology was his discovery that cirripeds are Crustacea; in the system proposed by Cuvier, they had been designated as a class of the Mollusca. By using his plankton net, Thompson captured some small translucent crustacean larvae, which he kept alive in captivity. He discovered that these animals metamorphosed and settled as acorn barnacles. His brilliant yet simple demonstration of the systematic position of the cirripeds was published in a fourth memoir in the *Zoological Researches . . .* (1830). Thompson's contribution to the biology of the cirripeds did not end with this study, for in 1836 he contributed a paper on the barnacle *Sacculina*, a parasite of the shore crab *Carcinus maenas*, in which he revealed its true nature and identified and described its larval forms.

Thompson's third major achievement in marine biology was the recognition of the class of animals he named Polyzoa. These animals had been formerly included as part of a heterogeneous collection of enigmatic invertebrates, the so-called zoophytes; but he showed that they were distinct from the colonial hydroids and the ascidians, with which they had been sometimes confused. The term Polyzoa received considerable usage, especially in Great Britain, but it was eventually dropped in favor of Bryozoa, which had been proposed almost contemporaneously.

John Vaughan Thompson was a practical naturalist; his use of the tow net and his observations of the living animals enabled him to make a very real contribution to marine zoology. Moreover, he showed an alert appreciation of the implications of his observations that were quite remarkable in a man untrained in the natural sciences and isolated from the mainstream of zoology. He was largely denied during his lifetime the acknowledgment that he deserved; and it has indeed only been during the second half of the twentieth century that his considerable contributions have been adequately recognized.

BIBLIOGRAPHY

I. ORIGINAL WORKS. The most important of Thompson's works on marine invertebrates are the *Zoological Researches and Illustrations* (Cork, Ireland, 1828–1834), a set of five scarce pamphlets, recently reprinted by the Society for the Bibliography of Natural History (London, 1968); and *The Memoir on the Pentacrinus europaeus: A Recent Species Discovered in the Cove of Cork* (Cork, 1827).

The following papers appeared in serial publications; (letter to the editor) concerning the metamorphosis in brachyuran crustacea *Zoological Journal*, **5** (1831), 383–384; "Memoir on the Metamorphosis and Natural History of the Pinnotheres, or Pea-Crabs," in *Entomological Magazine*, **3** (1835), 85–90; "Of the Double Metamorphosis in Macropodia Phalangium, or Spider-Crab . . .," *ibid.*, **3** (1836), 370–375; "Natural History and Metamorphosis of an Anomalous Crustaceous Parasite of *Carcinus Maenas*, the *Sacculina carcini*," *ibid.*, 452–456; "Memoir on the Star-Fish of the Genus *Comatula*," in *Edinburgh New Philosophical Journal*, **20** (1836), 295–300; and "Memoir on the Metamorphosis in the Macrourae or Long-tailed Crustacea, Exemplified by the Prawn (*Palaemon serratus*)," *ibid.*, **21** (1836), 221–223. The botanical works include *Catalogue of Plants Growing in the Vicinity of Berwick-upon-Tweed* (London, 1807); and *Catalogue of the Exotic Plants Cultivated in the Mauritius . . .* (Mauritius, 1816).

II. SECONDARY LITERATURE. See the introduction by Alwyne Wheeler to the facsimile of *Zoological Researches . . .*, published by the Society for the Bibliography of Natural History (London, 1968), i–vi, for an appreciation of Thompson's work. See T. R. Stebbing, *et al.*, "The Terms Polyzoa and Bryozoa," in *Proceedings of the Linnean Society of London*, session 123 (1910–1911), 61–72 for notes on the proposal of the term Polyzoa; and R. E. Vaughan, "A Forgotten Work by John Vaughan Thompson," in *Proceedings of the Royal Society of Arts and Sciences of Mauritius*, **1** (1953), 241–248, for an account of the catalogue of exotic plants in Mauritius.

ALWYNE WHEELER

THOMPSON, SILVANUS PHILLIPS (*b.* York, England, 19 June 1851; *d.* London, England, 12 June 1916), *applied physics, electrical engineering, history of science and technology.*

Thompson was the second of eight children of Silvanus Thompson, a Quaker schoolteacher, and Bridget Tatham, a member of another distinguished Quaker family. Richard and William Phillips, friends of Faraday, were his great-uncles. After sitting for the external B.A. at the University of London in 1869, Thompson taught at Bootham School in York, where his father was senior master. He continued his scientific studies and earned the B.Sc. (1875) and D.Sc. (1878).

While still a graduate student, he came close to making a discovery of the first order. Edison had noted that trains of sparks associated with electrical apparatus gave rise to effects that could be perceived some distance away, without intervening wires, and had concluded that these effects were a "new force." In a carefully designed experiment, Thompson showed that the mysterious effects were in fact electric; but by not pursuing the matter, he narrowly missed demonstrating experimentally Maxwell's theory of electromagnetic propagation, which Hertz accomplished in 1887–1888.

In 1876 Thompson was appointed lecturer in physics at the newly established University College, Bristol, and in 1878 he became the first professor of physics there. He quickly established himself as a popular and prolific lecturer and author of textbooks on electricity that made his name famous throughout the industrialized world. In 1885 he was appointed principal of Finsbury Technical College in London, one of two polytechnics sponsored by the City and Guilds of London Institute (the other, Central Technical College, later became part of Imperial College of Science and Technology of the University of London). He held this post until his death thirty-one years later.

In London, Thompson participated vigorously in scientific life and became the intimate of Lodge, FitzGerald, Crookes, and other luminaries. The thousands of graduates of Finsbury College, who came along at a time when England had virtually no engineering colleges of university level, represent perhaps his most important contribution. He also took a hand in the development of radiotelegraphy and wrote a privately printed pamphlet in support of Lodge's claims of priority over Marconi in the invention of a crucial feature, resonant tuning. Another popular work (until his death published anonymously), *Calculus Made Easy* (1910), is still in print three generations later.

In addition to his many technical contributions (notably in X rays, luminescence, magnetism, electrical machinery and illumination, and optics), Thompson was a notable historian of science and technology. His biographies of Gilbert, Faraday, and Kelvin are considered excellent of their sort, and he also published a highly polemic account of the life and work of Philipp Reis, a German schoolmaster whom Thompson persisted in regarding as the inventor of the telephone.

Thompson received many British and international honors but missed being named principal of the University of London when it was reorganized in 1901, possibly because of his stand on the Boer War: as an active Quaker, he openly castigated the British government for its inhuman treatment of civilians in the concentration camps of South Africa. In 1881 he married a fellow Quaker, Jane Smeal Henderson. They had four daughters, the second of whom collaborated with her mother in a biography of Thompson.

BIBLIOGRAPHY

I. ORIGINAL WORKS. Thompson was a prolific writer. The list of his books, pamphlets, translations, and privately published works is in the *British Museum General Catalogue of Printed Books* (1964). His most influential textbooks are *Elementary Lessons in Electricity and Magnetism* (London, 1881), *Dynamo-Electric Machinery* (London, 1884), *The Electromagnet and Electromagnetic Mechanism* (London, 1887), *Polyphase Electric Currents and Alternate-Current Motors* (London, 1895), *Light Visible and Invisible* (London, 1896), *Design of Dynamos* (London, 1903), and *The Manufacture of Light* (London, 1906). The ever-popular *Calculus Made Easy* was published first in 1910. He also wrote biographies of Philipp Reis (1883), Faraday (1898), and Kelvin (1910); and in 1901 he translated William Gilbert's *De magnete*. Lodge's priority over Marconi in the use of tuned circuits in radiotelegraphy was lucidly and succinctly argued in Thompson's 38-page pamphlet, *Notes on Sir Oliver Lodge's Patent for Wireless Telegraphy* (1911), which is of considerable historic interest.

II. SECONDARY LITERATURE. The biography by his wife and the second of his four daughters, J. S. and

H. G. Thompson, *Sylvanus Phillips Thompson. His Life and Letters* (London, 1920), contains a complete list of his publications. Short biographies appear in *Dictionary of National Biography* (1912–1921), 528–529; and in *Proceedings of the Royal Society*, **94A** (1917–1918), xvi–xviii, with a portrait.

CHARLES SÜSSKIND

THOMSEN, CHRISTIAN JÜRGENSEN (*b.* Copenhagen, Denmark, 29 December 1788; *d.* Copenhagen, 21 May 1865), *archaeology*.

Thomsen was the son of Christian Thomsen, a merchant and counselor-at-law (*Justitsieråd*), and Hedevig Margaretha Jürgensen. He was privately educated, since his father intended him to take over the family shipping business, and did not attend a university. Thomsen followed his father's wishes and entered a business career, but closed the family firm after the death of his mother in 1840. By that time he was firmly established in a second career as a museum director.

Thomsen had from his youth been interested in collecting art, antiquities, and, especially, coins, and his family's wealth allowed him to indulge these tastes. He was soon known for his numismatic knowledge and for his beautiful and well-organized collection of coins; in 1816, in spite of his youth and his lack of an academic degree, he was made secretary of the Danish Commission for the Preservation of Antiquities and put in charge of their museum. He arranged the collections, which he found in a sorry state, chronologically, and in 1820 divided prehistoric artifacts into representatives of the Stone, Iron, and Bronze Ages, an archaeological sequence that he mentioned in letters as early as 1818. This new chronology was soon widely accepted in English-speaking countries, in which Thomsen's claim to priority was also recognized. It was, however, disputed in Germany, as was Thomsen's assertion of priority, a situation that may have arisen because Thomsen only rarely published articles in scientific journals and, indeed, did not publish his chronology until 1836.

Thomsen was an organizer and modernizer. He was one of the first to use museums as a tool for popular education, and to this end took the almost unprecedented step of opening his collections to the public free of charge. He also lectured widely to lay audiences, hoping thereby both to encourage a general knowledge of antiquities and to create a climate favorable for the working archaeologist. He was successful in these aims, and encouraged a number of enthusiastic amateurs, who made a number of significant archaeological finds. In 1838 he was made inspector of a complex of museums of art, archaeology, and history in Copenhagen, and in 1849 succeeded to their directorship.

In 1841 Thomsen also established the first ethnographical museum, in which he designed exhibits focused upon the tools of ordinary life, showing how peoples really lived, rather than upon rarities. In this museum he also introduced the notion of organizing exhibits according to a "principle of progressive culture," to demonstrate cultural development. His ideas of archaeology, ethnography, and museum direction were all well in advance of his time. That they were widely accepted and emulated is a tribute to Thomsen's persuasive power and to his skill in winning professional agreement to his methods and public support for his interests.

BIBLIOGRAPHY

I. ORIGINAL WORKS. Since Thomsen published few works in scientific publications, his ideas are known chiefly through letters, newspaper articles, and museum pamphlets and catalogues of exhibitions. His prehistoric chronology is in *Ledetraad til Nordisk Oldkyndighed* (Copenhagen, 1836), translated into German as *Leitfaden zur nordischen Alterthumskunde,* . . . (Copenhagen, 1837).

II. SECONDARY LITERATURE. On Thomsen and his work, see V. Hermansen, *C. J. Thomsen and the Founding of the Ethnographical Museum* (Copenhagen, 1941); and "Christian J. Thomsen," in *Dansk Biografisk Lexicon*, XXIII (Copenhagen, 1942), 550–556; B. Hildebrant, "C. J. Thomsen och hans lärda förbindelser i Sverige 1816–1837," in *Kungliga Vitterhets, Historie och Antikvitets Akademiens Handlingar, 1937–1938* (1938); and H. Seger, "Die Anfänge des Dreiperioden-Systems," in *Schumacher-Festschrift zum 70. Geburtstag Karl Schumacher, 14. Oktober 1930* (Mainz, 1930).

NILS SPJELDNAES

THOMSEN, HANS PETER JÖRGEN JULIUS (*b.* Copenhagen, Denmark, 16 February 1826; *d.* Copenhagen, 13 February 1909), *chemistry.*

The son of Thomas Thomsen, a bank auditor, and the former Jensine Friederike Lund, Thomsen left secondary school without graduating. Since he was interested in chemistry, he planned to enter a pharmacy; but before he could do so, the professor of chemistry at the University of Copenhagen gave him the opportunity to work in his laboratory and at the same time to prepare for the entrance examination to the Polytekniske Laereanstalt, practical experience plus the examination being the alternative to the general certificate for admission to that school. Thomsen passed the examination in 1843 and obtained the candidate's degree (M.Sc.) in applied natural sciences in 1846. From 1847 to 1853 he was assistant in the chemical laboratory and, from 1850 to 1856, instructor in agricultural chemistry, at the Polytekniske Laereanstalt. He took time for a study tour to France and Germany in 1853–1854. He was director of weights and measures at Copenhagen from 1856 to 1859 and then, until 1866, taught physics at the Danish Military College. In addition, Thomsen was instructor (1864–1865), lecturer (1865–1866), and professor (1866–1901) of chemistry at the University of Copenhagen and head of the chemical laboratory, at the same time serving as professor of chemistry at the Polytekniske Laereanstalt.

Thomsen's first chemical work was elaboration of a method for the fabrication of soda from cryolite. He obtained a monopoly; and after overcoming some technical difficulties, he opened a factory at Copenhagen (1859), followed by others in Germany, Poland, and the United States. The Solvay method for manufacturing soda soon made cryolite commercially uncompetitive for use in soda production; but it proved to be a valuable raw material for making milk glass, enamel, and especially aluminum. Thus Thomsen's factory could continue separating cryolite from accompanying, less valuable minerals.

This technical achievement was, however, only a minor facet of Thomsen's work; his main activities were in pure science. In 1852 he had submitted "Bidrag til et Thermochemisk System" to the Royal Danish Academy of Sciences and Letters. For this paper he received the Academy's silver medal and 50 rigsdaler (at that time equivalent to $28) "to be used for the purchase of precision equipment." This was the start of a thirty-year program of thermochemical studies, during which Thomsen personally carried out more than 3,500 calorimetric measurements in a room kept at a temperature of 18° C. The results were later collected in the four-volume *Thermochemische Untersuchungen*, of which the three first volumes give the experimental material and the fourth Thomsen's theoretical reflections. His fundamental thought was that the evolution of heat accompanying a chemical reaction (which he called *varmetoning*, equivalent to enthalpy change) is an exact expression of the chemical affinity of the reaction.

Nearly the same theory was advanced a short time later by Berthelot, and a heated discussion between the two scientists took place and continued for several years. Supplementary experiments made by Thomsen (spontaneous reactions accompanied by "negative *varmetoning*," enthalpy loss— that is, endothermic reactions that are nevertheless spontaneous) led him to realize that his theory was only an approximation (it was later found that the theory is valid at absolute zero), and he publicly admitted its inexactitude. Berthelot, however, maintained the theory for many years, despite the facts that told against it.

Thermochemical studies were not Thomsen's only scientific contribution. He determined the heat of neutralization for acids and bases, and used the results to calculate the basicity of polybasic acids; through these and similar measurements he verified Guldberg and Waage's law of mass action. In his chemical experiments performed in galvanic cells, Thomsen found that the electromotive force can be used to calculate the mechanical work necessary for separating a compound into its elementary particles. In many instances, by measuring the electromotive force Thomsen obtained the same value for the affinity as in previous calorimetric experiments, but in other instances a difference was found. It is now known that the electrochemical measurements are theoretically correct, not the calorimetric ones. Thomsen discussed the constitution of benzene, and in a long series of papers he treated the theory that the atoms of an element are composed of smaller elementary particles; these speculations made him suggest a new way of presenting the periodic system of the elements. Just after the discovery of the first noble gas, he predicted the existence of five more members of this group; indicated their place in the periodic system of elements; and predicted their approximate atomic weights. All five were found in the next few years, and Thomsen's predictions of their atomic weights were astonishingly near the values found. It is interesting to note that Thomsen's periodic system was the one used by Niels Bohr when he gave his explanation of the periodic system based upon the number of electrons surrounding the nuclei of the atoms (1922).

The importance of Thomsen's scientific work was rapidly recognized both in Denmark and abroad. In 1860 he was elected a member of the Royal Danish Academy of Sciences and Letters. Nine years later he was nominated as professor of physical chemistry at the University of Leipzig, but he refused the offer. Many foreign scientists asked to work under his guidance, but he was afraid that the comparability of the results obtained would be endangered when more than one person performed the measurements and therefore refused all such requests. Thus no school was formed around him. Thomsen was a foreign member of various academies and honorary member of learned societies, and held honorary doctorates from several universities (but none in France, because of the conflict with Berthelot).

Thomsen was rector of the University of Copenhagen (1886–1887, 1891–1892), principal of the Polytekniske Laereanstalt (1883–1902), and president of the Royal Danish Academy of Sciences and Letters (1888–1909). He was an efficient administrator not only in science and education: He was a member of the Copenhagen city council (1861–1894), and a member of the commission for the reform of the Danish monetary system and system of weights and measures (1863). The conversion of Denmark's money to a decimal system was completed in 1874, and the reform of the system of weights and measures in 1910–1911. Upon his retirement from active service in 1902, Thomsen was appointed titular privy councillor in recognition of his public service.

BIBLIOGRAPHY

I. ORIGINAL WORKS. Thomsen's 227 papers in Danish and foreign scientific journals include "Thermochemische Untersuchungen I–XXXII," in *Poggendorffs Annalen der Physik* (1859–1873); *Journal für praktische Chemie* (1873–1880); and *Berichte der Deutschen chemischen Gesellschaft* (1873–1880); studies on electromotive forces in *Wiedemanns Annalen*, **11** (1880), 246–269; on the constitution of benzene, in *Berichte der Deutschen chemischen Gesellschaft*, **13** (1880), 1808–1811, 2166–2168; "Über die mutmassliche Gruppe inaktiver Elemente," in *Zeitschrift für anorganische . . . Chemie*, **8** (1895), 283–288; and "Systematische Gruppierung der chemischen Elemente," *ibid.*, **9** (1895), 190–193. His books include *Thermochemische Untersuchungen*, 4 vols. (Leipzig, 1882–1886); and *Systematische Durchführung thermochemischer Untersuchungen. Zahlenwerte und theoretische Ergebnisse* (Stuttgart, 1906).

II. SECONDARY LITERATURE. Obituaries are in *Berichte der Deutschen chemischen Gesellschaft*, **42** (1909), 4971–4988; and *Oversigt Dan. Vid. Selsk.* (1909), 27–31. See also *Dansk Biografisk Leksikom*, XXIII (1942), 568–575; and Stig Veibel, *Kemien i Danmark*, I (1939), 202–210; and II (1943), 426–444, with complete bibliography.

STIG VEIBEL

THOMSON, SIR CHARLES WYVILLE (*b*. Bonsyde, Linlithgow, Scotland, 5 March 1830; *d*. Bonsyde, 10 March 1882), *natural history, oceanography*.

Thomson was the son of Andrew Thomson, a surgeon in the East India Company. His earliest education was at Merchiston Castle School. When he was sixteen he matriculated at the University of Edinburgh to study medicine, a field that he was forced to give up after three years because of ill health. Moreover, his primary interest was natural history, especially zoology, botany, and geology. In 1853 he married Jane Ramage Dawson. Their only child, Frank Wyville, became a surgeon captain in the Third Bengal Cavalry.

Thomson held a number of academic positions. In 1851 he was a lecturer in botany at the University of Aberdeen; two years later, in 1853, he was appointed professor of natural history at Queen's College, Cork. In 1854 he became professor of geology at Queen's College, Belfast; and six years later, in 1860, he was named professor of zoology and botany at the same college. In 1868 Thomson accepted the professorship in botany at the Royal College of Science, Dublin, and in 1870 he assumed his last academic position, the regius professorship of natural history at the University of Edinburgh.

While at Belfast, Thomson began to establish himself as a talented marine biologist with his published studies of coelenterates, polyzoans and fossilized cirripeds, trilobites, and crinoids. He also became interested in determining whether life exists at great depths in the sea. Forbes suggested that below 300 fathoms there exists an azoic zone. In 1866, while visiting Michael Sars at Christiania (Oslo), Thomson had the opportunity to examine animals collected at depths below 300 fathoms. Thomson's interest in this question led him to embark upon a series of crucial deep-sea dredging voyages that culminated in the classic *Challenger* expedition of 1872–1876.

In 1868 Thomson and William Benjamin Carpenter, who was at the time vice-president of the Royal Society, persuaded the Society to seek Admiralty support for a deep-sea dredging project in the North Atlantic. Support was granted, and in August of 1868 Thomson and Carpenter began their project on board the paddle steamer H.M.S. *Lightning*. Despite stormy weather they were able to undertake some dredging and to obtain sponges, rhizopods, echinoderms, crustaceans, mollusks, and foraminifers below the 300-fathom mark. Perhaps the most surprising result of this cruise was

the discovery of diverse temperatures at similar depths in different regions. The discovery called into question the accepted theory of a relatively constant submarine temperature of 4° C. The success of the *Lightning* cruise led to additional Admiralty support, and in the summer of 1869 the survey ship H.M.S. *Porcupine* was placed at the disposal of the Royal Society. Thomson, Carpenter, and John Gwyn Jeffreys dredged and took serial temperatures off the west coast of Ireland and off the Shetlands. They also began to analyze the composition of seawater from various depths. After dredging in waters over a thousand fathoms below the surface, they obtained on 22 July 1869 samples of mud and marine animals from 2,435 fathoms down. The results of these two cruises clearly cast doubts upon the validity of the azoic theory.

All these findings contributed to a renewed interest in the science of the sea. In 1869 Thomson was made a fellow of the Royal Society for his work. He described the details and accomplishments of the two expeditions in his popular study *The Depths of the Sea* (1873). With the encouragement of Carpenter, the Royal Society again approached the Admiralty for support in extending the scope of the investigations from the North Atlantic to the oceans of the world.

The Admiralty agreed, and on 7 December 1872, H.M.S. *Challenger*, a steam-powered corvette of 2,300 tons, set forth from Sheerness. Thus began a three-and-a-half-year voyage of oceanographic exploration. Since Carpenter did not wish to command the expedition, Thomson was selected as head of the civilian scientists. Once at sea the staff of the *Challenger* began the arduous tasks of sounding, dredging, and taking serial temperatures and water samples. Their dredging confirmed that marine life exists at depths approaching three thousand fathoms. They also discovered nodules of almost pure manganese peroxide on the seafloor. As they dredged and sounded in deeper water, they discovered that a clay bottom is characteristic of great depths. The material of the ocean floor is the residue of a chemical process that removes the carbonate of lime from the calcareous skeletons of foraminifers, mollusks, and other species. In bottom deposits beyond four thousand fathoms in the Pacific Ocean, they discovered a seafloor with new characteristics—radiolarian ooze. John Murray, one of the staff naturalists, uncovered new data on the diurnal migration of plankton and the oceanic distribution of globigerina. The temperature readings at various depths in a number of areas contributed to the growing speculation as to the nature of oceanic circulation. This complex question was not resolved by the scientific staff of the *Challenger*, for there was no physicist aboard to analyze this problem. The *Challenger* expedition was weakest in its examination of the questions of physical oceanography. On 24 May 1876 the ship returned to her berth at Sheerness after a voyage of 68,890 nautical miles and after having made soundings at 362 stations.

Much of the work of the expedition still lay ahead, for the specimens and data collected had to be organized and distributed, and the scientific results published. Publication of this diverse information was an enormous task, one which ultimately cost the British Treasury over £100,000. Queen Victoria conferred a knighthood (1876) upon Thomson for his service to science. While Thomson established the format of the *Challenger Reports*, he did not live to see the completion of the publication of this multivolume work, which chronicled his epic years of oceanographic exploration.

BIBLIOGRAPHY

I. ORIGINAL WORKS. Thomson's scientific papers are listed in the Royal Society's *Catalogue of Scientific Papers*, V, VIII, XI, and XIX. For the cruises of the *Porcupine* and *Lightning*, consult *The Depths of the Sea* (London, 1873). A popular account of the *Challenger*'s activities in the Atlantic may be found in *The Voyage of the Challenger. The Atlantic. A Preliminary Account of the General Results of the Exploring Voyage of H.M.S. Challenger During the Year 1873 and the Early Part of the Year 1876*, 2 vols. (London, 1877). The scientific results were published in *Report on the Scientific Results of the Voyage of H.M.S. Challenger during the Years 1873–1876*, 50 vols. (London, 1880–1895).

II. SECONDARY LITERATURE. For a biographical sketch of Thomson by a former student and assistant, see William Herdman, "Sir C. Wyville Thomson and the 'Challenger' Expedition," in *Founders of Oceanography and Their Work* (London, 1923), 37–67. See also Margaret Deacon, "The Magnificent Generalization" and "The Voyage of H.M.S. Challenger," in *Scientists and the Sea, 1650–1900* (London, 1971), 306–332, 333–365. For an examination of the problems of publishing the reports of the expedition, consult Harold L. Burstyn, "Science and Government in the Nineteenth Century: the Challenger Expedition and its Report," in *Bulletin de l'Institut océanographique*, **2**, spec. no. 2 (1968), 603–611.

PHILLIP DRENNON THOMAS

THOMSON, ELIHU (*b.* Manchester, England, 29 March 1853; *d.* Swampscott, Massachusetts, 13 March 1937), *electrical engineering.*

Thomson was the second of ten children of Scots parents of the skilled artisan class. When he was five the family moved to Philadelphia, where he graduated from the Central High School (then an advanced academy of the Gymnasium type) shortly before his seventeenth birthday. He became the assistant of E. J. Houston and then a teacher at the school. With Houston, Thomson collaborated in experiments that refuted Edison's claim to have discovered a "new force" (wireless transmission) and in other inventions, notably arc lights. They also started the Thomson-Houston Co., a predecessor of the General Electric Co., with which Thomson remained associated throughout his long career.

Thomson's inventions made possible significant improvements in alternating-current motors and transformers, both developments of the first importance in the history of electrical engineering. He invented electric resistance welding and also contributed to improvements in electric control, instrumentation, and radiology. Altogether, Thomson was the recipient of more than seven hundred patents and many awards, not all of which were related to electrical engineering. For instance, he discovered that a mixture of helium and oxygen prevents caisson disease, or bends.

During World War I, Thomson and others attempted to create an engineering school (financed from a bequest by the industrialist Gordon McKay) that would be jointly operated by Harvard University and the Massachusetts Institute of Technology. The project came to nothing when the courts ruled against use of the bequest for that purpose. When the MIT presidency fell vacant in 1919, Thomson was asked to fill the post. He declined but was acting president from 1921 to 1923.

Thomson combined solid achievement with great ingenuity and an uncanny sense for turning ideas and inventions into practical and highly profitable devices. He is also reckoned as one of the pioneers of the electrical manufacturing industry in the United States, in the development of which he took an active part for over half a century.

BIBLIOGRAPHY

I. ORIGINAL WORKS. Thomson wrote no books; his writings are his patents and technical papers, several of which were deemed sufficiently important for inclusion in *Report of the Board of Regents of the Smithsonian Institution*; for example, see (1897), 125–136; (1899), 119–130; (1900), 333–358; (1904), 281–285; and (1913), 243–260. Thomson was also a prolific letter writer. His papers, comprising 13,600 items and 43 vols. of letter books, are in the library of the American Philosophical Society. Some of the letters that he wrote and received have been published in an annotated vol., H. J. Abrahams and M. B. Savin, eds., *Selections From the Scientific Correspondence of Elihu Thomson* (Cambridge, Mass., 1971); but they are limited to his scientific interests and throw only oblique light on his more important activities as a technologist.

II. SECONDARY LITERATURE. The only full-scale biography is D. O. Woodbury, *Elihu Thomson: Beloved Scientist, 1853–1937* (Cambridge, Mass., 1944, 1960), written in a popular style and lacking all bibliographical apparatus. See also *Dictionary of American Biography*, supp. 2 (New York, 1958), 657–659; *The National Cyclopaedia of American Biography*, XXVII (New York, 1939), 28–30; and Karl T. Compton, in *Biographical Memoirs. National Academy of Sciences*, **21** (1941), 143–179.

CHARLES SÜSSKIND

THOMSON, JOSEPH JOHN (*b.* Cheetham Hill, near Manchester, England, 18 December 1856; *d.* Cambridge, England, 30 August 1940), *physics*.

Thomson came to physics for want of money to enter engineering. His father, a bookseller, sent him to Owens College to mark time until a leading engineer, to whom he was to be apprenticed, had an opening; but the father died before the vacancy occurred, and the family then could not afford the premium. With the help of small scholarships Thomson continued to an engineering degree at Owens College, which had an excellent scientific faculty including Osborne Reynolds, Henry Roscoe, Balfour Stewart (under whom Thomson did his first experimental work [1]), and Thomas Barker, the professor of mathematics, a former senior wrangler. On Barker's advice Thomson remained at Owens in order to work for an entrance scholarship in mathematics offered by Barker's old college, Trinity (Cambridge). He won a minor scholarship and in 1876 went up to the university where he would spend the rest of his life [58:13–32].

He read for the mathematical tripos, which at that time covered a wide range of pure mathematics as well as applications to many branches of physics. To "wrangle" successfully, that is, to place high on the tripos list, one needed great facility at computation and an ability to cope with the sort of models, or "physical analogies," prized by

the school of Kelvin, Stokes, and Maxwell. But one required neither knowledge nor experience of experimental physics; and so Thomson, who prepared himself by following diligently the advice of his coach, E. J. Routh, did no more than put his foot into the Cavendish Laboratory, and never met Maxwell [58:95, 129], whose work was to inspire his own. He emerged second from the tripos of 1880, after Joseph Larmor, who, like himself, became a Cambridge professor.

Thomson stayed on at Trinity, which awarded him a fellowship in 1881. He followed three lines of mathematical work, apparently diverse in content and style, but forming a coherent group for disciples of Maxwell and continuing research interests for himself. He seldom abandoned an idea he had once developed.

Fellow of Trinity. In Maxwell's practice there is a play, and sometimes a tension, between advancing theory by developing special mechanical models or analogies and deducing basic equations from the most general dynamical relationships. In the first mood, for example, Maxwell reached the equations of electromagnetism via an elaborate picture of a hydrodynamical contrivance supposed responsible for the phenomena; in the second, he obtained them directly from a Lagrangian constructed from known relationships between measurable quantities. The advantage of the second procedure, as Maxwell emphasized, is that one need not know (as one did not know) anything about the "mechanism" at work. The advantage of the first procedure is that, as Thomson would say, it fixes ideas, aids the memory, and, above all, suggests unexpected new directions of experimentation [15:1].

Thomson's earliest effort at designing models was stimulated by the subject set for the Adams Prize of 1882, "a general investigation of the action upon each other of two closed vortices in a perfect incompressible fluid." In his winning *Treatise* [5] Thomson carried the matter further than required, to an application which, for him, gave it "the greater part of the interest it possesse[d]" [5: 2], namely Kelvin's theory of the vortex atom (1867). Here the atoms of a gas are represented as reentrant vortices in a frictionless fluid, rather like smoke rings in air; but the vortices, unlike the rings, are eternal, and therefore could reproduce the permanence of the Victorian atom.

The theory appealed to Thomson's romantic strain, to his recurrent wish for a quantitative, mechanistic, and "ultimate" [39:1]—by which he meant not "unique" but parsimonious [5:1]—account of the physical world. In this sense the theory of the vortex atom is perhaps the most fundamental ever started, for it hoped to make do with nothing besides the several perfections of its primitive fluid and pure mathematical analysis. "The difficulties of this method are enormous," Maxwell had written, "but the glory of surmounting them would be unique."[1] Thomson's *Treatise* is perhaps the most glorious episode in this hopeless struggle.

In adapting the pertinent hydrodynamics to the theory of the vortex atom, Thomson was guided, and perhaps even inspired, by the experiments of A. M. Mayer as interpreted by Kelvin [5:107]. Mayer, whose striking results would remain fresh in Thomson's mind [e.g., 26:313–314], had investigated the equilibrium configurations of n vertical magnetized needles floating on water and exposed to the attraction of a large fixed magnet. It appeared that if $n \leq 5$ the magnets would arrange themselves in a single circle, while for large n several concentric rings were required. On the basis of his kinetic representation of magnetism, Kelvin had inferred that to every stable arrangement found by Mayer there must be a counterpart formed by straight columnar vortices. Thomson therefore examined the stability of m vortex rings so coupled that their nearest portions always ran parallel, like threads wrapped symmetrically about a toroid, without crossing one another. Stability required that the vortices be of equal strength, and that $m \leq 6$.

To apply these results to the problem of chemical constitution (to which Thomson, in striking contrast to most physicists, gave continuing consideration [e.g., 39:120–141; 55:28–112]), observe that each of the linked threads in Thomson's arrangement can itself be a combination of n (≤ 6) vortices of equal strength. Let the strengths of all vortex atoms be multiples of that of hydrogen, taken as one. The oxygen atom clearly has strength two. Nitrogen gives trouble, apparently requiring a vortex of strength two in NO and of strength one in NH_3. Carbon likewise has its ambiguities (CO, CH_4); and in general the table of valences with which Thomson concluded his *Treatise* was useless for the chemist. But it was quite characteristic of him—at least in regard to "ultimate" theories—to be satisfied with gross *qualitative* agreement between experiment and the quantitative results he extracted at great labor from simple mechanical representations. Much of his important work on atomic structure, and the theories of chemical action [55:12–26] and of the nature of light [57] which he developed late in life show the same cu-

rious procedure: precise calculation and ingenious analogy applied with great virtuosity to secure only a rough fit with a few data. No doubt this method—or rather mood, for it by no means characterizes all of Thomson's work—helped him to those "happy intuitions" and "inspired generalizations," to that "abundance of ideas" and "endless fertility in invention" which led and impressed his contemporaries.[2] But it was also a method that became sterile in proportion to its success; for its qualitative conquests prepared the way for an exact physics that had no need for it.

A second line in Thomson's early researches descends from Maxwell's phenomenological strain. As part of the dissertation written for his fellowship [58:21], he elaborated an idea that had occurred to him at Owens College, and to which he would return [e.g., 53]—that the potential energy of a given system might be replaced by the kinetic energy of imaginary masses connected to it in an appropriate way. This notion, which anticipated the better-known scheme of Heinrich Hertz, could be made analytic by employing a form of Lagrange's equations worked out by Routh [12:12–15]. From the inspection of a Lagrangian, therefore, one not only cannot determine the underlying mechanism, but in general one cannot tell whether one confronts an ordinary system or one with Thomsonian masses.

Like Maxwell, Thomson was prepared to exploit this result in two ways. First, the fact that one can replace potential energy ("[which] cannot be said, in the strict sense of the term, to explain anything" [12:15]) by kinetic energy supported the hope for a theory based solely on the properties of matter in motion. "When we have done this we have got a complete explanation of any phenomenon and any further explanation must be rather metaphysical than physical" [*ibid.*]. Thomson had in mind a theory like the vortex-ring atom. But, second, the fact that a given Lagrangian is compatible with any number of models is a strong recommendation for avoiding them all, especially since a primary goal of physics—the discovery of new phenomena—can be reached merely by manipulating an appropriate Lagrangian in a prescribed manner.

In a series of papers [7, 9], lectures, and a book, *Applications of Dynamics* [12], Thomson illustrated how to guess at a term in the Lagrangian from a consideration of known phenomena and how, from the term once admitted, to deduce the existence and magnitudes of other effects. He also showed that a time-average of the Lagrangian could play the part of the entropy in certain problems usually handled by the second law of thermodynamics. One of his most important contributions in this line was the development of the notion, perhaps original with him, that electricity flows in much the same way in metals as in electrolytes [e.g., 12: 289–304]. He was to return to this idea in founding the electron theory of metals, first supposing the electrons free [30], as in Arrhenius' picture of a dilute solution, and then, in the hope of accounting for a difficulty in the theory of specific heats, allowing them only intermittent liberty [39:86–102], as in Grotthus' theory of electrolytic conduction [62:419–420, 425].

Three characteristics of these *Applications* deserve notice. For one, Thomson shows himself a master of the literature, not excluding the pertinent papers of German experimentalists. He was to keep fully abreast of the journals (from which he sometimes took ideas whose origin he later forgot) until World War I [59:150–151, 219]. Second, the moderate phenomenology of the *Applications*, a work which eschews the specification of dynamical processes, recurs in much of Thomson's later work. His pioneering theory of the conduction of electricity in gases [24, 28], for example, merely assumes the existence of ions, and describes their behavior not in terms of the electrodynamics of their interactions, but via parameters—especially measures of mobility and recombination—to be fixed by experiment. Only later [e.g., 45] did he sketch a theory of the process of ionization.

Third, Thomson, in common with most of the Cambridge school of mathematical physicists, took it for granted that an appropriate Lagrangian could always be found, or, in other words, that in principle all physical phenomena could be explained mechanically. Further, he thought that one or another of the possible dynamical explanations of a given phenomenon, whose existence is guaranteed by the Lagrangian, ought to be made explicit whenever possible. In this mood, as contrasted to that of the theorist of vortex atoms, Thomson did not require that models of diverse phenomena be consistent among themselves, nor that they avoid action at a distance; but that they admit only those sorts of forces and interactions with which physicists had become familiar since the time of Newton. He never totally abandoned this point of view, which caused him and contemporaries like Lodge and Schuster to deprecate the quantum theory as a screen of ignorance, a cowardly substitute for "a knowledge of the structure of the atom" [50a:27]. Sometimes, as in his theory of the speckled wavefront [34:63–65; 42], designed to explain the

selective ionizing power of X and γ rays, his efforts to cope with the quantum could advance the subject. But after 1910 his schemes for avoiding novelties like Einstein's approach to the photoeffect [49] and Bohr's deduction of the Balmer formula [52], would become increasingly farfetched and fruitless.

The last of Thomson's early research lines was the mathematical development of Maxwell's electrodynamics. His first important results included the discovery of the so-called electromagnetic mass, or extra inertia, possessed by electrified bodies in virtue of their charge [2], and the calculation (in error by a factor of two) of the force—now known as the Lorentz force—exerted by a magnetic field on a moving electrified sphere [*ibid*.]. These results were not only important in themselves: they also marked or sparked the beginning of the rapid harvest of Maxwellian fruits by Fitzgerald, Heaviside, Lamb, Poynting, and Thomson himself [e.g., 6].

One is struck by the literalness with which Thomson at first cultivated Maxwell's theory. Not that he clung slavishly to his model, for his thorough report on electrical theories to the British Association for the Advancement of Science [8] points to obscurities in Maxwell's formulation and discusses competing systems sympathetically. But he tried to remain true to what he considered the peculiar mark of Maxwell's theory: the dielectric "displacement" D, whose divergence represented what other electricians called the electric fluid and whose time rate of change, even in the absence of matter, gave magnetic effects like those of an ordinary current. By obscuring the concept of charge, displacement caused much of the malaise felt by Continental readers of Maxwell, and it could lead even English ones astray. In his important paper of 1881 [2], Thomson reached incorrect results by ascribing the magnetic field of a moving charged sphere solely to D outside it, thereby ignoring the most important factor, the convection of the charge [cf. 62:306–307; 60:24, 55].

In subsequent work Thomson replaced "displacement" (an "unfortunate" term [8:125]) by "polarization," which he represented in terms of electrostatic "tubes of force" supposed to begin and end on "atoms," each tube conferring the electrolytic unit of electricity, or "electron," on its termini [15:1–52]. From this representation, which in its ingenious details shows the hand of the essayist on vortex motion [cf. 58:94], Thomson recovered all the usual formulae of Maxwellian electrodynamics. He also thereby [15:13] stressed the notion of electromagnetic momentum stored in the medium (as a consequence of the translation of the tubes, the cause of magnetism), a notion used by himself [e.g., 39:24] and others to save the equality of action and reaction in electrodynamics [62:366], and to demonstrate the existence of "some invisible [material] universe, which we may call the ether" [36a:235].

It need scarcely be said that, although Thomson believed strongly that students should form some mental picture of the mechanism of the electromagnetic field, he did not urge his own as unique or even as particularly meritorious. "Which particular method the student should adopt is for many purposes of secondary importance, provided that he does adopt one" [15:vii]. "A theory of matter is a policy rather than a creed" [39:1]. He himself used models different in scope and degree of reduction, and, not seldom, conflicting in character; and after the discovery of the electron he freely admitted anti-Maxwellian bugaboos, like electric charge, into his partial pictures of metallic conduction [e.g., 30], atomic structure [e.g., 35], and chemical combination [39:120–139]. Such laxity of course could not be permitted in an "ultimate" theory of electricity [53, 56, 57].

Cavendish Professor. In 1884 Lord Rayleigh, who had succeeded Maxwell, resigned the Cavendish Professorship of Experimental Physics. Thomson had by then completed a few imperfect bits of laboratory work [cf. 44:80; 58:97], including a determination, at Rayleigh's suggestion, of the ratio of the electrostatic to the electromagnetic unit of electricity [4, corrected in 13]. Rayleigh had intended to collaborate in this work which, apart from its imperfection, was typical of the Cavendish during his era; but Thomson, unaware of many of the pitfalls, ran away with the project, published hastily, and gave his colleagues, including the Professor, to doubt that he had any future in experimental physics [59:18–20]. With these credits and his mathematics, he competed for the chair; much to his surprise [58:98], and to the great annoyance of some of his competitors, who included Fitzgerald, Glazebrook, Larmor, Reynolds, and Schuster, he was elected. It says much for the wisdom of the electors, among whom the ancient wranglers Stokes, William Thomson, W. D. Niven, and George Darwin, one of the judges of Thomson's Adams Prize essay, were probably most influential.

Luckily the personnel of the laboratory, including one who had expected to be its chief, remained on; and so the introductory courses set up in Rayleigh's time, and especially those for the many candidates for part I of the Natural Science Tripos, continued to function smoothly while the new Professor found his way. The same staff later (1888) introduced courses for intending physicians, whose fees quickly became an important part of the Cavendish's finances [44:84–89; 61:250–280; 59:19–21].

Thomson chose the phenomena of the gas discharge, whose study Maxwell had recommended, for experimental investigation. The subject had attracted attention in the early 1880's owing largely to the work of Crookes and Goldstein on the cathode rays [62:350–353]. Indeed, the ostensible motivation of Thomson's Maxwellian computations of 1881 was to provide a theoretical guide to the further study of the rays, which he, like Crookes, took to be "particles of matter highly charged with electricity and moving with great velocities" [2:229; 58:91–93]. Two years later Thomson had again turned his attention to the discharge, guided this time by the theory of the vortex atom [3].

The vortical mechanism for chemical bonding, he observed, works only when combining vortex rings have approximately the same size and velocity. Any disturbance in the medium, like the approach of another vortex atom, may alter the critical parameters and prevent linkage or disrupt unions. Now an electric field may be represented by a distribution of velocity in the medium; and the chemical decomposition it stimulates would be the immediate cause of the discharge. In this odd form Thomson introduced an idea of the utmost importance for future work: that the gas discharge proceeds in analogy to electrolysis, by the disruption of chemical bonds. Initially, as was only natural, he regarded the particles into which the molecules separated under the influence of the field as "atoms." Later researches (and, one presumes, a relaxation of his Maxwellian literalness) helped him to see the "atoms" first as "ions," that is, charge carriers of atomic dimensions, and then as mixtures of ions and "bodies much smaller than atoms."

The electrolytic analogy suggested that important clues to the mechanics of gas discharge might come from studies of dielectric breakdown in poorly conducting liquids, or from decomposition of polyatomic gases by sparks. Thomson and his students worked on the one [e.g., 11] and the other [10, the Bakerian lecture of 1887, continued in 16 and 18], and acquired many data without much advance in understanding. By the early 1890's he had concluded that a study of the striated positive light was the most promising avenue to the understanding of the discharge. As for the cathode rays, which had seemed significant in the early 1880's, they now appeared to him but a "local" and "secondary" matter [15:114–115].

Controversy returned the neglected cathode rays to the center of attention. Most English physicists, including Thomson, had taken them to be streams of charged particles, primarily because their paths curved in a magnetic field; while most German physicists, arguing chiefly from their ability to cause glass to fluoresce, had considered them an "aether disturbance" akin to ultraviolet light [62: 351–354]. In the early 1890's the English were put on the defensive by Philipp Lenard, who aggressively pursued the discovery of his master, Heinrich Hertz, that the rays could be passed through thin metal foil impermeable to particles of gas-theoretical dimensions. (Another objection, based on Hertz's inability to deflect the rays in an electrostatic field, was regarded less seriously; what weight it had was largely reduced by Perrin's direct detection of the charge carried by the rays, and vanished altogether when Thomson obtained the deflection in a better vacuum than Hertz had commanded [26:296].) Thomson tried in turn to undermine the position of the etherists by showing that the cathode rays moved at less than the velocity of light [17], but his results—off by two orders of magnitude—did not convince his opponents. At this point Röntgen prepared to enter the fray, and in the process discovered X rays.

Thomson, who had all the apparatus to hand, immediately found that the new rays turned gases they traversed into conductors of electricity [19, 20], and so offered a means much more convenient than disruptive discharge for producing gaseous ions [58:326]. Under his guidance the advanced students at the Cavendish rushed to exploit the new tool, and to make the accurate measurements of ionic parameters on which the Professor built his theory of gas discharge. The first edition of the famous *Conduction of Electricity Through Gases* [33] is a monument to these coordinated researches, in which McClelland [33], Rutherford [24], Townsend, and Zeleny played principal parts [59:74, 125; 60:38–41]. The presence at this time of these "research students"—graduates of other institutions allowed, by a reform introduced in 1895, to work for a research degree without first obtaining a Cambridge B.A.—was a great stroke of luck, as Thomson fully recognized [44:93; 58:325]. It provided talented and highly motivated men who not only developed the Professor's ideas in work

of the highest quality, but also helped raise the enthusiasm of younger recruits to the laboratory [61:269–271].

Thomson also saw in the X rays a possible explanation for the "startling" [37:3] transparency of metal foils to cathode rays: might it not be that in fact no penetration occurs, that cathode rays striking one surface of the metal produce X rays there which in turn create *new* "ions," alias "cathode rays," on the far side? [22] This ingenious subterfuge did not long survive the attacks of Lenard who, at Thomson's invitation [59:55], brought his campaign to the British Association in 1896. Thomson allowed himself to be persuaded of the importance of Lenard's work, and particularly of his discoveries that (*a*) the magnetic "deflectibility" of rays passed outside the tube depends only on the conditions within it, (*b*) that these external "Lenard rays" lost their power of causing fluorescence, that is, were absorbed, in proportion to the density, and independent of the chemical character, of the environment, and (*c*) that the mean free path of the rays outside the tube far exceeded the value to be expected if they consisted of gaseous ions [cf. 25: 430–431]. One suspects that it was in the process of digesting Lenard's results that Thomson first entertained the idea that the cathode rays consisted of bodies smaller than atoms.

To explore the matter further he employed Schuster's old technique of magnetic bending; for from the measured radius of curvature R of a beam of cathode rays deflected by a magnet of strength H one can infer a value for e/m, the ratio of the charge to the mass of the hypothetical cathode-ray particle ($e/m = v/HR$). Since the values for similar ratios, E/M, were known for ions produced in electrolysis, a comparison of e/m to E/M might provide a clue to the nature of the particle.[3]

To obtain e/m by Schuster's method the velocity v of the rays is required. If one takes for v either Thomson's faulty measurement [17] or, as Schuster had done, the mean speed of a gas molecule $(3kT/M)^{1/2}$, $e/m \sim E/M$, that is, one confirms the standard English theory which assimilated the rays to streams of charged particles of atomic dimensions. Lenard's intervention pushed Thomson to devise a more direct way of obtaining v. He found two. In the first [25:432; 26:302–306], the heat $T = nmv^2/2$ delivered by a stream of n "corpuscles" (as Thomson was to call the cathode-ray particle) to a Faraday cup was compared to the total charge, $Q = ne$, simultaneously conveyed, whence $v^2 = (e/m)$ $\cdot (2T/Q)$. In the second [26:307–309], which exploited Thomson's discovery of the electrostatic deflection of the rays, v came from balancing an electric force eF against a magnetic one $(e/c)vH'$ to give no net deviation of the beam, whence $v = cF/H'$. The rough result of these measurements was that e/m exceeded by a factor of 1,000 the E/M for the ion of hydrogen, which has the largest charge-to-mass ratio of the chemical elements. The same anomalous value characterized all the cathode rays Thomson tried, irrespective of the material of the electrodes or of the nature of the gas in the discharge tube in which they were produced [26:306, 309].

At least two other physicists—Emil Wiechert and Walther Kaufmann, both then beginning distinguished careers—had independently obtained the same sort of data about the rays, and had inferred the correct magnitude of e/m by deducing v from the energy which would be acquired by a particle falling through the full potential V of the tube ($mv^2/2 = eV$). The equation could scarcely be justified theoretically, as Thomson liked to observe [e.g., 58:339]; but it gave the right order, and for this reason had been rejected by Schuster before the advent of Lenard. Despite their possessing most or all of the relevant data, neither Wiechert nor Kaufmann discovered the electron. Wiechert came closest: guided by the older Continental ideas about electricity [62:198 ff.], then recently revived by Lorentz, he identified the cathode-ray particle as a disembodied atom of electricity, a fundamental entity distinct from common matter. Kaufmann found nothing at all but an argument against "the hypothesis that assumes the cathode rays to be charged particles shot from the cathode."[4]

When Thomson, following his method, sought a representation of his striking data, he did not forget his old concerns: the vortex atom and Mayer's magnets, the problem of chemical combination and the nature of electricity [cf. 58:94]. It was doubtless these which pushed him to "discover" the electron, that is, to claim far more for the "corpuscle" than the data authorized. For from its large e/m he inferred its small mass (by assuming that its charge was of the order of the electrolytic unit); from its small mass he inferred (what scarcely follows) its small size; from its small size, its penetrability, and an answer to Lenard; from its size again and from the apparent independence of its e/m from the circumstances of its production, that it is a constituent of all chemical atoms. Or, rather, *the* constituent: for, as Thomson pointed out [26:311–314], if the chemical atoms are built up of corpuscles, arranged in rings in the style of Mayer's mag-

nets, one immediately glimpses an electrodynamic explanation of the periodic properties of the elements and saves Prout's vexed hypothesis—that the elements are built up of multiples of a single basic unit, or "protyle"—from the old objections based on deviations of atomic weights from integers. And there is more. Although Thomson called his particle "corpuscle" in order not to prejudge the value of its charge, which he initially believed to be larger than the "electron" [26:312; 60:55], he came quickly to believe that the corpuscle carried the elementary unit of electricity [27:544–545]. Apparently the protyles of matter and electricity were inseparable.

The initial evidence for Thomson's claims consisted primarily of the values of e/m for cathode rays of different provenance and of Lenard's law of absorption, which would follow if atoms contained corpuscles (and nothing but corpuscles capable of slowing cathode rays) in proportion to their weights. (To this might be added the similar law for the absorption of X rays found by McClelland, which Thomson had earlier tied to Prout's hypothesis [21], and which no doubt aided his digestion of Lenard.) Few physicists in 1897 were prepared to believe on this basis that the world was made of corpuscles.

Two years later the claim seemed more than plausible. In the interim, Thomson, following up old experiments of Elster and Geitel [59:108–112], had managed to find other particles—those liberated from metals by ultraviolet light and from carbon filaments by heat—which possessed approximately the same value of e/m as the corpuscle [29]. Moreover, he had succeeded in measuring e alone by exploiting, in a way suggested by Townsend and with an apparatus designed by C. T. R. Wilson, his earlier study of the ability of charged particles to promote condensation of water vapor [14; cf. 58:342–343; 61:195–205; 59:101–105]. The measurement employed X rays or ultraviolet light to create ions in a saturated gas, ions which, as Wilson had painstakingly proved, did indeed serve as condensation nuclei. The gas was then expanded and n droplets formed; from the mass and rate of fall of the fog one can compute n, whence $e = Q/n$, Q being the total charge carried down by the droplets. The result, which agreed to order of magnitude with estimates of the electrolytic "electron" [27:544; 29:562–563], turned out to be 30 percent too high. A second try [31] erred equally by defect. Thomson liked to leave the second decimal place to someone else [60:169]; in this case he left the first as well.

All this evidence, however imposing, left a large logical gap in Thomson's theory; for, strictly speaking, it did not bear on his claim that the *normal* atom consisted of corpuscles. By great good luck this gap was filled even as Thomson prepared his first lecture on the cathode rays [25]. For just then Zeeman established that the particle that, on the theory of Lorentz, gave rise to the spectral lines split by his magnet, possessed an e/m 1,000 times that of electrolytic hydrogen. The corpuscle not only belonged in normal atoms, but was responsible for their line spectra. The weight of evidence tipped in Thomson's favor. When he outlined it to the British Association in 1889 [29] it immediately "carried conviction" [58:341]: "The scientific world seemed suddenly to awake to the fact that their fundamental conceptions had been revolutionized."[5]

Atomic Structure. After consolidating his evidence about the electron (as physicists renamed the corpuscle when they came to believe in it) Thomson returned to the problem he had raised when introducing it as Prout's protyle: what causes the electrons of an atom to arrange themselves in the periodic manner implied by the table of the elements? He aimed at a theory that would postulate nothing but a few properties of the universal corpuscle; even the positive electrification apparently needed to retain atomic electrons and to neutralize matter would, he hoped, be reduced to an electronic property [59:140–141]. There were many good reasons, some of which had been identified before 1900 by Fitzgerald, Larmor, and Rayleigh, for believing that such a theory (even admitting two sorts of charges) could not explain important atomic characteristics like the frequencies of spectral lines. Fortunately, Thomson disregarded this counsel of despair, which the failure or barrenness of models proposed by others had made the more compelling when he took up the work in 1903 [34:90–139].

He then represented the positive electrification, which he had not been able to eliminate, in a manner Kelvin had used for a primitive model of a radium atom: a diffuse sphere of constant charge density through which electrons move subject solely to electrostatic forces. Thomson always regarded this model as a *pis aller*, an unsatisfactory incarnation of that "something which causes the space through which the corpuscles [in an atom] are spread to act as if it had a [compensating] charge of positive electricity" [29:565]. But it was easily visualized, and yielded much of what he wanted: for assuming the electrons constrained to circulate in a single plane through the atom's center (another *pis aller*, to ease calculations) Thomson showed that to insure *mechanical* stability the electrons, under the influence of electrostatic forces alone, must distribute themselves into rings in the manner of Mayer's magnets [35].

He drew several important qualitative conclusions. First, since the electrons, unlike the magnets, move in accelerated paths, they must radiate, and consequently no arrangement of them can be permanent. This apparent menace proved a great advantage. The radiation from a ring of p electrons *decreases* very quickly as p increases, the radius and angular velocity of the particles remaining the same [37]; hence if the rings of an atom are well populated its internal motions might decay very slowly until a critical velocity is reached and the whole explodes. We call such explosions radioactivity. (The obvious inference, that all elements must be radioactive, kept several Cavendish men busy for years [cf. 61:235–237].) The relative stability of matter depends, in this theory, on n, the number of electrons in an atom. Since, in 1904, Thomson still took n to be on the order of 1,000 times the atomic weight A, he did not fear imminent radiation collapse.

Secondly, the electronic distributions calculated by Thomson supported analogies to the behavior of the chemical elements and, in particular, the conclusion that the electronic populations of the atoms of contiguous elements in the periodic table differ by a single unit. Had he made this a principle, it would probably have modified his thinking about the order of n; but, as was his practice with such models, he did not take the results of his calculations literally, never assigned the value of n for any given element, and, very probably, did not anticipate that exact assignments could soon be made.

In fact the first substantial advances in atomic theory arose from efforts to obtain n as a function of A. Here Thomson once again led the way by showing how to estimate n from measurements of the scattering of light (dispersion), X and β rays [36]. All the data, including some collected at the Cavendish, were interpreted via formulae computed by Thomson under the guidance of his model atom; and the formulae for the scattering of X [33:268] and of β rays [36:773] were the first of their kind. The upshot was that the population of the atom had been grossly overestimated, and that n appeared to lie between two-tenths and twice the atomic weight.

A great many experimental studies on the scattering of X, β, and γ rays were then put in train at the Cavendish [61:237]. The multiplication of data prompted Thomson to improve upon his theory of β scattering [43], which, however, rested on an unjustified assumption: that, regardless of the thickness of the scatterer, a β particle acquires a measurable deflection only as a result of encounters with a great many atomic electrons. It was this theory that served Rutherford first as pattern and then as counterfoil during his classical analysis of the scattering of α particles. Although the results of this analysis—the single-scattering theory, the new approximation $n = A/2$, and the nuclear atom—forced the rejection of Thomson's model, they should be viewed not as evidence of the failure, but as proof of the value, of his methods.

Thomson's discovery of the order of n did much more than recommend the cultivation of scattering theory. For one, it undermined the radiative stability of the atom and, by reducing the number of spectral emitters, made what Rayleigh called the "bog of spectroscopy" more mushy than ever. For another, it demonstrated that the chief part of the atomic mass must belong to the positive charge. Thomson tended to ignore the first set of problems, although he once troubled to suggest how a single electron might, during its capture by an ionized atom, emit most or all of the line spectrum [39: 157–162]. It was different with the new-found substantiality of the plus charge, which no longer could be referred persuasively to a "property of the corpuscle."

Thomson's last important experimental work, which extended over many years, was devoted to determining the nature of positive electricity. He concentrated on the "canal" or "positive" rays which can be constructed from the ions in a discharge tube by passing them through a perforated cathode. In earlier studies, by W. Wien in particular, the E/M of the rays had been found by deflecting them in superposed electric and magnetic fields, and catching them on a photographic plate; from the position of the traces on the film it appeared that they consisted of gaseous ions, and especially of hydrogen, which occurred irrespective of the gas filling the tube. Wien inclined to attribute the ubiquitous hydrogen to release of impurities absorbed by the walls of the tube. But this conclusion, as well as the general interpretation of Wien's results, was made problematic by the width of the traces, which Thomson ascribed to the neutralization of ions in the rays by collisions with molecules of the residual gas. His first effort, therefore, was to remove the molecules by realizing the highest vacuum obtainable [cf. 58:350–357]. Wien's bands then broke up, as theory required, into parabolic traces, each deposited by ions possessing different velocities and a common E/M [38].

Many ionic species disclosed themselves, and always H$^+$, which Thomson accordingly took to be the positive protyle for which he was looking [38: 575; 39:19, 23; 40:12–13]; but after a long exchange with Wien he conceded that the hydrogen was not protyle but impurity [46:248]. During the exchange Thomson introduced many ingenious improvements in experimental technique and in the analysis of the traces. By 1913 his instrument had become sensitive enough to distinguish ionic species of atomic weights 20 and 22 in a neon discharge. At first [48:593] he thought the heavier species a new element, or perhaps a molecular peculiarity, NeH$_2{}^+$; but eventually he came around to the new view of Rutherford's school and recognized that he had been the first to isolate isotopes of stable elements [54:88]. In this work Thomson had the help not only of his long-time assistant, E. Everett, but also of Francis Aston, who returned to it after the war and perfected the mass spectroscope, which brought him the Nobel Prize.

Teacher and Administrator. Aston was one of seven Nobel Prizemen, twenty-seven Fellows of the Royal Society, and dozens of professors of physics trained at the Cavendish during Thomson's tenure [58:435–438]. Thomson was an excellent teacher and, when in good form, an unsurpassable lecturer [61:257; 59:42–43], clever, challenging, presuming neither too much nor too little, enthusiastic, and imperturbable. He took pedagogy seriously, on all levels. He interested himself in the improvement of science education in the secondary schools [22, 47] as well as in the universities, for which he and his close friend J. H. Poynting prepared several excellent texts. He kept his own lectures up to date both at the Royal Institution, where he became Professor of Natural Philosophy in 1905 (in addition to his Cambridge post), and at the Cavendish [cf. 61:273–278]. For the benefit of the advanced students in the laboratory he established in 1893 the Cavendish Physical Society, a fortnightly seminar in the German manner in which recent work—including his own—was reviewed and criticized [61:226, 271; 59:41].

Thomson was not himself a good experimentalist, being clumsy with his hands [60:73; 58:118], but he had a genius for designing apparatus and diagnosing its ills [59:175]. This trait, together with his wide and up-to-date interests, his enthusiasm, imagination, and resourcefulness, made him an excellent director of research throughout his tenure of the Cavendish chair. He resigned the professorship in 1919, in favor of Rutherford [59:215–218], before his lack of sympathy for Bohr's new physics could do any damage.

Thomson made every effort to place his best students, and gave generously of his time to keep those who took professorships in the colonies alive professionally. He would see their papers through the press, select demonstrators for them, advise on job openings and laboratory construction, and report recent progress in physics. As administrator of the Cavendish he gave his demonstrators great freedom and interfered as little as possible with laboratory routine [61:226]. He extended the buildings twice, once with accumulated laboratory fees [59:46], and again with Lord Rayleigh's Nobel Prize money, generously given the University for the purpose [59:155–156]. For a time, particularly in the 1890's, the need to save for expansion left little for research [61:270; 59:47–48], and it may be that Thomson could then have done more to improve the finances of the laboratory. He had a good eye for investment himself, and died a moderately wealthy man [59:262].

Thomson received a great many honors, including the Nobel Prize (1906), a knighthood (1908), the Order of Merit (1912), and the Presidency of the Royal Society, which he assumed in 1915. He therefore bore the burden of directing the Society's efforts to assist in the war [cf. 51] and of restraining some of its superpatriots from trying to oust Fellows of German descent like Schuster [59:181–195]. The tact and energy with which he accomplished these tasks were widely recognized. In 1918 Thomson became Master of his old college, Trinity. He guided its affairs with his wonted geniality and good sense until a few months before his death.

NOTES

1. "Atom," in *Encyclopaedia Britannica* (9th ed., 1875).
2. The first two phrases are A. Righi's, "Sir J. J. Thomson," in *Nature*, **91** (1918), 4–5; the second pair come from N. Bohr, *ibid.*, **118** (1926), 879, and 59:150, respectively.
3. This agrees with the account in 37:3, with the order of ideas in 25:430–432, and with the order of events in 1896–1897. Lenard's role has become less prominent in Thomson's definitive announcement of his discovery [26], and has altogether disappeared from the retrospective account in 44:95, which ascribes the awakening of "doubts" about the ionic interpretation of the rays solely to the results of the bending experiments. Whittaker [62:361], Rayleigh [59:80], and G. P. Thomson [60:44–45] all follow this version, which Thomson enlarged in 58:333–335.

4. W. Kaufmann, "Die magnetische Ablenkbarkeit der Kathodenstrahlen und ihre Abhängigkeit vom Entladungspotential," in *Annalen der Physik*, **61** (1897), 544–552.
5. A. Schuster, *The Progress of Physics 1875–1908* (Cambridge, 1908), 70–71.

BIBLIOGRAPHY

I. Most of Thomson's important papers were published in the *Philosophical Magazine*, which he took to be, and helped to make, the leading English journal for physics. His results would often be reprinted, more or less reworked, in books, two of which became fundamental texts in their fields [33, 50]. No full bibliography of his works exists; the best, that in the obituary notice by the 4th Baron Rayleigh (*Obituary Notices of Fellows of the Royal Society*, **3** [1941], 587–609), contains some 250 items and yet is quite incomplete. It omits letters to *Nature*, at least one of which [19] was important; and misses contributions to cooperative works like the *Encyclopaedia Britannica*, Watt's *Chemical Dictionary*, and the *Recueil des travaux offerts . . . à H. A. Lorentz* (The Hague, 1900). Other important omissions include Thomson's Nobel Prize speech [37], his Rede lecture [21], and his contribution to *James Clerk Maxwell. A Memorial Volume* (New York, 1931). Additional items are supplied by Poggendorff and by Rayleigh [59:292]. A useful but incomplete list of Thomson's publications from 1880 to 1909 may be gathered from 61:285–323.

There follows a list in order of publication of the works of Thomson mentioned in the text (*PM* = *Philosophical Magazine*; *PCPS* = *Proceedings of the Cambridge Philosophical Society*; *PRI* = *Proceedings of the Royal Institution*; *PRS* = *Proceedings of the Royal Society*; *PT* = *Philosophical Transactions of the Royal Society*; *RBA* = *Reports of the British Association for the Advancement of Science*).

[1] "Experiments on Contact Electricity Between Non-Conductors," in *PRS*, **25** (1877), 369–372.
[2] "On the Electric and Magnetic Effects Produced by the Motion of Electrified Bodies," in *PM*, **11** (1881), 229–249.
[3] "On a Theory of Electric Discharge in Gases," in *PM*, **15** (1883), 427–434.
[4] "On the Determination of the Number of Electrostatic Units in the Electromagnetic Unit of Electricity," in *PRS*, **35** (1883), 346–347.
[5] *Treatise on the Motion of Vortex Rings* (London, 1883).
[6] "On Electrical Oscillations . . .," in *Proceedings of the London Mathematical Society*, **15** (1884), 197–218.
[7] "On Some Applications of Dynamical Principles to Physical Phenomena," in *PT*, **176** pt. 2 (1885), 307–342.
[8] "Report on Electrical Theories," in *RBA* (1885), 97–155.
[9] "Some Applications of Dynamical Principles to Physical Phenomena," *PT*, **178A** (1887), 471–526.

[10] "On the Dissociation of Some Gases by the Electric Discharge," in *PRS*, **42** (1887), 343–344.

[11] "On the Rate at Which Electricity Leaks Through Liquids Which Are Bad Conductors of Electricity," in *PRS*, **42** (1887), 410–429, written with H. F. Newall.

[12] *Applications of Dynamics to Physics and Chemistry* (London, 1888).

[13] "On Determination of 'v,' the Ratio of the Electromagnetic Unit of Electricity to the Electrostatic Unit," in *PT*, **181** (1889), 583–621, written with G. F. C. Searle.

[14] "The Electrolysis of Steam," in *PRS*, **53** (1893), 90–110.

[15] *Notes on Recent Researches in Electricity and Magnetism* (Oxford, 1893).

[16] "On the Effect of Electrification and Chemical Action on a Steam Jet . . .," in *PM*, **36** (1893), 313–327.

[17] "On the Velocity of the Cathode-Rays," in *PM*, **38** (1894), 358–365.

[18] "On the Electrolysis of Gases," in *PRS*, **58** (1895), 244–257.

[19] "The Röntgen Rays," in *Nature*, **53** (1896), 391–392.

[20] "On the Discharge of Electricity Produced by the Röntgen Rays," in *PRS*, **59** (1896), 274–276.

[21] "The Röntgen Rays," Rede lecture, in *Nature*, **54** (1896), 302–306.

[22] "Presidential Address," section A, in *RBA* (1896), 699–706.

[23] "On the Leakage of Electricity Through Dielectrics Traversed by Röntgen Rays," in *PCPS*, **9** (1896), 126–140, written with J. A. McClelland.

[24] "On the Passage of Electricity Through Gases Exposed to Röntgen Rays," in *PM*, **42** (1896), 392–407, written with E. Rutherford.

[25] "Cathode Rays," in *PRI*, **15** (1897), 419–432.

[26] "Cathode Rays," in *PM*, **44** (1897), 293–316.

[27] "On the Charge of Electricity Carried by the Ions Produced by Röntgen-Rays," in *PM*, **46** (1898), 528–545.

[28] "On the Theory of the Conduction of Electricity Through Gases by Charged Ions," in *PM*, **47** (1899), 253–268.

[29] "On the Masses of the Ions in Gases at Low Pressures," in *PM*, **48** (1899), 547–567.

[30] "Indications relatives à la constitution de la matière," in *Rapports du congrès international de physique* (Paris, 1900), III, 138–151.

[31] "On the Charge of Electricity Carried by Gaseous Ions," in *PM*, **5** (1903), 346–355.

[32] "The Magnetic Properties of Systems of Corpuscles Describing Circular Orbits," in *PM*, **6** (1903), 673–693.

[33] *Conduction of Electricity Through Gases* (Cambridge, 1903).

[34] *Electricity and Matter* (New Haven, 1904).

[35] "On the Structure of the Atom . . .," in *PM*, **7** (1904), 237–265.

[36] "On the Number of Corpuscles in an Atom," in *PM*, **11** (1906), 769–781.

[36a] *On the Light Shown by Recent Investigations of Electricity on the Relation Between Matter and Ether*, Adamson lecture (Manchester, 1907); reprinted in *Annual Report of the Smithsonian Institution* (1908), 233–244.

[37] "Carriers of Negative Electricity," in *Les prix Nobel en 1906* (Stockholm, 1908).

[38] "On Rays of Positive Electricity," in *PM*, **13** (1907), 561–575.

[39] *The Corpuscular Theory of Matter* (London, 1907).

[40] "Presidential Address," in *RBA* (1909), 3–24.

[41] "Positive Electricity," in *PM*, **18** (1909), 821–845.

[42] "On a Theory of the Structure of the Electric Field and Its Application to Röntgen Radiation and to Light," *PM*, **19** (1910), 301–313.

[43] "On the Scattering of Rapidly Moving Electrified Particles," in *PM*, **23** (1912), 449–457.

[44] "Survey of the Last Twenty-five Years," in *A History of the Cavendish Laboratory, 1871–1910* (London, 1910), 75–101.

[45] "Ionization by Moving Electrified Particles," in *PM*, **23** (1912), 449–457.

[46] "Further Experiments on Positive Rays," in *PM*, **24** (1912), 209–253.

[47] "The Functions of Lectures and Textbooks in Science Teaching," in *Nature*, **88** (1912), 399–400.

[48] "Some Further Applications of the Method of Positive Rays," in *PRI*, **20** (1913), 591–600.

[49] "On the Structure of the Atom," in *PM*, **26** (1913), 792–799.

[50] *Rays of Positive Electricity and Their Application to Chemical Analysis* (London, 1913).

[50a] *The Atomic Theory*, Romanes lecture (Oxford, 1914).

[51] "Presidential Address," in *PRS*, **93A** (1916), 90–98; *PRS*, **94A** (1917), 182–90; *PRS*, **95A** (1918), 250–257.

[52] "On the Origin of Spectra and Planck's Law," in *PM*, **37** (1919), 419–446.

[53] "Mass, Energy and Radiation," in *PM*, **39** (1920), 679–689.

[54] "Opening of the Discussion on Isotopes," in *PRS*, **99A** (1921), 87–94.

[55] *The Electron in Chemistry* (Philadelphia, 1923).

[56] "On the Analogy Between the Electromagnetic Field and a Fluid Containing a Large Number of Vortex Filaments," in *PM*, **12** (1931), 1057–1063.

[57] "On Models of the Electric Field and of the Photon," in *PM*, **16** (1933), 809–845.

[58] *Recollections and Reflections* (London, 1936).

II. Thomson's notebooks have been deposited at the Cambridge University Library (Add. 7654/NB), which also has three boxes of his correspondence, primarily incoming (Add. 7654 [ii]) and, in the Rutherford Papers (Add. 7653), some forty letters from him, bits of which were published by A. S. Eve, *Rutherford* (New York, 1939). The Royal Society Library also has a few Thomson autographs, primarily twenty-six letters to Schuster (Sch. 331–356). Indications of other holdings may be found in R. M. MacCleod, *Archives of British Men of*

Science (London, 1972), and in T. S. Kuhn *et al.*, *Sources for History of Quantum Physics* (Philadelphia, 1967).

III. The chief biographies of Thomson are the following:

[59] Lord Rayleigh, *The Life of Sir J. J. Thomson, O.M.* (Cambridge, 1943).

[60] G. P. Thomson, *J. J. Thomson and the Cavendish Laboratory in His Day* (New York, 1965).

For assessments of Thomson's work, see the following:

[61] H. F. Newall, E. Rutherford, C. T. R. Wilson, N. R. Campbell, L. R. Wilberforce *et al.*, *A History of the Cavendish Laboratory* (London, 1910).

[62] E. T. Whittaker, *A History of Theories of Aether and Electricity*. I. *The Classical Theories*, 2nd ed. (New York, 1951).

[63] R. McCormmach, "J. J. Thomson and the Structure of Light," in *British Journal for the History of Science*, **3** (1967), 362–387.

[64] V. M. Dukov, *Elektron*: *istoria otkritia i izuchenia svoistov* (Moscow, 1966), 108–154.

[65] J. L. Heilbron, "The Scattering of α and β Particles and Rutherford's Atom," in *Archive for History of Exact Science*, **4** (1968), 247–307.

[66] D. Topper, "Commitment to Mechanism: J. J. Thomson, The Early Years," *ibid.*, **7** (1971), 393–410.

J. L. HEILBRON

THOMSON, THOMAS (*b.* Crieff, Scotland, 12 April 1773; *d.* Kilmun, Scotland, 2 July 1852), *chemistry*.

Thomson was the seventh child and youngest son of John Thomson, a retired woolman, and Elizabeth Ewan. Having been educated mainly at home by his talented mother and by his brother James, he enjoyed a good classical training at the Burgh School of Stirling from 1786 to 1788. In 1788 he won a bursary to the local University of St. Andrews, where he studied classics, mathematics, and natural philosophy. With a medical career tentatively in mind, in 1791 he began attending a variety of classes at the University of Edinburgh, where in 1795–1796 he was inspired to devote his life to chemistry by Joseph Black's impeccably elegant lectures. Although he did not graduate M.D. until 1799, from 1796 until 1800 he replaced his brother James as assistant editor of the Supplement to the third edition of the *Encyclopaedia Britannica*, to which he contributed extensive articles on chemistry and mineralogy. After 1800 Thomson devoted himself largely to chemistry as teacher, researcher, textbook writer, editor, and historian. Between 1800 and 1811 he made a precarious living as a private lecturer on chemistry in Edin-

burgh. During this period he published, on the basis of his articles in the *Britannica*, his bestselling *A System of Chemistry* (Edinburgh, 1802). In 1805 he acted as a well-paid consultant for the Scottish Excise Board and in 1807, with characteristic enterprise, instituted a private laboratory class in practical chemistry. In 1808, as a pugnacious opponent of Edinburgh's Huttonian geologists, Thomson helped to found the Wernerian Natural History Society. Becoming a fellow of the Royal Society in 1811, Thomson launched himself as a historian with his unofficial *History of the Royal Society* (London, 1812). From 1813 to 1820 he edited, first in London (1813–1817) and then in Glasgow (1817–1820), his own journal *Annals of Philosophy*, which rapidly overtook its proprietary competitors. The last phase of his entrepreneurial career began in 1817, shortly after his marriage to Agnes Colquhoun, when he was unanimously elected lecturer in chemistry at the University of Glasgow. Within seven months his aggressive opportunism had elevated this post into a regius professorship, which he held until his death. Thomson worked hard to reestablish the distinguished tradition of chemistry at the university and to improve its growing medical school. Particularly during the 1830's he was centrally involved in the unsuccessful political attempts made to elevate the status and increase the rights of the regius professors in the university. Tired by his life of unremitting effort, in 1841 Thomson relinquished part of his lecturing and the supervision of the laboratory to his nephew Robert Dundas Thomson, whom he had groomed as his successor. From 1846 until 1852 all his duties were discharged by his nephew, who subsequently failed to acquire the chair.

A self-taught chemist, Thomson first secured his reputation through the publication in 1802 of his *System*, which was so popular that it went through six editions during the next eighteen years; it also received the further accolade of appearing in French, German, and American editions. As the first systematic treatise of a nonelementary kind to break the French monopoly of such works, Thomson's *System* tried patriotically to do justice to the contributions made by British chemists to the new chemistry, which had been established in the late eighteenth century. Unusual for British works of the time, this well-ordered and careful digest was based on a wide range of original and recent papers as well as on the standard works. Quite characteristically, Thomson tabulated numerical data and employed a style that was attractively clear, frequently succinct, and occasionally trenchant. In the third edition of his *System* (Edinburgh, 1807), he began a thirty years' stint as John Dalton's warmest advocate when he extended the latter's chemical atomic theory from gases to include acids, bases, and salts. In January 1808 Thomson was the first to submit an experimental illustration of the law of multiple proportions, doing so at least four months before the publication of Dalton's *New System of Chemical Philosophy* (1808). This paper, "On Oxalic Acid" (*Philosophical Transactions*, **98** [1808], 63–95), also established a useful method of determining empirical formulas. After 1808 Thomson's enthusiasm for chemical atomism and for its mathematical harmonies burgeoned, an enthusiasm palpably displayed in the successive editions of his *System*, and countervailing the cautious skepticism shown by Wollaston and, more strongly, by Davy. His fervor was also apparent in his journal, *Annals of Philosophy*, in which he printed abstracts of currently published research by Continental as well as by British workers; inaugurated annual reports on the progress of science; and offered well-documented scientific biographies. Not unexpectedly, chemistry was the dominant subject of the journal, and its columns a leading vehicle for Dalton's chemical atomic theory. In 1815 Thomson espoused a second and related quantitative chemical cause when he published in his journal William Prout's anonymous paper on the specific gravities of gases. From then on Thomson focused his research upon three connected aims: to put Dalton's theory on a wider and firmer experimental basis; to provide conclusive experimental evidence for Prout's hypothesis that the atomic weights of elements were whole-number multiples of that of hydrogen; and to extend his projected investigation of the composition and formulas of salts to encompass those of all known minerals, particularly those containing aluminum.

During his first five or six years at Glasgow, Thomson and his laboratory students tried to accomplish the first two of these aims; their results were finally revealed in Thomson's *An Attempt to Establish the First Principles of Chemistry by Experiment* (London, 1825). Doubtless Thomson felt that this ambitious work was the culmination not only of his atomic labors but also of a long and busy career. Yet his measurements of the specific gravities of gases, of which he was proud, were shown in 1825 by his friend Harry Rainy to be inaccurate. Worse still, in 1827 the reliability of his gravimetric analyses was severely assailed by Berzelius, at that time the dominant analytical chemist in Europe. His lethal conclusion that many of

Thomson's fundamental experiments were made at the writing table did not enhance the reputation of the dour Scot, although his atomic weights were widely accepted in Great Britain and in the United States between 1825 and about 1835. In 1836 Thomson completed his research program by publishing his *Outlines of Mineralogy, Geology, and Mineral Analysis* (London, 1836), in which he arranged minerals on the basis of their experimentally determined chemical composition and not on the basis of their physical properties. As he discovered no new elements and was working in a research field that had been already intensively developed, the work aroused little controversy or notice.

The outstanding pedagogic feature of Thomson's professorial work was his pioneering emphasis on the laboratory teaching of practical chemistry. By the autumn of 1818 he had extracted from the university a chemical laboratory in which he established the first school of practical chemistry in a British university. He trained his students in the qualitative and quantitative analysis of inorganic substances, particularly minerals. Many of his students seem to have subsequently worked in the Glasgow chemical industry. Some of the more competent pupils were recruited by Thomson to form a small research school. By the mid-1830's his laboratory had become a nursery from which ambitious chemists migrated to other laboratories, including that of Justus Liebig, to complete their training.

Although sometimes arrogant and perpetually sardonic, Thomson became a father figure for Glaswegian scientists during the 1830's. His *History of Chemistry* (London, 1830–1831), unique and authoritative from 1760 onward, was professional propaganda that *inter alia* legitimated chemistry for the educated layman as a noble, rational, and autonomous science. From 1834 until his death Thomson was the president and chief ornament of the Philosophical Society of Glasgow. Indeed, in 1834 he was largely responsible for changing the moribund society dominated by artisans into an intellectually and administratively competent one that under his supervision at last began to publish its *Proceedings* in 1841. Not surprisingly he acted as Glasgow's senior host to distinguished scientific visitors and eagerly supported the activities of the British Association for the Advancement of Science during its first crucial decade. The leadership that Thomson gave to Glaswegian science, like so much else that he did during his career, shows the sort of reward that could be won at that time in British science by an ambitious self-made chemist who was distinguished more for unflagging industry than for brilliant originality.

BIBLIOGRAPHY

I. ORIGINAL WORKS. Thomson's important books are listed by J. R. Partington, *A History of Chemistry*, III (London, 1962), 716–721. The *Catalogue of Scientific Papers Compiled by the Royal Society of London* (London, 1871), 5, 970–976, lists 201 items by him.

II. SECONDARY LITERATURE. The basic biographies remain R. D. Thomson, "Biographical Notice of the Late Thomas Thomson," in *Glasgow Medical Journal*, 5 (1857), 69–80, 121–153, 379–380; and W. Crum, "Sketch of the Life and Labours of Dr. Thomas Thomson," in *Proceedings of the Philosophical Society of Glasgow*, 3 (1855), 250–264. Further secondary sources and a discussion of his professorial career are given by J. B. Morrell, "Thomas Thomson: Professor of Chemistry and University Reformer," in *British Journal for the History of Science*, 4 (1969), 245–265; and "The Chemist-Breeders: the Research Schools of Liebig and Thomas Thomson," in *Ambix*, 19 (1972), 1–46.

J. B. MORRELL

THOMSON, SIR WILLIAM (Baron Kelvin of Largs) (*b.* Belfast, Ireland, 26 June 1824; *d.* Netherhall, near Largs, Ayrshire, Scotland, 17 December 1907), *physics.*

Thomson was the son of James Thomson, who, at the time of his son's birth, was professor of engineering at Belfast. In 1832 he became professor of mathematics at Glasgow. He was the author of several noted texts on differential and integral calculus, and he educated William and another son, James, at home. In 1834 both boys matriculated at Glasgow, where the environment was one characteristic of the Scottish universities of the time, which differed greatly from Cambridge. Whereas at Cambridge there was no chair in natural philosophy, nor much interest in the work of the Parisian analysts of the first third of the century, at Glasgow there was a professorship in natural philosophy (held by William Meickleham, who was succeeded by Nichol and then by William Thomson); there was also a chair in chemistry (held by Thomas Thomson).

Meickleham had a great interest in the French approach to physical science and much respect for it. In 1904 Thomson recalled how, "My predecessor in the Natural Philosophy Chair . . . taught his students reverence for the great French mathematicians Legendre, Lagrange, and Laplace. His immediate successor, Dr. Nichol, added Fresnel and Fourier to this list of scientific nobles."[1] Having been stimulated by Meickleham, Thomson avidly read Fourier's *Théorie analytique de la chaleur* and Laplace's *Mécanique céleste* during a trip to Paris in 1839. Indeed, Thomson's earliest interests centered on questions drawn from both these treatises. His first published paper (except for an early effort concerning the completeness of Fourier series) involved an attempt to find a method for determining the temperature in a heat-conducting solid outside a closed isothermal surface described within the solid. Thomson approached the problem by employing propositions drawn from Laplace's theory of attraction: the theory that treats the forces exerted by shells of attracting matter. In doing so he forged a formal relationship between the theory of the transfer of heat, on the one hand, and on the other, the general class of theories of attraction, in the particular instance of effects exerted by the electrical fluid.[2]

In the course of his analysis Thomson found that the Coulomb force which is exerted by electrical fluid in a state of equilibrium on the surface of a conducting body within which no fluid exists is mathematically parallel to the flow of heat produced by thermal sources distributed, in place of the electrical fluid, over the surface of the conductor. The formal relation assumes that the empty space in and around the conducting body is replaced by a heat-conducting solid, and that the surface of the conductor is itself replaced by a similarly shaped surface over which sources of heat are distributed in equilibrium. (The term "equilibrium" here means that the thermal surface has a constant temperature and does not enclose any sources of heat, all sources being located at the surface.) In stating this formal relation, Thomson was attempting, at this time (1842), only to find a method for solving problems in heat by use of the theory of electricity in equilibrium. The relationship between the theories of the transfer of heat and of electricity was thus purely formal, their connection being mathematical, not physical.

Between 1841 and 1845 Thomson attended Cambridge. His studies did not influence him as deeply as had those during his years at Glasgow, primarily because of the extreme importance attached to finishing in the first rank of the Senate-House examinations. This emphasis required the expenditure of much thought on the particular kinds of mathematical problems asked. Only rarely were those problems related to any physical question that was not contained in Newton's *Principia*.

Thomson did expand his knowledge of the French mathematical techniques and theories during these years, however; and soon after his graduation he journeyed again to Paris, at his father's suggestion, to work in Regnault's laboratory.

On arriving there for the second time, during the summer of 1845, Thomson was warmly received by Liouville and was soon introduced to Cauchy, Sturm, Biot, Dumas, and Regnault. His studies in Paris were crucial for the subsequent development of British physical science. During this period he developed the technique of electrical images, first read Clapeyron's explication of Carnot's theory of the motive power of heat, and formulated a methodology of scientific explanation that strongly influenced Maxwell.

Thomson's extensive contact with Liouville led him to think more deeply about electrical theory. Liouville had heard of Faraday's work in electrostatics, or at least of the aspects in which Faraday claimed to have found that electrical induction occurs in "curved lines." The conception seemed to conflict with the action-at-a-distance approach, and Liouville asked Thomson to write a paper clarifying the differences between Faraday on the one hand and Coulomb and Poisson on the other. This request prompted Thomson to bring together ideas he had been turning over in his mind during the previous three years.

Even in the 1842 paper on isothermal surfaces, Thomson did not treat the electrical fluid as Poisson had done. He knew of Poisson's mode of mathematical development, but he dealt with the fluid more in the manner of Coulomb—that is, without attributing to the imagined fluid the material properties of actual fluids known to experience. Poisson, for his part, had insisted on conceiving of electricity as a fluid that, like other material entities, occupies a finite region of space: the central problem of his theory was the determination of the actual thickness of the electrical layer at any point of a conducting surface.

In 1842, and again early in 1845, Thomson attempted to envision the physical characteristics of the electrical fluid, and reached disquieting conclusions. He found that if electricity is thought of as a fluid the parts of which exert only inverse-square forces upon one another, then the electrical layer at the surface of a conductor can have no physical thickness at all. That result implied that electricity must be a set of point centers of force. At the time he completely rejected that notion. Later, in 1860, he attributed it to Bošković. But this rejection made it increasingly difficult for him to conceive of

Poisson's fluid as a real physical entity at all. Thus, Liouville's request for a discussion of the issue between Faraday's approach and that of action-at-a-distance led Thomson to attempt a restatement of both theories in terms free from physical hypotheses (as he termed hypotheses concerning unobservable entities). In making that effort, Thomson found himself to be constructing an entire methodology for scientific explanation.[3]

He began by distinguishing the "physical" from the "mathematical" content of Poisson's theory, at first implicitly. In the "mechanical theory of electricity," as he termed the physical hypothesis of the electrical fluid,[4] there are fundamental difficulties which create doubt about the adequacy with which the hypothesis represents the nature of all matter. At the same time the "mathematical theory" developed by Poisson did seem to be extremely powerful and to be capable of dealing correctly with a vast range of particular cases. Prompted by the physical difficulty with Poisson's approach and concerned over the apparent conflict with Faraday's ideas, Thomson began to think more carefully about the actual nature of the action-at-a-distance theory. What did it assert that could be accepted without also accepting the electrical fluid as a real entity? For Thomson was caught between his great admiration for the mathematical power of Poisson's approach and his distaste for the electrical fluid. Hoping to resolve this dilemma, he undertook a series of researches that in effect led him to a proof of the equivalence of Faraday's approach with that of the action-at-a-distance school. He achieved that result by excluding all elements that depended on physical hypotheses from both theories.

From Thomson's new point of view, both the French approach to electrical theory and that of Faraday should consist only of sets of mathematical propositions about the "distribution of electricity" on conducting bodies. Of Coulomb, who had never written like Poisson of the "thickness" of the electrical layer, Thomson said that he had "expressed his theory in such a manner that it can only be attacked in the way of proving his experimental results to be inaccurate." He did not, therefore, believe that Coulomb's approach would stand or fall with the fate of the electrical fluid.

Of course, it may be wondered how Thomson could have employed the phrase "distribution of electricity" without believing that some hypothetical entity is implicated. He did not think so, however. Instead, by 1845 he was drawing a distinction between a "physical hypothesis" and an "elementary mathematical law." By a physical hypothesis he meant an assumption concerning the physical existence of an unobservable entity like the electrical fluid or Faraday's contiguous dielectric particles. By an elementary mathematical law he meant a statement that can be directly applied in experiments because its referents are phenomenal entities and mathematical propositions about them. For example, when it is a question of the "distribution of electricity," a phrase that might appear in an "elementary mathematical law," the actual subject concerns the effects produced when a proof-plane is applied to a point of an electrified conductor. The measure of those effects is the twist given to the torsion-bearing thread of an electrometer. Coulomb's laws, therefore, and also those aspects of Poisson's mathematical development of them that do not depend upon the conception of electricity as a physical fluid, were thus actually concise, mathematical laws applicable to the results of such experiments. They were not hypotheses concerning the nature of electricity.

If, however, neither Coulomb's nor Faraday's approaches really did contain physical hypotheses, and if both of them yielded correct laws for the same phenomena, then there should be no conflict. Indeed, thought Thomson, any two theories dealing with the same phenomena, however different they may appear to be, cannot conflict if their most elementary laws can be expressed mathematically with no referents except those that can be interpreted phenomenologically. But having asserted the equivalence of such theories, Thomson had now to provide a method by which equivalence in any particular instance could be demonstrated. He found just such a method in his 1842 connecting of the laws of the transfer of heat with the theory of electricity in equilibrium on conducting surfaces. His reading of George Green's *Essay on the Application of Mathematical Analysis to the Theories of Electricity and Magnetism* (1828) had made the connection even more cogent.

Thomson obtained a copy of Green's work early in 1845. He was especially struck by the proof that a knowledge of the electrical potential at all points suffices to determine both the forces and the distribution of electricity on conducting bodies and permits dispensing with Poisson's postulate of an electrical layer of finite depth. Thomson realized that his own paper of 1842 had actually been founded on a formal equating of temperature with potential, and Green's work convinced him that all of the propositions of the mathematical theory of electricity could be expressed solely in terms of the potential. The relation between the mathematics of heat transfer and of electrical equilibrium thus became even more convincing than he had thought.

This relation made it possible to express the elementary laws of the "mathematical theory" (namely, that containing Poisson's mathematical results but not the conception of electricity as a physical fluid) in the same terms as the laws of the uniform transfer of heat. For Green had actually proved that a knowledge of the potential is sufficient to solve all electrical problems. "We may," Thomson now noted, "employ the elementary principles of one theory, as theorems, relative to the other." That is, the mathematical theory could be expressed in such a fashion that its laws appear as theorems following out of the laws of the transfer of heat when a formal equation is made between temperature and potential.

Construing the mathematical theory in terms of a Fourier heat transfer provided Thomson with a technique for proving the equivalence of Faraday's approach with the mathematical theory. The method was to express the concepts underlying these approaches in propositions drawn from Fourier; if this could be done unambiguously for both, then their equivalence would, he thought, be manifest. If, now, Faraday's principles regarding the induction of electricity on conductors could be connected with the same hypothesis-independent laws to which those of the mathematical theory were linked, then the two methods would come to the same thing. And, indeed, Thomson saw Faraday's system almost as an immediate consequence of the application of Fourier's laws to electrical phenomena (supposing conductors to be separated only by air or a vacuum).

But what of the effects of nonconductors placed between conducting bodies? Thomson had in mind here the properties that Faraday had discovered and had taken for evidence telling in favor of his theory and against that of Poisson. That difficulty would be met, Thomson thought, provided the new law were to be admitted in order to express the effect of a dielectric intermediary, and provided its status were to be that of an elementary mathematical principle, and not of a physical hypothesis. Thomson assumed that the smallest parts of a dielectric under electrical influence possess a "polarity" the laws of which are the same as Poisson's mathematical laws of magnetic polarity. He was thereby able to replace the dielectric by equivalent charged surfaces of electrical equilibrium.[5]

Thomson's conceptions were a powerful technique for analyzing the relationship between theories that seem to conflict. His method for reconciling the systems was to scrutinize them in terms of what each asserted concerning phenomena that could be measured or detected and to try to eliminate whatever was hypothetical. Although there was no guarantee that this critique would always succeed, for Coulomb's and Faraday's theories it did.

Thus it was that Thomson started his policy of eliminating physical hypotheses in order to reconcile Faraday's work with Coulomb's. It was fortified by his aversion to the concept of an imponderable fluid, an idea that was contrary to his beliefs about the nature of matter. For after all his methodology could not be independent of his opinions regarding the actual structure of unobservable entities. Given his particular objections to the electrical fluid, the method that he created between 1842 and 1845 for the purpose of unifying theories had begun to assume a slightly different aspect by 1847. The emphasis now fell upon what the formally equivalent system can tell about the original system as well as upon how it can help eliminate physical hypotheses.

The original purposes, which had been to unify theory and eliminate hypothesis, did not disappear. Instead an element of conceptual elucidation was added that made possible the visualization of the theory in new terms. The elucidatory role of the technique of formal equivalence became very prominent in 1847. In that year Thomson made use of Stokes's 1845 equations for fluids and solids in order to bring out the analogies, first, between the internal linear displacements of an elastic solid and electrostatic force, and, second, between the internal rotational displacements and galvanic and magnetic forces. Thomson's representation was conditioned by Faraday's discovery in 1845 of the rotation of the plane of polarization of light passed through a transparent body subject to magnetic action (the Faraday effect). The rotational nature of the effect led Thomson to characterize magnetic and galvanic forces by internal rotations of elastic media.[6] This new aspect of the process of formal equivalence was elucidatory because Thomson related distinct forces (electric and magnetic) to the internal processes of a single medium. Instead of being entirely distinct phenomena, electrical force and magnetic force were thus linked to a common element.

Yet even here Thomson limited himself to the statement that Faraday's discovery ". . . suggests the idea that there may be a problem connected with the distribution of electricity on conductors, or with the forces of attraction and repulsion exercised by electrified bodies." The purpose of the "mechanical analogy" was different from that of heat representation. The attempt was not to prove the equivalence of theories dealing with the same phenomena, but rather to link theories of different, although related, phenomena (namely, electricity and magnetism) by demonstrating that they could be shown to serve a closely connected set of expressions. The 1845 conception of formal equivalence was not thereby displaced; instead, it was supplemented. Equivalents now made the underlying mathematical connections of phenomena that are quite different more understandable. It was the qualities of clarity and unity that equivalents brought to disparate areas which ultimately had the greatest influence on Maxwell's early work. For it was from Thomson that Maxwell appropriated the equivalence technique as a method for providing unity in place of discord.

After his 1845 sojourn in Paris, Thomson returned to Scotland, where he succeeded to the professorship in natural philosophy at Glasgow, a post that he held for the rest of his life. Neither in Scotland nor in England was there then a university research laboratory or any other in which students could work. Thomson, having had access to Regnault's laboratory, was interested in establishing similar opportunities for students, and he obtained a small sum from the university for that purpose. It made possible the first teaching laboratory in Britain. He was also greatly interested in developing highly accurate measuring instruments, and the facilities of his new laboratory in Glasgow made that possible also.

Thomson's studies in France not only led him to a new approach to electrical theory and to an interest in experimental work and instrumentation; he was also introduced to Sadi Carnot's theory of the motive power of heat, as developed analytically by Clapeyron in 1834. Thomson was deeply impressed by the power of Carnot's theory (although he had read only Clapeyron's explication of it at this date), and especially by the rationalization it afforded for the production of mechanical effect by thermal processes. In an 1848 paper Thomson employed Carnot's theory for the first time in an attempt to establish an "absolute" thermometric scale. The old scale was a merely "arbitrary series of numbered points of reference sufficiently close for the requirements of practical thermometry." By an absolute scale Thomson meant one based on some completely general natural law. That law he took from Carnot—a given amount of heat passing between two given temperatures can produce at most a certain amount of work. In the old scale, based on the air thermometer, the amount of work done by a standard quantity of heat in falling through one degree varied at different points of the scale, as Clapeyron had shown. An absolute scale would be one in which the "value of a degree" would be independent of temperature. Thomson constructed this measure using the results of Regnault, Steele, and others.[7] (The modern Kelvin scale was defined later, following the elucidation of the concept of the conservation of energy.)

Carnot's work was generally unknown, even in Paris; and his theory was new not only to Thomson but to the entire British physical community of the 1840's. A few months after the 1848 paper Thomson presented to the Royal Society of Edinburgh a general account of Carnot's findings. Thomson noted that Carnot's theory was founded on the concept that heat is a substance that, when employed in a complete cycle of operations, enters the body acting as an engine in a given amount. At the end of the cycle it is entirely removed, and the engine remains in its initial state. Carnot had likened the operation of such a heat engine to that of a column-of-water device in which a quantity of water falling through a fixed distance from a given height produces an invariable quantity of motive power, the water being fully transferred from its original height to a reservoir at a lower level. In Carnot's view heat acts in a similar manner: a given quantity of heat abstracted by an engine from a high-temperature reservoir effects changes in the volume of the engine and, at the end of a cycle in which the engine is restored to its original condition, the heat taken from the high-temperature source has been totally transferred to a reservoir at a lower temperature, the amount of power produced being fixed by the temperatures of the reservoirs and the quantity of heat transferred.

Even at this early date, Thomson was ambivalent in his views concerning the concept of heat as substance despite the seeming necessity of accepting that idea if Carnot's theory were to be employed. In his "Account of Carnot's Theory" (1849) he wrote,

> . . . all those assumptions depending on the idea that heat is a *substance*, invariable in quantity, not convertible into any other element, and incapable of being *generated* by any physical agency; in fact the acknowledged principles of latent heat; would require to be tested by a most searching investigation before

they ought to be admitted, as they have usually been, by almost every one who had been engaged on the subject.[8]

Thomson's ambivalence had two distinct sources. The first lay in his skepticism about the propriety of employing imponderable entities. Further, Fourier's theory of the transfer of heat had left open the question of the nature of heat, and Thomson felt this openness to be one of the most important characteristics of the theory. Thus, he would not have accepted the material theory of heat without misgivings, even had he not known the work of Joule, whom he met at the 1847 meeting of the British Association. That work furnished a second set of reasons for Thomson's ambivalence.

Joule believed that heat and mechanical effect are but different aspects of matter, motion, and force. Sensible heat, he supposed, is in reality the "living force of the particles of the bodies in which it is induced"; when in a latent form, heat consists in the "separation of particle from particle, so as to cause them to attract one another through a greater space." Living force and "attraction through space"—by which Joule intended not force alone but a force acting across a given space—are convertible and "equivalent" because "living force may be produced by the action of gravity [or any attractive or repulsive force] through a given distance of space." Conversely, particulate motion can be transformed into particulate arrangement under the action of force. Whenever the living force of macroscopic bodies disappears, an equivalent of either particulate live force or of mechanical rearrangement effected against force is produced.

Thus, according to Joule, heat can be absolutely generated by mechanical action or, indeed, by any physical agency in which mechanical force is the ultimate source of action (as, for example, in an electromagnetic engine turned by hand). Conversely, heat should be absolutely destroyed in those circumstances in which thermal agency effects mechanical action. Joule attempted to support his contentions through a series of experiments involving electromagnetic engines and the internal motions of viscous fluids. In the former case Joule argued that heat is actually generated in a current-bearing conductor by the action of the current directly and not by any transfer of heat from hotter to colder parts of the body. In the latter case, he produced motions in a viscous fluid by means of a paddle wheel run by mechanical force. Although the motions seem to disappear after a time, they are actually converted into the living force particles of the fluid—heat—as is evidenced by a rise in temperature.

These two experiments at best demonstrated, Thomson carefully noted, that heat can be produced by mechanical effect; but they did not prove the converse—that it can be destroyed through conversion into effect. Joule's experimental demonstrations enabled Thomson to keep his distance from the material hypothesis of heat, although he continued to accept what he believed to be Carnot's basic principles. He did not embrace Joule's wider schema of heat as motion and "attraction through space"; indeed, it is highly unlikely that he knew the details of Joule's ideas on these points in 1849 beyond the rather vague assertion that heat is particulate *vis viva*. Thomson probably did not yet fully grasp the conception of latent heat as the arrangement of particles under the action of force. Indeed, his presentation of "Carnot's axioms" would suggest that he did not.

In the 1849 "Account" Thomson rarely referred to the impossibility of perpetual motion, conceived then as the impossibility of obtaining motive power without a corresponding alteration in other conditions. He began directly with his own version of Carnot's two axioms, regarding them as the basis of a theory that makes possible the calculation of the mechanical effect that can be produced *solely* by thermal agency. He gave the following as the principal "questions to be resolved by a complete theory of the subject"; these questions, to which Carnot's theory provides one possible answer, were essentially pragmatic:

> 1. What is the precise nature of the thermal agency by means of which *mechanical effect* is to be produced, without effects of any other kind?
> 2. How may the amount of this thermal agency necessary for performing a given quantity of work be estimated?

Thomson answered the first question by a deduction from what he called Carnot's "fundamental axiom," *viz.*, that ". . . at the end of a cycle of operations, when a body is left in precisely its primitive physical conditions, if it has absorbed any heat during one part of the operations, it must have given out exactly the same amount during the remainder of the cycle." On the basis of this axiom, Thomson concluded that "the origin of motive power . . . must be found in the agency of heat entering the body and leaving it" because no other effects are produced during a complete cycle. The

precise mode in which mechanical effect is produced by heat transfer is specified in Carnot's second axiom: "The thermal agency by which mechanical effect may be obtained, is the transference of heat from one body to another at a lower temperature."

Combining these two propositions made it possible to derive a theorem of great importance, which states that a fixed quantity of effect, the maximum which can be obtained, is produced by all reversible engines from the transferral of a given quantity of heat between two specified temperatures: "A perfect thermodynamic engine is such that, whatever amount of mechanical effect it can derive from a certain thermal agency; if an equal amount be spent in working it backwards, an equal reverse thermal effect will be produced." The foregoing has the standing of a theorem, and not a definition, because the criterion of reversibility is implicated in the first axiom through the notion of cyclical processes. The theorem affords the answer to the second question because it is used to calculate the effect produced by the transfer of heat between two fixed reservoirs by a perfect engine.

Both axioms are necessary for the derivation of the perfection theorem, and the first axiom is additionally necessary when analyzing a cycle of operations to ensure that, in a complete cycle, the engine returns to its primitive state. Yet Thomson, troubled by the conception of heat as a substance, felt that he had to justify the fundamental (first) axiom and attempted to do so by asserting that "no operation is known by which heat can be absorbed into a body without either elevating its temperature, or becoming latent, and producing some alteration in its physical condition." But heat engines must return to their initial states at the end of a cycle if—and here is the true motive for Thomson's insistence on the first axiom—calculation of the effects that have purely thermal origins is to be possible. It is again evident that Thomson had not yet grasped Joule's conception of latent heat as converted heat. He had not assimilated the idea that a body does not have to part with heat *as* heat in order to be returned to its primitive state. Instead, it can effect the conversion of heat into "attraction through space," that is, into the configuration of external bodies between which forces act, and thereby return to its original condition. In Thomson's opinion heat had to be transferred as heat in order to appear once again as sensible or latent; it cannot "disappear."

Thus, what Thomson called Carnot's "fundamental axiom" asserted the inconvertibility of heat in the view he then took of it. At this stage in his thought, it was not because convertibility of heat to something else would permit perpetual motion that he objected to it. Rather, he wished to maintain what he took to be Carnot's theory, because abandoning either axiom would ruin any theory of the origins of mechanical effect from thermal agency. He justified the first and fundamental axiom by the lack of any known operation in which heat can be absorbed without the appearance of extraneous effects. It is obvious in retrospect that this position was tenuous because it actually depended upon Thomson's inability to conceive of latent heat as converted heat. It can therefore be seen that in 1849 Thomson did not so much hold to the conception of the materiality of heat as he held to certain propositions that appeared to be founded on that idea, but that are in reality acceptable on empirical and pragmatic grounds. Carnot had himself, toward the end of his short life, come to view the material theory of heat as untenable and had accepted the view that heat is a mode of motion. He had despaired of making his theory of motive power consonant with the kinetic model of heat. Thomson, however, knew nothing of Carnot's later ideas.

Despite Thomson's having accepted the two axioms, in particular the first, he was still not confident of the idea that heat is a substance. He reasoned that Carnot's fundamental axiom, while it "may be considered as still the most probable basis for an investigation of the motive power of heat," might, along with "every other branch of the theory of heat . . . ultimately require to be reconstructed upon another foundation, when our experimental data are more complete." Thomson's ambivalence depended in part upon his aversion to imponderable entities. Joule thought as he did, and wrote

> In our notion of matter two ideas are generally included, namely those of *impenetrability* and *extension*. . . . Impenetrability and extension cannot with much propriety be reckoned among the *properties* of matter, but deserve rather to be called its definitions, because nothing that does not possess the two qualities bears the name of matter. If we conceive of impenetrability and extension we have the idea of matter, and of matter only.

Joule's comments were printed in the Manchester *Courier* of 5 and 12 May 1847, but he may very well have discussed them with Thomson at the British Association meeting of that same year.

Thomson was also impressed by Joule's concep-

tion of conservation in general. As Joule had written in the *Courier*:

> . . . the phenomena of nature, whether mechanical, chemical, or vital, consist almost entirely in continual conversion of attraction through space, living force, and heat into one another. Thus it is that order is maintained in the universe — nothing is destroyed, nothing ever lost, but the entire machinery, complicated as it is, works smoothly and harmoniously. And though, as in the awful vision of Ezekiel, "wheel may be in the middle of wheel," and every thing may appear complicated and involved in the apparent confusion and intricacy of an almost endless variety of causes, effects, conversions, and arrangements, yet is the most perfect regularity preserved — the whole being governed by the sovereign will of God.

Thomson was clearly affected by this conception, for in a footnote to his 1849 "Account" he remarked:

> When thermal agency is spent in conducting heat through a solid, what becomes of the mechanical effect it might produce? Nothing can be lost in the operations of nature — no energy can be destroyed. What effect then is produced in place of the mechanical effect which is lost? . . . [A similar problem seems to exist in the question of the] mechanical effect lost in a fluid set in motion in the interior of a rigid closed vessel, and allowed to come to rest by its own internal friction; but in this case the foundation of a solution of the difficulty has been actually found, in Mr. Joule's discovery of the generation of heat by the internal friction of fluids in motion.

It can be seen that in 1849 Thomson was deeply puzzled by the apparently complete disappearance of effect in certain cases. His thoughts were more clearly defined during the following two years as the result of two experiments. One of them clearly lent weight to Carnot's theory, and the other seemed to support that part of Joule's conceptions in which heat is thought to be generated. (Although Thomson had, from 1847 on, been willing to consider the latter possibility, only in 1850 did he accept it as a proven fact.)

The first experiment, performed by his brother, James, confirmed the deduction from Carnot's theory (with both axioms) that the freezing point of water must be lowered when the pressure is increased. One of the most important aspects of that work lay, not so much in its direct test of the two axioms, as in its use of the theorem derived from them regarding the perfection of reversible engines. It was this theorem that James Thomson most frequently employed in his demonstration, thereby giving it a significance greater than that normally associated with a derivative proposition. The work on the lowering of the freezing point of water, therefore, helped to shift attention from the two axioms toward the theorem on the perfection of the reversible engine. This shift was important for William Thomson's subsequent reformulation of Carnot's theory, in that he was to reconstruct the theory by substituting for Carnot's dual axioms a single one from which the perfectibility theorem followed directly.[9]

The second circumstance was more complex than the first and involved the properties of saturated steam under high pressure escaping through an orifice. Rankine had observed that, when saturated steam is permitted to expand, the heat that becomes latent during expansion is greater than the heat that the expanding vapor would normally release as a result of its concomitant drop in temperature. If no part of the vapor is to become liquid, it follows that some external source must supply the extra heat necessary to maintain saturation. More specifically, as a gas expands adiabatically, its temperature drops; the drop in temperature was taken as an indication that a certain amount of the free heat of the gas had become latent. The expansion of the gas was supposed to be the result of this absorption of heat. (The modern explanation of the effect depends upon the negative slope of the temperature-entropy curve in the vapor portion of the liquid-vapor curve. The implication is that the specific heat of saturated steam is negative, meaning that heat is absorbed as its temperature falls. The physical explanation of the effect is that, as the vapor has its temperature lowered, it expands so much to avoid supersaturation that the external work that it performs is greater than the drop in its internal energy. The situation thus requires that heat be absorbed.)

Steam remains saturated during its expansion after its escape at high pressure through an orifice (an expansion rapid enough to be essentially adiabatic). Its condition is evident in that it does not scald, as it would had it become partially liquefied. By mid-1850 Thomson saw this phenomenon as conclusive evidence in favor of Joule's contention that heat can be generated from something else: Thomson thought he knew the source of this extra heat. "There is no possible way," he wrote to Joule, "in which the heat can be acquired except by the friction of the steam as it rushes through the orifice. Hence I think I am justified in saying that your discovery alone can reconcile Mr. Rankine's

discovery with known facts." It was at this time also that Thomson first learned of Clausius' work of the previous April; although he had not read it by October, he commented that Clausius' methods "differ from those of Carnot only in the adoption of your [Joule's] axiom instead of Carnot's. . . ." Within five months Thomson himself had assimilated in full the "dynamical theory of heat" and had so modified Carnot's theory as to be in accord with it—an act accomplished independently, without any detailed knowledge of Clausius' work of May 1850.[10]

Thomson's central concern during these months was the discovery of a principle from which the essential elements of Carnot's theory could be derived while dispensing with the fundamental axiom concerning the conservation of heat *qua* heat. This was not a simple task; without the fundamental axiom, it is extremely difficult to produce a measure of the effect resulting from purely thermal action. The beginning of a solution lay in the new meaning given to the concept of "latent heat" by the dynamical theory, where it is thought of as the work done against the internal, molecular forces of a body. They then store it in the resulting molecular configuration. This notion relieved Thomson of his earlier concern that a body can be returned to its initial state only if the entire amount of heat that has entered it leaves in the same form. He now understood that heat can be converted into a "new" form—"attraction through space" in Joule's terminology—and yet be entirely removed from the transferring engine because the "latent heat" of the engine, its forced molecular configuration, can be directly converted through the performance of work into something of the same kind, namely, the "attraction through space" of external bodies. The problem, therefore, became the discovery of a principle that could be taken as the expression of the essential contents of Carnot's theory once conversion had been admitted. In other words, now that heat could be envisioned as both *vis viva* and molecular configuration, the problem ceased to concern the way in which purely thermal actions could be measured, for thermal actions were reducible to mechanical processes. The problem now was to formulate the theory of heat engines.

As noted above, James Thomson's 1850 paper on the freezing point of water placed great emphasis on the ideal nature of reversible engines. The maximum mechanical effect from the transfer of a quantity of heat between two temperatures will be obtained from engines that yield a mechanical effect when run forward equal to that expended on them when run backward. Although derived from Carnot's two axioms, by 1850 Thomson had come to see this proposition as the central element of the theory. The theorem as stated is insufficient. It is necessary also to stipulate that the engine returns to its initial condition at the end of a cycle. Thomson had earlier believed that this requirement necessitated the acceptance of Carnot's fundamental axiom, but by March 1851 he knew that this was incorrect. Yet the theorem itself could not be derived if either of the two axioms was rejected. Neither was it tenable in its original form, if the dynamical theory was accepted, because it employed the concept of the complete transfer of heat. Thomson was able to reformulate the theorem without referring to transfer of heat. Instead, he referred to heat "quantity": "If an engine be such that, when it is worked backwards, the physical and mechanical agencies in every part of its motion are all reversed, it produces as much mechanical effect as can be produced by any thermodynamic engine, with the same temperatures of source and refrigerator, from a given quantity of heat." (The "quantity of heat" appears to be that which is abstracted from the high-temperature reservoir.) Thomson attributed this formulation to Carnot and Clausius, but the attribution to Carnot is misleading, because Carnot's statement referred to the transfer of heat *in toto* and not simply to heat "quantity" and thermal reservoirs. It was in the proposition on the ideal nature of reversible engines that Thomson located the essential content of Carnot's theory. This proposition, along with Joule's, is one of the two central propositions of the theory of heat engines.

Nonetheless, Thomson was not satisfied with the proposition on the perfection of reversible engines. He felt the need for a more elementary principle because the proposition did not appear to be self-evident, as Carnot's axioms had prior to Joule's work. Working independently of Clausius, Thomson now developed the concept of a new kind of perpetual motion and then deduced the perfection of reversible engines from the postulate of its impossibility. This new perpetual motion, were it possible, would produce useful effects solely by the conversion of heat directly into work—a possibility that is not in conflict with either Joule's proposition or with the impossibility of that kind of perpetual motion in which something for nothing is obtained. Thomson asserted the impossibility of what was later termed perpetual motion of the second kind in the following words: "It is impossible, by means of inanimate material agency, to derive

mechanical effect from any portion of matter by cooling it below the temperature of the coldest of the surrounding objects."[11]

After 1844 (at the latest) Thomson felt that Fourier's principles had been overlooked by those "geologists who uncompromisingly oppose all paroxysmal hypotheses, and maintain not only that we have examples now before us, on the earth, of all the different actions by which its crust had been modified in geological history, but that those actions have never, or have not on the whole, been more violent in past time than they are at present." Thomson had early thought the Uniformitarian approach to be untenable. He believed that if both the earth and the sun had once been molten balls cooling through radiation (the earth forming a crust and the sun, because of its peculiarly high temperature and the nature of its substance, remaining an "incandescent liquid mass"), then the dissipation of heat required by Fourier's laws must necessarily have been much more rapid in the past than in the present. If this were so, then clearly such phenomena as the winds, which depend upon thermal gradients, must have been much more vigorous in past times. In 1844 these views were merely beliefs. Because Thomson had not developed in detail the solutions to such problems of heat transfer, he had not investigated the modifications which such circumstances as the solidification of the earth's outer crust might have produced in the rate at which heat is dissipated. Most important, he did not have the full range of data needed for deducing numerical values.

By late 1852 Thomson's beliefs about the inadequacy of Uniformitarian assumptions had been made even more cogent as a result of the second law of thermodynamics. He now thought Fourier's theory of the conduction of heat to be "a beautiful working out of a particular case belonging to the general doctrine of the 'Dissipation of Energy.'" Thomson's earlier beliefs were now reinforced by the energy dissipation conception. He reasoned that geological actions, being ultimately mechanical and due, in cases like volcanism, to internal gradients in the heat of the earth, must have gradually decreased in intensity over time as energy was "dissipated" (or, as he later put it, as "potential energy is exhausted"). Even if the earth as a whole has not cooled appreciably since its formation, it must still follow that volcanic action must have been more intense in the past. For it is a particular case of the conversion of heat into mechanical effect, and the inevitable equalizing of temperature throughout the substance of the earth must ultimately lead to a state of quiescence. By 1852 Thomson also thought that Fourier's laws require both the earth and the sun to have cooled substantially over time (although he had not provided a detailed argument for this latter assertion). And however that may be, he thought that the second law of thermodynamics requires volcanic action to have been much more intense in the past than at present. (If, however, the sun has not cooled appreciably, then atmospheric phenomena on earth—though not necessarily geological—might not have altered radically over time.)

By 1862 Thomson had provided detailed support for the contention that the sun has cooled. It had previously been held that the sun, although an incandescent mass radiating heat, might have remained at about the same temperature, its heat replenished either by the influx of meteors or by the effects of shrinking under the influence of gravity, or by both factors. Thomson discounted these contentions by making numerical estimates. In the first case, he argued, the mass increase attendant on the meteoric influx would have affected planetary motion. In the second case, even if heat is generated by shrinkage—given reasonable estimates of the specific heat of the sun's mass obtained from "Stokes's principles of solar and stellar chemistry" (spectroscopic theory)—the correlation is very poor between the actual amount of heat radiated and the amount that would be provided by gravitational collapse. It is, therefore, most likely, argued Thomson, that the sun has cooled considerably and that it is an incandescent liquid mass receiving no heat from without. On that basis, Thomson further calculated, given his estimate of the solar specific heat and the present rate of radiation, that the sun probably has "not illuminated the earth for 100,000,000, and almost [certainly for not more than] 500,000,000 years."

Thomson's deduction of a maximum limit for the age of the sun was in direct conflict with those geological Uniformitarians who assumed that geological time cannot be given absolute limitations. Thomson soon presented a second paper supporting his earlier belief that the earth also must have been much hotter in the past. He showed that Fourier's laws of the transfer of heat require that, given the present rate of decrease of the heat of the earth with depth, the earth must have solidified from its primordial molten state not less than 20,000,000 and not more than 400,000,000 years ago. These limits were rigorous deductions from Fourier's laws applied to the case of a molten sphere cooling through emission of radiant heat.

They include a probable estimate of the magnitude of the effect due to the formation of the earth's crust; and they hold good provided that the earth has no sources of energy beyond its own central heat.

Thomson's original intention in writing the 1862 papers had been to attack Lyell and the extreme Uniformitarian approach to geology. The Uniformitarians, he felt, looked upon the sun "as Fontenelle's roses looked upon their gardener. 'Our gardener,' say they, 'must be a very old man; within the memory of roses he is the same as he has always been; it is impossible that he can ever be other than he is.' " Lyell had asserted that an absolute geochronology is not useful and most likely not possible. By 1865, however, British geologists were uncertain that Lyell had been correct on this point, and there was disagreement over whether the history of the earth could be absolutely dated. Some believed that it could be grouped in distinct sequences (Pre-Cambrian, Cambrian, etc.) with arbitrary time spans. Thomson unwittingly entered the midst of the geochronology controversy with his insistence that absolute times can, and indeed must, be assigned.

The idea that the central heat of the earth accounts for volcanic action and other geological processes involving thermal variations was assumed by most geologists of the time; and Thomson's criticism implied that, if that idea be accepted, it followed that for a long period the surface of the earth had been the scene of violent and often abrupt changes. This last point was especially damaging to the Darwinians, who had assumed that evolution, being a very slow, gradual process, must occur within the context of uniform geological change. For thirty years the geological and biological community had either to ignore the findings of physics, which few could do comfortably, or else with Huxley attempt to satisfy the demands of Thomson's limitations as best they could.[12]

It was Thomson's acceptance of the dynamical theory of heat and his subsequent reformulation of the axioms of thermodynamics that had led him to several of the conclusions resulting in the geological controversy. The effect of the dynamical theory was not limited to areas directly associated with thermal processes, however. In accepting the conception that sensible heat is particulate *vis viva* and that latent heat is the stored effect of molecular configuration, Thomson, for the first time in his career, deliberately did employ unobservable entities and make use of physical hypotheses. It must be recognized that Thomson's earlier exclusion of unobservables had been dependent upon his inability to attribute truly material properties to such entities. In contrast, the dynamical theory of heat did not require the acceptance of any particular conception of the ultimate nature of material particles. It required only that these particles exist and exhibit the properties of mass, motion, and the power to exert forces (although this latter aspect presents several difficulties). The idea that heat is a mode of particulate motion opened to Thomson a new approach to all physical theory, therefore. He wrote in 1872 of his thoughts before he had accepted the dynamical theory

> . . . [before 1847] I did not . . . know that motion is the very essence of what has hitherto been called matter. At the 1847 meeting of the British Association in Oxford, I learned from Joule the dynamical theory of heat, and was forced to abandon at once many, and gradually from year to year all other, statical preconceptions regarding the ultimate causes of apparently statical phenomena.

In 1855 Thomson wrote John Tyndall a letter in which he referred to the "mechanical qualities" of the medium that pervades all space. He now believed the ultimate explanation of electromagnetic phenomena lay in the structure of that medium, conceived dynamically. On 10 May 1856 Thomson submitted to the Royal Society a paper that employed the dynamical properties of molecular entities to explain the Faraday effect. By then he was willing to employ microstructural entities which possess the requisite material properties, and he argued that, from any galvanic current, there extends a moving spiral that coils about the line of magnetic force passing through the center of the axis of the current. Indeed, he intimated that the current itself consists of the trapping of a segment of this spiral in ponderable matter. Light waves are propagated by transverse vibrations of the particles of the moving spirals, and the plane of polarization of the waves will be rotated in a sense dependent upon the motion of the spiral, which, in turn, depends upon the direction of the magnetic force.[13] (See Fig. 1.)

Thomson believed that this representation afforded the ultimate representation of all electromagnetic effects. Magnetic forces were to be due to the screw motions of the spiraling helices which, when fixed in matter, become currents, and electrostatic forces to their compressions:

> We now look on space as full. We know that light is propagated like sound through pressure and mo-

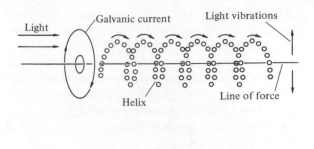

FIGURE 1

tion. . . . If electric force depends on a residual surface action, a resultant of an inner-tension, experienced by the insulating medium, we can conceive that electricity itself is to be understood as not an accident, but an essence of matter. Whatever electricity is, it seems quite certain that electricity in motion IS heat; and that a certain alignment of axes of revolution in this motion is magnetism. . . .[14]

It was this vision of Thomson's that Maxwell seized upon between 1857 and 1862 in his search for a new approach to electromagnetic theory.

Despite his influence upon Maxwell, Thomson was highly skeptical of Maxwell's approach to electromagnetic theory. The reasons for that skepticism lay in Thomson's developing beliefs regarding the nature of the hypotheses to be used in physical explanations. Although the dynamical theory of heat had opened Thomson's mind to the role of unobservable entities in theory, he still had very definite opinions on the nature of the admissible entities. "I have been led," he wrote in 1858 in an unpublished note,[15] ". . . to endeavour to explain some of the known properties of sensible matter by investigating the motion of [a fluid filling the interstices between detached solid particles] on strict dynamical principles." The sole attributes of the space-filling fluid are extension, incompressibility, and inertia; these, together with the laws of mechanics, constitute the "dynamical principles" to be used as the basis of physical theory. Evident in this is a clear reflection of Thomson's early revulsion from imponderable fluids and his strong conviction that it is in extended matter and inertial motion that the ultimate explanation of all physical processes is to be sought.

Yet one phenomenon above all stands in the path of any general theory of the type he desired, and that is elasticity. If nothing is to be admitted beyond matter and motion, then elastic reaction to compression and distortion must be explicable without recourse to "force" in the Newtonian sense. In 1858 Thomson had no theory that could explain elasticity solely on the grounds of extension and inertia. What put him on the track of a solution was Tait's 1867 translation of Helmholtz' 1858 paper on vortex motion in inviscid, incompressible fluids: such fluids are analyzable without recourse to any principles beyond inertia and extension. In his work, Helmholtz, with whom Thomson maintained a close personal friendship, had shown that linear fluid vortices, defined as lines drawn in the fluid along which the angular momentum of differential fluid elements is constant, influence one another's motions through the instantaneously propagated pressures that their existence produces in the fluid as a whole. The effects are instantaneous because the fluid is incompressible. Closed lines of vortex motion exhibit striking patterns: two such figures appear to repel or attract one another in a complex manner dependent upon their mutual orientation and the angular momenta of their constituent elements. These effects are the results solely of pressures produced in the medium.

In 1867 Thomson opened a paper entitled "On Vortex Motion" as follows: "The mathematical work of the present paper has been performed to illustrate the hypothesis that space is continuously occupied by an incompressible frictionless fluid acted on by no force, and that material phenomena of every kind depend solely on motions created in the liquid."[16] In subsequent papers Thomson attempted to demonstrate that closed vortex tubes (tori whose surfaces are formed of closed, linear vortex filaments) behave toward one another much as the material particles that constitute bodies are supposed to act: the tubes "repel" one another, and, under certain conditions, they "attract" — actions that are the results, not of "force," but of material motions alone. Thomson ultimately had to admit that his program could not be expanded to include electromagnetism or the electromagnetic theory of light, gravitation, and chemical phenomena; but throughout the period 1860–1880 he was imbued with the conception of "vortex atoms" — that is, with the idea that all material particles are actually vortex tubes in an all-encompassing medium. Although their initial creation is inexplicable mechanically, he believed that their actions provide the most fruitful basis for theoretical speculation. Helmholtz had shown that vortices, once established by some unknown means in an inviscid medium, have unalterable qualities that can neither be generated nor destroyed by mechanical processes, and so are eternal. Among these qualities, as noted

above, is a pseudoelasticity by which the vortices tend to avoid one another in an apparently elastic manner. Thomson saw in this the possibility of identifying the elastic atoms of kinetic theory with perpetually circulating vortices.

It was the strength of this conviction that accounts for his cold reaction to Maxwell's work. Maxwell, in 1861–1862, and again in 1864, had perforce to employ an unreduced "elasticity," a resistance to distortion of form, in his equations for the dynamical processes of the medium. Further, in their 1864 form the ethereal processes are difficult to visualize—they are dynamical, employing as primordial concepts material substance, momentum, and energy—but the structure of the medium is not necessarily supposed to be continuous, nor is it specified. Thomson regarded elasticity as a property that must be reduced completely to the effects of material motion. By 1867 he was greatly excited by the possibilities of his fluid medium, and he regarded Maxwell's system as at best a way station on the road to a more adequate representation. He could not accept a primordial elasticity. (For that matter, not many of Maxwell's British successors could accept it, and Maxwell himself was troubled by the question.) Also Thomson was not attracted to any dynamical theory that could not be fitted into the framework of a continuous, readily visualized medium. Although these hopes kept him from accepting Maxwell's scheme, and gradually opened a gap between him and the new generation of British "electricians" of the late 1870's and early 1880's, still his conceptions were generally regarded as the best chance for a truly dynamical theory. And Maxwell himself, despite Thomson's disagreement with his theory, was impressed by this vision. He saw in it at least an attempt to achieve ultimate mechanical simplicity; he, too, believed in this goal, having strayed only so far as he felt necessary in his approach to electromagnetism. Maxwell wrote of Thomson's vortices as follows:

. . . the greatest recommendation of this theory, from a philosophical point of view, is that its success in explaining phenomena does not depend on the ingenuity with which its contrivers "save appearances" by introducing first one hypothetical force and then another. When the vortex atom is once set in motion, all its properties are absolutely fixed and determined by the laws of motion of the primitive fluid, which are fully expressed in the fundamental equations. The disciple of Lucretius may cut and carve his solid atoms in the hope of getting them to combine into worlds; the follower of Boscovich may imagine new laws of force to meet the requirements of each new phenomenon; but he who dares to plant his feet in the path opened by Helmholtz and Thomson has no such resources. His primitive fluid has no other properties than inertia, invariable density, and perfect mobility, and the method by which the motion of this fluid is to be traced is pure mathematical analysis.[17]

Thomson's concern with the dynamical foundations of physical science, and his insistence that material substance be clearly conceived, are strikingly evident in the *Treatise on Natural Philosophy*, which he wrote with Peter Guthrie Tait in the early 1860's. "Thomson and Tait," as the work is generally known, and Maxwell's later *Treatise on Electricity and Magnetism* were the most influential British physical texts of the last half of the nineteenth century. Originally Thomson had envisioned a multivolume series giving a complete representation of all physical theory, including material processes, heat, light, and electricity and magnetism. He and Tait produced only the first two volumes, however—on kinematics and dynamics. The unfinished character of the work is evident in its continual references to future portions—as, for example, to a planned section on the properties of matter. Thomson and Tait presented in full the kinematics of point particles and the dynamics of motion under force; they placed heavy emphasis upon the dynamics of material media; and they made detailed use both of a new formulation of Lagrangean mechanics and the conservation of energy. The *Treatise on Natural Philosophy* introduced a new generation of British and American physical scientists to the details and concepts of mechanics.

In his attempt to achieve an alternative to Maxwell's theory of light, Thomson could find no clear help in his vortices, and in 1888 he began to look into the reasons for the failure of the elastic-solid theory of the luminiferous ether. He had particularly in view George Green's 1837 medium. Green had been obliged to assume that the ether is incompressible, in order to avoid instability and to remove longitudinal waves. On these grounds, however, he was unable to obtain Fresnel's tangent-law for the reflection and refraction of light for waves polarized normally to the plane of incidence. Encouraged by his vortex theory of the medium, Thomson at first imagined an inviscid fluid permeating the pores of an incompressible, spongelike solid, but he soon found that this structure only augmented the older difficulties. He therefore began to consider whether Green's comments on stability might not be open to doubt. As Thomson considered the problem, it occurred to him that the kind of instability envisaged by Green, that of a spontaneous shrinkage of finite ether volumes, would not occur "provided we either suppose the medium to extend all through boundless space, or give it a fixed containing vessel as its boundary."

By supposing the ether to have no resistance to compression by volume, Thomson was able to show that the hypothesis adopted makes it possible to obtain all of Fresnel's laws, while eliminating the longitudinal wave and avoiding instability. The work had an immediate and widespread impact on the Maxwellian community. Within a month Richard Tetley Glazebrook had written a paper successfully applying the new conception to double refraction, dispersion, and metallic reflection. In the United States, Willard Gibbs compared the new theory to the electrical theory:

> It is evident that the electrical theory of light has a serious rival, in a sense in which, perhaps, one did not exist before the publication of William Thomson's paper in November last. Nevertheless, neither surprise at the results which have been achieved, nor admiration for that happy audacity of genius, which seeking the solution of the problem precisely where no one else would have ventured to look for it, has turned half a century of defeat into victory, should blind us to the actual state of the question.
>
> It may still be said for the electrical theory, that it is not obliged to invent hypotheses, but only to apply the laws furnished by the science of electricity, and that it is difficult to account for the coincidence between the electrical and optical properties of media, unless we regard the motions of light as electrical. . . .[18]

Despite Thomson's deep theoretical concerns, he was always strongly interested in physical instrumentation. He felt that existing instruments were inadequate for precisely determining important physical constants. Instrumentation became even more important as electrical phenomena began to be employed in Britain's increasingly complex industrial economy, and Thomson was involved in the design and implementation of many new devices.

His interest and reputation brought him to the attention of a consortium of British industrialists who, in the mid-1850's, proposed to lay a submarine telegraph cable between Ireland and Newfoundland. Telegraphy by then was a well-developed and extremely profitable business, and the idea of laying such a cable was not new. The undertaking provides perhaps the first instance of a complex interaction between large-scale industrial enterprise and theoretical electricity. Thomson was brought in early in the project as a member of the board of directors, and he played a central role.

The directors had entrusted the technical details of the project to an industrial electrician, E. O. W. Whitehouse; and the many difficulties that plagued it from the outset resulted from Whitehouse's insistence on employing his own system of electrical signaling, despite theoretical objections from Thomson. Thomson had developed a very sensitive apparatus, the mirror-galvanometer, to detect the minuscule currents transmitted through miles of cable, but Whitehouse refused to use it. The Whitehouse-Thomson controversy stemmed primarily from Whitehouse's jealousy of Thomson's reputation. Thomson had asserted that the length of cable would, by a process of statical charging of its insulation, substantially reduce the rate at which signals could be sent unless small voltages were used, so small that only his galvanometer could detect the currents.

The first attempt to lay the cable, in 1857, ended when it snapped and was lost. The second attempt, a year later, was successful, but the large voltages required by the Whitehouse method reduced the ability of the cable to transmit signals rapidly, just as Thomson had predicted. Whitehouse privately recognized the inadequacy of his own instruments and surreptitiously substituted Thomson's galvanometer while claiming success for his own methods. This deception was soon discovered, and the ensuing controversy between Whitehouse, the board of directors, and Thomson combined theoretical science, professional vanity, and financial ignominy. A third cable was laid in 1865, and, with the use of Thomson's instruments, it proved capable of rapid, sustained transmission. Thomson's role as the man who saved a substantial investment made him a hero to the British financial community and to the Victorian public in general; indeed, he was knighted for it. It also was the foundation for a large personal fortune.

As the Atlantic cable affair demonstrates, Thomson was deeply involved in applying instrumentation designed for sensitive measurements to industrial concerns. His involvement in industry did not stem from a great desire to further the application of science to technology, although that motive was certainly there among others. Rather it was a consequence of his interest in instrumentation itself. The two central concerns of his life were the application of the ideas of mechanics to physics and the development of sensitive measuring devices. By the time of his death, Thomson, then Baron Kelvin of

Largs, while perhaps behind the times in his adherence to dynamical modes of thought, was generally looked upon as the founder of British physics. Together with Helmholtz in Germany, he had been the foremost figure in transforming—indeed, in creating—the science of physics as it was known in 1900.

NOTES

1. S. P. Thompson, *The Life of William Thomson*, I.
2. W. Thomson, "On the Uniform Motion of Heat in Homogeneous Solid Bodies, and its Connexion With the Mathematical Theory of Electricity," in *Cambridge Mathematical Journal*, 3 (1843), 71–84.
3. See S. P. Thompson, *op. cit.*, I.
4. W. Thomson, "Demonstration of a Fundamental Proposition in the Mechanical Theory of Electricity," in *Reprint of Papers on Electrostatics and Magnetism*, pp. 100–103.
5. W. Thomson, "On the Mathematical Theory of Electricity in Equilibrium," *op. cit.*, 15–37.
6. W. Thomson, "On a Mechanical Representation of Electric, Magnetic, and Galvanic Forces," in *Mathematical and Physical Papers*, I (Cambridge, 1911), 76–80.
7. W. Thomson, "On an Absolute Thermometric Scale, Founded on Carnot's Theory of the Motive Power of Heat, and Calculated From the Results of Regnault's Experiments on the Pressure and Latent Heat of Steam," *ibid.*, I, 100–106.
8. W. Thomson, "An Account of Carnot's Theory of the Motive Power of Heat, With Numerical Results Deduced From Regnault's Experiments on Steam," in *Transactions of the Royal Society of Edinburgh*, 16 (1849), 541–574.
9. James Thomson, "Theoretical Considerations on the Effect of Pressure in Lowering the Freezing Point of Water," in *Cambridge and Dublin Mathematical Journal*, 5 (1850), 248–255.
10. W. Thomson, "On a Remarkable Property of Steam Connected With the Theory of the Steam-Engine," in *Philosophical Magazine*, 27 (1850), 386–389.
11. W. Thomson, "On the Dynamical Theory of Heat; With Numerical Results Deduced From Mr. Joule's 'Equivalent of a Thermal Unit' and M. Regnault's 'Observations on Steam,'" in *Transactions of the Royal Society of Edinburgh*, 20 (1853), 261–288.
12. On the problems see P. Lawrence, "The Central Heat of the Earth," Ph.D. dissertation, Harvard University, 1973.
13. W. Thomson, "Dynamical Illustrations of the Magnetic and Helicoidal Rotatory Effects of Transparent Bodies on Polarized Light," in *Proceedings of the Royal Society*, 7 (1856), 150–158.
14. W. Thomson, Royal Institution Friday Evening Lecture, in *Reprint of Papers on Electrostatics and Magnetism*, pp. 208–226.
15. Cambridge University Library, MS Add. 7342, box I, notebook IV, pp. I–II. Quoted in Ole Kundsen, "From Lord Kelvin's Notebook: Ether Speculations," in *Centaurus*, 16 (1966), 41–53.
16. W. Thomson, "On Vortex Motion," in *Philosophical Transactions of the Royal Society of London*, 25, pt. 1 (1868), 217–260.
17. J. C. Maxwell, *Scientific Papers of James Clerk Maxwell* (New York, 1952), 445–484; from "Atomism," in *Encyclopaedia Britannica*, 9th ed., II (1875).
18. J. Willard Gibbs, "A Comparison of the Electric Theory of Light and Sir William Thomson's Theory of a Quasi-Labile Ether," in *American Journal of Science*, 37 (1889), 467–475.

BIBLIOGRAPHY

All of Thomson's papers are collected in two sets, *Reprint of Papers on Electrostatics and Magnetism* (London, 1872); and *Mathematical and Physical Papers*, 6 vols. (Cambridge, 1911). Occasional papers are not reprinted in the former collection, but in their absence a reference to their location in the journals is given. The *Treatise on Natural Philosophy*, 2 vols. (Oxford, 1867), written with P. G. Tait, went through numerous editions.

The only full-scale biography is S. P. Thompson, *The Life of William Thomson, Baron Kelvin of Largs*, 2 vols. (London, 1901). Although uncritical, it contains a vast selection from Thomson's correspondence and includes a complete bibliography of Thomson's papers. Thomson's "green notebooks," kept throughout his life, are unpublished but are available at the University Library, Cambridge. Brief accounts of Thomson's life and work include David Murray, *Lord Kelvin as Professor in the Old College of Glasgow* (Glasgow, 1924); Alexander Russell, *Lord Kelvin, His Life and Work* (London–Edinburgh–New York, 1939); and A. P. Young, *Lord Kelvin, Physicist, Mathematician, Engineer* (London, 1948).

See also Herbert Norton Casson, "Kelvin, His Amazing Life and Worldwide Influence," in *Efficiency Magazine* (1930); John Ferguson, "Lord Kelvin: a Recollection and an Impression," in *Glasgow University Magazine*, **20**, no. 9 (1908); Kelvin Centenary Oration and Addresses Commemorative (London, 1924); Agnes Gardner King, *Kelvin the Man. A Biographical Sketch by His Niece* (London, 1925); Émile Picard, "Notice historique sur la vie et l'oeuvre de Lord Kelvin," in *Annuaire de l'Académie des sciences de Paris* (1920); Robert H. Silliman, "William Thomson: Smoke Rings and Nineteenth-Century Atomism," in *Isis*, **54** (1963), 461–474; E. C. Watson, "College Life at Cambridge in the Days of Stokes, Cayley, Adams, and Kelvin," in *Scripta mathematica*, **6** (1939), 101–106.

JED Z. BUCHWALD

THORPE, JOCELYN FIELD (*b*. London, England, 1 December 1872; *d*. London, 10 June 1940), *chemistry*.

After studying engineering and chemistry at King's College and the Royal College of Science, Thorpe entered the University of Heidelberg in 1892; three years later he received a doctorate in chemistry. He joined the research group of William Henry Perkin, Jr., at the University of Manchester, where he became lecturer in organic chemistry. In 1908 he was elected to the Royal Society and was its Sorby Research Fellow from 1909 to 1913. Subsequently he was appointed to the chair of organic chemistry at the Imperial College of Science and Technology in London, a post he held until his retirement in 1938. He served on many government and industrial committees and was president of the Chemical Society from 1928 to 1931 and of the Institute of Chemistry from 1933 to 1936. He was knighted in 1939.

Thorpe's first researches in organic chemistry dealt with the synthesis of polybasic acids. He contributed an important method of preparation for dibasic acids, when he found that sodiocyanoacetic ester condenses with the cyanohydrins of aldehydes and ketones to form products that hydrolyze into substituted succinic acids. With Perkin, Thorpe investigated the structure of camphor and related compounds. They synthesized two oxidation products of camphor, camphoronic acid (1897) and camphoric acid (1903), and confirmed the formulas of Bredt for camphor and these acid derivatives. They also confirmed Baeyer's structures for carone and the caronic acids by synthesizing them in 1899.

Thorpe's most valuable contribution to chemistry was his study of the formation and reactions of imino compounds, resulting from his 1904 discovery of the condensation reaction of sodiocyanoacetic ester with the cyano group. He also found imino compounds to be the product of the condensation of nitriles with each other; dinitriles condense intramolecularly to form many new imino compounds.

In 1911 Thorpe established the existence of keto-enol tautomerism between an open chain compound and its cyclic isomer, while in 1919 he and C. K. Ingold proved the presence of "intraannular tautomerism" in bridged rings:

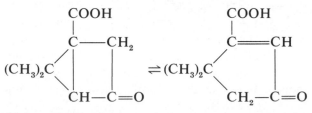

With Ingold, Thorpe collaborated from 1914 to 1928 on a study of valency and chemical bonding; they were the first to propose that the valency angles of the carbon atom may depart from the regular tetrahedral angles in the formation of highly substituted organic compounds.

BIBLIOGRAPHY

I. ORIGINAL WORKS. Thorpe wrote two books on dyes and colors: *The Synthetic Dyestuffs and the Inter-*

THORPE

mediate Products From Which They Are Derived (London, 1905), written with John C. Cain; and *Synthetic Colouring Matters: Vat Colours* (London, 1923), written with Christopher K. Ingold. With Martha A. Whiteley, Thorpe wrote *A Student's Manual of Organic Chemical Analysis* (London, 1925) and also edited the supplementary vols. (1934–1936) and the 4th ed. (1937) of T. E. Thorpe's *Dictionary of Applied Chemistry*.

Thorpe's important papers include "Synthesis of *i*-Camphoronic Acid," in *Journal of the Chemical Society*, **71** (1897), 1169–1194, written with W. H. Perkin, Jr.; "The Formation and Reactions of Imino Compounds," in three parts, *ibid.*, **85** (1904), 1726–1761, written with H. Baron and F. Remfry; **89** (1906), 1906–1935, written with E. Atkinson; **93** (1908), 165–187, written with C. Moore; "The Formation and Stability of Spiro Compounds," *ibid.*, **115** (1919), 320–383, written with C. K. Ingold; "Ring-Chain Tautomerism," *ibid.*, **121** (1922), 1765–1789, written with C. K. Ingold and E. Perren; "The Chemistry of Polycyclic Structures in Relation to Their Homocyclic Unsaturated Isomerides," *ibid.* (1922), 128–159, written with C. K. Ingold and E. Farmer; and "The Hypothesis of Valency Deflection," *ibid.* (1928), 1318–1321, written with C. K. Ingold.

II. SECONDARY LITERATURE. On Thorpe's life and work, with many references to his papers, see G. A. R. Kon and R. P. Linstead, "Sir Jocelyn Field Thorpe," in *Journal of the Chemical Society* (1941), 444–464, repr. in Alexander Findlay and William Hobson Mills, eds., *British Chemists* (London, 1947), 369–401.

ALBERT B. COSTA

THORPE, THOMAS EDWARD (*b.* Barnes Green, Harpurhey, near Manchester, England, 8 December 1845; *d.* Salcombe, England, 23 February 1925), *chemistry, history of science.*

Thorpe was the son of George Thorpe, a cotton merchant, and Mary Wilde. He received his early education in Manchester and in 1863 entered Owens College, Manchester, as a chemistry student under Roscoe's guidance. Much of his four years at Owens College was spent as Roscoe's private assistant, and he participated in the classical work on vanadium (which resulted in determining its true atomic weight) and on the percentage of carbon dioxide in the atmosphere.

After graduation Thorpe worked with Bunsen at the University of Heidelberg, where he received his doctorate. He then went to Bonn, where he studied ethylbenzoic acid with Kekulé. In 1870 he became professor of chemistry at the Andersonian College, Glasgow. Four years later he was appointed professor of chemistry at the new Yorkshire College of Science at Leeds. He resigned this post in 1885 in order to become Edward Frank-

land's successor at the Royal College of Science in London, which later became the Imperial College of Science and Technology. Between 1894 and 1909 he was director of the government laboratories, responsible for design and equipment. He returned to Imperial College in 1909 but resigned three years later.

Best known for his numerous textbooks and histories of chemistry, Thorpe was also an important figure in inorganic chemical research. His doctoral dissertation on the oxychlorides of chromium and sulfur led to a study of similar phosphorus compounds, resulting in the discovery of thiophosphoryl chloride ($PSCl_3$), phosphoryl fluoride (POF_3), and phosphorus pentafluoride (PF_5). This last discovery was of particular importance, since it necessitated postulating a valence of five for phosphorus. His atomic weight determinations of silicon and gold were the most accurate at the time for those elements. He also determined the weights of titanium, strontium, and radium. He carried out extensive studies of the critical temperatures, viscosities, and molecular volumes of liquids. His investigation of the vapor density of hydrofluoric acid revealed that at lower temperatures it is polymerized.

BIBLIOGRAPHY

I. ORIGINAL WORKS. Thorpe is most remembered for the large number of popular textbooks he wrote. Most of the following went through several editions: *A Dictionary of Applied Chemistry*, 3 vols. (London, 1893); the 3rd ed. (1921–1927), which he was preparing until a few days before his death, contained 7 vols. His other chemistry books were *A Manual of Inorganic Chemistry*, 2 vols. (London, 1898); *Qualitative Chemical Analysis and Laboratory Practice*, 8th ed. (London, 1894), written with M. M. Pattison Muir; *Coal, Its History and Uses* (London, 1879); and *A Series of Chemical Problems With Key* (London, 1907), written with W. Tate.

Thorpe's interest in the history of chemistry led to two books: *Essays in Historical Chemistry* (London, 1894, 1923) and *History of Chemistry* (London, 1909–1910, 1924). In addition he published the following short biographical sketches: *Humphry Davy, Poet and Philosopher* (London, 1901); *Joseph Priestley* (London, 1906); and *The Right Honorable Sir Henry Enfield Roscoe* (London, 1916). After his retirement he enjoyed yachting and wrote two books about his experiences: *The Seine From Havre to Paris* (London, 1913) and *A Yachtsman's Guide to the Dutch Waterways* (London, 1915). His published papers are listed in Poggendorff, III, 1345; IV, 1499; V, 1255.

II. SECONDARY LITERATURE. A detailed obituary notice is P. P. Bedson, "Sir Edward Thorpe," in *Journal*

389

of the Chemical Society, (1926), 1031–1050. See also the *Dictionary of National Biography 1922–1930*, pp. 842–843.

SHELDON J. KOPPERL

THOUIN, ANDRÉ (*b*. Paris, France, 10 February 1747; *d*. Paris, 27 October 1824), *botany*.

Thouin spent his entire life at the Jardin des Plantes in Paris. At age seventeen he succeeded his father as head gardener and became responsible for his family's financial support. He remained unmarried in order to care for his mother, sisters, and brothers, who lived with him in a small apartment in the annex of the old greenhouses. A student of Bernard de Jussieu and Buffon, Thouin assisted the latter in reorganizing the Jardin des Plantes and enriched its greenhouses and the collections of the École de Botanique through many exchanges of plants with foreign botanists. Thouin was a good conversationalist, and his manner was dignified and gentle. His friends included Malesherbes, who filled his pockets with plants and tree branches, and Rousseau, whose misanthropy gave way to openness in Thouin's company. Thouin also maintained contacts with a number of other naturalists, including Bernardin de Saint-Pierre, Bosc, Desfontaines, and Faujas de Saint-Fond.

An unassuming person who detested pomp, Thouin refused to wear the insignia of the Legion of Honor, which he thought should be reserved for soldiers, and donned the costume of the Institut de France only when obliged to do so. Always generous, he made an interest-free loan of 30,000 francs to a friend who was in difficulties. The money came from a sum left to Thouin by someone who was interested in agriculture and had been impressed by his outstanding integrity.

In collaboration with A. P. de Candolle, in 1806 Thouin observed the influence of light on a number of plants. They used six Argand lamps, believing that they thereby attained five-sixths the intensity of sunlight. Thouin made grafts and noted the influence of the stock on certain characteristics of the graft. He was also an early proponent of the teaching of agriculture and horticulture.

In 1802, with Desfontaines, Thouin made an inventory of the convents in the Paris region, as well as of the property of émigrés and of those who had been guillotined. The Convention authorized him to dispose of the fruit trees of the Carthusian convent in Paris; this was the origin of the nursery of the Muséum d'Histoire Naturelle. Appointed an army commissioner, Thouin confiscated rich collections in the Low Countries in 1794–1795 and others in Italy two years later. Surviving documents unfailingly show that he carried out his assignments with great honesty. He already had a considerable reputation at age thirty-nine, when he became a member of the Academy of Sciences.

In the last year of his life Thouin fell gravely ill. Realizing that he would soon die, he began to write up his observations and correct his manuscripts. His brother Jean (1756–1827) succeeded him as head gardener; and another brother, Gabriel (1747–1829), also devoted himself to horticulture. Thouin's herbarium eventually was left to the Faculty of Sciences of Montpellier.

BIBLIOGRAPHY

Works published during Thouin's lifetime are *Essai sur l'exposition et la division méthodique de l'économie rurale* (Paris, 1805); *Description de l'École d'agriculture pratique de Muséum d'histoire naturelle* (n.p., n.d. [Paris, 1814]); and *Monographie des greffes* ([Paris], 1821 [?]), a technical description of the methods for propagating plants. See also Royal Society *Catalogue of Scientific Papers,* V, 983–984, which lists 32 works.

His posthumously published writings include *Cours de culture et de naturalisation des végétaux* (Paris, 1827), published by his nephew, Oscar Leclerc; *Voyage dans la Belgique, la Hollande et l'Italie* (Paris, 1841), prepared from Thouin's journal by Baron Trouvé; and the supplement to François Rozier's course on agriculture.

Many of Thouin's articles appeared in *Mémoires de la Société d'agriculture; Mémoires de l'Académie des sciences; Dictionnaire d'histoire naturelle*, edited by Déterville; *Annales d'agriculture française;* and the *Annales* and *Mémoires du Muséum national d'histoire naturelle*.

P. JOVET
M. MALLET

THUE, AXEL (*b*. Tönsberg, Norway, 19 February 1863; *d*. Oslo, Norway, 7 March 1922), *mathematics*.

Thue enrolled at Oslo University in 1883 and became a candidate for the doctorate in 1889. From 1891 to 1894 he held a university scholarship in mathematics, and he was a professor of applied mathematics at Oslo from 1903 to 1922.

During 1890–1891 Thue studied at Leipzig under Sophus Lie, but his works do not reveal Lie's influence, probably because of Thue's inability to follow anyone else's line of thought. In 1909 he published his famous article "Über Annäherungswerte algebraischer Zahlen" in Crelle's *Journal*. In 1920 C. L. Siegel found a more precise expression for the approximation of algebraic numbers and K. F. Roth discovered the best possible equation in 1958. Nevertheless, Thue was able to draw a far-reaching conclusion in number theory. He showed that an equation like $y^3 - 2x^3 = 1$ cannot possibly be satisfied by an indefinite number of pairs of numbers x, y, when x and y must be a whole number. Generally formulated, the left side of the equation can be an irreducible homogeneous polynomial in x and y of a degree higher than 2, and the right side can be any whole number. Thue's theorem was characterized by Edmund Landau (1922) as "the most important discovery in elementary number theory that I know."

During 1906–1912 Thue published many articles on series, in one of which he said: "For the development of the logical sciences it will be important to find wide fields for the speculative treatment of difficult problems, without regard to eventual applications." His "Über die gegenseitige Lage gleicher Teile gewisser Zeichenreihen" was characterized as a basic work by G. A. Hedlund (1967).

Thue's most important work in applied mathematics was "De virtuelle hastigheters princip" ("The Principle of Virtual Velocity"), an original statement that has no parallel in the literature. One of the paradoxes Thue liked to state was "The further removed from usefulness or practical application, the more important."

BIBLIOGRAPHY

I. ORIGINAL WORKS. A list of 47 articles (1884–1920) is in *Norsk matematisk tidsskrift*, **4** (1922), 46–49. They include "Über Annäherungswerte algebraischer Zahlen," in *Journal für die reine und angewandte Mathematik*, **135** (1909), 284–305; "Eine Eigenschaft der Zahlen der Fermatschen Gleichung," in *Videnskabsselskabets skrifter* (Oslo) (1911), 1–21; and "De virtuelle hastigheters princip," in *Aars Voss'skoles festskrift* (Oslo, 1913), 194–213. *Selected Mathematical Papers of Axel Thue* (Oslo,   ), with an introduction by Carl Ludwig Siegel, is in press.

II. SECONDARY LITERATURE. There are biographies by C. Størmer, V. Bjerknes, and others in *Norsk matematisk tidsskrift*, **4** (1922), 33–46, with portrait. Viggo Brun and Trygve Nagell published a list of his posthumous works in *Videnskabsselskabets skrifter* (Oslo) (1923), 1–15. Also see G. A. Hedlund, "Remarks on the Work of Axel Thue on Sequences," in *Nordisk matematisk tidsskrift* (1967), 148–150.

VIGGO BRUN

THUNBERG, CARL PETER (*b.* Jönköping, Sweden, 11 November 1743; *d.* Tunaberg, near Uppsala, Sweden, 8 August 1828), *botany*.

After studying at Jönköping, Thunberg entered Uppsala University in 1761, where he soon came under the influence of Linnaeus. His dissertation for the medical degree, *De ischiade* (1770), was not botanical and Linnaeus did not preside over the disputation; but Thunberg's passion was, nevertheless, natural history and especially botany, and Linnaeus soon considered him a protégé. In order to complete his medical education, Thunberg went to Paris immediately after the disputation, the trip being made possible by a scholarship. Before reaching France he stayed for a while in Holland, where a letter of recommendation from Linnaeus opened the house of Jan and Nikolaus Laurens Burman to him; both were good botanists, and the father was an old friend of Linnaeus.

In Paris, Thunberg received an extraordinary offer: an invitation to follow a Dutch merchant ship to Japan, which was closed to all European nations except Holland. The Burmans had good connections with the rich bourgeoisie of Holland, among whom the enthusiasm for gardening was very great. Thunberg was expected to collect as many Japanese garden plants as possible for his employers. He was, of course, free to make his own purely botanical collections as well, a situation that pleased Linnaeus, with whom Thunberg maintained close correspondence during the voyage. In order to enter Japan, he had to behave in every respect like a good Dutchman. He learned Dutch by stopping off in South Africa, in Cape Colony, where he remained from April 1772 to March 1775, thus fortunately combining language studies with botanical excursions.

There had been very little true botanical investigation of the Cape Colony; during his stay Thunberg made three voyages into the interior, collecting and describing more than three thousand plants, of which about one thousand were new to science. On two trips he was accompanied by the gardener and plant collector Francis Masson, who had been sent to the Cape Colony by Kew Gardens in London. At this time Thunberg began describing species and revising genera from his collections, publishing his papers in the transactions of several Swedish and foreign academies.

In March 1775 Thunberg sailed on a Dutch ship to Batavia. From Java he continued on another Dutch vessel to the island of Deshima in Nagasaki harbor, the only Japanese port open to European trade. For a while Thunberg was able to make short excursions near the town, but bureaucratic difficulties soon curtailed even these few opportunities to collect Japanese plants. A journey to Tokyo with the Dutch ambassador did little to improve the situation. Thunberg nevertheless became the first Western scientist to investigate Japan botanically through the aid of the young Japanese interpreters employed by the traders. Some of them were physicians, eager to learn modern European medicine from Thunberg, who exchanged his knowledge for specimens of Japanese plants. He left the country in December 1776 with a rich collection for further analysis. On his way home he visited Java, Ceylon, and the Cape Colony. Having satisfied his Dutch employers, he went to London, its herbariums and collections being the most important at that time.

Thunberg reached Sweden in 1779 and was appointed botanical demonstrator at Uppsala University. Linnaeus had been succeeded by his son, and it soon became clear that Thunberg and young Linnaeus could not work well together. Although Thunberg was a demonstrator, Linnaeus did not allow him to enter the botanical garden. In 1784 Thunberg succeeded to the professorship of botany (in the Faculty of Medicine), a post he held until his death. He lived quietly on a little estate, Tunaberg, just outside Uppsala, traveling to his daily work in a strange, uncomfortable carriage, well-known among the students as "the rattlesnake." The major event during this long academic period was the transfer of the botanical garden from a low and often flooded region of the town to the much more suitable park of the royal castle, where it is still situated. Most of Thunberg's time as professor was occupied by writing about his extensive collections.

Thunberg's first major work after returning to Sweden was *Flora japonica* (1784), a fundamental account of the floristics and systematics of the vegetation of Japan that describes twenty-one new genera and several hundred new species. His only predecessor of any importance was Engelbert Kaempfer, who traveled in the Far East at the end of the seventeenth century and whose collections Thunberg studied in the British Museum during his visit to London. The vast and important material from the Cape Colony occupied Thunberg for the rest of his life. A preliminary work was *Prodromus plantarum capensium* (1794–1800), a summary of his findings. Much more detailed and important was *Flora capensis* (1807–1823), completed with the help of the German botanist J. A. Schultes. Among his many shorter works are monographs on *Protea*, *Oxalis*, *Ixia*, and *Gladiolus*.

Thunberg was exclusively a descriptive botanist who closely followed Linnaeus, using his methods and his already somewhat outmoded sexual system. He modified the latter slightly, reducing its twenty-four classes to twenty by excluding Gynandria, Monoecia, Dioecia, and Polygamia and distributing their members among the other classes. The aim of his reductions, however, seems to have been more practical than theoretical, the plants of the omitted classes often not being constant in their class characters and fitting more smoothly in other parts of the system. Although Linnaeus had been searching for a truly natural system, Thunberg seemed to have no penchant for speculation. His strong points were his keen eye in the field, his indefatigable spirit and eagerness in collecting, and his concise descriptions. Among his contemporaries he was perhaps the one who described the largest number of new plant genera and species. His aims certainly reached no further.

Thunberg's description of his great voyage, published in four parts in Swedish in 1788–1793 and soon translated into English as *Travels in Europe, Africa and Asia* (1793–1795), as well as in French and German, contains material of great ethnographical interest.

BIBLIOGRAPHY

I. ORIGINAL WORKS. T. O. B. N. Krok, *Bibliotheca botanica suecana* (Stockholm–Uppsala, 1925), 705–716, lists all Thunberg's botanical works. Letters from his many correspondents, both Swedish and foreign, are at the University Library, Uppsala, together with other MSS. His published works include *De ischiade* (Uppsala, 1770); *Flora japonica* (Leipzig, 1784); *Travels in Europe, Africa and Asia*, 4 vols. (London, 1793–1795), first published as 4 vols. (Uppsala, 1788–1793); *Prodromus plantarum capensium* (Uppsala, 1794–1800); and *Flora capensis*, 2 vols. (Uppsala, 1807–1823).

II. SECONDARY LITERATURE. See H. O. Juel, *Plantae Thunbergianae* (Uppsala, 1918), in German; and articles about Thunberg by N. Svedelius in *Isis*, **35** (1944–1945), 128–134; in S. Lindroth, ed., *Swedish Men of Science* (Stockholm, 1952), 151–159; and in *Svenska Linnésällskapets årsskrift*, **27** (1944), 29–64.

Thunberg and Cape Colony botany are treated by M.

Karsten, in *The Old Company's Garden at the Cape and Its Superintendents* (Cape Town, 1951), 132–134, *passim*; "Carl Peter Thunberg. An Early Investigator of Cape Botany," in *Journal of South African Botany*, **5** (1939), 1–27, 87–155; **12** (1946), 127–190. Thunberg and Japan are treated in C. Gaudon, *Le Japon du XVIIIe siècle vu par Ch. P. Thunberg* (Paris, 1966); and in *Forskningsmaterial rörande C. P. Thunberg* (Tokyo, 1953), in Japanese and Swedish.

See also G. Eriksson, *Botanikens historia i Sverige intill år 1800* (Uppsala, 1969), 258–260, 268–270, 321; and S. Lindroth, *Kungliga Svenska Vetenskapsakademiens historia*, II (Stockholm, 1967), 408–412 and *passim*.

THUNBERG, THORSTEN LUDVIG (*b*. Torsåker, Sweden, 30 June 1873; *d*. Lund, Sweden, 4 December 1952), *physiology*.

The son of Per Erik Thunberg, a merchant, and of Wendela Maria Elisabeth Hård, Thunberg studied medicine at the University of Uppsala from 1891 to 1900 and obtained the M.D. degree with a dissertation on epidermal sensory perception. He was demonstrator for Olof Hammarsten at the Institute of Physiological Chemistry in 1893–1894 and for Frithiof Holmgren at the Institute of Physiology at Uppsala in 1894–1896. He was reader in physiology at Uppsala in 1897–1904. Immediately after the death of Magnus Blix in 1904, Thunberg went to Lund as temporary occupant of the chair of physiology and embryology; the following year he was appointed to the chair of physiology, from which he retired in 1938.

Thunberg's first work, on sensory physiology, was published in 1893 and his last, in 1953. Thunberg extensively studied the physiology of epidermal sensations, showing, among other things, that a pinprick gives rise to two sensations of pain, the second occurring some seconds after the first. This phenomenon was interpreted much later by Zotterman, who demonstrated the existence of two groups of pain fibers, one of which transmits impulses more slowly than the other. In 1905 Thunberg wrote the chapter "Physiologie der Druck-, Temperatur- und Schmerzempfindungen" for Nagel's *Handbuch der Physiologie des Menschen*. With this work he left a field into which he had been led more by chance than by ability.

In 1903, when Thunberg began to study the elementary processes of metabolism—studies that constitute his major contributions to science—nothing was known of the oxidation processes in the tissue cells. Energy is derived in the cells by combustion (cellular respiration), whereby oxygen is consumed and carbon dioxide produced. Lavoisier had proved that respiration is chemically a combustion process in the 1770's. From then until 1875, the consumption of oxygen and the production of carbon dioxide were thought to be confined to the lungs and the blood. In that year Pflüger proclaimed: "Cells are constantly burning, although we do not see their light with our weak vision." Everyday experience shows that organic material does not burn in oxygen at body temperature, so it was assumed that oxygen was activated in some way. From about 1840 a series of oxygen activation theories appeared; but valid knowledge had to await the work of Thunberg, Otto Warburg, and Heinrich Wieland. Warburg introduced the term *Atmungsferment* and argued that this enzyme that catalyzed oxidation was an iron-pyrrole complex. His idea was based on the orthodox concept that the degradation and combustion of food to carbon dioxide and water took place through the direct attack of oxygen on the carbon atoms of the food. Thunberg and Wieland developed an entirely new conception, rivaling that of Warburg.

In 1908 Thunberg began to study the capacity of cells to burn various organic acids, including acetic, propionic, oxalic, malic, succinic, and citric. These acids were not then recognized as normal constituents of the body that played a role in intracellular metabolism; rather, they were known as products of putrefaction or fermentation. From among all the organic acids Thunberg chose precisely those that proved useful to his aims, thus revealing his unerring sense for the right path to follow.

Wieland turned to this area of investigation just when his cooperation was needed to elucidate the nature of the processes of biological oxidation. In 1912 he found that organic compounds can be oxidized through removal of hydrogen in the presence of a catalyst and that the hydrogen can be taken up by suitable acceptors, such as methylene blue. From 1910 Thunberg integrated Wieland's discoveries with his own, especially those on the biological oxidation of succinate, and initiated the concept of the specific, hydrogen-activating, chain-forming enzyme systems. When Thunberg began this work, all that was known of intracellular enzymes was merely that postmortem autolysis was catalyzed by proteolytic enzymes. Oxidases also had been found.

Thunberg saw that the oxidation of succinate was initiated by an agent in the cells that endowed a hydrogen group in the succinate with a reactivity that it had not previously possessed. The reactivity could easily be demonstrated with methylene blue, which was decolorized by hydrogen uptake. Under the influence of this agent in the cells, the succinate emerged as "hydrogen donator" and released a hydrogen group to the "hydrogen acceptor" methylene blue. The terms "donator" and "acceptor" were introduced by Thunberg and are now in general use. He called the enzymatic agent a dehydrogenase, in this case succinate dehydrogenase. The introduction of the methylene blue method in 1916 opened up a worldwide search for dehydrogenases. The chainlike degradation of the various organic molecules in the organism could now be charted.

Thunberg finally formulated the following generalization concerning the oxidative degradation of food: the degradation is accomplished by a chain of consecutive splittings of hydrogen atoms carried out by a series of dehydrogenases, each with a specific purpose.

With the discovery of a hydrogen-carrying flavoprotein, *das gelbe Atmungsferment*, Warburg in 1932 contributed substantially to Thunberg's conception of hydrogen transport from one system to another as a central mechanism in oxidative metabolism. Thunberg rightfully considered himself responsible for a revolution in the concept of the mechanism of biological oxidation.

In 1905, the year of his appointment to the chair of physiology at Lund, Thunberg recorded that nerve tissue respires, taking up oxygen and giving up carbon dioxide. It had previously been thought that nerve fibers conducted impulses like an electric cable, without measurable energy consumption. Thunberg made this discovery with his microrespirometer, an ingenious device with which he could measure oxygen consumption and carbon dioxide production in small units of tissue. Using this apparatus, he also could demonstrate that traces of certain metals, such as manganese salts, strongly catalyze tissue respiration. This field held his interest throughout his retirement.

Although a scientist first, Thunberg was not unfamiliar with the nonscientific world. As a student at Uppsala he was associated with the radical-liberal group Verdandis, headed by the physiologist Hjalmar Öhrvall. During five decades—through books, popular journals, pamphlets, and the daily press, and as an adviser to the government—he disseminated information on hygiene and medicine that in scope and quality was unparalleled in Sweden.

Thunberg's enormous capacity for work was combined with good health, and he reached the age of seventy before becoming seriously ill, with pneumonia, from which he recovered. He was fully active for more than nine years, until October 1952, when he stumbled over the doorstep of his house and broke his femur. Despite the best care, he died early in December. He had been elected a member of the Royal Swedish Academy of Sciences in 1928, and later of many foreign learned societies.

BIBLIOGRAPHY

Obituaries include Georg Kahlson, "Thorsten Thunberg," in *Acta physiologica scandinavica*, **30** (1953), supp. 111; and F. G. Young, "Prof. T. Thunberg," in *Nature* (12 Dec. 1953).

GEORG KAHLSON

THURET, GUSTAVE ADOLPHE (*b*. Paris, France, 23 May 1817; *d*. Nice, France, 19 May 1875), *botany*.

The third son of Isaac Thuret, consul general of the Netherlands in France, and Jacoba Henrietta van der Paedevoort, Thuret belonged to a French Protestant family that had emigrated to Holland following Louis XIV's revocation of the Edict of Nantes. He received a religious education and remained a strong Protestant. After being tutored in the classics, he studied law at Paris, and obtained the *licence* in 1838. During his youth he made many trips abroad, especially to England; and he spoke English fluently, having been taught it by his mother before he learned French.

Named attaché to the French embassy in Constantinople in 1840, Thuret soon gave up a diplomatic career to devote himself to botanical research. A very wealthy man, he remained an amateur, never seeking a university post. Nevertheless, the importance of his discoveries brought him a corresponding membership in the Académie des Sciences in 1857.

In order to further his research, Thuret hired an assistant—a medical student, Édouard Bornet (1828–1911) who soon became his collaborator and friend. While studying marine algae at Cherbourg, Thuret also drew on the services of the artist A. Riocreux, who skillfully reproduced Thuret's microscopical observations. The latter commenced in 1840 with the discovery of the flagella of the spermatozoids among the Characeae. This encouraged Thuret to look for similar locomotive organs among the other cryptogams, particularly the algae.

Working with Joseph Decaisne, Thuret attempted to study live *Fucus*, obtained from fish markets in Paris. They soon realized, however, that such observations could be made only at the seashore, where much more active live algae were available, along with seawater in which to observe them. Upon their return from a trip to the coast of Normandy, Decaisne and Thuret announced the discovery of the spermatozoids of *Fucus* to the Académie des Sciences on 11 November 1844. They described a red granule (stigma) and two unequal flagella, one pointing forward and the other backward. The subtlety and precision of their observations is remarkable, especially considering the imperfect state of the microscopes at their disposal.

The Académie des Sciences proposed the following subject for the grand prize in the physical sciences for 1847: "L'étude des mouvements des corps reproducteurs ou spores des Algues zoosporées et des corps renfermés dans les anthéridies des Cryptogames." The prize was shared by the two papers submitted, one by Thuret and the other by two naturalists from Marseilles, A. Derbes and A. J. J. Solier. Thuret's paper, however, was incontestably superior. Basing his analysis on the color of the zoospores and of the spermatozoids, as well as on the mode of insertion and orientation of the flagella, Thuret established, among the Zoosporeae classified by Decaisne, a very sharp distinction between the green algae (Chlorosporeae) and the brown algae (Phaeosporeae).

In 1852 Thuret left Paris and moved to Cherbourg, where he completed his initial investigation of *Fucus*. Through skillful fertilization experiments, in the course of which hybrid zygotes were obtained, he demonstrated the role of the spermatozoids in fertilization. Thus in 1854 he clarified the crucial phenomenon of fertilization, which had been shrouded in mystery. He was, however, unable to bring about the fusion of the male and female gametes, observed shortly afterward in another alga (*Oedogonium*) by Nathanael Pringsheim.

Thuret had verified the existence of spermatozoids and of mobile zoospores among green and brown algae, but the reproduction of the blue and red algae remained unknown, since no flagellated cell had been observed in either group. Thuret soon established, however, the absence of sexual reproduction among the blue algae, which multiply only by spores or by fragmentation of the trichomes into hormogonia. The problem of reproduction among the red algae appeared more intractable until 1866, when Thuret and Bornet ascertained that the male gametes (pollinia or spermatia), which never move, cling to and fuse with the hair (trichogyne) surmounting the female cell. They thereby discovered the wholly unexpected fertilization process that precedes the development of the carpospores. The formation of the carpospores, moreover, is accompanied by fusion phenomena that are often complex, involving the mother plant (auxiliary cells). Through the discoveries of Thuret and Bornet, the extremely varied reproductive modes of the different groups of algae, virtually unknown twenty-five years earlier, were definitively elucidated, at least in broad outline.

Thuret confirmed his discoveries by observations of a large number of species. In order to publicize them, he began two books, both of which were completed after his death by Bornet: *Notes algologiques* (1876–1880) and *Études phycologiques* (1878). They were illustrated with remarkable copperplate engravings of Riocreux's drawings that combined scientific exactitude with artistic beauty.

Thuret found it difficult to live in the humid climate of Cherbourg, and in 1856 he moved to the Mediterranean coast at Cap d'Antibes, which was then almost uninhabited. There he bought two fields and built a large villa where he continued his research on Mediterranean algae. His reputation attracted to Antibes a number of foreign botanists who wished to study algae: W. G. Farlow, E. de Janczewski, M. Woronin, and J. Rostafinski, among others. Thuret transformed the land surrounding the villa into a splendid botanical garden into which he introduced many exotic ornamental plants, which are now common in all the gardens along the Côte d'Azur. The "Villa Thuret," which its founder bequeathed to the nation, is now an agronomic research station. Thuret left his algologic collections and library to Bornet, who in turn gave them to the Muséum d'Histoire Naturelle in Paris.

The outstanding characteristic of Thuret's research was his constant concern to observe fully alive algae in their natural environment. This grasp of the necessity for working under conditions that permit the subject of study to remain alive was still unusual in Thuret's time, as was his broad biological conception of the methods suitable for the study of development and of the role of the reproductive organs. Together, these advanced views enabled Thuret to make a wealth of discoveries that revealed the extreme diversity in the reproductive modes of the algae and opened the way for further progress in the subject.

BIBLIOGRAPHY

An obituary is E. Bornet, "Notice biographique sur M. Gustave-Adolphe Thuret," in *Annales des sciences naturelles*, 6th ser., Botanique, **2** (1875), 308–361, and in *Mémoires de la Société impériale des sciences naturelles de Cherbourg*, **20** (1876).

JEAN FELDMANN

THURNAM, JOHN (*b*. Lingcroft, near York, England, 28 December 1810; *d*. Devizes, England, 24 September 1873), *psychiatric medicine, anthropology*.

Thurnam, as the son of a Quaker family, had a characteristically thorough early education. Subsequently, he studied medicine and received his first qualification in 1834. His relevant medical appointments were as medical superintendent at the celebrated asylum the Retreat, at York, between 1839 and 1849, and thereafter at the Wiltshire County Asylum, Devizes.

Thurnam's activities in psychiatry and anthropology mirrored widespread current interest in these subjects, and his studies were a powerful stimulus at the time, even if they are rarely remembered today. In medicine his most important work was *Observations and Essays on the Statistics of Insanity* (London, 1845), which played an immensely important role in the application of statistics to psychiatry. At a period when nonrestraint care was being generally introduced into asylums, when many clinical investigations were being made into psychiatric illnesses, and when numerous new drugs were being tried (at least in the 1860's), a statistical approach to results was essential for making assessments. Thurnam also recognized that such statistical information had to be standardized, and he devised a questionnaire for use at the Retreat. Thurnam contributed to the growing professional organization within psychiatric medicine, using such organization to promote his ideas and his standard questionnaire. He was an original member (1841) of the Medico-Psychological Association and president in 1844 and 1855. The success of Thurnam's work can be seen in innumerable publications, as, for example, W. C. Hood, *Statistics of Insanity* (London, 1855), while in 1882 Daniel Hack Tuke spoke of his work as "a Pharos to guide those who sail on waters where many are

shipwrecked" (*Chapters in the History of the Insane* [London, 1882], 492).

Of his work in anthropology, Thurnam was concerned mostly with the study of skulls, his notable contribution being his co-editorship of *Crania Britannica* (1865).

BIBLIOGRAPHY

I. ORIGINAL WORKS. The full title of Thurnam's celebrated work on statistics is *Observations and Essays on the Statistics of Insanity, and on Establishments for the Insane; to Which Are Added the Statistics of the Retreat Near York* (London, 1845). It superseded an earlier work, *The Statistics of the Retreat; Consisting of a Report and Tables Exhibiting the Experience of That Institution for the Insane From its Establishment in 1796 to 1840* (York, 1841).

Much of Thurnam's significant anthropological work appeared in the 1860's, notably his work with *Crania Britannica. Delineations and Descriptions of the Skulls of the Early Inhabitants of the British Islands* (London, 1865).

II. SECONDARY LITERATURE. There is no modern study of Thurnam, although he is remembered in R. Hunter and I. Macalpine, *Three Hundred Years of Psychiatry, 1535–1860* (London, 1963), 941–945. For useful notices see *Medical Times and Gazette*, **2** (1873), 479; and *Dictionary of National Biography*, **19** (1909), 831–832.

J. K. CRELLIN

THURNEYSSER, LEONHARD (or **Thurnyser, Lienhart**) (*b*. Basel, Switzerland, 5 August 1531; *d*. Cologne, Germany, 8 July 1596), *alchemy*.

Thurneysser was the son of Ursula and Jacob Thurneysser, a goldsmith. He took up his father's profession and also studied with a Dr. Huber, a physician and alchemist resident at Basel; he did not attend a university. He married Margarette Müllerin when he was sixteen but, when he was discovered to be selling gold-covered lead as pure gold, was forced to flee Basel in 1548, leaving his wife behind. He spent some time in Holland, northern Germany, France, and England, then in about 1552 returned to Germany to join the army of Albert, margrave of Brandenburg. He was captured by the Saxon army in the following year and put to work in the mines at Tarenz, in the Inn Valley. Following his release he worked as a goldsmith and smelter in Nuremberg, then returned to the Tyrol, where he was in the service of Archduke Ferdinand from 1560 to 1570. On Ferdinand's instructions he made journeys to England, France, Bohemia, Hungary, Italy, Spain, and North Africa to acquaint himself with metallurgical methods and medicine. His first book, the verse alchemical tract *Archidoxa*, was published in 1569; a similar work, *Quinta essentia*, was issued a year later.

Thurneysser moved in 1571 to Frankfurt an der Oder, where he wrote *Pison*, a kind of textbook of mineral-water analysis. This work came to the notice of Johann Georg, elector of Brandenburg, who summoned Thurneysser to his court. There Thurneysser cured Johann Georg's wife of a serious illness and was made court physician, despite his lack of an academic degree. Enjoying his patron's full confidence, Thurneysser acted as his adviser on metallurgy and mining and took advantage of his position in a masterly way. He established, at the Greyfriars monastery in Berlin, a laboratory — or, indeed, a factory — that employed 300 people in the production of saltpeter, mineral acids, alums, colored glass, drugs, essences, and even amulets. He also founded his own printing house, which published his calendars, prognostications, alchemical and medical tracts, and a wide variety of polemics.

The works that Thurneysser published at this time were impressive examples of the printer's art, illustrated with woodcuts and etchings, and incorporating Greek, Arabic, Syrian, Hebrew, and Chaldean typefaces. Since his books often contained words in languages that he did not know (some of the magic spells and terms that he gave have been identified as common Hungarian swearwords), he was publicly accused of harboring in his inkpot a devil who dictated to him. His chief alchemical works, *Megaln chymia* and *Melisath*, were both first published in Berlin in 1583. The latter is a kind of dictionary directed to clarifying the works and ideas of Paracelsus, whose follower Thurneysser purported himself to be. But although he frequently quoted from Paracelsus, Thurneysser often invented the passages cited himself; and the *Melisath* contains citations of some eighty tracts by Paracelsus that never existed outside Thurneysser's own mind. His works were severely criticized by other physicians, particularly Kaspar Hoffmann, professor of medicine at the University of Frankfurt an der Oder, and Thurneysser would certainly seem to have been a charlatan, whose methods and drugs had at best a dubious power to heal.

Nevertheless, Thurneysser became rich; he owned a large library, collected pictures and other works of art, and established a sort of museum of natural history. He had agents in a number of German and Polish cities, who advertised his wares and sold his drugs, cosmetics, and amulets to the gentry and wealthy burghers of Germany, Poland, and Denmark. He himself courted the favor of royalty, including the deranged Duke Albert Frederick of Prussia, Frederick II of Denmark, and Stephen Báthory, king of Poland. (He dedicated his *Historia sive descriptio plantarum* to the last, but when the king paid him less money than he felt was his due, dedicated the next edition of the work to his patron Johann Georg.)

In addition, Thurneysser conducted a sort of school of alchemy, which numbered the distinguished apothecary Michael Aschenbrenner among its students. He was not without enemies, however, and about 1572 was accused of participating in the murder of the alchemist Sebastian Siebenfreund.

In 1576 there was an outbreak of pestilence in Brandenburg, and Thurneysser, with the court, left Berlin for a period of several months. During this time his second wife, Anna Hüerlin, whom he had married in 1561, died, and his business, which he had left in the hands of his brother Alexander, suffered severely. By 1580 he had decided to move back to Basel, where he purchased an estate called "Zum Thurn," which enabled him to style himself grandly as Leonhard Thurneysser zum Thurn. He had brought a considerable amount of his money to Basel, and he there married his third wife, Marina Herbrodt. In divorce proceedings two years later, the Basel town council made over all of his remaining wealth to his wife, terms against which Thurneysser railed in a number of pamphlets.

Thurneysser returned to Brandenburg and spent the last years of his life attempting to make gold. After he failed to transmute a large quantity of silver, however, he left the service of Johann Georg and traveled to Italy, where he found a patron in Ferdinand de' Medici, grand duke of Tuscany. At this time he became a convert to Roman Catholicism. He returned to Germany shortly before his death in Cologne and in his will asked to be buried there beside Albert the Great, a wish that was never carried out.

BIBLIOGRAPHY

I. ORIGINAL WORKS. Thurneysser's publications include *Archidoxa* (Münster, 1569; Berlin, 1575); *Quinta essentia* (Münster, 1570); *Prokatalepsis* (Frankfurt an der Oder, 1571); *Pison* (Frankfurt an der Oder, 1572);

Chermeneia (Berlin, 1574); *Onomasticon polyglosson* (Berlin, 1574); *Eyporadelosis* (Berlin, 1575); *Bebaiosis agonismoy* (Berlin, 1576); *Historia sive descriptio plantarum* (Berlin, 1578); *Historia und Beschreibung influentischer, elementarische und natürlicher Wirckungen* (Berlin, 1583); *Megaln chymia* (Berlin, 1583); *Melisath* (Berlin, 1583); *Attisholtz oder Attiswalder Badordnung* (Cologne, 1590); *Reise und kriegs Apotecken* (Leipzig, 1602); and *Zehn Bücher von kalten (warmen) mineralischen und metallischen Wassern* (Strasbourg, 1612).

Until 1945 two unedited alchemical manuscripts and a number of letters were to be found in the Berlin Staatsbibliothek.

II. SECONDARY LITERATURE. On Thurneysser and his work, see *Allgemeine Deutsche Biographie*, XXXVII (1894), 226; Paul Diergart, "Mitteilungen zur Wertung des Paracelsisten. Leonhard Thurnyser," in *Beiträge aus der Geschichte der Chemie* (Leipzig-Vienna, 1909), 306–313; Fritz Ferchl, *Chemisch pharmazeutisches Bio- und Bibliographikon* (Mittenwald, 1937), 536; John Ferguson, *Bibliotheca chemica*, II (Glasgow, 1906), 450–455, which includes excerpts from some of Thurneysser's calendars; Stanisław Kośmiński, *Słownik lekarzów polskich* (Warsaw, 1883), with letter on p. 514 in which Thurneysser described for Stephen Báthory an "alexipharmacum" sovereign against all poisons; Hermann Kopp, *Die Alchemie*, 2 vols. (Heidelberg, 1886), *passim*; J. C. Moehsen, *Beiträge zur Geschichte der Wissenschaften in der Mark Brandenburg* (Berlin-Leipzig, 1783), 55–198; J. R. Partington, *A History of Chemistry*, II (London, 1961), 152–153; Will-Erich Peuckert, *Der Alchemist und sein Weib* (Stuttgart, 1956); Günther Bugge, *Der Alchimist* (Berlin, 1943), a novel based upon Thurneysser's life; B. Reber, "Zwei neue Dokumente über Leonhard Thurneysser zum Thurn," in *Mitteilungen zur Geschichte der Medizin und der Naturwissenschaften*, 5 (1906), 432–439; Karol Christoph Schmieder, *Geschichte der Alchemie* (Munich, 1927), 284–286; Karl Sudhoff, *Bibliographia Paracelsica* (Berlin, 1894), *passim*; and Laszlo Szathmary, *Magyar Alkemistak* (Budapest, 1928), 319–322.

WŁODZIMIERZ HUBICKI

THURSTON, ROBERT HENRY (*b.* Providence, Rhode Island, 25 October 1839; *d.* Ithaca, New York, 25 October 1903), *engineering education, steam engineering, testing of materials.*

Thurston was a mechanical engineer who exerted wide and lasting influence upon the American engineering profession. He was a prolific writer of textbooks, reference works, and technical and popular articles; and he organized and directed two mechanical engineering schools. In addition he organized and was an active member of professional societies and served on industrial and governmental committees.

Thurston was the eldest of the three children of Robert Lawton Thurston, a prominent steam-engine builder in Providence, and Harriet Taylor. Upon completion of high school, Thurston was expected to enter his father's shops; but he and his father were persuaded by one of his teachers that he should continue his education at Brown University, where he graduated in 1859 with a major in science and a minor in civil engineering.

After a short period as draftsman, Thurston represented his father's company in Philadelphia, where in 1861 his first published article appeared in the *Journal of the Franklin Institute*. Throughout the Civil War (1861–1865), he served as an assistant engineer in the navy, and at the end of the war he was assigned to the U.S. Naval Academy in Annapolis as assistant professor of natural and experimental philosophy. The pattern of his subsequent career was evident in his six years of teaching at the academy. Upon the death of the incumbent, he became head of his department. He designed and built a signaling lamp; experimented with lubricants; and published a number of descriptive technical reports and popular articles on naval armament, steam engines, and the manufacture of iron and steel.

Henry Morton, former editor of the *Journal of the Franklin Institute* and president of the newly formed Stevens Institute of Technology in Hoboken, New Jersey, invited Thurston to organize and to direct the school of mechanical engineering. It was during his fourteen years (1871–1885) at the institute that Thurston established his international reputation. In 1874 he persuaded the trustees of Stevens to equip a testing laboratory to serve commercial clients. Subsequently, laboratory work became a part of the engineering curriculum.

While teaching, Thurston invented testing machines and carried out extensive research on strength of materials and lubrication. He was one of the first to demonstrate that the elastic limit of ductile materials can be raised by the application of stress beyond the yield point. His series of public lectures on the history of the steam engine, published several years later, in 1878, was long a standard work on the subject. Major works—which were derived from his classroom lectures on materials of engineering, friction, and lubrication—were published while Thurston was at Stevens. During this period Thurston wrote large books on steam boilers and the steam engine. He served also as secretary of the U.S. Board to Test Iron, Steel, and Other Metals; as U.S. Commissioner to the 1873 Vienna International Exhibition; as an official of the 1876 Philadelphia Centennial Exhibition; and as first president of the American Society of Mechanical Engineers, which in 1880 he helped organize. He also published an extraordinary number of both technical and popular articles.

In 1885 Thurston moved to Cornell University, where he reorganized and directed the Sibley College of Mechanical Engineering. Through his publications and the considerable number of Cornell graduates who became teachers in engineering colleges throughout the country, Thurston influenced greatly the philosophy and direction of engineering education. In an engineering school he expected to treat only professional subjects and to relegate general education to a preparatory school. He considered general education as desirable but not essential; his successors gave only lip service to its desirability. Thurston suggested in 1893 ("Technical Education in the United States," p. 923n) that the ideal technical education was probably to be found in the military academies, where scientific and professional studies and physical training were all given due weight.

Thurston was diligent, enthusiastic, and persistent, and tended toward action rather than reflection. He made massive contributions to the order and the promulgation of the engineering sciences and to the promotion of organizations that were directed toward the increase of material wealth in a progress-oriented social order.

He was a member or honorary member of a score of technical societies in the United States and Europe. He received honorary degrees from Stevens Institute of Technology (1885) and Brown University (1889). Thurston was married in 1865 and, upon the death of his wife, remarried in 1880.

BIBLIOGRAPHY

I. ORIGINAL WORKS. Thurston edited *Reports of the Commissioners of the United States to the International Exhibition Held at Vienna 1873*, 4 vols. (Washington, 1875–1876). His other works include *A History of the Growth of the Steam-Engine* (New York, 1878); *The Materials of Engineering*, 3 vols. (New York, 1883–1884); *A Treatise on Friction and Lost Work in Machinery and Millwork* (New York, 1885); *A Manual of Steam-Boilers, Their Design, Construction, and Operation* (New York, 1888); *Reflections on the Motive Power of Heat* (New York, 1890), a trans. of N. L. S.

Carnot, *Reflexions sur la Puissance Motrice du Feu* (1824); *A Manual of the Steam-Engine: For Engineers and Technical Schools*, 2 vols. (New York, 1891); *Robert Fulton, His Life and Its Results* (New York, 1891); "Technical Education in the United States," in *Transactions of the American Society of Mechanical Engineers*, **14** (1893), 855–1013; and *The Animal as a Machine and a Prime Motor, and the Laws of Energetics* (New York, 1894). A list of Thurston's writings is in Durand's biography (see below), pp. 245–287.

II. SECONDARY LITERATURE. William F. Durand, *Robert Henry Thurston* (New York, 1929), is an uncritical but informative biography by a former associate and friend; a portrait appears as the frontispiece. See also Durand's article on Thurston in *Dictionary of American Biography*, **9** (1936), 518–520. A context is provided for Thurston's work in education and in the American Society of Mechanical Engineers in Monte Calvert, *Mechanical Engineering in America, 1830–1910* (Baltimore, 1967). Thurston's correspondence is in the Cornell University Library, Collection of Regional History and University Archives.

EUGENE S. FERGUSON

THYMARIDAS (*fl.* Paros, first half (?) of fourth century B.C.), *mathematics*.

An early Pythagorean of uncertain date, Thymaridas was a number theorist from the Aegean island of Paros. He defined a unit as a "limiting quantity" (see Iamblichus, *In Nicomachi . . .*, p. 11, 2–3); and he is said to have called a prime number $\varepsilon\dot{v}\theta v\gamma\rho\alpha\mu\mu\iota\kappa\acute{o}s$ ("rectilinear"), because it can only be established one-dimensionally (Iamblichus, *op. cit.*, p. 27, 4–5), since the only measures of a prime number are itself and one. But Thymaridas' chief contribution to number theory was his $\dot{\varepsilon}\pi\acute{\alpha}\nu\theta\eta\mu\alpha$ ("bloom"), which he expressed rather obscurely in generalized form (Iamblichus, *op. cit.*, p. 62, 18 ff.). The rule leads to the solution of a certain set of n simultaneous simple equations connecting n unknowns. The unknown quantity is called "an undetermined number of units" (that is, x); the known quantities are $\dot{\omega}\rho\iota\sigma\mu\acute{\varepsilon}\nu\alpha$ ("determined"). The principle of the rule has been explained by Heath as follows:

Let there be n unknown quantities

$$x, x_1, x_2, \cdots x_{n-1}$$

connected by n equations, in such a way that

$$x + x_1 + x_2 + \cdots + x_{n-1} = S$$
$$x + x_1 = a_1,$$

$$x + x_2 = a_2,$$

$$\cdots\cdots\cdots\cdots$$

$$x + x_{n-1} = a_{n-1},$$

the solution is

$$x = \frac{(a_1 + a_2 + \cdots + a_{n-1}) - S}{n-2}.$$

Iamblichus shows that other equations can be reduced to this form (Iamblichus, *op. cit.*, p. 63, 16 ff.); he gives as an example an indeterminate problem having four unknown quantities in three linear equations. It is not certain that Thymaridas was responsible for the extension of his method.

Of Thymaridas' life we are told only that he fell from prosperity to poverty and that consequently Thestor of Poseidonia sailed to Paros to help him with money specially collected for his benefit (Iamblichus, *De vita pythagorica*, p. 239). "Eumaridas" in a list of Parian Pythagoreans (Iamblichus, *op. cit.*, p. 267) may be a mistake for Thymaridas.

BIBLIOGRAPHY

On Thymaridas and his work, see T. L. Heath, *A History of Greek Mathematics*, I (Oxford, 1921), 69, 72, 94; Iamblichus, in *Nicomachi arithmeticam introductionem*, H. Pistelli, ed. (Leipzig, 1894), 11, 2–3; 27, 4–5; 62, 18 ff.; 63, 16 ff.; and *De vita pythagorica*, L. Deubner, ed. (Leipzig, 1937).

G. HUXLEY

IBN TIBBON, JACOB BEN MACHIR (*b.* Marseilles, France [?], *ca.* 1236; *d.* Montpellier, 1305), *astronomy, science translation.*

In Romance languages Ibn Tibbon is known as Don Profiat or Profeit, and in Latin as Prophatius Judaeus. These names come from translation of the Hebrew *mehir* into the languages of southern France.

His family, commonly designated by the patronymic Ibn Tibbon, came from Granada. His great-grandfather, Judah ben Saul ibn Tibbon (1120–*ca.* 1190), moved in 1150 to the south of France because of the unrest in Granada. He established himself at Lunel, where in 1160 Benjamin of Tudela found him practicing medicine. Having grown up in an Islamic country, Judah ben Saul spoke Arabic and was thus able to translate into Hebrew, for the benefit of his coreligionists, religious and philosophical works written in Arabic by Baḥya ibn Paquda, Solomon ibn Gabirol, Judah ha-Levi, Ibn Janah, and Saadia. His son, Samuel ben Judah (1150–1232), continued this work of translation; but it was his grandson, Moses ben Samuel (*fl.* 1240–1283), and his great-grandson, Jacob ben Machir, who brought the family greatest glory. The translations made by the family were among the most important cultural works of the time, at least from a historical point of view, since they were part of a process by which Arabic learning and, through that, Greek scientific traditions were made available to the scholars of medieval Europe.

Jacob studied medicine at Montpellier, and it appears that from 1266 to 1267 he lived in Gerona, Spain, where he was a follower of Moses ben Nahman. Ideologically he adhered to the Maimonidean philosophy and spent most of his life in Lunel and Montpellier.

Working from texts in Arabic, Ibn Tibbon rendered into Hebrew works by Autolycus of Pitane (*On the Moving Sphere*), Euclid (*Elements, Data*), Menelaus of Alexandria (*Spherics*), Qusṭā ibn Lūqā (*Use of the Celestial Globe*), Ibn al-Haytham (*On the Configuration of the World*), Ibn al-Ṣaffār (*On the Use of the Astrolabe*), al-Zarqālī (*Use of the Ṣafīḥa*), al-Ghazālī (*Balance of Knowledge*), Jābir ibn Aflaḥ (*Correction* [*iṣlāḥ*] *of the Almagest*), and Ibn Rushd (compendium of the Organon, commentary on Aristotelian zoology).

His own works, which deal with astronomy, are Prologue to Abraham bar Ḥiyya's *Calculation of the Courses of the Stars*, extracts from the *Almagest*, *Robaᶜ Yisrael*, and *Almanac*.

The *Robaᶜ Yisrael* ("Quadrant of Israel") was written between 1288 and 1293 in Hebrew, and was translated into Latin in 1299 by Armengaud, son of Blaise (*d.* 1314). In 1301 an expansion of this work appeared; the text has been lost but is preserved in the Latin translation (*ca.* 1309) by Peter of St.-Olmer, which was translated back into Hebrew. A new astronomical instrument is described in this work—the so-called *quadrans novus*, as distinct from the *quadrans vetus* of Robert the Englishman (*ca.* 1276) and the tenth-century *vetustissimus*. Examples of the *quadrans novus* have been preserved, and it apparently was much used in its time. It consists of a simplification of the face of the astrolabe by means of two successive rebates that have as their axes the north-south and east-west lines. Whatever connections may exist between this apparatus and similar instruments used by the Arabs have not been clearly established.

The *Almanac* is calculated for Montpellier and dated 1 March 1300 (1301 A.D.). In his prologue Ibn Tibbon notes that he was inspired by the almanac of King Tolomeus, which had been corrected by al-Zarqālī. Those corrections were insufficient, however, and, in addition, introduced new errors. For instance, al-Zarqālī did not take into account that some calculations had been made according to the Coptic calendar. Ibn Tibbon explains that he has followed the method of his predecessors, using the Toledan Tables as a basis; this is not quite correct, however, since his work is actually based on al-Zarqālī's completion of Ammonius' treatise on the almanac. But this distinction between tables and almanac was not usual; and for that reason several writers, among them Andalo di Negro, believed that Ibn Tibbon had used the Alfonsine Tables as a basis, since the prologue was not consistent with the tabular part of the work. The only exception to that model is the collection of lunar tables, inspired by those of al-Khwārizmī, known through al-Zarqālī. In the subsequent development of the work, Ibn Tibbon limits himself to the calculation of ephemerides and modifies the constant to be added at the end of the cycles. Later astronomers—Andalo di Negro, Levi ben Gerson, Abraham Zacuto—found errors that they corrected.

Ibn Tibbon's astronomical work was very highly regarded during the Renaissance and was cited by Copernicus, Reinhold, Clavius, and Kepler.

BIBLIOGRAPHY

I. ORIGINAL WORKS. For the MSS see Moritz Steinschneider, *Die hebräischen Übersetzungen des Mittelalters . . .* (Berlin, 1893; repr. Graz, 1956), index, 1057, and the references given there. For the trans. of the *Ṣafīḥa*, see the ed. and trans. by José María Millás Vallicrosa into Catalan, *Tractat de l'assafea d'Azarquiel* (Barcelona, 1933). One of the texts of the Latin trans. of the work on the *quadrans novus* is G. Bofitto and C. Melzi d'Eril, eds., *Il quadrante d'Israel* (Florence, 1922); the same authors also published *Almanach Dantis Alighieri sive Prophacii Judaei Montispessulani* (Florence, 1908).

II. SECONDARY LITERATURE. See Marion Boutelle, "The Almanac of Azarquiel," in *Centaurus*, **12**, no. 1 (1967), 12–19; P. Duhem, *Le système du monde*, III (Paris, 1915), 298–312; R. T. Gunther, *Early Science in Oxford*, II (Oxford, 1923), 163–169; H. Michel, *Traité de l'astrolabe* (Paris, 1947), 23–24; J. M. Millás Vallicrosa, *Estudios sobre Azarquiel* (Madrid–Granada, 1943–1950), 356–362, 402–404; E. Poulle, "Le quadrant nouveau médiéval," in *Journal des savants* (Apr.–

June 1964), 148–167, 182–214; E. Renan and A. Neubauer, *Rabbins français*, repr. from *Histoire littéraire de la France*, XXVII (Paris, 1877); and George Sarton, *Introduction to the History of Science*, II (Baltimore, 1931), 850–853 and index.

J. VERNET

IBN TIBBON, MOSES BEN SAMUEL (*b.* Marseilles, France; *fl.* Montpellier, France, 1240–1283), *medicine, philosophy, translation.*

Moses ben Samuel was related to Jacob ben Machir ibn Tibbon and father of the Judah ben Moses ibn Tibbon who took part in the struggles between Maimonideans and anti-Maimonideans that occurred at Montpellier, aligning himself with the former. He spent most of his life in Montpellier. He wrote a number of works, most of them commentaries on the Bible and the Talmud. Among them is one that deals with the weights and measures mentioned in those works.

Ibn Tibbon is most significant as a translator from Arabic into Hebrew of Ibn Rushd (commentaries on Aristotle: *Physics, De caelo et mundo, De generatione et corruptione, Meteora, De anima, Parva naturalia, Metaphysics, Problems*), Themistius (commentary on Book Λ of the *Metaphysics*), al-Baṭalyūsī (*Kitāb al-ḥadāʾiq*), al-Fārābī (*Kitāb mabādiʾ*), Maimonides (*Kitāb al-sirāj, Kitāb al-farāʾiḍ, Maqāla fī ṣinaʿat al-manṭiq* [dealing with philosophy and religion], and *Regimen Addressed, On Poisons and Antidotes, Commentary on the Aphorisms of Hippocrates* [on medicine]), Euclid (*Elements*), Geminus (*Introduction to Astronomy*), Theodosius of Bithynia (*Spherics*), Jābir ibn Aflaḥ (*Iṣlāḥ al-majisṭī*), Muhammad al-Ḥaṣṣār (treatise on arithmetic and algebra), al-Biṭrūjī (*Kitāb al-haiʾa*), Ibn Sīnā (*Canticum, The Small Canon*), Ibn al-Jazzār (*Viaticum peregrinantis*), Ḥunayn ibn Isḥāq (*Isagoge Johannitii ad tegni Galeni*), al-Rāzī (*Antidotary, Division and Distribution of Diseases*).

BIBLIOGRAPHY

For the MSS see Moritz Steinschneider, *Die hebräischen Übersetzungen des Mittelalters . . .* (Berlin, 1893; repr. Graz, 1956), index, 1062, and the references given there.

For general information, see E. Renan and A. Neubauer, *Rabbins français* (Paris, 1877), repr. from *Histoire littéraire de la France*; George Sarton, *Introduction to the History of Science*, II (Baltimore, 1931), 847 and index; and Max Schloessinger, in *Jewish Encyclope-*

dia, VI (New York, 1906), 545–548. Also see references in the article on Jacob ben Machir ibn Tibbon in this Dictionary.

J. VERNET

TIEDEMANN, FRIEDRICH (*b*. Kassel, Germany, 23 August 1781; *d*. Munich, Germany, 22 January 1861), *anatomy, physiology.*

Tiedemann was the son of Dietrich Tiedemann, a professor of philosophy, Greek, and classical literature, who took great interest in his son's early education. He attended the Marburg Gymnasium, then, in 1798, entered the university there to begin medical studies. His chief interest was medical theory, and in 1802 he began to concentrate on theoretical subjects at Bamberg and Würzburg, under the guidance of J. N. Thomann and Kaspar von Siebold; the inability of physicians to prevent his father's death of a contagious disease in 1803 further strengthened his aversion to practical medicine.

Tiedemann graduated from Marburg with the M.D. in 1804, then remained there to attend Franz Joseph Gall's courses on physiology, comparative osteology, and craniology. Gall's exceptionally skillful fine anatomical preparations set an example for Tiedemann's own later work. Tiedemann then returned to Würzburg to study with Schelling. He was, however, able to resist the seductiveness of *Naturphilosophie*—Schelling himself was responsible, Tiedemann later wrote, for his decision to remain faithful to the methods of empirical research and observation—and determined to go to Paris to study with Georges Cuvier. In the course of his journey he met S. T. Soemmerring, who was greatly impressed by Tiedemann's preparation of the nervous system of the pigeon. It was upon Soemmerring's recommendation that Tiedemann was in 1807 called to the Landshut Medical Faculty as professor of anatomy and zoology.

In Paris, under Cuvier's tutelage, Tiedemann became interested in comparative anatomy and morphology, and these studies formed the basis for the first works that he published in Landshut. Among these were three sections of a projected, but never completed, textbook on zoology. Three parts were brought out (in 1808, 1810, and 1814, respectively); of these the first dealt with problems of general zoology, and in particular the classification of mammals, while the second and third were devoted to birds. The published segments of the work were greeted as the most comprehensive

compendium of zoological data since Cuvier's own *Leçons d'anatomie comparée*. At the same time, Tiedemann also published a series of monographs summarizing his studies on specific subjects. These included a work on the heart in fish (1809), detailed studies of the anatomy and natural history of the great reptiles (1811 and 1817), and a number of works on the structural anatomy of birds and amphibia, especially the lymphatic vessels and respiratory organs of birds. His 1816 publication on echinoderms (holothurioidea [sea cucumbers], starfish, and sea urchins), a subject set by the Académie des Sciences, won its prize and Tiedemann was elected a corresponding member.

During the same period of his career, Tiedemann did further important research on morphology and embryology. He studied the fetal development of bone tissues and demonstrated beyond doubt that the maternal blood is not transmitted to the fetus, which rather has its own closed circulatory system, separate from (but closely associated with) the maternal one. His most important work in this area lay in his studies of the development of the brain; his *Anatomie und Bildungsgeschichte des Gehirns im Fötus der Menschen, nebst einer vergleichenden Darstellung des Hirnbaues in den Thieren*, dedicated to J. F. Blumenbach, was published in 1816.

In the preface to this work, Tiedemann stated that, since the fully developed fetal brain had been described exhaustively, it was therefore necessary to study its anatomical development in detail; anatomy, he added, would be a mature science only when the different stages of development and mutual relations of various structures had been examined so that the laws that governed them might be understood. Continuity of observation, Tiedemann stated, was essential, and his book represented the results of several years of continuous research. He was thus able to record the exact stage at which a number of structures first arose in the fetal brain, together with the duration of brain growth and the time of its completion. A comparison of the durable forms of the brain of various animals with the transitory embryonic configurations of the human brain allowed him to draw an analogy between the adult animal brain and the human brain at a certain stage of development; he was also able to detect the crossing of the pyramidal tracts in a very young embryo, the changes in the peripheral nerves, and the cranial shift of the sacral part of the spinal cord. His book contained a number of beautiful and accurate illustrations, and was later translated into French and English.

In 1816 Tiedemann went to the University of Heidelberg to take up an appointment as professor of anatomy, comparative anatomy, physiology, and zoology. The new post offered him greater resources (among other things, there was a more generous supply of cadavers for dissection), and brought him into contact with a younger colleague, the chemist Leopold Gmelin, whose work strongly influenced his own. Tiedemann's interests gradually became concentrated on problems of physiology, and with Gmelin he performed a considerable body of research, in which he assumed responsibility for animal experimentation and observation, while Gmelin carried out chemical examinations.

In 1820 Tiedemann and Gmelin published *Versuche über die Wege auf welchen die Substanzen aus dem Magen und Darm ins Blut gelangen, über die Verrichtung der Milz und über die geheimen Harnwege*, an account of their researches on the passage of various substances from the stomach or intestines to the blood, on the function of the spleen, and on the hypothetical hidden urinary ducts. The absorption of nutrients from the alimentary tract had long been of interest to Tiedemann — it had, in fact, motivated his previous studies on the lymphatic vessels — but his work on the spleen was something quite new. The role of the spleen had been hitherto only a subject of speculation; Tiedemann's attempts to prove experimentally, in horses and dogs, that the spleen secreted a fluid that passed through the lymphatic system to participate in the transformation of chyle into blood served as the basis for all further work on the part of the spleen in blood formation. Tiedemann and Gmelin also showed that the hidden urinary ducts posited by other workers could not exist.

In 1822 Friedrich Sigismund Leuckart assumed responsibility for the teaching of zoology and comparative anatomy at Heidelberg and Tiedemann was able to devote all his time to physiology. The following year the Paris Académie des Sciences announced a prize for the best work encompassing the chemical composition of the digestive juices, the digestion of simple and complex foodstuffs in animals (including mammals, birds, reptiles, amphibians, and fish), the contents of the stomach and intestines during periods of fasting and eating, and the passage of digested substances into the blood, lymph, and urine. Under this stimulus Tiedemann and Gmelin decided to expand their earlier work on digestion into a comprehensive study, using chemical methods as well as experimental and microscopic investigations, designed to satisfy the conditions of the award.

Digestion had been thought of as a single process, taking place in a single organ, the stomach. Tiedemann and Gmelin, however, observed the digestion of foodstuffs as they passed through the alimentary tract and investigated the assimilation of nutrients into the blood and lymph and the eventual elimination of waste products to demonstrate that digestion is in fact a complicated series of processes, involving a number of organs. They proved that for some substances digestion represents not a simple dissolution but rather a chemical transformation, as, for example, displayed by the conversion of starch into glucose. They showed experimentally that the digestive juices have discrete properties, as, for instance, the pancreatic juice, formerly thought to be an abdominal saliva, which they obtained through an experimentally induced abdominal fistula and tested chemically to demonstrate its difference from saliva.

Chief among their other findings was their discovery of a number of biliary substances, of which some (such as pigments) were merely excreted, while others played more important physiological roles, as in the absorption of fat, which diminished when bile was not present. They also (shortly after Prout, but independently and by a different method) detected the presence of hydrochloric acid in the stomach, and showed that it increases in quantity with the digestion of certain foods. They further described the color reactions of proteins during pancreatic digestion and discovered glucose, transformed chemically from starch and similar substances, in the blood.

Despite their remarkable achievement, Tiedemann and Gmelin did not win the Académie's prize. That body decided rather to divide the prize between them and two young French scientists, François Leuret and Jean-Louis Lassaigne, giving each entry half the prize and an honorable mention. Resentful, Tiedemann and Gmelin refused to accept any part of the award and announced that they would submit their work to the judgment of the entire scientific world; their *Die Verdauung nach Versuchen* was published in Heidelberg in 1826. The great chemist Berzelius characterized the book as "a long series of investigations about the process of digestion, in which everything that anatomy and chemistry could at present offer to its study was used," and praised it as "uncontestably the most complete physiological examination [of digestion], which has enriched the chemical study of the processes that occur in living animals." And indeed, further advances in the study of digestion became possible only with advances in chemistry.

By 1835 Tiedemann had begun to suffer from the eye complaint that eventually led to the loss of his sight. In that year he was relieved of his courses by his son-in-law, Theodor Bischoff, although he continued to carry out his own research. In 1836 he published, in English, what may be considered one of the earliest basic works of physical anthropology, *On the Brain of the Negro Compared With That of the European and the Orang-Outang*. In this surprisingly modern study, Tiedemann showed that, in contrast to the large difference between the forebrains of apes and men, no substantial differences could be found between the brains of the races of men; although the majority of Negro skulls and cranial cavities that he studied were smaller than those of European specimens, they had, by his measurement, contained brains as large and as heavy. He further stated his finding that there was no area of intellectual activity in which Negroes could not perform as well as European whites, and concluded that there was no natural formation or disposition of the brain in Negroes that would substantiate the notion of their predestined subservient state.

In 1844 Tiedemann took up the task of designing a new anatomical theater. His life was disrupted by the revolution of 1848–1849; not only was he opposed to popular uprisings, for political and philosophical reasons, but also three of his sons were army officers. The eldest, Gustav Nicolaus Tiedemann, was executed under martial law, and the two others had to flee into exile. In 1849 Tiedemann retired from the University of Heidelberg and settled first in Frankfurt am Main, and then, in 1856, in Munich. The fiftieth anniversary of his doctorate was celebrated by his friends and former students in 1854, and a medal was struck for the occasion. In the same year Tiedemann published his last book, a history of tobacco and its use.

BIBLIOGRAPHY

I. ORIGINAL WORKS. A bibliography of Tiedemann's works is found in Theodor Bischoff (see below). Works include *Zoologie*, 3 vols. (Landshut, 1808, 1810, 1814); *Anatomie des Fischherzens* (Landshut, 1809); *Anatomie und Naturgeschichte des Drachen* (Nuremberg, 1811); *Anatomie der kopflosen Missgeburten* (Landshut, 1813); *Anatomie und Bildungsgeschichte des Gehirns im Fötus der Menschen, nebst einer vergleichenden Darstellung des Hirnbaues in den Thieren* (Nuremberg, 1816), French ed. (Paris, 1823), English ed. (Edinburgh, 1826); *Anatomie der Röhrenholothurie, des pomeranzenfarbenen Seesterns und Seeigels* (Landshut, 1816); *Anatomie und Naturgeschichte des Krokodils* (Heidelberg, 1817), with M. Oppel and J. Liboschitz.

Other works include *Abhandlung über das vermeintliche bärenartige Faulthier* (Heidelberg, 1820); *Versuche über die Wege auf welchen die Substanzen aus dem Magen und Darm ins Blut gelangen, über die Verrichtung der Milz und über die geheimen Harnwege* (Heidelberg, 1820), French ed. (Paris, 1821), with Gmelin; *Icones cerebri simiarum et quorundam mammalium variorum* (Heidelberg, 1821); *Tabulae arteriarum corporis humani* (Karlsruhe, 1822); *Tabulae nervorum uteri* (Heidelberg, 1823); *Die Verdauung nach Versuchen* (Heidelberg, 1826, 1827), with Gmelin; *Physiologie des Menschen: I, Allgemeine Betrachtungen der organischen Körper* (Darmstadt, 1830); II, not published; III, *Untersuchungen über das Nahrungsbedürfniss, der Nahrungstrieb und die Nahrungsmittel der Menschen* (Darmstadt, 1836); *On the Brain of the Negro Compared With That of the European and the Orang-Outang* (London, 1836), German ed. (Heidelberg, 1837); *Von den Duverneyschen, Bartolinschen oder Cowperschen Drüsen des Weibes und der schiefen Gestaltung und Lage der Gebärmutter* (Heidelberg, 1840); *Von der Verengerung und Verschliessung der Pulsadern in Krankheiten* (Heidelberg, 1843); *Von lebenden Würmern und Insekten in den Geruchs-Organen des Menschen, den Zufällen, welche sie verursachen und den Mitteln sie auszutreiben* (Mannheim, 1844); *Zeitschrift für Physiologie*, ed. with G. R. and L. Ch. Treviranus; and *Geschichte des Tabaks und anderer ähnlichen Genussmittel* (Frankfurt am Main, 1854).

II. SECONDARY LITERATURE. An important study of Tiedemann's life and works is Theodor Bischoff, *Gedächtnissrede auf Friedrich Tiedemann* (Munich, 1861), with bibliography, pp. 36–39. Other biographical studies are P. Flourens, "Tiedemann, Friedrich," in *Biographie universelle ancienne et moderne*, XLI, 526–529, and in *Gazette médicale de Paris*, 29, no. 52 (1861); J. Pagel, in *Allegemeine Deutsche Biographie*, XXXVIII (1894), 577–578; F. Seitz, in *Biographisches Lexikon hervorragender Aerzte aller Zeiten und Völker*, V (1934), 586–587; E. Stübler, in *Geschichte der Medizinischen Fakultät der Universität Heidelberg, 1386–1925* (Heidelberg, 1926), 248–253.

Discussions of Tiedemann's work include (in chronological order) N. Mani, "Das Werk von Friedrich Tiedemann und Leopold Gmelin: 'Die Verdauung nach Versuchen,' und seine Bedeutung für die Entwicklung der Ernährungslehre in der ersten Hälfte des 19. Jahrhunderts," in *Gesnerus*, **13** (1956), 190–214; and H. Hoepke, "Der Streit der Professoren Tiedemann und Henle um den Neubau des Anatomischen Institutes in Heidelberg (1844–1849)," in *Heidelberg Jahrbuch 1961*.

VLADISLAV KRUTA

VAN TIEGHEM, PHILIPPE (*b*. Bailleul, Nord, France, 19 April 1839; *d*. Paris, France, 28 April 1914), *botany*.

Van Tieghem's father, a textile merchant, died in Martinique of yellow fever shortly before the birth of his son; and his mother died immediately afterward. Philippe was their fifth child and was brought up by his uncle and aunt, and later by his sisters. He received his *baccalauréat-ès-sciences* at the *collège* of Bailleul in 1856. As a scholarship student at the *lycée* of Douai, he prepared for the entrance examination to the École Polytechnique but decided instead to take the examination for the École Normale Supérieure, which he entered in 1858. After passing the *agrégation* in physical and natural sciences in 1861, van Tieghem became *agrégé-préparateur* in botany and mineralogy. Under Pasteur's supervision he prepared a dissertation on ammoniacal fermentation. Since his examiners considered that his research pertained essentially to chemistry, he was granted a doctorate in the physical sciences and not, as he had hoped, in the natural sciences. Wishing to become a botanist, he presented a second dissertation on the Araceae, which earned him the desired degree in 1867.

When Payer's chair at the École Normale Supérieure became vacant in 1864, van Tieghem was appointed his successor. Thus, at age twenty-five, he became *maître de conférences* in botany. From his marriage in 1862 to Hélène Sarchi he had four daughters and one son.

Because of the variety and the extent of van Tieghem's 328 recorded writings, a chronological list cannot provide a true picture of his work. Throughout his life he simultaneously studied several subjects; and his research covered five fields of botany: cryptogamy, fermentation, anatomy and biology of phanerogams, the application of anatomy to classification, and plant physiology.

In studying plant evolution and the reproduction of fungi, van Tieghem showed the value of using a pure culture of a single spore kept in a liquid medium. The spore must be protected from contamination by an enclosure yet remain accessible to microscopic observation. For his work on these monosperm cultures, van Tieghem was elected to the Académie des Sciences in 1877 and was appointed professor-administrator at the Muséum d'Histoire Naturelle in May 1879.

Van Tieghem was one of the first to reveal the relationship of blue algae to bacteria. In 1878 he studied "sugar gum" and established that it was a plant that lived on sugar. He described its development and proved that the insoluble substance, an isomer of cellulose, that forms the curd of the gum is excreted by the cells of the organism, which he named *Leuconostos mesenteroides*.

From 1877 to 1879 van Tieghem investigated *Bacillus amylobacter* and butyric fermentation. He demonstrated that only the membranes (whether cutinized, suberized, or lignified) of the submerged sections of aquatic plants can resist this bacterium, the role of which in the decomposition of complex organic substances into simple ones was soon confirmed. In collaboration with Bernard Renault, van Tieghem discovered that organisms closely related to *Bacillus amylobacter* were present in sections of carboniferous plant tissues, where they were preserved by silicification. The two scientists thus established the possibility that coal originated through the same fermentation process occurring in the remote past.

Van Tieghem created an anatomy founded on the homologies of tissues and on their origin from the initial cells. In addition to describing the tissues themselves, he considered the modes of their origin and the pattern of their differentiation. He distinguished three parts of the plant: root, stem, and leaf—a conception that won widespread acceptance largely for its simplicity. The principles of plant symmetry that van Tieghem established are classic. Having defined the organs by their structure, he applied his method to several unanswered questions: the structure of the pistil (his paper on this subject received the Bordin Prize of the Académie des Sciences in 1867), the organization of the ovule, the orientation of the embryo, and the composition of the seed. In 1871 he was awarded a grand prize for his work on the root. Moreover, in his anatomical research on the root and the stem, van Tieghem distinguished between primary and secondary tissues. Starting in 1871, he showed how anatomy could reveal the affinities between plants. He compared organs of the same species in different areas, thus initiating the study of the effect of the environment on plants.

Van Tieghem also did research in plant physiology. His experiments on the effect of cold on seeds and on the resultant "extreme slowing down" of their life processes were crucial. Through his work on the potential of the various parts of the embryo contained in the seed, he proved that each of the embryo's organs is autonomous and can grow without the others, whether or not the seed contains endosperm. He demonstrated that young embryos deprived of endosperm can be nourished by an artificial paste the chemical composition of which is close to that of specific endosperm.

After 1893 van Tieghem turned to work on parasites. He examined many exotic plants on which various degrees of degeneration of the ovule could be detected. His findings concerning this female organ led him to define the structure of the ovule and its integuments in a number of plants. Van Tieghem's work revealed the need for new classification of the phanerogams, based on the ovule and the seed, as well as a complete classification based on the ovule of plants.

Numerous and varied as they are, all van Tieghem's publications are characterized by an important new approach to botany: function is always studied in relation to structure and development.

In addition to conducting scientific investigations, van Tieghem held many official posts. From 1873 to 1886 he was professor of biology at the École Centrale des Arts et Manufactures; from 1885 to 1912, professor at the École Normale Supérieure des Jeunes Filles at Sèvres; and from 1898 to 1914, professor of plant biology at the Institut Agronomique. Students still find his *Traité de botanique* useful.

BIBLIOGRAPHY

I. ORIGINAL WORKS. Many of van Tieghem's writings are listed in *Notice sur les travaux scientifiques de M. Ph. Van Tieghem* (Paris, 1876). See also "Recherches sur la structure du pistil et sur l'anatomie comparée de la fleur, avec un atlas de 16 planches," in *Mémoires des savants étrangers*, **21** (1871), for which van Tieghem was awarded the Bordin Prize in 1867; "Recherches sur la symétrie de structure des plantes vasculaires," in *Annales des sciences naturelles*, Botanique, 5th ser., **12** (1871); *Traité de botanique conforme à l'état présent de la science*, 3rd. ed. (Paris, 1873), trans. into German by J. Sachs; *Traité de botanique* (Paris, 1884); *Éléments de botanique*, I (Paris, 1886), II (Paris, 1888); and "Recherches comparatives sur l'origine des membres endogènes dans les plantes vasculaires," in *Annales des sciences naturelles*, 7th ser., **8** (1889), written with Henri Douliot.

II. SECONDARY LITERATURE. See G. Bonnier, "L'oeuvre de Philippe Van Tieghem," in *Revue générale de botanique*, **26** (1914), 353–441; and J. Costantin, "Philippe Van Tieghem," in *Nature. Revue des sciences et de leurs applications aux arts et à l'industrie*, no. 2137 (1914), 394–396; and "Le rôle de Brongniart, de Renault et de Van Tieghem dans la chaire d'organographie du Muséum," in *Archives du Muséum nationale d'histoire naturelle*, 6th ser., **12** (1935), 319–324.

A. NOUGARÈDE

TIEMANN, JOHANN CARL WILHELM FERDINAND (*b.* Rübeland, Germany, 10 June 1848; *d.* Meran, Austria [now Merano, Italy], 14 November 1899), *chemistry.*

The son of William and Auguste Tiemann, Ferdinand Tiemann is primarily remembered for the synthesis of phenolic aldehydes, known as the Reimer-Tiemann reaction. He studied chemistry and pharmacy in Brunswick at the Collegium Carolinum (now known as the Technische Hochschule); briefly assisted his uncle, Carl Tiemann, a pharmacist; and entered the University of Berlin in 1870 to study chemistry under A. W. von Hofmann. Bertha Tiemann, the younger of his two sisters, married Hofmann in 1877. After serving in the Franco-Prussian War, he spent the rest of his life in the department at Berlin, where he became assistant in 1871, university lecturer in 1878, and professor in 1882. He was editor of the *Berichte der Deutschen chemischen Gesellschaft* from 1882 to 1897.

In 1870 Tiemann published the results of his earliest research on the derivatives of guanidine, trinitrotoluene, and diaminotoluene, and on the synthesis of dinitro- and trinitrobenzoic acids. In 1873 he began the first of many investigations on the purification and analysis of water. Tiemann and Wilhelm Haarmann obtained vanillin from the acid oxidation of conifer glucosides in 1874. During the next year they established the configuration of vanillin, and Tiemann synthesized it from protocatechuic acid. By heating guaiacol with chloroform and aqueous sodium hydroxide, Karl Ludwig Reimer obtained vanillin in 1876; and later that year he and Tiemann extended the reaction as a general method for synthesizing phenolic aldehydes. In 1891 Tiemann discovered the commercial method of preparing vanillin from eugenol (contained in oil of cloves) by the successive processes of rearrangement, acetylation, and oxidation of the side chain followed by hydrolysis. His other work included the synthesis of caffeic acid, the discovery of Ionone (ketones that have a strong odor of violets and are used especially in perfumes), elucidation of the structure of glucosamine, and extensive investigations of terpenes.

Tiemann enjoyed the reputation of being a fine teacher and a popular lecturer. With his students he published many papers on hydroxyaldehydes and related compounds. Failing health forced him to spend the winter of 1899 in the South Tirol, where he died of a heart attack, leaving a widow and three children.

BIBLIOGRAPHY

Some of Tiemann's contributions were first reported in the following papers: "Neue Guanidin-Abkömmlinge," in *Berichte der Deutschen chemischen Gesellschaft*, **3** (1870), 6; "Abkömmlinge des Trinitrotoluols und des Toluylendiamins," *ibid.*, p. 217; "Di- und trinitrirte Benzoesäuren," *ibid.*, p. 223, written with W. Judson; "Ueber das Coniferin und seine Umwandlung in das aromatische Prinzip der Vanille," *ibid.*, **7** (1874), 608, written with W. Haarmann; "Ueber eine synthetische Bildungsweise des Vanillins, über Hydrovanilloin und Vanillylalkohol," *ibid.*, **8** (1875), 1123; "Ueber die Einwirkung von Chloroform auf alkalische Phenolate," *ibid.*, **9** (1876), 824, written with K. L. Reimer; and "Ueber die Einwirkung von Chloroform auf Phenole und besonders aromatische Oxysäuren in alkalischer Lösung," *ibid.*, **9** (1876), 1268, written with K. L. Reimer.

See also "Synthese der Kaffeesäure, Abkömmlinge derselben und der Hydrokaffeesäure," *ibid.*, **11** (1878), 646, written with N. Nagai; "Ueber Vanillin," *ibid.*, **24** (1891), 2870; "Ueber Veilchenaroma," *ibid.*, **26** (1893), 2675, written with P. Krüger; and "Ueber das Glucosamin," *ibid.*, **27** (1894), 138, written with E. Fischer.

For a short biography, a review of his research, and a complete list of his publications, see Otto N. Witt, "Ferdinand Tiemann. Ein Lebensbild," in *Berichte der Deutschen chemischen Gesellschaft*, **34** (1901), 4403–4455.

A. ALBERT BAKER, JR.

TIETZ, J. D. See **Titius, Johann Daniel.**

AL-TĪFĀSHĪ, SHIHĀB AL-DĪN ABU'L-ʿABBĀS AḤMAD IBN YŪSUF (*b.* Tīfāsh, 1184; *d.* Cairo, 1253/1254), *mineralogy, physiology.*

Al-Tīfāshī began his education in Tīfāsh, three days' journey from Kairouan. At a very early age, he went to Cairo, where one of his teachers was the physician ʿAbd al-Laṭīf al-Baghdādī. After further studies in Damascus, he returned to Tīfāsh and obtained a judgeship. He later settled in Cairo, where he died.

Al-Tīfāshī's book on precious stones bears various names in the manuscripts; the generally accepted title is *Azhār al-afkār fī jawāhir al-aḥjār* ("Blossoms of Thoughts on Precious Stones"). It treats twenty-five stones in as many chapters. No critical edition of the book has been produced, but a text with Italian translation was printed in 1818. The work exists in a longer version, however, in a number of the surviving manuscripts, a fact established by J. J. Clément-Mullet, who used the trea-

tise as a principal source for his *Essai sur la minéralogie arabe*. Although he had the opportunity, Clément-Mullet unfortunately did not prepare a critical edition and omitted from his book much of the important information he had gathered.

Al-Tīfāshī states that he intends to treat stones from five points of view: the generation of the stones at the place of deposit; locations of deposits; types, qualities, and marks of genuineness; magical properties and uses; and prices. Clément-Mullet reproduced only those portions of the manuscripts relating to the first three topics, and even this was done unsystematically. J. Ruska was the first to offer longer selections from the text, based on various recensions in order to show that al-Tīfāshī had drawn on the so-called *Book of Stones* by Aristotle and the *Book of Causes* (or *Secret of the Creation*) attributed to Apollonius of Tyana (Balīnūs).

Al-Tīfāshī also wrote a book on sense perception, of which only the title of the original work is known. An extract is preserved in a manuscript by the fourteenth-century lexicographer Ibn Manzūr, but it has not been carefully studied.

Al-Tīfāshī also produced three books on sexual relations. One of these, which discusses the restoration of potency in old men, was reprinted several times and even appeared in an anonymous English translation. The first part deals with the sex organs, sexual hygiene, and aphrodisiacs, and includes quotations from a number of ancient and Islamic physicians. The second part is a sort of erotic guide for men. A second book, apparently more oriented toward hygiene, has not yet been studied. The third book comprises obscene anecdotes; several stories of this type also appear in the second part of the first of the books mentioned above.

BIBLIOGRAPHY

I. ORIGINAL WORKS. The text of the *Azhār*, with Italian trans., is A. R. Biscia, *Fior di pensieri sulle pietre preziose di Ahmad Teifascite* (Florence, 1818), Italian version also printed separately (Bologna, 1906). J.-J. Clément-Mullet reproduces portions of the MS in his *Essai sur la minéralogie arabe* (Paris, 1868). One of his books on sexual relations appeared as *The Old Man Young Again, Translated From the Arabic by an English Bohemian* (Paris, 1898). J. Ruska includes selections from the *Azhār* in his *Das Steinbuch des Aristoteles* (Heidelberg, 1912), 23–31; and *Tabula Smaragdina* (Heidelberg, 1926).

II. SECONDARY LITERATURE. See C. Brockelmann,

Geschichte der arabischen Literatur, I (Weimar, 1898), 495; and supp., I (Leiden, 1937), 904, and III (1942), 1243; Ibn Farḥūn, *Al-Dībāj al-mudhahhab fī maʿrifat aʿyān ʿulmāʾ al-madhhab* (Cairo, A.H. 1356 [A.D. 1937/1938]); G. Sarton, *Introduction to the History of Science*, II (Baltimore, 1931), 650; M. Steinschneider, "Arabische Lapidarein," in *Zeitschrift der Deutschen morgenländischen Gesellschaft*, **49** (1895), 254 ff.; and M. Ullmann, *Die Medizin im Islam* (Leiden, 1970), 196 f.

M. PLESSNER
F. KLEIN-FRANKE

TIKHOV, GAVRIIL ADRIANOVICH (*b.* Smolevichi, near Minsk, Russia, 1 May 1875; *d.* Alma-Ata, Kazakhstan S.S.R., 25 January 1960), *astrophysics, astrobotany.*

Tikhov was the son of a railway stationmaster. In 1893 he graduated from the Gymnasium in Simferopol with a gold medal and entered the mathematical section of Moscow University. He graduated in 1897 with a first-degree diploma. From 1898 to 1900 he studied in Paris at the Sorbonne and worked as a probationer in Jules Janssen's astrophysics observatory in Meudon. At Janssen's suggestion Tikhov, on 15 November 1899, observed a meteor shower from a balloon. Twice he ascended Mont Blanc to work at Janssen's mountain observatory.

After returning to Russia, Tikhov taught mathematics at a Moscow Gymnasium and then at the Ekaterinoslav Higher Mining School. He also studied meteors and variable stars. In 1906 he was named extra-staff adjunct-astronomer at the Pulkovo observatory. Using the so-called Bredikhin short-focus astrograph, Tikhov began work on photographic astrocolorimetry, using two parts of the spectrum, separated by special color filters. He sensitized films to the necessary portions of the spectrum and prepared gelatin filters colored with various dyes. In 1913 he successfully defended his dissertation for the degree of master of astronomy and geodesy.

From 1914 to 1917 at the Central Aeronautical Navigation Station of the Pilot Observer Military School, Tikhov worked on ways of improving visibility from airplanes and developed light filters and special photographic film for aerial photography. His first monograph on aerial photography (1917) dealt with methods for improving visual and photographic air reconnaissance. It was widely used by pilots of the Allied armies.

After the war Tikhov returned to Pulkovo, and

from 1919 to 1931 he also lectured on astrophysics at the University of Leningrad. From 1919 to 1941 he directed the astrophysics laboratory of the P. F. Lesgaft Scientific Institute.

In 1927 Tikhov was elected corresponding member of the Academy of Sciences of the U.S.S.R., and in 1935 he received the degree of doctor of physical and mathematical sciences. He observed the total solar eclipse of 21 September 1941 in Central Asia and subsequently worked at a branch of the U.S.S.R. Academy of Sciences. When the Kazakh S.S.R. Academy of Sciences was organized in 1946, he became an active member. In 1947 Tikhov became head of the section of astrobotany, which he had organized. In 1949 he became professor of astronomy. He was a member of the International Astronomical Union, the American Astronomical Society, and a number of Soviet scientific societies.

By means of colorimetry Tikhov studied the dispersion of light in interstellar space, that is, the rate of diffusion of light at various wavelengths. In this study he chose Algol variable stars, on which he detected a delay in the moment of eclipse in the shorter waves as compared to the longer waves. This phenomenon is now known as the Tikhov-Nordmann effect. (Charles Nordmann discovered this effect some time later.) The Soviet astrophysicist E. R. Mustel subsequently explained it in terms of the distortion of the form of the components and the presence of tidal waves of reduced temperature.

Tikhov later developed the method of the "longitudinal spectrograph," in which the optical imperfections of a poorly achromatized objective lens were used for quickly and conveniently estimating the color of stars; the technique led to the publication of extensive catalogs of star colors.

An extended series of works related to observation of the total solar eclipses of 1927, 1936, and 1941 resulted in the establishment of two structural peculiarities of the solar corona—the "globular," or "dispersed," corona and the "radiant" corona that penetrates the streamers.

Tikhov also made photographic observations of Mars using the thirty-inch refractor with light filters at the Pulkovo observatory. From this research later came the new fields of astrobotany and astrobiology. Tikhov conceived the idea of comparing the spectrophotometric properties of natural formations on the earth (mountains, soils, sands, ice, snow, and plant life) with corresponding properties of various formations on Mars. Specialized investigations of the reflecting abilities of vegetation growing under severe conditions and at high altitudes showed the great degree of adaptability of life and suggested the possible existence of vegetation on Mars. Tikhov himself participated in fifteen expeditions to various mountain regions and the Arctic in support of these ideas.

Tikhov's work on atmospheric optics was closely related to this research. In 1912 he invented an instrument for registering astral scintillation and elaborated a method for measuring the angular diameter of stars on the basis of their scintillation. He later studied the "green flash" that appears at sunset and discovered the anomalous dispersion of light in the earth's atmosphere. He investigated ashen light of the moon, in an attempt to determine how the light of the earth as a planet would be seen from outer space. To study atmospheric optics by daylight, in a clear sky, Tikhov designed an original cyanometer and a one-dimensional colorimeter with a dark blue wedge.

BIBLIOGRAPHY

I. ORIGINAL WORKS. Tikhov's basic works (from his 165 writings) were published as *Osnovnye trudy*, 5 vols. (Alma-Ata, 1954–1960). His autobiography is *Shestdesyat let u teleskopa* ("Sixty Years at the Telescope"; Moscow, 1959). His principal works in astrobotany and astrophysics (1912–1957) have appeared in English trans., 2 vols. (New York, 1960).

II. SECONDARY LITERATURE. On Tikhov's life and work, see the bibliography of his 165 published writings in *Izvestiya Akademii nauk Kazakhskoi SSR*, no. 90, Ser. astrobot., nos. 1–2 (1950), 5–13; N. I. Kucherov, "G. A. Tikhov," in *Izvestiya Glavnoi astronomicheskoi observatorii v Pulkove*, **22**, pt. 2 (1961), 2–5; M. A. Milkhiker and M. A. Daskal, "Gavriil Adrianovich Tikhov," in *Byulleten Vsesoyuznogo astronomo-geodezicheskogo obshchestva*, no. 28 (1960), 56–59; V. V. Sharonov, "Gavriil Adrianovich Tikhov," in *Priroda* (1950), no. 8, 85–88; and N. M. Shtaude, "Osnovnye cherty nauchnogo tvorchestva G. A. Tikhova po lichnym vpechatleniam za 40 let" ("The Basic Features of G. A. Tikhov's Scientific Work From Personal Impressions Over Forty Years"), in *Izvestiya Akademii nauk Kazakhskoi SSR*, no. 90, Ser. astrobot., nos. 1–2 (1950), 19–24.

P. G. KULIKOVSKY

TILAS, DANIEL (*b.* Gammelbo, Västmanland, Sweden, 11 March 1712; *d.* Stockholm, Sweden, 17 October 1772), *geology, mining.*

Tilas' father, Olof Tilas, was an officer and landowner who was knighted in 1719. His mother, Maria Hjärne, was the daughter of the scientist Urban Hjärne. As was usual among the Swedish landed gentry at that time, Tilas received his elementary education at home and was sent to the University of Uppsala in 1723, studying there until 1726 and again from 1728 to 1732. According to his unpublished autobiography, he did not spend much time on studies and gave the university little credit for his education. This is certainly unfair, for he received a good foundation in both Latin and the natural sciences, the latter most probably from his connection with the group around Linnaeus.

Tilas' interest in mining began early, and in 1732 he became assistant (*auskultant*) at the Office of Mines, the state organization that had administrative and legal control of the flourishing Swedish mining industry. He was greatly interested in the inspection of mines and took part in the work at mines and smelting plants. He discovered the need for exact mapping of the mineral veins in the mines, in order to form rational plans, and soon extended this work to mapping the geology of the surrounding areas, to facilitate prospecting for new mines.

Tilas developed an ambitious project to map all of Sweden geologically; and from his correspondence it seems that he also planned a geological map of the world. His inspiration certainly was Linnaeus' plans for similar inventories of the fauna and flora of the world. Tilas produced an unpublished geological map of two provinces of Finland and of a large number of mines. His grand designs were not approved by some of his older colleagues, but his results and ideas made him famous. He was a founding member of the Royal Swedish Academy of Sciences (1739) and served as its president for two terms. From 1741 to 1743 and in 1745 Tilas was a member of the international commission to establish the border between Sweden and Norway. With some of the younger members he walked along the boundary, making a number of interesting geological and other observations in relatively unknown and inaccessible areas.

In 1751 a fire destroyed Tilas' house; and his collections of rocks and minerals, and all his manuscripts and maps, were lost. Loss of the latter was especially disastrous to his great plans, and it was impossible for him to repeat all the fieldwork involved. Some of his results were published in 1765, but much of his scientific work remains in the manuscripts he managed to reconstruct and in the form of unpublished reports. Tilas' great importance lay not only in his plan to make geological maps of large regions but in his activity in other fields of geology. Some of his views on the origin of fossils and erratic boulders seem rather modern; and he introduced a number of terms, including the mineral name feldspar. He was also one of the first geologists to work with oil (1740) and to describe its economic exploitation.

Tilas was married in 1741 to Hedvig Reuterholm (d. 1743) and in 1743 to Anna Catharina Åkerhielm. Through both his marriages he became connected with influential political families and was active at the royal court. Also interested in genealogy and numismatics, Tilas became chamberlain in 1766 and state herald in 1768.

BIBLIOGRAPHY

I. ORIGINAL WORKS. Tilas' works include *En bergmanns rön och forsök i mineralriket* (Stockholm, 1738); "Mineralhistoria øfver Osmundsberget uti Rättviks Socken," in *Kungl. Vetenskaps akademiens Handlingar* (1740); *Stenrikets historia* (Stockholm, 1742); and *Utkast til Sveriges mineralhistoria* (Stockholm, 1765). Complete lists of his published papers are given in the secondary literature. His unpublished diaries and official reports, preserved in Swedish archives, have been used extensively in the study of the politics and culture of his time.

II. SECONDARY LITERATURE. Much of the extensive but rather scattered literature on Tilas is based on his unpublished diaries, MSS, and reports. See E. V. Falk, "Daniel Tilas och Fredrik Gyllenborg," in *Personhistorisk tidsskrift*, **36** (1936), 19–49; G. Regnell, "On the Position of Palaeontology and Historical Geology in Sweden Before 1800," in *Arkiv för Mineralogi och Geologi*, **1**, no. 1 (1949), 1–64; and N. Zenzen, "Geologiska kartor och geologisk kartläggning i Sverige føre upprättande av Sveriges Geologiska Undersökning," in *Geologiska föreningens i Stockholm förhandlingar*, **47** (1925), 311–343; "On the First Use of the Term 'Feldspat' (Feldspar etc.) by Daniel Tilas," *ibid.*, 385–405; and "Daniel Tilas om geologien i svensk-norska gränstrakter," *ibid.*, **53** (1931), 27–46.

NILS SPJELDNAES

TILDEN, SIR WILLIAM AUGUSTUS (*b.* London, England, 15 August 1842; *d.* London, 11 December 1926), *chemistry*.

The eldest son of Augustus Tilden, William had a mixed early education resulting from the numerous moves of his family. He attended East Dereham School briefly before being apprenticed in 1857 to the pharmaceutist Alfred Allchin, who so encouraged Tilden to chemistry that he allowed him to spend the last year of his apprenticeship studying at the Royal College of Chemistry. In 1863 Tilden became a demonstrator at the Pharmaceutical Society, a post he held for nine years while studying at London University for his B.Sc. (1868) and D.Sc. (1871).

Tilden married Charlotte Pither Bush in 1869 (*d.* 1905). He joined Clifton College as science master in 1872 and there began to investigate nitroso derivatives of terpenes, especially α-pinene and limonene. In 1880 he was elected a fellow of the Royal Society and the first professor of chemistry at Mason College. In 1894 he succeeded T. E. Thorpe as professor of chemistry at the Royal College of Science of London. Tilden married his second wife, Julia Mary Ramie, in 1907. He was named emeritus professor of Imperial College, which was formed from the Royal College of Science, and created a knight in 1909. Although retirement ended his bench chemistry, he continued to write and publish books.

Familiarity with aqua regia and nitrosyl chloride led Tilden to study hydrocarbon derivatives of NOCl, first with phenol, then with α-pinene and limonene. During this time the structures of the terpenes including pinene and limonene were subjects of controversy. The ease with which terpenes formed nitrosyl chlorides not only permitted characterization of these compounds but also provided ready intermediates for further reaction. Nitroso terpene derivatives, prepared from the nitrosyl chlorides by base hydrolysis, allowed Tilden to classify terpenes into a limited number of classes bringing some order to the previous chaos. His scheme divided terpenes into three types based on their nitroso derivatives: the turpentines, of which α-pinene is the principal constituent, gave derivatives m.p. 126°C; citrenes, of which limonene is the most commonly occurring, gave derivatives m.p. 76°C; and sylvestrene, which was recognized as different from the other two. Once this division was made, the structure determination of a terpene in a particular class was quite rapid. The first class would be recognized later as containing bicyclic terpenes, and the second and third as monocyclic terpenes, each of a different structure. From his first work in 1877 with the nitroso derivatives Tilden continued throughout his career to study terpenes. One further investigation led him to study the thermal decomposition of terpenes in a red-hot iron tube. He obtained, as one of the many products in the decomposition, isoprene, which is now recognized as the building block not only of the C_{10} terpenes but also the C_{15} sesquiterpenes, the C_{20} diterpenes, and the C_{30} triterpenes. The sticky material he obtained from isoprene exposed to sunlight was a precursor of synthetic rubber, but Tilden never pursued its uses.

The problem of relating specific heat to atomic weight caught Tilden's interest late in his career; he measured specific heat as a function of temperature for a number of metals and found that it was a marked function of temperature. His work demonstrated that specific heat was determined by uncertain physical forces and not the work required to separate the atoms of the substance.

Tilden served the Institute of Chemistry as president from 1891 to 1894, the Chemical Society as treasurer from 1899 to 1903 and as president from 1903 to 1905, and was awarded the Davy Medal in 1905.

BIBLIOGRAPHY

I. ORIGINAL WORKS. No collected volume of Tilden's papers is extant. Most of his terpene papers were published in *Journal of the Chemical Society* (1865–1907) and papers on specific heat in *Philosophical Transactions of the Royal Society*.

Preparation of α-pinene nitrosyl chloride appeared in *Journal of the Chemical Society*, **28** (1875), 514; and preparation of limonene nitrosyl chloride, *ibid.*, **31** (1877), 554.

Tilden wrote several books; the most signal are *A Short History of the Progress of Scientific Chemistry* (London, 1899), *The Elements* (London, 1910), *Chemical Discovery and Invention in the Twentieth Century* (London, 1917), *A Life of Sir William Ramsay* (London, 1918), and *Famous Chemists* (London, 1921).

II. SECONDARY LITERATURE. Two excellent biographical sketches are *Journal of the Chemical Society* (1927), 3190–3202; and *Proceedings of the Royal Society*, **117A**, no. 778 (1928), i–v, with bibliography.

GERALD R. VAN HECKE

TILLET, MATHIEU (*b.* Bordeaux, France, 10 November 1714; *d.* Paris, France, 20 December 1791), *agronomy, chemistry.*

Little is known about Tillet's early life. Like many other French scientists of the period he spent his early manhood in Bordeaux. His interest in science having been stimulated by the local academy, he went to Paris to practice it, and he remained there for the rest of his life. In 1758 he entered the Paris Académie des Sciences as a botanist; but he worked mainly as an assayer and chemist. Tillet enjoyed a string of promotions within the Academy, in the activities of which he took an energetic part. He was director in 1779 and treasurer at the time of his death. He apparently left the accounts (to his successor Lavoisier) in a chaotic state. Before going to Paris, Tillet was director of the mint at Troyes; later he became a *Commissaire du Roi pour les essais et affinage du Royaume*. He was also an enthusiastic member of the Société d'Agriculture.

Tillet's chemical papers, all of which were published by the Academy, sprang directly out of the practical concerns connected with assaying and refining metals for the mint. The papers deal almost exclusively with the metallurgy of gold and silver and are devoted to improving the precision and rationalizing the operations of assay by cupellation. Tillet made no very dramatic innovations in the course of this work, but he contributed in a sober and workmanlike way to the creation of accurate chemical standards, to which the French government scientists directed so much effort in the eighteenth and nineteenth centuries.

Tillet is best remembered for his investigations of wheat smuts and bunts, one genus of which, *Tilletia*, is named for him. In a long series of experiments carried out at Bordeaux and repeated at Paris, Tillet distinguished stinking smut (bunt) from loose smut, disproved the theories that these diseases of wheat were caused by climate or insects, and showed clearly the infectious nature of the dust by planting artificially infected seed among healthy plants and by noting the spread of the disease. He did not know the exact nature of the fungus causing the disease, but he did identify the dust as containing the agent.

BIBLIOGRAPHY

I. ORIGINAL WORKS. See *Dissertation sur la ductibilité des métaux, et les moyens de l'augmenter* (Bordeaux, 1750); *Dissertation sur la cause qui corrumpt et noircit les grains de bled dans les épis; et sur les moyens de prévenir ces accidens. Qui a remporté le Prix au Jugement de l'Académie Royale des Belles-Lettres, Sciences et Arts de Bordeaux* (Bordeaux, 1755), also in German as *Das Hern Tillets, . . . Abhandlung von der Ursache . . .* (Hamburg–Leipzig, 1757), and as *Dissertation on the Cause of the Corruption and Smutting of the Kernels of Wheat in the Head, and on the Means of Preventing These Untoward Circumstances*, H. B. Humphrey, trans. (Ithaca, N.Y., 1937); *Suite des expériences relatives à la meme dissertation* (Bordeaux, 1755); *Précis des expériences qui ont été faites par ordre du Roi à Trianon, sur la cause de la corruption des bleds et sur les moyens de la prévenir; à la suite duquel est une instruction propre à guider les laboureurs dans la manière dont ils doivent préparer le grain avant de le semer* (Paris, 1756); and *Histoire d'un insecte qui dévore les grains de l'Angoumois, avec les moyens que l'on peut employer pour le détruire* (Paris, 1762), written with Duhamel du Monceau.

See also *Essai sur le rapport des poids étrangers avec le marc de France* (Paris, 1766), also in Italian (Florence, 1769); *Observations faites par ordre du Roi sur les côtes de Normandie, au sujet des effets pernicieux qui sont attribués, dans le pays de Caux, à la fumée du Varech, lorsqu'on brûle cette plante pour la réduire en soude* (1772); *Rapport fait à l'Académie royale des sciences, au sujet d'une question relative à l'arpentage* (1772), written with l'Abbé Bossut; *Mémoire sur un moyen nouveau de faire avec exactitude, et tout-à-la-fois, le depart de plusieurs essais d'or, dans un seul et même matras* (Paris, 1779); *Expériences et observations sur le poids du pain au sortir du four et sur le règlement par lequel les boulangers sont assujetis à donner aux pains qu'ils exposent en vente un poids fixe et déterminé* (Paris, 1781); *Projet d'un tarif propre à servir de règle pour établir la valeur du pain proportionnément à celle du blé et des farines, avec des observations sur la mouture économique comme base essentielle de ce tarif, et sur les avantages du commerce des farines, par préférence à celui du blé en nature* (Paris, 1784); and *Rapport fait à l'Académie royale des sciences, relativement à l'avis que le Parlement a demandé à cette Académie sur la contestation qui s'est élevée à Rochefort au sujet de la taxe du pain* (Paris, 1785), written with Le Roy and Demarest.

Other works include *Observations de la Société Royale d'Agriculture sur l'uniformité des poids et mesures* (Paris, 1790), written with Abeille; *Extrait d'une partie du Rapport de l'Académie royale des sciences, fait par MM. Tillet, Leroy, Fourcroy, et Broussonnet, sur le foyer Franklin, perfectionné par M. Desarnad, et sur celui de son invention; Mémoire sur deux machines propres à donner le rapport que les différentes mesures à grains, ou celles des liquides, ont avec le boisseau ou la pinte de Paris* (Paris, n.d.).

To the list of Tillet's papers in Poggendorff, add the following: "Lettre à M. XXX," in *Mercure de France* (1757), 179; "Observations sur la maladie du Mais ou Blé de Turquie," in *Histoire de L'Académie royale des sciences pour l'année 1760* (1766), 254–261; and "Expériences et observations sur la végétation du Blé dans chacune des matières simples dont les terres labourables sont ordinairement composées et dans différens mélanges des ces matières par lesquels on s'est rapproché de ceux qui constituent ces mèmes terres à labour," *ibid.*, 1772 . . . (1775).

II. SECONDARY LITERATURE. See Michaud, *Biographie universelle*, XLI, 545; Poggendorff, II, 1108; and J. R. Partington, *A History of Chemistry*, III, 609–610. For Tillet's work on smuts and bunts, see N. E. Stevens, "Plant Pathology in the Penultimate Century," in *Isis*, **21** (1934), 98–122; and B. Wehnelt, "Mathieu Tillet.

Tilletia," in *Nachrichten über Schädlingsbekämpfung*, **2** (1937), 41–146.

STUART PIERSON

TILLO, ALEKSEY ANDREEVICH (*b.* Kiev, Russia, 25 November 1839; *d.* St. Petersburg, Russia [now Leningrad, U.S.S.R.], 11 January 1900), *geography, cartography, geodesy.*

Tillo's father, an officer in the engineering communications corps, was of French origin. From 1849 to 1859 Tillo studied at the military schools of Kiev and St. Petersburg. In 1862 he graduated from the Mikhaylov Artillery Academy and in 1864 completed the theoretical course of the geodesy section of the General Staff Academy. He subsequently carried out practical geodetic and astronomical work for two years at the Pulkovo observatory under the supervision of Otto Struve. From 1866 to 1871 he was director of the Military Topographical Section of the Orenburg Military District. From 1871 on he held a number of military command positions and received the rank of lieutenant general in 1894. In 1892 he was elected corresponding member of the Académie des Sciences and, in 1894, of the St. Petersburg Academy of Sciences. Tillo's research was associated mainly with the Russian Geographical Society, of which he became a member in 1868. From 1884 he was a member of the council of the society, and from 1889 he was president of its section of mathematical geography.

Tillo's specialty was geodesy, and his chief works were devoted to the study of the hypsometry and orography of Russia. Leveling carried out in the summer of 1874 led Tillo to determine that the level of the Aral Sea had risen seventy-four meters above that of the Caspian Sea. Tillo initiated the major leveling projects carried out in 1875 and 1877 in Siberia; the results of the surveys and the data from his own research provided the basis for his map of the altitudes of European Russia (1884) and his map of the lengths and descents of the rivers of European Russia (1888). Tillo's important hypsometrical map of European Russia (1889) was compiled from data on the altitudes of more than 51,000 points. The map established the presence in European Russia of two broad north-south elevations, which Tillo called the Mid-Russian and the Privolga; the ridges had previously— and incorrectly—been shown on maps as the Ural-Baltic and the Ural-Carpathian.

In an improved version of his map (1896) Tillo included those parts of Germany, Austria-Hungary, and Romania that bordered on Russia. He also studied meteorological phenomena, the hydrology of rivers and lakes, and the magnetism of the earth.

BIBLIOGRAPHY

I. ORIGINAL WORKS. There is a complete bibliography of Tillo's writings in Novokshanova (see below). They include *Opisanie Aralo-Kaspyskoy nivelirovki, proizvedennoy v 1874 godu po porucheniyu Russkogo Geografi cheskogo Obshchestva i Orenburgskogo ego otdela* ("A Description of the Aral-Caspian Leveling Carried Out in 1874, Commissioned by the Russian Geographical Society and Its Orenburg Section"; St. Petersburg, 1877); *Opyt svoda nivelirovok Rossyskoy imperii. Materialy dlya gipsometrii Rossii. S Atlasom prodolnykh profiley*, 4 pts. ("An Attempt at a Generalization Comparing the Levels of the Russian Empire. Materials for the Hyposometry of Russia. With an Atlas of Longitudinal Profiles"; St. Petersburg, 1881–1882); *Karta vysot Evropeyskoy Rossii* ("Map of the Altitudes of European Russia"; St. Petersburg, 1884); *Karta dliny i padenia rek Evropeyskoy Rossii* ("Map of the Lengths and Descents of the Rivers of European Russia"; St. Petersburg, 1888); *Gipsometricheskaya karta Evropeyskoy Rossii* ("Hypsometric Map of European Russia"; St. Petersburg, 1889); "Srednyaya vysota sushi i srednyaya glubina morya v severnom i yuzhnom polushariakh i zavisimost sredney vysoty materikov i sredney glubiny morey ot geograficheskoy shiroty" ("The Average Altitude of the Dry Land and the Average Depth of the Sea in the Northern and Southern Hemispheres and the Relation of the Average Altitude of the Continents and the Average Depth of the Seas to Geographical Latitude"), in *Izvestiya Imperatorskogo Russkogo geografichesko obshchestva*, **25**, no. 2 (1889), 113–134; "Raspredelenie atmosfernogo davlenia na prostranstve Rossyskoy imperii i Aziatskogo materika na osnovanii nablyudeny s 1836 po 1885 g." ("Distribution of Atmospheric Pressure in the Area of the Russian Empire and the Asian Continent Based on Observations From 1836 Through 1885"), in *Zapiski Imperatorskogo russkogo geograficheskogo obshchestva*, **21** (1890), 1–308; "Orografia Evropeyskoy Rossii na osnovanii gipsometricheskoy karty" ("The Orography of European Russian Based on a Hypsometric Map"), in *Izvestiya Imperatorskogo Russkogo geografichesko obshchestva*, **26**, pt. 1 (1890), 8–32; *Gipsometricheskaya karta Zapadnoy chasti Evropeyskoy Rossii, v svyazi s prilezhashchimi chastyami Germanii, Avstro-Vengrii i Rumynii* ("Hypsometric Map of the Western Part of European Russia Together with the Adjacent Parts of Germany, Austria-Hungary, and Romania"; St. Petersburg, 1896); *Karta basseynov vnutrennikh vodnykh putey Evropeyskoy Rossii s ukazaniem punktov meteorologicheskikh i vodomernykh nablyudeny* ("Map of the Basins of the Inland Water Routes of European Russia With an Indication of the Points of Meteorological and Water-Measuring Observations"; St. Petersburg, 1897); and *Atlas raspredelenia atmosfernykh osadkov Rossii po mesyatsam i za ves god na osnovanii dvadtsatiletnikh nablyudeny 1871–1890 gg.* ("Atlas of the Distribution of Atmospheric Precipitation in Russia by Months and the Entire Year Based on Twenty-Year Observations 1871–1890"; St. Petersburg, 1897).

II. SECONDARY LITERATURE. See L. S. Berg, "A. A. Tillo," in *Izvestiya Vsesoyuznogo geograficheskogo obshchestva*, **82**, no. 2 (1950), 113–125, published on the fiftieth anniversary of his death; and Z. K. Novokshanova, *Aleksey Andreevich Tillo* (Moscow, 1961).

I. FEDOSEYEV

TILLOCH, ALEXANDER (*b.* Glasgow, Scotland, 28 February 1759; *d.* Islington, London, England, 26 January 1825), *natural philosophy, science journalism.*

The son of John Tulloch, a tobacco merchant and magistrate, Alexander Tilloch attended the University of Glasgow, graduating in 1771. While working in his father's firm he experimented with printing, and in 1781 he rediscovered the method of printing books from plates (stereotyping) instead of from movable type. Stereoprinting had first been developed (unsuccessfully) by the Edinburgh jeweler William Ged in 1725. In 1784 Tilloch patented the process with Andrew Foulis, printer for the University of Glasgow, and together they produced several books. A man of considerable inventiveness, Tilloch filed other patents for mill drives and steam engines, and devised printing methods for the prevention of banknote forgeries.

In 1787, calling himself Tilloch rather than Tulloch, he moved to London, where, with the aid of friends, he bought an evening daily newspaper, *The Star*, which he edited until 1821. From 1809 he used this paper to expound his views on biblical prophecies. He joined the Sandemanian sect (Goswell Street Chapel) but, like Michael Faraday, he reconciled its fundamentalism with a scientific outlook. A gregarious man with pronounced antiquarian tastes, Tilloch belonged to innumerable societies, including William Allen's Askesian group.

In 1797 William Nicholson founded his *Journal of Natural Philosophy*. In June 1798, in direct competition, Tilloch published the monthly *Philosophical Magazine* in order "to diffuse Philosophical Knowledge among every class of Society, and to give the Public as early an Account as possible of every thing new or curious in the Scientific World, both at Home or on the [war-torn] Continent" (preface to the first volume). Launched in the educational spirit of the Scottish Enlightenment, the *Philosophical Magazine* in its early years catered more to artisans than to the educated scientific establishment. (Tilloch founded an explicit mechanics' journal, *Mechanic's Oracle*, in 1824.) From 1810 onward, through skillful journalism, because of the decline and takeover of Nicholson's *Journal* (in 1814), and because of the exciting competition from Thomas Thomson's *Annals of Philosophy* after 1812, Tilloch's *Philosophical Magazine* came to be of major importance for the dissemination of original scientific news.

BIBLIOGRAPHY

I. ORIGINAL WORKS. Eight of Tilloch's post-1800 papers are recorded in the Royal Society *Catalogue of Scientific Papers*, V (London, 1867–1925), 996. His biblical writings are cited in Carlyle (below). Files of the *Star* newspaper and the *Mechanic's Oracle and Artisan's Laboratory and Workshop* (July 1824–1825) are kept at the British Museum. The library of the University of Edinburgh possesses a few letters.

II. SECONDARY LITERATURE. Biographical notices with further references will be found in *Gentleman's Magazine*, 95 (1825), i, 276–281, and by E. Irving Carlyle in *Dictionary of National Biography*, LVI (1898), 391–392. See also W. I. Addison, *Matriculation Albums of the University of Glasgow* (Glasgow, 1913), 96; and J. Harrison, ed., *Printing Patents, 1617–1857* (London, 1859; repr. London, 1969), 93–95.

The foundation of the *Philosophical Magazine* is discussed by Allan and John Ferguson in a bicentenary commemoration number edited by A. Ferguson, *Natural Philosophy Through the Eighteenth Century and Allied Topics* (London, 1948); and S. Lilley, "Nicholson's Journal," in *Annals of Science*, 6 (1948–1950), 78–101.

W. H. BROCK

TILLY, JOSEPH-MARIE DE (*b.* Ypres, Belgium, 16 August 1837; *d.* Schaerbeek, Belgium, 4 August 1906), *geometry.*

Tilly, one of the most profound Belgian mathematicians, attained the rank of lieutenant general by the time of his retirement. As a second lieutenant in the artillery, he was assigned in 1858 to teach a course in mathematics at the regimental school; and it was there that he studied the principles of geometry. In 1860, in *Recherches sur les éléments de géométrie*, Tilly used Anatole Lamarle's methods to criticize Euclid's fifth postulate and achieved results that Lobachevsky had published but of which he was unaware until about 1866. In *Études de mécanique abstraite* (1870), based on the negation of Euclid's postulate, Tilly worked with a Lobachevskian space. He was the first to study non-Euclidean mechanics, a subject he virtually created. His research brought him into contact with Jules Houël, the only French mathematician then interested in the new geometries. Although they never met, their correspondence (1870–1885) was a valuable stimulus to Tilly, who had been working for nine years without guidance.

In *Essai sur les principes fondamentaux de la géométrie et de la mécanique* (1878), Tilly established the Riemannian, Lobachevskian, and Euclidean geometries on the concept of the distance between two points. In his formulation these geometries were based, respectively, on one, two, and three necessary and sufficient, irreducible axioms.

Tilly also wrote on military science and on the history of mathematics in Belgium, including the centenary report on the mathematical activities of the Belgian Royal Academy from 1772 to 1872. These studies were undertaken in the midst of Tilly's demanding professional duties as director of the arsenal at Antwerp and as commandant and director of studies at the École Militaire for ten years. In *Essai de géométrie analytique générale* (1892), the synthesis and crowning achievement of his work, Tilly stressed the fundamental relationship among the ten distances between any two of a group of five points. In brief, he established that geometry is the mathematical physics of distances.

Tilly's last years were marred by his unjust dismissal as commandant of the École Militaire in December 1899 and his forced early retirement in August 1900. The actions of the minister of war were motivated by complaints that Tilly had unduly emphasized the scientific education of future officers. The inspector of studies at the École Militaire, Gérard-Mathieu Leman (later a general), had forbidden Tilly to use the notions of the infinitely small and of the differential.

In 1870 Tilly was elected corresponding member and, in 1878, full member of the science section of the Belgian Royal Academy, of which he was president in 1887.

BIBLIOGRAPHY

See two articles by P. Mansion, in *Annuaire de l'Académie royale de Belgique*, **80** (1914), 203–285, with portrait and bibliography; and in *Biographie nationale* . . ., XXV (Brussels, 1930–1932), 264–269.

J. PELSENEER

IBN AL-TILMĪDH, AMĪN AL-DAWLA ABU'L-ḤASAN HIBAT ALLĀH IBN ṢAꜤĪD (*b.* Baghdad, *ca.* 1073; *d.* Baghdad, 11 February 1165), *medicine, pharmacy, logic, education, literature.*

Ibn al-Tilmīdh's maternal grandfather, Muꜥtamad al-Mulk Abu'l-Faraj Yaḥyā ibn al-Tilmīdh, was a physician. He made great efforts to secure a good education for his grandson, who assumed the patronymic Ibn al-Tilmīdh after the grandfather's death. Upon completion of his medical education, Ibn al-Tilmīdh went to Persia, where he practiced for several years in the Khurāsān region. There, according to Ẓahīr al-Dīn al-Bayhaqī (1106–1170), he learned the Persian language. Being a Syriac Christian and vitally interested in his church, its liturgy, and its activities, he also mastered the Syriac (Aramaic) language. Yāqūt al-Ḥamawī (1179–1229) affirmed that Ibn al-Tilmīdh knew Greek as well.

Ibn al-Tilmīdh conducted a lively correspondence with dignitaries, high government officials, colleagues, friends, and members of his family. His letters, collected during his lifetime in a large volume entitled *Tawqīꜥāt wa-murāsalāt*, include one of advice and admonition addressed to his son, who does not seem to have been very intelligent. He also wrote numerous short poems on general medicine, the value of learning, dietetics, mental health, friendship, clouds, hospitality, modesty, loneliness, romance, wine, fish, the balance, the astrolabe, armor, and shadows.

After his return to Baghdad, Ibn al-Tilmīdh served under several caliphs, especially al-Muqtafī (1136–1160), who appointed him court physician and chief of the ꜤAḍudī hospital, one of the most important institutions of its kind. He also was commissioned by the caliph to conduct licensing examinations for doctors, and he had the largest private medical school in Baghdad in his time. His fame as a medical educator attracted students from far and near.

Ibn al-Tilmīdh enjoyed an excellent reputation not only as an educator but also as a physician. His practice brought him wealth and prosperity, and he was very generous to his students and to the poor. He amassed a large library, most of which was dispersed after his death.

Ibn al-Tilmīdh wrote fourteen books, including pharmaceutical formularies and medical commentaries, some of which were cited by later Arab physicians for more than a century after his death. He was described as a highly respected man—gentle, eloquent, and very friendly—who died at an advanced age without loss of his mental faculties or dignified manners.

BIBLIOGRAPHY

I. ORIGINAL WORKS. Ibn al-Tilmīdh's literary contributions can be classified in four categories:

1. Independent medical works such as *Aqrābādhīn* (a pharmaceutical formulary in 20 chs., compiled from several earlier compendiums); a shorter version, in 13 chs. for use in hospitals only; the (*al-Amīniyya*) *fi'l-faṣd*, on phlebotomy, in 10 chs. (Lucknow, 1890); *Quwa 'l-adwiya al-mufrada* (on the effects of simple drugs used in hospitals), arranged alphabetically, with descriptions, identifications, synonyms (in Syriac, Greek, and Persian), and therapeutic uses of each; and *Mujarrabāt* (on clinical cases that he treated and experimented upon), containing several medical recipes with descriptions of pharmacological effects. Several MSS of these works are extant in many libraries, including the British Museum; Bodleian; Forschungsbibliothek, Gotha; Egyptian National Library, Cairo; and Damascus National Library.

2. Commentaries and selections from Greek medical texts, such as Hippocratic writings and their interpretations by Galen: *Aphorisms, Prognostic,* and *Substitution of Drugs.*

3. Commentaries and abstracts of leading Arabic medical works: as Ḥunayn ibn Isḥāq's *Isagoge* (*al-Masāꜥil*); al-Rāzī's *Continens* (*al-Ḥāwī*); Miskawayh's *On Wines and Waters* (*al-Ashriba*); al-Masīḥī's *Hundred Books on Medicine* (*al-Miꜥa*); Ibn Sīnā's *Canon* (*al-Qānūn*); and Ibn Jazla's *Minhāj.* Ibn al-Tilmīdh also wrote a commentary entitled *Medicine of the Prophet* (*Ṭibb al-nabī*), thereby becoming the first Christian physician to write on such traditional Muslim books of medical aphorisms. Unfortunately, all these commentaries are lost, except for a few quotations and references preserved by later authors.

4. Collection of his epistles and poems, of which only fragments are still known; see Louis Cheikho, *Al-machriq,* **24** (1921), 251–258, 339–350, and *Catalogue des manuscrits des auteurs chrétiens depuis l'Islam* (Beirut, 1924), 6.

II. SECONDARY LITERATURE. According to Ẓahīr al-Dīn al-Bayhaqī, *Taꜥrīkh al-ḥukamāꜥ,* M. Kurd ꜤAlī, ed. (Damascus, 1946), 144–146, the first to mention Ibn al-Tilmīdh was his contemporary, the historian al-ꜤImād al-Isfahānī, in his *Kharīdat al-Qaṣr.* More detailed biographies are given in Yāqūt al-Ḥamawī, *Dictionary of*

Learned Men, D. S. Margoliouth, ed., VII (London, 1931), 243–247; Abu'l-Faraj Ibn al-ʿIbrī (Bar Hebraeus), *Taʾrīkh Mukhtaṣar* (Beirut, 1958), 209–210; Ibn Khallikān, *Wafayāt al-aʿyān*, II (Cairo, 1892), 191–194; Ibn al-Qifṭī, *Taʾrīkh al-ḥukamāʾ*, J. Lippert, ed. (Leipzig, 1903), 340–342; Ibn Abī Uṣaybiʿa, *ʿUyūn al-anbāʾ*, I (Cairo, 1882), 259–295; and Abū Muḥammād ʿAbd Allāh al-Yāfiʿī, *Mirʾāt al-janān*, III (Hyderabad, 1920), 344, based on the above sources.

More modern reference works, listed chronologically, are F. Wüstenfeld, *Geschichte der arabischen Aerzte und Naturforscher* (Göttingen, 1840), 97–98; Lucien Leclerc, *Histoire de la médecine arabe*, II (Paris, 1876), 24–27; George Sarton, *Introduction to the History of Science*, II (Baltimore, 1931), 234; Carl Brockelmann, *Geschichte der arabischen Literatur*, 2nd ed., I (Leiden, 1943), 642, and supp., I (Leiden, 1937), 891; S. Hamarneh, "The Climax of Medieval Arabic Professional Pharmacy," in *Bulletin of the History of Medicine*, **42** (1968), 454–461; *Origins of Pharmacy and Therapy in the Near East* (Tokyo, 1973), 56–64, 87; and *Catalogue of Arabic Manuscripts on Medicine and Pharmacy at the British Library* (Cairo, 1975), nos. Or. 8293–8294.

SAMI HAMARNEH

TIMIRYAZEV, KLIMENT ARKADIEVICH (*b.* St. Petersburg, Russia [now Leningrad, U.S.S.R.], 3 June 1843; *d.* Moscow, U.S.S.R., 28 April 1920), *plant physiology.*

Timiryazev was the youngest of the seven children of Arkady Semenovich, director of the St. Petersburg customshouse, and Adelaida Klementevna, an Englishwoman. The Timiryazevs were fairly well-to-do, but after the father's retirement their financial position changed sharply. A knowledge of foreign languages enabled Timiryazev to set himself up as a reviewer of the English press for the newspaper *Golos* and to help his family by doing literary translations.

Timiryazev was educated at home and in 1860 entered St. Petersburg University in the natural sciences section of the Faculty of Physics and Mathematics. In 1862 he was expelled for participating in student disorders. After a year he renewed his studies at the university, but only as an auditor. He continued his work as a translator and also published an article on Darwin's *Origin of Species* (1864). For work on liverworts (1865) Timiryazev received a gold medal and the degree of Candidate of Sciences. After graduating he worked under Mendeleev in Simbirsk province, studying new methods of agrotechnology. He also carried out experiments in photosynthesis. In 1868, at the

First Congress of Naturalists and Physicians, Timiryazev gave a report on air feeding and the use of artificial light. In the same year, on the recommendation of Beketov he was sent abroad "for preparation for the rank of professor." In 1868–1870 he worked in Germany with Helmholtz, G. Kirchhoff, Bunsen, and Hofmeister; in France, he worked with Berthelot, J. B. Boussingault, and Claude Bernard. On his return to Russia, Timiryazev became a teacher of botany in the Petrov Agricultural and Forestry Academy (now K. A. Timiryazev Moscow Academy of Agriculture), defended his master's dissertation on the spectral analysis of chlorophyll (1871), and became extraordinary professor at the academy. In 1875 he defended his doctoral dissertation on the assimilation of light by plants, and became ordinary professor. In 1877 Timiryazev was elected professor of anatomy and plant physiology at the University of Moscow.

Timiryazev's career was marked by encounters with the government and in 1898 he was discharged as a full-time teacher from Moscow University. He did retain the management of the botanical laboratory. Only in 1917 was he restored to the title of professor at Moscow University, but because of illness he could no longer work in the department. Timiryazev ardently embraced the ideals of the October Revolution.

Timiryazev's basic research was in plant physiology. In the 1860's he began important experimental and theoretical work on photosynthesis. In his master's and doctoral dissertations, and also in a series of later works he first used spectral analysis to study thoroughly the optical properties of chlorophyll and the dependence of photosynthesis on those properties of chlorophyll and on various rays of the solar spectrum. Timiryazev refuted the incorrect opinion that maximum photosynthesis occurs in the yellow-green rays and showed that the process proceeds most intensively in the red part of the spectrum. He substantiated the applicability of the first law of photochemistry and the law of the conservation of energy to the process of photosynthesis.

Timiryazev developed the concept of chlorophyll not only as a physical but also as a chemical sensitizer immediately affected by the oxidation-reduction transformation in the course of photosynthesis. In 1890 he was one of the first to assert the existence of the second absorption band of chlorophyll and, consequently, of the second absorption band of photosynthesis. He studied the relation between photosynthesis and the intensity of illumination (1889) and gave the present generally known graphic expression of the light saturation of photosynthesis, approximately at half of full insolation. Timiryazev stated the basic results of his thirty-five-year research on photosynthesis in the Croonian lecture "The Cosmical Function of the Green Plant," read to the Royal Society of London in 1903. From 1874 to 1903 he prepared a number of works for publication in the collection *Sun, Life, and Chlorophyll* (1923). The theoretical basis he provided for the energetics of photosynthesis is still valid, even though the quantum theory of light has replaced the wave theory.

Timiryazev's success in his research in photosynthesis is explained to a large degree by the fact that he gave much attention to the working out of new methods and the study of physiological processes in plants, for which he himself constructed a number of instruments and devices. He formulated theoretical ideas on the watering and mineral feeding of plants. Timiryazev also felt that it was necessary to apply Darwinian principles, especially natural selection, to explain physiological processes in plants. He himself undertook an experiment to give such an explanation in relation to photosynthesis and the green color of chlorophyll. The fight to introduce the achievements of plant physiology into agriculture took up a large part of Timiryazev's time.

Timiryazev was instrumental in the defense and development of Darwinism, especially in Russia. When he was only a student, he became acquainted with *The Origin of Species* and was able to see in its evolutionary theory the basis of a general theory of the organic world and to understand its materialistic basis. His books "A Short Sketch of the Theory of Darwin" (1865) and "Charles Darwin and His Theory" went through fifteen editions from 1883 to 1941. The ideas of Darwin occupied a central place in the posthumous "Historical Method in Biology" (1922).

BIBLIOGRAPHY

I. ORIGINAL WORKS. Timiryazev's writings were published as *Sochinenia*, 10 vols. (Moscow, 1937–1940); see I, 475–495 for a bibliography of his works on plant physiology, Darwinism, and general questions of natural science. His selected works appeared as *Izbrannye sochinenia*, 4 vols. (Moscow, 1948–1949).

His works include "Über die relative Bedeutung von Lichtstrahlen verschiedener Brechbarkeit bei der Koh-lensäurezersetzung in Pflanzen," in *Botanische Zeitung*, **27** (1869), 169–175; *Spektralny analiz khlorofilla* ("The Spectral Analysis of Chlorophyll"; St. Petersburg, 1871); "Sur l'action de la lumière dans la décomposition de l'acide carbonique par la granule de chlorophylle," in *Atti del Congresso botanico internazionale* (Florence, 1876), 108–114; "Sur le rapport entre l'intensité des radiations solaires et la décomposition de l'acide carbonique par les végétaux," in *Comptes rendus . . . de l'Académie des sciences*, **109** (1889), 379–382; and "The Cosmical Function of the Green Plant," in *Proceedings of the Royal Society*, **72** (1903), 424–461, his Croonian lecture.

II. SECONDARY LITERATURE. On Timiryazev and his work, see (listed chronologically) V. L. Komarov, N. A. Maksimov, and B. G. Kuznetsov, *Kliment Arkadievich Timiryazev* (Moscow, 1945), with bibliography of secondary literature, 198–211; G. V. Platonov, *Mirovozzrenie K. A. Timiryazeva* ("Timiryazev's World View"; Moscow, 1952), 468–478; A. I. Korchagin, *Kliment Arkadievich Timiryazev. Zhizn i tvorchestvo* (". . . Life and Activity"), 3rd ed. (Moscow, 1957); and E. M. Senchenkova, *K. A. Timiryazev i uchenie o fotosinteze* (". . . and the Theory of Photosynthesis"; Moscow, 1961).

E. M. SENCHENKOVA

TINSEAU D'AMONDANS, CHARLES DE (*b.* Besançon, France, 19 April 1748; *d.* Montpellier, France, 21 March 1822), *mathematics.*

The sixth of the seven children of Marie-Nicolas de Tinseau, *seigneur* of Gennes, and Jeanne Petramand of Velay, Tinseau belonged to the nobility of the Franche-Comté. Admitted to the École Royale du Génie at Mézières in 1769, he graduated as a military engineer at the end of 1771 and until 1791 was an officer in the engineering corps. Gaspard Monge, his professor of mathematics at Mézières, awakened in Tinseau an interest in mathematical research; and in 1772 he presented two memoirs to the Académie des Sciences, one on infinitesimal geometry and the other on astronomy. The following year he was named Bossut's correspondent at the Academy; but after that he seems to have written only one paper, on infinitesimal geometry. Nevertheless, the few items that have survived from his correspondence with Monge before the Revolution attest to a continuing interest in mathematical research.

A participant in the efforts made by the nobility in 1788 to defend the *ancien régime*, Tinseau joined the émigrés gathered at Worms under the leadership of the prince of Condé in 1791.

From then on, he lived in various émigré communities, conducting a very active propaganda campaign against the Revolution and later against the Empire. He attempted to organize uprisings in France, and encouraged and aided the Allied powers in their fight against the French armies. Tinseau also fought in several campaigns and, according to his biographer, provided all the coalitions formed until 1813 with strategic plans of the French army. The intransigence of his anti-Revolution convictions is evident in the dozen political pamphlets that he published between 1792 and 1805 at Worms and London.

Devoted to the Bourbons, whom he considered the sole legitimate dynasty, Tinseau refused an offer of amnesty from Napoleon and rejected offers of naturalization extended by the British government. With the rank of brigadier general in the engineering corps, Tinseau acted as aide de camp to the future Charles X and did not return to France until 1816, at which time he immediately went into retirement.

Tinseau married three times. His first marriage took place in France before the Revolution, the other two in England during his exile. His four children from the first marriage all died without issue. From his third marriage he had a son who died in Africa and a daughter who married the engineer and mathematician François Vallès (1805–1887).

Two of the three memoirs that constitute Tinseau's *oeuvre* deal with topics in the theory of surfaces and curves of double curvature: planes tangent to a surface, contact curves of circumscribed cones or cylinders, various surfaces attached to a space curve, the determination of the osculatory plane at a point of a space curve, problems of quadrature and cubature involving ruled surfaces, the study of the properties of certain special ruled surfaces (particularly conoids), and various results in the analytic geometry of space. In these two papers the equation of the tangent plane at a point of a surface was first worked out in detail (the equation had been known since Parent), methods of descriptive geometry were used in determining the perpendicular common to two straight lines in space, and the Pythagorean theorem was generalized to space (the square of a plane area is equal to the sum of the squares of the projections of this area on mutually perpendicular planes).

Although Tinseau published very little, his papers are of great interest as additions to Monge's earliest works. Indeed, Tinseau appears to have been Monge's first disciple.

BIBLIOGRAPHY

I. ORIGINAL WORKS. Tinseau's two memoirs on infinitesimal geometry were published as "Solution de quelques problèmes relatifs à la théorie des surfaces courbes et des lignes à double courbure," in *Mémoires de mathématique et de physique présentés . . . sçavans,* **9** (1780), 593–624; and "Sur quelques propriétés des solides renfermés par des surfaces composées des lignes droites," *ibid.,* 625–642. An unpublished memoir dated 1772, "Solution de quelques questions d'astronomie," is in the archives of the Académie des Sciences.

Between 1792 and 1805 Tinseau published many violently anti-Revolution and anti-Napoleonic writings, eleven of which are cited in Michaud (see below).

II. SECONDARY LITERATURE. The only somewhat detailed article on Tinseau, by Weiss in Michaud's *Biographie universelle,* XLVI (Paris, 1826), 100–102, deals mainly with his political and military careers. Some observations on his mathematical work are in R. Taton, *L'oeuvre scientifique de Gaspard Monge* (Paris, 1951), see index; and C. B. Boyer, *History of Analytic Geometry* (New York, 1956), 207. Various documents concerning Tinseau are in his dossiers in the archives of the Académie des Sciences and at the Service Historique de l'Armée.

RENÉ TATON

TISELIUS, ARNE WILHELM KAURIN (*b.* Stockholm, Sweden, 10 August 1902; *d.* Stockholm, 29 October 1971), *physical biochemistry.*

Most of Tiselius' ancestors on both sides were scholars and many had shown great interest in science, especially biology. His father, Hans Abraham J:son Tiselius, had taken a degree in mathematics at Uppsala University. His mother, Rosa Kaurin, was the daughter of a Norwegian clergyman. His father died in 1906, and his mother moved with Tiselius and his sister to Göteborg, where her parents-in-law lived and the family had close friends.

Tiselius' profound interest in science was awakened in the grammar school at Göteborg, where he had an inspiring teacher of chemistry and biology. Gradually it became clear to him that he wanted to study at the University of Uppsala with The Svedberg, the leading physical chemist in Sweden. In September 1921 he entered that university, with which he remained associated for the rest of his life. In May 1924 he received the M.A. in chemistry, physics, and mathematics. In November 1930 he presented a doctoral dissertation on electrophoresis and was appointed docent in chemistry. A special chair in biochemistry was created for Tiselius at the Faculty of Science in 1938; he retired thirty years later.

Tiselius married Ingrid Margareta (Greta) Dalén in 1930. He was healthy for most of his life, although during the last few years he was told to reduce his activities in order not to overstrain his heart. It was difficult for him to follow this advice, and after an important meeting at Stockholm he suffered a severe heart attack and died the following morning.

Modest, quiet, and warm-hearted, Tiselius possessed a sense of humor that was both acutely witty and gentle. He was deeply interested in natural history and had a wide knowledge of botany and ornithology. He often made excursions into the countryside to watch and photograph birds.

Tiselius was awarded the 1948 Nobel Prize in chemistry "for his work on electrophoresis and adsorption analysis and especially for his discovery of the complex nature of the proteins occurring in blood serum." He received honorary doctorates from twelve universities and was a member or honorary member of more than thirty learned societies, including the National Academy of Sciences in Washington and the Royal Society.

In the summer of 1944 Tiselius became a member of a governmental committee established to recommend measures for improving conditions for scientific research, especially basic research. Most of the proposals were approved by the Swedish Parliament, and a number of improvements were introduced. When the Swedish Natural Science Research Council was established in 1946, Tiselius was appointed chairman for the first four years.

In 1947 Tiselius became member of the Nobel Committee for Chemistry and vice-president of the Nobel Foundation. At the International Congress of Chemistry held at London in 1947, he was elected vice-president in charge of the section for biological chemistry of the International Union of Pure and Applied Chemistry. Four years later, at the conference in New York, he was elected president of the union. In the 1960's he was active in the creation of the Science Advisory Council to the Swedish government, which, under the chairmanship of the prime minister, deals with Swedish research policy.

In the last decade of his life Tiselius was quite concerned about the problems created by the evolution of science; although eager for society to benefit from the advances, he was aware that scientific developments may present a severe threat to mankind. He gave much thought to the opportunity for the Nobel Foundation to use its unique position and status in a way that would complement its awarding of prizes. He took the initiative by starting Nobel symposia in each of the five prize fields. The participants not only discussed the latest developments but also attempted to assess their social, ethical, and other implications. He firmly believed that the Nobel Foundation could and should play an important role in bringing science to bear on the solution of the most pertinent problems of mankind.

Tiselius entered Svedberg's laboratory as research assistant in July 1925, at the beginning of an outstandingly fruitful intellectual period there. In September 1923 Svedberg had returned to Uppsala with many new ideas after eight months at the University of Wisconsin. He had constructed his first low-speed ultracentrifuge and was then developing the first high-speed device to be used to study the size and shape of protein particles. Svedberg also was interested in determining the electrophoretic properties of proteins, and Tiselius participated in this work. His first paper, published jointly with Svedberg (1926), described a new method for determining the mobility of proteins.

Svedberg was so heavily engaged in the development of his ultracentrifuges that he gave Tiselius free rein to continue the study of electrophoresis. Tiselius began to read biochemistry, which was not included in the chemistry curriculum at that time, and was fascinated by the enormous variability—and especially by the specificity—of biochemical substances.

In his daily work with electrophoresis, Tiselius was often worried by impure or badly defined materials. Even substances that were found to be homogeneous in the ultracentrifuge would often prove inhomogeneous in the electrophoresis experiments. This was particularly true with the serum proteins. He gradually concluded that definition and purification were all-important for the whole of biochemistry. Thus separation became the key problem, and Tiselius was convinced that a solution would require a number of methods besides electrophoresis and ultracentrifugation. He gave some thought to the further development of chromatographic and adsorption methods, and made some preliminary experiments with them. Finally he decided to continue the exploration of electrophoresis and presented his dissertation in November 1930. In the year of his retirement (1968) he described his feelings after the dissertation as follows:

I remember very vividly that I felt disappointed. The method was an improvement, no doubt, but it led me just to the point where I could see indications of very interesting results without being able to prove anything definite. I can still remember this as an almost physical suffering when looking at some of the electrophoresis photographs, especially of serum proteins. I decided to take up an entirely different problem, but a scar was left in my mind which some years later would prove to be significant.

After finishing his dissertation, Tiselius worked on new problems that gave him experience in other fields. He considered this important because he hoped to qualify for a chair in chemistry.

Through his reading Tiselius had learned about the unique capacity of certain zeolite minerals to exchange their water of crystallization for other substances, the crystal structure remaining intact even after the water of crystallization had been removed *in vacuo*. It was known that the optical properties changed when the dried crystals were rehydrated, but until then no quantitative study of the phenomenon had been made. Tiselius saw the possibilities of this accidental observation, found the governing factors, and developed a very elegant and accurate optical method for the quantitative measurement of the diffusion of water vapor and other gases into zeolite crystals. The later portion of the work was carried out at the Frick Chemical Laboratory at Princeton University in 1934–1935, while Tiselius held a Rockefeller Foundation fellowship for study under Hugh S. Taylor.

Even if Tiselius could not concentrate on biochemistry during his stay in the United States, it proved to be a very stimulating year that decisively influenced his career. The atmosphere in the Frick Laboratory was inspiring, but of even greater importance for Tiselius' later work was his frequent contact with research carried on by the Rockefeller Institute in its laboratories in Princeton and New York. This contact led to friendships with J. H. Northrop, W. M. Stanley, and M. L. Anson, as well as the opportunity to meet K. Landsteiner, M. Heidelberger, and L. Michaelis. From discussions with them it became clear to Tiselius that to solve some of their problems they needed some new methods that had been in his mind for years but that he had been unable to realize. Encouraged by the discussions with these friends, he was again convinced that the development of new and more efficient separation processes was a key problem in biochemistry and decided to concentrate on this problem. While still in the United States, he began a total reconstruction of the electrophoresis apparatus.

After his return to Uppsala, Tiselius radically redesigned the experimental technique. The apparatus he developed could be used safely with potential gradients in the U-tube at least ten times those in any earlier electrophoresis apparatus, and made it possible to obtain a much higher resolving power for protein mixtures. The movement of the boundaries could be followed optically by August Toepler's *Schlieren* method. The U-tube could be divided into well-defined sections after the conclusion of the experiments, thus allowing samples to be taken from different parts of the tube for chemical and biological analyses.

The first experiments, carried out with horse serum, immediately demonstrated the advantage of the new instrument. The *Schlieren* pattern showed four protein bands with different mobilities. The fastest-moving band corresponded to the serum albumin boundary; and the next three bands disclosed, for the first time, the presence of at least three electrophoretically different components in serum globulin. Tiselius tentatively named them α, β, and γ globulin. Serum from other animals yielded similar patterns, but with quantitative differences. It also was shown that the antibodies (immunoglobulins) usually were found in the γ globulin or between the β and γ globulin bands.

The method was subsequently tested by Tiselius and his co-workers in all possible ways, new and better refractometric methods were introduced, and various minor changes were made. The new technique also allowed the electrophoretic isolation of the three globulin fractions, and it was thus found that their chemical properties were different. Tiselius soon suspected that each of these three main globulin components consisted of several individual proteins that by chance had similar mobilities. Later methods have verified this suspicion, and many individual proteins have been isolated from the three main globulin fractions.

Tiselius had hoped that his new electrophoresis technique might also be useful in elucidating a problem of great interest to him, the isolation and identification of the large fragments and polypeptides obtained by a mild breakdown of protein molecules. In this respect the method was a disappointment; he felt that electrophoresis was hardly specific enough for separating the multitude of substances occurring in materials of biological origin. He then became interested in adsorption methods, which had been used to some extent in organic and biochemical preparations. The separation had hitherto been studied mainly on the column. Tiselius saw the possibility of developing a new quantitative analytical method in which the separation in the eluate emerging from the column could be observed by refractometric methods similar to those used in electrophoresis. He also gave a theoretical treatment that related the retardation volume of an adsorbed substance to its adsorption coefficient and the mass of adsorbent in the column. He considered the modification of adsorption behavior arising from the presence of a second, more strongly adsorbed solute. Specific retardation volumes were determined for a number of amino acids and peptides; and it was found that the length of the carbon chain had a decisive influence, each additional CH_2 group producing a marked increase. The retardation volumes of neutral amino acids remained unaffected over a wide range of pH, while those of the acidic and basic amino acids showed a strong pH dependence.

A very important technical improvement was made by Tiselius and S. Claesson in 1942 with their introduction of interferometric methods to measure the concentration of the eluate. The object of this development was to overcome the instability arising from the very slight density differences between neighboring layers of eluate by restricting convective mixing to very small volumes. The volume of the interferometric channel was only 0.13 ml. The experimental arrangement was exceptionally well suited for the detailed study of the different types of chromatographic processes and led to important theoretical advances and to their experimental verification.

All the early experiments were carried out by frontal analysis that allowed determination of the concentration of the components in a mixture but did not result in their separation. The latter could be done by using an elution method. The eluted components, however, showed a very marked "tailing." Tiselius showed in 1943 that this could be prevented by adding to the eluting solution a substance with higher adsorption affinity than any of the components in the mixture. The method has since been called displacement analysis.

In the following decade Tiselius and his co-workers made several modifications and improvements in this technique. In most of the work activated charcoal had been used as an adsorbent, and many attempts were made to modify its adsorptive properties by various pretreatments. Tiselius (1954) also tried to use calcium phosphate in the hydroxyl-apatite form as an adsorbent for proteins in conjunction with phosphate buffers as eluting agents, with some degree of success, but the definitive solution to the problem for protein chromatog-

raphy came with the development of the cellulose ion exchangers by E. A. Peterson and H. A. Sober (1956). Tiselius' decisive contribution to chromatography lay in the elucidation of the fundamental processes involved.

Until the mid-1940's Tiselius did a large part of the experimental work by himself, sometimes with the assistance of a technician. After that time great demands were made on him, and he could spend little time in his laboratory. Studies on paper electrophoresis and zone electrophoresis were continued by his co-workers and students under his direction, and much work on other separation problems was delegated to his collaborators. Two important new separation methods originated in Tiselius' laboratory. The dramatic separation of particles and of macromolecules, obtained by P. Å. Albertsson, used partition in aqueous polymer two-phase systems of, for instance, dextran and polyethylene glycol. In the gel-filtration method, devised by J. Porath and Per Flodin, fractionation is obtained according to size and shape of the dissolved molecules.

It was characteristic of Tiselius that he took up well-recognized qualitative experimental phenomena, analyzed them critically, and established their fundamental theoretical basis. As a consequence he was able to introduce essential improvements in experimental technique. His contributions to the development of new methods for analysis and separation of biological systems mark an era in the study of macromolecules and have contributed to the enormous development in biochemistry since the end of the 1930's.

BIBLIOGRAPHY

I. ORIGINAL WORKS. Only a few of Tiselius' 161 published papers can be mentioned here. A complete bibliography is in the biography by Kekwick and Pedersen (see below). They include "A New Method for Determination of the Mobility of Proteins," in *Journal of the American Chemical Society*, **48** (1926), 2272–2278, written with T. Svedberg; "Über die Berechnung thermodynamischer Eigenschaften von kolloiden Lösungen aus Messungen mit der Ultrazentrifuge," in *Zeitschrift für physikalische Chemie*, **124** (1926), 449–463; the revision and enlargement of Svedberg's *Colloid Chemistry* (New York, 1928); "The Moving Boundary Method of Studying the Electrophoresis of Proteins," in *Nova acta Regiae Societatis scientiarum upsaliensis*, 4th ser., **7**, no. 4 (1930), 1–107; "Adsorption and Diffusion in Zeolite Crystals," in *Journal of Physical Chemistry*, **40** (1936), 223–232; "A New Apparatus for Electrophoretic Analysis of Colloidal Mixtures," in *Transactions* *of the Faraday Society*, **33** (1937), 524–531, originally sent for publication to a biochemical journal but refused as being "too physical"; "Electrophoresis of Serumglobulin II. Electrophoretic Analysis of Normal and Immune Sera," in *Biochemical Journal*, **31** (1937), 1464–1477; "A New Method of Adsorption Analysis and Some of Its Applications," in *Advances in Colloid Science*, **1** (1942), 81–98; "Adsorption Analysis by Interferometric Observation," in *Arkiv för kemi, mineralogi och geologi*, **15B**, no. 18 (1942), 1–6, written with S. Claesson; "Displacement Development in Adsorption Analysis," *ibid.*, **16A**, no. 18 (1943), 1–11; "Electrophoresis and Adsorption Analysis as Aids in Investigations of Large Molecular Weight Substances and Their Breakdown Products," in *Les Prix Nobel en 1948*, 102–121, in *Nobel Lectures in Chemistry 1942–1962* (Amsterdam, 1964), 195–215; "Chromatography of Proteins on Calcium-Phosphate Columns," in *Arkiv för kemi*, **7** (1954), 443–449; "Separation and Fractionation of Macromolecules and Particles," in *Science*, **141** (1963), 13–20, written with J. Porath and P. Å. Albertsson; and the autobiographical essay "Reflections From Both Sides of the Counter," in *Annual Review of Biochemistry*, **37** (1968), 1–24.

II. SECONDARY LITERATURE. Tiselius' collaborator S. Hjertén published a biography of his former teacher, "Arne Tiselius 1902–1971," in *Journal of Chromatography*, **65** (1972), 345–348; a bibliography of Tiselius' papers is in R. A. Kekwick and K. O. Pedersen, "Arne Tiselius 1902–1971," in *Biographical Memoirs of Fellows of the Royal Society*, **20** (1974), 401–428. An earlier publication dealing with Tiselius' scientific life is K. O. Pedersen, "Arne Tiselius," in *Acta chemica scandinavica*, **2** (1948), 620–624. The important new approach to the chromatography of proteins is given in E. A. Peterson and H. A. Sober, "Chromatography of Proteins. I. Cellulose Ion-Exchange Adsorbents," in *Journal of the American Chemical Society*, **78** (1956), 751–755. In honor of Tiselius' sixtieth birthday a number of his friends published "Perspectives in the Biochemistry of Large Molecules," which is *Archives of Biochemistry and Biophysics*, supp. **1** (1962).

KAI O. PEDERSEN

TISSERAND, FRANÇOIS FÉLIX (*b.* Nuits-St.-Georges, Côte-d'Or, France, 15 January 1845; *d.* Paris, France, 20 October 1896), *celestial mechanics, astronomy.*

Tisserand was the younger son in a poor Burgundian family. His father, a cooper, died when Tisserand was very young; and his mother brought up the two children. Tisserand was a brilliant student at schools in Beaune and Dijon and later at the École Normale Supérieure, which he entered at age eighteen. Immediately after his graduation as *agrégé des sciences* in 1866, Le Verrier offered him the post of *astronome-adjoint* at the Paris observatory.

Le Verrier questioned the value of the lunar theory developed by Delaunay, his personal enemy. He entrusted the examination of the theory to Tisserand, who presented Delaunay's results concisely and demonstrated them in a new way, on the basis of Jacobi's principles of analytical mechanics. Tisserand also generalized the results to such an extent that Poincaré wrote: "[Tisserand] has grasped their true significance better, perhaps, than the author" (*Bulletin astronomique*, **13** [1896], 431).

This work constituted Tisserand's doctoral dissertation, which he defended in 1868. He then devoted some time to astronomy, participating in the mission sent to Malacca to observe the solar eclipse of 1868. At the Paris observatory he worked in the Service Méridien, the Service Géodésique, and the Service des Équatoriaux.

In 1873 Tisserand was named director of the Toulouse observatory and professor of astronomy at that city's university. During the next five years, besides reequipping the observatory, he did research on the theoretical and practical determination of the orbits of the asteroids and satellites, and on the perturbations in their orbits. He also contributed to potential theory. Having quickly established a reputation, he was elected a corresponding member of the Académie des Sciences in 1874, although he had not published a major work since his dissertation.

Tisserand was hired by the Paris Faculty of Sciences in 1878 to teach rational mechanics and, from 1883, celestial mechanics. Henceforth he devoted his research primarily to the latter subject, which he examined thoroughly, regularly publishing five or six notes or papers on it every year. In 1885 Tisserand obtained an important result on the three-body problem. Newcomb and, previously, Delaunay (for the case of the moon) had shown that the solutions can be expressed with the aid of purely trigonometric expansions; Tisserand gave a general method that, by means of a contact transformation, allows one actually to compute the expansions. In 1889 he established the relationship known as "Tisserand's criterion," which is applied to the two orbits described by an asteroid or comet before and after it passes close to a planet. The relationship is a function of the orbital elements that is not affected by the perturbation experienced by the body. This criterion is widely used to establish the identity, or lack of identity, of two objects observed at different times and following distinct orbits.

Tisserand's greatest work is his *Traité de mécanique céleste*, the publication of which, begun in 1889, was completed a few months before his death. The four volumes represent an up-to-date version of Laplace's *Mécanique céleste*. In them Tisserand sets forth the general theory of perturbations and the works of Le Verrier on the theory of the planets, and discusses the theories of the moon, the theory of the satellites, the computation of the perturbations of the asteroids, potential theory, and the theory of the shapes of the celestial bodies and of their rotational movements. In addition, he reviews the most significant recent studies on these subjects, up through those of Poincaré. Laplace integrated the works of his predecessors into his text and therefore often was credited with results that were not his own. Tisserand, on the other hand, presents each author's memoir, simplifies its exposition, and integrates into it the fruit of his own research, without always making clear what part of the work is his. Thirty papers are incorporated into the *Traité* in this fashion. Since the authors of modern works on celestial mechanics often derive more of their information from this treatise than from the original papers, Tisserand's contributions are now diffused without being credited to him. A very modest person, Tisserand no doubt would have approved of this situation.

Tisserand was appointed director of the Paris observatory in 1892. In this capacity he pursued the project begun by Admiral Ernest Mouchez of producing the *Catalogue photographique de la carte du ciel*, and in 1896 he presided over the Congrès International de la Carte du Ciel. He succeeded Le Verrier as member of the Académie des Sciences in 1878 and was elected a member of the Bureau des Longitudes in 1879.

Tisserand suffered a fatal stroke in 1896, and was survived by three daughters. He had married while at Toulouse and, having become a widower soon after the birth of his first daughter, remarried in 1885. His collaborators, all of whom were also his friends, described Tisserand as honest, kind, and very solicitous toward young astronomers. His lectures were said to be exceptionally clear. This gift for clarity also is evident in his writings, which are all the easier to read by virtue of the economy and elegance of their demonstrations.

BIBLIOGRAPHY

I. ORIGINAL WORKS. Tisserand's writings include "Extension d'après les principes de Jacobi de la méthode suivie par Delaunay dans sa théorie du mouvement de la lune," in *Journal de mathématiques pures et appliquées*, **13** (1868), 255–303; *Sur la théorie des perturbations planétaires* (Toulouse, 1875), repr. in *Annales scientifiques de l'École normale supérieure*, **7** (1878), 261–274; *Déplacement séculaire du plan de l'orbite du 8ème satellite de Saturne; mouvement des apsides des satellites de Saturne, masse de l'anneau de Saturne* (Toulouse, 1877), repr. in *Annales de l'Observatoire astronomique de Toulouse*, **1** (1880), A1–A71; "Développement de la fonction perturbatrice dans le cas d'une forte inclinaison; perturbation de Pallas par Jupiter," in *Annales de l'Observatoire de Paris*, **15** (1880), C1–C52; "Parallaxe du soleil," *ibid.*, **16** (1882), D1–D48; "Mouvement séculaire des plans des orbites de trois planètes," *ibid.*, E1–E57; "Sur le problème des trois corps," *ibid.*, **18** (1885), G1–G19; *Traité de mécanique céleste*, 4 vols. (Paris, 1889–1896; I and II repr. 1960); and *Leçons sur la détermination des orbites*, J. Perchot, ed. (Paris, 1899).

Tisserand published seventy notes in the *Comptes rendus . . . de l'Académie des sciences* (**70–122** [1870–1896]), most of which were incorporated into the articles and books cited above. In *Bulletin astronomique*, **1–13** (1884–1896), which he founded and edited, he published twenty-eight short articles, the most important of which are "Théorie de la capture des comètes . . .," **6** (1889), 241–257, 289–292, which contains Tisserand's criterion; "État actuel de la théorie de la lune," **8** (1891), 481–503; "Perturbations . . . dans un milieu résistant," **10** (1893), 504–517; "Déplacement séculaire de l'équateur d'une planète et du plan de l'orbite de son satellite," **11** (1894), 337–343; and "Libération des petites planètes," **12** (1895), 488–507.

In the field of teaching and scientific popularization, Tisserand published *Recueil d'exercices sur le calcul infinitésimal* (Paris, 1876; 2nd ed., enl., 1896) and *Leçons de cosmographie* (Paris, 1895), written with H. Andoyer. The latter work contains a chapter on the history of astronomy that consists mainly of the text of three articles that Tisserand had published in *Annuaire du Bureau des longitudes*: "Perturbations et découverte de Neptune" (1885), 805–845; "Mesure des masses en astronomie" (1889), 671–723; and "Accélération séculaire de la lune" (1892), B1–B32. Tisserand wrote four other historical or popular articles for the *Annuaire du Bureau des longitudes*: "Quelques observatoires français du 18ème siècle" (1881), 736–765; "Planètes intramercurielles" (1882), 729–772 (the subject is treated in more detail here than in the *Traité de mécanique céleste*, IV, 524–528); "Petites planètes" (1891), B1–B20; and "Mouvement propre du système solaire" (1897), A1–A32.

II. Secondary Literature. See the following, listed chronologically: "Discours prononcés aux obsèques de F. Tisserand," in *Bulletin astronomique*, **13** (1896), 417–439; O. Callandreau, "François Félix Tisserand," in *Monthly Notices of the Royal Astronomical Society*, **57** (1897), 231–233; L. Bassot, H. Poincaré, and M. Loewy, "Discours prononcés à l'inauguration de la statue de F. Tisserand à Nuits-St.-Georges . . .," in *Annuaire du Bureau des longitudes* (1900), E1–E19 (see also *Bulletin astronomique*, **16** [1899], 401); J. Bertrand, "Notice historique sur la vie et les travaux de F. Tisserand," in *Mémoires de l'Académie des sciences de l'Institut de France*, **47** (1904), 269–282; and A. Danjon and A. Léauté, "Inauguration du nouveau monument de F. Tisserand," in *Institut de France, Académie des sciences, notices et discours*, **4** (1962), 559–571.

The *Traité de mécanique céleste* was the subject of many reviews, the most detailed of which is R. Radau, in *Bulletin astronomique*, **6** (1889), 15–26; **7** (1890), 419–424; **11** (1894), 102–110; and **13** (1896), 300–306.

JACQUES R. LÉVY

TITCHMARSH, EDWARD CHARLES (*b.* Newbury, England, 1 June 1899; *d.* Oxford, England, 18 January 1963), *mathematics.*

Titchmarsh was the son of Edward Harper and Caroline Titchmarsh. In 1925 he married Kathleen Blomfield; they had three children. Titchmarsh received his mathematical training at Oxford; and, like most of his contemporaries, he did not take a doctorate. After teaching at University College, London (1923–1929) and the University of Liverpool (1929–1931), he became Savilian professor of geometry at Oxford. He held this position for the rest of his life.

All of Titchmarsh's extensive research was in various branches of analysis; and in spite of his professorial title, he even lectured exclusively on analysis. He made many significant contributions to Fourier series and integrals; to integral equations (in collaboration with G. H. Hardy); to entire functions of a complex variable; to the Riemann zeta-function; and to eigenfunctions of second-order differential equations, a subject to which he devoted the last twenty-five years of his life.

Titchmarsh wrote a Cambridge tract on the zeta-function (1930), and later expanded it into a much larger book (1951) containing practically everything that was known on the subject. His survey of Fourier integrals (1937) is a definitive account of the classical parts of the theory. His work on eigenfunctions appeared in two parts in 1946 and

1958. His text *The Theory of Functions* (1932) was his best-known book; a generation of mathematicians learned the theory of analytic functions and Lebesgue integration from it, and also learned (by observation) how to write mathematics. He also wrote *Mathematics for the General Reader* (1948).

Titchmarsh made many original contributions to analysis, but his influence was at least as great through his systematization of existing knowledge and his improvements of proofs of known results. He saw physics as a source of interesting mathematical problems; but his interest was exclusively in the mathematics, without any regard for its real applicability. The approach, so often sterile, was successful in his case, for it led him into his study of eigenfunctions, in which the importance of his results was less appreciated in Great Britain than in other countries, especially the Soviet Union.

BIBLIOGRAPHY

Titchmarsh's works are *The Zeta-Function of Riemann* (London, 1930); *The Theory of Functions* (Oxford, 1932); *Introduction to the Theory of Fourier Integrals* (Oxford, 1937); *Eigenfunction Expansions Associated With Second-Order Differential Equations*, pt. 1 (Oxford, 1946), pt. 2 (Oxford, 1958); *Mathematics for the General Reader* (London, 1948); and *The Theory of the Riemann Zeta-Function* (Oxford, 1951).

On Titchmarsh and his work, see the obituary by M. L. Cartwright, in *Journal of the London Mathematical Society*, **39** (1964), 544–565.

R. P. BOAS, JR.

TITIUS (TIETZ), JOHANN DANIEL (*b.* Konitz, Germany [now Chojnice, Poland], 2 January 1729; *d.* Wittenberg, Germany, 16 December 1796), *astronomy, physics, biology.*

Titius was the son of Barbara Dorothea Hanow, the daughter of a Lutheran minister, and Jacob Tietz, a draper and Konitz city councillor. His father died when he was young, and Titius was sent to Danzig to be brought up by his maternal uncle, the natural historian Michael Christoph Hanow, who encouraged his interest in natural science. Titius finished his studies at the Danzig grammar school, then, in 1748, entered the University of Leipzig, from which he received the master's degree four years later with a dissertation on Euler's theory of moonlight. In 1755 he became a private lecturer in the Leipzig Faculty of Philosophy; in

April 1756 he accepted an appointment as professor ordinarius for lower mathematics at the University of Wittenberg. In 1762 Titius became professor of physics and Senior of the Faculty of Philosophy at Wittenberg, while in 1768 he was appointed rector of the university. In addition to his courses in mathematics and physics, he also lectured on philosophy, natural theology, and natural law.

Titius was a versatile and industrious man who mastered the natural science of his time without making any significant original contribution to it. Although he only occasionally devoted himself to astronomy, he became famous chiefly for the law—now named for him—governing the distances between the planets and the sun, a law that he may have formulated without making observations. Titius' law was first stated in the 1766 translation of Charles Bonnet's *Contemplation de la nature*, published in Leipzig, and appeared as a note to a number of subsequent editions of this work. It states that the distances between the planets and the sun are laid down in the sequence

$$A = 4 + 2^n \cdot 3 \ (n = -\infty, 0, 1, \cdots, 4).$$

In 1772 this was confirmed by Bode, who placed a hypothetical planet between Mars and Jupiter, in the space that Titius had reserved for a satellite of Mars; it was in this spot that Ceres, the first planetoid, was discovered by Piazzi in 1801. Titius' law is accurate in accounting for the average distances between the planetoids and the sun and is also true for the planet Uranus, discovered by Herschel in 1781; it is, however, absolutely wrong for both Neptune and Pluto.

Titius' chief scientific activity was directed to physics and biology. He published a number of works on physical topics, including a set of conditions and rules for performing experiments. He was particularly concerned with thermometry; in 1765 he presented a survey of thermometry up to that date, with emphasis on the air thermometer, and also wrote a monograph on the metallic thermometer that had been constructed by Hanns Loeser in 1746–1747. In addition, Titius wrote treatises on both theoretical and experimental physics, in which he incorporated the findings of other workers (as, for example, the descriptions of experiments written by Georg Wolfgang Kraft in 1738).

Titius' biological work was influenced by that of Linnaeus. His most extensive publication on the subject, *Lehrbegriff der Naturgeschichte zum ersten Unterrichte* (Leipzig, 1777), is a systematic classification of plants, animals (based in part on the system of Jacob Theodor Klein), and minerals, as well as the elemental substances ether, light, fire, air, and water. In shorter works dealing with the classification of animals (1760) and minerals (1765), Titius attempted to emend Linnaeus' method. He also devoted two other short monographs to specific subjects, the penduline titmouse (1755) and a method for preventing the silting of the split near Danzig by planting acacias, seaweed, and broom (1768).

A number of Titius' other publications are devoted to questions of theology and philosophy as they pertain to science. He also wrote historical works, including a history of West Prussia and Wittenberg, a description of the conquest of West Prussia by Kasimir IV of Poland in 1454–1466, and, on the occasion of the building of a new bridge across the Elbe, a historical survey of earlier bridges at that spot.

Titius was further prominent as the editor of six series of periodicals chiefly concerned with natural science. These were written for the purpose of making new scientific results known to specialists and non-specialists alike and were also designed to entertain; for this reason they achieved considerable popularity. Among them, the *Allgemeines Magazin* was limited to translations of works by foreign authors, while Titius himself contributed articles to the *Neue Gesellschaftliche Erzählungen* and wrote fourteen of the thirty-two articles printed in the *Gemeinnützige Abhandlungen*, which dealt mainly with the natural history of Saxony. In his efforts to make foreign scientific writings available to the greatest number of readers, Titius was also active in promoting cheap reprints of important segments of the *Philosophical Transactions of the Royal Society*.

Although he was offered chairs in other universities, including those of Göttingen, Helmstedt, Danzig, and Kiel, Titius chose to spend forty years at Wittenberg. His son, Salomo Konstantin Titius, also taught at Wittenberg, where he held the third chair of medicine, which embraced anatomy and botany, from 1795 until his own death in 1801.

BIBLIOGRAPHY

I. ORIGINAL WORKS. The most detailed bibliography of Titius' writings is Johann Georg Meusel, *Lexikon der vom Jahre 1750–1800 verstorbenen teutschen Schriftsteller*, XIV (Leipzig, 1815), 74–81. See also Poggendorff and the extensive lists given in *Neues gelehrtes Europa*, pt. 19 (Wolfenbüttel, 1773), 630–642; J. F. Goldbeck, *Litterarische Nachrichten von Preussen*, pt.

1 (Leipzig–Dessau, 1781), 194–200; and F. C. G. Hirsching, *Historisch-litterarisches Handbuch berühmter und denkwürdiger Personen, welche in dem 18. Jahrhundert gelebt haben, fortgesetzt und herausgegeben von J. H. M. Ernesti*, XIV (Leipzig, 1810), 375–376, all of which also give brief biographical notes. An autobiographical note is in *Nachricht von den Gelehrten, welche aus der Stadt Conitz des Polnischen Preussens herstammen* (Leipzig, 1763), 69–74, which also contains Titius' own catalogue of his writings up to that time. His own list of writings up to 1773 is available in the Universitäts- und Landesbibliothek Sachsen-Anhalt, Halle.

Titius' monographs include *Luminis lunaris theoria nova, argumentis Euleri superstructa* (Leipzig, 1752); *Investigatio finium divinorum in rebus naturalibus necessaria, adversus Cartesium Princip. philos. I.28. III.2 defensa* (Leipzig, 1753); *Philosophische Gedanken von dem Wahren Begriffe der Ewigkeit—Eternity is All!* (Leipzig, 1755); *Parus minimus Polonorum remiz Bononiensium pendulinus descriptus* (Leipzig, 1775); *Feyerliches Denkmahl der Ehrfurcht und Treue, dem glorreichen Gedächtnisse Friedrich August's, Königs in Polen, und Kurfürst Friedrich Christian's gewidmet von der Teutschen Gesellschaft in Wittenberg* (Wittenberg, 1763); *Attributorum Dei, apto digestorum ordine, brevis expositio* (Leiden, 1763); *Ortus mundi necessarius a priori assertus* (Wittenberg, 1763); *Thermometri metallici ab inventione illustrissimi atque excellentissimi S.R.I. Comitis Loeseri descriptio* (Leipzig, 1765); *Die gänzliche Ergebung der Lande Preussen an Polen, mittelst des A. 1466, nach der Einnahme von Conitz, zwischen König Casimir dem IV und dem Hohmeister Ludwig von Erlichshausen geschlossenen Friedens, historisch vorgestellet* (Wittenberg, 1766); *Abhandlung über die von der naturforschenden Gesellschaft in Danzig aufgegebene Frage: Welches die dienlichsten und am wenigsten kostbaren Mittel sind, der überhandnehmenden Versandung in der Danziger Nähring vorzubeugen und dem weitern Anwachs der Sanddünen abzuhelfen* (Leipzig, 1768); *Physicae dogmaticae elementa, praelectionum causa evulgata* (Wittenberg, 1773); *Lehrbegriff der Naturgeschichte zum ersten Unterrichte* (Leipzig, 1777); *Grundsätze der theoretischen Haushaltungskunde zum Unterrichte der Anfänger und zur fernern Erklärung entworfen* (Leipzig, 1780); *Physicae experimentalis elementa praelectionum causa in lucem edita* (Leipzig, 1782); and *Nachricht von der vormaligen und der neu erbaueten Elbbrücke bey Wittenberg nebst einigen Beylagen mitgetheilet* (Leipzig, 1788).

The periodicals edited and in part written by Titius are *Allgemeines Magazin der Natur, Kunst und Wissenschaften*, 4 pts. (1753–1754); *Neue Erweiterungen der Erkenntnis und des Vergnügens*, 12 vols. (1753–1762); *Neue Gesellschaftliche Erzählungen für die Liebhaber der Naturlehre, der Haushaltungswissenschaft, der Arztneykunst und der Sitten*, 4 pts. (1758–1762); *Wittenbergisches Wochenblatt zur Aufnahme der Naturkunde,*

und des ökonomischen Gewerbes, 8 vols. (1768–1775); *Gemeinnützige Abhandlungen zur Beförderung der Erkenntniss und des Gebrauches natürlicher Dinge in Absicht auf die Wohlfahrt des Staates und des menschlichen Geschlechts überhaupt*, pt. 1 (1768); and *Nützliche Sammlung von Aufsätzen und Wahrnehmungen über die Witterungen, die Haushaltungskunde, das Gewerbe, die Naturkenntniss, Polizey und andere damit verknüpfte Wissenschaften, als die Fortsetzung des Wittenbergischen Wochenblatts*, 10 vols. (1783–1792).

II. SECONDARY LITERATURE. In addition to the biographical notes in the bibliographies cited above, see the brief notice by R. Knott, in *Allgemeine deutsche Biographie*. A portrait of Titius, engraved by S. Halle, is at the beginning of J. G. Krünitz, *Oeconomische Encyklopädie*, XLV (Berlin, 1789). See also M. M. Nieto, *The Titius-Bode Law of Planetary Distances: Its History and Theory* (Oxford, 1972).

MENSO FOLKERTS

TODHUNTER, ISAAC (*b*. Rye, Sussex, England, 23 November 1820; *d*. Cambridge, England, 1 March 1884), *mathematics*.

Todhunter was the second son of George Todhunter, a Congregational minister in Rye, and Mary Hume. Upon the death of his father, the family moved to Hastings, where his mother opened a school for girls and where Todhunter was educated in private schools. Although he is said to have been extremely backward as a child, Todhunter later made good progress under J. B. Austin, with whom he subsequently obtained employment as a schoolmaster. While teaching at schools in Peckham and in Wimbledon, he enrolled as an evening student at University College, London. In 1842 he was awarded the B.A. (obtaining a mathematical scholarship), and in 1884 he received the M.A. (with gold medal). In the same year—acting on the advice of Augustus De Morgan, professor of mathematics at University College—he entered St John's College, Cambridge, where he graduated B.A. (senior wrangler) in 1848 and was given the Smith Prize. Shortly after graduating he was awarded the Burney Prize for an essay in the field of moral science. The following year he was elected to a fellowship, and he remained at St John's College, where for fifteen years he tutored, lectured, wrote, and examined. According to the rules of the college, he resigned his fellowship upon his marriage in 1864 to Louisa Anna Maria Davies. In 1862 Todhunter was elected fellow of the Royal Society of London, and he served on the council of the society from 1871 to 1873. He was also a founding member of the London Mathematical Society.

Throughout his lifetime Todhunter gave much public service as an examiner for the University of Cambridge in moral sciences and also in the mathematical tripos; he also examined for the University of London and for the Indian Civil Service Commission. Most of his time he devoted to writing, and the formidable series of mathematical textbooks he produced established him as one of the most influential figures in mathematical education of the nineteenth century. The textbooks were full and thorough, and were written with meticulous care. Consequently they were extremely popular with schoolmasters and some titles, in particular the *Algebra* (1858) and the *Euclid* (1862), had fifteen or sixteen editions. Many boys went through school and university studying mathematics entirely from Todhunter's textbooks.

Todhunter had little sympathy for the growing spirit of reform and criticism in mathematical education as evidenced in the formation of the Association for the Improvement of Geometrical Teaching (1871). He resisted all attempts to displace Euclid's *Elements* from its central position in mathematics courses. He also defended vigorously the rigors of the examination system as the only sound basis for obtaining and maintaining high standards in mathematics teaching. In *The Conflict of Studies* . . . (1873) he discussed many matters raised by the new reform movements and defended a point of view that, even at that time, was thought conservative. The attack he made on the teaching of experimental science contains the much-quoted statement, "If he [the boy] does not believe the statements of his tutor—probably a clergyman of mature knowledge, recognized ability and blameless character—his suspicion is irrational and manifests a want of the power of appreciating evidence, a want fatal to his success in that branch of science which he is supposed to be cultivating."

Although Todhunter's textbooks continued in use for many years after his death, his reputation rests on the contribution he made to the history of mathematics. The most important works are *A History of the Progress of the Calculus of Variations During the Nineteenth Century (1861); A History of the Mathematical Theory of Probability From the Time of Pascal to That of Laplace (1865); and A History of the Mathematical Theories of Attraction and the Figure of the Earth From the Time of Newton to That of Laplace (1873).* A further work, *A History of the Theory of Elasticity*, was published posthumously (1886–

1893). In all of these works, Todhunter gave a close and carefully reasoned account of the difficulties involved and the solutions offered by each investigator. His studies and use of source material were thorough and fully documented.

In 1871 Todhunter won the Adams Prize of the Royal Society, for an essay, *Researches in the Calculus of Variations*. The subject arose out of a controversy that had been carried on in the *Philosophical Magazine* some years before, concerning the nature of discontinuity. Todhunter's thesis illuminated some special cases but was obscured by the lack of any adequate definition of continuity.

Todhunter was not an original mathematician. His textbooks were useful in mathematical education but soon became outdated; the histories are still valuable.

BIBLIOGRAPHY

I. ORIGINAL WORKS. None of Todhunter's biographers have found it worthwhile to compile a full list of his elementary textbooks, which ran into a great many editions in his lifetime and, after his death, were revised by others so that they might continue to be useful in schools. The library of St. John's College, Cambridge, contains most of these books and also a collection of journal articles. There is also a small MS collection, which includes the *Arithmetic* on which Todhunter was working immediately prior to his death.

The more important historical works of Todhunter are *A History of the Progress of the Calculus of Variations During the Nineteenth Century* (Cambridge, 1861); *A History of the Mathematical Theory of Probability From the Time of Pascal to That of Laplace* (Cambridge, 1865); *A History of the Mathematical Theories of Attraction and the Figure of the Earth From the Time of Newton to That of Laplace*, 2 vols. (London, 1873); *A History of the Theory of Elasticity and of the Strength of Materials From Galilei to the Present Time*, K. Pearson, ed., 2 vols. (Cambridge, 1886–1893). Essays on education are contained in *The Conflict of Studies and Other Essays* (London, 1873). The Adams Prize essay was printed as *Researches in the Calculus of Variations* (London, 1871). Todhunter also edited George Boole, *Treatise on Differential Equations* (London, 1865) and *William Whewell. An Account of His Writings, With Selections From His Literary and Scientific Correspondence*, 2 vols. (London, 1876).

II. SECONDARY LITERATURE. On Todhunter and his work, see J. E. B. Mayor, "In Memoriam," in *Cambridge Review*, 5 (1884), 228, 245, 260; E. J. Routh, in *Proceedings of the Royal Society*, 37 (1884), xxvii–

xxxii; and A. Macfarlane, *Lectures on Ten British Mathematicians of the Nineteenth Century* (New York, 1916), 134–146.

MARGARET E. BARON

TOEPLITZ, OTTO (*b*. Breslau, Germany [now Wrocław, Poland], 1 August 1881; *d*. Jerusalem, 19 February 1940), *mathematics*.

Toeplitz' father, Emil Toeplitz, and his grandfather, Julius Toeplitz, were both Gymnasium teachers of mathematics; and they themselves published several mathematical papers. In Breslau, Toeplitz completed the classical Gymnasium and then studied at the university, where he specialized in algebraic geometry and received his Ph.D. in 1905.

The following year Toeplitz moved to Göttingen, where he stayed until he obtained an appointment at the University of Kiel in 1913; he became professor ordinarius in 1920. In 1928 he accepted a chair at the University of Bonn, but soon after Hitler's rise to power in 1933, he was dismissed from the office by the National Socialist regime. For the next few years he was involved in organizational work for the declining Jewish community in Germany. In 1938 he moved to Jerusalem, where he was administrative adviser to the Hebrew University; he also continued to teach in a private seminar, in which he reported the results of his work with G. Köthe.

Toeplitz' chief interest was the theory of infinite linear, bilinear, and quadratic forms, and of the associated infinite matrices, as a framework for concrete problems of analysis. It appears that this interest was sparked by the influence of Hilbert's work on integral equations, which was in the process of publication when Toeplitz arrived in Göttingen; but it was also not unrelated to Toeplitz' earlier work. Thus, following Hilbert, Toeplitz transferred the classical theories on linear, bilinear, and quadratic forms in *n*-dimensional space as far as possible to the infinite-dimensional cases; and he applied the results to the theory of integral equations and to other areas of analysis, such as Fourier series and complex variable theory.

In 1927 Toeplitz published "Integralgleichungen und Gleichungen mit unendlich vielen Unbekannten," written with E. Hellinger, with whom Toeplitz had closely collaborated. Among the important notions and methods that are given in the article, one of the major concepts was that of a normal bilinear form, which is basic in operator theory.

In the 1930's Toeplitz' mathematical research was based on a more general point of view. With G. Köthe, Toeplitz aimed at the development of a general theory of infinite-dimensional coordinate spaces. By this time S. Banach had published his "Théorie des opérations linéaires," but Toeplitz, having himself contributed much to the emergence of a general theory of linear operators, was critical of the work of Banach and his associates, which he considered too abstract. On the other hand, by deemphasizing the importance of the norm in their theory of coordinate spaces, Toeplitz and Köthe helped to develop the even more general theory of locally convex spaces. As an offshoot of his general interest, Toeplitz established, quite early in his career, the "Toeplitz conditions," which are fundamental in the theory of divergent sequences.

Toeplitz was deeply interested in the history of mathematics and held that only a mathematician of stature is qualified to be a historian of mathematics. In particular, he investigated the relation between Greek mathematics and Greek philosophy. He also wrote "Die Entwicklung der Infinitesimalrechnung" (1949), which was intended as an introduction to the calculus on a historical basis; the work is an example of Toeplitz' concern for the teaching of mathematics at the high school and college level. With H. Rademacher, Toeplitz also wrote *Von Zahlen und Figuren* (1930), one of the most successful attempts to bring higher mathematics before the educated public.

Toeplitz was a typical German-Jewish intellectual, who, while retaining an interest in Jewish matters, felt himself to be a part of his country of birth.

BIBLIOGRAPHY

Toeplitz' major works are *Über Systeme von Formen, deren Funktionaldeterminante identisch verschwindet* (Breslau, 1905); "Über allgemeine lineare Mittelbildungen," in *Prace Matematyczno-fizyczne*, **22** (1911), 113–119; "Integralgleichungen und Gleichungen mit unendlich vielen Unbekannten," in *Encyklopädie der mathematischen Wissenschaften*, **2**, pt. 3 (1927), 1395–1597, written with E. Hellinger; *Von Zahlen und Figuren* (1930), written with H. Rademacher; and "Die Entwicklung der Infinitesimalrechnung," in G. Köthe, ed., *Grundlehren*, LXI (1949). See also Poggendorff, V, 1261–1262; VI, 2672; VIIA, 695.

On Toeplitz and his work, see H. Behnke and G. Köthe, "Otto Toeplitz zum Gedächtnis," in *Jahresbericht der Deutschen Mathematikervereinigung*, **66** (1963), 1–16.

ABRAHAM ROBINSON

TOLMAN, RICHARD CHACE (*b.* West Newton, Massachusetts, 4 March 1881; *d.* Pasadena, California, 5 September 1948), *physical chemistry, mathematical physics.*

Tolman came from a prosperous New England family with close ties to the business and academic world. Following in his father's footsteps, Tolman enrolled at the Massachusetts Institute of Technology after attending the public schools in West Newton. He received a bachelor of science degree in chemical engineering in 1903. He spent the following year in Germany, at the Technische Hochschule at Charlottenburg, and later at Crefeld in an industrial chemical laboratory. Upon his return to M.I.T. in 1904 as a graduate student, Tolman joined Arthur Amos Noyes's Research Laboratory of Physical Chemistry and earned his Ph.D. in 1910. Tolman taught briefly at the University of Michigan and the University of Cincinnati before going to the University of California, Berkeley (1912–1916). He became professor of physical chemistry at the University of Illinois in 1916.

In Washington, D.C., in 1918, while serving as chief of the dispersoid section of the Chemical Warfare Service, Tolman crossed paths again with Noyes, then chairman of the Committee on Nitrate Supply. Noyes was already working hard to persuade the government to continue after the war its research program on the nitrogen products used in explosives and fertilizers. His efforts led to the creation of the Fixed Nitrogen Research Laboratory in 1919, and to Tolman's appointment as associate director (1919–1920) and director (1920–1922). The laboratory flourished under Tolman's direction, and became a mecca for bright young physical chemists. In 1922 Tolman joined the faculty of the California Institute of Technology through Noyes's efforts. As professor of physical chemistry and mathematical physics, Tolman served as dean of the graduate school and was a member of the executive council for many years.

The main thrust of Tolman's work in statistical mechanics, relativistic thermodynamics, and cosmology was mathematical and theoretical. His earliest scientific research (1910) involved measuring the electromotive force produced when a centrifugal force is applied to an electrolytic solution. Tolman based the derivation of an expression for the electromotive force on kinetic arguments, in addition to the customary thermodynamic ones, and showed that both yield the same equation. Turning to metallic conductors next, Tolman, working with T. Dale Stewart at Berkeley, demonstrated the production of an electromotive force by measuring the flow of electric current when a coil of wire rotating about its axis is mechanically accelerated and then brought to a sudden halt. In 1916 they made the first laboratory determination of the mass of the electric carrier in metals.

Tolman also published a number of important papers in the field of chemical kinetics in gaseous systems, that is, the problem of accounting for the rate at which chemical reactions take place. His theoretical treatment of monomolecular thermal and photochemical reaction rates underscored the need to clarify the meaning of the loosely defined concept of the energy of activation. This done, Tolman turned to the experimental work of Farrington Daniels and his co-workers on the decomposition of nitrogen pentoxide, the best example of a first-order unimolecular reaction over a range of concentrations and at a series of temperatures, as a check on the proposed mechanisms of chemical reaction then current. In particular, he showed in 1925 that the simple radiation theory of reaction proposed by Jean Baptiste Perrin and W. C. McC. Lewis did not adequately account for known rates of reaction. The papers not only reveal Tolman's precise reasoning and great physical intuition, but also his consuming interest in the application of statistical mechanics to rates of physical-chemical change.

With Gilbert N. Lewis, Tolman published the first American exposition of the special theory of relativity in 1909. Tolman later wrote *The Theory of the Relativity of Motion* (Berkeley, 1917). This early interest in relativity theory was further stimulated by Hubble's discovery in 1929 that red shifts are proportional to distance, and led to a series of studies on the applications of the general theory to the overall structure and evolution of the universe. In his comprehensive treatise on relativistic thermodynamics, Tolman presented his theory of a universe expanding and contracting rhythmically like a beating heart, arguing that gravity has the effect of counteracting the influence of radiation, thus preventing the complete cessation of motion as predicted by the second law of thermodynamics.

During World War II, Tolman served as vice-chairman of the National Defense Research Committee, as scientific adviser to General Leslie R. Groves on the Manhattan Project, and as United States adviser to the wartime Combined Policy Committee. Afterwards, he became scientific adviser to Bernard Baruch on the United Nations Atomic Energy Commission. Honors received during his lifetime included the Medal for Merit and election to the National Academy of Sciences in 1923.

Tolman married Ruth Sherman, a psychologist, in 1924. They had no children. He willed the bulk of his estate to the California Institute of Technology.

BIBLIOGRAPHY

Tolman published four books and over 100 scientific papers, all of which are chronologically listed in the bibliography appended to the biographical introduction prepared by J. G. Kirkwood, O. R. Wulf, and P. S. Epstein, in *Biographical Memoirs. National Academy of Sciences*, **27** (1952), 139–153. In *Principles of Statistical Mechanics* (Oxford, 1938), a monograph that remains a classic in its field, Tolman refashioned statistical mechanics by using quantum rather than classical mechanics as the starting point for the science. Details about his family and childhood can be gleaned from his brother's autobiographical notes, found in B. F. Ritchie, "Edward Chace Tolman," *ibid.*, **37** (1964), 293–324. Bernard Jaffe, *Outposts of Science* (New York, 1935), 506–516, gives a vivid picture of Tolman's work in cosmology at Caltech in the 1930's. His World War II activities are thoroughly covered in Albert B. Christman's *Sailors, Scientists and Rockets*, I (Washington, D.C., 1971).

Manuscript sources include letters in the papers of Gilbert N. Lewis, now in the office of the Chemistry Department, Berkeley, and several boxes of correspondence and unpublished manuscripts in the archives of the California Institute of Technology.

JUDITH R. GOODSTEIN

TORRE, MARCANTONIO DELLA (*b.* Verona, Italy, 1481; *d.* Riva, Italy, 1511), *medicine, anatomy.*

Marcantonio della Torre received the doctorate in philosophy on 22 December 1497 and in medicine on 1 February 1501 at the University of Padua, where his father, Girolamo, was professor of medicine. Immediately appointed public instructor in medicine and later professor of the theory of medicine, Marcantonio della Torre continued to teach in Padua until 1510, when he transferred to the University of Pavia as professor of anatomy. During the following year his promising career was cut short by plague, contracted at Riva on Lake Garda, and his early death at the age of 30 was signaled by numerous humanist obituaries, including a poem by his celebrated compatriot Girolamo Fracastoro.

Little is known of della Torre's medical work, for no manuscripts or published works appear to have survived. His name lives, instead, because of his supposed collaboration with Leonardo da Vinci on a treatise on anatomy. The story of this collaboration, repeated as fact by many later writers, stems primarily from a passage in the second edition of Vasari's *Lives* (1568), added after Vasari had visited Leonardo's heir, Francesco Melzi, and had seen the manuscripts in his possession. That the two men were friends or acquaintances thus rests on a reliable source,[1] but their supposed collaboration, or the influence of Marcantonio upon Leonardo, is open to question on several counts. First of all, their association must have been brief, limited to the time between Marcantonio's move to Pavia in 1510 and his death in 1511. Leonardo was then nearly twice Marcantonio's age, and his interest in anatomy had been aroused as early as 1489, when Marcantonio was seven years old. Leonardo's anatomical dissections in Florence date from 1503, and he was writing about the anatomical text he hoped to publish long before he could have met the younger man. Indeed, about the time their encounter could have occurred, the greater part of Leonardo's anatomical work had already been done. In 1508 he was recording and organizing the results of the dissections done in Florence, and in 1510 wrote that "this winter of the year 1510 I hope to have completed all this anatomy."[2] Moreover, no change in style that might be attributable to Marcantonio's influence is observable in Leonardo's work at this time.[3]

That the two men would have been interested in each other because of their common interest in anatomy is clear. Yet Marcantonio was a classicist who supported traditional Galenism against the newer anatomy of Mondino de' Luzzi, while Leonardo was unfettered by scholasticism, and his anatomical researches sprang largely from his universal curiosity about the workings of nature. Thus the meeting and friendship of Leonardo da Vinci and Marcantonio della Torre appear highly probable, but the chronology of Leonardo's anatomical work and the disparity in their outlook, training, and temperament argue against their having actively collaborated in the preparation of a treatise on anatomy.

NOTES

1. Leonardo referred to a "Marcantonio" in the *Codex Atlanticus*, fol. 20v, 6, datable about 1508–1509; and on Windsor 19102 (C. III. 8), datable about 1510–1512, he wrote "book on water to Messer Marcho Antonio." This was a common name, however, and it is highly uncertain that della Torre was meant.
2. In the phrase "the winter of the year 1510," Leonardo may

have been following the Tuscan usage, meaning 1510–1511, for the Florentine year began March 25.

3. Kenneth Clark, *The Drawings of Leonardo da Vinci in the Collection of Her Majesty the Queen at Windsor Castle. Second Edition Revised with the Assistance of Carlo Pedretti*, I, appendix C, "The Anatomical Studies" (London, 1968–1969), xlvii.

BIBLIOGRAPHY

References to della Torre by sixteenth-century writers include Girolamo Fracastoro, "In obitu M. Antonii Turriani veronensis," in *Opera omnia* (Venice, 1584), ff. 199–200; and Giorgio Vasari, *Delle vite de' più eccellenti pittori scultori et architetti*, 2nd ed., I, pt. 3 (Florence, 1568), 7.

Other sources treating Leonardo's anatomic work and his possible collaboration with della Torre are Gerolamo Calvi, *I manoscritti di Leonardo da Vinci* (Bologna, 1925); Kenneth Clark, *The Drawings of Leonardo da Vinci in the Collection of Her Majesty the Queen at Windsor Castle*, 2nd ed., with Carlo Pedretti (London, 1968–1969); *Leonardo da Vinci. An Account of his Development as an Artist* (New York and Cambridge, 1939), 161; G. B. De Toni, "Frammenti vinciani. I. Intorno a Marco Antonio dalla Torre anatomico veronese del XVI secolo ed all' epoca del suo incontro con Leonardo da Vinci a Pavia," in *Atti del R. Istituto veneto di scienze, lettere ed arti*, 54 (Venice, 1895–1896), 190–203; Kenneth D. Keele, "Leonardo da Vinci's Influence on Renaissance Anatomy," in *Medical History*, 8 (1964), 360–370; C. D. O'Malley and J. B. de C. M. Saunders, eds., *Leonardo da Vinci on the Human Body. The Anatomical, Physiological, and Embryological Drawings. With Translations, Emendations, and a Biographical Introduction* (New York, 1952), 24–25, 31–35; Edmondo Solmi, "Leonardo da Vinci, il Duomo, il Castello, e l'Università di Pavia," in *Scritti vinciani* (Florence, 1924), 67.

MARTHA TEACH GNUDI

TORRES QUEVEDO, LEONARDO (*b.* Santa Cruz de Iguña, Santander, Spain, 28 December 1852; *d.* Madrid, Spain, 18 December 1936), *engineering.*

Born into a family of technicians, Torres Quevedo studied civil engineering (1870–1876) and for a time drew plans for railway lines in southern Spain. Provided with independent means, he traveled throughout Europe. At the request of the mathematician José Echegaray (1832–1916) Torres Quevedo made public his inventions, which won him wide recognition and official support. The Centro de Ensayos de Aeronáutica was created for him by royal decree in 1904, as was the Laboratorio de Mecánica Aplicada (1907, 1911), forerunner of the Centro de Investigaciones Físicas "Leonardo Torres Quevedo" of the Consejo Superior de Investigaciones Científicas.

Torres Quevedo disliked writing—"for me a form of martyrdom," he called it—and thus his scientific contributions must be traced from the few reports he did write and, especially, from the patents he obtained and the machines he built. He was frequently concerned with describing machines, as in his article "Sobre un sistema de notaciones y símbolos destinados a facilitar la descripción de las máquinas" (*Revista de la Real Academia de ciencias . . . de Madrid*, 4 [1906], 429–442).

In algebraic machines, the subject of his inaugural lecture to the Royal Academy of Sciences (1901), Torres Quevedo combined mechanical and electromechanical means to construct a machine that would solve algebraic equations of any degree. The fundamental element is an endless spindle designed to add the construction of one monomial with that of another, automatically carrying out the calculation of Gauss's additive logarithms and working out the formula

$$y = \log(10^x + 1).$$

Telekino, a remote-control system employing Hertzian waves (patented 10 December 1902), with which Torres Quevedo carried out numerous experiments, was completely developed in 1906. Although the military significance of this device did not elude its inventor, he never succeeded in resolving the problem of interference that enemy forces would be able to generate.

Aeronautics was developed in 1902–1909, during which period Torres Quevedo conceived a dirigible system in which three cables, instead of rigid metallic struts, divide the vessel longitudinally into three triangular sections and give the outer covering, after it has been filled with gas under pressure, the physical characteristics required for it to be properly navigable. The *Gaceta* of 31 December 1909 authorized the granting of the patent to the French company ASTRA, and such lighter-than-air craft were satisfactorily employed in the same field as the German zeppelin. (See Espitallier, "Le dirigeable trilobé de l'ingénieur espagnol Torres Quevedo," in *La technique aéronautique*, I [Paris, 1910], 20–28.)

In 1912 Torres built a robot capable of playing the chess endgame of king and rook against king and defeating a human adversary. This device, perfected in 1920, and the Telekino must be recognized as conceptually related to the calculating machine of Charles Babbage, as Torres Quevedo acknowledged in "Ensayos sobre automática. Su definición. Extensión teórica de sus definiciones" (*Revista de la Real Academia de ciencias . . . de Madrid*, **12** [1913], 391–419). His work in this field culminated in an electromechanical calculating machine introduced 26 June 1920, the prototype of which demonstrated that calculations of any kind can be effected by purely mechanical processes. In 1913 Torres Quevedo had established that a machine could proceed by trial and error, in contrast with current belief—"at least when the rules that have to be followed in trial and error are precisely known. . . ."

In 1909 Torres built the funicular railway on Mount Ulía in San Sebastián (280 meters long) and, beginning in 1914, the cable-car line at Niagara Falls, Ontario, inaugurated 10 February 1916 (580 meters long). The method employed was to suspend the car by several cables the tensions of which were made independent of the weight of the car by counterweights borne at the ends of each cable. As a result, the breaking of one cable involved no danger, since there would be no increase in the load carried by the others.

BIBLIOGRAPHY

An interesting biography (a condensed version of a carefully annotated one to be published by the same author) is Leopoldo Rodríguez Alcalde, *Leonardo Torres Quevedo* (Madrid, 1966). The lack of Torres' writings can be overcome, up to 1914, with José A. Sánchez Pérez, "Los inventos de Torres Quevedo," in *Sociedad matemática española* (1914), 24.

J. VERNET

TORREY, JOHN (*b*. New York City, 15 August 1796; *d*. New York City, 10 March 1873), *botany*.

Torrey was the son of William Torrey, a New York merchant of New England ancestry who had fought in the American Revolution. His mother was Margaret Nichols, the daughter of a successful cabinetmaker and owner of real estate. The family lived on the eastern side of the tip of Manhattan. They attended the Presbyterian church, of which John remained a member throughout life. He attended public school in New York and for one year in Boston.

John Torrey first became interested in botany in 1810, when he befriended the scientist Amos Eaton, who was in a prison administered by young

Torrey's father, William Torrey. At the time that Torrey's interest in botany first developed, the Linnaean system of classification was still in use in the United States, and the collecting activities of botanists had not as yet exhausted the novelties found even in the environs of New York City. By the time that Torrey's career ended in 1873, a natural system of classification was in use by American botanists, and the range of his own herbarium encompassed the entire North American continent.

Torrey initiated, with the first volume of his *Flora of the Northern and Middle Sections of the United States* (1824), the practice of gathering together in one work all that was known of North American flora. He led American botanists in the adoption of the natural system of classification, developed by Antoine-Laurent de Jussieu and A. P. de Candolle. He edited an American edition of John Lindley's *Introduction to the Natural System of Botany* (1831) and planned a work to be titled the *Flora of North America*, based on the new system. After his protégé Asa Gray joined him as a partner in 1836, he published several fascicles of the *Flora of North America*. He stopped publication in 1843, however, because Gray, who had accepted a position at Harvard College, was no longer in New York, and because both of them were inundated with botanical specimens as a result of western explorations.

In 1843 Torrey published *Flora of the State of New York*, in two volumes, as a part of the New York survey. This work, the most polished and finished to come from Torrey's hand alone, represents him at the height of his powers of taxonomic and nomenclatural discrimination. Between 1843 and his death in 1873 Torrey wrote no fewer than eighteen reports on the dried specimens brought back by explorers, mostly collectors with the topographical engineers, from the western United States. Torrey's herbarium, which went to Columbia College after his death, must be counted as one of his major scientific contributions; it became the foundation for the herbarium of the New York City Botanical Garden. During a period in the 1860's Torrey had in his possession the collections of the Smithsonian Institution, so that his taxonomic work is also embedded in the foundations of the United States National Herbarium.

Torrey wrote few textbooks and did not express himself on the great issues of biology surrounding the publication of Darwin's *Origin of Species*. The limitations preventing a well-rounded career in biology stem from Torrey's incomplete solution of the problem as to what constituted the professional role of a scientist in early- and mid-nineteenth-century America. His research was in botany, but his degree was in medicine (1818), and his teaching was in the fields of chemistry and mineralogy. In the 1820's he taught chemistry at West Point, the College of Physicians and Surgeons in New York, and, for brief periods, at Williams College, New York University, and before general subscription audiences. From 1830 to 1854 he was a professor at Princeton, but he taught there only during the summer term, spending the winters in New York.

In 1851 Torrey began to reorganize his whole pattern of living; he sold his house in Princeton and, a few years later, resigned his teaching posts. In 1853 he became assayer of the United States Mint in New York, which received in those years large shipments of gold from California. In 1856 he became a trustee of Columbia College and ·in 1860 moved to the campus, to a house that he received in return for his herbarium of 40,000 species and library of 600 volumes. Thus he continued to earn his living teaching chemistry, and to make contributions to science by spending every spare moment on his botanical studies.

Torrey's influence must include his friendships with many of the builders of the American scientific community, beginning with Amos Eaton. Torrey was close to Joseph Henry and played an important role in his appointment to Princeton in 1832. His protection and encouragement gave Asa Gray the status of professional botanist, a status that Torrey himself never achieved. Yet he remained able to work as a peer with his younger colleague to the very end, when Gray edited Torrey's report of the Wilkes expedition from northwestern North America as its author lay dying.

BIBLIOGRAPHY

The two major sources on John Torrey are Andrew Denny Rodgers III, *John Torrey: A Story of North American Botany* (Princeton; 1942); and Christine Chapman Robbins, "John Torrey (1796–1873). His Life and Times," in *Bulletin of the Torrey Botanical Club*, **95** (1968), 515–645. Both have lists of Torrey's works and extensive bibliographies. Robbins has a useful chronology. Extensive MS collections and the Torrey herbarium are at the New York Botanical Garden, Bronx, New York.

A. HUNTER DUPREE

TORRICELLI, EVANGELISTA (*b.* Faenza, Italy, 15 October 1608; *d.* Florence, Italy, 25 October 1647), *mathematics, physics*.

Eldest of the three children of Gaspare Torricelli and the former Caterina Angetti, Torricelli soon demonstrated unusual talents. His father, a textile artisan in modest circumstances, sent the boy to his uncle, the Camaldolese monk Jacopo (formerly Alessandro), who supervised his humanistic education. In 1625 and 1626 Torricelli attended the mathematics and philosophy courses of the Jesuit school at Faenza, showing such outstanding aptitude that his uncle was persuaded to send him to Rome for further education at the school run by Benedetto Castelli, a member of his order who was a mathematician and hydraulic engineer, and a former pupil of Galileo's. Castelli took a great liking to the youth, realized his exceptional genius, and engaged him as his secretary.

We have direct evidence on the scope and trend of Torricelli's scientific studies during his stay at Rome in the first letter (11 September 1632) of his surviving correspondence, addressed to Galileo on behalf of Castelli, who was away from Rome. In acknowledging receipt of a letter from Galileo to Castelli, Torricelli seized the opportunity to introduce himself as a mathematician by profession, well versed in the geometry of Apollonius, Archimedes, and Theodosius; he added that he had studied Ptolemy and had seen "nearly everything" by Brahe, Kepler, and Longomontanus. These studies had compelled him to accept the Copernican doctrine and to become "a Galileist by profession and sect"; he had been the first in Rome to make a careful study of Galileo's *Dialogo sopra i due massimi sistemi*, published in February of that year (1632).

After this letter there is a gap in the correspondence until 1640, and it is not known where Torricelli lived or what he did during this period. The most likely hypothesis so far advanced is that from the spring of 1630 to February 1641, he was secretary to Monsignor Giovanni Ciampoli, Galileo's friend and protector, who from 1632 was governor of various cities in the Marches and Umbria (Montalto, Norcia, San Severino, Fabriano). In 1641 Torricelli was again in Rome; he had asked Castelli and other mathematicians for their opinions of a treatise on motion that amplified the doctrine on the motion of projectiles that Galileo had expounded in the third day of the *Discorsi e dimostrazioni matematiche intorno a due nuove scienze . . .* (Leiden, 1638). Castelli considered the work excellent; told Galileo about it; and in April 1641, on his way from Rome to Venice through Pisa and Florence, after appointing Torricelli to give lectures in his absence, submitted the manuscript to Galileo, proposing that the latter should accept Torricelli as assistant in drawing up the two "days" he was thinking of adding to the *Discorsi*. Galileo agreed and invited Torricelli to join him at Arcetri.

But Castelli's delay in returning to Rome and the death of Torricelli's mother, who had moved to Rome with her other children, compelled Torricelli to postpone his arrival at Arcetri until 10 October 1641. He took up residence in Galileo's house, where Vincenzo Viviani was already living, and stayed there in close friendship with Galileo until the latter's death on 8 January 1642. While Torricelli was preparing to return to Rome, Grand Duke Ferdinando II of Tuscany, at Andrea Arrighetti's suggestion, appointed him mathematician and philosopher, the post left vacant by Galileo, with a good salary and lodging in the Medici palace.

Torricelli remained in Florence until his death; these years, the happiest of his life, were filled with the greatest scientific activity. Esteemed for his polished, brilliant, and witty conversation, he soon formed friendships with the outstanding representatives of Florentine culture; the painter Salvatore Rosa, the Hellenist Carlo Dati, and the hydraulic engineer Andrea Arrighetti. In fact, the regular meetings with these friends gave rise to the "Accademia dei Percossi," to whom Torricelli apparently divulged the comedies he was writing, which have not survived but were explicitly mentioned in the memoirs dictated on his deathbed to Lodovico Serenai (*Opere*, IV, 88).

In 1644 Torricelli's only work to be published during his lifetime appeared, the grand duke having assumed all printing costs. The volume, *Opera geometrica*, was divided into three sections: the first dealt with *De sphaera et solidis sphaeralibus libri duo*; the second contained *De motu gravium naturaliter descendentium et proiectorum* (the writing submitted to Galileo for his opinion); and the third section consisted of *De dimensione parabolae*. The work, soon known throughout Italy and Europe, had intrinsic value and, through its clear exposition, diffused the geometry of Cavalieri, whose writings were difficult to read.

The fame that Torricelli acquired as a geometer increased his correspondence with Italian scientists and with a number of French scholars (Carcavi, Mersenne, F. Du Verdus, Roberval), to whom he was introduced by F. Niceron, whom he met while in Rome. The correspondence was the means of communicating Torricelli's greatest scientific discoveries but also the occasion for fierce arguments on priority, which were common during that century. There were particularly serious polemics with Roberval over the priority of discovery of certain properties of the cycloid, including quadrature, center of gravity, and measurement of the solid generated by its rotation round the base. In order to defend his rights, Torricelli formed the intention of publishing all his correspondence with the French mathematicians, and in 1646 he began drafting *Racconto d'alcuni problemi proposti e passati tra gli matematici di Francia et il Torricelli ne i quattro anni prossimamente passati* (*Opere*, III, 1–32). But while he was engaged in this work he died of a violent illness (probably typhoid fever) lasting only a few days. In accordance with his wish he was buried in the Church of San Lorenzo in Florence, but the location of his tomb is unknown.

Mathematical research occupied Torricelli's entire life. During his youth he had studied the classics of Greek geometry, which dealt with infinitesimal questions by the method of progressive elimination. But since the beginning of the seventeenth century the classical method had often been replaced by more intuitive processes; the first examples were given by Kepler, who in determining areas and volumes abandoned Archimedean methods in favor of more expeditious processes differing from problem to problem and hence difficult to imitate. After many years of meditation, Cavalieri, in his geometry of indivisibles (1635), drew attention to an organic process, toward which Roberval, Fermat, and Descartes had been moving almost in the same year; the coincidence shows that the time was ripe for new geometrical approaches.

The new geometry considered every plane figure as being formed by an infinity of chords intercepted within the figure by a system of parallel straight lines; every chord was then considered as a rectangle of infinitesimal thickness—the indivisible, according to the term introduced by Galileo. From the assumed or verified relations between the indivisibles it was possible to deduce the relations between the totalities through Cavalieri's principle, which may be stated as follows: Given two plane figures comprised between parallel straight lines, if all the straight lines parallel thereto determine in the two figures segments having a constant relation, then the areas of the two figures also have the same relation. The principle is easily extended to solid figures. In essence Cavalieri's geometry, the first step toward infinitesimal calculus, replaced the potential mathematical infinity and infinitesimal of the Greek geometricians with the present infinity and infinitesimal.

After overcoming his initial mistrust of the new method, Torricelli used it as a heuristic instrument for the discovery of new propositions, which he then demonstrated by the classical methods. The promiscuous use of the two methods—that of indivisibles for discovery and the Archimedean process for demonstration—is very frequent in the *Opera geometrica*. The first part of *De sphaera et solidis sphaeralibus*, compiled around 1641, studies figures arising through rotation of a regular polygon inscribed in or circumscribed about a circle around one of its axes of symmetry (already mentioned by Archimedes). Torricelli observes that if the regular polygon has equal sides, one of its axes of symmetry joins two opposite vertices or the midpoints of two opposite sides; if, on the other hand, it does not have equal sides, one of its axes of symmetry joins a vertex with the midpoint of the opposite side. On the basis of this observation he classifies such rotation solids into six kinds, studies their properties, and presents some new propositions and new metrical relations for the round bodies of elementary geometry. The second section of the volume deals with the motion of projectiles, about which more will be said later.

In the third section, apart from giving twenty demonstrations of Archimedes' theorem on squaring the parabola, but without adding anything new of importance, Torricelli shows that the area comprised between the cycloid and its base is equal to three times the area of the generating circle. As an appendix to this part of the work there is a study of the volume generated by a plane area animated by a helicoid motion round an axis of its plane, with the demonstration that it equals the volume generated by the area in a complete rotation round the same axis. Torricelli applies this elegant theorem to various problems and in particular to the surface of a screw with a square thread, which he shows to be equal to a convenient part of a paraboloid with one pitch.

As Torricelli acquired increasing familiarity with the method of indivisibles, he reached the point of surpassing the master—as Cavalieri himself said. In fact he extended the theory by using curved indivisibles, based on the following fundamental concept: In order to allow comparison of two plane figures, the first is cut by a system of curves and the second by a system of parallel straight lines; if each curved indivisible of the first is equal

to the corresponding indivisible of the second, the two figures are equal in area. The simplest example is given by comparison of a circle divided into infinitesimal concentric rings with a triangle (having the rectified circumference as base and the radius as height) divided into infinitesimal strips parallel to the base. From the equality of the rings to the corresponding strips it is concluded that the area of the circle is equal to the area of the triangle.

The principle is also extended to solid figures. Torricelli gave the most brilliant application of it in 1641 by proving a new theorem, a gem of the mathematical literature of the time. The theorem, published in *Opera geometrica*, is as follows (*Opere*, I, 191–213): take any point of an equilateral hyperbola (having the equation $xy = 1$) and take the area comprised by the unlimited section of the hyperbola of asymptote x, asymptote x, and the ordinate of the point selected. Although such area is infinite in size, the solid it generates by rotating round the asymptote, although unlimited in extent, nevertheless has a finite volume, calculated by Torricelli as π/a, where a is the abscissa of the point taken on the hyperbola.

Torricelli's proof, greatly admired by Cavalieri and imitated by Fermat, consists in supposing the solid generated by rotation to be composed of an infinite number of cylindrical surfaces of axis x, all having an equal lateral area, all placed in biunivocal correspondence with the sections of a suitable cylinder, and all equal to the surfaces of that cylinder: the principle of curved indivisibles allows the conclusion that the volume of this cylinder is equal to the volume of the solid generated by rotation of the section of the hyperbola considered. In modern terms Torricelli's process is described by saying that an integral in Cartesian coordinates is replaced by an integral in cylindrical coordinates. Still using curved indivisibles, Torricelli found, among other things, the volume of the solid limited by two plane surfaces and by any lateral surface, in particular the volume of barrels. In 1643 the results were communicated to Fermat, Descartes, and Roberval, who found them very elegant and correct.

The example of the hyperbola induced Torricelli to study more general curves, defined today by equations having the form $x^m y^n = c^n$, with m and n positive whole numbers and $m \neq n$. He discovered that their revolution round an asymptote could generate an infinitely long solid with finite volume and that, under particular conditions, the area comprised between the asymptote and the curve could also be finite. Torricelli intended to coordinate all these results, communicated by letter to various mathematicians in 1646 and 1647, in a single work entitled *De infinitis hyperbolis*, but he died before it could be completed. Only after publication of the *Opere* was it possible to reconstruct the paper from scattered notes.

The geometry of indivisibles was also applied by Torricelli to the determination of the center of gravity of figures. In a letter to Michelangelo Ricci dated 7 April 1646, he communicated the "universal theorem," still considered the most general possible even today, which allows determination of the center of gravity of any figure through the relation between two integrals. Among particular cases mention should be made of the determination of the center of gravity of a circular sector, obtained both by the classic procedure and by the method of indivisibles. Torricelli arrived at the same result, perhaps known to him, that Charles de La Faille had reached in 1632.

Torricelli also directed his attention to rectification of arcs of a curve, which Descartes in his *Géométrie* of 1637 had declared to be impossible, after having learned from Mersenne that Roberval had demonstrated the equality of length of particular arcs of a parabola and of arcs of an Archimedean spiral. Having conceived the logarithmic spiral, which he termed "geometric," he taught a procedure allowing rectification with ruler and compass of the entire section comprised between any point on the curve and the center, to which the curve tends after an infinite number of revolutions. Torricelli further demonstrated that any Archimedean spiral—or "arithmetic spiral," as he called it—can always be made equal to any particular arc of a suitable parabolic curve.

In addition to these contributions to the integral calculus, Torricelli discovered many relationships of differential calculus. Among the applications he made to the concept of derivative, drawn from the doctrine of motion (see below), mention should be made of his research on maxima and minima. He showed that if the sum $x + y$ is constant, the product $x^m y^n$ is maximum if x and y have the same relation as the exponents. He also determined the point still known as Torricelli's point on the plane of a triangle for which the sum of the distances from the vertices is minimum; the problem had been proposed by Fermat.

Torricelli made other important contributions to mathematics during his studies of mechanics. In *De motu gravium* he continued the study of the parabolic motion of projectiles, begun by Galileo, and observed that if the acceleratory force were to

cease at any point of the trajectory, the projectile would move in the direction of the tangent to the trajectory. He made use of this observation, earning Galileo's congratulations, to draw the tangent at a point of the Archimedean spiral, or the cycloid, considering the curves as described by a point endowed with two simultaneous motions. In unpublished notes the question is thoroughly studied in a more general treatment. A point is considered that is endowed with two simultaneous motions, one uniform and the other varying, directed along two straight lines perpendicular to each other. After constructing the curve for distance as a function of time, Torricelli shows that the tangent at any point of the curve forms with the time axis an angle the tangent of which measures the speed of the moving object at that point. In substance this recognizes the inverse character of the operations of integration and differentiation, which form the fundamental theorem of the calculus, published in 1670 by Isaac Barrow, who among his predecessors mentioned Galileo, Cavalieri, and Torricelli. But not even Barrow understood the importance of the theorem, which was first demonstrated by Newton.

Full mastery of the new geometrical methods made Torricelli aware of the inherent dangers, so that his manuscripts contain passages against infinites. His unpublished writings, in fact, include a collection of paradoxes to which the doctrine of indivisibles leads when not applied with the necessary precautions.

In *De motu gravium* Torricelli seeks to demonstrate Galileo's principle regarding equal velocities of free fall of weights along inclined planes of equal height. He bases his demonstration on another principle, now called Torricelli's principle but known to Galileo, according to which a rigid system of a number of bodies can move spontaneously on the earth's surface only if its center of gravity descends. After applying the principle to movement through chords of a circle and parabola, Torricelli turns to the motion of projectiles and, generalizing Galileo's doctrine, considers launching at any oblique angle—whereas Galileo had considered horizontal launching only. He demonstrates in general form Galileo's incidental observation that if at any point of the trajectory a projectile is relaunched in the opposite direction at a speed equal to that which it had at such point, the projectile will follow the same trajectory in the reverse direction. The proposition is equivalent to saying that dynamic phenomena are reversible—that the time of Galileo's mechanics is ordered but without direction.

Among the many theorems of external ballistics, Torricelli shows that the parabolas corresponding to a given initial speed and to different inclinations are all tangents to the same parabola (known as the safety parabola or Torricelli's parabola, the first example of an envelope curve of a family of curves).

The treatise concludes with five numerical tables. The first four are trigonometric tables giving the values of sine 2α, $\sin^2\alpha$, $\frac{1}{2}\tan\alpha$, and sine α, respectively, for every degree between 0° and 90°; with these tables, when the initial speed and angle of fire are known, all the other elements characteristic of the trajectory can be calculated. The fifth table gives the angle of inclination, when the distance to which the projectile is to be launched and the maximum range of the weapon are known. In the final analysis these are firing tables, the practical value of which is emphasized by the description of their use in Italian, easier than Latin for artillerymen to understand. Italian is also the language used for the concluding description of a new square that made it easier for gunners to calculate elevation of the weapon.

The treatise also refers to the movement of water in a paragraph so important that Ernst Mach proclaimed Torricelli the founder of hydrodynamics. Torricelli's aim was to determine the efflux velocity of a jet of liquid spurting from a small orifice in the bottom of a receptacle. Through experiment he had noted that if the liquid was made to spurt upward, the jet reached a height less than the level of the liquid in the receptable. He supposed, therefore, that if all the resistances to motion were nil, the jet would reach the level of the liquid. From this hypothesis, equivalent to a conservation principle, he deduced the theorem that bears his name: The velocity of the jet at the point of efflux is equal to that which a single drop of the liquid would have if it could fall freely in a vacuum from the level of the top of the liquid at the orifice of efflux. Torricelli also showed that if the hole is made in a wall of the receptacle, the jet of fluid will be parabolic in form; he then ended the paragraph with interesting observations on the breaking of the fluid stream into drops and on the effects of air resistance. Torricelli's skill in hydraulics was so well known to his contemporaries that he was approached for advice on freeing the Val di Chiana from stagnant waters, and he suggested the method of reclamation by filling.

Torricelli is often credited—although the idea is sometimes attributed to the Grand Duke Ferdinando II—with having converted Galileo's primitive air thermoscope to a liquid thermometer, at first filled with water and later with spirits of wine. On the other hand, there is very good evidence of his technical ability in working telescope lenses, a skill almost certainly acquired during his stay in Florence. By the autumn of 1642 he was already capable of making lenses that were in no way mediocre, although they did not attain the excellence of those made by Francesco Fontana, at that time the most renowned Italian telescope maker. Torricelli had set out to emulate and surpass Fontana. By 1643 he was already able to obtain lenses equal to Fontana's or perhaps even better, but above all he had come to understand that what is really important for the efficiency of a lens is the perfectly spherical machining of the surface, which he carried out with refined techniques. The efficiency of Torricelli's lenses was recognized by the grand duke, who in 1644 presented Torricelli with a gold necklace bearing a medal with the motto "Virtutis praemia."

The fame of Torricelli's excellent lenses quickly became widespread and he received many requests, which he fulfilled at a good profit. He attributed the efficiency of telescopes fitted with his lenses to a machining process that was kept secret at the time but was described in certain papers passed at Torricelli's death to the grand duke, who gave them to Viviani, after which they were lost. An elaborate story has sometimes been woven round this "secret"; but from the surviving documents it seems possible to reconstruct the whole of Torricelli's "secret"—which, apart from the need to enhance the merits of his production in the grand duke's eyes, consisted mainly in very accurate machining of the surfaces, in selecting good-quality glass, and in not fastening the lenses "with pitch, or in any way with fire." But this last precaution—which, according to Torricelli, was known only to God and himself—had been recommended by Hieronymus Sirturi in his *Telescopium* as far back as 1618. In any event, one of Torricelli's telescope lenses, which is now preserved together with other relics at the Museo di Storia della Scienza, Florence, was examined in 1924 by Vasco Ronchi, using the diffraction grating. It was found to be of exquisite workmanship, so much so that one face was seen to have been machined better than the mirror taken as reference surface, and was constructed with the most advanced technique of the period.

The lectures given by Torricelli on various occasions, and collected by Tommaso Bonaventuri in the posthumous volume *Lezioni accademiche*, were by preference on subjects in physics. They include eight lectures to the Accademia della Crusca, of which he was a member (one lecture of thanks for admission to the academy, three on the force of impact, two on lightness, one on wind, and one on fame); one in praise of mathematics, given to the Studio Fiorentino; two on military architecture at the Academy of Drawing, and one of encomium for the "golden century," the fabled epoch of human perfection, delivered to the "Accademia dei Percossi."

From the point of view of physics, the lectures on the force of impact and on wind are of particular interest. In the former he said that he was reporting ideas expressed by Galileo in their informal conversations, and there is no lack of original observations. For example, the assertion that "forces and impetus" (what we call energy) lie in bodies was interpreted by Maxwell in the last paragraph of *A Treatise on Electricity and Magnetism* (1873) as meaning that the propagation of energy is a mediate and not remote action. In the lecture on wind Torricelli refuted the current theory on the formation of wind, which was held to be generated by vaporous exhalations evaporating from the damp earth; on the other hand, he advanced the modern theory that winds are produced by differences of air temperature, and hence of density, between two regions of the earth.

But Torricelli's name is linked above all to the barometric experiment named after him. The argument on vacuum or fullness goes back to the first Greek philosophical schools. In the Middle Ages, Catholic theology replaced Aristotle's doctrine that a vacuum is a contradiction in logic by the concept that nature abhors a vacuum (*horror vacui*). During the Renaissance the argument between supporters of vacuum and those of fullness flared up again. Galileo, joining the rationalist philosophers Telesio and Bruno, opposed Aristotle's arguments against the vacuum and about 1613 experimentally demonstrated the weight of air. But, like the majority of his contemporaries, he believed that an element does not have weight in itself; hence, on the basis of the ascertained weight of air, he was unable to deduce pressures within atmospheric air. To explain the phenomenon that in suction pumps the water does not rise more than eighteen *braccia* (about nine meters), as observed by the Florentine well diggers, Galileo advanced the hypothesis of a force—the "force of vacuum"—that occurred inside the pump and was capable of balancing a column of water eighteen *braccia* high.

In 1630, when Giovanni Battista Baliani asked him why a siphon that was to cross a hill about twenty-one meters high did not work, Galileo replied by reiterating his theory of the force of vacuum. Baliani retorted that in his opinion the failure of the siphon was due to the weight of the air, which by pressing on all sides supported the column of water not under pressure in the top part of the siphon, from which the air had been expelled by the water poured in to fill it. But Galileo did not accept Baliani's ideas, and in the *Discorsi* (1638) he continued to uphold the theory of the force of vacuum. After Galileo's death the discussion continued between his followers in Rome and Florence; and it is probable that the former turned to Torricelli to get his opinion on the working of suction pumps or on a similar experiment that Gasparo Berti is said to have carried out at Rome in 1640 for the purpose of showing that the water in suction pumps rose to more than eighteen *braccia*.

Torricelli, who was perhaps acquainted with Baliani's concept, proceeded to repeat Berti's or Baliani's experiment, using progressively heavier liquids such as seawater, honey, and mercury, which was mined in Tuscany. The use of mercury also allowed him to simplify the filling process by replacing Baliani's or Berti's siphon with a simple glass tube about one meter long. He planned to fill it to the rim with mercury, to close it with one finger and overturn it, and to immerse the open end in mercury in a bowl. To make such a long tube capable of withstanding the weight of mercury was not an easy task at that time (only in 1646 was Mersenne able to obtain a sufficiently strong tube from the French glassworks); Torricelli asked Viviani to make one, and hence the latter was the first to perform the experiment.

In a letter of 11 June 1644 to Michelangelo Ricci, Torricelli described the experiment and, rejecting the theory of the force of vacuum, interpreted it according to Baliani. But even before carrying out the experiment he was aware of the variations in atmospheric pressure, since in the letter he says that he "wished to make an instrument that would show the changes of air, now heavier and denser, now lighter and thinner." According to a fairly well founded hypothesis, he had acquired a knowledge of the variations in atmospheric pressure through skillful observation of the behavior of hydrostatic toys, perhaps invented by him and later called "Cartesian devils." According to Torricelli the force that supports the mercury column is not internal to the tube but external, produced by the atmosphere that weighs on the mercury in the bowl. If, instead of mercury, the tube had contained water, Torricelli predicted that the height of the column would have been greater by the proportion that the weight of mercury exceeds that of water, a result verified by Pascal in 1647. In confirmation of the hypothesis that the cause of support of the mercury is outside and not inside the tube, Torricelli describes other experiments with tubes blown into a sphere at the top, with which equal heights of the mercury column were obtained, so that the force was not due to the volume of vacuum produced and therefore was not a "force of vacuum."

In his reply to Torricelli's letter Ricci put forward three objections showing how difficult it was for contemporaries to understand the transmission of pressure in air: (1) If the bowl is closed with a lid, the air weighs on the lid and not on the mercury, which should therefore fall in the bowl; (2) The weight of the air acts in a vertical direction from top to bottom, so how can it be transmitted from bottom to top inside the tube? (3) Bodies immersed in a fluid are subject to Archimedes' thrust, so the mercury should be pushed upward by a force equivalent to an equal column of air. Torricelli replied in a letter of 28 June 1644, carefully refuting the objections as follows: (1) If the lid does not change the "degree of condensation" of the air locked between the lid itself and the mercury in the bowl, things remain as before—this is shown by the example of a wool cylinder loaded with a weight and cut crosswise by an iron plate, in which the lower part remains compressed as before; (2) Fluids gravitate downward by nature, but "push and spurt in all directions, even upward"; (3) The mercury in the tube is not immersed in air. In substance Torricelli's two letters elaborate the theory of atmospheric pressure, with a hint at what was to be Pascal's principle.

According to the writings of his contemporaries, Torricelli, after succeeding in the experiment, sought to observe the conditions of life of small animals (fish, flies, butterflies) introduced into the vacuum. The results obtained were almost nil, however, because the creatures were crushed by the weight of the mercury before reaching the top part of the tube; and attempts to ascertain whether sound is propagated in a vacuum also appear to have been unsuccessful. In testimony of his great appreciation Grand Duke Ferdinando II issued a decree praising this experiment of Torricelli's very highly.

Copies of Torricelli's two letters were circulated among Italian scientists and were sent to Mersenne, who, traveling to Italy in October 1644, passed through Florence and obtained a repetition of the experiment from Torricelli himself. On his return to France, he informed his friends of Torricelli's experiment, giving rise to flourishing experimental and theoretical activity. Discovery of the barometer, Vincenzo Antinori wrote, changed the appearance of physics just as the telescope changed that of astronomy; the circulation of the blood, that of medicine; and Volta's pile, that of molecular physics.

BIBLIOGRAPHY

I. ORIGINAL WORKS. The writings and scientific correspondence were published in *Opere di Evangelista Torricelli*, Gino Loria and Giuseppe Vassura, eds., 4 vols. in 5 pts. (I–III, Faenza, 1919; IV, 1944).

Individual works are *Opera geometrica. De sphaera et solidis sphaeralibus libri duo . . . De motu gravium naturaliter descendentium et proiectorum libri duo. De dimensione parabolae* (Florence, 1644), the first sec. repr. with its long title, *De sphaera et solidis sphaeralibus libri duo in quibus Archimedis doctrina de sphaera et cylindro denuo componitur, latius promovetur et in omni specie solidorum, quae vel circa, vel intra sphaeram, ex conversione poligonorum regularium gigni possint, universalius propagatur* (Bologna, 1692); *Lezioni accademiche*, Tommaso Bonaventuri, ed. (Florence, 1715; 2nd ed., Milan, 1813); and "Sopra la bonificazione della Valle di Chiana," in *Raccolta d'autori che trattano del moto delle acque*, IV (Florence, 1768). Other short writings were published in historical works, mentioned below.

The majority of Torricelli's MSS, after complicated vicissitudes and some losses, as recounted in the intro. to the *Opere*, are preserved at the Biblioteca Nazionale Centrale, Florence; Angiolo Procissi, in *Evangelista Torricelli nel terzo centenario della morte* (Florence, 1951), 77–109, gives an accurate catalogue raisonné. The autograph works, except for one, and the souvenirs kept at the Torricelli Museum in Faenza were destroyed in 1944.

There are two oil portraits of Torricelli in the Uffizi Gallery in Florence; another portrait, engraved by Pietro Anichini, is reproduced on the frontispiece of the *Lezioni accademiche*.

II. SECONDARY LITERATURE. All histories of mathematics or physics deal more or less fully with Torricelli's life and work. *Opere*, IV, 341–346, contains a bibliography. Some of the most significant works are Timauro Antiate (pseudonym of Carlo Dati), *Lettera ai Filaleti. Della vera storia della cicloide e della famosissima esperienza dell'argento vivo* (Florence, 1663), the first publication of the correspondence with Ricci on the barometric experiment; [Tommaso Bonaventuri], in *Lezioni accademiche*, preface, v–xlix; Angelo Fabroni,

Vitae Italorum doctrina excellentium qui saeculis XVII et XVIII floruerunt, I (Pisa, 1778), 340–399, the appendix of which contains *Racconto di alcuni problemi*; and Giovanni Targioni Tozzetti, *Notizie degli aggrandimenti delle scienze fisiche accaduti in Toscana nel corso di anni LX del secolo XVII*, 4 vols. (Florence, 1780).

See also Vincenzo Antinori, *Notizie istoriche relative all'Accademia del Cimento*, in the series Saggi di Naturali esperienze fatte nell'Accademia del Cimento (Florence, 1841), *passim*, esp. 27; Ernst Mach, *Die Mechanik in ihrer Entwickelung historisch-kritisch dargestellt*, 2nd ed. (Leipzig, 1889), 377 ff.; and Raffaello Caverni, *Storia del metodo sperimentale in Italia*, 6 vols. (Florence, 1891–1900; repr. Bologna, 1970)—vols. I, IV, V have unpublished passages from Torricelli.

After publication of the *Opere*, which contained many unpublished writings, the studies on Torricelli received a new impetus. The following works contain many other bibliographical references: Vasco Ronchi, "Sopra una lente di Evangelista Torricelli," in *l'Universo* (Florence), 5, no. 2 (1924); Mario Gliozzi, *Origini e sviluppi dell'esperienza torricelliana* (Turin, 1931), repr. with additions in *Opere*, IV, 231–294; C. de Waard, *L'expérience barométrique, ses antécédents et ses explications* (Thouars, 1936); Guido Castelnuovo, *Le origini del calcolo infinitesimale nell'era moderna* (Bologna, 1938; 2nd ed., Milan, 1962), *passim*, esp. 52–53, 58–62; Ettore Bortolotti, "L'opera geometrica di Evangelista Torricelli," in *Monatshefte für Mathematik und Physik*, **48** (1939), repr. in *Opere*, IV, 301–337; Ettore Carruccio, *De infinitis spiralibus*, intro., rearrangement, trans., and notes by Carruccio (Pisa, 1955); Giuseppe Rossini, *Lettere e documenti riguardanti Evangelista Torricelli* (Faenza, 1956); *Convegno di studi torricelliani in occasione del 350° anniversario della nascita di Evangelista Torricelli* (Faenza, 1959); and W. E. Knowles Middleton, *The History of the Barometer* (Baltimore, 1964), ch. 2.

MARIO GLIOZZI

TOSCANELLI DAL POZZO, PAOLO (*b*. Florence, Italy, 1397; *d*. Florence, 1482), *astronomy, geography, medicine.*

Toscanelli's father, Domenico, was a physician. Information on Toscanelli's work is scanty and incomplete, since only a few fragments of his writings are extant. He must have begun his studies in medicine, mathematics, and astronomy at the University of Florence but later transferred to the more famous University of Padua, where he formed a friendship with Nicolas of Cusa. While pursuing his medical studies at Padua, Toscanelli was drawn to astrology but nevertheless achieved important results in astronomy.

On his return to Florence, the *signoria* of the city assigned Toscanelli the treatment of "judicial astrology," then much in vogue. Deemed by Cusa and Regiomontanus as the most learned living mathematician, he was introduced to Brunelleschi, then busy with the construction of the large cupola of the basilica of Santa Maria del Fiore. The great height of the lantern above the cupola gave Toscanelli the idea of placing a gnomon there, the highest ever built. Very little information is available concerning this important astronomical instrument; but the testimony of Egnatio Danti, the cosmographer of Cosimo I de'Medici, states that Toscanelli pierced an opening at the base of the lantern, through which the rays of the sun passed. The purpose was to determine with accuracy the day of the solstice and other astronomical data. The opening is ninety meters above the floor, and at high noon during the summer solstice the sun's rays fall on the marble floor of the basilica.

Stone slabs have been embedded in the floor at various times. The oldest, according to Ximenes, who in 1755 studied and reconstructed this meridian line, was the one that Toscanelli placed there in 1468.

Toscanelli also demonstrated his ability in astronomy through his observations of the comets that appeared in 1433, 1449, 1456, 1457, and 1472. (It was not until 1864 that his manuscripts in the National Library at Florence were discovered.) Although these observations were made without instruments, his methods of cartographic representation were much more accurate than those then in common use. In fact Giovanni Celoria (1842–1920), director of the astronomical observatory at Brera (Milan), was able to calculate the cometary orbits on the basis of Toscanelli's drawings. Thus he ascertained that the comet Toscanelli observed in 1456 was the one now known as Halley's comet.

Cristoforo Landino, professor of rhetoric and poetry at the University of Florence and a friend of Toscanelli, states that the latter held many conversations on geography with travelers and navigators who passed through Florence. It was probably as a result of these conversations that he decided to construct a nautical map of the Atlantic Ocean, even though knowledge of the longitudes of various places was then quite imperfect. Therefore it is not surprising that the positions of Cathay and of the island of Cippangu—that is, of China and Japan—were only vaguely known. They were placed more than one hundred degrees too far to the east, halfway between their correct locations and Lisbon, a displacement toward Europe of about ten thousand kilometers. The purpose of the map was to demonstrate that if one sails west, one can reach the Orient by a shorter route and thus circumnavigate the globe. Documents of the period indicate that the map, which was later reconstructed, was sent by Toscanelli with a letter to Fernando Martins, canon of Lisbon, whom he had met in Italy at the time of Cusa's death. In the letter he demonstrated that it was possible to reach "the most noble and large city of Quinsay" (China) by crossing the Atlantic. At the end of his life, Toscanelli apparently sent a copy of his map to Christopher Columbus, urging him to use it for exploration.

BIBLIOGRAPHY

Gustavo Uzielli, *La vita e i tempi di Paolo dal Pozzo Toscanelli* (Rome, 1893), contains an extensive bibliography and was reprinted in *Pubblicazioni del R. Osservatorio astronomico di Brera*, no. 55 (1921).

See also Carlo Errera, *L'epoca delle grandi scoperte geografiche* (Milan, 1926); G. Fumagalli, *Bibliografia delle opere concernenti Toscanelli e Amerigo Vespucci* (Florence, 1898); Hermann Wagner, "Die Rekonstruktion der Toscanelli Karte von Jahre 1474 und die Pseudo-Facsimilia des Behaim Globus v.j. 1492," in *Nachrichten der K. Gesellschaft der Wissenschaften zu Göttingen*, Phil.-hist. Kl. (1894); and his review of H. Vigaud, "La lettre et la carte de Toscanelli sur la route des Indes par l'ouest . . .," in *Göttingischen gelehrten Anzeigen* (1902), no. 2; and L. Ximenes, *Del vecchio e nuovo gnomone fiorentino* (Florence, 1757).

G. ABETTI

TOULMIN, GEORGE HOGGART (*b.* Southwark, Surrey, England, September 1754; *d.* Wolverhampton, England, July 1817), *geology.*

Toulmin was the eldest son of Robert Toulmin, a prosperous soapmaker whose forebears had lived for many years in Westmorland, in northwest England. Young Toulmin studied medicine at Edinburgh University from 1776 until 1779, when he graduated M.D. with a thesis entitled *De cynanche tonsillari.* Little is known about Toulmin's career after graduation, but it seems likely that he practiced medicine for the rest of his life; at first probably in London, and later in Wolverhampton. He published two unimportant medical works in 1789 and 1810. In the second work he states that he had lectured in London in 1795 on the subjects treated in the book; and a notice of the second book in the *Gentleman's Magazine* (London, 1810) describes him as Dr. G. H. Toulmin of Wolverhampton.

Soon after graduating Toulmin published his only geological work, *The Antiquity and Duration of the World* (London, 1780). This book, reprinted with some changes in title and content in 1783, 1785, and 1789, is chiefly remarkable for having anticipated in a very general way some of the conclusions reached by James Hutton in his *Theory of the Earth* (1788). In his book Toulmin rejected contemptuously earlier attempts to establish a chronology of the earth's history, including, by implication, the Old Testament chronology, and he accepted the Aristotelian belief in the eternity of the world. He claimed that the matter of which the earth is composed, both organic and inorganic, is in a state of constant motion, resulting from decay and erosion; and that new fossiliferous sediments are being deposited in the oceans. He recognized that mountains are destroyed by erosion and supposed that new ones would be formed by elevation. He also claimed that the operations of nature proceed in a slow and uniform manner; and that each part of the universe operates in a manner designed to secure the preservation of both the parts and the whole.

Although reprinted three times, Toulmin's book seems to have been almost completely ignored by contemporary geologists. G. F. Richardson, in his *Geology for Beginners* (London, 1842), stated that "Dr. Toulmin, although doubted and disbelieved in his own day, has expressed opinions which contain the substance of the system of Dr. Hutton, and the principles of Mr. Lyell."

While there are similarities in both the philosophy of the two authors and in the geological conclusions they reached, there is a fundamental difference between the two books. The geological conclusions reached by Hutton are to a large extent based on the extensive studies of rocks in the field which he made before publishing his *Theory*, but Toulmin adduces no evidence at all to suggest that his book was similarly based. On the contrary, he makes much use of previously published literature, notably John Whitehurst's *An Inquiry into the Original State and Formation of the Earth* (London, 1778). This, alone, may have accounted for the neglect of Toulmin's work by geologists; but an additional reason may have been his atheistical tendencies.

Toulmin and his book were forgotten until 1948, when S. I. Tomkeieff commented on the similarities of Toulmin's views to some of the conclusions reached by Hutton. In 1963 D. B. McIntyre drew attention to certain statements in the 1788 version of Hutton's *Theory* that are strikingly similar, textually, to statements to be found in Toulmin's book, and he concluded that Hutton must have read this book before writing his *Theory*. In 1967 G. L. Davies discussed fully the evidence bearing on the question whether Hutton, in compiling his *Theory*, was in any way indebted to Toulmin and concluded that there was no evidence supporting the suggestion; although he surmised that Toulmin, during his stay in Edinburgh, may have read a rough draft of Hutton's *Theory*, which could account for the textual similarities to be found in Toulmin's book. Whatever the truth may be, Toulmin's book can only be regarded as an academic exercise, rather than an original contribution to the development of geological ideas in the eighteenth century.

BIBLIOGRAPHY

I. ORIGINAL WORKS. Toulmin's published works on geology are *The Antiquity and Duration of the World* (London, 1780; repr., 1824); *The Antiquity of the World* (London, 1783); *The Eternity of the World* (London, 1785); and *The Eternity of the Universe* (London, 1789; repr., 1825, 1837). The last three works repeat, with little change, the text of the first.

His published works on medicine are *The Instruments of Medicine, or the Philosophical Digest and Practice of Physic* (London, 1789); *Elements of the Practice of Medicine on a Popular Plan . . . an Elementary Work for Students* (London, 1810).

II. SECONDARY LITERATURE. See S. I. Tomkeieff, "James Hutton and the Philosophy of Geology," in *Transactions of the Edinburgh Geological Society*, **14** (1948), 253–276, and *Proceedings of the Royal Society of Edinburgh*, **5** (1950), 387–400; D. B. McIntyre, "James Hutton and the Philosophy of Geology," in C. C. Albritton, ed., *The Fabric of Geology* (Reading, Mass.– Palo Alto–London, 1963), 1–11; and G. L. Davies, "George Hoggart Toulmin and the Huttonian Theory of the Earth," in *Bulletin of the Geological Society of America*, **78** (1967), 121–124.

V. A. EYLES

TOURNEFORT, JOSEPH PITTON DE (*b.* Aix-en-Provence, France, 3 June 1656; *d.* Paris, France, 28 November 1708), *botany, medicine.*

Tournefort, who had one brother and seven sisters, came from a family of the minor nobility. His father, Pierre Pitton, a lawyer and royal secretary, was *seigneur* of Tournefort; his mother, Aimare de Fagoue, was the daughter of a royal counselor at the chancellery of Provence. Destined at first for the Church, Tournefort received an excellent education in the classical languages and science from the Jesuits. His father's death in 1677 enabled him to prepare for his future vocation, natural history,

especially botany. Until 1683 he divided his time between herborizing and courses in chemistry, medicine, and botany (taught by Magnol) at the University of Montpellier. For several months each year he traveled through the countryside and mountains of the Alps, the Midi, the Pyrenees, and Spain — often accompanied by such botanist friends as Charles Plumier and Pierre Garidel.

In 1683, at the recommendation of Mme de Venelle, a grande dame at court and originally from Aix, Tournefort was chosen as substitute for Guy Fagon, professor at the Jardin du Roi, in Paris. His new post required him not only to teach botany but also to enrich the holdings of live plants in the garden. Each year between 1685 and 1689 he undertook long herborizing expeditions in the Midi and to Holland, England, and especially to the Iberian Peninsula, where he stayed for over a year. In 1691, at the nomination of the Abbé Bignon, he entered the Académie des Sciences; and from 1693 he was Fagon's sole substitute at the Jardin du Roi.

Although Tournefort had published only an edition of his lecture notes entitled *Schola botanica* (1689) and prepared by one of his English students, William Sherard, he was already one of Europe's most noted botanists and had dozens of correspondents, including Magnol at Montpellier and Herman at Leiden.

Between 1694 and his death in 1708 Tournefort's work was marked by two major events. The first was the publication of his *Élémens de botanique* (1694), which appeared in three volumes, two of them consisting of illustrations executed by Claude Aubriet; the work was translated into Latin as *Institutiones rei herbariae* (1700). The second was his voyage to the Levant (1700–1702). Tournefort's account of this voyage, published posthumously in 1717 and translated into several languages, still makes interesting reading. Tournefort's subsequently published writings represent only a small portion of his scientific work, however. At his death, the result of an accident, he left twelve folio volumes on botany, two of which were ready for the press: "Herborisations aux environs de Paris" and "Nomenclature des plantes observées en France, en Espagne, et en Portugal."

The study of living nature, especially of plants, was characterized in the seventeenth century principally by two major currents of research, one dealing with classification and the other with the inner structures of plants and their functions. These movements were not unrelated, and naturalists such as John Ray and Sébastien Vaillant introduced into classification certain fundamental notions from anatomy and biology. Tournefort was less open in this respect: he knew nothing of plant sexuality, refused to employ the microscope, and divided the plant into almost independent parts that he considered as separate entities. These important limitations in his work provoked widespread and often severe criticism. Yet this criticism was unfair to the extent that it failed to take into account Tournefort's overall intentions and the rigor with which he carried them out.

What botany owes to Tournefort is not the invention of the biotaxonomic genus, which had imposed itself empirically on observers since antiquity, but rather the creation of the concept of the genus in the modern sense and its first skillful application. His teacher at Montpellier, Magnol, had refined the concept of family (1689), although no doubt prematurely, for it was not taken up again for more than half a century. The classificatory unit that most attracted Tournefort was the genus—a "cluster of species," as he put it—a natural grouping having a real existence, independent of the observer, and identifiable. His goal was to "reduce each species to its true genus" and to define the genus by character or, as it would be called today, by diagnosis. Once identified, each genus was to receive a name that would evoke only the characteristic expressed in its description, and the name was to be as simple as possible—although tradition should not be completely disregarded. Above all, Tournefort carefully distinguished the act of describing from that of naming.

Tournefort's conception of genus contains a fundamental new contribution that was elaborated in the work of Linnaeus, Bernard de Jussieu, and Adanson. The distinct paths of taxonomy and nomenclature were now acknowledged. Linnaeus defined the species and, in a completely natural way, imposed the binary nomenclature; Jussieu and Adanson made knowledge of natural units at all levels the aim of their research.

In addition to genera, Tournefort suspected the existence of higher units, which he called classes, but in practice he scarcely treated them as such. Rather, like the divisions, he used them most often as quite arbitrary means of identifying species. Absorbed in the huge task of making an inventory of the genera in the material at hand, Tournefort did not have time to consider each species in detail. He was satisfied simply to rely on Gaspard Bauhin's *Pinax*, which, in his opinion, contained a perfectly satisfactory definition of species.

Tournefort's revolution was aided by his exceptionally broad botanical experience, the fame he acquired following his trip to the Levant, and his personality. His deep concern for clarity, simplicity, and rigor in his writings was the source of his attractive style and convincing argumentation. Unfortunately, it also resulted in a certain schematism and, ultimately, led to the superficiality of his method. The *Élémens* and the *Institutiones* are milestones in the history of taxonomy not only for the conceptual advances they reflect but also for the wholly new form in which they are cast. The text of the *Élémens* is in French, accompanied by a technical dictionary, and it is closely related to Aubriet's illustrations. The result is a well-integrated and easily accessible whole that could not fail to produce a sensation. Thus, although Tournefort's work disregarded the major biological discoveries of the seventeenth century, within its self-imposed limits it clearly outlined the avenues of study that led to the modern system of classification.

On the level of principles, Tournefort contributed powerfully and brilliantly to the establishment of objectivity in taxonomy and of research methods suitable for a natural method of classification. (His own system, based upon the flower and the fruit, chiefly the corolla, was, however, highly artificial.) While he was far from discovering the principle of subordination of characteristics, his method displayed a certain subordination related to his recognition of natural units existing at different levels. Further, Tournefort played a decisive role in the emancipation of botany from medicine.

Tournefort's genera—he accepted 725—have largely been retained, through the work of the leading taxonomists of the eighteenth century. Almost one-third of the genera of French flora derive from Tournefort. His herbarium, one of the treasures of the Muséum d'Histoire Naturelle at Paris, contains 6,963 species.

A well-rounded naturalist, Tournefort was also interested in minerals and shells, and his natural history collection included three thousand specimens of shells (G. Brice, cited by G. Ranson in *Tournefort* [Paris, 1957], 106). In addition, Tournefort was a physician with a considerable practice. Through his teaching and his publications he exerted an enormous influence until the end of the eighteenth century.

BIBLIOGRAPHY

I. ORIGINAL WORKS. Tournefort's first publication was a selection from his lectures at the Jardin du Roi, edited by William Sherard under the pseudonym of Simon Warton: *Schola botanica . . .* (Amsterdam, 1689). He subsequently published *Élémens de botanique ou méthode pour connoître les plantes,* 3 vols. (Paris, 1694).

Tournefort's other publications include the four-page pamphlet *Quaestio medica . . . discutienda . . . die Francisco Afforty . . . praeside: An potio e salvia salubris?* (n.p., n.d. [Paris, 1695]); *Histoire des plantes qui naissent aux environs de Paris avec leur usage en médecine* (Paris, 1698), a review of which appeared in *Nouvelles de la république des lettres,* **12** (Mar. 1699); a letter from Tournefort to the author at the beginning of D. Tauvry, *Nouvelle pratique des maladies aiguës et de toutes celles qui dépendent de la fermentation des liqueurs* (Paris, 1698); *Institutiones rei herbariae,* 3 vols. (Paris, 1700); "Observations sur les plantes qui naissent dans le fond de la mer," in *Mémoires de l'Académie royale des sciences,* for 1700 (1703), 27–36; *Corollarium institutionum rei herbariae, in quo plantae 1356 munificentia Ludovici Magni in orientalibus regionibus observatae recensentur* (Paris, 1703), a supp. to the *Institutiones* written by Tournefort after his return from the Levant; "Description du labirinthe de Candie, avec quelques observations sur l'accroissement et sur la génération des pierres," in *Mémoires de l'Académie royale des Sciences* for 1702 (1704), 217–234; "Persicaria orientalis nicotiniae folio, calyce florum purpureo corol. hist. rei herbar," *ibid.,* for 1703 (1705), 302–304; "Description de deux espèces de Chamaerhododendros observés sur les côtes de la Mer Noire," *ibid.,* for 1704 (1706), 345–352; "Description de l'oeillet de la Chine," *ibid.,* for 1705 (1706), 264–266; "Suite de l'établissement de quelques nouveaux genres de plantes," *ibid.,* for 1705 (1706), 83–87, 236–241; "Observation sur les maladies des plantes," *ibid.,* 27–36; "Observations sur la naissance et sur la culture des champignons," *ibid.,* for 1707 (1708), 58–66; and *Materia medica . . .,* (London, 1708), translated from Tournefort's lectures at the Jardin des Plantes and published in English before appearing in French.

Posthumous publications include *Tournefortius contractus sub forma tabularum sistens Institutiones rei herbariae juxta methodum modernarum . . .* (Frankfurt, 1715); *Traité de la matière médicale . . .,* 2 vols. (Paris, 1717); *Relation d'un voyage du Levant fait par ordre du roy . . .,* 2 vols. (Paris, 1717), with maps prepared by Claude Aubriet—this work consists of letters addressed to the count of Pontchartrain during the voyage of 1700–1702 and is preceded by Fontenelle's *éloge* of Tournefort; *Institutiones rei herbariae,* 3rd ed., 3 vols. (London, 1719), with app. by Antoine de Jussieu—this ed. contains the *Isagoge in rem herbarium,* about two-thirds of which (all of the portion on the history of botany) is completely new with respect to the intro., written in French, to the *Élémens de botanique; Histoire des plantes qui naissent aux environs de Paris avec leur usage dans la médecine,* 2nd ed., rev. and enl. by Bernard de Jussieu, 2 vols. (Paris, 1725); *Tournefort's History of Plants Growing About Paris,* John Martyn,

trans. (London, 1732); *Beschryving van eene reize naar de Levant . . . door den Hr Pitton de Tournefort . . .,* 2 vols. in 1 (Amsterdam, 1737); *Abrégé des "Élémens de botanique ou méthode pour connoître les plantes" par M. de Tournefort* (Avignon, 1749); *Matière médicale extraite des meilleurs auteurs et principalement du traité des médicamens de M. de Tournefort et des leçons de M. Ferrein,* 3 vols. (Paris, 1770), which was attributed to C. L. F. Andry, by A. A. Barbier, in *Dictionnaire des ouvrages anonymes . . .,* III (Paris, 1875), col. 82; and *Beschreibung einer auf königlichen. Befechl unternommenen. Reise nach der Levante,* G. W. F. Panzer, trans., 3 vols. plus 1 vol. of plates (Nuremberg, 1776–1777).

Later versions are *Élémens de botanique ou méthode pour connoître les plantes par Pitton de Tournefort . . .,* N. Jolyclerc, ed., 6 vols. (Lyons, 1797); [*Epistola D. D. Volkamero, apud Norinbergenses archiatio*]. *Panzer Georgio Wolfgang Panzero . . . gratulatur simulque quaedam de D. Joanne Georgio Volcamero . . . additis duabus ad illum epistolis Hermann Boerhaave & Jos. Pitt. Tournefort exponit D. Georg. Wolfgang Franciscus Panzer* (Nuremberg, 1802); *Joseph Pitton Tournefort de optima methodo instituenda in re herbaria, ad . . . Gulielmum Sherardum . . . epistola, in qua respondetur dissertationi: D. Raii de variis plantarum methodis* (n.p., n.d.), the letter being dated "Parisiis ex Horto regio, sept. MDCXCVII"; *Réponse de M. Chomel à deux lettres écrites par M. P. C. sur la botanique* (n.p., n.d. [Paris, 1696])—according to J. M. Quérard, the true author is Tournefort (this response is addressed to Philibert Collet, who, in his letters of 1695, spoke of the *Élémens de botanique* as a trans. and abridgement of John Ray's *Historia plantarum*); and "Etablissement de quelques nouveaux genres de plantes par M. Tournefort," in *Mémoires de l'Académie royale des sciences* (1706), 236–241; and *Tableau synoptique de la méthode botanique de Tournefort* (Paris, 1796). See also *Isagoge in rem herbarium (Introduction à la botanique),* translated by G. Becker from the 1719 ed. of the *Institutiones,* in *Tournefort, Muséum d'histoire naturelle* (Paris, 1957), 239–306.

II. SECONDARY LITERATURE. See G. Becker et al., "Les grands naturalistes français," in *Tournefort, Muséum d'histoire naturelle* (Paris, 1957); and H. Daudin, *De Linné à Jussieu* (Paris, 1926).

JEAN F. LEROY

TOWNELEY, RICHARD (*b.* Towneley Hall, near Burnley, Lancashire, England, 1629; *d.* York, England, 22 January 1707), *natural philosophy.*

Towneley was a member of a celebrated Roman Catholic family which, from the reign of Elizabeth I, was burdened by the penal measures of a succession of Protestant rulers, although wealth and ingenuity were sufficient to preserve both their religious integrity and their large estates. These circumstances partly explain Towneley's aversion to publicity and his retiring disposition.

Towneley was the eldest son of Charles Towneley, who was killed at the Battle of Marston Moor (1644). Richard married Margaret Paston, a Norfolk Catholic, and established a large family at Towneley Hall. In spite of the premature accretion of family responsibilities, he was able to devote most of his energies to science; the interest was probably stimulated by his uncle, Christopher Towneley (1604–1674), who had known the northern astronomers Horrocks, Crabtree, and Gascoigne. Following their deaths during the Civil War, Christopher Towneley collected and preserved their manuscripts.

Almost all of Towneley's work took place in his home. He accumulated an outstanding library of scientific works and attracted many local collaborators, mainly Catholic gentry, but also Henry Power and John Flamsteed. With Power, Towneley made early, fruitful investigations concerning air pressure. They repeated and augmented the classical experiments of Torricelli, Pascal, and Pecquet; and in 1660 and 1661 undertook experiments that led to a recognition of the air pressure–volume relationship, subsequently known as Boyle's law. Their discovery was published in 1661, but the law was not generally known until Boyle's *New Experiments Physico-Mechanical* (2nd edition, 1662). Boyle acknowledged Towneley's assistance in arriving at this generalization. Towneley's interest in air pressure continued, with attempts to measure altitudes barometrically and investigations of capillarity and the meteorological use of barometers. The interest widened to include other meteorological records; particularly important were his detailed measurements of rainfall, kept between 1677 and 1704.

Perhaps Towneley's most significant achievement was the improvement of the micrometer. Working from the principle discovered by Gascoigne, Towneley produced a sophisticated micrometer, which he applied to astronomical uses. He introduced this instrument to Flamsteed and the Royal Society. From 1670 he and Flamsteed collaborated on routine astronomical observations.

Towneley's position in English natural philosophy was distinctive, since he was one of the very few thoroughgoing Cartesians.

BIBLIOGRAPHY

I. ORIGINAL WORKS. Towneley's MSS were dispersed at the Victorian sale of the Towneley library; few of the MSS have been traced. His few publications were communicated by correspondents and friends. *Mercurial Experiments Made at Towneley Hall in the Years 1660 and 1661* was known in September 1661, but no copy has survived; it was reprinted in Henry Power, *Experimental Philosophy* (London, 1664). Towneley's micrometer was described in *Philosophical Transactions of the Royal Society*, 2, nos. 25, 29 (1667), 457–458, 541–544. For Flamsteed's communication of Towneley's account of the eclipse of 1676, see *Philosophical Transactions of the Royal Society*, 11 (1676), 602–604. For Towneley's rainfall records, see *ibid.*, 18 (1699), 51; 21 (1702), 47; and 25 (1705), 1877–1881.

Towneley's most substantial surviving MSS are "Considerations upon Mr. Hooke's attempt for ye Explication of ye Expt. of ye waters ascent into small Glasse canes" (1665) and "A preliminarie discourse wherein . . . the existence or qualitie and motion of a subtle matter is proved" (1667), in the Fulton Library, Yale University. For his correspondence, see Webster (1966), below. Particularly important is the Flamsteed-Towneley correspondence, Royal Society MS 243.

II. SECONDARY LITERATURE. Towneley is not mentioned in the standard biographical dictionaries. His scientific work is summarized in A. Wolf, *History of Science and Technology in the Sixteenth and Seventeenth Centuries*, 2nd ed. (London, 1962). For more detailed discussion, see the following articles by C. Webster: "Richard Towneley and Boyle's Law," in *Nature*, 197 (1963), 226–228; "The Discovery of Boyle's Law and the Concept of the Elasticity of Air in the Seventeenth Century," in *Archive for History of Exact Sciences*, 2 (1965), 441–502; "Richard Towneley, the Towneley Group and Seventeenth-century Science," in *Transactions of the Historic Society of Lancashire and Cheshire*, 118 (1966), 51–76; and "Henry Power's Experimental Philosophy," in *Ambix*, 14 (1967), 150–178.

CHARLES WEBSTER

TOWNSEND, JOHN SEALY EDWARD (*b.* Galway, Ireland, 7 June 1868; *d.* Oxford, England, 16 February 1957), *physics.*

Townsend is best known for his research concerning the kinetics of ions and electrons in gases. The son of a college professor, he was educated at Trinity College, Dublin. He studied mathematics and physics, receiving his degree in 1890. After five years of teaching mathematics, in 1895 Townsend became one of the first outside research students to enter the Cavendish Laboratory under J. J. Thomson.

In 1897 Townsend made a direct determination of the absolute unit of charge using an original method, which "included practically all the ideas which were later used in accurate measurements of the charge."[1] Using Stokes's law, Townsend measured the rate of fall of a cloud that had condensed on an electrified gas, which had been liberated in electrolysis and then bubbled through water. By February 1898 he published the unit of charge as 5×10^{-10} esu.[2] In 1898 Townsend proved that the fundamental constant of electrolysis was equivalent to the charge carried by a gaseous ion whatever its mode of production. In that same year he also developed a method for determining the rate of ion diffusion indirectly using the ion mobility. By August 1900, the year of his election as Wykeham professor of physics at Oxford, Townsend had published a preliminary statement of his unique collision theory of ionization. Considering

FIGURE 1: Based upon J. S. Townsend, *The Theory of Ionization of Gases by Collision* (London, 1910), p. 1, and extended on the basis of R. Papoular, *Electrical Phenomena in Gases* (London, 1965), p. 123, and A. von Engel, *Ionized Gases*, 2nd ed. (Oxford, 1965), p. 223.

Schematic current-voltage characteristics for gaseous discharge at low pressure (*ca.* 1 mm Hg).

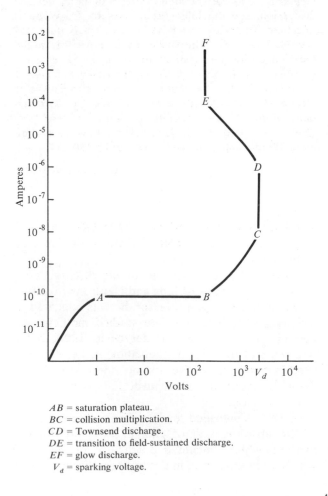

AB = saturation plateau.
BC = collision multiplication.
CD = Townsend discharge.
DE = transition to field-sustained discharge.
EF = glow discharge.
V_d = sparking voltage.

the ionization potential to be less than 15 volts instead of more than 150 volts, as was then commonly held, Townsend established that the motion of ions under the influence of an electric field was sufficient to form secondary ions in the gas. The ionization by collision was caused mainly by the "negative ions," which Townsend considered "the same as the negatively charged particles which are given off when ultra-violet light falls on a zinc plate. It has been shown by Professor [J. J.] Thomson that the mass of these particles is 1/500 of the mass of a molecule of hydrogen."[3] The rate of secondary ionization by electrons was a function of the pressure and the applied voltage. His theory could adequately account for the anomalous increase in conductivity under ultraviolet light observed already in 1890 by Stoletow. By 1903, the year of his election as fellow of the Royal Society, Townsend had included the role of the positive ions in his collision theory. He developed an expression,[4] ultimately containing his two well-known ionization coefficients α and γ, by which he could describe the Townsend discharge and also the breakdown or spark discharge (see Figure 1).

The collision principle was the basis of the 1908 particle detector of E. Rutherford and H. Geiger. Townsend had written to Rutherford that

> . . . the dodge of multiplying small conductivity by collisions works very well. . . . The case of a wire inside a cylinder has been worked out by Kirkby.[5] . . . You are certain to get unsteady effects if you try to multiply by too big a factor as the small variations produced in [the coefficients] α and β by variations of EMF or pressure have a large effect on the multiplier when it rises to the value of 500 or 1000.[6]

Kirkby and Townsend also quantitatively investigated electrochemical effects of the ionization of gases. Townsend studied the motion of electron swarms, noting that individual electrons may have random velocities much greater than the mean drift velocity of the swarm. He also noted that the mean free path of electrons in gases is energy-dependent. By the end of World War I Townsend was fifty, but during the subsequent two decades he averaged over two scientific papers a year and published five books. During the early 1920's Townsend, independently of C. Ramsauer, discovered a new physical effect. He reported in 1924 the fact that the monotomic gases, especially argon and helium, seemed particularly transparent to low energy electrons, since these could traverse such gaseous media without "feeling" its presence. Ramsauer had observed the diminished dispersion for such slow-speed electrons compared with swifter ones. Although Townsend did not himself become involved with quantum theory, this Ramsauer-Townsend effect[7] was the analogue in gases of the results with solid-state targets obtained a few years later by C. J. Davisson and independently by G. P. Thomson, and it thus became important in the understanding of the wave nature of the electron. In 1941 Townsend was knighted in recognition of his many scientific contributions, and he died in his eighty-eighth year.

NOTES

1. E. Rutherford, "The Development of the Theory of Atomic Structure," in J. Needham and W. Pagel, eds., *Background to Modern Science* (Cambridge, 1938), 64–65.
2. This result compared favorably with that of R. A. Millikan, who, like Townsend, had avoided the expansion principle and who had closely approximated by 1911 the accepted value of 4.8×10^{-10} esu. Using an expansion chamber to form a cloud, J. J. Thomson published a result of 6.5×10^{-10} esu in December 1898.
3. J. Townsend, "The Conductivity Produced in Gases by the Motion of Negatively Charged Ions," in *Philosophical Magazine*, **1** (1901), 198–227. Considerable confusion could arise concerning Townsend's term "negative ion," for it could be taken as indicating a massive particle that had acquired a negative charge. However, whether he described the negatively charged particle as having passed from an ionic state into an electronic state (*Electricity in Gases* [1915], p. 119) or as simply electrons (*Electrons in Gases* [1947], p. 92), his negative ions were very small with respect to the molecule of hydrogen.
4. Townsend's first expression was contained in "Some Effects Produced by Positive Ions," in *Electrician*, **50** (1903), 971.

$$n = n_0 \frac{(\alpha - \beta) \exp (\alpha - \beta) a}{\alpha - \beta \exp (\alpha - \beta) a}.$$

The α and β were his first set of ionization coefficients, where α was the number of collisions or ion pairs produced per centimeter of path by an electron, and where β was the number of ion pairs produced per centimeter by a positive ion. The number of electrons produced by the external radiation was "n_0," "n" represented the total number of electrons arriving at the anode, and "a" was the distance between the electrodes. The dominant secondary effect of the positive ions, however, was not in gaseous collisions but was the release of secondary electrons at the cathode. In addition to α (the ionization coefficient representing the electrons released by other electrons colliding with the gas on their way to the anode), Townsend introduced his secondary emission coefficient γ, which represented the ionizing electrons released at the cathode. The general expression accordingly became:

$$n = n_0 \frac{\exp \alpha a}{1 - \gamma (\exp \alpha a - 1)}.$$

The sparking potential was a maximum value, and Townsend emphasized that the potential required for sustained discharge was normally significantly less. The conditions for breakdown were obtained on either expression by letting "n" approach infinity. For a given applied voltage and pressure the critical distance "d" for the spark discharge (the end of the region of Townsend discharge and the beginning of the region of the field-sustained discharge) was thus described on the earlier formulation by $\alpha = \beta \exp (\alpha - \beta) d$, and on the later formulation by $1 = \gamma (\exp \alpha d - 1)$.

5. P. J. Kirkby, a research student of Townsend, "On the Electrical Conductivities Produced in Air by the Motion of Negative Ions," in *Philosophical Magazine*, **3** (1902), 212–225.
6. Townsend letter to E. Rutherford, 10 March 1908, in Cambridge University Library, Add. MSS 7653/T76.
7. A. von Engel, *Ionized Gases*, 2nd ed. (Oxford, 1965), 31. J. Townsend, *Motion of Electrons in Gases* (Oxford, 1925), 26–29, an address to the Franklin Institute, Philadelphia, Sept. 1924.

BIBLIOGRAPHY

Townsend published over one hundred papers and several books as listed by his biographer A. von Engel, in "John Sealy Edward Townsend, 1868–1957," in *Biographical Memoirs of Fellows of the Royal Society*, **3** (1957), 257–272; and in his notice for the *Dictionary of National Biography: 1951–1960*, pp. 983–985. A small collection of his correspondence exists at the Cambridge University Library Add. MSS 7653/T71–T89; but T. S. Kuhn has noted, in *Sources for History of Quantum Mechanics* (Philadelphia, 1967), p. 92b, that no extensive collection is likely to exist. See also A. von Engel, in *Nature*, **179** (1957), 757–758, and Maurice de Broglie, "Notice nécrologique sur Sir John Townsend," in *Comptes rendus hebdomadaires des séances de l'Académie des sciences*, **244** (1957), 3105–3106. In *A History of the Cavendish Laboratory* (London, 1910), E. Rutherford in ch. 6 and C. T. R. Wilson in ch. 7 discussed the early work of Townsend. After over 40 years of continuous service at Oxford, at his retirement a notice of his work appeared in *Nature*, **157** (1946), 293. A valuable article is by C. A. Russell, in T. I. Williams, ed., *A Biographical Dictionary of Scientists* (London, 1969), 517–518. The work of Townsend concerning diffusion of ions in gases and also regarding the fundamental unit of charge is considered in detail in N. Feather, *Electricity and Matter* (Edinburgh, 1968), 306–313; and in R. A. Millikan, *The Electron* (Chicago, 1963), facsimile of 1917, 34–38, 43–47, 51–52, 123–125, esp. in appendices A and B.

The development of the expression for the Townsend discharge and the breakdown equation is discussed in J. A. Crowther, *Ions, Electrons, and Ionizing Radiations* (London, 1961), 54–56; and is treated technically in A. von Engel, *Ionized Gases*, 2nd ed. (Oxford, 1965), 171–182.

THADDEUS J. TRENN

TOWNSEND, JOSEPH (*b.* London, England, 4 April 1739; *d.* Pewsey, Wiltshire, England, 9 November 1816), *medicine, geology, economics.*

Townsend was the fourth son of Bridget Phipps

Townsend and Chauncy Townsend, a linen merchant, mine inspector, and member of Parliament. He attended Clare Hall, Cambridge University, and received his B.A. in 1762 and his M.A. in 1765. In 1762–1763 Townsend studied medicine in Edinburgh, attending the classes of William Cullen in anatomy, Robert Whytt in physiology, and John Hope in botany.

While a student Townsend came under the influence of Calvinistic Methodism and was ordained a minister in 1765. He was an unusually tall man and a powerful speaker, and for a number of years he traveled through England as an evangelical minister. The experience was unpleasant, and his enthusiasm gradually waned. Richard Graves satirized Townsend's ministry in a novel, *The Spiritual Quixote* (1772). In 1773 he married Joyce Nankivell, by whom he had two daughters and four sons. She died in 1785 and in 1790 he married Lydia Hammond Clerke, widow of Sir John Clerke. She died in 1814.

Townsend traveled to France, Holland, and Flanders in 1770 as chaplain to the duke of Atholl. In 1786–1787 he traveled through Spain and wrote an important account of the Spanish economy, similar to those travel accounts Arthur Young was writing on Britain and France. Townsend's *Journey Through Spain* (3 vols., 1791; 3rd ed. 1814) was popular enough to be translated into German (1792), Dutch (1792–1793), and French (1800).

In 1786 Townsend published an attack on British charity for being too indulgent to the poor, and in his *Journey Through Spain* he extended this attack to Spanish institutions. He argued that when the poor depended upon charity, the increase of their population would deplete the wealth of the country. Realizing that the population of Spain had declined, he analyzed the causes. (The population of Spain had declined sharply in the seventeenth century, but at the time he was writing this, it was actually increasing rapidly.) His discussion contributed to the awareness of the importance of population as an economic factor. Malthus claimed not to have known Townsend's writings on population until after publishing the first edition of his *Essay on the Principle of Population* (1798), but he expressed an appreciation for Townsend's writings in the second and subsequent editions of his *Essay*.

Townsend wrote two very popular manuals for the practice of medicine: *The Physician's Vade Mecum* (1781; 10th ed., 1807) and *Elements of Therapeutics, or a Guide to Health* (1795; 3rd ed., 1801). The latter work contains the first English description of Antonio de Gimbernat's operation for strangulated femoral hernia, and Townsend also published the first English description of pellagra (under the name of "mal de la rosa") in his *Journey* (II, 10).

Townsend developed an early interest in geology and paleontology, perhaps because of his father's influence. The *Journey* contains numerous geologic descriptions and speculations. He became friends with William Smith, who in 1799 explained to him the method of correlating strata by the kinds of fossils in them. Townsend published one of the first and clearest accounts of Smith's discovery in the first volume of *The Character of Moses Established for Veracity as an Historian, Recording Events From the Creation to the Deluge* (2 vols., 1813–1815). Townsend used Smith's discovery to attack James Hutton's assertion that there is no evidence concerning the origin of the earth. In spite of his doctrinaire stand, there is considerable merit to Townsend's geological discussion. At the founding of the Geological Society of London in 1807, Townsend was elected an honorary member.

BIBLIOGRAPHY

I. ORIGINAL WORKS. For a list of Townsend's writings, see the *General Catalogue of Printed Books* of the British Museum. This list does not include his now rare treatise *On the Agency of Vital Air in the Cure of Various Diseases, With Cases*, 2nd ed. (London, 1824), later retitled *Townsend on Vital Air, Being Numerous Cases Showing the Effects of Vital Air and Other Factitious Airs: As Judiciously Practiced by Dr. Thornton*, 9th ed. (London, 1827); and as *Townsend on Pneumatic Medicine*, 10th ed. (London, 1830). The only known copies of the 2nd and 9th editions have been in private hands and are described briefly by A. D. Morris (see below).

II. SECONDARY LITERATURE. The best account of Townsend's life and career and of his medical contributions is by A. D. Morris, "The Reverend Joseph Townsend MA, MGS (1739–1816) Physician and Geologist — 'Colossus of Roads,'" in *Proceedings of the Royal Society of Medicine*, **62** (1969), 471–477.

For other biographical information and a discussion of Townsend's geology, see A. G. Davis, "The Triumvirate: A Chapter in the Heroic Age of Geology," in *Proceedings of the Croydon Natural History and Scientific Society*, **11** (1943), 122–146. See also Charles Coulston Gillispie, *Genesis and Geology: A Study in the Relations of Scientific Thought, Natural Theology, and Social Opinion in Great Britain, 1790–1850* (Cambridge, Mass., 1951; New York, 1959), for a discussion of Townsend's *The Character of Moses*. . . .

Townsend's demographic ideas have been discussed by Kenneth Smith, *The Malthusian Controversy*

(London, 1951) and by Ashley Montagu and Mark Neuman in an edition of Townsend's *A Dissertation on the Poor Laws by a Well-Wisher to Mankind* (Berkeley, 1971). On Spain's population at the time of Townsend's visit, see Earl J. Hamilton, "The Decline of Spain," in *Economic History Review*, **8** (1938), 168–179; Massimo Livi-Bacci, "Fertility and Population Growth in Spain in the Eighteenth and Nineteenth Centuries," in *Daedalus*, **97** (1968), 523–535; and Jorge Nadal, *La Poblacion Española, Siglos XVI a XX* (Barcelona, 1966). For a discussion of the Spanish economy, see Earl J. Hamilton, *War and Prices in Spain, 1651–1800* (Cambridge, Mass., 1947; New York, 1969).

FRANK N. EGERTON III

TOZZI, DON BRUNO (*b.* Florence, Italy, 27 November 1656; *d.* Vallombrosa, Italy, 24 January 1743), *botany*.

Tozzi was the son of Francesco Simone Tozzi. Although his family was of modest means, Don Bruno was nevertheless able to pursue a formal study of philosophy and theology before his investiture, at age twenty, as a monk in the order of Vallombrosa. He was successful in the performance of his religious duties but repeatedly refused promotions. He eventually did become procurator general and abbot of the order. At the same time he managed to pursue his interest in botany. His ecclesiastical duties required frequent journeys, and he availed himself of the opportunity to study and collect plants as he made his way from place to place on foot.

An endowment allowed Tozzi to obtain a choice collection of scientific books. He was a teacher and friend of Pier Antonio Micheli, and their lifelong friendship was enhanced by the many excursions they made together collecting plants. Micheli named the rare genus *Tozzia* for his mentor.

Abbot Tozzi not only had a keen eye for finding and collecting plants, but he also became adept at watercolor illustration of phanerogams as well as cryptogamic species. A number of his works were devoted exclusively to fungi, lichens, algae, and bryophytes. He generously shared his collections and drawings with prominent botanical figures of the day, including William Sherard, who sent him books. He also kept an active correspondence and exchange of materials with Hermann Boerhaave, James Petiver, and Hans Sloane. Tozzi became well-known as an able teacher and authority on the Italian flora. As many as 200 plants are illustrated in his *Catalogus plantarum etruriae et insularum adjacentium*. Along with his friend Micheli, he was

a founder of the Società Botanica Fiorentina, and he was elected to the Royal Society of London. He declined offers to teach in London because of advancing age and duties to his order. After retirement he began some folios of birds and insects, and devoted himself largely to his botanical interests until his death.

BIBLIOGRAPHY

I. ORIGINAL WORKS. Tozzi's contributions to botany are too numerous to list individually. Manuscripts by Tozzi not sent to his contemporaries are preserved at the Biblioteca Nazionale Centrale in Florence. Some watercolor drawings sent to Sherard are at the University of Oxford. The Sloane collections in the British Museum (Natural History) include some of Tozzi's color illustrations as well as some letters written to Petiver and Sloane. A nearly complete list of Tozzi's works are cited in P. A. Saccardo and F. Cavara, "Funghi di Vallombrosa," in *Nuovo giornale botanico italiano e Bolletino della Società botanica italiana*, n.s. **7** (1900), 272–310.

II. SECONDARY LITERATURE. The number of works containing information on Tozzi is scarcely indicative of the importance of this man to early European botany. Holdings of Tozzi's at the University of Oxford are listed by H. N. Clokie, *An Account of the Herbaria of the Department of Botany in the University of Oxford*, VIII (Oxford, 1964).

A tribute to Tozzi was made on the occasion of the 200th anniversary of Micheli's death in a small paper presented at the Italian Botanical Society by G. Negri, "Don Bruno Tozzi (1656–1743)," in *Nuovo giornale botanico italiano e Bolletino della Società botanica italiana*, n.s. **45** (1939), cix–cxiv.

A few insights concerning Tozzi and his works can be found in J. Proskauer, "Bruno Tozzi's Little Mystery, or a Quarter Millennium of Confusion," in *Webbia*, **20** (1965), 227–239.

DALE M. J. MUELLER

TRADESCANT, JOHN (*b.* Suffolk [?], England, 1570/1575; *d.* South Lambeth, Surrey, England, 15/16 April 1638), *natural history*.

In 1773 Ducarel wrote that Tradescant may be "justly considered the earliest collector (in this kingdom) of every thing that was curious in Natural History, viz., minerals, birds, fishes, insects, &c . . . coins and medals of all sorts, besides a great variety of uncommon rarities." Tradescant's father, Thomas Tradescant (a descendant of Willelmus Treluskant of Suffolk), in 1578 left Suffolk, where John was probably born, for London; his mother's name is unknown. The first verified record is John's marriage to Elizabeth Day at Meopham, Kent, on 18 June 1607. Their only son, John, was born the following year. Beginning in 1604 Tradescant was gardener for the properties of Robert Cecil, earl of Salisbury. There is some evidence that before 1600 he had been gardener to William Brookes at Cobham Hall.

Tradescant made his first (?) collecting trip to Flanders for Cecil in 1610, and it was probably then that he introduced the large-leaved Brussels strawberry into England. In 1611 he visited the Lamont nursery at Rouen and the apothecary garden of Jean Robin on the Île Notre-Dame. He also introduced species to the gardens at Hatfield, until its sale on the earl's death in 1612.

Six years later Tradescant made the first botanical visit to Russia when he accompanied Sir Dudley Digges, who was sent by James I under the Muscovy Company to negotiate a loan to the emperor of Russia. They reached Archangel on 16 July 1618, and Tradescant noted larch, white hellebore, and other plants (Allan, pp. 84–89), especially on the islands about the mouth of the Dvina River. On 5 August 1618 they set sail for England. Tradescant wrote an account of the expedition (Konovalov, pp. 130–141).

In 1620 Tradescant joined Sir Samuel Argall's expedition against the Barbary corsairs, taking the opportunity to collect garden seeds and fruits (Allan, pp. 101–103) and *naturalia*, including the first specimens of gutta-percha and mazer wood to be seen in England. After a short employment with George Villiers, duke of Buckingham, from 1625 to 1628, during which service he joined a military expedition to La Rochelle, Tradescant used the nucleus of his own collections to set up a garden and a museum in South Lambeth, a pioneer enterprise. His museum was enriched by gifts from virtuosi (sea captains supplied "such toyes as they could bring from other parts") and visited by Charles I and nobility. Doubtless the most famous exhibit was the stuffed dodo, seen by Willughby and Ray.

During this time Tradescant became gardener to Charles I and Queen Henrietta Maria. In 1631 René Morin began to send novelties. The following year Tradescant testified that an alleged unicorn's horn was that of a narwhal "yet very precious against poison."

His *Catalogus* (1634), the only known copy of which is in Magdalen College, lists 750 garden plants grown at South Lambeth, arranged alphabetically, and concludes with a catalog of fruits.

Forty Virginia species have been recognized in this *Catalogus* upon which the *Musaeum Tradescantianum* (1656) was based.

The generic name *Tradescantia* dates from H. B. Ruppius, *Flora Jenensis* (1718), and was accepted by Linnaeus. Tradescant "liv'd till [he] had travelled art and nature thro" and was buried on 17 April 1638, to the southeast of Lambeth Church.

BIBLIOGRAPHY

I. ORIGINAL WORKS. John Goodyer's copy of Tradescant's *Plantarum in Horto Iohannem* [sic] *Tradescanti nascentium catalogus* (1634) survives as the only known copy in Magdalen College, Oxford; and as Gunther suggested, it is almost certainly a copy made up from printer's proof, judging from the error on the title page. Many Tradescant curiosities, for example, chief Powhatan's feather cape, although often without precise provenance, are preserved in the (new) Ashmolean Museum. An album of Tradescant's "choicest Flowers and Plants exquisitely limned on vellum by Mr. Alex: Marshall" is in the library of Windsor Castle (see A. P. Oppé, *English Drawings, Stuart and Georgian Periods, in the Collection of His Majesty the King at Windsor Castle* (London, 1950), 74–75.

II. SECONDARY LITERATURE. Classic accounts of Tradescant and his work are William Watson, "Some Account of the Remains of John Tradescant's Garden at Lambeth," in *Philosophical Transactions of the Royal Society*, **46** (1752), 160–161; and Andrew Coltee Ducarel's letter to Watson, *ibid.*, **63** (1773), 79–88, plate 4, also published as a separately paginated reprint (London, 1773). Both accounts were used by Richard Pulteney, in his *Historical and Biographical Sketches of the Progress of Botany in England*, I (London, 1790), 175–179.

See also Edward F. Rimbault, "Family of the Tradescants," in *Notes and Queries*, **3** (1851), 353–355; and esp. G. S. B[oulger], in the *Dictionary of National Biography*, **57** (1899), 143–147. The latest biography, emphasizing the genealogy and botany, is Mea Allan, *The Tradescants* (London, 1964). Tradescant's 1618 Russian journal (Ashmole MS 824, xvi) has been published verbatim by S. Konovalov, "Two Documents Concerning Anglo-Russian Relations in the Early Seventeenth Century," in *Oxford Slavonic Papers*, **2** (1951), 130–141. The manuscript's identity was established by Joseph von Hamel, "Tradescant der Aeltere 1618 in Russland . . .," in *Recueil des actes de la séance publique l'Académie impériale des sciences de Saint-Petersbourg* (1847), 85–348, with portrait and map; also issued as a separately paginated reprint, and abridged in book form as *England and Russia: Comprising the Voyages of John Tradescant the Elder* [etc.], translated by John Studdy Leigh (London, 1854), reissued with only title page altered, as *Early English Voyages to Northern Russia* (London, 1857). Marjorie F. Warner, "The Morins," in *National Horticultural Magazine*, **33** (1954), 168–176, summarizes René Morin's contacts with Tradescant.

For documented commentary on relationships with Ashmole, see C. H. Josten, *Elias Ashmole (1617–1692)*, 5 vols. (Oxford, 1966), 2048–2049.

JOSEPH EWAN

TRADESCANT, JOHN (*b.* Meopham, Kent, England, 4 August 1608; *d.* South Lambeth, Surrey, England, 22 April 1662), *natural history*.

Traveler, collector, and gardener, Tradescant carried on the activities of his father of the same name. At the age of eleven he was a pupil at King's School, Canterbury, and at twenty-six was sworn into the Company of Master Gardeners of London. In 1637 he was in Virginia "gathering all varieties of flowers, plants, shells, &c" for his father's museum at South Lambeth. After his father's death he succeeded him as gardener to Queen Henrietta Maria. Tradescant married twice: first Jane Hurte, on 29 February 1627, by whom he had a daughter and son; and, after her death, Hester Pooks, on 1 October 1638. He may have made a second trip to Virginia in 1642.

The first use of "ark" for the museum appeared about 1645 in a poem mentioning "Tradeskin and his ark of novelties." His first meeting with Elias Ashmole was evidently in 1650. A draft of a catalog of the Tradescant collections was prepared by Ashmole and Thomas Wharton (Josten, I, 94), four years before the publication of *Musaeum Tradescantianum* (1656) under Tradescant's name. The *Musaeum* contains references to Aldrovandi, Belon, L'Écluse, Rondelet, Moffett, and Markgraf; and it constitutes an inventory of worldwide curiosities. Of the some two hundred Barbadian and Virginian plants identified in the two lists of 1634 and 1656, ten plants date from before 1600; but the remainder are notable introductions into horticulture.

The circumstances surrounding Tradescant's bequest of the museum to Ashmole are confused (see Josten, II, 768; and Whitehead, 54). In 1659 during a drinking party, Ashmole seems to have obtained a signed bequest from Tradescant, but in 1661 Tradescant willed his "closet of rarities" to his wife Hester, stipulating that on her death they go to Oxford or Cambridge "to which of them shee shall think fitt." In 1674 Ashmole removed the Tradescant collections to his own house and three

years later delivered his collections and Tradescant's "rarities" to Oxford, where they were displayed next to the Sheldonian in a building reputedly designed by Christopher Wren. It was not long before Hester was found drowned in her pond. The "name of Tradescant was unjustly sunk in that of Ashmole" (Pulteney, I, p. 179).

BIBLIOGRAPHY

I. ORIGINAL WORKS. The G. Wharton copy of *Musaeum Tradescantianum: or a Collection of Rarities Preserved at South-Lambeth Near London* (London, 1656) is in Morton Arboretum Library; it is reproduced as Old Ashmolean Reprint I (Oxford, 1925), with omission of pp. 74–178, and in toto in Mea Allan, *The Tradescants* (London, 1964), 247–312. The only authenticated specimen of Tradescant's shell collection is the holotype of *Strombus listeri* (S. Peter Dance, *Shell Collecting* [1966], 37). His miscellaneous numismatic, archaeological, and zoological collections originally in the "Old Ashmolean" were dispersed in 1831 to various Oxford museums. His *hortus siccus* is in the Bodleian (Ashmole MS 1465).

II. SECONDARY LITERATURE. See John Tradescant, *ante*, since most accounts include father and son. See also Richard Pulteney, *Historical and Biographical Sketches of the Progress of Botany in England*, I (London, 1790), 179; and S. W. Singer, "Tradescants and Elias Ashmole," in *Notes and Queries*, 5 (1852), 367–368, 385–387. Résumés of his respective fields are Dorothy Gardiner, "The Tradescants and Their Times," in *Journal of Royal Horticultural Society*, **53** (1928), 308–317; and P. J. P. Whitehead, "Museums in the History of Zoology," in *Museums Journal*, **70** (1970), 50–57. Commentary on Tradescant's "dodar" is given in Masauji Hachisuka, *The Dodo and Kindred Birds* (London, 1953); and references to Tradescant portraits are in David Piper, *Catalogue of the Seventeenth Century Portraits in the National Portrait Gallery, 1625–1714* (Cambridge, 1963), 350–351. For his relationship with Ashmole see C. H. Josten, *Elias Ashmole (1617–1692)*, 5 vols. (Oxford, 1966).

JOSEPH EWAN

TRAGUS, HIERONYMUS. See **Bock, Jerome.**

TRAUBE, MORITZ (*b.* Ratibor, Silesia [now Racibórz, Poland], 12 February 1826; *d.* Berlin, Germany, 28 June 1894), *physiological chemistry*.

Traube was the son of a Jewish wine merchant. His elder brother Ludwig (1818–1876), a specialist in internal medicine at Berlin, became famous through his work in experimental pathology. His father and brother quickly recognized the scientific abilities of young Moritz, who at the age of sixteen completed his Gymnasium studies with outstanding grades in the humanities.

Traube began his scientific education in Berlin but soon transferred to Giessen, where he studied under Liebig. At twenty-one he earned the doctorate with a work on chromium compounds. He founded a physical society with his brother Ludwig, who also encouraged him to study medicine. In 1849, however, Traube had to abandon his medical studies because of family obligations: his younger brother died unexpectedly, and his father asked him to take over the management of the large family business.

Traube's decision to comply with his father's wishes undoubtedly was a difficult one, and he subsequently led a double existence as a businessman and a researcher. With modest means he fitted out a private laboratory, where he spent his free hours. The first was in an attic room in Ratibor; later he built another in Breslau, where he transferred the wine business in order to facilitate his research; and the third was in Berlin. In Breslau, Traube worked in the laboratory of the physiologist Rudolf Heidenhain but later used his own facilities and engaged two assistants. Despite the great care with which he conducted his research and the originality of his ideas, Traube encountered considerable prejudice because he held no established academic post. Eventually, however, he achieved recognition, and in 1867 the University of Halle granted him an honorary doctorate.

Traube had two sons and three daughters. One of his sons, Hermann, became professor of mineralogy at the University of Berlin. In the last years of his life, which he spent in Berlin, Traube devoted himself entirely to scientific work until he succumbed to diabetes in 1894. He had begun to investigate the biochemical process of diabetes mellitus in man in 1852 and had distinguished two forms of the disease.

Traube's experiments extended over much of physiological chemistry but proved of great importance for general chemistry as well. In his *Handbuch zur Geschichte der Naturwissenschaft und der Technik* (1908), Darmstaedter draws attention to three of Traube's discoveries: oxygen-carrying ferments, or as they are now called, enzymes (1858); semipermeable membranes (1867); and artificial models of the cell (1875). Traube's most interesting studies were on the source of the energy for muscle contraction, on the nature of the ac-

tion of ferments, and on the formation of precipitation membranes.

Traube maintained that the energy source of muscle activity was the combustion of nitrogen-free substances. In 1861 he proposed that the organized portion of the muscle is not destroyed during work, urea is not a measurement of the production of muscle force, and albuminous substances (now called proteins) are not decomposed through muscle activity. This hypothesis, which contradicted Liebig's views, was sharply criticized by Georg Meissner in *Bericht über die Fortschritte der Anatomie und Physiologie* (1861–1863). Traube's position was not vindicated until Pettenkofer and Voit published results showing that carbohydrates could be interpreted as a source of energy. In this area Traube appears even to have anticipated the Bohr effect.

In his investigation of the action of ferments, Traube distinguished two types of "dialysis," one involving reduction and the other oxidation. In the reduction process the ferment removes oxygen from a substance and releases it either to another substance or to the air; whereas in the oxidation, the ferment takes oxygen from the air and releases it to an oxidizable substance. In Traube's view, the effectiveness of the ferment derives solely from the transfer of oxygen (*Platzwechsel*, or "transposition"). He found a simple model for such a process in finely divided platinum (platinum sponge), which decomposes hydrogen peroxide without limit (reduction) and recombines unlimited amounts of hydrogen and oxygen into water (oxidation). According to Traube, biological oxidation takes place in two steps. First, a substance A, together with oxygen and water, forms hydrogen peroxide in the presence of an oxidase; then a substance B is oxidized with the assistance of the hydrogen peroxide thus formed. This scheme can be represented by means of the following equation:

$$A + O_2 + 2H_2O \longrightarrow A(OH)_2 + H_2O_2$$
$$B + H_2O_2 \longrightarrow BO + H_2O$$

If this oxidation of B is viewed as the dehydrogenation of a substance RH_2, then the re-formation of A can be understood by means of an extension of this scheme:

$$RH_2 \longrightarrow R + 2H$$
$$A(OH)_2 + 2H \longrightarrow A + 2H_2O$$

(see W. Bladergroen, *Physikalische Chemie in Medizin und Biologie* [Basel, 1949], 623–624). Traube believed that ferments were specific substances, similar to proteins, that could not be obtained in pure form because of the ease with which they decompose.

Traube's discoveries of the formation of precipitation membranes (1864, 1867) were especially significant. He produced homogeneous membranes in the forms of closed cells by placing gelatin in tannic acid solution. The sphere became covered with a membrane and gradually increased considerably in volume through absorption of water; the contents remained clear, transparent glue, however, and no tannic acid entered. Open glass tubes were closed off by metalliferous membranes formed from cupric ferrocyanide and Prussian blue. According to Traube, the endosmotic process occurring in the case of such homogeneous membranes is the result of the attraction of the solute for the solvent (*endosmotische Kraft*). The most diffusible substances cannot penetrate certain membranes if the molecular interstices of the latter are smaller than the entering molecules. These findings permitted the development of a technique for measuring the magnitude of the attraction of various substances for water. Further, Traube's discovery of the semipermeable membrane provided the basis for Pfeffer's measurement of osmotic pressure and for van't Hoff's far-reaching theoretical interpretation of osmosis.

In the last years of his life Traube worked on problems pertaining to uric acid synthesis and to autoxidation, as well as on developing a process for producing sterile water.

BIBLIOGRAPHY

I. ORIGINAL WORKS. Traube's papers on general chemistry appeared mainly in *Poggendorff's Annalen der Chemie* and in *Berichte der Deutschen chemischen Gesellschaft*, and those on physiology in *Virchows Archiv* and in *Archiv für Anatomie und Physiologie*, as well as in *Zentralblatt für die medicinischen Wissenschaften*. Detailed reports on Traube's earlier works are in the *Bericht* that Henle and Meissner prepared for *Fortschritte der Anatomie und Physiologie*. Some of Traube's studies on ferment chemistry were reviewed in Leo Maly's *Jahresbericht für Thierchemie* by Nathan Zuntz, among others.

Traube published a monograph entitled *Theorie der Fermentwirkungen* (Berlin, 1858). His scattered papers were posthumously edited by H. and W. Traube as *Gesammelte Abhandlungen von Moritz Traube* (Berlin, 1899).

Traube's papers include "Ueber die Beziehung der Respiration zur Muskelthätigkeit und die Bedeutung der Respiration überhaupt," in *Virchows Archiv*, 21 (1861), 386–414; "Experimente zur Theorie der Zellenbildung," in *Medizinische-Zentralblatt*, no. 39 (1864): "Experimente zur Theorie der Zellenbildung und Endosmose," in *Archiv für Anatomie und Physiologie* (1867), 87–165; "Ueber das Verhalten der Alkoholhefe in sauerstoffgasfreien Medien," in *Berichte der Deutschen chemischen Gesellschaft*, 10 (1877), 510–513; "Zur Lehre von der Autoxydation," *ibid.*, 22 (1889), 1496–1514; and "Einfaches Verfahren, Wasser in grossen Mengen keimfrei zu machen," in *Zeitschrift für Hygiene*, 16 (1894), 149–150.

II. SECONDARY LITERATURE. See G. Bodländer, "Nekrolog auf M. Traube," in *Berichte der Deutschen chemischen Gesellschaft*, 28 (1894), 1085; E. von Meyer, "Moritz Traube," in *Handwörterbuch der Naturwissenschaften*, X (Jena, 1915), 43–44; and K. Müller, "Moritz Traube (1826–1894) und seine Theorie der Fermente" (M.D. diss., Zurich, 1970).

Further information on Traube's life and works is in W. Bladergroen, *Physikalische Chemie in Medizin und Biologie* (Basel, 1949), 623–624; L. Darmstaedter, *Handbuch zur Geschichte der Naturwissenschaften und der Technik* (Berlin, 1908), 585, 664, 734; F. Lieben, *Geschichte der physiologischen Chemie* (Leipzig–Vienna, 1935; repr. Hildesheim–New York, 1970), 117, 237–239; and Poggendorff, II, 1126; III, 1363; and IV, 1519.

G. RUDOLPH

TRAVERS, MORRIS WILLIAM (*b*. Kensington, London, England, 24 January 1872; *d*. Stroud, Gloucestershire, England, 25 August 1961), *physical chemistry, cryogenics, industrial chemistry*.

Travers actively collaborated with William Ramsay in the discovery and specification of the inert gases. The second of the four sons of a London physician, Travers was schooled from 1879 to 1882 at Ramsgate and from 1882 to 1885 at Woking. In the spring of 1885 he transferred to Blundell's School (Tiverton), which was equipped with a good chemistry laboratory. From 1889 to 1893 he studied at University College London taking his B.Sc. in 1893. Intending to specialize in organic chemistry, he worked with Alban Haller at the University of Nancy during early 1894. Returning to work with Ramsay in late 1894, just at the time of the discovery of argon, Travers took a position as demonstrator at University College London and continued research in organic chemistry under Collie. In 1898 he took his D.Sc. and became assistant professor.

After the discovery of helium in 1895, Travers

assisted Ramsay in the determination of the properties of argon and helium. They also heated minerals and meteorites for new gases, but inevitably only helium was evolved. For some time it had been suspected that yet another gas might accompany argon, and accordingly they prepared a large quantity of this gas by removing oxygen and nitrogen from air and by forcing the residue into a bulb. In order to apply the technique of fractional distillation, it was first essential to liquefy this argon residue. With the assistance of Hampson, Travers and Ramsay obtained in May 1898 a large quantity of liquid air for this purpose. Practicing with air to prepare themselves for an investigation of the argon, Travers evaporated a small quantity of the liquid air and collected the least volatile fraction. A spectrum analysis of the residue yielded the new lines of krypton. (Travers collected the gas from the last ten cubic centimeters of 750 cc of evaporating liquid air. After removing the oxygen and nitrogen, leaving a gaseous residue of about 26 cc, he observed on 31 May 1898 with Ramsay the new spectral lines. They telegraphed the news to Berthelot in Paris and sent their communication to the Royal Society on 3 June. It was announced on 6 June in the Paris Academy and on 9 June in London.) If the argon residue contained a constituent of lower boiling point (namely, greater volatility), it would distill over first. Accordingly they liquefied the argon and upon evaporation collected the most volatile fraction. A spectrum analysis showed the new lines of neon, the suspected companion of argon. (Travers prepared the most volatile fraction on 11 June. With Ramsay he observed the new spectral lines on 12 June. The paper was read on 16 June to the Royal Society, London, and announced in Paris on 20 June 1898.) A further unexpected companion, "metargon," proved to be a mistake, like the sensational "etherion" of Brush. Metargon was merely argon contaminated by carbon monoxide. C. F. Brush on 23 August announced the existence of an alleged gaseous constituent having a density 10^{-4} that of hydrogen (*Science*, **8** [1898], 485–494).

Travers and Ramsay next turned their attention toward the task of obtaining quantities of each inert gas sufficient to determine the properties. In spite of its low volatility, krypton proved difficult to obtain in isolated quantities. It was found to have an even less volatile companion, xenon, identified spectroscopically about 12 July 1898 and announced to the British Association on 8 September 1898. Since the neon fraction from the argon residue also contained helium, liquid air proved insufficient; it was necessary to employ liquid hydrogen for the condensation.

Although Dewar had successfully liquefied hydrogen by May 1898, Travers independently constructed the required apparatus. With liquid hydrogen they were able to condense the neon portion, while the helium remained gaseous. Evaporating this liquid, they obtained sufficient neon by July 1900 to complete their study of the inert gases. Continuing his cryogenic research, Travers made probably the first accurate temperature measurements of liquefied gases, and set up several experimental liquid air plants in Europe. In November 1903 Travers replaced S. Young as professor of chemistry at University College, Bristol, and contributed to that institution receiving a university charter. He was elected a fellow of the Royal Society in 1904, and two years later went to Bangalore as director of the Indian Institute of Science, which opened to students in 1911. In 1909 Travers married the sister of R. Whytlaw-Gray. During this period Travers conducted an interesting but controversial study on boron.

Returning to England in July 1914, Travers directed glass manufacture at Walthamstow (Duroglass, Ltd.) throughout World War I, and later became president of the Society of Glass Technology. From 1920 he was concerned with high-temperature furnaces and fuel technology, including the gasification of coal, and in 1925 took part in founding the Institute of Fuel. Travers was made honorary professor of chemistry at Bristol in 1927 and established a research group that worked on thermal decomposition of organic vapors and also gaseous and heterogeneous reactions. He also awakened the youthful scientific interest of A. B. Pippard during this period. He was president of the Faraday Society from 1936 to 1938 and retired in 1937. Then Travers began his historical research on Ramsay, organizing the Ramsay papers and compiling and working on twenty-four volumes of documentation. During World War II, Travers served in an advisory capacity and was a consultant to the explosives section of the Ministry of Supply from 1940 to 1945. Traveling extensively, he was a general trouble-shooter concerned with a variety of technical problems. From 1953 Travers resumed his biography of Ramsay and completed it in 1955.

BIBLIOGRAPHY

I. ORIGINAL WORKS. A nearly complete list of Travers' publications is in C. E. H. Bawn, "Morris William

Travers 1872–1961," in *Biographical Memoirs of the Fellows of the Royal Society*, **9** (1963), 301–313. Travers also wrote *William Ramsay and University College London*, a small booklet privately issued by University College London for the Ramsay centenary, and "Sir William Ramsay," in *Endeavour*, **11** (1952), 126–131. The best source on the discovery of the inert gases is *The Discovery of the Rare Gases* (London, 1928). For a brief account see Travers' "The Rare Gases of the Atmosphere," in E. F. Armstrong, ed., *Chemistry in the Twentieth Century* (London, 1924), 82–87. An extensive MS collection of Travers is incorporated with the Ramsay Papers (esp. items 82–105) in the library at University College London. R. M. MacLeod and J. R. Friday, *Archives of British Men of Science* (London, 1972), notes items in the Royal Society.

II. Secondary Literature. On Travers and his work, see D. H. Everett, in *Nature*, **192** (1961), 1127–1128; W. L. Hardin, *The Rise and Development of the Liquefaction of Gases* (New York, 1899), which contains a relevant discussion of the then current state of cyrogenics and also of the discovery of krypton, neon, metargon, and etherion; D. McKie, "Morris William Travers 1872–1961," in *Proceedings of the Chemical Society* (1964), 377–378, which mentions an autobiography, the draft of which is in the library of University College London; P. Walden, "Lothar Meyer, Mendelejeff, Ramsay und das periodische System der Elemente," in Günther Bugge, ed., *Das Buch der Grossen Chemiker*, 2nd ed., II (Weinheim, 1955), 229–287; Weeks, *Discovery of the Elements*, 7th ed. (Easton, 1968), 750–773, 868–896; and T. I. Williams in his *A Biographical Dictionary of Scientists* (London, 1969), 518–519.

Thaddeus J. Trenn

TREBRA, FRIEDRICH WILHELM HEINRICH VON (*b*. Allstedt, Weimar, Germany, 5 April 1740; *d*. Freiberg, Germany, 16 July 1819), *mining*.

Trebra was the eldest son of Christoph Heinrich von Trebra, a courtier at Weimar, and his wife, born Albertina Amalia Karolina von Werder. After attending the monastery school in Rossleben, he studied law, philosophy, mathematics, and natural science for seven semesters at the University of Jena. Pursuing his inclination for science, he enrolled in 1766 in the newly founded mining academy at Freiberg, Saxony.

Only one year later Trebra was serving as assessor for the Bureau of Mines (Oberbergamt) at Freiberg. He rapidly acquired considerable technical knowledge and carried out his assignments to the complete satisfaction of his superiors. As a result he was appointed inspector of mines at Marienberg, Saxony, on 1 December 1767. He was resolute in enforcing the regulations and strict and merciless in punishing infractions. Since he also introduced many technical improvements into silver mining, he brought the industry in this region to a new level of prosperity.

In recognition of his services Trebra was named Commissioner of Mines (*kommissionsrat*) in 1770 and, in 1773, assistant supervisor of mines for the Bureau of Mines at Freiberg. In 1776 the duke of Weimar commissioned him to conduct a study of the underlying copper-bearing schist near Ilmenau. There he met Goethe, who had charge of the Ilmenau mines. The two remained good friends for nearly forty years.

In 1779 Trebra became an inspector of mines for the government of Hannover, working for more than a decade at Zellerfeld, in the Harz Mountains, and furthering the development of the metal-mining industry in the Upper Harz. His tireless efforts to increase the productivity of the mines under his jurisdiction finally led to his appointment, in 1791, as royal supervisor of mines for Great Britain and Electoral Brunswick-Lüneburg in the mining city of Clausthal.

For reasons that have not been established, Trebra resigned his post as inspector of mines in 1795 and retired to his estate, Bretleben, on the Unstrut River. There he devoted himself to breeding sheep, growing hemp, operating a distillery, and producing saltpeter and starch. This retirement was regretted by many, not least by Goethe.

A few years later Trebra accepted an offer from the government of Saxony of a post as chief mining inspector and director of the *Oberbergamt* of Freiberg. Upon assuming this office in 1801 he became head of the Saxon mining industry, retaining the post until his death in 1819. He was highly effective in this capacity; and in recognition of his outstanding accomplishments, he was appointed a commander of the Royal Order of the Saxon Civil Service.

BIBLIOGRAPHY

I. Original Works. Trebra's books include *Erklärung der Bergwerks-Charte von dem wichtigsten Theile der Gebürge im Bergamtsrefier Marienberg* (Annaberg, 1770), also translated into Dutch; *Erfahrungen vom Innern der Gebirge nach Beobachtungen gesammelt* (Dessau–Leipzig, 1785), also translated into French; *Bergbaukunde*, edited with J. von Born, 2 vols. (Leipzig, 1789–1790); *Mineralien-Kabinet . . .* (Clausthal, 1795); *Das Silberausbringen des Königlich Sächsischen Erzgebirges auf die nächst verflossenen 40 Jahre von 1762 bis 1801* (Freiberg, 1802); *Merkwürdigkeiten der tie-*

fen Hauptstöllen des Bergamtsreviers Freyberg (Freiberg, 1804); and *Bergmeisterleben und Wirken in Marienberg* (Freiberg, 1818).

His articles include "Kalkhaltiges phosphorescirendes Steinmark," in *Chemische Annalen für die Freunde der Naturlehre*, pt. 1 (1784), 387–389; "Über die vom Himmel gefallenen Steine," in *Monatliche Correspondenz zur Beförderung der Erd- und Himmelskunde*, **9** (1804), 137; and "Über die innere Temperatur der Erde," *ibid.*, 349–350.

II. SECONDARY LITERATURE. See von Gümbel's notice on Trebra, in *Allgemeine deutsche Biographie*, XXXVIII (1894), 550–551; "Friedrich . . . von Trebra," in C. Schiffner, *Aus dem Leben alter Freiberger Bergstudenten*, I (Freiberg, 1935), 115–191; "Friedrich . . . von Trebra," in Walter Serlo, *Männer des Bergbaus* (Berlin, 1937), 145–146; Walter Herrmann, "Goethe und Trebra. Freundschaft und Austausch zwischen Weimar und Freiberg," in *Freiberger Forschungshefte*, ser. D, no. 9 (1955); and A. F. Wappler, *Oberberghauptmann von Trebra und die drei ersten sächsischen Kunstmeister Mende, Baldauf und Brendel* (Freiberg, 1906).

M. KOCH

TRELEASE, WILLIAM (*b.* Mount Vernon, New York, 22 February 1857; *d.* Urbana, Illinois, 1 January 1945), *botany.*

Trelease bridged the era of Asa Gray, whom he knew, and the twentieth century to become an internationally known botanist, teacher, and administrator. He was the son of Mary Gandall and Samuel Ritter Trelease, of Dutch and Cornish ancestry. After attending schools in Branford, Connecticut, and Brooklyn, New York, he entered Cornell University, where he studied under the botanist A. N. Prentiss and the entomologist John H. Comstock. While still an undergraduate he published four papers on pollination in *American Naturalist* and the *Bulletin of the Torrey Botanical Club*, and made field studies for the United States government on cotton insects in Alabama. Following his graduation (B.S., 1880), he entered Harvard to study fungi under William G. Farlow. During his Harvard year he came under the influence of Gray, Sereno Watson, George L. Goodale, and Samuel H. Scudder.

Beginning in 1881 Trelease taught systematic botany, horticulture, forestry, and economic entomology at the University of Wisconsin. To these courses he added bacteriology, the first time it was offered in the United States. In 1884 he was awarded the science doctorate at Harvard; his thesis concerned the zoogloeae. George Engelmann

and Gray urged Henry Shaw to appoint Trelease the head of the newly established Missouri Botanical Garden in St. Louis, popularly known as Shaw's Gardens, to be patterned after the Royal Botanic Gardens at Kew. In twenty years Trelease brought together a garden of 12,000 species under cultivation, a notable library of some 70,000 books (including the E. L. Sturtevant pre-Linnaean collection), and a herbarium of 700,000 specimens.

Following his resignation in 1912 and a year in Europe, Trelease assumed the headship of the department of botany at the University of Illinois, where he remained until his retirement in 1926. Among his 300 published papers and books were monographs on the genus *Agave*, mistletoes, and oaks, and an unfinished work on Piperaceae begun when he was seventy-five years old. Trelease described more than 2,500 species and varieties of plants. Addicted to bibliographic thoroughness, he was able to provide in his work a base for modern research involving supplemental techniques. Nonetheless, Trelease found time to serve as president of the leading organizations of his profession.

BIBLIOGRAPHY

I. ORIGINAL WORKS. For a bibliography of Trelease's writings see Kunkel (below). Trelease's noteworthy writings include *Botanical Works of the Late George Engelmann* (Cambridge, 1887), with Asa Gray; articles for L. H. Bailey's *Cyclopedia of American Horticulture* (New York, 1900–1902); *Agave in the West Indies* (Washington, D.C., 1913); *The Genus Phoradendron* (Urbana, Illinois, 1916); and the *American Oaks* (Washington, D.C., 1924).

The Piperaceae of Northern South America (Urbana, 1950) was completed by T. G. Yuncker. Trelease's papers on Mexican botany are listed with annotations in Ida K. Langman, *A Selected Guide to the Literature on the Flowering Plants of Mexico* (Philadelphia, 1964).

Four scrapbooks of letters, clippings, and memorabilia are preserved at the Missouri Botanical Garden.

II. SECONDARY LITERATURE. The fullest sketch is L. O. Kunkel, in *Biographical Memoirs. National Academy of Sciences*, **35** (1961), 307–332, with a portrait and bibliography of his writings by T. G. Yuncker for the years 1879–1950. See also L. H. Bailey in *Yearbook. American Philosophical Society* (1945), 420–425; and J. M. Greenman, in *Missouri Botanical Garden Bulletin*, **33** (1945), 71–72. Personal tributes are J. Christian Bay, *William Trelease, 1857–1945, Personal Reminiscences* (Chicago, 1945); and L. H. Pammel, *Prominent Men I Have Met*, III (Ames, Iowa, 1927), both privately printed.

JOSEPH EWAN

TREMBLEY, ABRAHAM (*b.* Geneva [now Switzerland], 3 September 1710; *d.* Petit Sacconex, near Geneva, 12 May 1784), *zoology.*

Abraham Trembley's father, Jean, was an officer in the Genevan army and rose to be its commander, the syndic of the guard. Abraham was educated at the Academy of Geneva, and in 1733 found employment as a tutor in Holland. His career was much influenced by his residence at Leiden, where he was in close touch with several distinguished scientists in the university. It was probably here that he met Count Bentinck, a curator of the university; and he became tutor to the latter's two sons at the mansion of Sorgvliet, near The Hague. Here he carried out the researches on the hydra that gained him a fellowship in the Royal Society in 1743 and made him famous. The duke of Richmond witnessed some of his experiments at Sorgvliet, and young Trembley made a deep impression on him. On his deathbed in 1750, the duke consigned to Trembley the care and education of his son and heir, then aged fifteen. Trembley conducted the youth on an extensive tour of the Continent. When they parted in 1756, he was so generously rewarded by the young duke that it was never again necessary for him to work for a living. In 1757 he returned to Geneva, married, and bought the country house at Petit Sacconex in which he lived for the rest of his life. Trembley devoted himself mainly to the instruction of his children and to writing books on education, politics, religion, and moral philosophy. His methods of instruction were novel and anticipated many later developments in educational theory. He was deeply religious, a Christian without strictly adhering to any particular sect.

It was in June 1740 that Trembley had his first opportunity to study the hydra. He had taken into his room at Sorgvliet some ditch water containing aquatic plants. He noticed a green hydra (*Chlorohydra viridissima*) attached to one of the plants, and at first took it to be itself a plant. He noticed, however, that the tentacles moved, and soon found that organisms of this species could change their positions; but he still hesitated to call them animals. He decided to determine the matter by cutting one of them in two, on the supposition that if both parts survived, the organism would clearly be classifiable as a plant. The cut was made in such a way that one of the parts possessed all the tentacles. He watched the regeneration of both fragments during the following days until regeneration was complete, when both parts were tentaculate; they were indistinguishable from one another.

Nevertheless, the apparent spontaneity of the hydra's movements made it difficult for him to accept the conclusion that these were in fact plants. To obtain help in reaching a decision, he sent some specimens to Réaumur and wrote him a very long letter about his observations. The letter was read in full at two sessions of the Académie Royale des Sciences in Paris in March 1741. Living specimens were also exhibited at the Academy.

Trembley accepted Réaumur's assurance that the organisms were unquestionably animals. A related species, probably the brown *Hydra vulgaris*, had in fact been discovered by Leeuwenhoek in 1702, and a note on it had been published. Professor Émile Guyénot has shrewdly remarked that if Trembley had been aware that animals of this sort were already known he would probably not have studied them so attentively; and if his first specimen had been *H. vulgaris* or *Pelmatohydra oligactis* (also brownish), he would not have been likely to think it was a plant. It would not then have occurred to him to make the experiment that resulted in the discovery of multiplication by artificial division. Trembley eventually studied all three species, but their modern names were not introduced in his time.

Réaumur checked for himself the truth of Trembley's account, and both Bentinck and Richmond wrote to the Royal Society to confirm it. It is not easy today to recapture the sense of utter amazement caused by the realization that an animal could be multiplied by cutting it in pieces. Voltaire refused to believe it. Long afterwards he still persisted in denying the possibility and dismissed the subject contemptuously, describing the animal in print as "a kind of small rush."

Trembley pursued his investigations on the hydra. He described the characteristics of the hydra's living substance (afterwards named protoplasm); investigated its reactions to light and to changes in temperature; watched it capturing its prey, eating, and digesting; and he found that *vulgaris* and *oligactis* could be colored red, black, or a feeble green by supplying suitable foods. His feeding experiments led to the introduction of a particularly interesting technique. Drawing no sharp distinction between the granules of the endoderm on one hand and the nematocysts of the ectoderm on the other, he thought that the animal might perhaps be able to nourish itself if turned inside out. He succeeded in this operation, despite the almost incredible difficulty presented by the minute size of the animals. He proved that a reversed *H. vulgaris* can, indeed, survive and feed without re-reversal, that is, without returning to its original form. Long afterwards there were still biologists who could not believe this, but the experiment was successfully repeated by M. Nussbaum in 1887. The ectoderm cells of reversed hydras are known nowadays to be able to migrate singly or in groups to the exterior, without any re-reversal of the organism as a whole.

Trembley devoted much time to a detailed study of the budding process, regeneration, and the artificial production of monsters. He then set to work to find out whether multiplication by division could be achieved in reverse, that is, whether two hydras could be transformed into one. This operation was perhaps the most dramatic of all his experiments. He placed one hydra within another, pushing it in tail first through the mouth of the other specimen until its tail projected from near the tail of the other, while its head had still not entered the mouth. The posterior end of the internal animal was permanently grafted, and a single individual with two tails resulted, one derived from each of the two original animals. This, the first permanent graft of animal tissues, was done in October 1742. Both constituent parts of the composite organism multiplied by budding. Several modifications of the grafting process were carried out successfully.

It is noteworthy that Trembley tried on hydra nearly every possible experiment in regeneration and grafting that was likely to give interesting results. He was exploring territory that was almost entirely unknown; yet the planning of his work was so complete, and its execution so thorough, that he might almost have been performing routine experiments on a system established by the long experience of others. The only important exception is that he did not try to find out whether the polarity of a body part could be reversed so that its anterior-posterior axis could be changed.

Trembley was persuaded by Réaumur to bring together the results of his work on the hydra in a book. The result was a beautifully produced volume entitled *Mémoires, pour servir à l'histoire d'un genre de polypes d'eau douce, à bras en forme de cornes* (1744), with very fine illustrations by Pieter Lyonet.

Although Trembley's study of the hydra is the best known of his works, it is arguable that some of his other researches are of equal importance. He was the first to describe multiplication and colony formation in Protozoa and multiplication by budding in Oligochaeta and Polyzoa, and he was also the first to give a full account of the anatomy of the individual in any member of the latter group. Until he discovered reproduction by budding in Oligo-

chaeta and Polyzoa, it had never been seen in any animal other than the hydra. Some twenty years later, while living at Petit Sacconex, he was the first to witness cell division in the strict sense of the term (division of a uninucleate cell). Still, it was not possible in Trembley's time for him or anyone else to recognize the full significance of some of his discoveries. When he discovered that Protozoa multiplied by division, for example, no one had yet suggested the separation of these animals into a distinct phylum; and when he watched cell division in *Synedra*, it was not known that this diatom was a single cell.

Trembley was above all a student of processes, and in this respect he led the way in zoology. It is often said that he was the father of experimental zoology, but it is doubtful whether he would have approved of this description. He used both observation and experiment freely, according to which method was most likely to serve his ends in a particular case. His only purely morphological study, however, was on the anatomy of the *Lophopus* (Polyzoa). G. J. Allman, in his *Monograph of the Fresh-Water Polyzoa* (1856), said of Trembley's work on this animal, "The description is wonderfully accurate, and the anatomical details have been in few points surpassed by subsequent observers." Trembley's accuracy of observation was one of his most striking characteristics. He had a passion for demonstrable facts and perhaps an exaggerated dislike of hypothesis.

BIBLIOGRAPHY

I. ORIGINAL WORKS. Important works by Trembley are *Mémoires, pour servir à l'histoire d'un genre de polypes d'eau douce, à bras en forme de cornes* (Leiden, 1744); and *Instructions d'un père à ses enfans, sur la nature et sur la religion* (Geneva, 1775).

II. SECONDARY LITERATURE. Works on Trembley are J. R. Baker, *Abraham Trembley of Geneva: Scientist and Philosopher, 1710–1784* (London, 1952); [Jean Trembley] *Mémoire historique sur la vie et les écrits de Monsieur Abraham Trembley* (Neuchâtel, 1787); and Maurice Trembley, *Correspondence inédite entre Réaumur et Abraham Trembley comprenant 113 lettres recueillies et annotées par Maurice Trembley*, with an introduction by É. Guyénot (Geneva, 1943).

JOHN R. BAKER

TREUB, MELCHIOR (*b.* Voorschoten, Holland, 26 December 1851; *d.* St. Raphael, France, 3 October 1910), *botany*.

Treub's father was burgomaster of Voorschoten, a small village; both his parents were of Swiss extraction, and spoke French at home. Treub himself was also fluent in English, German, and Dutch, but preferred French for his scientific publications. He attended secondary school at Leiden, then entered the university there, where he won a gold medal for a report on the true nature of lichens, written in response to a prize question. He expanded this work into the thesis for which he was granted the doctorate, *summa cum laude*, in 1873. Treub remained at Leiden for the next seven years as docent and assistant in the botanical institute under his former tutor, Professor W. F. R. Suringar. During this period he wrote twenty-nine papers on a variety of subjects—especially plant cytology, histology, nucleus division, and embryology—that demonstrated his acute powers of observation, manual dexterity in cutting sections, and skill as a draftsman. He was nominated to the Netherlands Academy of Sciences at the unusually early age of twenty-eight.

In 1880 Treub was called to the directorship of the botanical gardens at Buitenzorg (now Bogor), West Java, where he succeeded R. H. C. C. Scheffer. The complex consisted of the gardens themselves; a building housing administrative offices, a museum, an herbarium, and a library; the Cultuurtuin, a garden devoted to the cultivation of plants of economic importance, attached to a school of agriculture; and a mountain garden at Tjibodas (at 1,400 meters). The institution also published two periodicals, the *Annales du jardin botanique de Buitenzorg* and the *Jaarverslag*, its annual report, but these, like the entire establishment, had fallen into disarray. Treub set out to revitalize the institution, and in so doing developed formidable administrative skills and powers of persuasion.

Since a scientific center was, in a colonial commercial society, almost a luxury, Treub sought to publicize its merits. Many decisions about the Buitenzorg garden came from The Hague, which also set the budget, so Treub therefore wrote a number of articles for a literary journal in the Netherlands, by which he made the public aware of the economic potential of the colony. He published the annual reports of the garden punctually, and used these documents as a means of informing both the government authorities and the general public about the work being done at the garden and about its goals. Through the *Annales* and through a series of basic studies (on the embryology of Cycadaceae, Loranthaceae, and Burmanniaceae, and on the latex of Euphorbiaceae, classes of climbing plants, pitcher plants, and the structure of plants infested by ants) Treub also won the attention of the international botanical community.

By 1881 Treub had redesigned the curriculum of the agricultural school and had hired an assistant director, W. Burck, who began to develop the museum along economic botanical lines. Burck also did research on caoutchouc (rubber) trees and on commercial products of the Dipterocarpaceae and cultivated caoutchouc trees in a special garden at Tjipetir. The results of his work were too voluminous to be published in the annual report, so Treub got permission to start a new periodical, the *Mededeelingen*, which first appeared in 1883. As foreign scientists began to visit the gardens in increasing numbers, Treub equipped a nearby abandoned military hospital as a laboratory; this opened in January 1885, and became known as the Treub Laboratory. The results of the work done there were published in the *Annales*; Treub had thus assured himself of the unpaid services of a whole staff of eminent botanists.

Treub's campaign was successful and both the government and the community of planters became convinced of the value of applied scientific research. He secured additional staff, again at no cost to the institution, by suggesting an arrangement whereby the planters assumed the salaries of his assistants, while the government agreed to let their work proceed under Treub's supervision and their results be published in the *Mededeelingen*. Under this system, researches were made concerning diseases of tobacco, tea, coffee, indigo, and cacao plants. A chain of experimental stations was established since much of the necessary work could not be performed in Buitenzorg's climate and soil conditions.

As the facilities and staff for applied botanical research were expanded, Treub began to plan new divisions for basic research. In 1887, while on sick leave in Europe, he approached both the Netherlands and foreign governments and obtained "Buitenzorg funds," annual or biennial grants for prominent botanists to work in Java; during the same leave, he also sought private funds to finance explorations of Indonesia. (The latter effort resulted in the foundation, in 1890, of the Society for the Promotion of the Natural Sciences in the Netherlands Indies, a body that still exists and is commonly called the "Treub Society.")

Following his return to Java, Treub supervised the further expansion of the botanic garden. A phytochemical-pharmacological laboratory was established in 1887 and an agricultural chemistry laboratory in 1890; by 1894 Treub was able to found a zoological museum and to hire an agricultural zoologist, J. C. Koningsberger, whose work eventually led to the foundation of an institute of plant diseases. He further acquired a forest preserve adjacent to the mountain garden at Tjibodas, and in 1891 erected a field laboratory there.

During this time Treub also conducted a major study on rice; his own research on food crops, coupled with his new laboratories, was the nucleus from which the Java General Agriculture Experiment Station grew. In addition, Treub encouraged the publication of the journal *Teysmannia* (begun in 1894), which was devoted largely to practical short notes from the botanic garden; in 1900 he also laid out a series of demonstration fields that were intended to benefit farmers as well as administrators. A new library was built in 1896, and by 1905 the complex that Treub had built up was elevated to a full civil department, of which Treub was named director. He continued to serve at the same time as director of the gardens themselves.

A number of significant botanical studies were published during Treub's tenure as director, chief among them a *Flore de Buitenzorg* and the *Icones Bogoriensis*. In 1894 he started yet another periodical, the *Bulletin du jardin botanique de Buitenzorg*, which was designed to reach the international scientific community. Despite the pressures of his administrative duties, Treub also did research of his own and published his results. These studies include a work on the embryology and biohistory of the club ferns, a study of a previously unknown form of fertilization in Casuarina (chalazogamy), writings on the embryology of Ficus and Elatostema, a theory of the origin of proteins based on the finding of prussic acid in Pangium, and works on the sociology of the rain forest and the new flora of Krakatoa. He also, in 1886, wrote a history of the Buitenzorg botanic garden.

By the end of 1909 Treub's health had begun to fail, and he retired from his posts to the south of France, where he planned to start a garden of exotic plants and to pursue the microscopic study of tropical plants. He was able to publish only one paper, on the embryology of Garcinia, before his death a year later.

BIBLIOGRAPHY

I. ORIGINAL WORKS. The notice by F. A. F. C. Went, cited below, lists some 103 books and papers by Treub; of these the scientific works are in French, while a number of others on a variety of subjects are in Dutch. See especially Treub's commentaries in the *Jaarverslag* for the years 1880 to 1910 and, of the individual works, *Onderzoekingen over de natuur der Lichenen*, his thesis (Leiden, 1873); *Onderzoekingen over serehziek suikerriet gedaan in 's-Lands Plantentuin te Buitenzorg* (Djakarta, 1885); *Geschiedenis van 's-Lands Plantentuin te Buitenzorg* (Djakarta, 1889); *Korte geschiedenis van 's-Lands Plantentuin* (Djakarta, 1892); *De beteekenis van tropische botanische tuinen* (Djakarta, 1892); *Over de taak en werkkring van 's-Lands Plantentuin te Buitenzorg* (Buitenzorg, 1899); and the posthumously published *Landbouw, Januari 1905-October 1909. Beredeneerd overzicht der verrichtingen en bemoeiingen met het oog op de praktijk van land-, tuin-, en boschbouw, veeteelt, visscherij en aanverwante aangelegenheden* (Amsterdam, 1910).

II. SECONDARY LITERATURE. See F. A. F. C. Went, "In Memoriam," in *Annales du jardin botanique de Buitenzorg*, 2nd ser., **9** (1911), i–xxxii.

C. G. G. J. VAN STEENIS

TREVIRANUS, GOTTFRIED REINHOLD (*b.* Bremen, Germany, 4 February 1776; *d.* Bremen, 16 February 1837), *zootomy, physiology.*

Treviranus was the eldest son of Joachim Johann Jacob Treviranus, merchant and later a notary, and brother of the botanist Ludolph Christian Treviranus. He introduced the notion of biology as a distinct discipline into Germany and was one of the first to express the idea that the cell is the structural unit of living matter.

Treviranus was a keen observer and an able theorizer. As an adherent of *Naturphilosophie*, he supposed that the universal laws of nature were represented by general ideas and that these ideas were the instruments to throw the light of knowledge over the darkness of the world of facts and phenomena. All his studies centered on the theme "What laws underlie living nature?" In order to answer this question, he studied life in all its aspects: generation, food and feeding, psychical processes, geographical distribution, the interaction between mind and body, and the relationship between the organism and its environment. Even before Lamarck published his *Philosophie zoologique*, Treviranus stated that changes in the physical environment could induce corresponding changes in organic structures—or, as he wrote in his *Biologie* (1802), any living creature has the ability to adapt its organization to changing external conditions. As a consequence Treviranus was an opponent of Cuvier's theory of catastrophism. Both Ernst Haeckel and August Weismann considered Treviranus as one of their predecessors. He was so, however, only within the limits of *Naturphilosophie*; nowhere did Treviranus explain how changes in organic structures were induced nor how they could become hereditary.

From 1793 to 1796 Treviranus studied medicine and mathematics at the University of Göttingen. In the latter year, after having written his doctoral dissertation, he returned to Bremen, where he established a practice as a consulting physician. In his spare time he made observations on the structure and function of living beings, especially of the invertebrates. He was an accomplished microscopist. He prepared most of his beautiful illustrations himself.

In 1797 Treviranus was appointed professor of mathematics and medicine at the Bremen lyceum, and in the same year he published the first volume of *Physiologische Fragmente*. In 1800 he published the results of a series of experiments concerning the influence of certain chemical substances—particularly of drugs such as opium and belladonna—on plants and animals.

Soon after he had settled in Bremen, Treviranus wrote his magnum opus, *Biologie* (1802–1822), in which he sought to summarize all basic knowledge of his time about the structure and function of living matter. This six-volume work, intended to be a modernization of Haller's *Elementa physiologiae*, greatly influenced his contemporaries. Volume I treats the interpretation of living nature, the basic laws of biology, the empirical basis of biology, the definition of life, and the principles of classification; volume II, the organization of living nature, the distribution of plants and animals, and the influence of external conditions; volume III, growth and development; volume IV, nutrition and the digestive systems in plants and animals, respiration, and circulation; volume V, animal health, animal electricity, phosphorescence, automatic movements in animals and plants, the organization of the nervous system, and instinct; and volume VI, relation between the physical and the psychical worlds, the mind-body problem, and the objective and subjective worlds of the senses.

Treviranus published his ideas in a more condensed form in *Erscheinungen und Gesetze* (1831–1832), a classic in theoretical biology. In this work he also incorporated an account of the advances made in biology during the preceding thirty years. He paid greater attention to mind-body relations, the process of generation, periodicity, constitution, health and disease, and temperament. Some of these subjects were considered in greater detail in *Beiträge zur Aufklärung* . . .

(1835–1837). In the first and third volumes, Treviranus tried to prove mathematically that the structure of the crystalline lens is responsible for man's ability to see things in perspective; the second volume contains microscopical investigations of animal tissues.

These theoretical studies induced Treviranus to undertake research in many fields; the results have been recorded in some of his collections, such as *Vermischte Schriften* (1816–1821); *Beobachtungen aus der Zootomie*, published by his brother (1839); and *Zeitschrift für Physiologie*, which he founded in 1824 with his brother Ludolph Christian and Friedrich Tiedemann.

Of particular interest are Treviranus' anatomical studies on invertebrates, such as those he made on the reproductive organs of worms, mollusks, insects, and arachnids; and on the respiratory and circulatory organs of crustaceans and other invertebrates. Also noteworthy are his monographic studies on the anatomy of the louse, of wingless insects, of snails, and of arachnids. In addition Treviranus performed many microscopic-anatomical studies on vertebrates: the reproductive organs of fishes, amphibians, the tortoise, the mole, the hedgehog, and the guinea pig; the ears of birds and the eye of the narwhal; and the nervous system of birds.

Treviranus paid special attention to the anatomy and physiology of the sensory organs. In *Beiträge zur Anatomie* he formulated mathematical laws of diffraction in order to discover the physical basis of vision. More particularly he was interested in determining which mechanism in the eye is responsible for our seeing things in their relative positions and what the function may be of such structures as the cornea, lens, and retina. This work contains many comparative studies of the visual processes in the various classes of animals.

BIBLIOGRAPHY

I. ORIGINAL WORKS. Treviranus' earlier writings include *De emendanda physiologia* (Göttingen, 1796), his inaugural dissertation; *Physiologische Fragmente*, 2 vols. (Hannover, 1797–1799); "Über den Einfluss des galvanischen Agens . . .," in *Nordisches Archiv für Natur- und Arzneiwissenschaft*, **1**, no. 2 (1800), 240–305; *Biologie, oder Philosophie der lebenden Natur für Naturforscher und Aerzte*, 6 vols. (Göttingen, 1802–1822); "Ueber den innern Bau der Arachniden," in *Abhandlungen der Physikalisch-medizinischen Societät in Erlangen* (1812), no. 1, 1–48; *Vermischte Schriften anatomischen und physiologischen Inhalts*, 4 vols.

(Göttingen–Bremen, 1816–1821), written with L. C. Treviranus; "Ueber die Zeugungstheile und die Fortpflanzung der Mollusken," in *Zeitschrift für Physiologie*, **1** (1824), 1–55; "Ueber den innern Bau der Schnecke des Ohrs der Vögel," *ibid.*, 188–196; "Ueber die Harnwerkzeuge und die männlichen Zeugungstheile der Schildkröten überhaupt und besonders der *Emys serrata*," *ibid.*, **2** (1827), 282–288; *Beiträge zur Anatomie und Physiologie der Sinneswerkzeuge des Menschen und der Thiere* (Bremen, 1828); "Ueber das Gehirn und die Sinneswerkzeuge des virginischen Beutelthieres," in *Zeitschrift für Physiologie*, **3** (1829), 45–61; and "Ueber die Entstehung der geschlechtslosen Individuen bei den Hymenopteren, besonders der Bienen," *ibid.*, 220–234.

Later works are "Ueber die hinteren Hemisphären des Gehirns der Vögel, Amphibien und Fische," in *Zeitschrift für Physiologie*, **4** (1831), 39–67; "Ueber das Nervensystem des Scorpions und der Spinne," *ibid.*, 89–96; "Ueber die Zeugung der Egel," *ibid.*, 159–167, and **5** (1833), 133–136; *Die Erscheinungen und Gesetze des organischen Lebens*, 2 vols. (Bremen, 1831–1832); "Ueber die Verbreitung des Antlitznerven im Labyrinth des Ohrs der Vögel," in *Zeitschrift für Physiologie*, **5** (1833), 94–96; "Ueber die Zeugung des Erdregenwurms," *ibid.*, 154–156; *Beiträge zur Aufklärung der Erscheinungen und Gesetze des organischen Lebens*, 3 vols. (Bremen, 1835–1837); and *Beobachtungen aus der Zootomie und Physiologie*, L. C. Treviranus, ed. (Bremen, 1839).

II. SECONDARY LITERATURE. Biographies are by G. Barkhausen, G. H. Schumacher, and G. Hartlaub, in *Biographische Skizzen verstorbener Bremischer Aerzte und Naturforscher* (Bremen, 1844), 433–590; and K. F. P. von Martius, *Akademische Denkreden* (Leipzig, 1866), 55–69. There is a critical evaluation of Treviranus' study of mollusk reproduction by Lorenz Oken, in *Isis* (1827), esp. 752–754.

P. SMIT

TREVIRANUS, LUDOLPH CHRISTIAN (*b*. Bremen, Germany, 18 September 1779; *d*. Bonn, Germany, 6 May 1864), *plant anatomy, plant physiology*.

Treviranus was particularly interested in the basic structural unit of living beings—the cell—and in the forces causing structural differentiation, and he therefore studied the various aspects of the relation between structure and function during the ontogeny of plants.

Ludolph Christian was three years younger than his brother, Gottfried Reinhold. Their father, Joachim Johann Jacob Treviranus (*d*. 1806), was a merchant who, after a business failure, became a notary.

Treviranus studied medicine at the University of Jena, where F. W. Schelling was one of his teachers. The greatest philosophical influence on him, however, was that of his brother Gottfried. As an adherent of *Naturphilosophie*, Ludolph Christian sought the causes of the vital processes in life itself; and, like his brother, he denied any difference between organic and inorganic forces, and rejected any physical explanation of the phenomena of life.

After completing his doctoral dissertation (1801), Treviranus established himself as a consulting physician in Bremen. On the basis of his work on the inner structure of plants (1806), which contains interesting observations on the structure and function of the reproductive organs, the University of Rostock offered him the chair of botany. In 1816 he went to Breslau; and in 1830 he and Nees von Esenbeck of Bonn exchanged positions. Treviranus showed a lively interest in the organization and scientific function of botanical gardens; his writings in this field (1843, 1848), however, caused him much trouble, for his ideas did not win the support he needed from colleagues in either Breslau or Bonn.

Treviranus' major work is *Physiologie der Gewächse* (1835–1838), a study devoted to the relation between structure and function in plants. It deals with differences between plant and animal life, the elementary structures of plants (cells, sap and spiral vessels), tissues and organs, movements of sap, excretion of water and absorption of light by the leaves, growth and generation, various forms of reproduction, environmental influences, rest and movements of plants, and length of life. The book is still of interest because of the authoritative historical introductions to the subjects, an approach that was characteristic of all Treviranus' publications. Its practical contents were of less value. Treviranus preferred to use simple magnifying glasses, which prevented him from discovering such fundamental phenomena as the process of fertilization and the formation of the seeds; thus many of his observations were superseded during his lifetime. According to his point of view, influenced by *Naturphilosophie*, fertilization—in plants as well as in animals—should be mediated by a "palpable matter" (1822, 1831).

Of more importance from a purely physiological point of view were Treviranus' observations on the influence of chemical substances on plants, a series of experiments that were continued by Heinrich Göppert, his pupil at Breslau; his research on the movement of particles in the cell; and his studies on the movement of sap in trees (1811, 1817).

With his brother Gottfried, Treviranus published a series of essays on anatomy and physiology (1816–1821). The fourth volume (1821) contains contributions by Ludolph Christian on the formation and structure of the epidermis, the structure of stomata, honeydew as an excretion of plant lice and as a symptom of plant disease, sexuality and germination of plants, propagation by means of bulbs, and reproduction in cryptogamic plants.

With Friedrich Tiedemann the brothers founded *Zeitschrift für Physiologie* (1824), which includes essays by Ludolph Christian on the anatomy and function of sap vessels, the structure of the reproductive organs, the evaporation of water in plants, luminescence and the production of heat in plants, and the impossibility of visualizing the act of fertilization (1831).

Treviranus' interest in history and the arts culminated in a booklet on woodcuts (1855), in which he considered their use as an aid to botanical learning in the Renaissance (Otto Brunfels, Jerome Bock, Leonhard Fuchs), their improvement (by Conrad Gesner, Matthioli, Dodoens, L'Obel, L'Écluse [Clusius], and Rudolf Camerarius), their decline in the seventeenth century, and their revival in the eighteenth century (Thomas Bewick). In the last years of his life, Treviranus wrote a series of monographs on plant genera, including *Delphinium*, *Aquilegia*, *Durieua*, *Astilbe*, and *Lindernia*.

BIBLIOGRAPHY

Among Treviranus' earlier works are *Quaedam ad magnetismum sic dictum animalem spectantia* (Jena, 1801), his doctoral dissertation; "Vom Bau der cryptogamischen Wassergewächse," in F. Weber and M. Mohr, eds., *Beiträge zur Naturkunde*, I (1805); *Vom inwendigen Bau der Gewächse und von der Saftbewegung in denselben* (Göttingen, 1806); *Beyträge zur Pflanzenphysiologie* (Göttingen, 1811), which includes the German trans. of a series of essays by Thomas Knight on the movement of sap in trees; "Ueber die Ausdünstung der Gewächse und deren Organe," in G. R. and L. C. Treviranus, *Vermischte Schriften . . .*, I (Göttingen, 1816), 171–188; "Fernere Beobachtungen über die Bewegung der grünen Materie im Pflanzenreiche," *ibid.*, II (Bremen, 1817), 71–92; "Abhandlungen phytologischen Inhalts," *ibid.*, IV (Bremen, 1821), 1–222; *Die Lehre vom Geschlechte der Pflanzen in Bezug auf die neuesten Angriffe erwogen* (Bremen, 1822); "Ueber den eigenen Saft der Gewächse . . .," in *Zeitschrift für Physiologie*, 1 (1824), 147–180; "Bemerkungen über den Bau der Befruchtungstheile und das Befruchtungsgeschäft der Gewächse," *ibid.*, 2 (1827), 185–187; "Etwas über die wässerigen Absonderungen blättriger Pflanzentheile," *ibid.*, 3 (1829), 72–78; and "Entwickelt sich Licht und Wärme beim Leben der Gewächse?" *ibid.*, 257–268.

Later works are *Caroli Clusii Atrebatis et Conradi Gesneri Tigurini, epistolae ineditae* (Leipzig, 1830); "Gelangt die Befruchtungsmaterie der Gewächse zu deren Samen-Anlagen auf eine sichtbare Weise?" in *Zeitschrift für Physiologie*, 4 (1831), 125–145; *Physiologie der Gewächse*, 2 vols. (Bonn, 1835–1838); "Ueber die Gattung *Lindernia* . . .," in *Linnaea*, 16 (1842), 113–126; *Theorie der Gartenkunde . . .* (Erlangen, 1843), German trans. of John Lindley, *The Theory of Horticulture* (London, 1840); *Bemerkungen über die Führung von botanischen Gärten . . .* (Bonn, 1848); *Caricis specierum in imperio Rutheno huiusque lectarum enumeratio* (Stuttgart, 1852); "Ueber die umbelliferen-Gattung *Durieua*," in *Botanische Zeitung*, 11 (1853), 193–195; "Ueber die Gattung *Astilbe*," *ibid.*, 13 (1855), 817–820; *Die Anwendung des Holzschnittes zur bildlichen Darstellung von Pflanzen nach Entstehung, Blüthe, Verfall und Restauration* (Leipzig, 1855; repr. Utrecht, 1949); "Ueber einige Stellen in des älteren Plinius Naturgeschichte der Gewächse," in *Botanische Zeitung*, 17 (1859), 321–325; and "Lebens-Abriss von Ludolph Christian Treviranus," *ibid.*, 24 (1866), supp., with an incomplete bibliography.

A biography is in K. F. P. von Martius, *Akademische Denkreden* (Leipzig, 1866), 523–538.

P. SMIT

TREVISANUS. See **Bernard of Trevisan.**

TRIANA, JOSÉ GERÓNIMO (or **JERÓNIMO**) (*b.* Zipaquirá, Colombia, 1826; *d.* Paris, France, October 1890), *botany.*

The botanical sciences were not firmly established in Colombia until the 1930's, when the Colombian National Herbarium and the Botanical Institute of the National University were founded at Bogotá. Until then the investigation of the rich and interesting Colombian flora had been carried on by a series of more or less self-taught individuals without institutional affiliation. Working with very little bibliographical information, they had to deal with an extremely mountainous area in which each climatic zone and mountain range posed different problems. Thus it is all the more extraordinary that from the arrival of José Celestino Mutis at Cartagena in 1760 until the 1930's botanical study was uninterrupted in Colombia.

Triana began the study of botany at Bogotá as the private pupil of Francisco Javier Matis, the last survivor of the Mutis botanical expedition. In 1850 the government appointed him associate botanist on the commission (headed by Agustín Codazzi) charged with preparing and publishing a geographical map of Colombia that would establish its borders. Triana traveled with the commission throughout Andean Colombia collecting plants in order to verify his catalog of the flora, and recording the place and date of collection, barometric pressure, common name, and popular use of each species. Triana's herbarium, amassed through tedious observations, was presented to the government in 1855 in thirty-eight volumes, each containing about 100 species. He also gathered data on the ethnobotanic legacy of Colombia: botanic medical traditions of the native medicine men, the raw materials of primitive industries, and the home remedies of the mestizo societies. Together with his herbarium, Triana's data on economic and medicinal botany established his scientific reputation both in Colombia and in Europe.

While still in Colombia, Triana had begun correspondence with foreign botanical explorers of Colombia, including Luis Schlim, J. Linden, Julian Warscewiez, J. J. Jewies, H. Holton, and Herrmann Karsten. Interest in the Colombian flora increased in the botanical centers and gardens of France, England, Belgium, and Germany; and in 1850–1857 Triana benefited from the company of explorers sent from Europe to be trained as botanists.

In 1856 Triana was commissioned by the government to go to Europe for two years in order to publicize Colombian plants of economic value. When he reached Paris, Triana met the botanist Descaine. He collaborated on the publication of the *Flora de la Nueva Granada* with Jules Planchon, with whom he worked at Montpellier in 1858 and 1859; at the end of this time he left ready for the press *Mémoire sur la famille des guttifères*, which appeared in 1860. At the end of his career he won the esteem of Filippo Parlatore, professor of botany at Florence.

In 1865, at the Horticultural Exposition of Amsterdam, Triana presented his *Monografía de las melastomáceas*, which was published at London in 1871 and was awarded the Candolle Prize.

Triana's greatest ambition was to publish a flora of his country; but the government, impoverished by civil wars, withdrew financial support. He therefore chose to prepare a systematic work in collaboration with Planchon and others, *Prodromus florae Novogranatensis, ou énumération des plantes de la Nouvelle Grenade*. Triana used the illustrations and descriptions prepared by Mutis and Francisco José Caldas for their *Historia de los árboles de quina*, which were in Madrid, when he published his *Nouvelles études sur les quinquinas* (1870).

Triana's study of the bibliographical sources started in London (1865–1867). He traveled to Madrid twice in order to study Mutis' material on quinine and prevailed upon Queen Isabella II to instruct the administrators of the Madrid Botanical Garden to give him access to the icons. Triana immediately made a new and extensive systematic recension of the *Cinchona* species. He also obtained permission to present Mutis' *Quinología* at the Universal Exposition of Paris in 1867. This exhibit brought him many honors and prizes.

Two of Triana's most valuable botanical works are still unpublished, "Catálogo metódico de los dibujos de la Flora de Nueva Granada hechos bajo la dirección de don José Celestino Mutis" and "Catálogo de los ejemplares que componen el herbario formado por José J. Triana. . . ."

In 1889 Triana was struck by a carriage, an accident that apparently aggravated some of his preexisting ailments. He underwent an operation in 1890 and died that October. In 1857, fifteen days before his departure from Bogotá for Europe, he married Mercedes Umaña, who bore him fifteen children.

BIBLIOGRAPHY

Triana's writings include *Nuevos jeneros i especies de plantas para la flora Neo-Granadina* (Bogotá, 1854); *Prodromus florae Novogranatensis,* 2 vols. (Paris, 1862–1867), written with J. E. Planchon, which also appeared as a series of memoirs in *Annales des sciences naturelles* (Botany), 3rd ser., **17**–4th ser., **17** (1862–1873); *Nouvelles études sur les quinquinas, d'après les matériaux présentés en 1867 à l'Exposition universelle de Paris* (Paris, 1870); and "Les mélastomacées," in *Transactions of the Linnean Society of London,* **28** (1871), 1–188, also published separately (London, 1871).

On his life and work, see *Abhandlungen herausgegeben vom Naturwissenschaftlichen Verein zu Bremen,* **3** (1873), 393–403; and **5** (1878), 29–33; and *Journal of Botany, British and Foreign,* **29** (1891), 46–47.

ENRIQUE PÉREZ ARBELÁEZ

TRILIA, BERNARD OF. See **Bernard of Le Treille.**

TRISMEGISTUS. See **Hermes Trismegistus.**

TROJA, MICHELE (*b.* Andria, Apulia, Italy, 23 June 1747; *d.* Naples, Italy, 12 April 1827), *medicine.*

Troja studied medicine at Naples and then won a competition for the post of assistant surgeon at that city's Hospital of San Giacomo degli Spagnoli. In 1774 he obtained a scholarship for postgraduate study that enabled him to go to Paris, where he began the research on the formation of bone callus and bone regeneration that made him famous. For this work, which continued that of Henri-Louis Duhamel du Monceau, he was nominated corresponding member of the Paris Academy and was invited by Diderot to write a number of articles for the supplement of the *Encyclopédie*.

When he returned home in 1779, Troja was given the chair of ophthalmology at the University of Naples, a post established especially for him, since the subject had not been taught there until then. In the following year he became surgeon of the king's chamber for having successfully cured the crown prince of a disease. In 1802 Troja campaigned successfully for the creation of a commission to spread the knowledge and use of Jenner's smallpox vaccination.

Troja is known especially for his studies on the nutrition and regeneration of bones, a subject that was the focus of academic interest at that time. Even Spallanzani became interested in it; and in his letters he referred to the work of Troja, although apparently without great enthusiasm. Such an unfavorable judgment does not appear justified today, for Troja considerably improved the techniques of study. For instance, he used immersion in nitric acid to bring out bone structure and applied zinc sulfate to obtain coloration of the cells and improve the visibility of microscopic structures.

Troja's research on the eye is preserved in a volume of lectures on eye diseases. In urology he studied the diseases of the bladder and of the urinary system in general, and invented the flexible catheter. This invention derived from his active interest in and knowledge of India rubber, which had just been introduced into Europe.

In addition to his own work in anatomy and microscopy, Troja collaborated with G. S. Poli for many years in the latter's investigations on the anatomy of mollusks.

BIBLIOGRAPHY

I. ORIGINAL WORKS. Troja's writings include *De novorum ossium in integris aut maxime ob morbis deperditionibus regeneratione experimenta* (Paris, 1775); *Lezioni intorno alle malattie degli occhi* (Naples, 1780); *Lezioni intorno ai mali della vescica orinaria e delle sue appartenenze . . . Colla giunta di una memoria sulla costruzione dei cateteri flessibili* (Naples, 1785–1793); and *Osservazioni ed esperimenti sulle ossa; in supplemento ad un'opera sulla rigenerazione delle ossa, impressa nel 1775* (Naples, 1814).

II. SECONDARY LITERATURE. See M. del Gaizo, "Della vita e delle opere di Michele Troja," in *Atti della R. Accademia medico-chirurgica* (Naples), **52** (1899), 191; and **53** (1899), 351; Gianni Randelli, "Ripetizione degli esperimenti di Michele Troja sulla rigenerazione delle ossa," in *Physis*, **6** (1964), 45–64; and A. von Schoenberg, *Biographie des Dr. und Professor M. Troja* (Erlangen, 1828).

CARLO CASTELLANI

TROMMSDORFF, JOHANN BARTHOLOMÄUS (*b.* Erfurt, Germany, 8 May 1770; *d.* Erfurt, 8 March 1837), *chemistry, pharmacy.*

Chemistry and pharmacy loomed large in Trommsdorff's youthful environment. Not only was his father, Dr. Wilhelm Bernhard Trommsdorff, the owner of an apothecary shop but he was also a successful chemistry teacher in the University of Erfurt and the chief local representative of chemistry in Erfurt's revitalized Academy of Useful Sciences. However, young Trommsdorff never had the advantage of his father's instruction, for, two days before his twelfth birthday, his father died. Financial difficulties soon arose, compelling Trommsdorff to abandon plans for a higher education and enter pharmacy. He went to Weimar, where he served as an apprentice under his father's old friend the chemist Wilhelm Heinrich Bucholz and Bucholz's employee the chemist Johann Friedrich Göttling. Thanks to their instruction and encouragement, he published his first note in Lorenz von Crell's *Chemische Annalen* in 1787. That same year he also completed his apprenticeship. After two and a half years as a journeyman in Erfurt, Stettin, and Stargard, he took over the family apothecary shop in Erfurt.

Trommsdorff continued publishing articles and small monographs on various chemical and pharmaceutical topics. By early 1793 he felt confident enough to venture into the debate over the composition of mercuric oxide that was raging between the antiphlogistonist Sigismund Friedrich Hermbstaedt in Berlin and the phlogistonist Friedrich Albrecht Carl Gren in Halle. He sided with his boyhood friend Gren, who maintained that completely fresh mercury calx per se did not yield dephlogisticated air when reduced. To his chagrin, he and his allies were soon discredited by Hermbstaedt's party in this crucial controversy in the German antiphlogistic revolution. Trommsdorff's first reaction was to renounce all theorizing. However, influenced by the works of Kant and Georg Christoph Lichtenberg, he was soon calling for the unification of physics, chemistry, and natural history. For the next few years, he showed considerable interest in attaining this elusive goal of the *Naturphilosophen*. In the early 1800's, however, the empiricist in him triumphed. From then on his research was limited to turning out hundreds of useful, but essentially routine, chemical studies.

Although Trommsdorff's work as a chemist was valued highly enough for him to hold a chair of chemistry at Erfurt University and to be offered several other chairs, including that of Martin Heinrich Klaproth in Berlin, his work as a scholarly pharmacist was of greater significance. His numerous texts were exceptionally popular, most of them going through many editions in Germany and abroad. His *Journal der Pharmacie* (1794–1834) was the leading periodical for pharmacy and pharmaceutical chemistry until Justus von Liebig began publishing his *Annalen der Pharmacie* in 1832. And his "Chemical-physical-pharmaceutical Boarding School," attended by over 300 students between 1795 and 1828, played a major role in the training of the founding generation of the German drug industry.

BIBLIOGRAPHY

For a complete bibliography of Trommsdorff's more than four hundred publications, see Adolph Peter Callisen, *Dem Andenken des verdienten Chemiker Dr. Joh. Barthol. Trommsdorff* (Copenhagen, 2nd ed., 1837).

For his life and influence, see Hermann Trommsdorff, "Johann Bartholomä Trommsdorff und seine Zeitgenossen," in *Jahrbuch der Akademie gemeinnütziger Wissenschaften in Erfurt*, new ser., **53** (1937), 5–55; and **55** (1941), 131–234.

Other studies of Trommsdorff include Christa Caumitz, "Johann Bartholomäus Trommsdorff (1770–1837): Ein Begründer der wissenschaftlichen deutschen Pharmazie," a manuscript in the Archives of the Deutsche Akademie der Naturforscher, Leopoldina (Halle, German Democratic Republic); Hermann Gittner, ed., *Die Harzreisen des Johann Bartholomä Trommsdorff 1798 und 1805* (Oberhausen, 1957); and "Die Rheinreise des Johann Bartholomai Trommsdorff zur 13. Naturforscherversammlung in Bonn anno 1835," in *Deutsche Apothekerzeitung*, **99** (1959), 31–36; Horst Rudolf Abe et al., "Johann Bartholomäus Trommsdorff und die Begründung der modernen Pharmazie," in *Beiträge zur Geschichte der Universität Erfurt*, **16** (1971–1972); and

Wilhelm Vershofen, *Die Anfänge der chemisch-pharmazeutischen Industrie*, I (Berlin-Stuttgart, 1949), and II (Aulendorf, 1952).

KARL HUFBAUER

TROOST, GERARD (*b.* 's Hertogenbosch, Netherlands, 15 March 1776; *d.* Nashville, Tennessee, 14 August 1850), *geology, mineralogy, paleontology, natural history.*

Troost was the son of Everhard Joseph Troost and Anna Cornelia van Haeck. He attended the University of Leiden and the Athenaeum in Amsterdam, where he specialized in chemistry, geology, and natural history. He received his master of pharmacy from the Athenaeum and his doctorate of medicine at Leiden. He never practiced medicine, and although he was briefly a pharmacist in Amsterdam and The Hague and later in the United States, his interest in geology gradually became dominant.

In 1807 Louis Bonaparte, the appointed king of Holland, sent Troost to Paris, where, as a colleague of Haüy, he became skilled in mineralogy and crystallography. For two years Troost collected for the king specimens of minerals from various parts of Europe. He also studied with A. G. Werner, whom he accompanied on geologic field trips. He translated Humboldt's *Ansichten der Natur* into Dutch, and as a result the two men became lifelong friends. In 1809 Troost accompanied a Dutch scientific expedition that sailed for Java by way of the Cape of Good Hope. Although the ship was captured by French pirates, Troost eventually made his way back to Europe and soon tried to reach Java again, by way of the United States. But in 1810, while he was in Philadelphia, Louis Bonaparte, who in too many matters put the interest of his subjects ahead of those of his brother Napoleon, was forced to abdicate; and Holland was incorporated for a while into the French empire. Therefore, Troost decided to stay in the United States. He became an American citizen and established a pharmaceutical and chemical laboratory in Philadelphia. In 1811 Troost married Margaret Tage of Philadelphia, by whom he had two children, Caroline and Lewis. She died in 1819, and he then married a Mrs. O'Reilly of Philadelphia.

Troost was short and portly and had a kindly disposition. He was a polished man of the world and a profound scholar, and his manner was always unassuming. He was proficient in several languages, but Americans noted that he always spoke English with a Dutch accent. He won the respect and friendship of all classes of people.

Troost was one of seven men who in 1812 founded the Academy of Natural Sciences of Philadelphia, and he was its first president. In 1826 a geologic map of Philadelphia and environs, which he had prepared, was published by the Philadelphia Society for Promoting Agriculture.

In 1825 Troost joined Robert Dale Owen, who with Maclure, Say, and Lesueur, made up what they described as a "boatload of knowledge." Their boat took them down the Ohio River to New Harmony, Indiana, where they planned to establish a utopian society. Interest waned at New Harmony, however, and in 1827 Troost moved to Nashville, Tennessee, where he lived for the rest of his life.

In 1828 Troost was appointed professor of geology and mineralogy at the University of Nashville, where he also taught chemistry. He held this post until his death and was esteemed by his students. He was state geologist of Tennessee from 1831 to 1839, and he prepared the first geologic map of the state. He was one of the early workers in stratigraphy in the United States and contributed to the knowledge of the mineral resources of Tennessee. He housed his extensive collections of minerals, rocks, fossils, shells, Indian relics, and mounted birds in a private museum at Nashville that was open to the public and considered one of the finest museums west of the Appalachians.

In mid-July 1850, only four weeks before his death, Troost finished the manuscript of his study of the fossil crinoids of Tennessee. He had written it with much difficulty; in his introduction to the manuscript he expressed a fear that since his memory and sight were both sadly impaired, the work might contain some inaccuracies. The manuscript was received 18 July 1850 by the Smithsonian Institution, which undertook to publish it, subject to the editorial approval of Louis Agassiz. After Agassiz had kept the paper for five years without expressing his opinion of its worth, it was sent for review to James Hall, Jr., in Albany, New York. But the manuscript, with Troost's collection of Tennessee crinoids, was still in Hall's possession at the time of his death more than forty years later. The fossils and the manuscript were then returned to the Smithsonian Institution.

Hall and his colleagues may have attributed their unconscionable delay to Troost's misgivings about possible inaccuracies, although Hall had introduced under his own authorship four of Troost's genera, quoting Troost's descriptions for three of them. Troost's paper was finally published in 1909 with supplementary descriptions and observations by Elvira Wood. But by that time most of the species and genera originally recognized by Troost had been described by others, and his memory was deprived of the credit that would have been accorded it if his important monograph had been printed when it was received more than half a century earlier.

BIBLIOGRAPHY

I. ORIGINAL WORKS. A bibliography of Troost's papers is in L. C. Glenn (see below). Papers on mineralogy, published from 1821 to 1848, are primarily in *American Journal of Science* and *Journal of the Philadelphia Academy of Sciences*. Papers on paleontology, published from 1834 to 1850, are primarily in *Transactions of the Geological Society of Pennsylvania*. Papers on the geology of Tennessee, published from 1835 to 1849, are in *American Journal of Science*, *Journal of the Tennessee Senate* (Nashville), and Tennessee Senate and House documents (Knoxville).

II. SECONDARY LITERATURE. See J. M. Clarke, "Prof. James Hall and the Troost Manuscript," in *American Geologist*, **35**, no. 4 (1905), 256–257, and *James Hall of Albany, Geologist and Paleontologist, 1811–1898* (Albany, N.Y., 1923), 233; L. C. Glenn, "Gerard Troost," in *American Geologist*, **35**, no. 2 (1905), 72–94; Phillip Lindsley, "The Life and Character of Professor Gerard Troost, M.D.," in *The Works of Phillip Lindsley*, I (Philadelphia, 1859), 541–588; Dumas Malone, ed., "Gerard Troost," in *Dictionary of American Biography*, XVIII (1938), 647–648; G. P. Merrill, *The First One Hundred Years of American Geology* (New York, 1964), 111, 138, 215–216; H. G. Rooker, "A Sketch of the Life and Work of Dr. Gerard Troost," in *Tennessee Historical Magazine*, 2nd ser., **3**, no. 1 (1932), 3–19, with portrait opposite p. 3; and Elvira Wood, "A Critical Summary of Troost's Unpublished Manuscript on the Crinoids of Tennessee," in *Bulletin. United States National Museum*, **64** (1909), with portrait.

ELLEN J. MOORE

TROOST, LOUIS JOSEPH (*b.* Paris, France, 17 October 1825; *d.* Paris, 30 September 1911), *chemistry.*

After receiving his *agrégé* at the École Normale Supérieure in Paris in 1851, Troost taught briefly at the Lycée d'Angoulême and at the Lycée Bonaparte in Paris. He received his doctorate in 1857 and continued to work in Deville's thermochemical laboratory alongside researchers who included

Henri Debray, F. Isambert, Paul Hautefeuille, and Alfred Ditte. In 1874 he was appointed to the chair of chemistry at the Sorbonne and in 1884 was elected to the Académie des Sciences.

Troost's first studies concerned preparations of salts of lithium, but the greater part of his research focused on isomerism, allotropy, and dissociation. Together with Deville he studied the variations with rising temperature of vapor densities of a number of substances, including iodine, phosphorus, arsenic, and zirconium. They confirmed Dumas's observation that the vapor density of sulfur near its boiling point corresponds to a hexatomic molecule and found that sulfur vapor becomes diatomic above 800°C. Their determinations indicated analogous vapor-density variations for selenium and tellurium and also aided in the clarification of the chemistry of niobium and tantalum. All their observations were couched in terms of equivalents and volumetric considerations rather than atoms.

In 1868 Troost commenced a long period of collaboration with Hautefeuille. Their researches included the conditions of transformation of cyanogen into paracyanogen and of cyanic acid into cyanuric acid; the allotropic conversions of white phosphorus into red phosphorus and of oxygen into ozone; and the preparations of new compounds of boron and silicon, particularly their chlorides. With Hautefeuille, Troost also analyzed the absorption of hydrogen by sodium, potassium, and palladium; and they studied the roles of manganese and silicon in iron metallurgy. Their investigations of the introduction of nitric acid into hydrocarbons supported Berthelot's conclusion that there is much greater mechanical work available in the nitric ethers (such as nitroglycerine) than in nitrobenzene and similar products.

BIBLIOGRAPHY

I. ORIGINAL WORKS. Troost wrote two principal textbooks: *Précis de chimie*, 2nd ed. (Paris, 1867; 45th rev. ed., with E. Pechard, 1932); and *Traité elémentaire de chimie comprenant les principales applications à l'hygiène, aux arts et à l'industrie*, 2 vols. (Paris, 1865; 24th rev. ed., with E. Pechard, 1948), which became a classic text in secondary education. The most complete list of Troost's publications is in his own *Notice sur les travaux scientifiques de M. Louis Troost* (Paris, 1888). Several of his papers are reprinted in Henri Le Châtelier, ed., *Les classiques de la science*: vol. III, *Eau oxygénée et ozone* (Paris, 1913), and vol. VI, *La fusion du platine et dissociation* (Paris, 1914).

II. SECONDARY LITERATURE. On Troost and his work, see Armand Gautier, "Séance du lundi 2 octobre 1911," in *Comptes rendus hebdomadaires des séances de l'Académie des sciences*, **153** (1911), 611–615, esp. 613–615; and an unsigned obituary, "Louis Joseph Troost," in *Nature*, **87** (1911), 491–492. There are also discussions of the researches of Troost and Hautefeuille, in Georges Lemoine, "Les travaux et la vie de Paul Hautefeuille," in *Revue des questions scientifiques*, **55** (1904), 5–25; and Alfred Lacroix, "Gabriel Hautefeuille (1836–1902)," in Lacroix's *Figures de savants*, 2 vols. (Paris, 1932), vol. I, 81–89.

MARY JO NYE

TROOSTWIJK, ADRIAAN PAETS VAN (*b.* Utrecht, Netherlands, 4 March 1752; *d.* Nieuwersluis, Netherlands, 3 April 1837), *chemistry.*

Nothing is known of van Troostwijk's education. From the age of eighteen until his retirement in 1816 he worked in Amsterdam as a merchant. He was also an important Dutch chemist and published thirty-five works between 1778 and 1818. From 1806 to 1816 he was a member of the Royal Institute of Sciences, Literature, and Fine Arts (the present Royal Netherlands Academy of Sciences). In 1816 he moved to Nieuwersluis, where he remained until his death.

Van Troostwijk was greatly influenced by his friend the physician Jan Rudolph Deiman (1743–1808) and by Martinus van Marum, director of Teyler's Museum in Haarlem. From 1778 until 1792 van Troostwijk published the results of his own research and of work done in collaboration with Deiman, van Marum, and Krayenhoff. With Deiman he investigated the improvement of air by growing plants (1778), the nature and properties of carbon dioxide (1781), and the influence of galvanism on both the sick and the healthy. In 1783 he published a work written with van Marum on the electrophorus and, four years later, a joint work on the noxious fumes in swamps, drains, mines, and factories. Using van Marum's electrical machine, they investigated the chemical action of electricity on various gases and on metal oxides. After sparking dephlogisticated air (oxygen), they remarked that it "had acquired a very strong smell, which to us very much resembled the strong smell of electric matter, only much more so than we had ever smelled before" (observation of ozone). When they sparked fixed air (carbon dioxide) its volume was slightly increased. They put equal amounts of electrified and unelectrified fixed air over water and found that after two days only one-tenth of the latter but two-fifths of the former remained. They did not, however, realize that the electrified fixed air was partially decomposed into carbon monoxide and oxygen. During their first experiments on the decomposition of water by electric sparks, Deiman and van Troostwijk also subjected carbon dioxide to violent electric discharges. They found that it produced a much larger volume of inflammable air than water. They did not recognize that the inflammable air obtained in this way was carbon monoxide, and not hydrogen, and they came to the wrong conclusion that fixed air contains water.

In 1785 van Troostwijk published a treatise on the recently discovered types of air, and he was co-author with Krayenhoff of a work on the use of electricity in physics and medicine (1788). A phlogistonist until 1788, van Troostwijk renounced his former belief chiefly through the influence of the publications of van Marum (1787) and Alexander Petrus Nahuys (1788). In 1789 van Troostwijk and Deiman published the results of their experiments on the decomposition of water by static electricity and its synthesis by combustion.

Around 1791 van Troostwijk, Deiman, Pieter Nieuwland, and Nicolaas Bondt founded the Batavian Club, better known as the Society of Dutch Chemists, a circle of friends who met to study chemistry. The apothecary Anthonie Lauwerenburgh and the physician Gerard Vrolik later became members of the group. The society was instrumental in securing recognition in the Netherlands for Lavoisier's discoveries and published many articles in support of the new oxidation theory. Van Troostwijk was, in all probability, the leader of the society, which remained active until 1808. Articles published by the Dutch chemists were collected in the journal *Recherches physico-chimiques* (1792–1794) and later appeared in an enlarged Dutch translation as *Natuur-scheikundige verhandelingen* (Amsterdam, 1799–1801).

Van Troostwijk also investigated the preparation of olefiant gas (ethylene) from the action of concentrated sulfuric acid on ethyl alcohol and the preparation of ethylene chloride from the action of chlorine on ethylene (1794). The latter compound is still known as Dutch oil or Dutch liquid. Also that year he reported on the glow resulting from the mixture of sulfur and various metals heated in the absence of oxygen.

BIBLIOGRAPHY

I. ORIGINAL WORKS. There is a bibliography of van Troostwijk's writings in H. P. M. van der Horn van den Bos, "Bibliographie des chimistes hollandais dans la période de Lavoisier," in *Archives du Musée Teyler*, 2nd ser., **6** (1900), 375–420. His works include *Verhandeling over het nut van den groeij der boomen en planten, tot zuivering der lucht* (Amsterdam, 1780), written with J. R. Deiman; *Verhandeling over de vaste lucht* (Rotterdam, 1781), written with Deiman; *Verhandeling over de vorderingen in de luchtkennis* (Amsterdam, 1785); *De l'application de l'électricité à la physique et à la médecine* (Amsterdam, 1788), written with C. R. T. Krayenhoff; and "Lettre à M. de la Métherie, sur une manière de décomposer l'eau en air inflammable et en air vital," in *Journal de physique, de chimie et de l'histoire naturelle*, **35** (1789), 369–378, written with Deiman.

Later writings are *Beschrijving van een electriseermachine en van proefnemingen met dezelve in het werk gesteld* (Amsterdam, 1790), written with Deiman; "Expériences sur l'inflammation du mélange de soufre et de métaux, sans la présence de l'oxigène," in *Recherches physico-chimiques*, **3** (1794), 71–96, written with Deiman *et al.*; "Recherches sur les divers espèces des gaz, qu'on obtient en mêlant l'acide sulfurique concentré avec l'alcool," in *Journal de physique* . . ., **45** (1794), 178–191, written with Deiman, Bondt, and Lauwerenburgh.

II. SECONDARY LITERATURE. On van Troostwijk and his work, see H. P. M. van der Horn van den Bos: *De Nederlandsche scheikundigen van het laatst der vorige eeuw* (Utrecht, 1881); *Het aandeel dat de Scheikundigen in Frankrijk, Engeland, Duitschland en Noord- en Zuid-Nederland hebben gehad in het tot algemeene erkenning brengen van het Systeem van Lavoisier* (Amsterdam, 1895); "Matériaux pour l'histoire de la chimie dans les Pays-Bas. A. Paets van Troostwijk, un chimiste d'Amsterdam de la fin du 18e siècle, 1752–1837," in *Archives du Musée Teyler*, 2nd ser., **9**, pt. 2 (1904), 155–199; and "Adriaan Paets van Troostwijk," in *Chemisch weekblad*, **6** (1909), 1–35. See also E. Cohen, *Das Lachgas. Eine chemisch-kulturhistorische Studie* (Leipzig, 1907), 14–21; and H. A. M. Snelders, "Uiteenzettingen van het stelsel van Lavoisier door Nederlanders in het laatste kwart van de achttiende eeuw," in *Scientiarum historia*, **8** (1966), 89–100.

H. A. M. SNELDERS

TROPFKE, JOHANNES (*b.* Berlin, Germany, 14 October 1866; *d.* Berlin, 10 November 1939), *history of mathematics.*

Tropfke came from a wealthy family. A bright student, he was encouraged to study a number of different subjects at the Friedrichs Gymnasium, and his wide-ranging interests at the University of Berlin are reflected in the list of subjects Tropfke prepared for the state examination in 1889: mathematics, physics, philosophy, botany, zoology, Latin, and Greek. His dissertation dealt with a topic in the theory of functions. An enthusiastic teacher, he was director of the Kirschner Oberrealschule from 1912 to 1932.

Tropfke's program for changing the secondary school mathematics curriculum, presented in 1899, was published in expanded form as *Geschichte der Elementarmathematik in systematischer Darstellung* (1902–1903). Even in this form, however, it was still based mainly on a study of secondary literature that was largely unchecked by an examination of original sources. Tropfke subsequently produced a second, seven-volume edition (1921–1924) that benefited from the constructive and sympathetic criticism of Heinrich Wieleitner and Gustaf Eneström. This work offered what was, at the time, an excellent overall account of the subject, enriched by a wealth of extremely valuable citations and references. Moreover, it exerted a decisive influence on the reorganization of mathematical education, encouraging teachers to devote greater attention to historical development.

Advances in the study of the history of mathematics led Tropfke to undertake a third, revised and enlarged edition of his work; but it was not completed. He died shortly after the beginning of the war; and the remaining volumes, already in manuscript, were destroyed.

BIBLIOGRAPHY

Tropfke's writings include *Zur Darstellung des elliptischen Integrals erster Gattung* (Halle, 1889), his dissertation; *Erstmaliges Auftreten der einzelnen Bestandteile unserer Schulmathematik* (Berlin, 1899); *Geschichte der Elementarmathematik in systematischer Darstellung*, 2 vols. (Leipzig, 1902–1903; 2nd ed., 7 vols., Leipzig–Berlin, 1921–1924; 3rd ed., 4 vols., Leipzig–Berlin, 1930–1940); "Archimedes und die Trigonometrie," in *Archiv für Geschichte der Mathematik, der Naturwissenschaften und der Technik*, n.s. **10** (1928), 432–461; "Zur Geschichte der quadratischen Gleichungen über dreieinhalb Jahrtausende," in *Jahresberichte der Deutschen Mathematiker-vereinigung*, **43** (1933), 98–107; and **44** (1934), 26–47, 95–119; and "Die Siebenecksabhandlung des Archimedes," in *Osiris*, **1** (1936), 636–651.

An obituary by J. E. Hofmann, with portrait and bibliography, is in *Deutsche Mathematik*, **6** (1941), 114–118.

J. E. HOFMANN

TROUGHTON, EDWARD (*b.* Corney, Cumberland, England, October 1753; *d.* London, England, June 1836), *mathematics, optics, physics.*

Troughton was one of the most competent mathematical instrument makers of the late eighteenth and early nineteenth centuries. In many ways his career was parallel to that of Jesse Ramsden, his earlier counterpart, whom he was to replace as the foremost instrument maker of England.

In 1770 Troughton was apprenticed to his elder brother, John, who specialized in dividing and engraving instruments for other makers. His shop was on Surrey Street, in the Strand. In 1779 John and Edward Troughton became partners, and in 1782 they bought the business of Benjamin Cole at "The Sign of the Orrery," at 136 Fleet Street. This was a well-established enterprise, having been founded by John Worgan about 1680 and continued, in turn, by John Rowley, Thomas Wright, and the two Benjamin Coles, father and son.

John Troughton died in 1784; and Edward conducted the business alone until 1826, when he joined with William Simms, a skilled instrument maker. The firm was renamed Troughton and Simms and, after Troughton's retirement in 1831, continued under that name until 1922 when, through a merger, it became Cooke, Troughton and Simms Ltd.

Troughton's reputation rested on the accuracy and beautiful proportions of his instruments. In 1822 he wrote, "The beauty of the instrument lies not in the flourishes of the engraver, chaser and carver but in the uniformity of figure and just proportion alone."

Troughton made many contributions to the development of instrument making: in 1788 an improvement of Hadley's quadrant; in 1790 a mercurial pendulum; and in 1796 a refined version of the Borda, or reflecting circle. He was responsible for substituting spider web filaments for hair or wire in his optical micrometers.

Troughton's most notable achievement was the improvement of the method of dividing a circle. His paper on this in 1809 won him the Copley Medal from the Royal Society of London, which elected him a fellow the following year. In 1822 he was elected a fellow of the Royal Society of Edinburgh. He was a founding member of the Royal Astronomical Society.

Examples of his instruments are to be found in the Kensington Science Museum, London; the museums of the history of science in Oxford and Florence; the Whipple Museum, Cambridge; the National Maritime Museum, Greenwich; the Peabody Museum, Salem, Massachusetts; the Conservatoire des Arts et Métiers, Paris; and the Smithsonian Institution, Washington, D.C.

BIBLIOGRAPHY

I. ORIGINAL WORKS. Troughton's works are "An Account of a Method of Dividing Astronomical and Other Instruments by Ocular Inspection, in Which the Usual Tools for Graduating Are Not Employed, etc.," in *Philosophical Transactions of the Royal Society*, **99**, pt. 1 (1809), 105–145; *On the Repeating and Altitude-Azimuth Circle* (London, 1812); and "An Account of the Repeating Circle and of the Altitude and Azimuth Instrument, Describing Their Different Constructions, Etc.," in *Memoirs of the Astronomical Society*, **33** (1821), and in *Philosophical Magazine* (1822).

II. SECONDARY LITERATURE. On Troughton's life and work, see the *Dictionary of National Biography*, XIX (London, 1917), 1186–1187. Other works include Maria Luisa Bonelli, *Catalogo degli Strumenti del Museo di Storia della Scienza* (Florence, 1954), pp. 67, 204, 206, 225; Maurice Daumas, *Les instruments scientifiques au XVII et XVIII siècles* (Paris, 1953), 320–321; Nicholas Goodison, *English Barometers, 1680–1860* (New York, 1968), 240; Henry C. King, *The History of the Telescope* (London, 1955), 230–236; J. A. Repsold, *Zur Geschichte der astronomischen Messwerkzeuge, 1450–1830* (Leipzig, 1908), 118–122; E. G. R. Taylor, *The Mathematical Practitioners of Hanoverian England* (London, 1966), 298–299; and E. Wilfred Taylor and J. Simms Wilson, *At the Sign of the Orrery*, pp. 24–30.

RODERICK S. WEBSTER

TROUTON, FREDERICK THOMAS (*b.* Dublin, Ireland, 24 November 1863; *d.* Downe, Kent, England, 21 September 1922), *physics.*

Trouton came from a wealthy and prominent Dublin family. He performed brilliantly in his undergraduate work at Trinity College, Dublin, taking degrees in both engineering and physical science. In recognition of this work, he was awarded the Large Gold Medal, an honor rarely bestowed for work in science. Trouton remained at Trinity College as FitzGerald's assistant. Trouton and FitzGerald remained the closest of colleagues and confidants until FitzGerald's death in 1901. In 1902 Trouton was appointed Quain professor of physics, University College London. At London he pursued his interests in both engineering and physics until 1912, when he was struck by a severe illness that led to permanent paralysis in both legs. Trouton's active scientific career was at an end, but his spirit was not broken, and the wit and charm for which he was noted were not dampened even after the loss of his two sons in World War I. He continued to advise students and colleagues from his sickbed until his death at the age of fifty-eight.

Throughout his career, Trouton occupied himself with problems in both engineering and physical science. As an undergraduate, he discovered a relationship—known as Trouton's Law—between the latent heat and the molecular weight of a substance. According to the law, the ratio of the product of the molecular weight and the latent heat to the absolute temperature is a constant. The relationship is not precise and Trouton himself held it to be of little significance. It was also during his undergraduate days that Trouton took an active role in surveying for a railway.

Trouton's dual interests in applied research and physics continued throughout his career. He devoted considerable energy to investigations of the viscosity of pitch and molten glass at a variety of temperatures; the dynamics of the condensation of water vapor on glass, glass wool, and related substances; the effects of surface moisture on the conductivity of glass; and the relationship between the concentration and the adsorption of dyestuffs on sand. The practical implications of these studies were an explicit motivation for carrying them out.

The influence of FitzGerald seems to have been decisive in Trouton's more abstract research. Thus, shortly after Hertz published his startling discovery of the propagation of electromagnetic fields, Trouton and FitzGerald undertook a series of replicate investigations. But the investigations for which Trouton is remembered were those in which he attempted to determine the relative velocity of the earth and ether.

Independent of Hendrik A. Lorentz, FitzGerald had suggested that the null result of the Michelson-Morley experiment could be accounted for if one assumed that material objects contracted in the direction of motion as a result of interaction with ether. In 1903 Trouton and H. R. Noble undertook an experiment to measure the torsional force on a suspended charged plate condenser as a result of the interaction of the charges in the plates with the ether wind. The widely publicized results were, of course, null.

In 1908, in association with Alexander O. Rankine, Trouton undertook yet another ether drift experiment. They attempted to measure the change in resistance of a copper wire when the wire is rotated parallel and transverse to the direction in which the earth moves around the sun. As was the case with the Trouton-Noble experiment, the experiment was an extremely delicate one, calling for a considerable degree of virtuosity and cleverness. But again the results were null.

Such research placed Trouton in the great tradition of nineteenth-century British physics. He was, perhaps, the last of the well-trained British ether-mechanists.

BIBLIOGRAPHY

I. ORIGINAL WORKS. Trouton's published articles include "On Molecular Latent Heat," in *Philosophical Magazine*, **18** (1884), 54–57; "Repetition of Hertz's Experiments and Determination of the Direction of the Vibration of Light," in *Nature*, **39** (1889), 391–393; "Electrolysis Away From Electrodes," in *Electrician*, **43** (1899), 294; "Flow of Liquid Through Partitions," *ibid.*, 596–597; "Effect on Charged Condenser of Motion through the Ether," in *Transactions of the Royal Dublin Society*, **7** (1902), 379–384; "Forces Acting on a Charged Condenser Moving Through Space," with H. R. Noble, in *Proceedings of the Royal Society*, **72** (1903), 132–133; "Forces Acting on a Charged Condenser Moving Through Space," with H. R. Noble, in *Philosophical Transactions of the Royal Society*, **202A** (1904), 165–181; "Viscosity of Pitch-like Substances," with E. S. Andrews, in *Philosophy Magazine*, **7** (1904), 347–355; and in *Proceedings of the Physical Society*, **19** (1904), 47–56; "Coefficient of Viscous Traction and Its Relation to That of Viscosity," in *Proceedings of the Royal Society*, **77A** (1906), 426–440; "Vapour Pressure in Equilibrium With Substances Holding Varying Amounts of Moisture," *ibid.*, 292–314; "Leakage Currents on Glass Surfaces," with C. Searle, in *Philosophy Magazine*, **12** (1906), 336–347; "Condensation of Water Vapour on Glass Surfaces," in *Proceedings of the Royal Society*, **79A** (1907), 383–390; "Condensation of Moisture of Solid Surfaces," in *Chemical News*, **96** (1907), 92–93; "Rate of Recovery of Residual Charge in Electric Condensers," with S. Russ, in *Philosophical Magazine*, **13** (1907), 578–588; "Electrical Resistance in Moving Matter," in *Proceedings of the Royal Society*, **80A** (1908), 420–435; "Mechanism of the Semipermeable Membrane and a New Method of Determining Osmotic Pressure," *ibid.*, **86A** (1912), 149–154.

II. SECONDARY LITERATURE. An obituary may be found in *Nature*, **110** (1922), 490–491. For biographical sketches, see *Proceedings of the Royal Society*, **110A** (1926), iv; and E. Scott Barr, "Anniversaries in 1963," in *American Journal of Physics*, **31** (1963), 85–86.

STANLEY GOLDBERG

TROUVELOT, ÉTIENNE LÉOPOLD (*b*. Guyencourt, Aisne, France, 26 December 1827; *d*. Meudon, France, 22 April 1895), *natural history, astronomy.*

A keen observer and skillful artist, Trouvelot spent several years (1872–1874) working with the fifteen-inch refractor at Harvard Observatory. The drawings he made there and elsewhere are still widely known. Except for Rutherfurd's wet-plate photographs of the sun and moon, made in 1865, Trouvelot's drawings were considered the most accurate pictures of celestial objects available until the perfection of dry-plate photography.

Little is known about Trouvelot's life before he came to America in 1857; there is no indication that he was especially interested in astronomy during his early years. Interested in silkworm culture, he thought the European gypsy moth, *Porthetria dispar*, might serve the same purpose. In 1869 he imported to Medford, Massachusetts, some live egg clusters for experimentation. Unfortunately, a few of the moths escaped, and after a decade began to proliferate alarmingly. This was the origin of the defoliation of trees in the northeastern United States.

A member of the Boston Natural History Society, Trouvelot presented papers on a variety of topics—mostly concerned with zoology—at society meetings. His earliest major contribution to astronomy, published in 1875 in *Silliman's Journal* (now the *American Journal of Science*), was a paper on sunspots. Some one thousand of his sunspot drawings were deposited at the Harvard College Observatory. In 1881 Trouvelot was elected to the American Academy of Arts and Sciences.

In 1882 Trouvelot returned to France to join the staff of the new observatory at Meudon. While at Meudon he was particularly successful in his observations of solar prominences. In 1883 he went to the Caroline Islands to observe the total eclipse of the sun; he searched without avail for a supposed intra-Mercurial planet to account for the anomaly in the motion of Mercury.

Trouvelot published some fifty astronomical papers covering a wide range of topics, the most important being on the sun and Venus. He presented his last paper, concerning the transit of Mercury, on 12 November 1894 at the French Academy.

BIBLIOGRAPHY

I. ORIGINAL WORKS. For reproductions of Trouvelot's astronomical drawings, see *The Trouvelot Astronomical Drawings Manual* (New York, 1882); also see *Annals of Harvard College Observatory*, VIII, pt. 2 (1876), containing engravings prepared under the direction of Joseph Winlock. For references to Trouvelot's published astronomical papers, see Poggendorff, III, 1368; IV, 1526.

II. SECONDARY LITERATURE. Obituaries are contained in *Nature*, **52** (1895), 11; and *Observatory*, **18** (1895), 245–246. For mentions of Trouvelot's work, see Edward H. Forbush and Charles H. Fernald, "The Gypsy Moth," in *Report. Massachusetts Department of Agriculture* (1896); and *Annals of Harvard College Observatory*, **8**, pt. 1 (1876), 53, 55, 64.

E. DORRIT HOFFLEIT

TROWBRIDGE, JOHN (*b*. Boston, Massachusetts, 5 August 1843; *d*. Cambridge, Massachusetts, 18 February 1923), *physics*.

Trowbridge was a pioneer in the movement that established serious scientific research in America in the latter decades of the 19th century. The son of a prominent New England family, John Trowbridge studied at the Boston Latin School and graduated in 1865 with highest honors from the Lawrence Scientific School of Harvard University. After five years of teaching, he became professor of physics at Harvard (1870), serving in this capacity for forty years until his retirement in 1910.

Trowbridge was a strong advocate of laboratory practice as an integral part of scientific education. To this end he formally urged, as early as 1877–1878, the endowment of a "building devoted to physical investigation," with a staff dedicated to scientific research. He pointed out that while "there are no precedents for the endowment of a Physical Laboratory in connection with an American University, there is the greater honor in becoming the leader." He then designed and carried out the construction at Harvard of the Jefferson Physical Laboratory. He served as titular head upon its completion in 1884 and as director from 1888 until his retirement.

Trowbridge's main line of research was concerned with electrical phenomena. He devised the cosine galvanometer (1871) to measure strong electrical currents. With W. C. Sabine in 1890 he investigated high-frequency electrical oscillations using a revolving mirror. As early as 1890 Trowbridge supported the view that the carriers of electricity in wires were something other than atoms. By 1894 he investigated the magnetic effect of high-frequency oscillations and was one of the many pioneers of remote signaling. In 1895 he investigated with Duane the velocity of propagation of electrical waves. He undertook studies of the discharge of electricity through gases and, from 1896, examined both the production and effect of Röntgen radiation. In 1897 he studied with Theodore W. Richards the spectrum of argon and other gases. Aware of the need for a constant source of

high voltage, he developed, also in 1897, a storage battery of 10,000 cells. In addition to his scientific work he was the associate editor of the *American Journal of Science* from 1880 to 1920.

BIBLIOGRAPHY

I. ORIGINAL WORKS. Trowbridge published over one hundred original papers and several books dealing with scientific subjects. His most important book is *What is Electricity?* (London, 1897). A partial bibliography is included in Edwin H. Hall, "John Trowbridge: 1843–1923," in *Biographical Memoirs. National Academy of Sciences*, **14** (1930), 185–204, which also includes a discussion of some of the papers. This list is supplemented by the *Royal Society Catalogue of Scientific Papers*, XIX, 214–215.

Trowbridge wrote "Recent Advance in Physical Science," in *International Monthly*, **1** (1900), 123–132; and "Progress of Electricity From 1800 to 1900," in *The Nineteenth Century: A Review of Progress* (New York–London), 417–427. His "The Endowment of the Physical Laboratory at Harvard College" (Cambridge, Mass., *ca*. 1877), in the Harvard University Archives, HUF 693.77.24, includes a bibliography of the published research under the direction of Trowbridge between 1871 and 1877 in support of his proposal. He also described the endowment and construction of the laboratory in "The Jefferson Physical Laboratory," in *Science*, **5** (1885), 229–231.

Trowbridge's correspondence is in the Harvard College Library and in the Harvard University Archives.

II. SECONDARY LITERATURE. Edwin H. Hall contributed the article on Trowbridge for the *Dictionary of American Biography*. Theodore Lyman wrote the biographical article "John Trowbridge 1843–1923," in *Proceedings of the American Academy of Arts and Sciences*, **60** (1925), 651–654. Further biographical literature is cited in Max Armin, ed., *Internationale Personalbibliographie*, II, 687. The work of Trowbridge on remote signaling is considered by E. Hawks in *Pioneers of Wireless* (London, 1927), 121–128.

THADDEUS J. TRENN

TRULLI, GIOVANNI (*b*. Veroli, Frosinone province, Italy, 1598; *d*. Rome, Italy, 27 December 1661), *medicine*.

The years of Trulli's youth are rather obscure. We only know that he went to France for training in surgery, particularly lithotomy. In 1636 he settled in residence in Rome as surgeon to Cardinal Francesco Barberini, nephew of Pope Urban VIII, and at the University of Rome as special professor of surgery. He was relieved of this post after the death of Urban VIII, whose corpse he dissected on 29 July 1644, finding cardiac ossification (left ventricle), as well as gallstones and kidney stones. He was also surgeon at the Santo Spirito Hospital in Rome.

Trulli probably played a role in the contacts between Francesco Barberini and William Harvey, who was in Rome during September and October 1636. In the winter of 1636–1637, he formed a friendship with the German physician P. M. Schlegel, who gave public anatomical demonstrations in Rome to illustrate the doctrine of circulation of the blood. A firm supporter of this doctrine, Trulli was enthusiastic in his efforts to disseminate it. His opinion is known to us rather by indirect evidence and by his correspondence with M. A. Severino than by writings specifically devoted to the problem of circulation.

Toward the end of 1637 Galileo had become completely blind. On 23 January 1638 P. B. Borghi sent him advice from Rome, praising the surgeon who had given it to him. Galileo then sent a report to Rome on his vision (a document now lost), on the basis of which Trulli was able to provide a full consultation. Forwarded to Galileo by Borghi on 20 February 1638, this consultation constitutes the most important medical document on Galileo's blindness.

BIBLIOGRAPHY

I. Original Works. Trulli's consultation on Galileo's blindness is in *Le Opere di Galileo Galilei*, Edizione Nazionale, XIX, 552–554. His letter "De serie venarum" is in M. A. Severino, *Seilophlebotome castigata, sive de venae salvatellae usu et abusu* (Hanau, 1654), 150–153.

II. Secondary Literature. See Luigi Belloni, "La dottrina della circolazione del sangue e la scuola Galileiana 1636–61," in *Gesnerus*, **28** (1971), 7–34; and Felice Grondona, "In tema di etiogenesi della cecità di Galileo," in *Atti del Symposium internazionale di storia, metodologia, logica e filosofia della scienza "Galileo nella storia e nella filosofia della scienza" (Firenze–Pisa, 14–16 settembre 1964)* (Florence, 1967), 141–154.

Luigi Belloni

TRUMPLER, ROBERT JULIUS (*b*. Zurich, Switzerland, 2 October 1886; *d*. Oakland, California, 10 September 1956), *astronomy*.

The third of ten children born to a Swiss industrialist, Wilhelm Ernst Trümpler, and his wife,

Luise Hurter, Trumpler lived and studied in Zurich until age twenty-one. This period included two years at the University of Zurich, which he left in 1908 for the University of Göttingen; two years later he received his Ph.D. with a dissertation written under Leopold Ambronn.

Following a postdoctoral year at Göttingen, Trumpler served four years in the Swiss Geodetic Survey. He determined latitudes and longitudes, but he also became interested in the way stars in the Pleiades cluster move together across the sky. Such annual proper motions also interested Frank Schlesinger, then director of the Allegheny Observatory near Pittsburgh. He met Trumpler in 1913 at a meeting of the German Astronomical Society and invited him to come to Allegheny. Trumpler arrived in 1915 and began making comparative studies of galactic star clusters—so named because they are located in the disk of our galaxy. In August 1916 Trumpler married Augusta De La Harpe; three daughters and two sons were born to them.

At the invitation of W. W. Campbell, Trumpler went to the Lick Observatory in 1919. He joined the staff in 1920 and rose by 1929 to the post of astronomer. In 1938 he was named professor of astronomy on the Berkeley campus of the parent organization, the University of California, a position he retained until his retirement in 1951.

At Lick, Campbell chose Trumpler to assist him, in 1922, in a test of the general theory of relativity. The test involved an expedition to Wallal, on the northwest coast of Australia, to photograph stars in the sky near the totally eclipsed sun, for comparison with their positions as photographed at night four months earlier in Tahiti. The data, after suitable statistical treatment, showed an outward deflection at the edge of the sun of $1.75 \pm 0.09''$ (compared to Einstein's prediction of $1.745''$), a result considerably more accurate than that obtained by Eddington three years earlier.

Trumpler used the thirty-six-inch Lick refractor to study Mars during the favorable opposition of 1924. To his surprise, he concluded that the long dark markings, named canals by Schiaparelli, were real—but neither as straight nor as sharp and narrow as Lowell believed them to be. Trumpler's feeling that a "canal" such as Coprates might be a volcanic fault received some support in 1972 from close-up photographs taken by Mariner 9.

Trumpler's work on galactic star clusters proved to be his most significant contribution. In 1925 he published evidence that the mix of stars in galactic clusters differs markedly; some clusters contain massive blue stars but no yellow or red giants, while in others the opposite is true. In the hands of later workers, such as Baade and Sandage, these findings were developed into the currently accepted picture of how individual stars evolve with time. And in 1930, in a paper including data on 334 galactic clusters, Trumpler showed that distances to galactic clusters were being overestimated because interstellar material, previously thought to be nonexistent, was dimming the starlight by an average of 0.67 magnitudes for every kiloparsec of distance. This discovery brought distances measured in the galactic disk into agreement with those found by Shapley above and below the disk, and showed why estimates of galactic size, as made for instance by Kapteyn, were too small.

Trumpler was elected to the National Academy of Sciences in 1932. The Astronomical Society of the Pacific elected him president in 1932 and again in 1939 and has established an award in his memory, given annually to a promising postdoctoral astronomer.

BIBLIOGRAPHY

I. ORIGINAL WORKS. Trumpler's dissertation was "Eine Methode zur photographischen Bestimmung von Meridian-durchgängen." His work confirming the general theory of relativity appeared in two papers (both written with W. W. Campbell): "Observations on the Deflection of Light in Passing Through the Sun's Gravitational Field, Made During the Total Solar Eclipse of September 21, 1922," in *Lick Observatory Bulletin*, **11** (1923), 41–54; and "Observations Made With a Pair of Five-foot Cameras on the Light Deflections in the Sun's Gravitational Field at the Total Solar Eclipse of September 21, 1922," *ibid.*, **13** (1926), 130–160.

Trumpler's study of Mars, including both photographs and drawings, can be found in "Observations of Mars at the Opposition of 1924," *ibid.*, **13** (1926), 19–45.

Trumpler's first paper on galactic star clusters, "Die relativen Eigenbewegungen der Plejadensterne," is in *Astronomische Nachrichten*, **200** (1915), cols. 217–230. Another early contribution, "Comparison and Classification of Star Clusters," is in *Publications of the Allegheny Observatory, University of Pittsburgh*, **6** (1922), 45–74. His system for classifying galactic clusters on the basis of the spectra of their constituent stars appears in "Spectral Types in Open Clusters," in *Publications of the Astronomical Society of the Pacific*, **37** (1925), 307–318. His discovery of the interstellar absorption of light, including the selective way it operates, is described in "Preliminary Results on the Distances, Dimensions, and Space Distribution of Open Clusters," in *Lick Observatory Bulletin*, **14** (1930), 154–188. A summary of what galactic clusters can—and cannot—reveal about intraga-

lactic distances and galactic structure is contained in a paper Trumpler read at the dedication of the McDonald Observatory in 1939, published as "Galactic Star Clusters," in *Astrophysical Journal*, **91** (1940), 186–201.

Trumpler's book, *Statistical Astronomy*, written with Harold F. Weaver (Berkeley, 1953; repr., 1962), is the distillation of a graduate course he taught for over fifteen years. No complete list of Trumpler's publications has been published. Besides the above book, he wrote nine summarizing articles and approximately sixty-five research reports.

II. SECONDARY LITERATURE. An obituary notice on Trumpler, written by Harold and Paul Weaver, appeared in *Publications of the Astronomical Society of the Pacific*, **69** (1957), 304–307, with portrait and facs. signature.

SALLY H. DIEKE

TSCHERMAK, GUSTAV (*b*. Littau [now Litove], near Olomouc, Czechoslovakia, 19 April 1836; *d*. Vienna, Austria, 4 May 1927), *petrography, mineralogy*.

Tschermak grew up in the small Moravian town in which his grandfather had been a teacher and his father, Ignaz Czermak, was a tax collector. Despite the spelling of their name, the family considered themselves German. Tschermak began his secondary studies with a private tutor, then in 1850 entered Olomouc Gymnasium. He found the German-language instruction there to be inadequate, and this, together with his reaction to the rising tide of Czech national consciousness that followed the revolution of 1848 in Bohemia and Moravia, intensified his own feeling of Germanness and led him to found an anti-Slavic German student union. At the same time, he Germanized the spelling of his name. He distinguished himself in science during these years, and also founded a student natural history club. He was encouraged in these interests by one of his teachers, a Dr. Schwippel, and by the astronomer Julius Schmidt, who was then working in the private observatory in Olomouc.

In 1856 Tschermak enrolled in the Faculty of Philosophy of the University of Vienna. He began to study chemistry with Joseph Redtenbacher and learned the techniques of morphological and optical crystallography from Wilhelm Joseph Grailich. Although he attended no mineralogy lectures, he frequently visited the excellent imperial mineral collection. His first petrological work, "Das Trachytgebirge bei Banow," was published in 1858, while he was still a student. In 1860 Tschermak passed his teacher's examinations and was appointed assistant by the mineralogy professor Franz Xaver Zippe; he received the doctorate from the University of Tübingen later in the same year, and in 1861 qualified as *Privatdozent* in chemistry and mineralogy at the University of Vienna. In 1862 he became second assistant curator of the imperial mineralogical collection, and a few years later, first assistant curator.

During the 1860's Tschermak began the series of petrographical researches that, with his later work on meteorites, were to bring him an international reputation. He investigated the paragenesis of minerals in several granites, the quartz content in plagioclase, and the role of olivine in various rocks. He also contributed to the newly emerging methodology of microscopic investigation of rocks by means of using pleochroism to distinguish minerals of the augite, amphibole, and biotite groups. Dissatisfied with current knowledge about the most important rock-forming minerals, he set out to ascertain their crystal forms, their physical properties, and their compositional variations. He was thereby able to present the relationships between these mineral groups and to establish the prerequisites for an exact systematics, to which his chemical analysis of minerals, conducted with his friend Ernst Ludwig, was of fundamental importance.

Tschermak's most significant contribution in this direction lay in his work on feldspar. He realized that the many varieties of this mineral that had previously been distinguished could be derived from three compounds (which also occur in nature in almost pure form)—potash feldspar, albite, and anorthite. From this he was able to demonstrate that the various calcium-sodium feldspars form a homogeneous isomorphous series from pure calcium to pure sodium feldspar, of which the physical properties are a function of the proportion of the end members, that is, albite and anorthite.

Tschermak published his feldspar theory in *Die Feldspatgruppe* (1864), a work by which he, after a long dispute, firmly established his point of view. He made this theory the basis for his subsequent research, investigating almost all the important rock-forming silicates to confirm his idea that the great variety of chemical composition demonstrated in this group may be explained by the isomorphic mixture of simple compounds, from which changes in physical properties emerge naturally and in obedience to a law. A further petrographical book, *Die Porphyrgesteine Österreichs aus der mittleren geologischen Epoche*, embodying his previous research and the results of extensive investigatory travels, won a prize from the Vienna

Academy of Sciences in 1867 and was published as a book two years later.

In spring 1868 Tschermak was named associate professor of petrography at the University of Vienna, and in the autumn of the same year he was made director of the imperial mineral collection. He carried on an active research program, which attracted a number of young scientists, and, in order to make their results more widely known, founded the *Mineralogische Mitteilungen*, of which the first volume appeared in 1871. This periodical soon attracted foreign contributors; its first numbers were published as supplements to the *Jahrbuch der K. K. geologischen Reichsanstalt*, but after 1878 it was issued independently as *Tschermaks mineralogische und petrographische Mitteilungen*.

Tschermak began his work on meteorites in 1870, investigating the mineral content and inner structure of specimens from the imperial collection. He presented a theory of the origin of meteorites whereby these objects were cast off from small celestial bodies by volcanic activity—or, more precisely, by explosions of gases. In 1883 he published *Die mikroskopische Beschaffenheit der Meteoriten*, which became a standard work on the subject.

During this period Tschermak's academic career also advanced. In 1873 he was made full professor of mineralogy and petrography at the university (while retaining his curatorial post); in 1876 he received an offer, which he declined, from the University of Göttingen; and in 1877 he gave up his directorship of the imperial collection to devote all of his time to his work at the university where, the following year, a mineralogy and petrology institute was put at his disposal. He was elected dean of the Faculty of Philosophy in 1883 and rector of the university ten years later. He also continued to do research on silicates and meteorites, supplementing it with other petrological and mineralogical works, until his retirement in 1906. His *Lehrbuch der Mineralogie* was published in 1883, and went through a number of editions, while in 1907, after he had left the university, he was able to demonstrate that certain periodic meteor showers are characterized by petrographical conformity.

Tschermak's works brought him many honors. He became a member of the Vienna Academy of Sciences in 1875, was awarded the title "Hofrat" in 1886, and, on his retirement in 1906, was ennobled (subsequently styling himself "Tschermak von Seysenegg"). He was one of the founders of the Austrian Mineralogical Society and was elected its honorary president in 1910, on the occasion of the fiftieth anniversary of his doctorate. He was either a member or an honorary member of almost every important scientific society and natural history association. Of the four children of his two marriages, one daughter and two sons became distinguished scientists.

BIBLIOGRAPHY

I. ORIGINAL WORKS. Tschermak's writings include "Das Trachytgebirge bei Banow," in *Jahrbuch der Kaiserlichen Königlichen geologischen Reichsanstalt,* **9** (1858), 63–79; *Ein Beitrag zur Bildungsgeschichte der Mandelsteine* (Vienna, 1863); *Chemisch-mineralogische Studien. I, Die Feldspatgruppe* (Vienna, 1864); *Beobachtungen über die Verbreitung des Olivins in den Felsarten* (Vienna, 1867); *Quarzführende Plagioklasgesteine* (Vienna, 1867); *Die Porphyrgesteine Österreichs aus der mittleren geologischen Epoche* (Vienna, 1869); *Beitrag zur Kenntnis der Salzlager* (Vienna, 1871); *Ein Meteoreisen aus der Wüste Atacama* (Vienna, 1871); *Die Bildung der Meteoriten und der Vulkanismus* (Vienna, 1875) ; *Die Glimmergruppe* (Vienna, 1877); *Die mikroskopische Beschaffenheit der Meteoriten* (Vienna, 1883); *Die Skapolithreihe* (Vienna, 1883); and *Lehrbuch der Mineralogie* (Vienna, 1884).

In addition to memoirs in *Mineralogische und petrographische Mitteilungen,* Tschermak published articles in *Justus Liebigs Annalen der Chemie, Neues Jahrbuch für Mineralogie, Geologie und Paläontologie,* Poggendorff's *Annalen der Physik und Chemie, Almanach der Akademie der Wissenschaften in Wien, Denkschriften der Akademie der Wissenschaften* (Vienna), and *Sitzungsberichte der Akademie der Wissenschaften in Wien.*

II. SECONDARY LITERATURE. The most extensive obituary is by Tschermak's student and successor as professor, Friedrich Becke, in *Mineralogische und petrographische Mitteilungen,* **39** (1928), i–x. Other obituaries are by E. S. Dana, in *American Journal of Science,* 5th ser., **14** (1927), also in *American Mineralogist,* **12** (1927); and by J. W. Evans, in *Nature,* **120** (1927), 195–196. *Mineralogische und petrographische Mitteilungen,* **25** (1906), dedicated to Tschermak on his retirement, contains a signed photographic portrait.

HANS BAUMGÄRTEL

TSCHERMAK VON SEYSENEGG, ERICH (*b.* Vienna, Austria, 12 November 1871; *d.* Vienna, 11 October 1962), *botany, genetics.*

Tschermak came from a family of scholars. His father, Gustav Tschermak, was director of the Imperial Mineralogical Museum and, from 1873, professor of mineralogy and petrography at the University of Vienna. He was created a member of the hereditary nobility with the title "von Seysenegg." His mother, Hermine Fenzl, was a daughter of the botanist Eduard Fenzl, director of the Botanical Institute and Garden of the University of Vienna. Tschermak's older brother Armin, who married a daughter of the geologist Albrecht Penck, became professor of physiology at Ferdinand University in Prague and, after 1945, at the University in Regensburg for a few years. His sister Silvia was a mineralogist.

With his brother, Tschermak attended the humanistic Gymnasium at the Kremsmünster monastery (in Upper Austria). In 1891 he enrolled simultaneously at the University of Vienna and at the Hochschule für Bodenkultur at Vienna. After two semesters he volunteered for one year's work on a nobleman's estate near Freiberg, Saxony, in order to learn the basics of agricultural practice. He subsequently continued his studies at the University of Halle, where he took the agricultural examination for the agricultural diploma in 1895 and the following year obtained the Ph.D. with a dissertation in botany.

Tschermak, a Roman Catholic, married twice but had no children. In his autobiography he writes that he was a weak and sickly child; nevertheless, he lived to be nearly ninety-one. Although he suffered greatly in his last years from arthritis in his hands, he never lost his zest for work, his good humor, his kindness, or his enjoyment of social life.

Tschermak held honorary doctorates from the universities of Vienna, Giessen, and Ghent as well as from the agricultural universities of Vienna, Berlin, and Brno. He was a member of the Institut de France, of the Leopoldina Carolina in Halle and of the Max Planck Society, as well as numerous scientific societies and associations. He was awarded the Cothenius Medal and the Goethe Medal.

After completing his studies at Halle, Tschermak was employed at the agricultural stations at Stendal and Quedlinburg, Germany. In 1898, in Ghent, he studied breeding of vegetables and flowers. Stimulated by Darwin's *The Effects of Cross and Self Fertilization in the Vegetable Kingdom* (1876), Tschermak began hybridization experiments with various types of peas at the botanical garden in Ghent. The results of this research led to his rediscovery of Mendel's laws of heredity, which had been disregarded until then and had been rediscovered independently and simultaneously by Hugo de Vries in Amsterdam and by

Carl Correns in Leipzig. The publications of these three investigators appeared nearly simultaneously in 1900. Tschermak's papers appeared in *Zeitschrift für das landwirtschaftliche Versuchswesen in Österreich* and in summary form in *Berichte der Deutschen botanischen Gesellschaft.*

Tschermak's greatest service was his exclusive, immediate recognition of the importance of Mendel's laws of heredity and his application of these laws in his own breeding experiments. In 1900 Tschermak became an academic lecturer at the Hochschule für Bodenkultur, where he taught theory of plant production, commercial cultivation of plants, and production of vegetables in fields. In 1902 he became assistant to the professor of the theory of plant breeding; in 1906 he was appointed extraordinary professor; and in 1909 he was made full professor. In addition to teaching, Tschermak was for several years director of the Royal Institute for Plant Breeding of the Prince of Liechtenstein (later the Mendel Institute) in Eisgrub, Moravia.

Tschermak traveled extensively to acquire new experience in his field. He made four visits to Sweden, where he served as adviser on the expansion of the Swedish Seed Association at Svalöf. He had a warm relationship with the director of this institute, Nilsson-Ehle, and with his successor. In 1909 Tschermak traveled to the United States with his friend Kurt von Rümker, primarily to meet Luther Burbank and to study his methods. He revisited the United States the following year.

While he was at the Hochschule für Bodenkultur, Tschermak made many new crosses of cultivated plants that increased their diversity and value. Since he had only limited experimental facilities available, he frequently turned over the testing and propagation of his new plants to capable agricultural businesses and to interested farmers, many of whom had established test plots at his suggestion. Of special practical importance were Tschermak's new types of rye, wheat, barley, oats, and legumes. His breeding of short-shooted edible types of pumpkins with soft-shelled, oil-rich seeds (later known as Tschermak's pumpkin) made possible a broader use. Also of great value were his new varieties of flowers, such as the gillyflower (*Matthiola*), and many new types of primroses.

Tschermak's more than 100 publications are impressive because of the diversity and originality of his investigations, observations, and theories. His most important achievement, the rediscovery of Mendel's laws, was closely related to his observations of the xenia phenomenon of various plants: in certain instances the seeds in the female plant show effects that are transmitted through the pollen of the male plant. Tschermak investigated the xenia phenomenon in a group of legumes as well as in various types of corn and in the gillyflower. The well-known xenia of the corncob, which manifests itself in various colors and types of surfaces of the kernels, has been extensively investigated by Correns.

Tschermak also was interested in the stimulation effects of alien pollen. He interpreted his findings on fertilization by irritation to mean that nonfertilizing pollen and even dehydrating agents can cause a physiological stimulation of the mature egg cell, and initiate parthenogenetic development.

Tschermak's discovery and elucidation of a cryptomeric heredity among the gillyflowers is a classic work in theoretical genetics. Here, white-flowered hybrids from white-flowered parents can produce "nova" plants bearing colored flowers in the F_2 generation, if each of the parents possesses a dominant and a recessive gene for white flowers.

Tschermak's investigations of intergeneric hybridization led to basic discoveries about hybridization. He suspected that various of his fertile intergeneric hybrids, such as that of wheat and rye—the fertile hybrid of *Aegilops ovata* ($2n = 28$) and *Triticum dicoccoides* ($2n = 28$)—had been produced by the fertilization of unreduced F_1 gametes. For this hybrid, *Aegilotriticum* ($2n = 56$), the additive hybrid number of chromosomes could be demonstrated by cytological examination. This was the first artificially produced and cytologically demonstrated additive intergeneric hybrid of the Gramineae. Today the polyploidization of sterile F_1 hybrids is one of the techniques for the experimental investigation of relationships, as well as for the breeding of artificial, synthetic types of cultivated plants.

Tschermak demonstrated his diverse abilities in the breeding of agricultural and garden plants, for which he used his highly developed technique of hybridization. He was concerned primarily with such difficult problems as combining early ripening with high yield, which he achieved.

The Tschermak-grafted Marchfeld rye, originally bred by selection of the grain and of the offspring without interbreeding with foreign stock, is the only grain variety that has not yet been surpassed in yield (Marchfeld, near Vienna) by any other type, either foreign or domestic. For the self-pollinating types of grain such as wheat, barley, and oats, on the other hand, the new varieties obtained by continuous hybridization yielded 25–50 percent more than the older ones.

Today Tschermak's fundamental idea, the systematic combination of genes, and the method derived from Mendel's "laws of segregation" for the investigation of the offspring of single individuals isolated from hybrid populations, have become a matter of routine in the breeding of cultivated plants.

BIBLIOGRAPHY

A detailed account of Tschermak's life and a complete bibliography of his works are in his autobiography, *Erich von Tschermak-Seysenegg, Leben und Wirken* (Berlin–Hamburg, 1958).

His works include "Über künstliche Kreuzung von *Pisum sativum*," in *Zeitschrift für das landwirtschaftliche Versuchswesen in Österreich*, **3** (1900), 465–555, summarized in *Berichte der Deutschen botanischen Gesellschaft*, **18** (1900), 232–239; "Über die Züchtung neuer Getreiderassen mittels künstlicher Kreuzung," in *Zeitschrift für das landwirtschaftliche Versuchswesen in Österreich*, **4** (1901), 1029–1060, and **9** (1906), 699–743; "Über den Einfluss der Bestäubung auf die Ausbildung der Fruchthülle," in *Berichte der Deutschen botanischen Gesellschaft*, **20** (1902), 7–16; "Über Züchtung landwirtschaftlich und gärtnerisch wichtiger Hülsenfrüchte," *Arbeiten der Deutschen Landwirtschaftsgesellschaft für Österreich*, no. 4 (1920); "Über fruchtbare Aegilops-Weizenbastarde," in *Berichte der Deutschen botanischen Gesellschaft*, **44** (1926), 110–132, written with H. Bleier; "Zur zytologischen Auffassung meiner Aegilotricum-Bastarde und der Artbastarde überhaupt. Theorie der Chromosomenaddition oder Kernchimärie," *ibid.*, **47** (1929), 253–261; "Bemerkungen über echte und falsche Grössen-Xenien," in *Zeitschrift für Pflanzenzüchtung*, **17** (1932), 447–450; "Über einige Blütenanomalien bei Primeln und ihre Vererbungsweise," in *Biologia generalis*, **8** (1932), 337–350; "Der schalenlose Kürbis als Ölfrucht," *Deutsche Landwirtschaftliche Presse*, **61**, no. 3 (1934); and "Reizfruchtung (Samenbildung ohne Befruchtung)," in *Biologia generalis*, **19** (1949), 3–50.

Richard Biebl

TSCHIRNHAUS, EHRENFRIED WALTHER (*b.* Kieslingswalde, near Görlitz, Germany, 10 April 1651; *d.* Dresden, Germany, 11 October 1708), *mathematics, physics, philosophy.*

Tschirnhaus was the youngest son of Christoph von Tschirnhaus, a landowner, and Elisabeth Eleonore Freiin Achyll von Stirling, who belonged to a collateral branch of the mathematically gifted Stirling family. His mother died when he was six, but he was brought up by a loving stepmother. After receiving an excellent education from private tutors, Tschirnhaus entered the senior class of the Görlitz Gymnasium in 1666. In the autumn of 1668 he enrolled at the University of Leiden to study philosophy, mathematics, and medicine. He was deeply impressed by the tolerant atmosphere there, as well as by the fiery philosopher Arnold Geulincx, an occasionalist, and the distinguished physician F. de la Boë (Sylvius), who taught Harvey's theory of the circulation of the blood. The most profound influence on him in these years, however, was that of Descartes's philosophy and mathematics, to which he was introduced in private instruction by Pieter van Schooten.

At the beginning of the war between Holland and France in 1672, Tschirnhaus joined the student volunteer corps but did not see action. Following a short visit to Kieslingswalde in 1674, he returned to Leiden and was introduced by his school friend Pieter van Gent to Spinoza, whose teachings he immediately adopted. With a letter of recommendation from Spinoza, he went to London in May 1675 to see Henry Oldenburg. Tschirnhaus had become an excellent algebraist and was able to make a persuasive presentation of his methods for solving equations. He visited John Wallis at Oxford and held discussions with John Collins, to whom he showed examples of his methods. On closer examination, however, they proved to be special cases of a previously known solution.

Bearing recommendations from Oldenburg addressed to Huygens and Leibniz, Tschirnhaus moved to Paris in the fall of 1675. He did not then know French, and when engaged to teach mathematics to one of Colbert's sons, did so in Latin. In an animated exchange with Leibniz, Tschirnhaus reported in general terms on his own methods but only half listened to what Leibniz told him concerning his recent creation of a symbolism for infinitesimal processes. In fact, Tschirnhaus never did grasp the significance of Leibniz' disclosure, and throughout his life he considered the infinitesimal symbolism to be of limited applicability.

Leibniz introduced Tschirnhaus to Clerselier, who had custody of Descartes's papers and allowed them to look through unpublished manuscripts. The two also had an opportunity to examine the posthumous papers of Pascal and Roberval. Tschirnhaus reported on the progress of his studies at Paris in a number of interesting letters to Pieter van Gent, Spinoza, and the latter's friend G. H. Schuller. In the summer of 1676 he corresponded with Oldenburg concerning Descartes's mathematical methods. Tschirnhaus considered them unsurpassable, but Collins had expressed considerable skepticism about them. Consequently, the reports in which Oldenburg and Newton communicated the results obtained by expansions of series were addressed jointly to Leibniz and Tschirnhaus. In his reply of 1 September, Tschirnhaus judged these results somewhat disparagingly; Collins responded with a strong rebuttal, as did Newton in a second letter to Leibniz and Tschirnhaus (3 November 1676).

Also in 1676 Tschirnhaus accompanied Count Nimpsch of Silesia on a trip to southern France and Italy. Everywhere he went, Tschirnhaus sought contact with leading scientists, collected observations, and reported interesting discoveries to Leibniz. Among the matters he communicated to Leibniz was an algorithmic method of reduction that he wrongly believed could be applied to equations of any higher degree. (This method was published in *Acta eruditorum* in 1683.) He also reported on a supposedly new method of quadrature that was in fact merely the result of recasting a procedure devised by Gregory of Saint-Vincent in 1647 in a form better suited for computation. (The improvement had been effected by the use of indivisibles of zero width.) During his return trip in 1679, Tschirnhaus stopped at Paris, at The Hague (where he saw Huygens), and at Hannover (where he visited Leibniz).

While continuing his mathematical research Tschirnhaus constructed effective circular and parabolic mirrors, with which he obtained high temperatures by focusing sunlight. He also made burning glasses, though not without flaws. During a trip to Paris in the summer of 1682, he became a member of the Académie des Sciences. He did not, however, receive the hoped-for royal pension that would have enabled him to pursue his scientific work free from financial concern. After returning from Paris, Tschirnhaus married Elisabeth Eleonore von Lest, who took over most of the details of managing the estate his father had left him, thus permitting him to devote his time entirely to study. Among his achievements was the rediscovery of the process for making hard-paste porcelain. J. F. Böttger, who is usually given the credit, was a skilled craftsman; but all his work was done under Tschirnhaus' supervision.

Tschirnhaus exhausted his mathematical talents in searching for algorithms. Lacking insight into the more profound relations among mathematical propositions, he was all too ready to assert the existence of general relationships on the basis of particular results that he obtained. Further, he was unwilling to accept suggestions directly from other mathematicians, although he would later adopt them as his own inventions and publish them as such. This tactic led to bitter controversies with Leibniz, Huygens, La Hire, and Jakob I and Johann I Bernoulli; and it ultimately cost him his scientific reputation. Without going into details, we may mention two of these disputes. The first, with Leibniz, concerned the possibility of algebraic quadratures of algebraic curves (1682–1684). The second, with Fatio de Duillier (1687–1689), was provoked by Tschirnhaus' publication of an incorrect method of finding tangents to curves generated by the motion of a drawing pencil within a system of taut threads. The method appeared in a major work of considerable philosophical importance, *Medicina corporis et mentis* (1686–1687), which was influential in the early stages of the Enlightenment. Another work by Tschirnhaus, *Gründliche Anleitung zu den nützlichen Wissenschaften* (1700), was highly praised by Leibniz in 1701. Both books deeply impressed Leibniz' disciple Christian Wolff.

Tschirnhaus was essentially an autodidact. During his university years he lacked the guidance of a kind, experienced, yet strict teacher, who could have restrained his exuberant temperament, moderated his excessive enthusiasm for Descartes's ideas, and instilled in him a greater measure of self-criticism. Even so, Tschirnhaus' achievements—often accomplished with insufficient means—were far more significant than the average contribution made by university teachers of science during his lifetime. Indeed, even his errors proved to be important and fruitful stimuli for other scientists.

BIBLIOGRAPHY

I. ORIGINAL WORKS. The major portion of Tschirnhaus' unpublished papers is in the MS division of the library of the University of Wrocław and among the Leibniz MSS of the Niedersächsische Landesbibliothek, Hannover.

His books are *Medicina corporis et mentis*, 3 pts. in 2 vols. (Amsterdam, 1686–1687; 2nd ed., Leipzig, 1695), also translated into German (Frankfurt, 1688; 2nd ed., Lüneburg, 1705–1708) and recently retranslated into German by J. Haussleiter, in *Acta historica Leopoldina* (Leipzig, 1963), with biography, portrait, and detailed bibliography prepared by R. Zaunick; and *Gründliche Anleitung zu den nützlichen Wissenschaften* (n.p., 1700; 2nd ed., 1708; 3rd ed., 1712).

Tschirnhaus' mathematical papers and reviews appeared in *Journal des sçavans* (Amsterdam), no. 15 (8 June 1682), 210–213; in the following issues of *Acta eruditorum*: (1682), 364–365, 391–393; (1683), 122–124, 204–207, 433–437; (1686), 169–176; (1687), 524–527; (1690), 68–73, 169–172, 481–487, 561–

565; (1695), 322–323, 489–493; (1696), 519–524; (1697), 113, 220–223, 409–410; (1698), 259–261; and in *Mémoires de physique et de mathématique de l'Académie royale des sciences* for 1701 (1704), 291–293, and for 1702 (1704), 1–3.

His papers on the burning glass were published in the following issues of *Acta eruditorum*: (1687), 52–54; (1688), 206; (1691), 517–520; (1696), 345–347, 554; (1697), 414–419; (1699), 445–448; and in *Histoire de l'Académie royale des sciences* for 1699 (1702), 90–94, and for 1700 (1703), 131–134.

Some of his correspondence has been published in Huygens, *Oeuvres complètes*, VIII and IX (The Hague, 1899–1900); Spinoza, *Opera*, 3rd ed., III (The Hague, 1914); and in Leibniz, *Briefwechsel mit Mathematikern*, C. I. Gerhardt, ed. (Berlin, 1899; repr. Hildesheim, 1962). The entire Leibniz-Tschirnhaus correspondence will eventually be published in Leibniz, *Sämtliche Schriften und Briefe*, 3rd ser.

II. SECONDARY LITERATURE. See H. Weissenborn, *Lebensbeschreibung des E. W. v. Tschirnhaus . . . und Würdigung seiner Verdienste* (Eisenach, 1866); and the following, more recent, works of J. E. Hofmann: "Das *Opus geometricum* des Gregorius a S. Vincentio und seine Einwirkung auf Leibniz," in *Abhandlungen der Preussischen Akademie der Wissenschaften*, Math.-naturwiss. Kl. (1941), no. 13, 55–69; *Die Entwicklungsgeschichte der Leibnizschen Mathematik während des Aufenthaltes in Paris (1672–1676)* (Munich, 1949), enl. English ed., *Leibniz in Paris, 1672–1676* (London–New York, 1974); *Über Jakob Bernoullis Beiträge zur Infinitesimalmathematik* (Geneva, 1956); "Aus der Frühzeit der Infinitesimalmethoden: Auseinandersetzung um die algebraische Quadratur algebraischer Kurven in der zweiten Hälfte des 17. Jahrhunderts," in *Archive for History of Exact Sciences*, **2**, no. 4 (1965), 270–343; and "Drei Sätze von E. W. v. Tschirnhaus über Kreissehnen," in *Studia Leibnitiana*, **3** (1971), 99–115. See also E. Winter, *E. W. von Tschirnhaus und die Frühaufklärung in Mittel- und Osteuropa* (Berlin, 1960).

J. E. HOFMANN

TSERASKY (or CERASKY), VITOLD KARLO-VICH (*b.* Slutsk, Minsk guberniya, Russia, 9 May 1849; *d.* Meshcherskoe, near Podolsk, Moscow oblast, U.S.S.R., 29 May 1925), *astronomy*.

Tserasky's father was a secondary school geography teacher. The discovery of Donati's comet in 1858 awakened his interest in astronomy. In 1867 he entered Moscow University and while a second-year student worked at the observatory as part-time calculator. Tserasky received a gold medal for a student work on the motion of Mars. After graduating he became a supernumerary assistant at the observatory. In 1874 he took part in an arduous expedition to Kyakhta, on the Chinese border, to observe the transit of Venus.

After returning to Moscow, Tserasky began systematic photographic study of the sun, but in 1877 he became deeply involved in instrumental astrophotometry. Simultaneously with the Potsdam and Harvard observatories, he conducted pioneering work in precise stellar photometry. In 1878 he was designated astronomer-observer at the Moscow observatory. In 1883 he defended his master's dissertation on the determination of the brightness of white stars. The astrophotometer of Zöllner led him to invent an instrument (the Zöllner-Tserasky photometer) that became the subject of his doctoral dissertation (1887).

At the end of the 1870's Tserasky began teaching at the Higher School for Women, which were begun by a number of progressive professors—advocates of higher education for women, who did not have the right to study in universities during the tsarist period. From 1882 he was lecturer at the University of Moscow; in 1884 he became *Privatdozent*; and in 1889 he was elected professor of astronomy. His public lectures also were very successful.

In 1884 Tserasky married Lidia Petrovna Shelekhova, later known for her discoveries of more than 200 variable stars on the negatives of the Moscow Observatory. In 1890 Tserasky succeeded Bredikhin as director of the Moscow observatory, and from 1895–1903 he supervised the reconstruction of the observatory and the renovation of its equipment. In 1914 he was elected corresponding member of the St. Petersburg Academy of Sciences. After retiring in 1916 because of his health, he settled in Feodosiya, in the Crimea. In 1922 he moved to the home of his son, a physician, not far from Moscow, where he died three years later.

In addition to his numerous works in photometry, Tserasky made in 1895 the first experimental determination of the lower limit of the temperature of the sun (3,500°K.), by melting a number of refractory minerals at the focus of a concave mirror having a diameter and focal length both of one meter. (On the basis of these data Scheiner computed the temperature of the surface of the sun at 6,600°K., which approximates the correct value.) Following his discovery, at the end of the last century, of a few variable stars, Tserasky organized systematic astrophotographic studies using a wide-angled, short-focus astrograph (the "equatorial camera") built according to his design. From the resulting negatives L. P. Tseraskaya discovered more than 200 variable stars. In 1885 Tserasky discovered luminous (silver) clouds and with Belopolsky determined their altitude at 80 kilometers (actual value ~ 82 km.). Tserasky studied meteors and invented an original instrument for determining their angular velocity. In 1911 he published the results of his photometric comparison of the stellar magnitude of the sun with that of Venus and a number of bright stars; his value of the stellar magnitude of the sun (−26.50) has become an important weight in world summaries. To determine the degree of flattening of the sun's sphere Tserasky devised an original heliometric objective and, for detailed study of sunspots, a specially constructed eyepiece. In 1908 he constructed a device that used solar energy to set off an electric bell on his desk.

An unpublished photometric catalog of 466 circumpolar stars, found among Tserasky's papers, was edited by G. A. Manova and was included in a collection of his selected works (1953).

BIBLIOGRAPHY

I. Original Works. Tserasky's 92 published writings include *O prokhozhdenii Venery po disku Solntsa v 1874 g.* ("On the Transit of Venus Across the Disk of the Sun in 1874"; Moscow, 1875); "Ob opredelenii yarkosti belykh zvezd" ("On the Determination of the Brightness of White Stars"), in *Uchenye zapiski Moskovskogo universiteta*, Otd. fiz.-matem., no. 4 (1882), 105–176, his master's diss.; "Astronomichesky fotometr i ego prilozhenia" ("The Astronomical Photometer and Its Uses"), in *Matematichesky sbornik*, **13** (1886), 551–632, his doctoral thesis; "Sur les nuages lumineux," in *Annales de l'Observatoire astronomique de Moscou*, 2nd ser., **2**, bks. 1–2 (1890), 177–180; "Études photométriques sur l'amas stellaire χ Persei," *ibid.*, **3**, bk. 2 (1896), 1–24; "Sur la température du soleil," *ibid.*, 121–122, also in J. Scheiner, *Strahlung und Temperatur der Sonne* (Leipzig, 1899); "Ob opredelenii formy solnechnogo diska" ("On the Determination of the Form of the Solar Disk"), in *Izvestia Akademii nauk*, **11**, no. 2 (Sept. 1899), 59–60; "Études photométriques sur l'amas stellaire Coma Berenices," in *Annales de l'Observatoire astronomique de Moscou*, 2nd ser., **4** (1902), 87–120, and **6** (1917), 33–44; "Détermination photométrique de la grandeur stellaire du soleil," in *Astronomische Nachrichten*, **170** (1905), 135–138; "Sur une équation personnelle dans les observations photométriques," *ibid.*, **171** (1906), 135–136; *Sfericheskaya astronomia. Lektsii, chitannye v 1909–1910 gg.* ("Spherical Astronomy. Lectures Given in 1909–1910"; Moscow, 1910); "Détermination photométrique de la grandeur stellaire du soleil," in *Annales de l'Observatoire astronomique de Moscou*, 2nd ser., **5** (1911), 1–30; "Un oculaire pour l'étude détaillée des taches solaires," *ibid.*, 31–33; "Un objectif héliométrique pour la détermination de la forme du disque solaire," *ibid.*, 34–35; "Détermination des erreurs constantes des observations photométriques," *ibid.*, **6** (1917), 45–61; and *Izbrannye raboty po astronomii* ("Selected Works on Astronomy"; Moscow, 1953).

II. Secondary Literature. On Tserasky and his work, see S. Blazhko, "W. Ceraski," in *Astronomische Nachrichten*, **225** (1925), 111–112; "Nauchnye raboty professora V. K. Tseraskogo" ("The Scientific Works . . ."), in *Russky astronomichesky kalendar* for 1925, 128–134; and "Vitold Karlovich Tserasky. Zhizneopisanie" (". . . A Description of His Life"), in Tserasky's *Izbrannye raboty po astronomii* ("Selected Works on Astronomy," V. V. Podobed, ed., Moscow, 1953), 11–29; I. A. Kazansky's bibliography of Tserasky's works, *ibid.*, 46–52; Y. G. Perel, "K voprosu o mirovozzrenii V. K. Tseraskogo" ("Toward the Question of Tserasky's World Views"), in *Istoriko-astronomicheskie issledovaniya* (1955), no. 1, 323–334; and "Vitold Karlovich Tserasky," in *Vydayushchiesya russkie astronomy* ("Outstanding Russian Astronomers"; Moscow, 1951), 63–84; K. D. Pokrovsky, "V. K. Tserasky," in *Russky astronomichesky kalendar* for 1925, 115–127, published for his seventy-fifth birthday; B. A. Vorontsov-Velyaminov, "Nauchnaya deyatelnost V. K. Tseraskogo" ("The Scientific Activity of V. K. Tserasky"), in Tserasky's *Izbrannye raboty po astronomii*, 30–45; and F. Y. Zotov, "Vospominania o V. K. Tseraskom" ("Recollections. . ."), in *Istoriko-astronomicheskie issledovaniya* (1955), no. 1, 335–342.

P. G. Kulikovsky

TSIOLKOVSKY, KONSTANTIN EDUARDOVICH (*b*. Izhevsk, Ryazan guberniya, Russia, 17 September 1857; *d*. Kaluga, U.S.S.R., 19 September 1935), *mechanics, aeronautics, astronautics.*

Tsiolkovsky was the son of a forester. At the age of nine he became almost completely deaf following a serious illness. Unable to continue in school, he was obliged to study on his own, using his father's library. From the age of thirteen Tsiolkovsky began systematically to study the natural sciences. It was at this time that his inclination for invention became apparent.

In 1873, his father sent him to Moscow to continue his self-education. Studying on his own, Tsiolkovsky completed the entire secondary-school course and a considerable part of the university course.

After having passed the teaching examination in 1879 — without attending lectures — Tsiolkovsky was appointed in 1880 to the Borovsk district school, sixty miles southwest of Moscow, where he taught arithmetic and geometry. He devoted most of his free time to scientific investigations.

In the mid-1880's, Tsiolkovsky began research in aerostatics. He worked out a project for an all-metal dirigible with a corrugated metal shell, the volume of which could be varied in flight. Tsiolkovsky further developed his dirigible theory in "Aerostat metallichesky upravlyaemy" ("A Controlled Metal Dirigible," 1892).

In "K voprosu o letanii posredstvom krylev" ("On the Question of Winged Flight"), completed in 1890, Tsiolkovsky investigated the magnitude of forces acting upon a moving disk. In this work he made the first attempt to evaluate quantitatively the influence of the length of the disk on the magnitude of the aerodynamic forces. In 1891, part of the work was printed by the Society of Friends of Natural Science under the title "Davlenie zhidkosti na ravnomerno dvizhushchuyusya v ney ploskost" ("The Pressure of a Fluid on a Plane Moving Uniformly Through It"). It was Tsiolkovsky's first published work.

In 1892 Tsiolkovsky moved to Kaluga, where he continued to teach without interrupting his scientific research. In 1894 his work "Aeroplan ili ptitsepodobnaya (aviatsionnaya) letatelnaya mashina" ("The Aeroplane, or A Flying Birdlike Machine [Aircraft]") was published in *Nauka i zhizn*. In this work he proposed a plan for a plane having a metal frame (similar to contemporary aircraft)—a monoplane with a streamlined fuselage, freely supported wings, a thick profile with a rounded forward edge, a wheeled undercarriage, and an internal combustion engine. He also suggested using twin screw propellers rotating in opposite directions. He expounded the idea of using the gyroscope in aircraft as a simple automatic pilot.

While working on these projects Tsiolkovsky came to grips with the unavoidable necessity of obtaining precise data on the resistance of a medium. A series of experiments under natural conditions led him to test his models in an artificial airstream. In 1897 he constructed a wind tunnel, the first in Russia to be used in aviation.

Of greater significance are Tsiolkovsky's works on outer space. He became interested in questions of interplanetary travel at the age of sixteen. In "Svobodnoe prostranstvo" ("Free Space," 1883), he examined phenomena that occur in a medium in which the forces of gravity—for all practical purposes—are not active. This paper included the first formulation of the possibility of applying the prin-

ciple of reactive motion for flight in a vacuum, which led to a simple plan for a spaceship. Tsiolkovsky also considered several questions concerning the necessary conditions of life for plants and animals in space.

In 1896 Tsiolkovsky began to explore the possibility of interplanetary travel by means of rockets. In 1897 he formulated his now widely known formula establishing the analytical dependence between the velocity of a rocket at a given moment, the velocity of the expulsion of gas particles from the nozzle of the engine, the mass of the rocket, and the mass of the expended explosive material.

In "Issledovanie mirovykh prostranstv reaktivnymi priborami" ("A Study of Atmospheric Space Using Reactive Devices," 1903), Tsiolkovsky set forth his theory of the motion of rockets, established the possibility of space travel by means of rockets, and adduced the fundamental flight formulas.

Tsiolkovsky contributed to the recently established mechanics of bodies of changing mass. He evolved a theory of rocket flight taking into account the change of mass while in motion; he suggested the concept of gas-driven rudders for guiding a rocket in a vacuum; and he determined the coefficient of a rocket's practical operation.

From 1903 to 1917 Tsiolkovsky offered several plans for constructing rocket ships. He considered such questions as guiding a rocket in a vacuum, the use of a fuel component to cool the combustion chamber walls, and the application of refractory elements.

Tsiolkovsky's advanced ideas did not find acceptance. He was met with indifference and disbelief, and many considered this autodidact to be a rootless dreamer. Having received neither material nor moral support, Tsiolkovsky was left to his own resources. "It has been difficult for me," he wrote with bitterness, "to work alone for many years under unfavorable conditions and not even to see the possibility for hope or assistance."

The conditions of life and work for Tsiolkovsky changed radically after the October Revolution. In 1918 he became a member of the Academy, and in November 1921 he was allotted a personal pension. It became possible for him to devote himself completely to his scientific work.

During the 1920's Tsiolkovsky continued his investigations in aeronautics, and he elaborated his theory of multistage rockets. He also began working out his theory of the flight of jet airplanes, devoting a number of papers to this question.

In 1921 Tsiolkovsky conceived the idea of building a transport vehicle that would be carried on a cushion of air. This idea was further developed in "Soprotivlenie vozdukha i skory poezd" ("Air Resistance and the Express Train," 1927) and "Obshchie uslovia transporta" ("General Conditions for Transport," 1934).

In the mid-1920's, Tsiolkovsky's works on rocket engineering and space flight began to win international recognition. Hermann Oberth, the German rocket technologist, wrote to Tsiolkovsky in 1929: "You have ignited the flame, and we shall not permit it to be extinguished; we shall make every effort so that the greatest dream of mankind might be fulfilled."

Despite old age, Tsiolkovsky continued his scientific work. In "Dostizhenie stratosfery" ("Reaching the Stratosphere," 1932), he formulated the requirements of explosive fuel for use in jet engines. In 1934 and 1935 he proposed using clusters of rockets in order to reach great speeds.

"The main motive of my life," Tsiolkovsky wrote in evaluating his activity, "has been to . . . move humanity forward if only slightly. This is exactly why I have been interested in those things that never yielded either bread or strength. But I hope that my labors perhaps . . . may give to society mountains of bread and infinite power."

BIBLIOGRAPHY

Tsiolkovsky's collected works were published as *Sobranie sochineny*, 5 vols. (Moscow, 1951–1967). On his life and work, see *Konstantin Eduardovich Tsiolkovsky (1857–1932)* (Moscow–Leningrad, 1932), a jubilee collection published to commemorate his seventy-fifth birthday; and M. S. Arlazorov, *K. E. Tsiolkovsky, ego zhizn i deyatelnost* (". . . His Life and Work"; Moscow, 1962).

A. T. GRIGORIAN

TSU CH'UNG-CHIH (*b.* Fan-yang prefecture [modern Hopeh province], China, *ca.* A.D. 429; *d.* China, *ca.* A.D. 500), *mathematics*.

Tsu Ch'ung-chih was in the service of the emperor Hsiao-wu (*r.* 454–464) of the Liu Sung dynasty, first as an officer subordinate to the prefect of Nan-hsü (in modern Kiangsu province), then as an officer on the military staff in the capital city of Chien-k'ang (modern Nanking). During this time he also carried out work in mathematics and astronomy; upon the death of the emperor in 464, he left the imperial service to devote himself entirely to science. His son, Tsu Keng, was also an accomplished mathematician.

Tsu Ch'ung-chih would have known the standard works of Chinese mathematics, the *Chou-pi suan-ching* ("Mathematical Book on the Measurement With the Pole"), the *Hai-tao suan-ching* ("Sea-island Manual"), and especially, the *Chui-chang suan-shu* ("Mathematical Manual in Nine Chapters"), of which Liu Hui had published a new edition, with commentary, in 263. Like his predecessors, Tsu Ch'ung-chih was particularly interested in determining the value of π. This value was given as 3 in the *Chou-pi suan-ching*; as 3.1547 by Liu Hsin (*d.* 23); as $\sqrt{10}$, or $\frac{92}{29}$, by Chang Heng (78–139); and as $\frac{142}{35}$, that is, 3.155, by Wan Fan (219–257). Since the original works of these mathematicians have been lost, it is impossible to determine how these values were obtained, and the earliest extant account of the process is that given by Liu Hui, who reached an approximate value of 3.14. Late in the fourth century, Ho Ch'êng-tien arrived at an approximate value of $\frac{22}{7}$, or 3.1428.

Tsu Ch'ung-chih's work toward obtaining a more accurate value for π is chronicled in the calendrical chapters (*Lu-li chih*) of the *Sui-shu*, an official history of the Sui dynasty that was compiled in the seventh century by Wei Cheng and others. According to this work,

> Tsu Ch'ung-chih further devised a precise method. Taking a circle of diameter 100,000,000, which he considered to be equal to one *chang* [ten *ch'ih*, or Chinese feet, usually slightly greater than English feet], he found the circumference of this circle to be less than 31,415,927 *chang*, but greater than 31,415,926 *chang*. [He deduced from these results] that the accurate value of the circumference must lie between these two values. Therefore the precise value of the ratio of the circumference of a circle to its diameter is as 355 to 113, and the approximate value is as 22 to 7.

The *Sui-shu* historians then mention that Tsu Ch'ung-chih's work was lost, probably because his methods were so advanced as to be beyond the reach of other mathematicians, and for this reason were not studied or preserved. In his *Chun-suan-shih Lung-ts'ung* ("Collected Essays on the History of Chinese Mathematics" [1933]), Li Yen attempted to establish the method by which Tsu

Ch'ung-chih determined that the accurate value of π lay between 3.1415926 and 3.1415927, or $\frac{355}{113}$.

It was his conjecture that

"As $\frac{22}{7} > \pi > 3$, Tsu Ch'ung-chih must have set forth that, by the equality

$$\pi = \frac{22x + 3y}{7x + y} = 3.14159265,$$

one can deduce that

$$x = 15.996y, \text{ that is, that } x = 16y.$$

Therefore

$$\pi = \frac{22 \times 16y + 3y}{7 \times 16y + y} = \frac{22 \times 16 + 3}{7 \times 16 + 1} = \frac{355}{113}.$$"

For the derivation of

$$\pi = \frac{22x + 3y}{7x + y},$$

when a, b, c, and d are positive integers, it is easy to confirm that the inequalities

$$\frac{a}{b} \geqslant \frac{a+c}{b+d} \geqslant \frac{c}{d}$$

hold. If these inequalities are taken into consideration, the inequalities

$$\frac{22}{7} \geqslant \frac{22x + 3y}{7x + y} \geqslant \frac{3}{1}$$

may be derived.

Ch'ien Pao-tsung, in *Chung-kuo shu-hsüeh-shih* ("History of Chinese Mathematics" [1964]), assumed that Tsu Ch'ung-chih used the inequality

$$S_{2n} < S < S_{2n} + (S_{2n} - S_n),$$

where S_{2n} is the perimeter of a regular polygon of $2n$ sides inscribed within a circle of circumference S, while S_n is the perimeter of a regular polygon of n sides inscribed within the same circle. Ch'ien Pao-tsung thus found that

$$S_{12288} = 3.14159251$$

and

$$S_{24576} = 3.14159261,$$

resulting in the inequality

$$3.1415926 < \pi < 3.1415927.$$

Of Tsu Ch'ung-chih's astronomical work, the most important was his attempt to reform the calendar. The Chinese calendar had been based upon a cycle of 235 lunations in nineteen years, but in 462 Tsu Ch'ung-chih suggested a new system, the Ta-ming calendar, based upon a cycle of 4,836 lunations in 391 years. His new calendar also incorporated a value of forty-five years and eleven months a *tu* (365¼ *tu* representing 360°) for the precession of the equinoxes. Although Tsu Ch'ung-chih's powerful opponent Tai Fa-hsing strongly denounced the new system, the emperor Hsiao-Wu intended to adopt it in the year 464, but he died before his order was put into effect. Since his successor was strongly influenced by Tai Fa-hsing, the Ta-ming calendar was never put into official use.

BIBLIOGRAPHY

On Tsu Ch'ung-chih and his works see Li Yen, *Chung-suan-shih lun-ts'ung* ("Collected Essays on the History of Chinese Mathematics"), I–III (Shanghai, 1933–1934), IV (Shanghai, 1947), I–V (Peking, 1954–1955); *Chung-kuo shu-hsüeh ta-kang* ("Outline of Chinese Mathematics"; Shanghai 1931, repr. Peking 1958), 45–50; *Chun-kuo suan-hsüeh-shi* ("History of Chinese Mathematics"; Shanghai, 1937, repr. Peking, 1955); "Tsu Ch'ung-chih, Great Mathematician of Ancient China," in *People's China*, 24 (1956), 24; and *Chun-kuo ku-tai shu-hsüeh shi-hua* ("Historical Description of the Ancient Mathematics of China"; Peking, 1961), written with Tu Shih-jan.

See also Ch'ien Pao-tsung, *Chung-kuo shu-hsüeh-shih* ("History of Chinese Mathematics"; Peking, 1964), 83–90; Chou Ch'ing-shu, "Wo-kuo Ku-tai wei-ta ti k'o-hsüeh-chia: Tsu Ch'ung-chih" ("A Great Scientist of Ancient China: Tsu Ch'ung-chih"), in Li Kuang-pi and Ch'ien Chün-hua, *Chung-kuo k'o-hsüeh chi-shu fa-ming ho k'o-hsüeh chi-shu jēn-wu lun-chi* ("Essays on Chinese Discoveries and Inventions in Science and Technology and the Men Who Made Them"; Peking, 1955), 270–282; Li Ti, *Ta k'o-hsüeh-chia Tsu Ch'ung-chih* ("Tsu Ch'ung-chih the Great Scientist"; Shanghai, 1959); Ulrich Libbrecht, *Chinese Mathematics in the Thirteenth Century* (Cambridge, Mass., 1973), 275–276; Mao I-shēng, "Chung-kuo yüan-chou-lü lüeh-shih" ("Outline History of π in China"), in *K'o-hsüeh*, 3 (1917), 411; Mikami Yashio, *Development of Mathematics in China and Japan* (Leipzig, 1912), 51; Joseph Needham, *Science and Civilization in China*, III (Cambridge, 1959), 102; A. P. Youschkevitch, *Geschichte der Mathematik im Mittelalter* (Leipzig, 1964), 59; and Yen Tun-chieh, "Tsu Keng pieh chuan" ("Special Biography of Tsu Keng") in *K'o-hsüeh*, 25 (1941), 460.

AKIRA KOBORI

TSVET (or TSWETT), MIKHAIL SEMENOVICH (*b*. Asti, Italy, 14 May 1872; *d*. Voronezh, Russia, 26 June 1919), *plant physiology*, *plant biochemistry*.

Tsvet was the son of Semen Nikolaevich Tsvet, a Russian civil servant, and Maria de Dorozza, an Italian who had been raised in Russia. His parents had stopped in Asti en route to Switzerland for a cure when he was born. His mother died soon after Tsvet's birth, and his father had to leave the infant in Lausanne with a nurse while he returned to Russia.

Tsvet's childhood and youth were spent in Lausanne and Geneva. In 1891 he entered the department of mathematics and physics of the University of Geneva, where his special interests were chemistry, physics, and botany. While still a student, he did his first scientific work on plant anatomy, which received the Davy Prize and was published in 1894. After receiving the baccalaureate in physical and natural sciences in 1893, Tsvet continued work in the general botanical laboratory on his doctoral dissertation, "Études de physiologie cellulaire," which he defended in 1896.

In the summer of 1896 Tsvet moved to Russia, and from the beginning of 1897 he continued his investigations at the laboratory of plant anatomy and physiology of the Academy of Sciences and especially at the St. Petersburg Biological Laboratory, where, however, he did not have an academic post. Not until the autumn of 1897 did he become a botany teacher in the women's courses at the laboratory.

Since foreign scientific degrees were not legally recognized in Russia, in 1901 Tsvet passed the examination for the master's degree in botany at Kazan University and defended his thesis, "Fiziko-khimicheskoe stroenie khlorofilnogo zerna" ("The Physicochemical Structure of the Chlorophyll Grain"). In January 1902 he became supernumerary laboratory assistant in the department of plant anatomy and physiology at Warsaw University, and in 1903 he was appointed *Privatdozent*. Tsvet took on the added duty of teaching botany and microbiology at the Warsaw Veterinary Institute in 1907; a year later he began teaching these subjects at Warsaw Technical University, at which time he resigned from the university. He received the doctorate in botany in 1910 after defending the dissertation on chromophils in the plant and animal kingdoms.

World War I interrupted Tsvet's scientific work. In the summer of 1915 the Warsaw Polytechnical Institute was evacuated to Moscow and, in 1916,

to Nizhni Novgorod (now Gorky). Tsvet devoted much time and effort to organizing the work of the botanical laboratory in both cities and, at Nizhni Novgorod, participated in the organization of the Society of Natural Scientists and of the advanced agricultural courses.

In March 1917 Tsvet became professor of botany and director of the botanical garden at Yuryev (now Tartu) University, and that autumn he began teaching. He worked in Yuryev for only a short time, however. On 23 February 1918 Austrian and German soldiers entered the town, and Yuryev University soon ceased to function as a Russian institution. After the signing of the Treaty of Brest-Litovsk, the university was transferred to Voronezh in August 1918. Tsvet was able to work here for less than a year. His health, uncertain since birth, was finally ruined by excessive work, the displacements, and the hardships of the war years. He died of a chronic heart ailment at the age of forty-seven.

Tsvet's scientific legacy consists of sixty-nine publications, produced in the relatively short period from 1894 to 1916. He began research at a time when the data and methods of chemistry and physics were becoming more widely used for the discovery of the nature of the life processes. This aided the establishment of plant physiology as an independent science in the mid-nineteenth century and, toward the end of the century, contributed to the formation within plant physiology of such areas of research as cytophysiology. It was in the latter field that Tsvet saw the great possibilities for applying the results of chemical research and methods to achieve a better understanding of the nature of the plant organism. Even in his earliest works, on cytology and plant anatomy, he tried not only to describe the structures but also to discover their significance and functions, thereby creating new techniques and methods that were clearly expressed in his doctoral dissertation.

This tendency appeared more broadly and fruitfully in Tsvet's research at St. Petersburg. In his Geneva dissertation the central topic was the structure of chloroplasts, while in his later research the main subject was chlorophyll. In "O khloroglobine" ("On Chloroglobin") and "O prirode khloroglobina" ("On the Nature of Chloroglobin"; both 1900), Tsvet showed that the green pigment is found in the chloroplasts in the form of the chlorophyll-albumin complex, which, in analogy with hemoglobin, he called "chloroglobin." This term is now generally accepted; but at that time it met with sharp criticism from Tsvet's contemporaries,

486

who doubted the precision of his research methods.

In "Khlorofilliny i metakhlorofilliny" ("Chlorophyllins and Metachlorophyllins"; 1900) Tsvet contested the widespread view that only two pigments were present in the leaf: green chlorophyll and yellow xanthophyll. Using the five existing methods of physical analysis (fractional solution, differential solution, fractional precipitation, "wet sublimation," and diffusion) to separate the pigments with the least possible alteration, he established that in leaves there are two green pigments—chlorophyll α and β (now known as chlorophyll a and b), differing in color, fluorescence, and spectral absorption. Tsvet obtained a pure sample of the α form of chlorophyll but not of the β. This led him to attempt to develop a method that would consider the properties of the relationships of the chloroglobin pigments by means of adsorption. Tsvet decided to make the principle of adsorption the basis of this new method that, like filter paper, would allow the extraction from a solution of pigments in unchanged form. He stated his preliminary ideas on this question in his master's thesis, which contains, as he later recognized, the embryonic form of the method of chromatographic adsorption analysis that he soon developed.

On 30 December 1901, Tsvet presented a report to the Eleventh Congress of Russian Natural Scientists and Physicians at St. Petersburg, "Metody i zadachi fiziologicheskogo issledovania khlorofilla" ("Methods and Problems of Physiological Research on Chlorophyll"), in which he revealed his adsorption method and demonstrated its effects. He made a special, detailed report on 8 March 1903 to the biological section of the Warsaw Society of Natural Scientists, "O novoy kategorii adsorbtsionnykh yavleny i o primenenii ikh k biokhimicheskomu analizu" ("On a New Category of Adsorption Phenomena and on Its Application to Biochemical Analysis"). In it Tsvet described how he set himself the problem of creating a physical method that, in distinction from the chemical method, would, by using adsorption, allow the isolation of plant pigments and the separation of a mixture of such pigments in unchanged form. He experimentally substantiated that many substances could be adsorbed and explained the nature of this phenomenon. He also stated the theoretical bases and practical uses of the method.

In 1906, in *Berichte der Deutschen botanischen Gesellschaft*, Tsvet published two articles on his method and the data he had obtained with it on the pigment composition of plant leaves. In it he made the first suggestion to call the new method "chromatography" and formulated the law of adsorption replacement, giving a full description of the entire chromatographic setup, including sketches. He also provided a detailed account of the techniques of chromatographic experiments in general and in the study of chlorophyll in particular. His work on the creation of chromatography and its theoretical basis was summed up in his Russian doctoral dissertation, in which he gave a full demonstration of the difference of the chromatographic method from Friedrich Goppelsröder's capillary analysis.

Having tried 126 different powdered adsorbents, Tsvet found that those most effective for isolating plant pigments were calcium carbonate, sugarcane, and inulin. Grinding fresh leaves in a mixture of petroleum ether and a small amount of alcohol, he obtained an extract that he shook with distilled water to remove the alcohol and then filtered through a tube filled with powdered adsorbent. According to the strength of the various adsorptive capacities, the pigments were distributed into six differently colored layers in the tube. Taking the adsorbent from the tube, he obtained a column of powder that could be cut with a knife, after which each pigment could be washed from it separately. Thus Tsvet obtained in a pure form both chlorophyll a and chlorophyll b, and could separate from brown and diatomic algae the previously unknown chlorophyll c (in Tsvet's terminology, chlorophyll γ) and a number of previously unknown forms of xanthophyll: α, α', α'', and β (xanthophyll α later became known as lutein and xanthophyll β as taraxanthin). In 1911 Tsvet discovered in the leaves of *Thuja*, and isolated in pure form, a red-yellow pigment that he called rodoxanthin. Having discovered many forms of xanthophyll and their chemical relationship with the yellow pigment carotene, Tsvet suggested in 1911 that they be considered as one general group and called "carotenoids"—a term that has now won general acceptance.

Although Tsvet's chromotographic method was known to many of his contemporaries and was even used successfully in several laboratories to obtain pure forms of chlorophylls and carotenoids, its acceptance was very limited. The wide use of chromatography began in the 1930's, when Richard Kuhn, L. Zechmeister, and Paul Karrer simultaneously used it to study the chemistry of carotene and vitamin A. Dozens of other previously unknown forms of carotenoids and their products also were obtained, and colorless substances were isolated and purified: vitamins, hormones, enzymes. On the basis of Tsvet's method of chromatographic adsorption, a number of new forms of chromatography have been developed: ion-replacement, gas, distributive on paper, thin-layer, sedimentary. They have been widely used in biochemistry, analytical chemistry, biology, medicine, agriculture, and in a number of industries—chemical, pharmaceutical, food processing—where it is necessary to obtain absolutely pure substances, to separate complex mixtures, or to identify unknown compounds.

BIBLIOGRAPHY

I. ORIGINAL WORKS. Tsvet's writings include "Études de physiologie cellulaire," in *Bulletin du Laboratoire de botanique générale de l'Université de Genève*, **1**, no. 1 (1896), 123–206, his Geneva doctoral diss.; "Fiziko-khimicheskoe stroenie khlorofilnogo zerna" ("The Physicochemical Structure of the Chlorophyll Grain"), in *Trudy Kazanskogo obshchestva estestvoispytatelei*, **35**, no. 3 (1901), 1–268, his master's thesis at Kazan; "O novoy kategorii adsorbtsionnykh yavleny i o primenenii ikh k biokhimicheskomu analizu" ("On a New Category of Adsorption Phenomena and on Its Application to Biochemical Analysis"), in *Trudy Varshavskago obshchestva estestvoispytatelei*, Otd. biol., **14** (1903), 20–39; "Physikalisch-chemische Studien über das Chlorophyll. Die Adsorptionen," in *Berichte der Deutschen botanischen gesellschaft*, **24** (1906), 316–323; "Adsorptionsanalyse und chromatographische Methode. Anwendung auf die Chemie des Chlorophylls," *ibid.*, 384–393; *Khromofilly v rastitelnom i zhivotnom mire* ("Chromophils in the Plant and Animal Kingdoms"; Warsaw, 1910), for which he received the doctorate in botany; and "Über das makro- und mikrochemischen Nachweis des Carotins," in *Berichte der Deutschen botanischen Gesellschaft*, **29** (1911), 630–636.

II. SECONDARY LITERATURE. See C. Dhéré, "Michel Tswett," in *Candollea* (Geneva), **10** (1943), 23–63; T. Robinson, "Michael Tswett," in *Chimia Annual Studies in the History of Chemistry*, **6** (1960), 146–161; E. M. Senchenkova, *Mikhail Semenovich Tsvet* (Moscow, 1973), with a bibliography of works about Tsvet to 1973; "Otkrytie khromatografii i Akademia nauk" ("The Discovery of Chromatography and the Academy of Sciences," in *Priroda* (1974), no. 5, 92–101; and "Michail Semenovic Tsvet und die Chromatographie," in *Schriftenreihe für Geschichte der Naturwissenschaften, Technik und Medizin*, **12** (1975), 111–126; and R. L. M. Singe, "Tsvet, Willstätter, and the Use of Adsorption of Proteins," in *Archives of Biochemistry and Biophysics*, supp. 1 (1962), 1–6.

E. M. SENCHENKOVA

IBN ṬUFAYL, ABŪ BAKR MUHAMMAD (Latin, **Abubacer**) (*b.* Guadix, Spain, before 1110; *d.* Marrakesh, Morocco, 1185), *medicine, philosophy.*

Ibn Ṭufayl was a Spanish Muslim who received a broad education in the religion of Islam and the Arabic secular sciences. His professional career was that of a physician, first at Granada, Ceuta, and Tangier, and later (1163–1182) as court physician to the Almohad sultan of Morocco and Andalusia. He introduced Ibn Rushd to the sultan (*ca.* 1169) and commissioned him to write his commentaries on the works of Aristotle.

Ibn Ṭufayl is best known for his philosophical book *Ḥayy ibn Yaqẓān* ("The Living, Son of the Wakeful"). After a valuable introduction surveying the rise of philosophy in western Islam, the author presents Neoplatonic philosophy in the form of a myth. Ḥayy is a boy born on a desert island and reared by a doe. As he grows up he teaches himself, entirely by his own observation and reasoning, some practical arts and the rudiments of the empirical sciences. In his adult life he proceeds by reasoning and intuition to an understanding of metaphysics and theology and to an ascetic practice, all of which culminate in mystical visions by his intellect of God, the Necessary Being and Cause of the world. In later experiences he converses with a devout Muslim, and they agree that there is no difference in doctrine between Ḥayy's philosophy and the revealed religion of Islam, but that it is useless to teach philosophy to most people, for whom only the simplest practice of Islam is helpful.

The main aims of the myth appear to be to show (1) that the Neoplatonic philosophy is that which a rational man, undistracted by social interests or prejudices, will naturally arrive at, and (2) that the practice implied in this philosophy leads to the supreme happiness for man, which is the mystical state of the soul. In details Ibn Ṭufayl generally follows Ibn Sīnā, but there are some differences. For example, Ibn Ṭufayl thinks it unproved that the world is eternal rather than created in time, and holds that intelligibles are abstracted by the human intellect, not presented to it by an external Active Intellect.

Ḥayy ibn Yaqẓān has always been widely read in Arabic, and appeared in several European translations from 1671 onward; it probably influenced Defoe's *Robinson Crusoe* (1717).

Another work by Ibn Ṭufayl, *Rajaz ṭawīl fī ʿilm al-ṭibb* ("Long Poem in *Rajaz* Meter on Medical Science"), was discovered recently in manuscript at Rabat. He is also known to have influenced his pupil al-Biṭrūjī to abandon the Ptolemaic astronomy of eccentrics and epicycles in favor of a more Aristotelian system, but no astronomical writings by the master have survived.

BIBLIOGRAPHY

Texts of Ibn Ṭufayl's *Ḥayy ibn Yaqẓān* include the French ed. and trans. of L. Gauthier (2nd ed., Beirut, 1936); that of Aḥmad Amīn (Cairo, 1952); a partial English trans. by G. N. Atiyeh, in R. Lerner and M. Mahdi, *Medieval Political Philosophy* (Chicago, 1963), 134–162. and an English trans., intro., and notes by L. Goodman, *Ibn Ṭufayl's Ḥayy ibn Yaqẓān* (New York, 1971).

For studies of Ibn Ṭufayl and his work, see M. Cruz Hernandez, *Historia de la filosofia Hispano-musulmana*, I (Madrid, 1957), ch. 11; L. Gauthier, *Ibn Thofaïl, sa vie, ses oeuvres* (Paris, 1909); A.-M. Goichon, "Ḥayy b. Yakẓān," and B. Carra de Vaux, "Ibn Ṭufayl," both in *Encyclopaedia of Islam*, new ed. (Leiden, 1960–), III; G. F. Hourani, "The Principal Subject of Ibn Ṭufayl's *Ḥayy b. Yaqẓān*," in *Journal of Near Eastern Studies*, **15** (1956), 40–46; A. Pastor, *The Idea of Robinson Crusoe* (Watford, 1930); T. Sarnelli, "Primauté de Cordoue dans la médecine arabe d'Occident," in *Actas del Primer Congreso de Estudios Arabes y Islamicos* (Madrid, 1964), 441–451, describing the medical poem; and S. S. Hawi, *Islamic Naturalism and Mysticism, a Philosophic Study of Ibn Ṭufayl's Ḥayy ibn Yaqẓān* (Leiden, 1974).

GEORGE F. HOURANI

TULASNE, LOUIS-RENÉ (*b.* Azay-le-Rideau, France, 12 September 1815; *d.* Hyères, France, 22 December 1885), *mycology.*

Tulasne studied law in Poitiers with the intention of becoming a solicitor. In 1839, however, he inherited a considerable sum of money from his father and went to Paris to join his brother Charles, who was conducting medical studies there. The two brothers decided to give up their previous careers and to devote themselves to a life of botany, Christian religion, and charitable activities. They cooperated in these efforts until 1884, when Charles Tulasne died. Of the fifty-seven botanical works that Louis René Tulasne eventually published, his brother, who was also a talented and dexterous draftsman and illustrator, assisted him in the composition of fifteen.

In Paris, Tulasne attended the lectures of Brongniart, A. de Jussieu, and J. H. Léveillé and became a collaborator of Auguste de Saint-Hilaire at the Muséum National d'Histoire Naturelle. His first memoir, on the structure of the *Elaphomyces* fungi, was published in 1841. He then went on to study the results obtained by the British scientist Miles Berkeley, who had demonstrated that there are two fruiting forms in four genera of Gasteromycetes. He confirmed Berkeley's findings and generalized them in a series of ten memoirs, of which the last, *Fungi hypogaei* (Paris, 1851), remains one of the foundations of the modern study of this group.

At this time the Uredinales and Ustilaginales — the rusts and smuts that cause serious plant diseases — were little known, and some taxonomists thought them to be related to the Gasteromycetes. Tulasne began to study these parasites and was able to determine by experimentaton that in them the germination of teleutospores gives an intermediate promycelial stage, homologous to a basidium, which produces basidospores. Cell continuity, he established, was in these instances of prime importance. He then demonstrated the various fruiting forms borne in the growth of a single thallus in many species. He published, in addition to an important memoir on Ustilaginales, a precise explanation of the life-cycle of rye ergot (*Claviceps purpurea*), descriptions of the genus *Hypoxylon*, and various notes about *Erysiphaceae* (the powdery mildews).

Tulasne also did research on the reproduction and physiology of lichens, demonstrating that they display a filamentous habit rather similar to the mycelium of a fungus in their first stages of growth. Working with almost every European species of lichen, he determined the presence of spermatogonia and pycnidia in them and simultaneously succeeded in cultivating some species through sowing spores. In recognition of this work, as well as his important contributions to mycology, Tulasne was in 1854 elected to the Académie des Sciences.

Although his scientific reputation was based largely upon his work on cryptogams, Tulasne conducted other significant research on flowering plants. In 1849, having made a thorough study of the important herbaria of Paris and London, he brought out a paper on the Podostemeae, a group of plants similar to the mosses and ferns in appearance but belonging to a higher order because of their dicotyledonous embryos. He also published, between 1853 and 1855, two memoirs on American Leguminosae, four books on the flora of Colombia, a series of notes on the flora of Madagascar, four papers on the Monimiaceae, a work on American Gnetaceae, and a memoir, with descriptions of new species, on the two American genera *Antidesma* and *Stilaginella*.

Tulasne's major publication, written with his brother, was *Selecta fungorum carpologia*, published in three volumes between 1857 and 1865. At its completion, when he was fifty years old, Tulasne believed that his health was failing. He therefore presented his rich herbarium to the Muséum National d'Histoire Naturelle, gave his library to the Paris Université Catholique, and retired with his brother to the south of France, where they lived quietly for the rest of their lives.

BIBLIOGRAPHY

On Tulasne and his work, see E. Bornet, "Notice sur M. L. R. Tulasne," in *Comptes rendus hebdomadaires des séances de l'Académie des Sciences*, **103** (1886), 957–966; M. Chadefaud, "Mycologie," in A. Davy de Virville, *Histoire de la botanique en France* (Paris, 1954), 219–234; and P. Duchartre, "Notice sur M. L. R. Tulasne et sur son oeuvre botanique," in *Comptes rendus hebdomadaires des séances de l'Académie des Sciences*, **101** (1885), 1438–1444.

G. VIENNOT-BOURGIN

TULP, NICOLAAS (*b*. Amsterdam, Netherlands, 11 October 1593; *d*. The Hague, Netherlands, 12 September 1674), *medicine, anatomy*.

Nicolaas Tulp was the son of Pieter Dirkz, a wealthy merchant of Amsterdam, and Grietje Dirks Poelenburgh. Dirkz, meaning son of Dirk (Henry), was not a family name. According to Busken Huet, Tulp's real name was Claes (Nicolas) Pieterz. He took the name Tulp ("tulip") from the sculpture on the gable of his house on the Keizersgracht in Amsterdam.

On 19 February 1611, Tulp matriculated at the University of Leiden under the name of Nicolaas Petraeus. He obtained his medical degree on 30 September 1614, after defending his dissertation, *De cholera humida*. Tulp then settled in Amsterdam, where he soon had a lucrative practice. It is said that he was the first physician in town to visit his patients in a carriage.

Tulp was appointed *praelector* of anatomy in 1628, succeeding Joannes Fonteyn. He had the personal title *professor anatomiae* and was charged with teaching the surgeons of the city and illustrating the lectures, whenever possible, with public dissections.

Tulp is perhaps best known from the painting by Rembrandt commissioned by the Surgeons Guild in 1632. He is portrayed giving a lecture demonstration with an opened body. The painting, the famous "Anatomy Lesson of Dr. Tulp," is in the Mauritshuis in The Hague.

One of Amsterdam's leading citizens, Tulp served as a member of the city government, including four terms as mayor. He was also a curator of the Athenaeum, the city's school of higher learning.

In 1652, because of the pressures of his civic and professional duties, Tulp resigned his position as *praelector*. He was succeeded by J. Deyman.

Tulp's main work, the *Observationum medicarum libri tres* (1641), contains descriptions of 228 cases. Most of them cannot stand the test of modern criticism, but there are some valuable observations. For example, he described the ileocecal valve, sometimes called Tulp's valve, which is located at the junction of the large and small intestines, and he gave a correct description of its function. He also described the chyle vessels of the small intestine, which actually was a rediscovery. According to Baumann, both Herophilus and Erasistratus knew of these vessels but the knowledge was lost. Tulp also was the first to describe beriberi.

Tulp is also sometimes credited with the first description of the orangutan, about a half century before Tyson (1699), but incorrectly so. What Tulp described was a chimpanzee, which does appear to have been the first in Europe.

A great admirer of Hippocrates, Tulp opposed the new ideas of the iatrochemists, of whom J. B. van Helmont was the most notable. He was especially against the use of antimony, which was beginning to be prescribed.

The first pharmacopoeia of the Netherlands was compiled at Tulp's suggestion, He proposed the idea to a group of six physicians during a dinner at his house on 18 April 1635. A committee was formed, and on 5 May 1636 (date of the preface) the book was published. Since the time was so short, it is generally believed that Tulp had most of the manuscript ready when he made the proposal and that the book was therefore largely from his own hand. The municipality of Amsterdam ruled that this pharmacopoeia was henceforth to be the only one used in the city. Thus was formed the Collegium Medicum Amstelaedamense, set up to enforce the decree. The Collegium soon developed into a municipal committee for health care, the earliest example of governmental concern with public health in the Netherlands.

BIBLIOGRAPHY

I. Original Works. The *Pharmacopoea Amstelaedamensis, senatus auctoritate munita* (Amsterdam, 1636) went into many editions, the most recent being a facsimile edition of 1961. *Observationum medicarum libri tres* (Amsterdam, 1641) also had several eds., some with slightly changed titles (Amsterdam, 1652, 1672, 1685; and Leiden, 1716, 1739). The fifth ed. has a biography and the sixth ed. has the funeral oration by L. Wolzogen, professor of church history at the Athenaeum of Amsterdam.

Dutch translations are *De drie boecken der medicijnsche aanmerkingen* (Amsterdam, 1650); *Geneeskundige waarnemingen, Naar den zesden druk uit het latijn vertaald, Hier is bijgevoegd de lijkrede van L. Wolzogen* (Leiden, 1740); and *Hippocrates, Aphorismen, of kortbondige spreuken. Beneffens desselfs wet en vermaningen. Alsmede d'aanmaningen van N. Tulp. Vertaald door Steph. Blankaart* (Amsterdam, 1680 [?]; 2nd ed., 1714).

II. Secondary Literature. See H. F. Thijssen, "Voorlezing over Nicolaas Tulp," in *Magazijn voor wetenschappen, Kunsten en Letteren van N. G. van Kampen,* **3** (1824); L. H. van Bochove, *Dissertatio historica-medica inauguralis de Nicolao Tulpio, anatomes practicae strenuo cultore* (Leiden, 1846); H. C. Rogge, "Nicolaas Tulp," in *De Gids,* 3rd ser., **18** (1880), 77–125; E. H. M. Thijssen, *Nicolaas Tulp als geneeskundige geschetst. Eene bijdrage tot de geschiedenis der geneeskunde in de achttiende eeuw* (Amsterdam, 1881); and C. Busken Huet, *Het land van Rembrandt,* 2nd ed. (Haarlem, 1886), II B, 57–61.

Other works are E. D. Baumann, "Nicolaas Tulp" in *Nieuw Nederlandsch Biografisch Woordenboek,* III (1914), 1250–1251; J. S. Theissen, "Nicolaas (Claes Pieterz) Tulp," in *Gedenkboek van het Athenaeum en de Universiteit van Amsterdam* (Amsterdam, 1932), 695–696; A. Bredius, *Rembrandt, schilderijen* (Utrecht, 1935); P. van der Wielen, "De eerste Nederlandsche Pharmacopee," in *Bijdragen tot de Geschiedenis der Geneeskunde,* **16** (1936), 57–63; E. D. Baumann, *Uit drie eeuwen Nederlandsche Geneeskunde* (Amsterdam, 1951), esp. 64–71; and A. Querido, "Nicolaas Tulp en zijn manuscript," in *Spiegel Historiael,* **5** (1970), 305–311, on Tulp's own Dutch translation of the *Observationum.*

Peter W. van der Pas

TUNSTALL, CUTHBERT (*b.* Hackforth, Yorkshire, England, 1474; *d.* London, England, 18 November 1559), *theology, diplomacy, mathematics.*

Tunstall was the natural son of Thomas Tunstall and a daughter of Sir John Conyers, and he was later legitimated (in canon law) by their marriage. He attended Oxford (*ca.* 1491) and Cambridge (*ca.* 1496) but removed to Padua in 1499, where he remained for about six years and became doctor of both canon and civil (Roman) laws. He was appointed bishop of London (1522) and later bishop of Durham (1530, deprived 1552, restored 1553, deprived 1559). Although of strong religious convictions, he was humane and moderate, and was respected even by his opponents in matters of religion. While remaining faithful to Roman Catholic dogma, he was aware that reform was needed. He would protest decisions of Henry VIII (who often kept him away from London when unpopular decisions were to be made), but once they had been made, he would submit. Under Mary he refrained from persecuting Protestants. An outstanding classical scholar, Tunstall was a close friend of Sir Thomas More, to whom his arithmetic was dedicated, and of Erasmus, whom he assisted in the preparation of the second edition of his Greek New Testament.

Tunstall's Latin arithmetic, *De arte supputandi* (1522), was published as a farewell to secular writings just before he was consecrated bishop of London. The work made no claim to originality of material but had been compiled over the years from all available works in Latin or other languages that Tunstall understood. As master of the rolls (1516–1522), and on diplomatic missions to the Continent, he had felt the need to refresh his memory of arithmetic to protect himself in monetary transactions. From the material he had collected he determined to write such a clear treatise that no one who knew Latin would lack an instructor in the art of reckoning. The work seems not to have been popular in England. It has never been translated into English, and all editions but the first were printed on the Continent, where it was greatly admired. For example, Simon Grynaeus dedicated the first Greek text of Euclid's *Elements* (Basel, 1533) to Tunstall, since he had explained the calculating of numbers in so excellent a manner. England had lagged behind the rest of Europe in mathematics. Only a chapter on "Arsemetrike and Whereof It Proceedeth," in Caxton's *The Mirrour of the World* (1481), had preceded Tunstall's *De arte supputandi*; and it was not until 1537 that an arithmetic appeared in English.

BIBLIOGRAPHY

In addition to the London eds. of *De arte supputandi* (1522), there were Paris eds. (1529, 1535, 1538) and

Strasbourg eds. (1543, 1544, 1548, 1551). For Tunstall's ecclesiastical writings, see Charles Sturge, *Cuthbert Tunstal* (New York, 1938), which also contains a chapter on the arithmetic. For Erasmian humanism and religious developments in England during Tunstall's lifetime, see L. B. Smith, *Tudor Prelates and Politics, 1536–1558* (Princeton, 1953) and J. K. McConica, *English Humanists and Reformation Politics* (Oxford, 1965).

JOY B. EASTON

TUPOLEV, ANDREY NIKOLAEVICH (*b.* Pustomazovo, Tver [now Kalinin] guberniya, Russia, 10 November 1888; *d.* Moscow, U.S.S.R., 23 December 1972), *mechanics, aeronautical engineering.*

The son of a notary, Tupolev studied at the Tver provincial Gymnasium from 1900 to 1908 and in 1909 entered Moscow Technical School (now the N. E. Bauman Moscow Higher Technical School). Under the influence of N. E. Zhukovsky he became interested in aviation and joined a club of aeronautics enthusiasts that fostered the activities of many scientists and aeronautical engineers who later became well known. He designed, built, and flew training gliders; planned and constructed wind tunnels; and participated in the creation of an aerodynamic laboratory at the Technical School. In 1916 Tupolev and other members of the group under Zhukovsky's guidance took part in the creation of a bureau for experimental testing of aeronautical designs, one of the first scientific research institutions of its kind.

After graduating in 1918, Tupolev and the other members of Zhukovsky's collective organized the Central Aerohydrodynamics Institute in Moscow. Tupolev devoted much time and energy to this institute, serving as assistant director from 1918 to 1935. The office of design, headed by Tupolev and established at the institute in 1922, established a project for the first in a series of airplanes built by Tupolev. An independent design office was organized with Tupolev as director in 1936. Tupolev was the first designer in the Soviet Union to use all-metal construction in both civil and military aviation.

In 1933 Tupolev became a corresponding and, in 1953, active member of the Academy of Sciences of the U.S.S.R. His services were also recognized in Italy, England, and the United States. In 1970 an Italian national center for the development of methods of air transport in Italy awarded Tupolev the Leonardo da Vinci Prize "for planning the world's first supersonic passenger airplane, the Tu-144." Also that year the Royal Aircraft Establishment of England elected him honorary member and awarded him a special diploma, and in 1971 he became an honorary member of the American Institute of Aeronautics and Astronautics.

Under Tupolev's leadership more than 100 types of aircraft were designed, from light fighter planes to huge long-range passenger aircraft.

Tupolev's airplanes played a major role in the study of the Arctic. A series of record flights were made in his airplanes, including the 1937 nonstop Moscow–Vancouver flight over the North Pole of V. P. Chkalov in an airplane of the ANT-25 type.

In 1955 Tupolev built the first Russian jet passenger airplane, the Tu-104. In December 1968 he completed the first test flight of a supersonic passenger airplane, the Tu-144. For his military airplanes, which played an important role in World War II, Tupolev was awarded the title of lieutenant general in the engineering-technical service.

Continuing Zhukovsky's work, Tupolev further developed the principles of aerodynamics and the calculation of stability. Although skilled in computation, he could extract from mathematical formulas physical implications and technical ideas and could evaluate them with profound scientific and technical insight. This gift for observing physical phenomena behind a mathematical framework allowed Tupolev to solve the most complex problems of such varied disciplines as gas dynamics, automation, the static and dynamic strength of structures, and radiotechnology—fundamental aspects of modern aeronautical science.

BIBLIOGRAPHY

Tupolev's writings include "Aerodinamichesky raschet aeroplanov" ("An Aerodynamic Account of Aeroplanes"), in *Trudy Aviatsionnogo raschetno-ispytatelnogo byuro,* no. 1 (1917); and "Pervy sovetsky metallichesky samolet ANT-2" ("The First Soviet All-Metal Airplane ANT-2"), in *Samolet,* no. 8 (1924), 12–18. For biographical details, see the article in *Bolshaya sovetskaya entsiklopedia* ("Great Soviet Encyclopedia"), 2nd ed., XLIII (Moscow, 1956), 415.

A. T. GRIGORIAN

TÜRCK, LUDWIG (*b.* Vienna, Austria, 22 July 1810; *d.* Vienna, 25 February 1868), *medicine, laryngology, neurology.*

Türck's father, the jeweler to the Austrian imperial family and nobility, provided for his son generously, so that his economic and social positions were secure. The family was highly cultured and, apparently, devoted to music. Ludwig himself was reputedly a virtuoso cellist. At his death, his estate included two extremely valuable instruments. His brother, Joseph, owned a large and valuable collection of violins, said to be one of the finest in its time.

After study in the Gymnasium and the medical school in Vienna, Ludwig qualified as a physician there in 1836. His economic independence enabled him to devote himself to research, and by 1840 he was deeply involved in intensive studies of the anatomy and pathology of the nervous system. In 1844 he went to Paris to extend his studies under the great French physicians, who led the world in this field at the time. In Austria the outstanding leader in medical education was Baron Türkheim, and Türck's aggressive talents and brilliant intellectual endowments brought him to the baron's attention. Türkheim was director of the General Hospital in Vienna and took Türck under his patronage after his return from Paris. He arranged for a special division for nervous diseases to be established in the hospital with young Türck in charge. Here Türck remained for thirteen years and built up a solid scientific reputation by his intensive investigations in the neurological clinic. He published the results of these investigations both in periodicals and as monographs. Besides his early monograph on spinal irritation (1843), there were numerous contributions on the tracts in the spinal cord and their origins, on the roots of the trigeminal nerve, and on the results of tests of cutaneous sensibility. Türck's name is preserved in the nomenclature of the mammalian temporo-pontine tract, which is termed the bundle of Türck.

In 1857 the largest hospital in Vienna was established and Türck was appointed physician in chief. In the same year the direction of his principal researches shifted to laryngoscopy, to the nearly complete exclusion of other research. Manuel García, the renowned singer and vocal teacher in London, had sought with the aid of a mirror to observe the production of the voice and the visible alterations of the vocal organs that accompany its modulations. Even earlier, Senn, in Geneva, had suggested making visible the interior of the larynx by means of a small mirror inserted in the throat, and in the following decade prominent physicians in France and England, particularly Trousseau and Liston, had employed such instruments, but without useful results. When García published an account of his observations in 1855, Türck realized the possibilities for valuable clinical applications and, although ignorant of the details of the earlier procedures, he constructed an apparatus forthwith and went on to use it for diagnostic and operative purposes. Persistent experiments and abundant observations in the daily routine of hospital practice enabled him to develop and improve his instruments and soon the idea was crowned with brilliant success.

The earlier reports in no way detract from the originality of Türck's discovery. Not only was he unacquainted with the manner of García's investigations, but the aims and methods of the two men were totally different and unrelated. In 1857 Türck displayed to Ludwig the interior of the larynx of a patient in his ward and thereby found a practical solution for a problem that had long been troubling the physiologists and clinicians.

In March 1858 appeared an article by Czermak in the *Wiener medizinischen Wochenschrift* urgently recommending to physicians the practical application of the laryngeal mirror—giving rise to a bitter dispute over priority. This lasted for years until, after Türck's death, a professional declaration affirmed "that the history of medicine must forever link the name of Türck with laryngoscopy. To him alone is due the practical application of the laryngoscope for diagnostic and operative purposes."

BIBLIOGRAPHY

See *Abhandlung über Spinalirritation nach eigenen, grösstentheils im Wiener allgemeinen Krankenhause angestellten Beobachtungen* (Vienna, 1843); *Ph. Ricord's Lehre von der Syphilis. Nach dessen klinischen Vorträgen dargestellt von Ludwig Türck* (Vienna, 1846); "Fortsetzungen zum Gehirns," in *Sitzungsberichte der K. Akademie der Wissenschaften zu Wien*, Math.-nat. Cl., VI, 228; *Praktische Anleitung zur Laryngoskopie* (Vienna, 1860); *Recherches cliniques sur diverses Maladies du Larynx, de la trachée et du pharynx etudiées a l'aide du laryngoscope* (Paris, 1862); *Klinik der Krankheiten des Kehlkopfes und der Luftröhre. Nebst einer Anleitung zum Gebrauche des Kehlkopfrachenspiegels und zur Localbehandlung der Kehlkopfkrankheiten* (Vienna, 1866); *Atlas dazu. In 27 chromolithogr. Tafeln von A. Elfinger und C. Heitzmann* (Vienna, 1866); *Ueber Hautsensibilitätsbezirke der einzelnen Rückenmarknervenpaare. Aus dessen literarischen Nachlasse zusammengestellt von Professor Dr. C. Wedl* (Vienna, 1869); *Gesammelte neurologische Schriften* (Leipzig, 1910). Türck's articles in *Allgemeinen Wiener medizinischen Zeitung* provide a true record of the progress of his research.

E. HORNE CRAIGIE

TURGOT, ANNE-ROBERT-JACQUES (*b*. Paris, France, 10 May 1727; *d*. Paris, 18 March 1781), *economics*, *philosophy*.

The most famous member of a distinguished family, Turgot was the third son of Michel-Étienne Turgot, prévôt des marchands de Paris, city planner, and sponsor of the survey map of Paris known as the Turgot map. An older brother, Étienne-François, served briefly as governor of French Guiana and was a competent botanist and agronomist.

Turgot was originally intended for the priesthood and studied at the Séminaire St.-Sulpice and the Sorbonne. In 1751, recognizing that he had no religious vocation, he decided to follow the family tradition of public service. He was appointed intendant of Limoges in 1761, and his reforms there, over a period of thirteen years, made him a figure of national prominence. Perhaps best known was his abolition of the *corvée* (forced labor on the roads); by using professional rather than peasant labor, he achieved results of such quality that in 1787 the roads of Limousin were still being described as the best in France.[1] Offered transfers to more prosperous regions, Turgot preferred to remain in Limousin; he left the area only in 1774, when he was appointed minister of the navy in the first government formed by Louis XVI. One month later he was named controller general of finance, a post he was to hold for less than two years (August 1774–May 1776). In that capacity he attempted bold reforms on a national scale, thus antagonizing many special interest groups and earning an enduring reputation as the most courageous and enlightened official of the old regime.

Turgot's interests and talents were encyclopedic, extending far beyond his modern image as an economist. He knew five foreign languages well, studied two more, and published poetry and prose translations from English, German, and Latin. He displayed similar versatility in the sciences; his writings dealt with aspects of physics, chemistry, and geology. In addition, he reportedly knew enough astronomy, geography, and navigational theory and practice to be an unusually well-qualified minister of the navy.

Turgot's formal education in the sciences included the study of Newtonian physics with the Abbé Sigorgne and chemistry with Guillaume-François Rouelle. In 1748, while still a student, Turgot drafted an essay on "the causes of progress and decline in the arts and sciences," which he intended to submit for a prize then being offered by the Academy of Soissons. That year he also composed a brief and interesting critique of Buffon's cosmology and geology, the principles of which had just been published in a prospectus for Buffon's *Histoire naturelle*. Turgot's only other foray into geology was a series of field notes based on travels during the year 1760.

The one scientific work by Turgot published during his lifetime was the article "Expansibilité," in the Diderot *Encyclopédie*.[2] Here he was concerned with distinguishing between vaporization and evaporation, the latter defined as a loss of volume from the surface of a liquid or solid exposed to the atmosphere; he defined vaporization as the result of forces of repulsion—he elaborated at length upon this Newtonian theme—which act at the particulate level and produce a change of state. His article apparently had some influence on Lavoisier during the 1760's, and Condorcet later declared that Turgot had "opened new views in natural philosophy."[3] During the last years of his life Turgot was able to return to some of the topics raised in his article, and especially to the study of distillations *in vacuo* and under changing temperature conditions.

Turgot's talents as a chemist are revealed in the letters he exchanged with Condorcet in 1771–1772. Anticipating some of the ideas of Lavoisier, he argued persuasively that the gain in weight of a metallic calx (oxide) should be explained as a combination of the metal with "air." As he admitted, he had not tested his conclusions in the laboratory, and his argument was a logical, inductive one.

More significant than Turgot's own scientific activities was his role as a patron and a public official who regularly sought the advice of scientific experts. His recourse to scientists was both frequent and imaginative, suggesting not a series of ad hoc decisions but rather a general philosophy put into practice. Influenced by both Vincent de Gournay and the physiocrats, Turgot believed it desirable to free agriculture, industry, and commerce from excessive governmental regulation; the inescapable corollary to this doctrine was that laissez-faire would ensure progress and prosperity. But to this idea he added a conviction that was to him of equal weight: the results of scientific research, applied to technology and taught to peasants, craftsmen, manufacturers, and others, could provide a firm foundation for progress. These beliefs are apparent in many of his actions, such as his appointment of geologist Nicolas Desmarest as inspector of manufactures in Limousin[4] and his pioneering efforts to gather accurate statistical data about Limousin and, eventually, all of France.

Turgot's views were not new and, in fact, were shared by contemporaries ranging from the Trudaines to the encyclopedists. If the differences between Turgot and others are matters of degree rather than of kind, the consistency of his policies elevates him to a position of distinction among royal ministers, while his political power separates him from other philosophers. Furthermore, Turgot's own knowledge and ability in the sciences made him an intelligent judge of the ability of others, and he purposely increased his acquaintance with such subjects as agronomy in order to understand more fully the advice given him by the scientists he consulted. His attitude in this respect was succinctly summarized by Condorcet:

> He was not afraid to consult men of science, because he was not afraid of truth. . . . But he knew at the same time that the learned, accustomed to system and demonstration, carried sometimes to excess the spirit of scepticism and uncertainty; and that in consulting them, it is necessary both to seek to understand, and to be capable of understanding them. . . . [He] regarded the *encouragement of the arts and sciences* as an indispensable duty of his office.[5]

Translated into policy, his attitude led Turgot to devise some projects of his own, solicit suggestions from scientists, sponsor translations of scientific treatises, and encourage the work of inventors.

While an intendant, Turgot's major concern was the improvement of agriculture in a region as poor as Brittany and subject to endemic and epidemic famine. Aware of the studies of agronomists, he became convinced that potatoes were hardy enough to thrive where wheat could not, and that the potato was a food nourishing to both human beings and livestock. His efforts to persuade his peasants to make the experiment eventually met with some success, years before the potato became common in other French provinces. Turgot was also the patron of the Society of Agriculture of Limoges, founded by his predecessor, Pajot de Marcheval, in 1759. He doubted that experiments done in common could be done properly, but he attended some meetings, donated equipment, and used his own funds to establish prizes for essays on agricultural subjects. In 1766 he founded a short-lived school of veterinary medicine in Limoges, patterned upon the school in Lyons to which Turgot had sent students since its opening in 1762. When the Collège de Limoges was undergoing reform after 1762, Turgot used his influence to see that the sciences were given some prominence in the new curriculum.

As controller general, Turgot's concern with agriculture was expressed in two especially significant ways. A serious outbreak of murrain in 1774 led him to send Félix Vicq d'Azyr to the afflicted southwestern provinces to study the disease and to recommend remedies. The problems of diagnosis and control suggested to Turgot that the study of epidemics be undertaken systematically, and he and Vicq became founders of a society formed for that purpose and for the improvement of medical education and research. The society, which first met in 1776, later became the Société Royale de Médecine with Vicq d'Azyr its first secretary. At the same time, Turgot continued his efforts to introduce new crops. As an intendant, he had brought to Limousin crops already being raised elsewhere in France, but as controller general he extended his interests to the genuinely exotic. In 1775 he arranged the mission of naturalist Joseph Dombey to South America, instructing Dombey to bring back to France plants of botanical interest and of potential agricultural value. Turgot was intimately involved in planning this voyage, for which he sought the advice of Condorcet and the botanists Antoine-Laurent de Jussieu and André Thouin.

The voyages of Dombey and others were not wholly agricultural in purpose. One of Turgot's broader aims, which he shared with the physiocrats, was to bring about a more rationally organized world trade, with each country growing and producing those goods for which its soil, climate, and technological skills were best suited. But in addition Turgot dreamed of being able to send scientists all over the world as a kind of "traveling academy" for the collection of scientific information.[6] His view, not uncommon at the time, that science belonged to all humanity rather than to particular nations was made explicit in a memorandum written after 1776 and addressed to Louis XVI; Turgot urged the king (who accepted his advice) that, with France on the verge of war with England and with Captain Cook engaged in the third of his voyages, all French ships should be ordered not to molest Cook in any way.

The scientist consulted most regularly by Turgot was Condorcet, who was a personal friend and seems to have served informally as Turgot's liaison with the Académie Royale des Sciences. Among the many projects in which Condorcet played a part was Turgot's plan to introduce a uniform system of weights and measures, a reform long considered desirable. Like the later designers of the metric system, Turgot thought it best to select a natural constant — the length of a seconds pendulum at a given latitude—for the unit of length; a standard of weight should be determined in some comparable way, and the coinage should then be issued in units corresponding to divisions of weight. It was on Condorcet's advice that Turgot asked the astronomer Charles Messier to carry out the preliminary measurements, and in 1775 Turgot and Condorcet drew up instructions for Messier. Although the work was begun, it was discontinued when Turgot fell from power.

Turgot's interest in the system of canals and natural waterways of France originated from his desire to improve internal commerce. In 1775, on the advice of Condorcet, he created a committee of three eminent scientists—Condorcet, Bossut, and d'Alembert—to examine proposals for new canals and to inspect those already under construction. The scientists proposed that they work without salary, but Condorcet was rewarded with an appointment as director of the mint, while Bossut was named to a newly created post of professor of hydrodynamics. The committee was abolished upon Turgot's dismissal from office.

To reform the manufacture of gunpowder, Turgot created the Régie des Poudres in 1775, appointing Lavoisier one of the *régisseurs*. This government agency not only administered nationally the manufacture of saltpeter, but it also encouraged research to improve the quality and increase the quantity of saltpeter used for gunpowder. Research continued—much of it by Lavoisier—long after Turgot's dismissal, with results soon visible during the American Revolution and later during the French Revolution.

Turgot's activities during his twenty months as controller general—and for eight of the twenty months he was confined to bed with severe attacks of gout—were remarkable for their number, variety, and intelligence. His efforts can be considered the logical culmination of his earliest ideas and of his work as an intendant, and they bear witness to the consistency with which he tried to put into practice his ideals as an enlightened reformer. Although few of his reforms outlasted his term in office—several were reintroduced in later decades—his philosophy was to leave its mark upon subsequent generations.

NOTES

1. Arthur Young, *Travels in France During the Years 1787, 1788, 1789* (many editions), entry dated 6 June 1787.
2. Denis Diderot and Jean Le Rond d'Alembert, *Encyclopédie, ou Dictionnaire raisonné des sciences, des arts et des*

métiers, VI (1756), 274–285, and the important errata, VII (1757), 1028–1029. Reprinted in Schelle, *Oeuvres*, I, 538–576.
3. Condorcet, *Life*, 30–31.
4. Letter from Turgot to Daniel Trudaine, 10 September 1762, in Pierre Bonnassieux and Eugène Lelong, *Conseil de commerce et Bureau du commerce 1700–1791. Inventaire analytique des Procès-Verbaux* (Paris, 1900), xlv, col. 2, n. 2.
5. Condorcet, *op. cit.*, 136–137, 144.
6. Dupont de Nemours, *Mémoires*, I, 122. Cf. Schelle, *Oeuvres*, II, 523–533.

BIBLIOGRAPHY

I. ORIGINAL WORKS. 1. *Publications*: The best of several editions of Turgot's works is *Oeuvres de Turgot et documents le concernant*, Gustave Schelle, ed., 5 vols. (Paris, 1913–1923), although the editor's transcriptions are sometimes faulty, and he omitted much of value, including letters addressed to Turgot. Still indispensable, therefore, is the *Correspondance inédite de Condorcet et de Turgot, 1770–1779*, Charles Henry, ed. (Paris, 1883).

The authorship of published geological notes, attributed to Turgot, remains in some doubt, although it is certain that Turgot did make geological observations during his travels. Relevant texts and discussion are in *Oeuvres*, II, 604, and in *Oeuvres de M. Turgot, ministre d'état*, P.-S. Dupont de Nemours, ed., 9 vols. (Paris, 1808–1811), I, 52–53; III, 376–447.

2. *Manuscripts*: There are three major repositories, one of them private; the others are the Archives Nationales, Paris, and the Eleutherian Mills Historical Library, Wilmington, Delaware. Cf. John B. Riggs, *A Guide to the Manuscripts in the Eleutherian Mills Historical Library: Accessions Through the Year 1965* (Greenville, Del., 1970). Most documents were published by Schelle, but the footnotes in his edition provide a guide to some of the manuscripts he decided to omit.

II. SECONDARY LITERATURE. P. F. C. Foncin, *Essai sur le ministère de Turgot* (Paris, 1877); Douglas Dakin, *Turgot and the Ancien Régime in France* (London, [1939]), with valuable bibliography and notes; Henry Guerlac, *Lavoisier—The Crucial Year: The Background and Origin of His First Experiments on Combustion in 1772* (Ithaca, New York, [1961]), ch. 5; Roger Hahn, "The Chair of Hydrodynamics in Paris, 1775–1791: A Creation of Turgot," in *Actes du Xe Congrès international d'histoire des sciences*, II (Paris, 1964), 751–754; Rhoda Rappaport, "Government Patronage of Science in Eighteenth-Century France," in *History of Science*, VIII (1969 [publ. 1970]), 119–136; Jerry Gough, "Nouvelle contribution à l'étude de l'évolution des idées de Lavoisier sur la nature de l'air et sur la calcination des métaux," in *Archives internationales d'histoire des sciences*, **22** (1969), 267–275.

See also Denis I. Duveen and Herbert S. Klickstein, *A Bibliography of the Works of Antoine Laurent Lavoisier 1743–1794* (London, 1954), esp. 219–222; a subject index to this volume is in Duveen, *Supplement to a Bibliography of the Works of Antoine Laurent Lavoisier 1743–1794* (London, 1965).

The many general studies of Turgot tend to minimize or ignore scientific questions, but still valuable are the earliest biographies: P.-S. Dupont de Nemours, *Mémoires sur la vie et les ouvrages de M. Turgot, ministre d'Etat*, 2 vols.-in-1 (Philadelphia, 1782); and Marquis de Condorcet, *Vie de Monsieur Turgot* (London, 1786), translated anonymously as *The Life of M. Turgot* (London, 1787); also published in *Oeuvres de Condorcet*, A. C. O'Connor and F. Arago, eds., 12 vols. (Paris, 1847–1849), V, 1–233.

For discussions of Turgot's relations with the scientific community, see Keith M. Baker, *Condorcet, From Natural Philosophy to Social Mathematics* (Chicago, 1975); and C. C. Gillispie, "Probability and Politics: Laplace, Condorcet, and Turgot," in *Proceedings of the American Philosophical Society*, **116** (1972), 1–20.

RHODA RAPPAPORT

TURGOT, ÉTIENNE-FRANÇOIS (*b.* Paris, France, 16 June 1721; *d.* Château of Bons, Calvados, France, 25 December 1788), *botany, agronomy*.

An older brother of the famous reformer, the Chevalier Turgot, knight of the Order of Malta and Marquis de Soumont, served briefly as the governor of Guiana (1764–1765). After his retirement from public life in 1765, he devoted himself to agricultural experiments and study, interests which had already led him to introduce the cultivation of exotic crops in Malta and Guiana. Like his friends Malesherbes and Duhamel du Monceau, with whom he corresponded on agricultural subjects, Turgot used a large part of his land in Normandy for the naturalization of foreign trees and the cultivation of botanical rarities. He also maintained a residence in Paris, where he was able to introduce one of his protégés, Hector Saint-John de Crèvecoeur, to other naturalists and agronomists. He was a member of the Académie Royale des Sciences (1765), and a founding member of the Société d'Agriculture de Paris (1761).

Turgot is usually said to have died on 21 October 1789. The date 25 December 1788 adopted here is taken from the announcement in the *Journal de Paris* (1 January 1789, p. 4).

BIBLIOGRAPHY

I. ORIGINAL WORKS. Works by Turgot include *Mémoire instructif sur la manière de rassembler, de pré-* *parer, de conserver, et d'envoyer les diverses curiosités d'histoire naturelle* (Paris–Lyons, 1758); and *Essai sur les arbres d'ornement, les arbrisseaux, et arbustes de pleine terre* (Amsterdam–Paris, 1778). The second of these is a partial translation, with added material, of Philip Miller, *The Gardener's Dictionary*, 7th ed. (London, 1759; repr. Dublin, 1764).

Turgot wrote several articles in *Mémoires de l'Académie royale des sciences*, and in *Mémoires d'agriculture* of the Société Royale d'Agriculture (Paris). Most extant manuscripts are in private collections.

II. SECONDARY LITERATURE. References to Turgot and his work are found in the eulogies by P.-A.-M. Broussonet, in *Mémoires d'agriculture*, trimestre d'automne (1789), and the Marquis de Condorcet, in *Histoire de l'Académie des sciences, 1789* (1793), 31–38; and in Alfred Lacroix, *Notice historique sur les membres et correspondants de l'Académie des sciences ayant travaillé dans les colonies françaises de la Guyane et des Antilles de la fin du XVIIe siècle au début du XIXe* (Paris, 1932); and *Figures de savants*, III (Paris, 1932–1938), 61–69.

RHODA RAPPAPORT

TURING, ALAN MATHISON (*b.* London, England, 23 June 1912; *d.* Wilmslow, England, 7 June 1954), *mathematics, mathematical logic, computer technology*.

Turing was the son of Julius Mathias Turing and Ethel Sara Stoney. After attending Sherborne School he entered King's College, Cambridge, in 1931. He was elected a fellow of the college in 1935 for his dissertation "On the Gaussian Error Function," which won a Smith's prize in the following year. From 1936 until 1938 Turing worked at Princeton University with Alonzo Church.

While at Princeton Turing published one of his most important contributions to mathematical logic, his 1937 paper "On Computable Numbers, With an Application to the *Entscheidungsproblem*," which immediately attracted general attention. In it he analyzed the processes that can be carried out in computing a number to arrive at a concept of a theoretical "universal" computing machine (the "Turing machine"), capable of operating upon any "computable" sequence—that is, any sequence of zeros and ones. The paper included Turing's proof that Hilbert's *Entscheidungsproblem* is not solvable by these means. Church had, somewhat earlier, solved Hilbert's problem by employing a λ-definable function as a precise form of the intuitive notion of effectively calculable function, while in 1936, S. C. Kleene had proved the equivalence of λ-definability and the Herbrand-Gödel theory of general recursiveness. In his "Computability and λ-Definability" of 1937, Turing demonstrated that his and Church's ideas were equivalent.

In 1939 Turing published "Systems of Logic Based on Ordinals," in which he examined the question of constructing to any ordinal number α a logic $L\alpha$, such that any problem could be solved within some $L\alpha$. This paper had a far-reaching influence; in 1942 E. L. Post drew upon it for one of his theories for classifying unsolvable problems, while in 1958 G. Kreisel suggested the use of ordinal logics in characterizing informal methods of proof. In the latter year S. Feferman also adapted Turing's ideas to use ordinal logics in predicative mathematics.

In 1939 Turing returned to King's College, where his fellowship was renewed. His research was interrupted by World War II, however, and from the latter part of 1939 until 1948 he was employed in the communications department of the Foreign Office; he was awarded the O.B.E. for his work there. After the war, he declined the offer of a lectureship at Cambridge and, in autumn of 1945, joined the staff of the National Physical Laboratory to work on the design of an automatic computing engine (ACE).

In 1948 Turing became a reader in the University of Manchester and assistant director of the Manchester automatic digital machine (MADAM). He also continued to work in mathematical theory, and improved E. L. Post's demonstration of the existence of a semigroup with unsolvable word problem by exhibiting a semigroup with cancellation for which the word problem is (recursively) unsolvable. He made further contributions to group theory and performed calculations on the Riemann zeta-function in which he incorporated his practical work on computing machines.

In 1950 Turing took up the question of the ability of a machine to think, a subject that had gained general interest with the increasing application of mechanical computing devices to more and more complex tasks. His "Computing Machinery and Intelligence" was addressed to a broad audience and marked by a lively style. *The Programmer's Handbook for the Manchester Electronic Computer*, produced under his direction, was published in the same year.

Throughout his life Turing was also interested in applying mathematical and mechanical theory to the biological problem of life forms. He made a promising approach to this question in his 1952 publication "The Chemical Basis of Morphogene-

sis." In this work he exploited the mathematical demonstration that small variations in the initial conditions of first-order systems of differential equations may result in appreciable deviations in the asymptotic behavior of their solutions to posit that unknown functions might function biologically as form-producers; he was thus able to account for asymmetry in both mathematical and biological form. He was at work on a general theory when he died of perhaps accidental poisoning.

BIBLIOGRAPHY

I. ORIGINAL WORKS. An edition of Turing's collected works is in preparation by Professor Dr. R. O. Gandy. See especially Turing's "On Computable Numbers, With an Application to the *Entscheidungsproblem*," in *Proceedings of the London Mathematical Society*, **42** (1937), 230–265; "On Computable Numbers, With an Application to the *Entscheidungsproblem*. A Correction," *ibid.*, **43** (1937), 544–547; "Computability and λ-Definability," in *Journal of Symbolic Logic*, **2** (1937), 153–163; "Systems of Logic Based on Ordinals," in *Proceedings of the London Mathematical Society*, **45** (1939), 161–228; "The Word Problem in Semigroups With Cancellation," in *Annals of Mathematics*, **52** (1950), 491–505; "Computing Machinery and Intelligence," in *Mind*, **59** (1950), 433–460, repr. as "Can a Machine Think?" in J. R. Newman, *The World of Mathematics*, IV (New York, 1956), 2099–2133; and "The Chemical Basis of Morphogenesis," in *Philosophical Transactions of the Royal Society*, **237** (1952), 37–72.

II. SECONDARY LITERATURE. S. Turing, *Alan M. Turing* (Cambridge 1959), includes a bibliography of works by and about Turing. See also M. Davis, *Computability and Unsolvability* (New York, 1958); S. Feferman, "Ordinal Logics Re-examined," in *Journal of Symbolic Logic*, **23** (1958), 105; "On the Strength of Ordinal Logics," *ibid.*, 105–106; "Transfinite Recursive Progressions of Axiomatic Theories," *ibid.*, **27** (1962), 259–316; and "Autonomous Transfinite Progressions and the Extent of Predicative Mathematics," in B. van Rootselaar and J. F. Staal, eds., *Logic, Methodology and Philosophy of Science*, III (Amsterdam, 1968), 121–135; S. C. Kleene, *Introduction to Metamathematics* (Amsterdam–Groningen, 1952); and *Mathematical Logic* (New York, 1967); G. Kreisel, "Ordinal Logics and the Characterization of Informal Concepts of Proof," in *Proceedings of the International Congress of Mathematicians, 1958* (Cambridge, 1960), 289–299; and M. H. A. Newman, "Alan Mathison Turing," in *Biographical Memoirs of Fellows of the Royal Society 1955*, I (London, 1955), 253–263, which also has a bibliography.

B. VAN ROOTSELAAR

TURNER, EDWARD (*b*. Kingston, Jamaica, July 1796; *d*. Hampstead, London, England, 12 February 1837), *analytical chemistry*.

Turner was the second son of Dutton Smith Turner, a prosperous planter, and Mary Gale Redwar, a Creole of English ancestry. Her relatives raised and educated him in England. After attending Bath Grammar School he was apprenticed to a local country doctor from 1811 to 1814. He then spent two years walking the wards of the London Hospital before studying medicine at the University of Edinburgh from 1816 to 1819. At Edinburgh, where he was president of the student medical society, he formed a deep friendship with the energetic Robert Christison, a fellow medical student.

In August 1820, following an unsatisfactory attempt to practice medicine at Bath, Turner and Christison went to Paris for further study. Here Turner became attracted toward chemistry and physics by the lectures and experimental activities of Gay-Lussac, Pelletier, and Robiquet. From the spring of 1821 until the summer of 1823 he studied mineral analysis and chemistry at Göttingen with Friedrich von Stromeyer, who had a small teaching laboratory. Encouraged by Christison, he returned to Edinburgh in 1823 and became an important private, or extramural, lecturer in chemistry, exploiting Thomas Charles Hope's failure to provide practical chemistry teaching within the university by mounting laboratory classes. He also acted as chemical editor for David Brewster's *Edinburgh Journal of Science*. In 1827, through the influence of Leonard Horner, and supported by Brewster, Christison, Hope, Jameson, and Thomas Thomson, he was appointed professor of chemistry and lecturer in geology at the new University of London (University College, London). His teaching here ensured the popularity of chemistry among London medical students and his own financial success. From the opening of classes in 1829 he held a laboratory demonstration course (assisted by Robert Warrington). The college also provided him with a small research laboratory.

An excellent lecturer, Turner enchanted his listeners, who found him gentle and easy to approach. He was always a devout Christian, but after his health broke in 1834 he underwent evangelical conversion and hoped to impart moral and religious, as well as scientific, instruction to his students. He is distinguished as the author of one of the best nineteenth-century textbooks on chemistry, for his determination of atomic weights, and

for his attitude toward Prout's hypothesis that atomic weights were integral multiples of the atomic weight of hydrogen. His many mineralogical analyses were unexceptional.

He began his career as a naïve disciple of Thomas Thomson, whose *First Principles of Chemistry* (1825) he admired as a work of "profound sagacity." He was, therefore, initially convinced of the soundness of the Prout-Thomson multiple weights hypothesis, although like other chemists he stressed the hypothetical character of Dalton's atomism compared with the laws of chemical combination. His essay on this distinction (1825) was the foundation for his popular up-to-date textbook *Elements of Chemistry* (1827).

Through his mineralogical interests Turner was led to investigate the atomic weight of manganese, which Thomson had determined by the precipitation reaction between manganese sulfate and barium chloride, but which Berzelius had shown to be inaccurate. In 1828 Turner decided to place himself in the delicate position of "umpire between two of the greatest of living chemists" by investigating the discrepancies between Thomson's and Berzelius' atomic weights. He found immediately that Berzelius' criticism of Thomson's careless use of the reagent barium chloride was justified. From 1829 to 1833 he gradually showed that the remarkable edifice raised by Thomson's *Principles* was a house of cards. At the meeting of the British Association for the Advancement of Science held at Oxford in 1832, and at the Royal Society in 1833, Turner demonstrated by careful analyses that Thomson's atomic weights for chlorine, nitrogen, sulfur, lead, and mercury were in serious error, that his own values confirmed those of Berzelius, and, consequently, that although integral atomic weights might be used as convenient approximations by "medical men, students, and manufacturers," the true values were inconsistent with Prout's original hypothesis.

It is clear, however, that Turner believed (perhaps as a result of his friendship with Prout, or because of his own latent enthusiasm for mathematics) that chemists might one day find a simple relationship between atomic weights. He has sometimes been criticized for this wavering conclusion; but it was consistent with his empiricism and his positivistic view of physical theory. Turner believed that analytical chemistry was open to further improvements; until such time, however, chemists had no right to make unqualified guesses either way about mathematical relationships between the elements. Turner's emphasis upon the analyst as critical arbiter of theory, as well as his exacting standards, stimulated the later researches of F. Penny and J. S. Stas.

BIBLIOGRAPHY

I. ORIGINAL WORKS. Forty papers by Turner are listed in the Royal Society *Catalogue of Scientific Papers*, VI (London, 1867–1925). His books are *De Causis Febris Epidemicae nunc Edinburgi grassantis* (Edinburgh, 1819), his M.D. thesis; *Introduction to the Study of the Laws of Chemical Combination and the Atomic Theory* (London, 1825), with German trans. (Tübingen, 1828); *Elements of Chemistry* (Edinburgh, 1827; 2nd ed., London, 1828, and German trans., Leipzig, 1829; 3rd ed., London, 1831; 4th ed., London, 1833, which introduced formulas; 5th ed., London, 1834). Each of these eds. received American printings. There were three posthumous eds. by J. Liebig; W. G. Turner (1811–1855), Turner's brother, an industrial chemist; W. Gregory (London, 1842); and by Liebig and Gregory (London, 1842, 1847). Turner also published with Anthony Todd Thomson, *Two Letters to the Proprietors of the University of London, In Reply to Some Remarks in Mr. [G.S.] Pattison's Statement* (London, 1831), 16 pp.

For letters to Berzelius, see H. G. Söderbaum, ed., *Jac. Berzelius Bref* (Uppsala, 1912–1935), III, vii, 273–285. There is a small collection of Turner's college correspondence at University College, London.

II. SECONDARY LITERATURE. The most informative accounts of Turner are R. Christison, *Biographical Sketch of the late Edward Turner, M.D.*, two eds. (Edinburgh, 1837), 36 pp.; anon., "Edward Turner," in *Gentleman's Magazine*, 1 (1837), 434–435; W. Whewell, "Address to the Geological Society," in *Proceedings of the Geological Society*, 2 (1833–1838), 626–627; and the curious funeral sermon by Rev. Thomas Dale, *The Philosopher Entering . . . the Kingdom of Heaven* (London, 1837). Biographical accounts which assess his analytical work are Henry Terrey, "Edward Turner, M.D., F.R.S. (1796–1837)," in *Annals of Science*, 2 (1937), 137–152, with portrait; and J. S. Rowe, "Chemical Studies at University College, London," unpub. Ph.D. thesis, 1955.

W. H. BROCK

TURNER, HERBERT HALL (*b.* Leeds, England, 13 August 1861; *d.* Stockholm, Sweden, 20 August 1930), *astronomy, seismology.*

Turner, the son of John Turner, an artist, gained high honors in mathematics at Cambridge and was second wrangler in 1882. He was chief assistant at the Royal Observatory, Greenwich, from 1884 to 1893 and Savilian professor of astronomy at Oxford from 1893 until his death in 1930. He became a fellow of the Royal Society of London in 1897 and a correspondent of the Paris Academy of Sciences in 1908.

Turner's fame rests considerably on his ability and energy as an organizer of international scientific projects. He was a principal coordinator of work on the astrographic chart that began in 1887 and made extensive use of the new science of photography. He was active in establishing and contributed to eclipse expeditions to the West Indies in 1886, Japan in 1896, India in 1898, Algiers in 1900, and Egypt in 1905.

Turner's interests turned to seismology following the death in 1913 of his friend John Milne, who had been publishing regular analyses of instrumental records of great earthquakes. Turner took over this task, at first on a temporary basis; but the work soon became one of his major interests and culminated in the publication of the *International Seismological Summary*. This quarterly publication was a compendium of information derived from instrumental records on all well-recorded earthquakes over an uninterrupted period from 1918 to 1963. It included the estimated origin times, epicenters, and focal depths, as well as much auxiliary numerical detail, and has supplied the principal source material over several decades for some of the most important research on earthquakes and the internal structure of the earth.

In computing the origin times of earthquakes, Turner adapted Zöppritz' tables, which gave values for the travel times of earthquake waves through the earth in terms of the distances covered. These tables, known as the Zöppritz-Turner tables, were widely used into the 1930's.

Turner held several high international offices in both astronomy and seismology. He died while presiding at a meeting of the Seismology Section of the International Union of Geodesy and Geophysics.

BIBLIOGRAPHY

Turner's major publication was the quarterly *International Seismological Summary* for the years 1918–1927, published at Oxford under his editorship. He also wrote some 180 scientific papers, most of them published in *Monthly Notices of the Royal Astronomical Society*, and four semipopular books, published in London: *Modern Astronomy* (1901); *Astronomical Discovery* (1904); *The Great Star Map* (1912); and *A Voyage in Space* (1915).

There is a short notice by R. A. Sampson in *Dictionary of National Biography, 1922–1930*.

K. E. BULLEN

TURNER, PETER (*b*. London, England, 1586; *d*. London, January 1652), *mathematics*.

Turner was the son of Dr. Peter Turner and Pascha Parr, and the grandson of William Turner, the physician and naturalist and dean of Wells. He received his B.A. in 1605 and M.A. in 1612 at Oxford, and became a fellow of Merton College in 1607. Turner was the second Gresham professor of geometry (1620–1630) and second Savilian professor of geometry (1630–1648), in both cases succeeding Henry Briggs. He retained his Merton fellowship, going to London for his Gresham lectures in term time. In 1629 he was appointed to a commission charged with the revision of the Oxford statutes. The final draft was largely the work of Brian Twynne, but it was polished for the press by Turner, who was noted for his Latin style.

He was one of the first scholars to enlist for King Charles in 1641. He was captured at the battle of Edgehill and imprisoned for a time. He was ejected both from his fellowship and his professorship by the Parliamentary Visitors in 1648, and retired to live in straitened circumstances with his widowed sister in Southwark. Both Turner and the Savilian professor of astronomy, John Greaves, were replaced by Cambridge men—Turner by John Wallis, and Greaves by Seth Ward.

It is impossible to judge Turner's abilities in mathematics. He left no mathematical writings, and, indeed, seems to have been noted rather as a Latinist and a linguist, being skilled in Greek, Hebrew, and Arabic. According to Wood he destroyed many of his writings, being of too critical a mind. Further, his effects at Oxford were seized during the Civil War. Some translations from Greek to Latin of the church fathers in the possession of his colleague Mr. Henry Jacobs; Latin poems to the memory of Sir Thomas Bodley (1613); and the preface to the revised Oxford Statutes (1634) are all that are known to have survived.

BIBLIOGRAPHY

Turner's life can be found in John Ward, *Lives of the Professors of Gresham College* (1740; Johnson repr., Sources of Science, no. 71). See also C. E. Mallet, *A History of the University of Oxford*, II (Oxford, 1924– 1928; repr., New York, 1968); and the *Calendar of State Papers, Domestic*, during the reign of Charles I.

JOY B. EASTON

TURNER, WILLIAM (*b*. Morpeth, Northumberland, England, 1508; *d*. London, England, 7 July 1568), *natural history*, *medicine*.

Very little of what is recorded of Turner's family and early life in the northern counties is other than conjectural. His first appearance in the official records is as a student of Pembroke Hall, Cambridge, in 1526. He graduated B.A. in 1529/1530, and M.A. in 1533; he was a fellow of Pembroke Hall between 1530 and 1537, when he married Jane Auder of Cambridge. Under the influence of Hugh Latimer, Turner became an ardent religious reformer. His views were first made apparent in his translation of the *Comparison Betwene the Olde Learnynge and the Newe* (1537) by the German theologian Urbanus Regius.

Turner produced numerous religious tracts of the same fierce and uncompromising tone, concluding with *A Newe Booke of Spirituall Physic* (1555). His career was considerably affected by his extreme religious position. Although inclined from an early age to the tranquil study of natural history, he was forced by the threat of religious persecution to spend long periods in exile. During the first of these periods (1540–1546), Turner studied medicine in Italy, obtaining an M.D. at either Ferrara or Bologna, and traveled extensively in Germany and Switzerland, forming friendships with Konrad Gesner and other European naturalists. Having returned to England, Turner found that recognition came slowly. He was made dean of Wells Cathedral in 1551 and held this position until 1553. He incorporated for an M.D. at Oxford; Turner's work on natural history shows a consistently medical bias, and he seems to have combined medical and clerical duties throughout his career. A second period of exile (1553–1558), following the death of Edward VI, was chiefly spent as a medical practitioner in Weissenburg. Although Turner's foreign journeys were undertaken reluctantly out of necessity, they proved of inestimable value to his scientific work. He became fully acquainted with the Continental literature and with the latest trends in the research being conducted by the flourishing school of humanist naturalists. He was also able to extend his knowledge of the flora and fauna of Europe.

Some time after his second return to England,

Turner was restored to the deanery of Wells. His final years were spent in the undisturbed study of botany, in collaboration with a wide circle of friends who ranged from apothecaries to gentleman patrons.

Turner's vocation as a field naturalist emerged early. His publications include reference to material collected during his youth at Morpeth and as a student in East Anglia. At Cambridge he became dissatisfied with the derivative herbals and natural histories then in use, which gave little real impression of the local flora and fauna. He set out to produce reliable lists of English animals and plants using approved nomenclature based on classical sources and humanist usage. But Turner did not allow the scholarly aspect of his work to overshadow the results of his firsthand observations relating to morphology, distribution, behavior, and pharmacology. His main difficulty in carrying forward his botanical studies, in the troubled period of the Reformation, was in securing a subsistence and adequate toleration of his religious views. He made a modest beginning to his program with *Libellus de re herbaria* (1538), a list of 144 plants, the names of which were given in alphabetical order in Latin, with English and Greek synonyms. At this stage Turner had a good knowledge of the classical languages but not of the most recent work of humanist naturalists. This defect was supplied, and his next works written, during his periods in exile abroad. *Avium praecipuarum* (1544) follows the pattern of the *Libellus* and is a tentative list of birds mentioned in Pliny and Aristotle, with identifications of northern European species. Turner's information provides valuable evidence about the distribution of species during the sixteenth century. A further excursion into ornithology was his edition of the *Dialogus de avibus et earum nominibus*, written by his recently deceased friend Gisbert Longolius. Turner's work on birds progressed no further, his attention turning instead to fishes, on which he composed a preliminary essay addressed to Konrad Gesner. This study was primarily a list of English fishes with notes on their distribution. It shows little acquaintance with the recent writings of Belon and Rondelet in ichthyology.

Turner was more successful in completing his botanical studies. No doubt inspired by the Continental herbalists, he composed a Latin herbal; but he abandoned this project after his first return to England, when he became convinced of the necessity of first studying the British flora in its entirety. He also decided to publish in the vernacular, rec-

ognizing the need to diffuse botanical and medical knowledge as widely as possible among his countrymen, even at the cost of limiting the European influence of his work. The *Libellus* was accordingly expanded into *The Names of Herbes* (1549). For this larger collection of species, Turner drew on his Continental experience to include German and French names, with details of distribution. This publication served as an advertisement for the first section of his *New Herball* (1551), in which plants were again listed alphabetically under their Latin names, for the letters from *A* to *F*. Synonyms were given in English and other languages. Turner's descriptions were unorthodox, since he expressed these in vivid vernacular and usually included evidence drawn from firsthand observations. He showed little inclination to follow authorities and was scornful of much long-cherished herbal lore. The medical bias of the book was particularly marked, Turner intending it for use by apothecaries or laymen with medical interests. One unsatisfactory aspect of the *Herball* was the quality of its illustrations, which were poor copies of those in Leonhard Fuchs's *De historia stirpium* (1542). Turner was also arbitrarily selective, including some quite rare herbaceous plants but omitting common trees, grasses, and sedges. His second exile delayed the latter part of the *Herball* until 1562. This section, from *F* to *P*, was improved by his more extensive knowledge of German plants and by his access to Pietro Mattioli's translation of Dioscorides. He further reinforced the medical aspect of the work by including a treatise on baths, the first of numerous English works on this subject. Turner was mainly concerned with Bath, but he also made reference to baths in Italy and Germany. The first complete edition of the *Herball* appeared in 1568. Part I had been revised and expanded, Part II was unaltered, and a new Part III had been added to complete the alphabet. The quality of the descriptions was maintained: Turner wisely resisted the temptation to multiply species in the quest for encyclopedic coverage.

W. A. Cooke has estimated that Turner's pioneering flora provided the first descriptions of a total of 238 species of native plants. The vernacular names coined by Turner for indistinctly recognized species have passed into general use. In spite of its originality, Turner's work was not particularly well known to later botanists; Jean Bauhin and John Ray were exceptional in making active use of his *Herball*. It is evident that Turner's great competence in botany carried over to other spheres of natural history. Only the turmoil of his life prevented him from expanding his informative essays on birds and fishes. The preface to *The Names of Herbes* and his letter appealing for patronage to Sir William Cecil (1550) indicate that he planned books on fishes, stones, and minerals, and also a corrected translation of the New Testament. Turner's liberal interests as a naturalist provided a blueprint of the design for a system of nature that was made manifest by John Ray in the next century.

BIBLIOGRAPHY

I. ORIGINAL WORKS. A complete list of Turner's works, including those not published, or lost, is given by Charles H. Cooper, *Athenae Cantabrigenses*, I (Cambridge, 1858), 256–259. Cooper lists thirty-four titles. Turner's botanical works are *Libellus de re herbaria* (London, 1538); reprinted with a biographical introduction by B. D. Jackson (London, 1877), who also gives a list of Turner's works; *The Names of Herbes in Greke, Latin, Englishe, Duch and Frenche* (London, 1548/1549); reprinted, J. Britten, ed., English Dialect Society (London, 1882). The editions of Jackson and Britten have been reprinted, with a new introduction by W. T. Stearn, by the Ray Society (London, 1965). Turner's major botanical work is *A New Herball Wherein are Conteyned the Names of Herbes* [first part] (London, 1551); *The Seconde Parte* (Cologne, 1562), including "A Book of the Bath of Baeth"; *The First and Seconde Partes of the Herbal . . . With the Third Parte* (Cologne, 1568).

Turner's zoological writings are *Avium praecipuarum quarum apud Plinium et Aristotelem mentio* (Cologne, 1544); "Epistola Conrardo Gesnero," in Konrad Gesner, *Historia animalium*, IV (Zurich, 1558), 1294–1297.

II. SECONDARY LITERATURE. See A. Arber, *Herbals, Their Origin and Evolution*, 2nd ed. (Cambridge, 1938); W. A. Cooke, *First Records of British Flowering Plants*, 2nd ed. (London, 1900); T. P. Harrison, "William Turner, Naturalist and Priest," in *University of Texas Studies in English*, XXXIII (1954), 1–12; R. Pulteney, *Historical and Biographical Sketches of the Progress of Botany*, I (London, 1790), 40–70; C. E. Raven, *English Naturalists from Neckam to Ray* (Cambridge, 1947), by far the most extensive account of Turner as a naturalist.

CHARLES WEBSTER

TURNER, WILLIAM (*b.* Lancaster, England, 7 January 1832; *d.* Edinburgh, Scotland, 15 February 1916), *anatomy, academic administration.*

William Turner was the son of a cabinetmaker. The father died in 1837, and the boy was brought up in poor circumstances by his mother (*née* Margaret Aldren), a woman of strong character and simple faith. He was educated at a private school and apprenticed at the age of fifteen to Christopher Johnson, a local general medical practitioner.

At sixteen he proceeded to St. Bartholomew's Hospital, London, and qualified with the membership of the Royal College of Surgeons of England in the summer of 1853. His subsequent career was distinguished by parallel activities in both academic and administrative spheres.

In 1861 Turner became a fellow of the Royal Society of Edinburgh and followed Kelvin as its president in 1908. He was made fellow of the Royal Society of London in 1877, president of the Royal College of Surgeons of Edinburgh in 1882 (although he never practiced medicine or surgery), president of the Anatomical Society of Great Britain in 1892, and president of the British Association at its Bradford meeting in 1900. He was knighted in 1886 and was president of the General Medical Council of Great Britain from 1898 to 1904.

Turner's portrait, painted by Sir George Reid in 1895, shows a genial shrewd gentleman in characteristic pose. He was also painted in full academic dress by Sir James Guthrie in 1913; the portrait is now in the Court Room of the Old College, Edinburgh University.

In 1862 Turner married Anne Logan; they had three sons, two of whom practiced medicine, and two daughters.

One year after qualifying, on the recommendation of Sir James Paget, Turner was made senior demonstrator to John Goodsir, professor of anatomy at the University of Edinburgh. This school of anatomy was then the most distinguished in Britain. Turner succeeded to the chair in 1867, resigning only in 1903 when he took up the position of principal of the university, which he held until his death. He had then been a member of its Senate for forty-nine years.

In each of the bodies that he led, Turner's intimate knowledge of medical legislation, his scientific attainments, and his force of character were used to carry through important programs and reforms. Thus in Edinburgh he was instrumental in raising funds needed for the building of the new university; and when reform of medical education became imperative in the 1880's, Turner's minority report to the Royal Commission of 1881 (the Medical Acts Commission) was ultimately used as the basis of the Medical Act of 1886, an enactment that still largely governs medical education in Britain. Curiously, for one with so enlightened an outlook, Turner was consistently against the education of women alongside men in medicine, although he would have agreed to the separate establishment of medical colleges for women.

At the same time as these multifarious duties, he conducted full scientific and teaching activities. Arthur Keith wrote "on the thread of his life [are] strung all the beads of British anatomy for half a century and more." From his school at Edinburgh came graduates occupying no fewer than thirty-six chairs of anatomy, from Glasgow to Calcutta.

Turner inaugurated the *Journal of Anatomy and Physiology* in 1867 and was its editor for many years. In 1887 he and his friend and mentor George Murray Humphry, of Cambridge, founded the Anatomical Society of Great Britain and Ireland. These were important events for the teaching and influence of British anatomy.

From 1854 onward Turner published many papers, taking anthropological and comparative anatomy as his main interests. His publications list contains 276 titles. Edinburgh anatomists had long taken a wide view of their subject, based upon comparative studies. Turner broadened this basis and British anthropology attained a new eminence in world science.

Turner used his knowledge of craniology to support Huxley's defense of evolutionary theory, and his correspondence with Darwin (on rudimentary vestigial organs) is quoted by his son Logan Turner. Many of his observations were included in *The Descent of Man*. He was critical of Dubois's work on *Pithecanthropus erectus*, which he did not see as a new species intermediate between man and ape, but, in the modern light, as an early evolutionary form.

This active, conscientious, able, and amiable man was another example of anatomist-administrator. He placed British anthropology on a new footing, and his teaching in the Edinburgh anatomy department greatly influenced other schools. But his most lasting contribution probably lay in the field of medical education, in which he carried his colleagues and the government with him in opposing a "one portal" system of entry into medicine. He insisted on the right of universities to grant their own medical degrees, while supporting the idea of joint qualifying boards outside the universities; for example, the Conjoint Board of the two royal colleges and the triple diploma of the Glasgow colleges. His concept still forms the basis of British qualification in medicine.

BIBLIOGRAPHY

I. ORIGINAL WORKS. Turner's 276 papers are in his *List of Published Writings 1854–1910* (1915), of which copies are in the possession of his grandson and in the library of Edinburgh University. The subjects in this list include anatomy and physiology, comparative anatomy and zoology, pathological anatomy and anthropology, together with his many presidential addresses.

Among the titles may be noted Joseph Lister and William Turner, "Observations on the Structures of Nerve Fibres," in *Quarterly Journal of Microscopical Science*, **8** (1860), 29–34, also published separately (London, 1859); it includes a neat drawing by Lister himself. His long series of classical papers on the comparative anatomy of the placenta is exemplified by "Placentation in the Cetacea," in *Transactions of the Royal Society of Edinburgh*, **26** (1871), 467–504.

The 1875 edition of the *Encyclopaedia Britannica* contains Turner's article on "Anatomy," the historical section of which is described by Garrison as the best monograph on the subject in English.

Anthropology is represented by *The Comparative Osteology of the Races of Man*, constituting parts XXIX and XLVII of the zoological series of the *Scientific Results of the Voyage of H.M.S. Challenger* (Edinburgh, 1884–1886). His many contributions to craniology include those on the "People of Scotland" and the "People of India," in *Transactions of the Royal Society of Edinburgh, passim*.

Turner's collection of Cetacea made over fifty years is described in *The Marine Mammals in the Anatomical Museum of the University of Edinburgh* (Edinburgh, 1913).

A paper on "M. Dubois' Description. . . . of Pithecanthropus Erectus" is in *Journal of Anatomy and Physiology*, **29** (1895), 424–445.

II. SECONDARY LITERATURE. The main source is the biography by his son A. Logan Turner, *Sir William Turner, A Chapter in Medical History* (London, 1919). Many journals published obituary notices, the fullest account being in *British Medical Journal* (1916), **1**, 326–331. Others may be found in *Lancet* (1916), **1**, 484–486; *Nature*, **96** (1916), 79; and *The Student. Turner Memorial Number* (11 July 1916), published by the Students' Council, University of Edinburgh.

K. BRYN THOMAS

TURNER, WILLIAM ERNEST STEPHEN (*b.* Wednesbury, Staffordshire, England, 22 September 1881; *d.* Sheffield, England, 27 October 1963), *glass technology*.

Turner was the eldest son and the second of seven children of William George Turner and Emma Blanche Turner. His working-class parents sacrificed so that he could gain an education. Turner progressed from a Smethwick board school to King Edward VI Grammar School, Birmingham, and then in 1898 to Mason University College (which became Birmingham University in 1900). He graduated with a bachelor of science in 1902 and earned a master of science in 1904. Turner's first post was at Sheffield University under W. P. Wynne, where he early showed his characteristic capacity for organization. He lectured on physical chemistry for metallurgical students. His earlier experimental research was in conventional physical chemistry (for example, solubility and molecular weights in solution).

During this part of his career Turner continually urged the employment of scientists in industry and the establishment of a closer liaison between universities and industry. On the outbreak of war in 1914, he successfully advocated the formation of a Sheffield University technical advisory committee to consider problems raised by the cutting off of supplies from Germany. Although the initial problems lay in the field of metallurgy, glass soon became an issue. Turner drew up a report on the glass industry of Yorkshire, in which he dealt with the poor practical methods then in use, the paucity of technical literature on glass, and the need for teaching and research. He recommended that Sheffield become a center for instruction in glass manufacture. It was a triumph for Turner that, owing to his foresight, a Department of Glass Technology was created in the middle of the war.

At this time the government was promoting research associations (supported by both industry and government), but Turner resisted this type of organization and retained, through an appointed committee known as the Glass Delegacy, a high degree of independence for his department from the university, government, and industry while also securing the support of each. A separate organization, the Glass Research Association, foundered in 1925, and Turner's Department of Glass Technology held unchallenged world leadership in glass research for a generation. The research was directed mainly toward industrial problems, his view being that it was "wiser to tackle the immediate problems first and then let the need for the long dated, fundamental problems grow out of the imperative need for more information or for sounder basic principles" (Mellor Memorial Lecture, 1957). Typical problems had to do with the composition of raw materials for lead crystal, the resistance of chemical glass to reagents, and the design of furnaces. Fundamental studies emerged, for ex-

ample, on the variation of the physical properties of glass over a range of compositions, and the effect of small quantities of minor additives on these properties. Demands of other industries also raised problems, including that of the design of glass-to-metal seals in electrical construction.

World War II limited the freedom that Turner and his department had hitherto enjoyed. But the department continued to give valuable technical service, and even to increase its student enrollment. The Department of Glass Technology later reverted to a more orthodox form of administration comparable to that found in other university departments.

In 1916 Turner established the Society of Glass Technology, and a *Journal* began appearing in 1917. He was the editor until it ceased publication in 1959. By that time the form and content of the journal seemed no longer to meet the needs of a science and industry that he himself had done so much to change. Turner promoted international exchanges and was president of an International Commission for Glass Technology from 1933 to 1953.

During his retirement Turner encouraged the growing application of science to the archaeology of glass. He was an inveterate traveler, and although physically handicapped by the results of childhood poliomyelitis, he was a vigorous walker, even in the Alps.

Turner was married twice, first to Mary Isobel Marshall (died 1939), who bore him four children, and then in 1943 to Annie Helen Nairn, an artist in glass, who designed the presidential badge of the Society of Glass Technology. He was an officer of the Order of the British Empire (1918), fellow of the Royal Society (1938), and the holder of many foreign honors.

BIBLIOGRAPHY

For a list of Turner's writings, see *Biographical Memoirs of Fellows of the Royal Society*, X (1964), 325–356. This work lists twenty papers from the period 1905–1914, mainly on physical chemistry; some 240 research papers from 1914–1954, on glass technology; some eighty lectures and addresses on general industrial problems; and some thirty papers on glass archaeology.

An obituary notice is in *Glass Technology*, 4 (Dec. 1963), 165–169, with two portraits.

Personal reminiscences are in W. E. S. Turner, "The Department of Glass Technology and Its Work Since 1915," in *Journal of the Society of Glass Technology*,

21 (1937), transactions 5–43; R. W. Douglas, "W. E. S. Turner–Applied Scientist," in *Glass Technology*, **8** (February 1969), 19–28.

FRANK GREENAWAY

TURPIN, PIERRE JEAN FRANÇOIS (*b.* Vire, France, 11 March 1775; *d.* Paris, France, 1 May 1840), *botany*.

Turpin was the son of an impoverished artisan. He studied drawing at the École des Beaux-Arts in Vire, then, in 1780, enlisted as a soldier in the Calvados battalion. In 1794 he was sent to Haiti, where he met Alexandre Poiteau, a gardener at the Paris Muséum d'Histoire Naturelle, who taught him botany. Turpin and Poiteau collaborated in a study of Haitian flora; they collected an herbarium of some 1,200 plants, of which Turpin made drawings of a large number, and of which they together described about 800 species. They took this material to France, but Turpin soon returned to make a further exploration of Hispaniola and of the island of Tortuga, which lies off its northwest coast. In 1800 he made a trip to the United States, where he met Humboldt, but returned again to Haiti to serve as an army pharmacist in the campaign against Toussaint-L'Ouverture that was being conducted by General Leclerc. In 1802 Turpin settled in France to devote himself to botany and botanical illustration.

As a botanical artist Turpin achieved a fame equal to that of Redouté. He collaborated on a number of the most important botanical publications of the early nineteenth century, including Humboldt's *Plantae aequinoctiales . . . in ordem digessit Amatus Bonpland*, Benjamin Delessert's *Icones selectae plantarum pr. part.*, and J. L. M. Poiret's *Leçons de flore*, to which he contributed fifty-seven plates. He also made a number of drawings for the less distinguished *Flore du dictionnaire des sciences médicales* of F. P. Chaumeton, Chambéret, and Poiret. He himself composed a flora of Paris, then collaborated on another with Poiteau, who had also published a previous work on the same subject. Only the first eight parts of their joint work was printed, as *Flore parisienne contenant la description des plantes qui croissent naturellement aux environs de Paris* (1808–1813). Poiteau and Turpin also collaborated on a new, admirably illustrated edition of Duhamel du Monceau's *Traité des arbres fruitiers* of 1768; this work, which was important for distinguishing botanical species from the races or varieties known to gardeners, had lacked good drawings. In the new recension, published in 1808–1835, the work became one of the most beautiful books on fruit trees ever published.

Turpin's own botanical research reflected the broad scientific concerns of his time. A systematist by temperament, he believed in the great chain of being and in the continuity of forms and organs. He thus sought an archetypal model to explain the constitution of plants, and was particularly impressed by Goethe's notion of the leaf as the archetypal organ of the plant. (Charles Gaudichaud-Beaupré had proposed that this fundamental organ be called the "phyton," because it was formed by both the leaf–the phyllome–and the base that forms part of the stem, the phyllopodium.)

Turpin defended the idea of organ types in a number of works, including "Mémoire sur l'inflorescence des Graminées et des Cypéracées" (1819), "Organographie végétale" (1827), *Mémoire sur l'organisation intérieure et extérieure des tubercules du Solanum tuberosum* (1828), "Mémoire de nosologie végétale" (1833), and "Observations générales sur l'organogénie et la physiologie des végétaux" (1835). His *Examen d'une chloranthie ou monstruosité observée sur l'inflorescence du saule marceau* of 1833 is a related teratological study. In 1837 Turpin presented to the Académie des Sciences a drawing, executed in 1804, of the plant type that he had first conceived in Haiti. He intended this to illustrate the unity of organic composition and the original identity of all the foliaceous and lateral appendicular organs of the plant; the engraving was one of several published in C.-F. Martins's edition of the *Oeuvres d'histoire naturelle de Goethe* (1837). Goethe himself had, shortly before his death, asked Turpin to illustrate the theory that he had presented in his *Versuch die Metamorphose der Pflanzen zur erklaeren* of 1790.

Turpin also participated in the elaboration of the cell theory. His writings on the subject, published in 1820, were largely influenced by Spengler's idea that the "utricle" (cell) contained vesicles and granules, including the chlorophyll granules that played an active part in cellular development. From Sprengler, too, Turpin derived the notion of the plant as an aggregate of independent, completely individualized cells. Turpin did further research on the lower plants, and made a number of contributions to the systematics of freshwater algae. In addition, he was one of the first to confirm the conclusion of C. Cagniard de la Tour and T. Schwann that yeast is a living organism that reproduces by budding.

BIBLIOGRAPHY

Turpin's writings include *Flore parisienne contenant la description des plantes qui croissent naturellement aux environs de Paris*, 8 pts. (Paris, 1808–1813), written with A. Poiteau; "Mémoire sur l'inflorescence des Graminées et des Cyperacées," in *Memoires du Muséum d'histoire naturelle*, **5** (1819), 426–492; "Organographie végétale," ibid., **14** (1827); *Mémoire sur l'organisation intérieure et extérieure des tubercules du Solanum tuberosum* (Paris, 1828); *Examen d'une chloranthie ou monstruosité observée sur l'inflorescence du saule marceau* (Paris, 1833); "Mémoire de nosologie végétale," in *Mémoires présentés par divers savants*, **6** (1835), 217–240; and "Observations générales sur l'organogénie et la physiologie des végétaux," in *Mémoires de l'Académie des sciences*, 2nd ser., **14** (1835). He also collaborated with Poiteau on a new ed. of Duhamel du Monceau's *Traité des arbres fruitiers*, 6 vols. (Paris, 1808–1835).

In addition, Turpin contributed to Humboldt's *Plantae aequinoctiales . . . in ordinem digessit Amatus Bonpland*, 2 vols. (Paris, 1805–1818); F. P. Chaumeton, Chambéret, and J. L. M. Poiret's *Flore . . . médicale*, 8 vols. (Paris, 1814–1820); Poiret's *Leçons de flore*, 3 vols. (Paris, 1819–1820); and Benjamin Delessert's *Icones selectae plantarum pr. part.* (Paris, 1820–1823).

Twenty-five artistic items by Turpin are now in the Lindley Library.

M. HOCQUETTE

TURQUET DE MAYERNE, THEODORE (*b.* Mayerne, near Geneva, Switzerland, 28 September 1573; *d.* London, England, 15/16 March 1655), *medicine, chemistry.*

Turquet de Mayerne was the son of the noted Huguenot historian and political theorist Louis Turquet de Mayerne. Following early schooling at Geneva, he went to the University of Heidelberg and thence to Montpellier, where he graduated M.D. in 1597. In his subsequent career, that of an eminently successful court physician in both France and England, he displayed a remarkable ability to survive professional and political upheaval. Although not a prominent scientific figure in his own right, he was influential in the introduction and support of chemical therapeutics in medicine.

After graduating at Montpellier, Turquet went to Paris, where he became the protégé of Jean Ribit, first physician to Henry IV and a fellow Calvinist. He became a royal physician, and as Ribit's disciple he built up a successful practice that included many notables, particularly but not exclusively among the Huguenots. On Ribit's death in 1605, Turquet inherited their joint clientele. Ribit and

Turquet both endorsed the use of chemical remedies in their practice, and fostered the training of apothecaries in the preparation of these new medicaments. They probably were instrumental in establishing Jean Beguin's chemistry courses in Paris.

This advocacy of chemical therapeutics aroused the hostility of the Paris Medical Faculty, and Turquet became personally embroiled in the bitter polemics that ensued between the Faculty and proponents of Paracelsian therapy. In 1603 yet another Calvinist royal physician, Joseph Duchesne (Quercetanus), wrote a treatise defending Paracelsian-Hermetic medicine, which promptly elicited an anonymous and vituperative reply from the Faculty (most probably written by the elder Jean Riolan). In response to this Faculty-sponsored attack, Turquet published in the same year (1603) a moderate defense of chemical therapeutics arguing that the new remedies did not contravene the principles of medicine as set down by Hippocrates and Galen. This publication, however, was sufficient to bring him the official censure of the Faculty on 5 December 1603. As a privileged royal physician, Turquet was able to continue in practice, despite the fulminations of the Faculty.

Following the assassination of Henry IV, Turquet moved permanently to England in 1611; he had visited there in 1606, when he was incorporated M.D. at the University of Oxford. He came as first physician to James I and later served Charles I and his queen in a similar capacity. His professional career in England was a dazzling success and made him very rich. Turquet was elected a fellow of the Royal College of Physicians in 1616; he bought the *seigneurie* of Aubonne (near Lausanne) in 1621; and he was knighted by James in 1624. Following the outbreak of the English Civil War, he retired to Chelsea, where he died in 1655; he was buried in St. Martin-in-the-Fields. Only one daughter of his seven children by two marriages survived him.

In England, Turquet continued his interest in chemical therapeutics and the training of apothecaries. In association with Henry Atkins, several times president of the Royal College of Physicians, he helped establish the Worshipful Society of Apothecaries, which gave English pharmacists distinct corporate status and distinguished them from the grocers. He also served on the Royal College's committee that produced the first edition of the *Pharmacopoeia Londinensis* (1618), intended to provide the first standardized English formulary. It generally has been assumed that he was influential in the inclusion of chemical remedies in this text. It should be noted, however, that when the first specific proposals for the *Pharmacopoeia* were drawn up in 1589, such remedies were included. Also, Turquet did not join the College's committee on the *Pharmacopoeia* until shortly before its publication. He wrote the dedicatory epistle to James I, which should not be confused with the preface to the reader in which chemical remedies are defended. Turquet developed some chemical prescriptions of his own, including the popular *lotio nigra*, the main ingredient of which was mercuric oxide. He also experimented with pigments and included among his friends the artists Rubens, Van Dyke, Peter Lely, and Jean Petitot. It was also through his efforts that the manuscript of Thomas Moffett's *Theatrum insectorum* was published in 1634.

BIBLIOGRAPHY

I. ORIGINAL WORKS. Turquet de Mayerne published little in his lifetime. An early travel book attributed to him is entitled *Sommaire description de la France, Allemagne, Italie et Espagne* (Geneva, 1591; 1653). His defense of chemical remedies is *Apologia in qua videre est, inviolatis Hippocratis et Galeni legibus, remedia chymice preparata tuto usurpari posse, ad cujusdam anonymi calumnias responsio* (La Rochelle, 1603). Turquet did, however, keep extensive personal and clinical records throughout his life, the bulk of which became the property of Sir Hans Sloane and are now in the Sloane collection of the British Museum (for description see Edward J. L. Scott, *Index to the Sloane Manuscripts in the British Museum* [London, 1904], 349–350).

Turquet's MSS formed the basis of several posthumously published collections of his clinical case histories. The distinction of his patients gives these added historical interest. The first such collection was published, along with a treatise on gout, as *Tractatus de arthritide. Accesserunt ejusdem consilia aliquot medicinalia* (Geneva, 1674), translated into English by Thomas Sherley, 2 vols. (London, 1676–1677). A more comprehensive and systematic collection was published with a preface by Walter Charlton as *Praxeos Mayernianae in morbis internis* (London, 1690, 1695; Augsburg, 1691; Geneva, 1692 [as *Praxis medica*]). The last and most complete collection was edited by Joseph Browne as *Theodori Turquet Mayernii . . . opera medica, complectentia consilia, epistolas, et observationes, pharmacopeam, variasque medicamentorum formulas* (London, 1700, 1701, 1703).

II. SECONDARY LITERATURE. Accounts of Turquet's life and writings include the following, listed chronologically: Norman Moore, "Mayerne, Sir Theodore Turquet de," in *Dictionary of National Biography*; Thomas Gib-

son, "A Sketch of the Career of Theodore Turquet de Mayerne," in *Annals of Medical History*, n.s. 5 (1933), 315–326; "An Account of Dr. Theodore Turquet de Mayerne's 'Praxis Medica.' Augsburg 1691," *ibid.*, 438–443; and "Letters of Dr. Theodore Turquet de Mayerne to the Syndics and Executive Council of the Republic of Geneva," *ibid.*, n.s. 9 (1937), 401–421; and William B. Ober, "Sir Theodore Turquet de Mayerne, M.D., F.R.C.P. (1573–1655); Stuart Physician and Observer," in *New York State Journal of Medicine*, **70** (1970), 449–458. Most of these sources contain factual inaccuracies and must be used with caution.

For Turquet's association with Jean Ribit, see Hugh Trevor-Roper, "The Sieur de la Rivière, Paracelsian Physician of Henri IV," in *Science, Medicine and Society in the Renaissance, Essays to Honor Walter Pagel*, Allen G. Debus, ed., II (New York, 1972), 227–250. The Paris dispute over chemical therapy is discussed in W. P. D. Wightman, *Science and the Renaissance*, I (Edinburgh–London–New York, 1962), 256–263.

For Turquet's relationship with the English apothecaries, see C. Wall, H. Charles Cameron, and E. Ashworth Underwood, *A History of the Worshipful Society of Apothecaries of London*, I (London, 1963), *passim*. His role in the publication of the *London Pharmacopoeia* is discussed by George Urdang in the historical intro. to the facs. repro. of the 1618 ed. of *Pharmacopoeia Londinensis* (Madison, Wis., 1944); also see Urdang's "How Chemicals Entered the Official Pharmacopoeias," in *Archives internationales d'histoire des sciences*, n.s. 7 (1954), 303–314; and Allen G. Debus, *The English Paracelsians* (New York, 1966), 150–156. These should be assessed, however, in the light of Sir George Clark, *A History of the Royal College of Physicians of London*, I (Oxford, 1964), 227–230.

OWEN HANNAWAY

AL-ṬŪSĪ, MUḤAMMAD IBN MUḤAMMAD IBN AL-ḤASAN, usually known as **NAṢĪR AL-DĪN** (*b.* Ṭūs, Persia, 18 February 1201; *d.* Kadhimain, near Baghdad, 26 June 1274), *astronomy, mathematics, mineralogy, logic, philosophy, ethics, theology.*

Life. Naṣīr al-Dīn, known to his compatriots as Muḥaqqiq-i Ṭūsī, Khwāja-yi Ṭūsī, or Khwāja Naṣīr, is one of the best-known and most influential figures in Islamic intellectual history. He studied the religious sciences and elements of the "intellectual sciences" with his father, a jurisprudent of the Twelve Imām school of Shīʿism at Ṭūs. He also very likely studied logic, natural philosophy, and metaphysics with his maternal uncle in the same city. During this period he also received instruction in algebra and geometry. Afterward he set out for Nīshāpūr, then still a major center of learning, to complete his formal advanced education; and it was in this city that he gained a reputation as an outstanding scholar. His most famous teachers were Farīd al-Dīn al-Dāmād, who through four intermediaries was linked to Ibn Sīnā and his school and with whom Ṭūsī studied philosophy; Quṭb al-Dīn al-Maṣrī, who was himself the best-known student of Fakhr al-Dīn al-Rāzī (1148–1209), with whom al-Ṭūsī studied medicine, concentrating mostly on the text of Ibn Sīnā's *Canon*; and Kamāl al-Dīn ibn Yūnus (1156–1242), with whom he studied mostly mathematics.

This period was one of the most tumultuous in Islamic history: Mongols were advancing toward Khurasan from Central Asia. Therefore, although already a famous scholar, al-Ṭūsī could not find a suitable position and the tranquillity necessary for a scholarly life. The only islands of peace at this time in Khurasan were the Ismāʿīlī forts and mountain strongholds, and he was invited to avail himself of their security by the Ismāʿīlī ruler, Naṣīr al-Dīn Muḥtashim. Al-Ṭūsī accepted the invitation and went to Quhistan, where he was received with great honor and was held in high esteem at the Ismāʿīlī court, although most likely he was not free to leave had he wanted to. The date of his entrance into the service of the Ismāʿīlī rulers is not known exactly but was certainly sometime before 1232, for it was during that year that he wrote his famous *Akhlāq-i nāṣirī* for the Ismāʿīlī ruler. During his stay at the various Ismāʿīlī strongholds, including Alamut, al-Ṭūsī wrote a number of his important ethical, logical, philosophical, and mathematical works, including *Asās al-iqtibās* (on logic) and *Risāla-yi muʿīniyya* (on astronomy). His fame as a scholar reached as far as China.

Hūlāgū ended the rule of the Ismāʿīlīs in northern Persia in 1256. His interest in astrology, and therefore his respect for astronomers, combined with al-Ṭūsī's fame in this field, made Hūlāgū especially respectful toward him after he had captured Alamut and "freed" al-Ṭūsī from the fort. Henceforth al-Ṭūsī remained in the service of Hūlāgū as his scientific adviser and was given charge of religious endowments (*awqāf*) and religious affairs. He accompanied Hūlāgū on the expedition that led to the conquest of Baghdad in 1258 and later visited the Shīʿite centers of Iraq, such as Ḥilla.

Having gained the full confidence of Hūlāgū, and benefiting from his interest in astrology, al-Ṭūsī was able to gain his approval to construct a major observatory at Marāgha. Construction began in 1259, and the Īlkhānī astronomical tables were completed in 1272 under Abāqā, after the death of

Hūlāgū. In 1274, while at Baghdad, al-Ṭūsī fell ill and died a month later. He was buried near the mausoleum of the seventh Shīʿite imām, Mūsā al-Kāzim, a few miles from Baghdad.

Works. Nearly 150 treatises and letters by Naṣīr al-Dīn al-Ṭūsī are known, of which twenty-five are in Persian and the rest in Arabic. There is even a treatise on geomancy that al-Ṭūsī wrote in Arabic, Persian, and Turkish, demonstrating his mastery of all three languages. It is said that he also knew Greek. His writings concern nearly every branch of the Islamic sciences, from astronomy to philosophy and from the occult sciences to theology. Of the two, Ibn Sīnā was the better physician and al-Ṭūsī the greater mathematician and more competent writer in Persian. But otherwise their breadth of knowledge and influence can be compared very favorably. Moreover, the writings of al-Ṭūsī are distinguished by the fact that so many became authoritative works in the Islamic world.

Al-Ṭūsī composed five works in logic, of which *Asās al-iqtibās* ("Foundations of Inference"), written in Persian, is the most important. In fact, it is one of the most extensive of its kind ever written, surpassed only by the section on logic of Ibn Sīnā's *al-Shifāʾ*. In mathematics al-Ṭūsī composed a series of recensions (*taḥrīr*) upon the works of Autolycus, Aristarchus, Euclid, Apollonius, Archimedes, Hypsicles, Theodosius, Menelaus, and Ptolemy. The texts studied by students of mathematics between Euclid's *Elements* and Ptolemy's *Almagest* were known as the "intermediate works" (*mutawassiṭāt*); and the collection of al-Ṭūsī's works concerning this "intermediate" body of texts became standard in the teaching of mathematics, along with his recensions of Euclid and Ptolemy. He also wrote many original treatises on arithmetic, geometry, and trigonometry, of which the most important are *Jawāmiʿ al-ḥisāb biʾl-takht waʾl turāb* ("The Comprehensive Work on Computation with Board and Dust"), *al-Risāla al-shāfiya* ("The Satisfying Treatise"), and *Kashf al-qināʿ fī asrār shakl al-qitāʿ*, known as the *Book of the Principle of Transversal*, which was translated into Latin and influenced Regiomontanus. The best-known of al-Ṭūsī's numerous astronomical works is *Zīj-i īlkhānī* ("The Īlkhānī Tables"), written in Persian and later translated into Arabic and also partially into Latin, by John Greaves, as *Astronomia quaedam ex traditione Shah Cholgii Persae una cum hypothesibus planetarum* (London, 1650). Other major astronomical works are *Tadhkirah* ("Treasury of Astronomy") and his treatises on particular astronomical subjects, such as that on the astrolabe. He also translated the *Ṣuwar al-kawākib* ("Figures of the Fixed Stars" of ʿAbd al-Raḥmān al-Ṣūfī from Arabic into Persian. In the other sciences al-Ṭūsī produced many works, of which *Tanksūkh-nāma* ("The Book of Precious Materials") is particularly noteworthy. He also wrote on astrology.

In philosophy, ethics, and theology al-Ṭūsī composed a commentary on *al-Ishārāt waʾl-tanbīhāt* ("The Book of Directives and Remarks") of Ibn Sīnā; the *Akhlāq-i nāṣirī* (*Nasirean Ethics*), the best-known ethical work in the Persian language, and the *Tajrīd* ("Catharsis"), the main source book of Shiʿite theology, upon which over 400 commentaries and glosses have been composed. Al-Ṭūsī wrote outstanding expositions of Ismāʿīlī doctrine, chief among them the *Taṣawwurāt* ("Notions"), and composed mystical treatises, such as *Awṣāf al-ashrāf* ("Qualifications of the Noble").

Al-Ṭūsī also composed lucid and delicate poetry, mostly in Persian.

Scientific Achievements. In logic al-Ṭūsī followed the teachings of Ibn Sīnā but took a new step in studying the relation between logic and mathematics. He also elucidated the conditional conjunctive (*iqtirānī*) syllogism better than his predecessor. He converted logical terms into mathematical signs and clarified the mathematical signs employed by Abuʾl-Barakāt in his *Kitāb al-muʿtabar* ("The Esteemed Book"). Al-Ṭūsī also distinguished between the meaning of "substance" in the philosophical sense and its use as a scientific term, and clarified the relation of the categories with respect to metaphysics and logic.

In mathematics al-Ṭūsī's contributions were mainly in arithmetic, geometry, and trigonometry. He continued the work of al-Khayyāmī in extending the meaning of number to include irrationals. In his *Shakl al-qitāʿ* he showed the commutative property of multiplication between pairs of ratios (which are real numbers) and stated that every ratio is a number. *Jawāmiʿ al-ḥisāb*, which marks an important stage in the development of the Indian numerals, contains a reference to Pascal's triangle and the earliest extant method of extracting fourth and higher roots of numbers. In collaboration with his colleagues at Marāgha, al-Ṭūsī also began to develop computational mathematics, which was pursued later by al-Kāshī and other mathematicians of the Tīmūrid period.

In geometry al-Ṭūsī also followed the work of al-Khayyāmī and in his *al-Risāla al-shāfiya* he examined Euclid's fifth postulate. His attempt to prove it through Euclidean geometry was unsuc-

cessful. He demonstrated that in the quadrilateral *ABCD*, in which *AB* and *DC* are equal and both perpendicular to *BC*, and the angles *A* and *D* are equal, if angles *A* and *D* are acute, the sum of the angles of a triangle will be less than 180°.[1] This is characteristic of the geometry of Lobachevski and shows that al-Ṭūsī, like al-Khayyāmī, had demonstrated some of the properties of the then unknown non-Euclidean geometry. The quadrilateral associated with Saccheri was employed centuries before him by Thābit ibn Qurra, al-Ṭūsī, and al-Khayyāmī.

Probably al-Ṭūsī's most outstanding contribution to mathematics was in trigonometry. In *Shakl al-qitāʿ*, which follows the earlier work of Abuʾl-Wafāʾ, Manṣūr ibn ʿIrāq, and al-Bīrūnī, al-Ṭūsī for the first time, as far as modern research has been able to show, developed trigonometry without using Menelaus' theorem or astronomy. This work is really the first in history on trigonometry as an independent branch of pure mathematics and the first in which all six cases for a right-angled spherical triangle are set forth. If c = the hypotenuse of a spherical triangle, then:

$$\cos c = \cos a \cos b \qquad \cot A = \tan b \cot c$$
$$\cos c = \cot A \cot B \qquad \sin b = \sin c \sin B$$
$$\cos A = \cos a \sin B \qquad \sin b = \tan a \cot A.$$

He also presents the theorem of sines:

$$\frac{a}{\sin A} = \frac{b}{\sin B} = \frac{c}{\sin C}.$$

It is described clearly for the first time in this book, a landmark in the history of mathematics.

Al-Ṭūsī is best-known as an astronomer. With Hūlāgū's support he gained the necessary financial assistance and supervised the construction of the first observatory in the modern sense. Its financial support, based upon endowment funds; its lifespan, which exceeded that of its founder; its use as a center of instruction in science and philosophy; and the collaboration of many scientists in its activities mark this observatory as a major scientific institution in the history of science. The observatory was staffed by Quṭb al-Dīn al-Shīrāzī, Muḥyi ʾl-Dīn al-Maghribī, Fakhr al-Dīn al-Marāghī, Muʾayyad al-Dīn al-ʿUrḍī, ʿAlī ibn ʿUmar al-Qazwīnī, Najm al-Dīn Dabīrān al-Kātibī al-Qazwīnī, Athīr al-Dīn al-Abharī, al-Ṭūsī's sons Aṣīl al-Dīn and Ṣadr al-Dīn, the Chinese scholar Fao Mun-ji, and the librarian Kamāl al-Dīn al-Aykī. It had excellent instruments made by Muʾayyad al-Dīn al-ʿUrḍī in 1261–1262, including a giant mural quadrant, an armillary sphere with five rings and an alidade, a solstitial armill, an azimuth ring with two quadrants, and a parallactic ruler. It was also equipped with a fine library with books on all the sciences. Twelve years of observation and calculation led to the completion of the Zīj-i īlkhānī in 1271, to which Muḥyī 'l-Dīn al-Maghribī later wrote a supplement. The work of the observatory was not confined to astronomy, however; it played a major role in the revival of all the sciences and philosophy.

Al-Ṭūsī's contributions to astronomy, besides the Zīj and the recension of the Almagest, consist of a criticism of Ptolemaic astronomy in his Tadhkira, which is perhaps the most thorough exposition of the shortcomings of Ptolemaic astronomy in medieval times, and the proposal of a new theory of planetary motion. The only new mathematical model to appear in medieval astronomy, this theory influenced not only Quṭb al-Dīn al-Shīrāzī and Ibn al-Shāṭir but also most likely Copernicus, who followed closely the planetary models of Naṣīr al-Dīn's students. In chapter 13 of the second treatise of the Tadhkira, al-Ṭūsī proves that "if one circle rolls inside the periphery of a stationary circle, the radius of the first being half the second, then any point on the first describes a straight line, a diameter of the second."[2] E. S. Kennedy, who first discovered this late medieval planetary theory issuing from Marāgha, interprets it as "a linkage of two equal length vectors, the second rotating with constant velocity twice that of the first and in a direction opposite the first."[3] He has called this the "Ṭūsī-couple" and has demonstrated (see Figures 1 and 2) its application by al-Ṭūsī, Quṭb al-Dīn, and Ibn al-Shāṭir to planetary motion and its comparison with the Ptolemaic model.[4]

This innovation, which originated with al-Ṭūsī, is without doubt the most important departure from Ptolemaic astronomy before modern times. Except for the heliocentric thesis, the "novelty" of Copernicus' astronomy is already found in the works of al-Ṭūsī and his followers, which probably reached Copernicus through Byzantine intermediaries.

The most important mineralogical work by al-Ṭūsī is Tanksūkh-nāma, written in Persian and based on many of the earlier Muslim sources, such as the works of Jābir ibn Ḥayyān, al-Kindī, Muḥammad ibn Zakariyyāʾ, al-Rāzī, ʿUṭārid ibn Muḥammad, and especially al-Bīrūnī, whose Kitāb al-jamāhir fī maʿrifat al-jawāhir ("The Book of Multitudes Concerning the Knowledge of Precious Stones") is the main source of al-Ṭūsī's work. In fact the Tanksūkh-nāma, which derives its name

from the Turco-Mongolian word meaning "something precious," probably is second in importance in the annals of Muslim mineralogy only to al-Bīrūnī's masterpiece.

Al-Ṭūsī's work comprises four chapters. In the first he discusses the nature of compounds; the four elements, their mixture, and the coming into being of a "fifth quality" called temperament (mizāj), which can accept the forms of different species; and the role of vapors and the rays of the sun in their formation, in all of this following closely the theories of Ibn Sīnā's De mineralibus. An interesting section is devoted to colors, which al-Ṭūsī believes result from the mixture of white and black. In jewels, colors are due to the mixture of earthy and watery elements contained in the substance of the jewel.

The second chapter is devoted exclusively to jewels, their qualities, and their properties. Special attention is paid to rubies, the medical and occult properties of which are discussed extensively. In the third chapter al-Ṭūsī turns to metals and gives an alchemical theory of metallic formation, calling sulfur the father and mercury the mother of metals. He also enumerates the seven traditional metals, including khārṣīnī. Like so many Muslim philosopher-scientists, al-Ṭūsī accepts the cosmological and mineralogical theories of alchemy concerning the formation of metals without belonging to the alchemical tradition or even discussing the transmutation of base metal into gold. A section on perfumes ends the book, which is one of the major sources of Muslim mineralogy and is valuable as a source of Persian scientific vocabulary in this field.

Of all the major fields of science, al-Ṭūsī was least interested in medicine, which he nevertheless studied, generally following the teachings of Ibn Sīnā. He also composed a few works on medicine including Qawānīn al-ṭibb ("Principles of Medicine") and a commentary on Ibn Sīnā's Canon, and exchanged letters with various medical authorities on such subjects as breathing and temperament. He expressed certain differences of opinion with Ibn Sīnā concerning the temperament of each organ of the body but otherwise followed his teachings. Al-Ṭūsī's view of medicine was mainly philosophical; and perhaps his greatest contribution was in psychosomatic medicine, which he discusses, among other places, in his ethical writings, especially Akhlāq-i nāṣirī (Nasirean Ethics).

Al-Ṭūsī was one of the foremost philosophers of Islam, reviving the Peripatetic (mashshāʾī) teachings of Ibn Sīnā after they had been eclipsed for

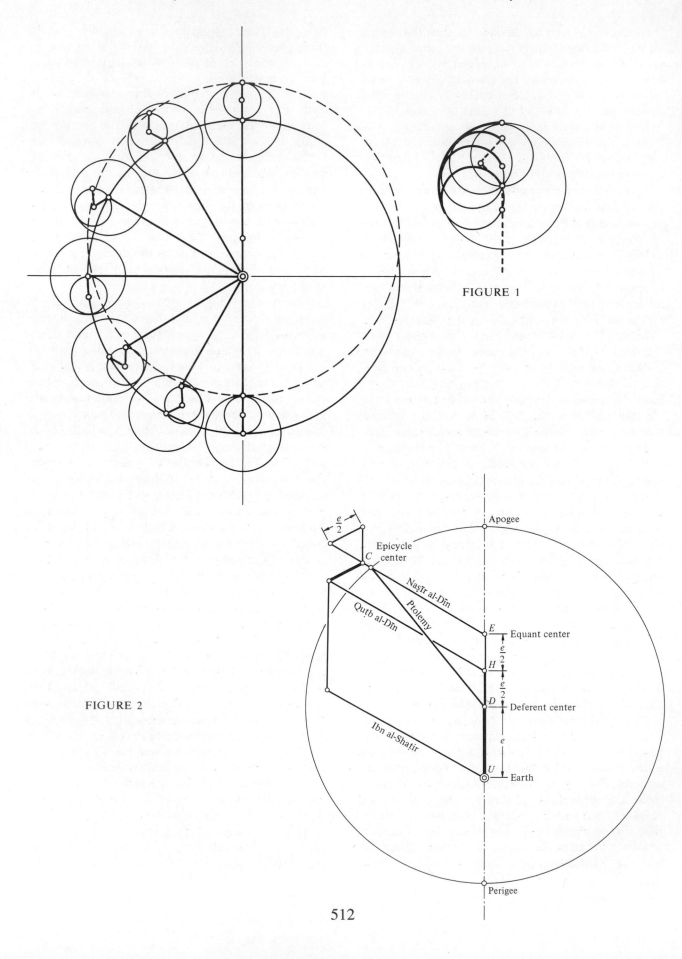

FIGURE 1

FIGURE 2

$\frac{e}{2}$

Epicycle
C   center

Naṣīr al-Dīn

Quṭb al-Dīn

Ptolemy

Ibn al-Shaṭir

Apogee

E   Equant center

$\frac{e}{2}$

H

$\frac{e}{2}$

D   Deferent center

e

U   Earth

Perigee

nearly two centuries by *Kalām*. He wrote a masterful commentary on the *Ishārāt waʾl-tanbīhāt* of Ibn Sīnā, which Fakhr al-Dīn al-Rāzī had attacked severely during the previous century. In this work, which is unusual among Muslim philosophical works for its almost mathematical precision, al-Ṭūsī succeeded in rekindling the light of philosophy in Islam. But while claiming in this work to be a mere follower of Ibn Sīnā, in several places questions of God's knowledge of particulars, the nature of space, and the createdness of the physical world clearly shows his debt to Shihāb al-Dīn al-Suhrawardī and some of the Muslim theologians. Al-Ṭūsī in fact marks the first stage in the gradual synthesis of the Peripatetic and Illuminationist (*ishrāqī*) schools, a tendency that became clearer in the writings of his foremost student, Quṭb al-Dīn al-Shīrāzī. He also wrote many philosophical treatises in Persian, so that his prose in this field must be considered, along with the writings of Nāṣir-i Khusraw, Suhrawardī, and Afḍal al-Dīn al-Kāshānī, as the most important in the Persian language.

In ethics al-Ṭūsī composed two major works, both in Persian: the *Akhlāq-i muḥtashimī* ("The Muḥtashimī Ethics") and the much better-known *Nasirean Ethics*, his most famous opus. Based upon the *Tahdhīb al-akhlāq* ("The Refinement of Character") of Muskūya (Miskawayh), the *Nasirean Ethics* expounds a philosophical system combining Islamic teachings with the ethical theories of the Aristotelian and, to a certain extent, the Platonic traditions. The work also contains an elaborate discussion of psychology and psychic healing. For centuries it has been the most popular ethical work among the Muslims of India and Persia.

In Twelve Imām Shiʿism, al-Ṭūsī is considered as much a theologian as a scientist and philosopher because of his *Tajrīd*, which is still central to Shiʿite theological education. A work of great intellectual rigor, the *Tajrīd* represents the first systematic treatment of Shiʿite *Kalām* and is therefore the foundation of systematic theology for the Twelve Imām Shiʿites. In the history of Islam, which is known for its multitalented figures of genius, it is not possible to find another person who was at once an outstanding astronomer and mathematician and the most authoritative theologian of a major branch of Islam.

Influence. Al-Ṭūsī's influence, especially in eastern Islam, was immense. Probably, if we take all fields into account, he was more responsible for the revival of the Islamic sciences than any other individual. His bringing together so many compe-

tent scholars and scientists at Marāgha resulted not only in the revival of mathematics and astronomy but also in the renewal of Islamic philosophy and even theology. Al-Ṭūsī's works were for centuries authoritative in many fields of Islamic learning; and his students, such as Quṭb al-Dīn and ʿAllāma Ḥillī, became outstanding scholars and scientists. His astronomical activities influenced the observatories at Samarkand and Istanbul and in the West to a much greater extent than was thought to be the case until recently; and his mathematical studies affected all later Islamic mathematics. In fact, the work of al-Ṭūsī and his collaborators at Marāgha moved eastward to influence Chinese science, which, as a result of the Mongol invasion, had a much closer relationship with Islam. The school of al-Ṭūsī also influenced later Indian science as cultivated under the Moguls and even as late as the eighteenth century, as can be seen in the observatory constructed by Jai Singh II, which indirectly reflects the observatory of Marāgha.

In the West al-Ṭūsī is known almost entirely as an astronomer and mathematician whose significance, at least in these fields, is becoming increasingly evident. In the Muslim East he has always been considered as a foremost example of the "wise man" (*ḥakīm*), one who, while possessing an acute analytical mind, which he devoted to mathematical, astronomical, and logical studies, extended the horizon of his thought to embrace philosophy and theology and even journeyed beyond the limited horizon of all mental activity to seek ultimate knowledge in the ecstasy provided by gnosis (*ʿirfān*) and Sufism.

NOTES

1. E. S. Kennedy, "The Exact Sciences in Iran Under the Seljuqs and Mongols," 664.
2. E. S. Kennedy, "Late Medieval Planetary Theory," 369.
3. *Ibid.*
4. *Ibid.*, 369, 367.

BIBLIOGRAPHY

Al-Ṭūsī's major published work is *The Nasirean Ethics*, translated by G. M. Wickens (London, 1964).

Secondary literature includes A. Carathéodory Pasha, *Traité de quadrilatère* (Constantinople, 1891); B. Carra de Vaux, "Les sphères célestes selon Nasīr-Eddīn Attūsī," in P. Tannery, ed., *Recherches sur l'histoire de l'astronomie ancienne* (Paris, 1893), app. 4, 337–361; A. P. Youschkevitch, and B. A. Rosenfeld, *Die Mathematik der Lander des Ostens in Mittelalter* (Berlin, 1960), 277–288, 304–308; E. S. Kennedy, "Late Medieval Planetary Theory," in *Isis*, **57** (1966), 365–378; and "The Exact Sciences in Iran Under the Seljuqs and Mongols," in *Cambridge History of Iran*, V (Cambridge, 1968), 659–679; M. Mudarris Raḍawī, *Aḥwal wa āthār-i ustād bashar . . . Khwāja Naṣīr al-Dīn* (Teheran, A.H. 1334, 1955 A.D.); S. H. Nasr, *Three Muslim Sages* (Cambridge, Mass., 1964); and *Science and Civilization in Islam* (Cambridge, Mass., 1968; New York, 1970); G. Sarton, *Introduction to the History of Science*, II, pt. 2 (Baltimore, 1931), 1001–1013; A. Sayili, *The Observatory in Islam* (Ankara, 1960); B. H. Siddiqui, "Naṣīr al-Dīn Ṭūsī," in M. M. Sharif, ed., *A History of Muslim Philosophy*, I (Wiesbaden, 1963), 564–580; A. S. Saidan, "The Comprehensive Work on Computation With Board and Dust by Naṣīr al-Dīn al-Ṭūsī," in *Al-abḥāth*, **20**, no. 2 (June 1967), 91–163, and no. 3 (Sept. 1967), 213–293, in Arabic; and *Yādnāmāyi Khwāja Naṣīr al-Dīn Ṭūsī*, I (Teheran, A.H. 1336, 1957 A.D.), in Persian.

SEYYED HOSSEIN NASR

AL-ṬŪSĪ, SHARAF AL-DĪN AL-MUẒAFFAR IBN MUḤAMMAD IBN AL-MUẒAFFAR (*b.* Ṭūs [?], Iran; *d.* Iran, *ca.* 1213/1214), *astronomy, mathematics.*

The name of Sharaf al-Dīn's birthplace, Ṭūs, refers both to a city and to its surrounding region, which with Mashhad and Nīshāpur formed a very prosperous area in the twelfth century.[1] A century earlier, Ṭūs had given Islam one of its most profound thinkers, al-Ghazālī (*d.* 1111); and it was soon to produce a great astronomer and theologian, Naṣīr al-Dīn (*d.* 1274). Nothing is known about the first years of al-Ṭūsī's life; but it is reported that, faithful to the tradition of medieval scholars, he went on a long journey to some of the major cities of the time. His itinerary can be reconstructed from undated information preserved in biographies of his contemporaries.

Al-Ṭūsī taught at Damascus, probably about 1165.[2] His most distinguished student there was Abu'l-Faḍl (*b. ca.* 1135), an excellent carpenter who helped make the wood paneling of the Bīmāristān al-Nūrī (1154–1159) before discovering the joys of Euclid and Ptolemy.[3] Al-Ṭūsī most probably then stayed at Aleppo, where one of his pupils was a respected member of the city's Jewish community, Abu'l-Faḍl Binyāmīn (*d.* 1207/1208), whom he instructed in the science of numbers, the use of astronomical tables, and astrology, and, at a less advanced level, in the other rational sciences.[4] From the nature of these courses, it is reasonable to suppose that they lasted about three years.

Al-Ṭūsī's most outstanding pupil, however, was Kamāl al-Dīn Ibn Yūnus (*d.* 1243) of Mosul, through whom al-Ṭūsī's teachings passed to Naṣīr al-Dīn and Athīr al-Dīn al-Abharī (*d.* 1263/1265).[5] Al-Ṭūsī was apparently in Mosul in the years preceding 1175,[6] for around this date two physicians from Damascus went there to study with him, but he had already left.[7] One of them then went to the neighboring city of Irbil, where he became a pupil of Ibn al-Dahhān.[8] About this time, however, the latter left Irbil to join Saladin, who had just seized Damascus (1174).[9] Al-Ṭūsī returned to Iran, where he died around 1213, at an advanced age.

Al-Ṭūsī is known for his linear astrolabe (al-Ṭūsī's staff), a simple wooden rod with graduated markings but without sights. It was furnished with a plumb line and a double cord for making angular measurements and bore a perforated pointer. This staff reproduced, in concrete form, the meridian line of the plane astrolabe—that is, the line upon which the engraved markings of that instrument are projected. (These markings are of stars, circles of declination, and heights.) Supplementary scales indicate the right ascensions of the sun at its entry into the signs of the zodiac as well as the hourly shadows. Al-Ṭūsī described the construction and use of the linear astrolabe in several treatises, praising its simplicity and claiming that an amateur could build it in about an hour. His staff made it possible to carry out the observations used to determine the height of the stars, the time, the direction of the Kaʿba, and the ascendants. The instrument, although inexpensive to construct, was less accurate than the ordinary astrolabe. It also was less decorative, and perhaps for this reason it was of little interest to collectors. In any case, not a single linear astrolabe has survived.[10]

Al-Ṭūsī's greatest achievement is recorded in a work that has not yet been analyzed by historians, the manuscript Loth III, 767, in the collection of the India Office, London. This manuscript is actually a reworking of the original by an unknown author who proudly states that he has eliminated the mathematical tables and shortened some of the long passages. He makes no further claims; and even if he had wished to make more substantial changes, the great difficulty of the work would have discouraged him. The entire contents of the work may, therefore, confidently be attributed to al-Ṭūsī. The treatise, which may have been mentioned by al-Sinjārī,[11] is not the first of its kind by an Arab author. A cross check of citations from Jamshīd al-Kāshī and Ṭāsh Kopru Zādeh reveals that al-Masʿūdī, a disciple of al-Khayyāmī, wrote on the numerical solution of third-degree equations.[12] The existence of an earlier author is not explicitly indicated, but, about 1350, Yaḥyā al-Kāshī noted several similar writings, without specifying dates or names.[13] In the following paragraphs we shall present the most remarkable results in al-Ṭūsī's treatise, but we cannot state the degree of originality for each.

The treatise divides the twenty-five equations of degree $n \leq 3$ into three groups. The first includes twelve equations: those of degree $n \leq 2$ or that reduce to that degree, plus the equation $x^3 = a$. The second contains the eight equations of the third degree that always admit one (positive) solution.[14] The third group is composed of the five equations that can give rise to impossible solutions:[15]

$$x^3 + c = ax^2$$

$$x^3 + c = b^2x$$

$$x^3 + 3ax^2 + c = 3b^2x$$

$$x^3 + b^2x + c = 3ax^2$$

$$x^3 + c = 3ax^2 + 3b^2x$$

We shall not give details of the geometric solutions, since they do not differ from those presented by al-Khayyāmī. (The care that al-Ṭūsī bestows on the study of the problem of the relative position of two conics is, however, worth noting.) On the other hand, the outstanding discussion of the existence of the roots of the group of equations that can give rise to impossible solutions merits the closest examination. Accordingly, we shall outline, by way of example, al-Ṭūsī's treatment of the fourth equation of this group, which, like the others, is based on the calculation of a maximum. Given that $x^3 < 3ax^2$; therefore $x < 3a$. Then $b^2x < x^2(3a - x)$, so that $b^2 < x(3a - x)$. The maximum of $x(3a - x)$ is $(3a/2)^2$.[16] Therefore $b < 3a/2$. We consider $x^2 + b^2/3 = 2ax$ and take its root $x_1 = a + \sqrt{a^2 - b^2/3}$. A discussion of its existence does not arise, since $b < 3a/2$. We form $f(x_1) = x_1^2(3a - x_1) - b^2x_1$. If $f(x_1) = c$, the equation $x^3 + b^3x + c = 3ax^2$ has a

solution $x = x_1$. If $f(x_1) < c$, there is no solution. If $f(x_1) > c$, the equation has two roots separated by x_1. Turning to an evaluation of al-Ṭūsī's treatment in the light of the differential calculus, we set $f(x) = 3ax^2 - x^3 - b^2x$; then $f'(x) = 6ax - 3x^2 - b^2$. Thus $f'(x)$ reduces to zero when $x^2 - 2ax + b^2/3 = 0$. Accordingly, the roots x_0 and x_1 are equal to $a \pm \sqrt{a^2 - b^2/3}$. Finally, $f(x_1) > 0$ implies $b < 3a/2$.

x	0	x_0		x_1		$3a$
$f'(x)$		$- \ 0$		$+ \ 0$		$-$
$f(x)$	0	$\searrow f(x_0)$	$\nearrow$	$f(x_1)$	$\searrow$	$-3ab^2$

The text does not say what led al-Ṭūsī to such profound and beautiful results. The idea of determining the maximum of $x^2(a - x)$, $x(b^2 - x^2)$, $\cdots$ might have been suggested by the solution of $x(a - x) = b^2$. The value of the maximum of $x^2(a - x)$ might have been borrowed from Archimedes, who, unlike al-Ṭūsī, established it geometrically.[17] Yet, even if al-Ṭūsī started from this point, he still had far to go. Pursuing his solution of the equation $x^3 + bx^2 + c = 3ax^2$, he shows that the two solutions are, respectively, $x_1 + X$, where X is the root of $X^3 + 3(x_1 - a)X = f(x_1) - c$, and $x_1 - X$, where X is the root of $X^3 + f(x_1) - c = 3(x_1 - a)X$. This method contains the genesis of a genuine change of variables, and one must admire the author's intention of interrelating the various equations—an approach quite different from traditional Arab thinking on this topic, which emphasized independent solutions of problems (as in the classic solution of the second-degree equations).

We shall conclude with a very schematic presentation of al-Ṭūsī's solution of the equation $x^3 + 3ax = N$, using the example $x^3 + 36x = 91,750,087$.[18] Let x_1 be the number in the hundreds' place of the root; then x_1^3 will represent millions and $3ax_1$ will represent hundreds. Therefore, we place x_1 in the millions' box (the upper line in Table I) and $a = 12$ in the hundreds' box (on the lower line; actually, since a is greater than nine, it is carried over

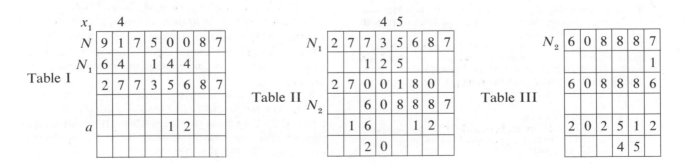

into that of the thousands). We then calculate the greatest x_1 such that $x_1^3 \leq 91$; this yields $x_1 = 4$. We remove $x_1^3 + 36x_1$ from N, obtaining $N = 27,735,687$. We next place $x_1^2 = 16$ under x_1 in the line containing a and decrease the lower line by one rank and x_1 by two. The result is Table II.

We now calculate the figure in the tens' place. It will be the greatest x_2 such that $3x_2$ multiplied by 16 can be subtracted from 277. Accordingly, $x_2 = 5$, and we place it to the right of 4 in the upper line. In the lower line we put $x_1 x_2$ in the position under $x_1 = 4$. We then subtract from N_1 the total of x_2^3 and the product of $3x_2$ times the lower line—that is, $3x_2(x_1^2 + x_1 x_2 + a) = 15(180,012)$. This yields N_2. We add $x_1 x_2$ (that is, 20) to the lower line in the position under $x_1 = 4$ and $x_2^2 = 25$ in the position under $x_2 = 5$. The line becomes 202,512. We decrease it by one rank and decrease the upper line by two. The result is Table III.

Finally, we calculate x_3 such that the product of $3x_3$ times $20 \leq 60$. Thus $x_3 = 1$. We place it to the right of 5. To the lower line we add 45 and subtract from N_2 the total of x_3^3 and the product of $3x_3$ times the lower line (202,962). The remainder is 0. The root of the equation is therefore 451. The method is independent of the system of numeration and permits as close an approximation of the root as desired; it suffices to add a row of three to the last remainder and to continue operating in the same manner. The treatise also gives analogous methods of numerical resolution for the other equations, even for those of the second degree.

NOTES

1. Guy Le Strange, *The Lands of the Eastern Caliphate* (Cambridge, 1909). See the chapter on Khurāsān (with references to the Arab geographers).
2. See Ibn Abī Uṣaybiʿa. *ʿUyūn al-anbāʾ*, II, 190–191.
3. This was a hospital built by Sultan Nūr al-Dīn ibn Zenki, famous for his wars against the Crusaders. See Ibn al-Athīr, *al-Tārīkh al-Bāhir fiʾl dawl ʾl-atābikiyya*, A. A. Ṭulaymāt, ed. (Cairo, 1963), 170; and Shawkat al-Shaṭṭī, *Mūjaz tārīkh al-ṭibb ʿind al-ʿArab* (Damascus, 1959), 22. See also Ibn Abī Uṣaybiʿa, *loc. cit.*
4. Ibn al-Qifṭī. *Tārikh* (Cairo, 1948), 278.
5. See Ibn Khallikān, *Wafayāt al-aʿyan*, IV, no. 718; and G. Sarton, *Introduction to the History of Science*, II, 600, and II, pt. 2, 1001–1013.
6. In 1193 Ibn Yūnus went to Baghdad to continue his religious studies; see Ibn Khallikān, *loc. cit.* See also Tāsh Kopru Zādeh, *Miftāḥ al-saʿāda*, II, 214–215.
7. They were Ibn al-Ḥajib and Muwaffaq al-Dīn. See Ibn Abī Uṣaybiʿa, II, 181–182, 191–192.
8. *Ibid.*
9. See Ibn Khallikān, IV, no. 655.
10. See Henri Michel, *Traité de l'astrolabe*, 22. The same point is also made in L. A. Mayer, *Islamic Astrolabists and Their Works* (Geneva, 1956).

11. Al-Sinjārī, *Irshād al-qāṣid* (Beirut. 1904), 124. Although probably valid, the citation raises some doubt. In fact, the title, *Kitāb al-Muẓaffar al-Ṭūsī*, becomes, in certain editions of Ṭāsh Kopru Zādeh's *Miftāḥ al-saʿāda* (for instance, I, 327) which, however, derive from al-Sinjārī: *Kitāb al-Ẓafar of al-Ṭūsī* (Naṣīr al-Dīn).
12. Jamshīd al-Kāshī, *Miftāḥ al-ḥisāb*, MS Paris Ar. 5020, fol. 98; and Ṭāsh Kopru Zādeh, *Miftāḥ al-saʿāda*, I, 327. Sharaf al-Dīn Muḥammad ibn Masʿūd ibn Muḥammad al-Masʿūdī is cited in the article on Muḥammad ibn Aḥmad al-Shurwāni in Ṣafadī, *al-Wāfī*, Ritter, ed. (Istanbul), II, 497, as having taught the *Ishārāt* of Ibn Sīnā to Fakhr al-Dīn al-Rāzi (1164–1238) after having studied under al-Khayyām. He is the author of *al-Kifāya fiʾl-hidāya*; see Ḥājjī Khalīfa, *Kashf al-Ẓunūn*, II, col. 1500. Khalīfa also cites his algebra (I, col. 857).
13. Yaḥya al-Kāshi, *al-Lubāb fiʾl-Ḥisāb*, Aya Sofya MS 2757. See fol. 65r, l. 21; fol. 65v, l. 3; and fol. 67r, l. 25. The MS, written in 1373, bears notes in the author's hand. See the article on al-Kāshi in Sarton, *Introduction to the History of Science*, III, pt. 1, 698.
14. Only $x^3 + ax = bx^2 + c$ can admit up to three positive solutions.
15. *Kitāb fiʾl-jabr waʾl-muqābala*, India Office (London), Loth 767. The equations are found on pp. 101r–112r; 112r–121r; 121r–130r; 130r–142v; and 142v–179r.
16. This is an immediate consequence of Euclid's *Elements*, II, 5.
17. T. L. Heath, *The Works of Archimedes* (New York, 1953), 67–72.
18. In the treatise (fols. 54v–55v) the equation actually solved is $x^3 + 36x = 33,087,717$, the root of which is 321.

BIBLIOGRAPHY

I. ORIGINAL WORKS. Al-Ṭūsī's works include the following:

1. *Kitāb fiʾl jabr waʾl muqābala*, India Office (London), Loth 767.
2. *Risāla fiʾl-asṭurlāb al-khaṭṭī*, British Museum, Or. 5479.
3. *Maʿrifat al-asṭurlāb al-musaṭṭaḥ waʾl-ʿamal bihi*, Leiden 1082. The MS does not bear this title, which was erroneously given to it by some bibliographers, and discusses the linear astrolabe, not the plane astrolabe. The third part, containing demonstrations, is missing from the MS.
4. *Kitāb fi maʿrifat al asṭurlāb al-musaṭṭaḥ waʾl ʿamal bihi*, Seray 3505, 2nd. If Max Krause's identification of this MS with Leiden 1082 is correct, it would be necessary to conclude that we do not have al-Ṭūsī's treatise on the plane astrolabe.
5. *Risāla fiʾl-asṭurlāb al-Khaṭṭī*, Seray 3342, 7.
6. *Risāla fiʾl-asṭurlāb al-Khaṭṭī*, Seray 3464, 1.
7. *Jawāb ʿalā suʾāl liʾamīr al-umarāʾ Shams al-Dīn*, Leiden 1027; Columbia University, Smith, Or. 45, 2. This work concerns the division of a square into three trapezoids and a rectangle, with the relationships preassigned.
8. *Fiʾl-Khaṭṭayn alladhayn yaqrubān wa la yaltaqiyān*, Aya Sofya 2646, 2, 71r–v, deals with the existence of an asymptote to the (equilateral) hyperbola and contains the same demonstration as in *Kitāb fiʾl-jabr waʾl-muqābala*, (1), fols. 38r–40r.

II. Secondary Literature. See the following:

9. Ibn Khallikān, *Wafayāt al-aʿyān* (Cairo, 1948).

10. Ibn Abī Uṣaybiʿa, *ʿUyūn al-anbāʾ* (Cairo, 1882).

11. Ṭāsh Kopru Zādeh, *Miftāḥ al-saʿāda* (Hyderabad, 1910–1911).

12. Ḥājjī Khalīfa, *Kashf al-ẓunūn* (Istanbul, 1941–1943).

13. H. Suter, *Die Mathematiker und Astronomen der Araber* (Leipzig, 1900), 134 (no. 333).

14. Max Krause, "Stambuler Handschriften islamischer Mathematiker," in *Quellen und Studien zur Geschichte der Mathematik, Astronomie und Physik*, Abt. B, Studien, **3** (1936), 437–532, see 490.

15. C. Brockelmann, *Geschichte der arabischen Literatur*, I, 2nd ed. (Leiden, 1943), 472, and supp. I (Leiden, 1937), 858.

16. G. Sarton, *Introduction to the History of Science*, II, pt. 2 (Baltimore, 1950), 622–623.

17. Carlo Nallino, article on the astrolabe (*asṭurlāb*) in *Encyclopaedia of Islam*, 1st ed., I (1913); and by Willy Hartner, *ibid.*, 2nd ed., I, 722–728.

18. Henri Michel, *Traité de l'astrolabe* (Paris, 1947), 115–122; and "L'astrolabe linéaire d'al-Ṭūsī," in *Ciel et terre* (1943), nos. 3–4. A description, sketch, and note on the use of al-Ṭūsī's linear astrolabe can be found on p. 21.

19. R. Carra de Vaux, "L'astrolabe linéaire ou bâton d'al-Tousi," in *Journal asiatique*, 11th ser., **5** (1895), 464–516. This article reproduces the text of al-Ḥasan al Marrākushī with a French translation.

Adel Anbouba

TUTTON, ALFRED EDWARD HOWARD (*b.* Stockport, Cheshire, England, 22 August 1864; *d.* Dallington, Sussex, England, 14 July 1938), *crystallography.*

The only child of James Tutton, a venetian blind manufacturer, Alfred Tutton left school at fourteen. He subsequently won a scholarship to the Royal College of Science in London, where in 1886 he graduated with the principal prizes for geology, physics, and chemistry. In 1889 he became lecturer in chemical analysis. In 1895 he was appointed inspector of technical schools and served successively in the Oxford, London, and Plymouth districts. Tutton retired to Cambridge in 1924 and occasionally lectured for the university. From 1895 until 1931, when he moved to Dallington, Sussex, he maintained a crystallographic laboratory in his various houses. On his final retirement in 1931 his instruments were purchased by Manchester University, which had awarded him an honorary D.Sc. in 1926.

Tutton married Margaret Loat of Cumnor Place, Oxford, on 18 June 1902. They had two sons and four daughters. Throughout his life he enjoyed excellent health, although he suffered a serious climbing accident in the Alps in 1926, and in his last years was afflicted with failing eyesight.

In 1899 Tutton was elected a fellow of the Royal Society and served as president of the Mineralogical Society of Great Britain from 1912 to 1915. His principal interests besides crystallography were climbing and glaciology; all three were united in his book *The Natural History of Ice and Snow* (1927).

Tutton's earliest researches with Thomas E. Thorpe (1890–1891) were purely chemical and concerned the lower oxides of phosphorus. During this period also he assisted Thorpe and Arthur W. Rücker with the magnetic survey of Scotland and England.

Early in his career Tutton began the program of research that was to occupy him for the next forty years: the precise goniometric and optical study of isomorphous salts. He began with the series R_2XO_4 where R = K, Rb, Cs, NH_4, and Tl; and X = S, Se. Next came the series $R_2M(XO_4)_2 \cdot 6H_2O$, with R and X the same and M = Mg, Zn, Fe, Ni, Co, Mn, Cu, Cd. For each series he demonstrated, using goniometric and optical techniques at the highest level of refinement, that physical properties vary regularly with the atomic properties of the substituent elements. The same general conclusion was verified later for the alkali perchlorates and for the double chromates of the alkalis. Tutton's results were published in about fifty papers between 1890 and 1929. The essentials were republished and his apparatus described in detail in *Crystalline Structure and Chemical Constitution* (1910), *Crystallography and Practical Crystal Measurement* (1911; 2nd ed., 2 vols., 1922), and *Crystalline Form and Chemical Constitution* (1926). He also wrote a general survey of crystallography in *Crystals* (1911).

Out of the highly precise crystallographic measurements in which Tutton was so expert came the interferential comparator that he applied to a comparison of the substandards of the yard with the Imperial standard yard and, following Michelson, the evaluation of the standard yard in terms of the wavelength of cadmium red.

Tutton's reputation rests on the outstanding precision of his goniometric and optical work, notable in that it was achieved while he was busily occupied with official duties. The rapid development of X-ray crystallography diverted his type of work from the mainstream of crystallographic research, but nevertheless his data, although not fundamental, added substantially to the understanding of isomorphism; and his ingeniously designed apparatus formed the basis of later instruments useful in a wide range of fields.

BIBLIOGRAPHY

I. ORIGINAL WORKS. Important works by Tutton are *Crystalline Structure and Chemical Constitution* (London, 1910); *Crystals* (London, 1911); *Crystallography and Practical Crystal Measurement* (London, 1911; 2nd ed., London, 1922); *The Natural History of Crystals* (London, 1924); *Crystalline Form and Chemical Constitution* (London, 1926); and *The Natural History of Ice and Snow, Illustrated From the Alps* (London, 1927). There are also many papers in *Proceedings of the Royal Society, Journal of the Chemical Society*, and other journals.

II. SECONDARY LITERATURE. For discussions of Tutton and his work, see J. R. Partington, *Nature*, **142** (1938), 321–322; and L. J. Spencer, *Mineralogical Magazine and Journal of the Mineralogical Society*, **25** (1939), 301–303. See also *Obituary Notices of Fellows of the Royal Society of London*, **2** (1939), 621–626.

DUNCAN MCKIE

TWENHOFEL, WILLIAM HENRY (*b.* Covington, Kentucky, 16 April 1875; *d.* Atlanta, Georgia, 4 January 1957), *geology.*

Twenhofel's parents, Ernst A. H. J. Twenhofel and Helena Steuwer Twenhofel, of German ancestry, obtained a scant livelihood from cultivating a small farm near Covington. Twenhofel became acquainted at an early age with the rigors of farm life, for he had to help earn his own way. As a result of his work on the farm, he developed the physique and self-reliance that were to serve him well in later life when he carried on his geologic fieldwork in remote parts of North America. He also developed a keen interest in the outdoors, and especially in the reaction of plants and animals to their environment. His interest in nature continued throughout his life, and some of his most important scientific work concerned the formation, erosion, and preservation of soils, the action of plants and animals in producing and modifying sediments, and the ultimate deposition of the sediments and their organic constituents to form sedimentary rocks.

In 1899 Twenhofel married his childhood sweetheart, Virgie Mae Stephens; they had three children, Lilian Helena, Helen Vivian, and William Stephens Twenhofel. Observant and ambitious, and keenly interested in understanding nature, the youthful Twenhofel taught in the local schools for six years until he could earn enough to enter National Normal University at nearby Lebanon, Kentucky, in 1902. Awarded his baccalaureate in 1904, he next taught science and mathematics in East Texas Normal College from 1904 to 1907. He entered Yale University at age thirty-two. While earning three degrees in geology, the B.A. in 1908, M.A. in 1910, and Ph.D. in 1912, he came under the influence of Charles Schuchert and Joseph Barrell. Twenhofel became a devoted follower of both men, finding in their teachings the stimulation to extend and diversify his interest in nature.

Using the college campus as a base of operations, and teaching as a means of livelihood, he began his geological career while still a graduate student at Yale by accepting an assistant professorship at the University of Kansas in 1910. In 1916 he moved on to the University of Wisconsin, where he joined Charles R. Van Hise, Charles K. Leith, Alexander N. Winchell, Warren J. Mead, and Armin K. Lobeck. These men, Twenhofel's colleagues for the next thirty years, had a great effect on his scientific career.

When Twenhofel entered Yale, Schuchert was involved in a controversy concerning the Ordovician-Silurian boundary, and had decided that the solution lay in rocks of the Maritime Provinces of Canada. Twenhofel joined him on a field reconnaissance expedition in 1908; he later chose as the subject of his doctoral thesis the critical section on Anticosti Island, Quebec. Later in his career Twenhofel published important papers and reports on the Silurian section at Arisaig, Nova Scotia (1908), the Ordovician-Silurian strata of Anticosti Island (1927), the geology of the Mingan Islands of Quebec (1938), the Mid-Paleozoic rocks of Newfoundland (1937, 1954) and the Baltic Provinces of Europe (1916), and the Silurian of Maine (1941). These important contributions, which brought him international recognition as an authority on Ordovician and Silurian stratigraphy and paleontology, demonstrated the transitional nature of the Ordovician-Silurian boundary in northeastern North America.

While carrying on his stratigraphic studies and teaching his classes at the University of Wisconsin, Twenhofel also continued his interest in sedimentation. While at the University of Kansas Twenhofel studied the remarkable Wreford and Foraker cherts and the Comanchean deposits of central Kansas. Soon after going to Wisconsin he became involved in a far-reaching controversy with Edward O. Ulrich concerning the stratigraphy of some Upper Cambrian formations of the Upper Mississippi Valley. Ulrich argued for the traditional layer-cake concept, placing the Mazomanie glauconitic beds above the Franconia formation. Twenhofel considered the two sequences essentially contemporaneous and laterally transitional, which was a novel and revolutionary interpretation for the time, but one that he and his graduate students ultimately established by their detailed fieldwork. First as member and later as chairman of the Committee on Sedimentation of the National Research Council during the three decades from 1919 to 1949, he greatly stimulated research in sedimentation, along with T. Wayland Vaughan, Edward M. Kindle, and Arthur C. Trowbridge. His work as author of the monumental *Treatise on Sedimentation* (1926; 2nd ed., 1932) was internationally recognized.

When Raymond C. Moore launched the *Journal of Sedimentary Petrology* in 1931, Twenhofel became one of the associate editors. He served as editor from 1933 to 1946, guiding the struggling publication through difficult times to an established position among geologic journals. Twenhofel's discussions of black shales stimulated renewed interest in those controversial rocks; his papers on ancient coral reefs and related subjects contributed to increased emphasis on paleoecology; and his early concerns over soil erosion and conservation were ahead of their time. Studies that he and his students made of the sediments of Wisconsin lakes greatly stimulated limnological research, and his reports on the black sands of the Oregon beaches called attention to those deposits of winnowed sands as possible sources of certain valuable minerals, as magnetite and ilmenite.

More than anyone else in his time, Twenhofel led and promoted the study of sedimentation as a branch of geology, and the present great strength and importance of the subject are largely the result of his leadership as investigator, teacher, author, and editor.

BIBLIOGRAPHY

I. ORIGINAL WORKS. Twenhofel's scientific writings cover a broad range of geologic subjects and reveal an unusual ability to organize and interpret large amounts of descriptive matter. He wrote more than seventy-five important articles and reports, and five widely used textbooks, all on some aspect of sedimentation, stratigraphy, and paleontology. His writings are listed in the Bibliographies of North American Geology, published as *Bulletins of the United States Geological Survey*. His five

major works are *Treatise on Sedimentation* (Baltimore, 1926; 2nd ed., 1932); *Invertebrate Paleontology*, with R. R. Shrock (New York, 1935); *Principles of Sedimentation* (New York, 1939); *Methods of Study of Sediments*, with S. A. Tyler (New York, 1941); and R. R. Shrock and W. H. Twenhofel, *Principles of Invertebrate Paleontology* (New York, 1953).

Major reports dealing with both stratigraphy and paleontology include "The Geology and Invertebrate Paleontology of the Comanchean and 'Dakota' Formations of Kansas," *Kansas State Geological Survey*, bulletin 9 (1924); *et al.*, "Geology of Anticosti Island," *Canadian Geological Survey*, memoir 54 (1927); "The Building of Kentucky," *Kentucky Geological Survey*, ser. 6, **37** (1931); *et al.*, "Geology and Paleontology of Mingan Islands, Quebec . . .," *Geological Society of America*, special paper 11 (1938); "Soil, the Most Valuable Mineral Resource; Its Origin, Destruction, and Preservation," *Oregon Department of Geology and Mineral Industries Bulletin*, 26 (1944).

II. SECONDARY LITERATURE. Additional biographical and bibliographical data are included in R. R. Shrock, "William Henry Twenhofel—Honorary Member," in *Bulletin of the American Association of Petroleum Geologists*, **31** (1947), 835–840; "Memorial to William Henry Twenhofel (1875–1957)," in *Journal of Sedimentary Petrology*, **27** (1957), 203; "William Henry Twenhofel (1875–1957)," in *Bulletin of the American Association of Petroleum Geologists*, **41** (1957), 978–980; C. O. Dunbar, "Memorial to William Henry Twenhofel (1875–1957)," in *Proceedings. Geological Society of America*; annual report for 1960 (1962), 151–156.

ROBERT R. SHROCK

TWORT, FREDERICK WILLIAM (*b.* Camberley, London, England, 22 October 1877; *d.* Camberley, 20 March 1950), *microbiology*.

Twort was the eldest of the eleven children of William Henry Twort, a medical practitioner in Camberley. He attended St. Thomas' Hospital Medical School in London, where he qualified in 1900 as member of the Royal College of Surgeons of England and licentiate of the Royal College of Physicians of London. He carried out no clinical practice and in 1901 was appointed assistant to Louis Jenner, the superintendent of the Clinical Laboratory of St. Thomas' Hospital. In the following year (1902), Twort entered the field of microbiology, in which discipline he remained for the rest of his professional career, as assistant to William Bulloch, bacteriologist to the London Hospital. He stayed there for seven years, during which time he gained wide experience in hospital bacteriology while beginning his own investigations. By 1907 the latter had become of primary importance to him, and he obtained the position of superintendent of the Brown Animal Sanatory Institution, a veterinary dispensary in London where Charles Sherrington and Victor Horsley had worked. Here Twort isolated himself from his colleagues in bacteriology and engaged only in research. Being by nature a recluse and an outstanding example of the independent research worker, he remained in this post for thirty-five years, except for a period of military service during World War I. He was appointed professor of bacteriology in the University of London in 1919 and was elected a fellow of the Royal Society in 1929.

Twort possessed great industry and powers of concentration as well as unusual ability; his remarkable technical skills were of the utmost advantage in his work. His aloofness and his inability to commit himself in his scientific writings militated against dissemination of his undoubtedly outstanding and original contributions to bacteriology. He was a kind and gentle person with a simple, uncomplicated nature; but he was also shy, naïve, slightly paranoid, and without much humor. Nevertheless, he could be aggressive and obstinate in defense of a principle, as for example the financial support of research. Biographers vaguely mention controversies and a "combative personality" (*Lancet*, 1950), but do not elaborate. He has also been styled "an erratic genius" (*British Medical Journal*, 1950).

Twort married Dorothy Nony Banister, daughter of F. J. Banister, an architect, and she helped him in his work. They had three daughters and a son who also entered the medical profession.

Twort's work in bacteriology was based on the premise that pathogenic bacteria must have evolved from wild, free-living organisms, an original theme at a time when bacteriologists were studying pathogens *per se* almost exclusively. Among several of his original contributions the most important was the discovery of the lytic phenomena now known to be caused by bacteriophage. Twort was working on the purification of vaccinia virus in an attempt to discover nonpathogenic ultramicroscopic viruses when he encountered a substance that could dissolve the bacterium *Staphylococcus aureus* in culture. He isolated it by ultrafiltration, and was able to transmit it indefinitely to further generations of micrococci. It is now known that this substance is a virus that attacks bacteria. Although Twort made this suggestion, he also advanced other suggestions, and, as usual, did not commit himself to any one. His classic paper on ultramicroscopic viruses, published in

Lancet in 1915, was in the form of a preliminary communication, but the expected sequel appeared during World War I and excited little interest. Moreover, in 1915 Twort joined the army, and on his return to his investigations in 1919 he did not continue what eventually became a most fruitful field of research. In 1917 Félix d'Hérelle discovered the same phenomenon and named it bacteriophage. The attempts he made to establish his own priority only served to reaffirm that of Twort.

In his other researches Twort also made original contributions that led eventually to fundamental advances in bacteriology. His first important paper, published in 1907, established the essentials of the adaptation and mutation of bacteria, showing, for example, that a nonpathogenic microorganism could become pathogenic. Once again his work gained little recognition at the time. It was the same with his paper published in 1909 on the factors that affect the growth of bacteria; the significance of these factors was not recognized until twenty years later. Twort's studies of Johne's bacillus, a mycobacterium responsible for a chronic intestinal disease of cattle, carried out with G. L. Y. Ingram in 1912, revealed an essential growth factor that, when present, allowed the organism to be cultured and a protective vaccine to be prepared. It opened up the whole field of the nutritional needs of bacteria, a field that could only be developed as biochemistry advanced. During World War I Twort investigated dysentery in the Middle East and discovered special forms of the causative bacillus; but his speculations on them were vague (1920) and the only result was his demonstration that these bizarre forms could be induced.

After World War I, Twort's researches became increasingly insignificant as he struggled to prove his thesis that pathogens derive from wild ancestors, that bacteria evolve from viruses, and that viruses come from even more primitive forms of life. The outcome of all these studies seems of little importance; they were terminated abruptly in 1944 by the destruction of his laboratory and equipment by enemy action.

BIBLIOGRAPHY

I. ORIGINAL WORKS. Twort's classic paper, on what is now termed bacteriophage, is "An Investigation of the Nature of Ultra-Microscopic Viruses," in *Lancet* (1915), **2**, 1241–1243. It is reprinted in full in N. Hayon, ed., *Selected Papers on Virology* (Englewood Cliffs, N.J., 1964), 97–102, and extracts appear in H. A. Lechevalier and M. Solotrorovsky, *Three Centuries of Microbiology* (New York, 1955), 303–306.

A list of Twort's papers, containing twenty-two items, is in P. Fildes' obituary (see below), 517. Those of importance are "The Fermentation of Glucosides by Bacteria of the Typhoid-coli Group and the Acquisition of New Fermenting Powers by *Bacillus dysenteriae* and other Micro-organisms. Preliminary Communication," in *Proceedings of the Royal Society*, series B, **79** (1907), 329–336; "The Influence of Glucosides on the Growth of Acid-fast Bacteria," *ibid.*, **81** (1909), 248; "A Method for Isolating and Cultivating the *Mycobacterium enteritidis chronicae pseudo-tuberculosae bovis*, Johne, . . .," with G. L. Y. Ingram, *ibid.*, **84** (1912), 517–542; and "Researches on Dysentery," in *British Journal of Experimental Pathology*, **1** (1920), 237–243.

II. SECONDARY LITERATURE. The only extended discussion of Twort and his work is by P. Fildes, *Obituary Notices of Fellows of the Royal Society*, **7** (1951), 505–517. Obituaries are in *British Medical Journal* (1950), **1**, 788–789, with a portrait; *Lancet* (1950), **1**, 648–649; and *Nature*, **165** (1950), 874. There is a portrait of Twort when working with W. Bulloch in C. E. Dolman, "Paul Ehrlich and William Bulloch: a Correspondence and Friendship (1896–1914)," in *Clio Medica*, **3** (1968), 65–84, fig. 9.

EDWIN CLARKE

TYNDALL, JOHN (*b*. Leighlinbridge, County Carlow, Ireland, 2 August 1820; *d*. Hindhead, Surrey, England, 4 December 1893), *natural philosophy, microbiology, popularization of science.*

Tyndall was the son of John Tyndall, an ardent Orangeman who was at different times a small landowner, shoemaker, leather dealer, and member of the Irish constabulary. Educated until he was nineteen at the national school in Carlow, Tyndall gained a vision of science, self-instruction, and moral duty shaped by his private reading of Carlyle, Emerson, and Fichte. Tyndall began work as a draftsman and civil engineer in the Irish Ordnance Survey but in 1842 was transferred to the English survey at Preston, Lancashire. In England for the first time, Tyndall witnessed economic depression and civil strife. Carlyle's *Past and Present* moved him deeply and, in 1843, focused his opposition to the oppressive policies and incompetent management of the ordnance survey. His protests rejected, Tyndall was dismissed and returned briefly to Ireland. He then found work in Lancashire and Yorkshire as a surveyor and engineer during the railway mania of 1844–1845. In 1847, once again unemployed, he was befriended by George Edmondson, a Quaker from Preston. Edmondson had recently begun at Queenwood College, Hampshire,

one of the first schools in England to have a laboratory for the teaching of science. At Queenwood, where Tyndall taught mathematics and drawing, he was joined by his friend the geometer Thomas Archer Hirst and the chemist Edward Frankland. Under Frankland's influence, Tyndall was introduced to German science. In 1848, Tyndall left Queenwood with Frankland to study at the University of Marburg. There, living on his savings, Tyndall completed a mathematical dissertation for the doctorate under Friedrich Stegmann, and then entered the laboratory of Karl Herrmann Knoblauch, recently arrived from Berlin, who was at that time extending the work of Faraday and Plücker on diamagnetism. Tyndall's first scientific research was undertaken in collaboration with Knoblauch; his first article, on the behavior of crystalline bodies between the poles of a magnet, was published in the *Philosophical Magazine* in 1851.

From 1851 Tyndall's life in both science and public affairs followed clear lines of development — as researcher, educator, popularizer, and controversial public figure. Like other men of science of his generation Tyndall had great difficulty in obtaining paid work in science. Jobless in England for two years, rejected from two posts in Ireland and (with his close friend T. H. Huxley) by the universities of Sydney and Toronto, Tyndall was obliged, like Huxley, to write, lecture, and examine. By the mid-1850's, Tyndall's prospects improved. In 1851 Huxley was elected a fellow of the Royal Society; Tyndall, aided by the patronage of Faraday, followed in 1852. In the following year, with a growing reputation, Tyndall became professor of natural philosophy at the Royal Institution, where, under Faraday's guidance, Tyndall developed his natural talents for lecturing and research. In 1867 he succeeded Faraday as superintendent of the Royal Institution and as adviser to Trinity House and the Board of Trade. From 1867 to 1885 his position at the Royal Institution gave him a central vantage point in British science.

Tyndall's research can be arbitrarily described in two phases: the first, between 1853 and 1874, witnessed a steady progression within physics, while the second, between 1874 and the early 1880's, saw the amplification of his work in other domains. In the first phase, his work on diamagnetism, involving the effects of compression on hundreds of crystalline substances (1851–1856), led to the study of Penrhyn slate and the problem of "slaty cleavage" (1854–1856). Generalizing from the effects of pressure on slate led him to the study of glacial movement (1856–1859); in turn, glaciers fostered a passion for mountaineering and a fascination for what was to become his major work – the effects of solar and, later, heat radiation on atmospheric gases (1860 – 1870). He then considered the scattering of light particles in the atmosphere (the "Tyndall effect") and explained the blue color of the sky ("Rayleigh scattering"). The scattering of sunlight by dust particles (much evident in the dust-laden air of Albemarle Street) led him to consider means of destroying airborne organic matter by heat; this in turn kindled his interest in the case against spontaneous generation (1870 – 1876) and brought him to the defense of Pasteur. This formidable capacity to move from electromagnetism through thermodynamics and into bacteriology was the hallmark of Tyndall's genius. No less formidable were his talents in describing, with charm and lucidity, the phenomena of physics to large audiences.

The enormous range of Tyndall's inquiries reflected many different intellectual influences. An explicit discussion of these influences in their context has yet to be undertaken. We lack any comprehensive review of Tyndall's work on optical and crystalline structure; on magnetism, radiation, and mountaineering; and on the relationship between his several research programs. Tyndall is remembered chiefly for his efforts to verify the high absorptive and radiative power of aqueous vapor; to measure the absorption and transmission of heat by many different gases and liquids; to explain the selective influence of the atmosphere on different sounds; and to establish the principle of "discontinuous heating" ("Tyndallization") as a sterilizing technique. Practical applications of his work in meteorology, fog signaling, and bacteriology were seen within his lifetime. In other ways his work anticipated important later developments. His explanations of diamagnetic phenomena and mechanical pressure – and their relation to molecular forces – could not be confirmed in the absence of a comprehensive theory of atomic structure. Yet his early research, extending the association of diamagnetisim with induced polarity, still relates to problems and techniques in high-pressure research in solid state and applied physics. In other fields his work has worn less well. His explanations of glacial movement by fracture and regelation were not conclusive; the conjectures of his adversary James D. Forbes on the viscosity and plasticity of glacial behavior, for example, were subsequently supported by applications of thermodynamic principles to continuous deformation under stress, and as a result have since widely prevailed.

Public demands on Tyndall's time were enormous, with the Royal Institution absorbing most of his energies. In his thirty-three years there he delivered over fifty Friday discourses, over 300 afternoon lectures, and twelve Christmas courses for young people. In addition he served as examiner for the Royal Military College (1855 – 1857), professor of physics at the Royal School of Mines (1859 – 1868), and lecturer at Eton (1856) and the London Institution (1856 – 1859). Much of his additional lecturing and examining were undertaken to supplement his salary at the Royal Institution, and many of his textbook commissions were accepted for the same reason.

Tyndall's influence upon what *Nature* called the scientific movement was direct and profound. He occupied a unique place in the popular exposition of science. In 1859 he joined with Huxley in writing a regular column for the *Saturday Review*. In 1863 – 1867 he acted as scientific adviser to *The Reader*, and in 1869 he helped inaugurate the journal *Nature*. In 1871, with Spencer and Huxley, he advised Edward Livingston Youmans on the *International Scientific Series* (to which he contributed Volume I [1872]). Tyndall's prolonged debates with publishers and his evidence to the Royal Commission on Copyright (1878) reveal the difficulties of earning a living as a scientific author. Tyndall contended with this partly by republishing his popular essays and lectures. For example, the American edition of *Fragments of Science*, which appeared in 1871, was sold out on the day of publication; and his *Forms of Water* (1872) went through twelve English editions by 1897.

Among his fellow members of the famous "X Club" (founded 1864) and his scientific contemporaries in the Metaphysical Club (founded 1869), Tyndall became an evangelist for scientific naturalism and the public support of research. He contributed "Science Lectures for the People" (begun in 1862) and gave evidence to the Select Committee on Scientific Instruction (1867 – 1868). In 1866 – 1867 he contributed to the British Association committee on the teaching of science; and in 1868 he became president of Section A, and 1874, president of the British Association at Belfast. By 1872, *Vanity Fair* spoke glowingly of his energy, imagination, and rhetoric, "at all times to be envied, and at nearly all times to be admired." This was the spirit in which his American tour (1872 – 1873) was conducted. The conclusion to his *Lectures on Light* and his bequest for fellowships at Harvard, Columbia, and Pennsylvania resonate with his hopes for the encouragement of scientific research.

With his flair for public debate, Tyndall earned the sobriquet "Xccentric" from the X Club. What Oliver Lodge called Tyndall's "wholesome rightness" came to the defense of many whom he believed ill used. Thus he advanced Monseigneur Rendu's claims against those of J. D. Forbes on the movement of glaciers; and he defended J. D. Hooker against intervention by A. S. Ayrton's Office of Works. His sincerity had the defects of its virtues; conviction bred defensiveness, even obstinacy, in celebrated debates with Forbes (1857–1867), C. A. Akin (1862–1863), P. G. Tait and William Thomson (1873–1874), Henry C. Bastian (1870–1873), and, notoriously, with John Ruskin (1874).

But these intellectual skirmishes were overshadowed by the battle that followed the "Belfast Address," Tyndall's presidential address to the British Association in 1874. Tyndall's quixotic conflicts with religious authority—notably about prayer and miracles—were intense and sustained. His devotion to experiment and verification, and his determination to find the truth, to reject metaphysics, and to reveal the ultimate mechanism of natural phenomena, had impelled his search for "agents of explanation" which would unify the physical relations of heat, magnetism, electricity and sound, and even the "ultra-scientific region" of the mind. This program was hardly new in 1874. But the explicit confrontation between materialism and revealed religion, provoked by the archdemocrat of science before the "parliament of science," left deep scars. Caustically satirized in William Hurrell Mallock's *New Republic* in 1877, Tyndall became to many more villain than hero.

If the year 1874 was a climacteric in Tyndall's public reputation, 1876 was a watershed in his private life. In that year, when he was fifty-six, he married Louisa Charlotte Hamilton, then aged thirty-one, the eldest daughter of Lord Claud Hamilton. The late 1870's and 1880's, however, were years of persistent illness, requiring frequent recuperative trips to his favorite retreat at Bel Alp, above the Rhone Valley. During the early 1880's, he continued to serve as "scientific adviser" to government and undertook fresh responsibilities with the Royal Commission on Accidents in Coal Mines (1879–1886). But by 1884 his relations with government were strained by a violent dispute with Joseph Chamberlain over lighthouse policy, which led to his resignation as scientific adviser to Trinity House and the Board of Trade. Politically, Tyndall always considered himself "in some sense Liberal, in some sense, Radical." As an Orange-

man, he admired Parnell and denounced the "Romish hierarchy of the National League." In 1885, rejecting Gladstone's policies for home rule in Ireland, and outraged by the government's failure in the Sudan, he broke finally with Liberalism. He was even moved to consider standing as a Unionist candidate for a Glasgow constituency in the election of May 1885.

In 1886 Tyndall fell seriously ill, and the following year he retired from the Royal Institution and withdrew to his house at Hindhead, near Haslemere, Surrey. Bedridden by insomnia and indigestion, in 1893 he died from an accidental overdose of chloral, tragically administered by his devoted wife, who survived him by forty-seven years.

Although he received five honorary doctorates and was an honorary member of thirty-five scientific societies, Tyndall was never offered national honors.

Tyndall's contemporaries did not view his work uncritically. Perhaps the least complimentary review of his work appeared in the tenth edition of the *Encyclopaedia Britannica* (1902), in an article by Oliver Lodge. Lodge claimed Tyndall's knowledge was "picturesque and vivid" rather than "thorough and exact"; that Tyndall never popularized anything especially recondite, yet "never hesitated to elaborate the simple"; that his research lacked originality and definition, so that his superficial understanding of physical issues promoted unnecessary disputes. There are difficulties with Lodge's interpretation, especially in relation to Tyndall's work on radiant heat and spontaneous generation. After protests from Tyndall's colleagues, Lodge removed the more inflammatory passages in the eleventh edition of the *Britannica*. Subsequently, little has appeared to qualify the received impression of a sensitive observer, a skillful experimentalist, a dedicated "field physicist" and Alpinist, an inspired communicator, and a "shining beacon to struggling self-taught youth," who, in *Nature*'s words, brought "democracy into touch with scientific research."

BIBLIOGRAPHY

I. ORIGINAL WORKS. Tyndall published more than 180 experimental papers, of which the Royal Society Catalogue lists more than 140, and more than sixty scientific lectures, addresses, and reviews, in addition to a considerable number of popular essays on literature, religion, mountaineering, and travel, many of which appeared in series and embodied material that he repeated in different forms and in different languages.

The most important of Tyndall's essays and lectures

are reproduced in several books, all published during his lifetime. These and other major books are *The Glaciers of the Alps* (London, 1860); *Heat Considered as a Mode of Motion* (London, 1863); *On Sound* (London, 1867; 4th ed., 1883), a later edition of which is *The Science of Sound* (New York, 1964); *Researches on Diamagnetism and Magne-Crystallic Action* (London, 1870); *Hours of Exercise in the Alps* (London, 1871); *Fragments of Science for Unscientific People* (London, 1871); *Contributions to Molecular Physics in the Domain of Radiation Heat* (London, 1872); *The Forms of Water in Clouds, Rivers, Ice, and Glaciers* (London, 1872; 12th ed., 1897); *Six Lectures on Light, Delivered in America, 1872–1873* (London, 1873; 5th ed., 1895); *The Floating Matter of the Air in Relation to Putrefaction and Infection* (London, 1881); *New Fragments* (London, 1892).

An outline of Tyndall's writings would be incomplete without a notice of the many contributions he made to the *Liverpool Mercury* under the name "Spectator," and to the *Carlow Sentinel* and *Preston Chronicle* under the name Wat Ripon between 1843 and 1849.

By far the greatest archive of Tyndall's papers exists at the Royal Institution of Great Britain. This collection, together with his published writings and much of his correspondence, has been catalogued, and the catalogue is available in microfiche with an accompanying printed introduction by J. Friday, R. MacLeod, and P. Shepherd, *John Tyndall, Natural Philosopher, 1820–1893* (London, 1974).

II. SECONDARY LITERATURE. The most accessible sources of biographical material on Tyndall are in *Nature*, **49** (1894), 128; *Dictionary of National Biography*, XIX, 1358–1363; and Oliver Joseph Lodge, in *Encyclopaedia Britannica*, 10th ed., XXXIII (1902), 517–521; and 11th ed., XXVII (1910–1911), 499–500, in which passages offending Mrs. Tyndall were removed.

Tributes to Tyndall are by Herbert Spencer, "The Late Professor Tyndall," in *Fortnightly Review*, **55** (1894), 141–148; T. H. Huxley, "Professor Tyndall," in *Nineteenth Century*, **35** (1894), 1–11; and Edward Frankland, "John Tyndall, 1820–1893," in *Proceedings of the Royal Society*, **55** (1894), xviii–xxxiv.

Mrs. Tyndall hoped, but failed, to complete a life of her husband. Owing to the circumstances of Tyndall's death, this biography was repeatedly delayed. Following Louisa Tyndall's death, a biography was completed by A. S. Eve and C. H. Creasey, *Life and Work of John Tyndall* (London, 1945).

There are several vignettes of Tyndall including D. Thompson, "John Tyndall (1820–1893), A Study in Vocational Enterprise," in *Vocational Aspects of Secondary and Further Education*, **9** (1957), 38–48; and J. G. Crowther, "John Tyndall," in *Scientific Types* (London, 1968).

Many informal details of Tyndall's social and scientific life are revealed in the diaries of Thomas Archer Hirst, perhaps Tyndall's closest friend, which repose in the Royal Institution, and which have been edited by W. H. Brock and R. MacLeod.

There have been few sustained assessments of Tyndall, the exceptions being Lord Rayleigh, "The Scientific Work of Tyndall," in *Royal Institution Library of Science*, **4** (1894), 273–281; and W. Bragg, "Tyndall's Experiments on Magne-Crystallic Action," *ibid.*, **9** (1927), 131–154. Aspects of his work have also been treated by James Bryant Conant, "Pasteur's and Tyndall's Study of Spontaneous Generation," in *Harvard Case Histories in Experimental Science*, case 7 (Cambridge, Mass., 1953), 487–539; E. J. Wiseman, "John Tyndall: His Contributions to the Defeat of the Theory of Spontaneous Generation of Life," in *School Science Review*, **159** (1965), 362–367; J. K. Crellin, "Airborne Particles and the Germ Theory, 1860–1880," in *Annals of Science*, **22** (1966), 49–60; and "The Problem of Heat Resistance of Micro-Organisms in the British Spontaneous Generation Controversy of 1860–1880," in *Medical History*, **10** (1966), 50–59; Glenn Vandervliet, *Microbiology and the Spontaneous Generation Debate During the 1870s* (Lawrence, Kansas, 1971); J. Friday, "A Microscopic Incident in a Monumental Struggle: Huxley and Antibiosis in 1875," in *British Journal for the History of Science*, VII (1974), 61–71; and some more general references that are in William Bulloch, *The History of Bacteriology* (London, 1938).

There has recently been growing interest in the substance of Tyndall's scientific and political controversies. Cf. Bernard Semmel, *The Governor Eyre Controversy* (London, 1962), 123–128; R. MacLeod, "Science and Government in Victorian England: Lighthouse Illumination and the Board of Trade, 1868–1886," in *Isis*, **60** (1969), 5–38; Frank M. Turner, "Rainfall, Plagues and the Prince of Wales: A Chapter in the Conflict of Religion and Science," in *Journal of British Studies*, **13** (May 1974), 46–65. The controversy with Forbes on glacier motion has been described by J. S. Rowlinson, "The Theory of Glaciers," in *Notes and Records of the Royal Society*, **26** (1971), 189–204. The Mayer-Joule controversy is dealt with in T. S. Kuhn, "Energy Conservation as an Example of Simultaneous Discovery," in M. Claggett, ed., *Critical Problems in the History of Science* (Madison, Wis., 1959), and in J. T. Lloyd, "Background to the Joule-Mayer Controversy," in *Notes and Records of the Royal Society*, **25** (1970), 211–235.

A comprehensive review of Tyndall's work on optical and crystalline structure, on magnetism, radiation, and mountaineering, as well as the relationships between his several "research programmes" is lacking. The historical record has stressed his activities as popularizer, lecturer, and man of letters.

ROY MACLEOD

TYRRELL, JOSEPH BURR (*b.* Weston, Ontario, Canada, 1 November 1858; *d.* Toronto, Canada, 26 August 1957), *geology, exploration, mining.*

Tyrrell was the son of William Tyrrell, a building contractor (later reeve of York Township and of Weston) and Elizabeth Burr, the daughter of Rowland Burr, a mill architect. He was educated at the Old Grammar School, Weston, and at Upper Canada College, Toronto; it is significant that he became an expert shot with the pistol at an early age.

At the University of Toronto he had a distinguished undergraduate career, gaining first-class honors in chemistry, biology, mineralogy, and geology, and winning the only natural sciences scholarship awarded in his year. After graduation he began studies leading to a career in the legal profession, but a threat of tuberculosis caused him to change to the outdoor life of a geologist.

His first appointment was with the Geological Survey of Canada, already a well-established organization, directed by A. C. Selwyn. Tyrrell was assigned as field assistant to the assistant director, Dr. George Dawson, who had already made a considerable reputation for his exploration and geological reconnaissance work in the more remote parts of Canada. Together they made traverses through the Crows Nest, Kootenay, and Kicking Horse passes in the Rocky Mountains. Tyrrell also made geological surveys of the Cretaceous coal measures of the foothills between Calgary and Edmonton, discovering in the course of this work the first remains of giant carnivorous dinosaurs found in Canada. In old age he was to describe this as "one of the most pleasurable thrills" of his life.

In the 1890's Tyrrell's attention turned to the Pre-Cambrian shield area of northern and arctic Canada, and he made a series of arduous journeys there by wagon and canoe. These trips were important for the geological surveys achieved, for apart from the sparse indigenous population of Indians and Eskimos, the only previous visitors had been white trappers. The territory included what are now parts of northern Manitoba and Saskatchewan. The two most noteworthy expeditions (1893 and 1894) were his crossings of the Barren Lands, the treeless arctic wastes lying to the west of Hudson Bay. In each case the starting point was the Lake Athabasca Post of the Hudson's Bay Company. The goal was the company station at Fort Churchill. The first expedition reached Hudson Bay at Chesterfield Inlet at latitude 63° 58'. The journey had proved dangerous. Had they not come upon herds of caribou, they would have starved. Winter overtook them early during the 500-mile journey along Hudson Bay to Fort Churchill. Tyrrell noted a great river discharging into Hudson Bay and resolved to return to investigate it the fol-

lowing year. He did so and named the river after R. Munro Ferguson, a member of the group. Maps were prepared by Tyrrell during these expeditions, and the scientific results were embodied in very full reports, parts of which remain the only authoritative accounts of this area.

Tyrrell was also a keen naturalist and his writings include a catalogue of the mammals of Canada, descriptions of the winter home of the caribou, and an account of the distribution of conifers. Scientifically, however, he is remembered for his contributions to glacial geology at this stage, notably the recognition that three major Pleistocene ice sheets—which he called the Labradorean, the Patrician, and the Keewatin—had covered northern and eastern Canada.

Still more significant were his later contributions to economic geology. He had already noted seepages of oil in the foothills zone north of Edmonton before 1893 and had urged investigation by drilling. This petroleum field was not adequately explored until the 1950's, however. He had also discovered amber deposits at Cedar Lake.

In 1898, after writing up his northern expeditions, he was assigned to the Yukon, where the Klondike gold rush, the most spectacular in Canadian history, was at its height. Tyrrell reported on the geological situation for the government, but upon his return to Ottawa at the end of the year he had come to the conclusion that he wished to take a more active part in the mining industry. Accordingly he left the Geological Survey to return in a private capacity to the Yukon. He became a geological and mining consultant and quickly won the confidence of the gold miners. He then spent seven years in the Yukon.

In 1894 Tyrrell married Mary Edith Carey, daughter of the Reverend Dr. G. M. W. Carey, of New Brunswick. After he became established in Dawson City his wife and small daughter Mary joined him.

Tyrrell's career in the Yukon spanned the changeover from streaming to large-scale hydraulic mining, and he learned and contributed much to the geology of alluvial gold. In 1895 he returned to the east, however, and after a short period as mining adviser to Sir William Mackenzie, the railroad developer, he set up as a consultant in Toronto. He was retained by the Anglo-French Mining Company of London, to which he began to make regular visits.

Tyrrell's influence on the development of metalliferous mining in Canada was considerable; he took a great interest in the famous silver mining district of Cobalt, Ontario, but his greatest achievement was the discovery of the Kirkland Lake gold deposit, which he predicted from structural reasoning. The sinking of a 600-meter shaft proved the orebody and led to the founding of the highly successful Kirkland Lake Gold Mining Company. Tyrrell was president of the company until a few years before he died.

BIBLIOGRAPHY

I. ORIGINAL WORKS. Tyrrell's works include a series of accounts of his expeditions in *Report. Geological Survey of Canada.* See especially Assiniboine and Saskatchewan, **2** (1887), E1–152; northwestern Manitoba, **5** (1892), E1–235; country between Athabasca Lake and Churchill, **6** (1893), D1–120; Doobaunt, Kazam, and Ferguson rivers, **9** (1896), F1–218.

Among his numerous published papers the following deserve mention: "The Glaciation of North Central Canada," in *Journal of Geology*, **6** (1898), 147–160; "Natural Resources of the Barren Lands of Canada," in *Scots. Geogr. Mag.*, **15** (1900), 126–138; "The Gold-Bearing Alluvial Deposits of the Klondike District," in *Transactions of the Institution of Mining and Metallurgy*, **8** (1900), 217–229; "Concentration of Gold of the Klondike," in *Economic Geology*, **2** (1907), 393–399; "The Law of the Pay Streak in Placer Deposits," in *Transactions of the Institution of Mining and Metallurgy*, **21** (1912), 593–605. He was responsible for the descriptions of the geology and mineral resources of the Yukon and the Northwest Territories in A. Shortt and A. G. Doughty, eds., *Canada and Its Provinces*, XXII (Ottawa, 1914), 583–660.

II. SECONDARY LITERATURE. For a biography up to year 1930, see W. J. Loudon, *A Canadian Geologist* (Toronto, 1930), with photograph. See also "Award of the Murchison Medal," in *Proceedings of the Geological Society*, **54** (1918), xlii–xliv; "Award of the Wollaston Medal," *ibid.*, **103** (1947), xxxvi–xxxviii; and obituary by D. R. D(erry), *ibid.*, no. 1563 (1958), 130–133.

K. C. DUNHAM

TYSON, EDWARD (*b.* Bristol, England, 20 January 1650/1651; *d.* London, England, 1 August 1708), *comparative anatomy, medicine.*

Tyson was born into a good Church of England family of some means. After attending private schools in Bristol, Tyson entered Magdalen Hall, Oxford, in 1667 where he was strongly influenced by Plot. From Oxford he received the B.A. in 1670 and M.A. in 1673. During this six-year period Tyson performed many dissections on diverse animals and worked in botany, being influenced by Grew's *The Anatomy of Vegetables Begun* (1672).

In 1673 Tyson began medical studies, receiving a bachelor of medicine degree from Oxford in 1677. In the same year his first publication appeared in Plot's *Natural History of Oxfordshire.*

Ready to begin practicing medicine, Tyson moved to London in 1677 and took up residence with his brother-in-law Richard Morton, in whose house he carried on various experiments, particularly in anatomy. He soon became affiliated with several members of the Royal Society and began publishing in the *Philosophical Transactions* in February 1678. Almost immediately Tyson developed a close relationship to Hooke, who made numerous references to Tyson in his *Diary*. During his first several years in London, Tyson published a handful of papers on morbid anatomy and pathological subjects in the *Philosophical Transactions* and Bartholin's *Acta medica et philosophica hafniensa.*

Tyson's first major contribution in comparative anatomy, published in 1680 under the title *Phocaena, or the Anatomy of a Porpess . . .*, was a description of a dolphin. A full quarter of the forty-eight pages is devoted to "A Preliminary Discourse Concerning Anatomy and a Natural History of Animals," in which Tyson presents his ideas on the importance of comparative anatomy and gives an outline for a proposed natural history of animals. Tyson criticizes the earlier encyclopedic style of natural history, which placed more emphasis on other authors than on the natural objects. He argues for beginning with the simplest animals and ascending through each of the tribes of animals. Here and in other of his anatomical works Tyson repeats his belief in the Great Chain of Being as seen in a gradation between all animals and the existence of intermediate types between each of the major groups. Tyson thinks his "Porpess" is the transitional link between the fishes and the land quadrupeds. This "Preliminary Discourse" contains a clear expression of the principles and methodology of comparative anatomy. In these ideas and the role it played the "Discourse" is very similar to the admirable, anonymous, introductory essay by Claude Perrault in *Mémoires pour servir à l'histoire naturelle des animaux* (1671–1676). These two essays did much to set the style and direction for the significant quantity of comparative-anatomical work in the late seventeenth century in Paris and London. Whether Tyson was acquainted with the work of Perrault and "the Parisians" in 1680 is indeterminable, although likely, since he had reviewed for the *Philosophical Collections* the *Mémoires pour servir à l'histoire des plantes* (1679), also produced under the auspices of the Paris Academy of Sciences.

Like "the Parisians," Tyson well recognized that before a general natural history of animals could be written there had to be an accumulation of observations and descriptions of many different kinds of animals. The starting point for such a project should be very good descriptions of representative animals, which can serve as reference points and points of comparison for many similar animals. He thought his description of the "Porpess" might serve as the representative of the cetaceans. Through arrangements made by Hooke—who attended the dissection and did the drawings that were later engraved and published in Tyson's *Phocaena*—Tyson was able to dissect the dolphin in November 1679. Tyson hoped the description he presented of his "Porpess" would serve as a model and provide inspiration for others. It was a good description on which others could build and which could help serve as the basis for a general natural history. The following year, in his preface to the English edition, which he arranged to have translated, of Swammerdam's *Ephemeri vita* (London, 1681), Tyson repeated the idea that studies of individual species would be the basis of any general natural history.

By 1681 Tyson was well established in London as a comparative anatomist and as a physician. He was elected a fellow of the Royal Society (1679), received a doctorate of physics from Cambridge and was admitted a candidate of the Royal College of Physicians in 1680, and was elected to the first of many terms on the council of the Royal Society (1681). In 1683 Tyson was appointed one of the two curators of the Royal Society who were responsible for providing demonstrations at each meeting. Tyson was also elected a fellow of the Royal College of Physicians; later he served as a censor of the college. The following year Tyson was appointed to two positions which had just become vacant—the Ventera readership in anatomy at the Surgeons Hall, from which he retired in 1699, and physician to Bethlehem and Bridewell Hospitals (now the Royal Bethlehem Hospital), where he also later served as a governor. In 1686 Tyson was elected a member of the Philosophical Society of Oxford.

After 1680 Tyson published just over two dozen works, mostly in the *Philosophical Transactions,* about half of which dealt with natural history. The balance of his output described several pathological cases, instances of monstrous development, and abnormal births. In 1683 Tyson described the anatomy of a rattlesnake, which had been brought to England from Virginia. This very thorough description may then have been the most complete study of any reptile. Later in the same year he described both the broad tapeworm and the roundworm of man as well as a specimen of the Mexican warthog. Because decomposition had begun on the latter, Tyson concentrated on the animal's dorsal scent gland. Glands, and particularly scent glands, were a subject of recurring interest to Tyson. His first publication (1677) was on scent glands. Over many years he gathered information on human and nonhuman glands, which he brought together in "Adenologia," the manuscript of which was never published and has been lost.

In 1685 Tyson contributed two descriptions, of a shark embryo and of the lumpfish, to John Ray's edition of Francis Willughby's *History of Fishes* (1686). Also in 1685 Tyson supplied a considerable amount of comparative-anatomical material to Samuel Collins for the latter's *A Systeme of Anatomy.* In his own *Myotomia Reformata* (1694) William Cowper published Tyson's discovery of the preputial and coronal glands in the glans penis of man. This discovery is perhaps the only thing for which Tyson may be remembered in medicine.

A live opossum was taken to London from Virginia in 1697. Its death in April 1698 provided Tyson with the material for one of his best anatomical descriptions. Fortunately for Tyson the specimen was a female, and he focused on the peculiarities of the reproductive system. He described the marsupium and the marsupial bones. In this paper, also published in 1698 as a separate work, he reiterates the principles of comparative anatomy, which he set forth in his *Phocaena.* In 1704 Tyson published an anatomy of a male opossum, on which Cowper collaborated with him.

In 1699 Tyson published his best-known work, *Orang-Outang, Sive Homo Sylvestris: or, the Anatomy of a Pygmie Compared With That of a Monkey, an Ape, and a Man.* The animal described was actually a young (two to three years old) chimpanzee. The term "Orang-Outang" is a native Malaysian term for "man of the woods" and was long used as a generic term for the larger nonhuman primates. Similarly, "ape" was applied to many of the Old World, tailless monkeys, as with the macaque still known as the "Barbary ape." Tyson was ably assisted on the *Orang-Outang* by Cowper, who did the section on myology, did the drawings for all of the plates, and mounted the skeleton, which is now at the British Museum (Natural History).

Generally the anatomical description is quite thorough and competent, particularly considering how little comparative, nonhuman primate material was then known in Europe. For comparative material Tyson relied quite heavily on the description of monkeys in Alexander Pitfeild's English translation of the Parisians' *Mémoires*. Tyson concluded with a table of the ways his "Pygmie" more resembled a man than an ape, and vice versa, concluding that it belonged between man and the apes. He was surprised that the orangutan's brain was so similar to that of man, because there is so much difference between a man's soul and the soul of the brutes that one would expect a greater difference in their respective organs of the soul. For Tyson, comparative anatomy was a means of understanding and of determining the order of the animals on the Great Chain of Being. Tyson repeatedly emphasizes how close the structure of his Pygmie is to that of man and that the Pygmie is the closest approach of the animal kingdom to the rational qualities of man. While the notion of the Great Chain has a history that long antedates Tyson, he did, in this first anatomical description of one of the great apes, clearly identify an occupant for the rung immediately below man. The identification of such gradational links was one of his objectives for comparative anatomy.

The last section of Tyson's *Orang-Outang* is devoted to "A Philological Essay Concerning the Pygmies of the Ancients." In this major, early contribution to the study of the folklore of the primates Tyson tried to demonstrate that the many references to assorted, but similar, creatures in ancient literature really referred to a nonhuman primate such as his orangutan. Two years later Tyson did a similar philological study regarding the mantichora (a mandrill in the genus *Papio*), which remained unpublished until Montague's biography of Tyson. Apparently Tyson intended this and other material on primates to be an appendix to the *Orang-Outang*. After the publication of the *Orang-Outang*, Tyson published several more papers in the *Philosophical Transactions*, the most interesting of which was on the male opossum and a fish, the yellow gurnard (sea robin).

By no means all of Tyson's scientific work appeared in print. There are many references in the records of the Royal Society to the research that Tyson was doing. These are sometimes referring to specimens turned over to Tyson for dissection (in one case the Society bought an ostrich for him to dissect), and sometimes are Tyson's reports. In the "Tyson Folio" at the Royal College of Surgeons are Tyson's research notes from numerous dissections as well as original drawings for his papers, both published and unpublished.

Tyson did not publish a large number of either anatomical or medical works, of which the most important was the *Orang-Outang*. Tyson carried on an active medical practice from 1677 until his sudden death in 1708. During much of this period he lectured on anatomy at Surgeons Hall and served as physician to Bethlehem and Bridewell Hospitals, where a wing is named in Tyson's memory. Tyson was a quiet man of orderly habits who occurs seldom in contemporary references and correspondence. Apparently his chief delight came from his studies.

BIBLIOGRAPHY

I. ORIGINAL WORKS. Tyson's two major writings were *Phocaena, or the Anatomy of a Porpess, Dissected at Gresham College: With a Preliminary Discourse Concerning Anatomy, and a Natural History of Animals* (London, 1680); and *Orang-Outang, Sive Homo Sylvestris: or, the Anatomy of a Pygmie Compared with That of a Monkey, an Ape, and a Man. To Which Is Added, A Philological Essay Concerning the Pygmies, the Cynocephali, the Satyrs, and Sphinges of the Ancients. Wherein It Will Appear That They Are All Either Apes or Monkeys, and Not Men, as Formerly Pretended* (London, 1699). A facs. ed. of *Orang-Outang* (London, 1966) has an introduction by M. F. A. Montague; a 2nd ed., entitled *The Anatomy of a Pygmy* (London, 1751), also included several of Tyson's shorter writings. Most of Tyson's other writings appeared in *Philosophical Transactions of the Royal Society*. A complete bibliography of Tyson's writings appears in Montague (see below).

At the Royal College of Surgeons, in folio vol. no. 324, are preserved a number of MSS by Tyson and many drawings of his dissections. The British Museum (MS Sloane 2770) has Tyson's MS of the myology portion of his anatomy lectures. At least six partial syllabi of his anatomy lectures exist at the British Museum and the Bodleian Library.

II. SECONDARY LITERATURE. The standard source for Tyson's life is M. F. Ashley Montague, *Edward Tyson, M.D. F.R.S. 1650–1708 and the Rise of Human and Comparative Anatomy in England* (Philadeophia, 1943). Montague exhaustively searched the contemporary literature and records for references to Tyson, and has brought his results together in this volume. A bibliography of Tyson's writings is included.

WESLEY C. WILLIAMS

UBALDO, GUIDO. See **Monte, Guidobaldo, Marchese del.**

UKHTOMSKY, ALEXEI ALEXEIVICH (*b.* Rhurik, Russia, 20 September 1875; *d.* Leningrad, U.S.S.R., 31 August 1942), *physiology.*

Ukhtomsky was descended from an ancient princely line whose name sprang from the Ukhtoma river that flowed through their ancestral domain in Rhurik in the province of Yaroslav. After receiving his secondary education at the military college in Nizhny Novgorod (now Gorki), he enlisted in the army as a cadet. Moved by strong religious beliefs, Ukhtomsky resigned from the army to enter the Moscow Theological Academy at Zagorsk. There was little inkling then of a future career in science; theology, church history, psychology, philosophy, and rhetoric absorbed his attention. In this religious climate he developed an intense interest in the faith of the Old Believers, or Roskolniks, a dissenting group in the Russian Orthodox Church. The group held tenaciously to the ritualistic practices that had been abandoned during Patriarch Nikon's reforms in the seventeenth century.

During a pilgrimage to visit their monasteries, he visited Tyumen, Siberia, where he met Rasputin. Ukhtomsky later invited him to St. Petersburg and introduced him into the religious salons of the aristocracy.

In 1902 Ukhtomsky, influenced by Wedensky, entered the University of St. Petersburg. Making a complete change, he entered the physicomathematical faculty and specialized in animal physiology under Wedensky. He first studied the effects of anemia, oxygen lack, and fatigue on neuromuscular preparations.

After graduating from the university, he took a postgraduate course and soon became assistant in the physiological department, demonstrating experiments for the lecturers. During this time he carried out research with Wedensky on "The Reflexes of Antagonistic Muscles to Electrical Stimulation of a Sensory Nerve."

It was while working as a demonstrator that he stumbled on the phenomenon that led to his theory of a dominant focus of cortical excitation operating to exclude and inhibit other concurrent functions. He had to prepare for the class an experiment on electrical stimulation of the motor cortex of the dog. To his dismay, stimulation produced no movement, even when he increased the strength of the current. Suddenly the dog defecated, and immediately following this, cortical stimulation once again produced a motor response.

Ukhtomsky was so struck by this observation that he put it to experimental investigation and made it the subject of his thesis "On the Dependence of Cortical Motor Effects on Secondary Central Influences," which he defended for a master's degree in 1912. This was his last laboratory work and for the remaining thirty years of his life he made no further experiments, but in this thesis was incorporated the main theme of all Ukhtomsky's future concepts, namely the principle of "dominanta." This term appeared in 1923 in the title of the first of his many publications on the subject.

On gaining his master's degree he was appointed a docent in physiology, responsible for lecturing on such subjects as the physiology of the sense organs and of the central nervous system. In all his scientific teaching he upheld the tenets of the Wedensky school. His broad education in history and philosophy and his wide knowledge of the physiological literature made him a fine lecturer, but he did not refrain, even in the laboratory, from trying, often successfully, to convert his pupils to his religious faith. He was kind and generous to impecunious students, often gaining help for them through his position as churchwarden at St. Nicholas, the Old Believers' church in St. Petersburg.

Ukhtomsky relinquished none of his religious observances. In 1912 he attended the All-Russian Old Believer Congress, at which he reported on "The Splendor of Church Singing." He observed all the religious rites both at home and in the laboratory; during Lent he came to the lecture room carrying a rosary of leather beads and wearing a black wooden cross around his neck.

Simple in tastes, he lived in a two-room flat surrounded by books. Many were physiological texts (some were library books that he could not bring himself to part with), and others were rare, old, handwritten religious books. Even when, in 1922, he was appointed to the chair in physiology and could have afforded more comfortable living quarters, he preferred to remain in his small flat. He never married but lived alone, reading and drawing icons of the Old Believer pattern. He chose to dress as a rich peasant—wearing hunting boots, a coarse jacket, and underclothes made from linen woven by the peasants. He wore his hair long in moujik fashion and, by religious observance, never shaved his beard.

During the October Revolution he was arrested and imprisoned. His many friends at the University of Petrograd appealed on his behalf and he was freed. He was reinstated, and on the death of Wedensky in 1922 succeeded to the chair in physiology. As head of the department he began to develop his own ideas of central nervous system function. He spoke vaguely of processes that could not be observed experimentally, such as "the learning of a rhythm" by nerve cells, nerve endings, and muscles; of "constellations and excitations"; of "active rest"; and so on. His followers, recognizing his brilliance at the same time that they recognized his failings as an experimental scientist, strove to advance his philosophical views by presenting them as close to those of dialectical materialism, and indeed his report to the All-Russian Physiological Congress was published, not in a physiological journal, but in a philosophical one, the *Pod Znamenem Marxisma*.

Ukhtomsky remained in favor and became a member of the Academy of Sciences of the U.S.S.R. and was honored by having the Ukhtomsky Institute of Physiology in Leningrad University named for him.

Known principally for his concept of dominanta, Ukhtomsky's ideas evolved substantially from his academic pedigree. Sechenov (1829–1905) had discovered that inhibition could be an active process in the nervous system (not merely a suppression or occlusion of excitation). His pupil Wedensky developed further the ideas of excitation and inhibition, and his pupil's pupil Ukhtomsky derived his unified theory of dominanta. Sechenov held that all forms of activity of the central nervous system were derivatives of the simplest act—the reflex. He envisioned three main links in the reflex: (1) stimulation of sensory receptors, (2) action of a reflex center, and (3) excitation of the effector systems (muscles and glands). It was the second of these that Ukhtomsky developed into the concept of dominanta.

The rhythm of the respiratory movements and the reciprocal innervation of limb muscles were two of the outstanding physiological systems that suggested a central control mechanism, one which Ukhtomsky envisaged as ensembles of excitation and of inhibition responsible for these rhythmic activations. Both he and Wedensky attempted to apply this principle to the nerves themselves, calling this "the rhythm of nerves."

An important feature of the concept of dominance was the lability by which the controlling nerve center could establish new functional connections between various centers, ensuring a specific reaction of the central nervous system to the particular stimulation it received (a concept one meets again in Pavlovian theories of conditioned reflexes). In other words, the balance of excitation and inhibition in a system was labile and not an automatism. This broke away from the automatic alternation previously conceived as operating in reciprocal innervation as described by Sherrington.

The concept that in the West was to develop into the recognition of homeostasis was called by Ukhtomsky "rest" or "balance." He envisaged it as the goal of a biological system following any stimulation or disturbance. His ideas along these lines extended into metabolism and the phenomena of fatigue states.

During the siege of Leningrad in World War II, Ukhtomsky's institute was evacuated to Saratov on the Volga, but he remained in the city. He studied shock in the wounded and continued his activities at the university. Suffering already from incipient cancer of the throat, chronic hypertension, and gangrene in his legs, his death was hastened by starvation and, on 31 August 1942, he died.

BIBLIOGRAPHY

The complete works of Ukhtomsky have been published in *Sobranie Sochineny* ("Collected Works"), 5 vols. (Leningrad, 1945–1954). An English trans. by D. B. Lindsley is being prepared by the American Psychological Association.

MARY A. B. BRAZIER

ULLOA Y DE LA TORRE GIRAL, ANTONIO DE (*b*. Seville, Spain, 12 January 1716; *d*. Isla de Léon, Cádiz, Spain, 5 July 1795), *natural history*.

A mariner by profession, Ulloa was commissioned by the government, along with Jorge Juan y Santacilla, to accompany the expedition sent to America by the Paris Academy of Sciences to measure an arc of meridian (1736–1745). While returning to Spain he was captured by the English but took advantage of his stay in Britain to further his education. Upon reaching Madrid, he published, with Jorge Juan, *Relación histórica del viaje a la América meridional* (1748). The sections devoted to geology and other technical matters, written by Ulloa, include the first scientific description of the platinum found in the sands of the Río Pinto (Magdalena) in Colombia in 1736: "a stone of such resistance that it is very difficult to break or shatter it by striking it on a steel anvil." It was studied by William Watson (1750) and by François Chavanneau in the Vergara laboratory (1786). Ferdinand VI sent Ulloa on a mission throughout Europe to learn about the most recent scientific discoveries.

Ulloa participated in the creation of the royal natural history collection (1752) and of the naval observatory at Cádiz (1754). In 1758 he was appointed general manager of the mines of Huancavélica, Peru, and later assumed high posts in the Spanish navy. He also served as first Spanish governor of Louisiana (1766–1768).

Ulloa's observations embraced many fields. In the catalog of nature that he entitled *Noticias americanas: Entretenimiento físico-histórico sobre América meridional y septentrional-oriental* (1772) he discussed "climates and the products of the three kingdoms—vegetable, animal, and mineral." The work called *Observación en el mar de un eclipse de sol* (1778) presents a certain interest. His scientific avocations so absorbed Ulloa that he began to neglect his duties as a high-ranking naval officer and was court-martialed, although he was cleared of the charges. *Conversaciones . . . con sus tres hijos* may be considered a didactic work.

Noticias secretas de América (1826), published after Ulloa's death and that of Juan y Santacilla, is a confidential report on the situation in America that had been sent to the marquis of Ensenada.

BIBLIOGRAPHY

I. ORIGINAL WORKS. Ulloa's writings include *Relación histórica del viaje a la América meridional . . .*, 4 vols. (Madrid, 1748), written with Jorge Juan y Santacilla; *Noticias americanas: Entretenimiento físico-histórico sobre América meridional y septentrional-oriental* (Madrid, 1772); *Observación en el mar de un eclipse de sol* (Madrid, 1779); *Conversaciones de Ulloa con sus tres hijos* (Madrid, 1795); and *Noticias secretas de América* (London, 1826), written with Juan y Santacilla.

II. SECONDARY LITERATURE. Juan Sempere y Guarinos, *Escritores del reinado de Carlos III*, VI (Madrid, 1785), 158–176, is important. See also Julio Fernández Guillén y Tato, *Los tenientes de navio Jorge Juan y Santacilla y Antonio de Ulloa y de la Torre-Giral y la medición del meridiano* (Madrid, 1935). On his description of platinum, see Mary Elvira Weeks, *Discovery of the Elements*, 6th ed. (Easton, Pa., 1956), ch. 16, esp. 409–412.

J. VERNET

ULRICH, EDWARD OSCAR (*b*. Cincinnati, Ohio, 1 February 1857; *d*. Washington, D.C., 22 February 1944), *stratigraphy, paleontology.*

Ulrich's career was typical of those nineteenth-century American paleontologists who, beginning as self-taught amateur collectors, reached professional status through initial independent publication, then commissions for state or territorial geologic surveys, and finally, a permanent position with the federal survey, a large museum, or a major university.[1]

Ulrich was one of eight children of an immigrant Alsation carpenter,[2] later a contractor in the Cincinnati area. Ulrich's formal education was limited to intermittent terms at two Ohio colleges during the 1870's.[3] He resumed carpentry with his father and continued collecting from the extensive and highly fossiliferous Upper Ordovician rocks of Cincinnati. In 1877 the Cincinnati Society of Natural History recognized his abilities with a small-salaried curatorship. He resigned the post in 1879 and spent a lively two years superintending silver mines near Boulder, Colorado.

Relocated at Newport, Kentucky, by 1884 Ulrich had published in the *Journal of the Cincinnati Society of Natural History* six brief paleontological papers and one major systematic investigation of American Paleozoic bryozoans, to which he expanded the new techniques of thin sections.[4]

With contracts from the Illinois and Minnesota geologic surveys for further studies of Paleozoic bryozoans, sponges, and mollusks, he combined efforts in 1885 with Charles Schuchert.[5] Both men became able lithographic illustrators.

Ulrich made fundamental taxonomic contributions to a dozen major marine invertebrate taxa. Preparation of bryozoan collections for the British Museum (Natural History) and the museum of the University of Munich led to his contributions on the bryozoans and ostracod crustaceans in the first English edition of Karl A. von Zittel's *Text-book of Palaeontology*, Charles R. Eastman, trans. (London, 1896). Between 1885 and 1897 Ulrich also described Paleozoic faunas and conducted stratigraphic studies for the Ohio and Kentucky surveys, served five years as curator of geology for the Cincinnati Society, and for nine years was associate editor of the *American Geologist*.

In 1897 Ulrich's reputation brought him a temporary appointment to the U.S. Geological Survey. This post, which became permanent in 1901, marked a significant shift in research emphasis from paleontology to stratigraphy. Relocation at Washington, D.C., renewed Ulrich's association with Schuchert until 1904; they wrote "Paleozoic Seas and Barriers in Eastern North America" during this interval. When Raymond Smith Bassler, who had been Ulrich's assistant during the previous decade at Newport, joined the U.S. National Museum, they continued close professional ties in major studies of bryozoans (1904).[6] Paleozoic ostracods (1923), and the enigmatic conodonts (1926).

In later years Ulrich considered himself first and foremost a stratigrapher and believed stratigraphic syntheses to be his most lasting contributions. Geologic mapping experience in the Upper Mississippi Valley[7] and Appalachians culminated in the article "Revision of the Paleozoic Systems" (1911). Among modifications and proposed additions to the standard geologic time scale were two new lower Paleozoic time-stratigraphic units of systemic rank, the Ozarkian and Canadian, inserted between the restricted Cambrian and Ordovician systems.

In his publications on stratigraphic methods and philosophy, Ulrich wholeheartedly adopted Thomas Chrowder Chamberlin's concept that records of diastrophic events were the natural and ultimate bases for defining and correlating stratigraphic units. In Ulrich's view, the differential isostatic adjustments yielded oscillatory littoral displacements, which produced abrupt discontinuities in geologic and faunal sequences deposited in multiple isolated epicontinental basins. These basins were alternately flooded from opposite directions by oceans flanking the North American continent. Rock units and their faunal assemblages bounded by these disconformities were discontinuous both spatially and temporally. Mutually exclusive, they were terminated by nondeposition rather than facies—lateral gradation to coeval units, formed in different depositional environments, an alternate concept popularized in the United States by Amadeus William Grabau[8] and adopted by Schuchert.

Ulrich's stratigraphic models were initially of value in interpreting the midcontinent region but failed to explain the more complex Appalachian geology. Ulrich used index or guide-fossil techniques at the most discrete taxonomic levels to make the initial identifications of the datum planes, not to define or correlate tectonic event-based broader stratigraphic units. He considered recognition of the introduction of new generic types a complementary and less than precisely coincident verification of physical boundaries, in contrast to Schuchert's insistence that the nonrepetitive aspect of organic evolution made fossils fundamental determinants of time and event.

Albertina Zuest, whom Ulrich married in Cincinnati in 1886, died in 1932 after a decade of disabling illness; their union was childless. The following year he married Lydia Sennhauser, his first wife's nurse during the early stages of her illness. Ulrich was appointed associate in paleontology at

the U.S. National Museum in 1914, and occupied that position after his formal retirement from the U.S. Geological Survey in 1932. He continued his studies, accumulating paleontologic evidence for his Ozarkian and Canadian systems, and supplying stratigraphic data for systematic investigations contributed mostly by younger museum associates. These studies failed to provide an acceptable paleontological base[9] for Ulrich's systemic units; the Ozarkian is not part of present usage, which considers the Canadian the basal series of the Ordovician system.

Ulrich was an eminent authority on American lower Paleozoic stratigraphy during the first three decades of the twentieth century. His vast experience and encyclopedic knowledge enabled him to dominate the discipline. Perhaps his most important influence during his years on the U.S. Geological Survey was the controversial aspect of his research and his disputative nature, which caused contemporaries to reexamine critically their own investigations.

NOTES

1. Raymond Smith Bassler, "Development of Invertebrate Paleontology in America," in *Bulletin of the Geological Society of America*, **44** (1933), 268.

2. Edward was the eldest of the five children born to Charles Ulrich and his first wife, Julia Schnell.

3. German Wallace College, now Baldwin-Wallace College, Berea, Ohio, which Ulrich attended in 1874–1875, awarded him the honorary degrees of Master of Arts (1886) and Doctor of Science (1892).

4. Henry Alleyne Nicholson's work in the previous decade had shown the need for continuing investigations of bryozoans by this method, one that disclosed the usefulness of internal structures in recognizing widespread external homeomorphy.

5. Schuchert later recalled their association in Newport (1881–1888), especially the four years during which he worked as Ulrich's assistant. See unpublished MS autobiography, ch. 7, p. 30; box XLIII, Charles Schuchert Papers, Manuscripts and Archives Division, Sterling Library, Yale University.

6. Bassler, who prepared the bryozoan section for the 2nd ed. (1913) of the work by Karl A. von Zittel, culminated his systematic work within the Ulrichian framework of ideas in *Treatise on Invertebrate Paleontology, Part G, Bryozoa* (Lawrence, Kansas, 1953); its excellent organization and bibliography reflect his abilities as a compiler. In Ulrich and Bassler's investigations, thin sections were studied primarily with the 10-power hand lens. Their contemporaries, Edgar Roscoe Cumings and Jesse James Galloway at the University of Indiana, made initial microscopic studies of bryozoan modes of growth and functional morphology, techniques now being applied to investigations of systematics and phylogeny for the revision volume of the *Treatise*.

7. The only major unpublished work from this period is the joint geologic mapping and stratigraphic study with Nevin Melancthon Fenneman in 1904–1914 of the Cincinnati East 15-minute quadrangle. The map and accompanying MS formerly in the survey's Washington open files is no longer ex-

tant. The Department of Geology of the University of Cincinnati presently holds a photostatic copy. Ulrich's adamant positioning of the Richmondian stage as basal Silurian disagreed with the usage of the Geological Names Committee of the U.S. Geological Survey, and most contemporary usage, which held it to be uppermost Ordovician. See William Henry Shideler, "The Ordovician-Silurian Boundary," in *Ohio Journal of Science*, **16**, no. 8 (1916), 329–335.

8. A comparison and critique of Ulrichian and Grabauan stratigraphic methods and philosophies is Carl Owen Dunbar and John Rodgers, *Principles of Stratigraphy* (New York, 1957), 136, 284–288.

9. Charles Schuchert, "Ozarkian and Canadian Brachiopods," in *American Journal of Science*, **237**, no. 2 (1939), 135–138.

BIBLIOGRAPHY

I. ORIGINAL WORKS. A large collection of papers, field notebooks, locality registers, monthly reports, a partly published MS, and memorabilia is in the Paleontology and Stratigraphy Branch, U.S. Geological Survey, National Museum of Natural History, Washington, D.C.

A second unpublished MS is held by the Denver Library of the survey, which also preserves the 1912–1917 correspondence between Ulrich and George Willis Stose. Folder 8, Geological Division General File (Chief Geologist), 1901–1916, Records Group 57 (Records of the Geological Survey) of the National Archives, Washington, D.C., contains field correspondence sent by Ulrich during 1902–1915. Letters sent in 1888–1893 by Josua Lindahl, then Illinois state geologist, to Ulrich are on microfilm in the Augustana College Library, Rock Island, Illinois. The department of geology, University of Iowa, Iowa City, holds copies of 1934 correspondence between Ulrich and A. C. Trowbridge.

Ulrich's 141 published titles are listed in the several bibliographies of North American geology, *Bulletin of the United States Geological Survey*, nos. 745 (1923), 1031–1033; 823 (1931), 624–625; 937 (1944), 961–963; and 1049 (1957), 927.

Among his paleontological writings are "American Paleozoic Bryozoa," in *Journal of the Cincinnati Museum of Natural History*, **5** (1882), 121–175, 232–257; **6** (1883), 82–92, 148–168, 245–279; and **7** (1884), 24–51; "American Paleozoic Sponges," in *Illinois Geological Survey*, **8**, pt. 2, *Palaeontology* (1890), 209–241, 243–251, 253–282 (the last section with Oliver Everett); "Paleozoic Bryozoa," *ibid.*, 283–688, pls. XXIX–LXXVIII; "New and Little Known American Paleozoic Ostracoda," in *Journal of the Cincinnati Society of Natural History*, **13** (1890–1891), 104–137, 173–211, pls. 7–18; "On Lower Silurian Bryozoa of Minnesota," in *Geological and Natural History Survey of Minnesota, Final Report*, **3**, *Paleontology*, pt. 1 (1895), 96–332, pls. 1–28 [folio]; "New Lower Silurian Lamellibranchiata of Minnesota," *ibid.*, pt. 2 (1897), 475–628, pls. XXXV–XLII; "The Lower Silurian Ostracoda of Minnesota," *ibid.*, 629–693, pls. XLIII–XLVI; "The Lower Silurian Gastropoda of Minnesota," *ibid.*, 813–1081, pls. LXI–LXXXII, with Wilbur H. Scofield; "A Revision of the Paleozoic Bryozoa," pt. 1, "On Genera and Species of Ctenostoma," in *Smithsonian Miscellaneous Collections*, **45**, no. 1452 (1904), 256–294, pls. LXV–LXVIII, pt. 2, "On Genera and Species of Trepostoma," *ibid.*, **47**, no. 1470 (1904), 15–55, pls. VI–XIV, with Raymond Smith Bassler; "Paleozoic Ostracoda: Their Morphology, Classification, and Occurrence," in *Maryland Geological Survey*, *Silurian* (Baltimore, 1923), 271–391, pls. XXXVI–LXV, with Bassler; "A Classification of the Toothlike Fossils, Conodonts, With Descriptions of American Devonian and Mississippian Species," in *Proceedings of the United States National Museum*, **68**, no. 2613 (1926), 1–63, pls. 1–11, with Bassler; "The Cambrian of the Upper Mississippi Valley," pt. 1, "Trilobita; Dikelocephalinae and Osceolinae," in *Bulletin of the Public Museum*, **12**, no. 1 (1930), 1–122, pls. 1–23; pt. 2, "Trilobita; Saukiinae," *ibid.*, **12**, no. 2 (1933), 123–306, pls. 24–45, with Charles Elmer Resser; "Cambrian Bivalved Crustacea of the Order Conchostraca," in *Proceedings of the United States National Museum*, **78**, no. 2847 (1931), 1–130, pls. 1–10, with Bassler; "Ozarkian and Canadian Brachiopoda," in *Special Papers of the Geological Society of America*, no. 13 (1938), viii, 1–323, pls. 1–58, with Gustav Arthur Cooper; "Ozarkian and Canadian Cephalopods," pt. 1, "Nautilicones," *ibid.*, no. 37 (1942), x, 1–157, pls. 1–57, with August Frederick Foerste, William Madison Furnish, and Arthur K. Miller; pt. 2, "Brevicones," *ibid.*, no. 49 (1943), x, 1–240, pls. 1–70, with Foerste and Miller; pt. 3, "Longicones and Summary," *ibid.*, no. 58 (1944), x, 1–226, pls. 1–68, with Foerste, Miller, and Athel Glyde Unklesbay.

Ulrich's stratigraphic publications include "The Lower Silurian Deposits of the Upper Mississippi Province: a Correlation of the Strata With Those in the Cincinnati, Tennessee, New York, and Canadian Provinces, and the Stratigraphic and Geographic Distribution of the Fossils," in *Geological and Natural History Survey of Minnesota, Final Report*, **3**, *Paleontology*, pt. 2 (1897), lxxxiii–cxxviii [folio], with Newton Horace Winchell; "Paleozoic Seas and Barriers in Eastern North America," in *Bulletin of the New York State Museum*, no. 52, Paleontology no. 6 (1902), 633–663, with C. Schuchert; "Columbia Folio, Tennessee," in *U.S. Geological Survey, Geological Atlas*, fol. no. 95 (1903), 1–6, 8 pls., with Charles Willard Hayes; "The Lead, Zinc, and Fluorspar Deposits of Western Kentucky, Part I, Geology and General Relations," in *Professional Papers. U.S. Geological Survey*, no. 36 (1905), 15–105, pls. I–VII; "Revision of the Paleozoic Systems," in *Bulletin of the Geological Society of America*, **22** (1911), 281–680, pls. 25–29, "Index . . .," *ibid.*, **24** (1913), 625–668; "The Chattanoogan Series, With Special Reference to the Ohio Shale Problem," in *American Journal of Science*, 4th ser., **34**, no. 200 (1912), 157–183; "The Ordovician-Silurian Boundary," in *Congrès Géologique International, Compte-Rendu de la XIIIe Session, Canada, 1913* (Ottawa, 1914), 593–669; "Correlation by Displacements of the Strand-line and the Function and Proper Use of Fossils in Correlation," in *Bulletin of the Geological Society of America*, **27** (1916), 451–490; "Major Causes of Land and Sea Oscillations," in *Journal of the Washington Academy of Sciences*, **10**, no. 3 (1920), 57–78, reprinted in *Smithsonian Institution, Annual Report for 1920* (1922), 321–337; "Some New Facts Bearing on Correlations of Chester Formations," in *Bulletin of the Geological Society of America*, **33** (1922), 805–852; "American Silurian Formations," in Maryland Geological Survey, *Silurian* (Baltimore, 1923), 233–270, with Bassler; "Notes on New Names in Table of Formations and on Physical Evidence of Breaks Between Paleozoic Systems in Wisconsin," in *Transactions of the Wisconsin Academy of Sciences, Arts and Letters*, **21** (1924), 71–107; "Relative Values of Criteria Used in Drawing the Ordovician-Silurian Boundary," in *Bulletin of the Geological Society of America*, **37** (1926), 279–348; "Ordovician Trilobites of the Family Telephidae and Concerned Stratigraphic Correlations," in *Proceedings of the United States National Museum*, **76**, no. 2818 (1930), 1–101, pls. 1–8.

II. SECONDARY LITERATURE. On Ulrich and his work, see R. S. Bassler, "Edward Oscar Ulrich (1857–1944)," in *Bulletin of the American Association of Petroleum Geologists*, **28**, no. 5 (1944), 687–689; and "Memorial to Edward Oscar Ulrich," in *Proceedings. Geological Society of America* (1945), 331–351, pl. 23; G. Arthur Cooper, "Edward Oscar Ulrich," in *Dictionary of American Biography*, supp. 3, pp. 782–783; Percy Edward Raymond, "Edward Oscar Ulrich," in *Science*, **99**, no. 2570 (1944), 256; Rudolf Ruedemann, "Biographical Memoir of Edward Oscar Ulrich, 1857–1944," in *Biographical Memoirs. National Academy of Sciences*, **24**, no. 7 (1947), 259–280, with portrait; and *The National Cyclopaedia of American Biography*, XXXIII (1947), 63–64.

CLIFFORD M. NELSON

ULRICH OF STRASBOURG (or **ULRICUS DE ARGENTINA** or **ULRICH ENGELBERTI**) (*b.* early thirteenth century; *d.* Paris, *ca.* 1278), *natural philosophy.*

A student of Albertus Magnus at Cologne (1248–1254), Ulrich became his devoted disciple. He lectured at Strasbourg for many years before serving as provincial of the German Dominicans from 1272 to 1277, when he was sent to Paris to lecture on Peter Lombard's *Sentences* and to obtain the degree of master; but he died shortly after arriving there.

Among Ulrich's writings are a lost treatise on meteors, a commentary on the *Sentences*, and his chief work, the *Summa de summo bono* ("A Summary Concerning the Supreme Good"), projected for eight books but extant only to the fifth treatise

of the sixth book. This is a Neoplatonic work that is metaphysical in tone and is heavily indebted to Arab thought. Duhem translated and analyzed portions concerned with medieval astronomy and found that they are largely derived from Albertus Magnus. For example, Ulrich cited Ptolemy and a spurious work of Alpetragius (al-Bitrūjī); Denys the Carthusian (1402–1471) attempted to correct the latter reference, noting that it should be attributed to al-Fārābī (see Duhem, p. 360). Ulrich probably used only Albertus' report of their teachings. Ulrich held that there are ten celestial spheres, and was mainly concerned with linking them to intelligences as movers, and with explaining the characteristics of the various planets in terms of the primary qualities associated with their spheres. He mentioned the precession of the equinoxes incidentally as being one degree each hundred years, but otherwise adduced no astronomical data; he seems not to have been himself an observer of the heavens. Ulrich's importance for medieval science would seem to reside in the witness he provides to the all-pervading influence of Albertus Magnus as an authority, on the Continent at least, in matters scientific.

BIBLIOGRAPHY

Étienne Gilson, *History of Christian Philosophy in the Middle Ages* (New York–London, 1955), 431–433, 751–753, references the edited portions of Ulrich's *Summa*, summarizes its teaching, and provides a guide to bibliography. See also Pierre Duhem, *Le système du monde*, III (Paris, 1915; repr. 1958), 358–363; and Caroline Putnam, "Ulrich of Strasbourg and the Aristotelian Causes," in *Studies in Philosophy and the History of Philosophy*, **1** (1961), 139–159.

WILLIAM A. WALLACE, O.P.

ULSTAD, PHILIPP (*fl.* early sixteenth century), *medicine, alchemy.*

Little is known of Philipp Ulstad's life other than that he was a Nuremberg patrician who taught medicine at the Academy in Fribourg, Switzerland, during the first half of the sixteenth century. Aside from a small treatise on the plague, he published one book of significance for the history of science: *Coelum philosophorum* . . . (1525). This work was extremely popular, going through more than twenty editions and serving as a standard authority on the preparation and use of distillates for nearly a century. Ulstad emphasized the medical efficacy of chemical distillates, thus departing somewhat from conventional medieval pharmacology and preparing the way, in part, for the more intimate connection between chemistry and medicine effected by his contemporary Paracelsus and the latter's disciples in the second half of the sixteenth century.

Ulstad's work was based mainly on the writings attributed to Ramon Lull, Albertus Magnus, Arnald of Villanova, and John of Rupescissa. He was most clearly indebted to John of Rupescissa's doctrine of the fifth essence, namely, the substance that can be extracted from all mundane bodies by ordinary chemical methods and that is the chemically active principle of each body. Ulstad was primarily concerned with the curative and preservative properties of rectified alcohol—which he denoted variously as the fifth essence, *aqua vite*, *aurum potabile*, and *coelum philosophorum*. He maintained that the fifth essence, although not incorruptible, was less corruptible than the four elements and owed its medical value to its ability to regulate the bodily humors and thereby preserve the human body from decay.

Despite his use of alchemical terminology, Ulstad clearly dissociated himself from the enigmatic aspects of the alchemical tradition in offering his concise and rational account of the preparation of distilled remedies. Concerned with culling from the medieval alchemical corpus those techniques and ideas of practical utility, he ensured that they were made available to as large an audience as possible, including all apothecaries, surgeons, and medical doctors.

The lucidity of his technical directions was a major reason for the influence exerted by Ulstad. His discussion of apparatus and manipulative procedures afforded the sixteenth-century investigator an accurate summary of the best distilling theory then available. Of particular importance is Ulstad's description and woodcut of a distilling column with vertical water-cooled coils that, although not original with him, contributed to the decline of the less efficient and uncontrollable air-cooling methods commonly employed. He also clearly presented a rudimentary dephlegmation technique based on the introduction of oil-soaked sponges into the still head to retain the phlegm and obtain better fractionation. Ulstad's recipes for the extraction of the fifth essence dealt with a wide variety of sources, including gold, spices, herbs, fruits, flowers, precious stones, and metals, and he specified the particular ailments most responsive to each essence.

A codifier rather than an innovator, Ulstad contributed to the rise of iatrochemistry by demonstrating that drugs and other medicinals depend for their efficacy upon pure spirits or essences that can be extracted by the methods of chemistry. His ideas reappear in the writings of many prominent scientific figures, including Konrad Gesner and Andreas Libavius.

BIBLIOGRAPHY

I. ORIGINAL WORKS. Ulstad's major book is *Coelum philosophorum seu de secretis naturae liber* (Fribourg, 1525; 1st French trans., Paris, 1546; 1st German trans., Strasbourg, 1527). The later editions and translations have more elaborate titles. I have used the following edition: *Le Ciel des Philosophes, ou sont contenus les secrets de nature et comme l'homme se peult tenir en santé, et longuement vivre . . . extraict des livres de Arnould de Ville neuve, du grand Albert, Raymont Lulle, Jehan de la Roche Tranchée* (Paris, 1550). Ulstad's other work is *De epidemia tractatus* (Basel, 1526).

II. SECONDARY LITERATURE. There is no full-scale biography of Ulstad. Details concerning his work are found in Lynn Thorndike, *A History of Magic and Experimental Science*, V (New York, 1941), 541–542, 602, 621; James R. Partington, *A History of Chemistry*, II (London, 1961), 84–86; J. Ferguson, *Bibliotheca chemica*, II (Glasgow, 1906), 482–483; and Edward R. Atkinson and Arthur H. Hughes, "The 'Coelum Philosophorum' of Philipp Ulstad," in *Journal of Chemical Education*, 16 (1939), 103–107. R. J. Forbes, *Short History of the Art of Distillation* (Leiden, 1948), 127–130, states that Ulstad was probably an associate of Hieronymus Brunschwig, although he gives no proof for the claim.

MARTIN FICHMAN

ULUGH BEG (*b.* Sulṭāniyya, Central Asia, 22 March 1394; *d.* near Samarkand, Central Asia [now Uzbek S.S.R.], 27 October 1449), *astronomy*.

Ulugh Beg, which means "great prince," was a title that replaced his original name, Muḥammad Taragay. He was raised at the court of his grandfather, Tamerlane, and from 1409 was the ruler of Maverannakhr, the chief city of which was Samarkand.

In contrast with his grandfather, Ulugh Beg was not interested in conquest but gained fame as a scientist. At Samarkand in 1420 he founded a *madrasa*, or institution of higher learning, in which astronomy was the most important subject. Ulugh Beg himself selected the scientists who taught there, first interviewing them to determine their qualifications. His *madrasa* differed from others of that time both in the content and in the level of the subjects taught there. Besides Ulugh Beg, the lecturers included Ṣalāḥ al-Dīn Mūsā ibn Maḥmūd (Qāḍī Zāda), and Ghiyāth al-Dīn Jamshīd al-Kāshī.

Four years after founding the *madrasa*, Ulugh Beg erected a three-story observatory. At the instigation of the jurists, however, the building was reduced to ruins by the beginning of the sixteenth century, and in time apparently disappeared. Its precise location remained unknown until 1908, when the archaeologist V. L. Vyatkin found its remains.

The main instrument of the observatory proved to be—not a quadrant, as Vyatkin thought—but a "Fakhrī sextant." A trench about two meters wide was dug in a hill, along the line of the meridian, and in it was placed a segment of the arc of the instrument. The part that is preserved, which was in the trench, consists of two parallel walls faced with marble, fifty-one centimeters apart.

The main use of the Fakhrī sextant was in determining the basic constants of astronomy: the inclination of the ecliptic to the equator, the point of the vernal equinox, the length of the tropical year, and other constants arising from observation of the sun. Thus it was built chiefly for solar observations in general and for observations of the moon and the planets in particular (an arc of 60° is sufficient). Other instruments used were an armillary sphere, a triquetrum, an astrolabe, and a *shāmila* (an instrument serving as astrolabe and quadrant).

With the aid of the Fakhrī sextant one could determine at noon every day the meridional height of the sun, its distance from the zenith, and its declination; and from this information one could deduce the latitude and the inclination of the ecliptic, such that between the latitude φ, the distance from the zenith z, and the declination δ there is the known relationship $\varphi = z + \delta$. For example, letting ϵ be the inclination of the ecliptic, the distance from the zenith at noon on the day of the summer solstice is $z_1 = \varphi - \epsilon$ and on the day of the winter solstice $z_2 = \varphi + \epsilon$, equations that lead to $\epsilon = 1/2 (z_2 - z_1)$. The value obtained by Ulugh Beg for the inclination of the ecliptic, $\epsilon = 23° 30' 17''$, differs by only 32″ from the true value (for his time).[1] According to him, the latitude of Samarkand was 39° 37′ 33″.[2]

The radius of the Fakhrī sextant in Ulugh Beg's observatory was 40.04 meters, which made it the largest astronomical instrument in the world of that type. On the arc of the sextant are divisions in which 70.2 centimeters corresponds to one degree; 11.7 millimeters (or, if rounded, 12 millimeters)

represents one minute; 1 millimeter is five seconds; and 0.4 millimeter is two seconds. It has been experimentally established that with unrestricted time for observation and sufficient training of the observer, the value of the threshold of angular discrimination can be considered as two to five seconds. Thus the choice of the scale of the main instrument, and its smallest divisions, was made with consideration for the limits of angular discrimination.

An important result of the scientific work of Ulugh Beg and his school was the astronomical tables called the *Zīj* of Ulugh Beg or the *Zīj-i Gurgānī* (Guragon, the title of Genghis Khan's son-in-law, was also used by Ulugh Beg). This work, originally written in the Tadzhik language, consists of a theoretical section and the results of the observations made at the Samarkand observatory; the latter include actual tables of calendar calculations, of trigonometry, and of the planets, as well as a star catalog.

The basis of Ulugh Beg's trigonometric tables was the determination of sin 1° with great accuracy. One of the methods of solving this problem was Ulugh Beg's, and another was that of Al-Kāshī.[3] Both lead to the solution of the third-degree algebraic equation with the form

$$x^3 + ax + b = 0,$$

where $x = \sin 1°$. Solving this equation by an original method of subsequent approximations, one obtains

$$x = \sin 1° = 0.017452406437283571.$$

In his trigonometric tables Ulugh Beg gives the values of sines and tangents for every minute to 45°, and for every five minutes from 45° to 90°; the values of cotangents are given for every degree. Comparing the values of the sines of any angles—for example, 20°, 23°, and 26°—with the corresponding true values, we obtain the following:

According to Ulugh Beg		True Value	
20°	0.342020142	20°	0.342020143
23°	0.390731129	23°	0.390731128
26°	0.438371147	26°	0.438371147

Also strikingly accurate is the study of the yearly movements of the five bright planets known in the time of Ulugh Beg, as is evident below:[4]

	According to Ulugh Beg	True Value	
Saturn	12°13′39″	12°13′36″	(d'Alembert)
Jupiter	30°20′34″	30°20′31″	(d'Alembert)
Mars	191°17′15″	191°17′10″	(Lalande)

Venus   224°17′32″   224°17′30″ (Lalande)
Mercury 53°43′13″   53°43′3″ (Lalande)

Thus the difference between Ulugh Beg's data and that of modern times relating to the first four planets falls within the limits of two to five seconds.

In the case of Mercury the difference is somewhat larger — ten seconds at most — because, of the planets mentioned, Mercury has the greatest orbital velocity. In addition, the eccentricity of its orbit is 0.206 — that is, it is considerable in comparison with the eccentricity of the four other planets — while the greatest visible angular distance of Mercury from the sun's disk is only about 28°. These peculiarities of the planet make observation of it with the naked eye fairly difficult, and consequently have an adverse effect on the accuracy of the results of observation. The yearly precession was determined by Ulugh Beg[5] to be 51.4″, while the true value is 50.2″.

The situation is somewhat different with Ulugh Beg's values for the positions of the stars. After that of Hipparchus, the star catalog of Ulugh Beg was the second in seventeen centuries. It contains 1,018 stars, the positions of some of which were determined mainly from observations made at the Samarkand observatory, and others from observations made before the beginning of 1437 (A.H. 841).[6] The latter were taken from the star catalog of al-Sūfī, who apparently borrowed them from Ptolemy. Thus the star catalog of Ulugh Beg has great value, since it is basically original, but nevertheless was influenced by Ptolemy, at least in respect to its coordinates.

In 1941 an expedition under the leadership of T. N. Kari-Niazov discovered the tomb of Ulugh Beg in the mausoleum of Tamerlane in Samarkand. In contrast with the Islamic custom of burying the dead only in a shroud, Ulugh Beg lay fully clothed in a sarcophagus, in agreement with the prescription of the *shariat*: a man who died as a *shakhid* (martyr) had to be buried in his clothes. On the skeleton, traces of his violent death are clear: the third cervical vertebra was severed by a sharp instrument in such a way that the main portion of the body and an arc of that vertebra were cut off cleanly; the blow, struck from the left, also cut through the right corner of the lower jaw and its lower edge.

NOTES

1. Ulugh Beg, *Zīj Guragoni*, Biruni Institute of Oriental Studies, Uzbek S.S.R. Academy of Sciences, MS 2214, 1.11a.

2. *Ibid.*, l. 102b.
3. Birjantsi, *Sharḥ, Zīj Guragoni*, Biruni Institute of Oriental Studies, Uzbek S.S.R. Academy of Sciences, MS 704, 1. 49a.
4. J. B. J. Delambre, *Histoire de l'astronomie indienne orientale* (Paris, 1787), 155.
5. Ulugh Beg., *op. cit.*, ll. 117b, 118a.
6. *Ibid.*

BIBLIOGRAPHY

See Abū Ṭahir Hoja, *Samaria*, from Tadzhik into Russian, V. L. Vyatkin, trans. (Samarkand, 1899); Z. Babur, *Babur-name*, M. A. Sale, trans. (Tashkent, 1948); V. V. Bartold, *Istoria kulturnoy zhizni Turkestana* ("History of the Cultural Life of Turkestan"; Leningrad, 1927); F. Baily, "The Catalogues of Ptolomey, Ulug-Beigh, Tycho Brahe, Halley and Hevelius, Deduced From the Best Authorities, With Various Notes and Corrections," in *Memoirs of the Royal Astronomical Society* (London, 1843); G. Bigourdan, *L'astronomie* (Paris, 1925); F. Boquet, *Histoire de l'astronomie* (Paris, 1925); C. Brockelmann, *Geschichte der arabischen Literatur* (Weimar, 1898); J. B. J. Delambre, *Histoire de l'astronomie du moyen âge* (Paris, 1819); I. Greave, *Binae tabulae geographicae, una Nassir-Eddini Persae, altera Ulug-Beigi Tartari* (London, 1652); and T. Hayde, *Tabulae longitudinis et latitudinis stellarum fixarum ex observatione Ulug-beighi* (Oxford, 1665).

Also see T. N. Kari-Niazov, *Observatoria Ulugbeka v svete novykh dannykh* ("The Observatory of Ulugh Beg in the Light of New Information"; Tashkent, 1947); and *Astronomicheskaya shkola Ulugbeka* ("The Astronomical School of Ulugh Beg"; Moscow, 1950; 2nd ed., enl., Tashkent, 1967); P. S. Laplace, *Précis de l'histoire de l'astronomie* (Paris, 1865); E. B. Knobel, *Ulughbeg's Catalogue of Stars* (Washington, D.C., 1917); Salih Zaki, *Asar-i Bakiya* ("Eternal Monument"; Constantinople, 1911); G. Sarton, *Introduction to the History of Science*, II (Baltimore, 1931); L. Sédillot, *Prolégomènes des tables astronomiques d'Oloug-Beg* (Paris, 1853); G. Sharpe, *Tabulae longitudinis et latitudinis stellarum fixarum ex observatione Ulugbeighi* (Oxford, 1767); V. P. Shcheglov, "K voprosu o geograficheskikh koordinatakh i azimute sekstanta observatorii Ulugbeka a g. Samarkande" ("Toward the Question of the Geographical Coordinates and the Azimuth of the Sextant at the Observatory of Ulugh Beg and of the City of Samarkand"), in *Astronomicheskiy zhurnal*, **30**, no. 2 (1953); H. Suter, *Die mathematiker und Astronomen der Araber und ihre Werke* (Leipzig, 1900); and V. L. Vyatkin, "Ochet o raskopkakh observatorii Mirza Ulugbeka v 1908 i 1909 godakh" ("An Account of the Excavations of the Observatory of Mirz Ulugh Beg in 1908 and 1909"), in *Izvestiya Russkago komiteta dlya izucheniya srednei i vostochnoi azii*, 2nd ser. (1912), no. 11.

T. N. KARI-NIAZOV

ULYANOV, VLADIMIR ILYICH. See **Lenin (Ulyanov), Vladimir Ilyich.**

ᶜUMAR AL-KHAYYĀMĪ. See **ᶜAl-Khayyāmī (or Khayyām), Ghiyāth al-Dīn Abu'l-Fatḥ ᶜUmar ibn Ibrāhīm al-Nīsābūrī (or al-Naysābūrī),** also known as **Omar Khayyam.**

ᶜUMAR IBN AL-FARRUKHĀN AL-ṬABARĪ (*fl.* Baghdad, Iraq, 762–812), *astrology, astronomy.*

Abū Ḥafṣ ʿUmar was the son of a native of Ṭabaristān, the Iranian province just south of the Caspian Sea, who bore the ancient Persian name Farrukhān; he was thus one of those Persian scholars who made the early Abbasid court a center for the translation of Pahlavi scientific texts into Arabic. He first appears on the scene as one of the group of astrologers, including Nawbakht, Māshāʾallāh, and al-Fazārī, whom al-Manṣūr asked to select an auspicious time for the foundation of Baghdad; they chose 30 July 762[1]. The latest date that we have for him is Shawwāl of A.H. 196 — that is, 15 June–13 July of A.D. 812 — when he finished his version of Ptolemy's *Kitāb al-arbaᶜa* (*Tetrabiblos*). These dates make it evident that Abū Maᶜshar was wrong in stating, as reported by his pupil Shādhān in his *Mudhākarāt*[2] and repeated by Ṣāᶜid al-Andalusī[3] and Ibn al-Qifṭī,[4] that ʿUmar was called to Baghdad by the wazīr, al-Faḍl ibn Sahl (*d.* 818), and introduced to al-Maʾmūn. Abū Maᶜshar's other statement[5] that he was devoted to Yaḥyā ibn Khālid ibn Barmak (*d.* 807) may well be true.

Of ʿUmar's personal life nothing else is known save that he had a son, Abū Bakr Muḥammad, who also wrote extensively on astrology and astronomy. Unfortunately, Ibn al-Nadīm[6] has often confused the father and son in his lists of their works. The following titles of ʿUmar's works, therefore, belong primarily to those texts known to us from more reliable sources.

1. A *tafsīr* or paraphrase of Ptolemy's *Tetrabiblos* finished between 15 June and 13 July of 812. This is preserved in Uppsala, Universitetsbibliotheket MS Arab. 203. According to the introduction, ʿUmar himself translated the text, presumably from a Pahlavi version; Ibn al-Nadīm states that he used the translation of Abū Yaḥyā al-Baṭrīq, presumably from the original Greek. The truth may be that he wrote his paraphrase, based on the Pahlavi, at the request of al-Baṭrīq.

2. A *tafsīr* of the astrological work of Dorotheus of Sidon, based on a Pahlavi recension of the early fifth century. This is preserved in two manuscripts: Yeni Cami 784 and Berlin or. oct. 2603. The present author is preparing an edition of this text.

3. *Mukhtaṣar masāʾil al-Qayṣarānī* ("Abridgment of the Caesarean (?) Interrogations") in 138 chapters. This work has been preserved in many manuscripts; I have examined Berlin Ar. 5878 and 5879, Escorial Ar. 938, and Beirut, Univ. St. Joseph Ar. 215. Though the name Qayṣarānī remains obscure, it certainly has nothing to do with the *Jāmiᶜ al-kitāb* of Abū Yūsuf Yaᶜqub ibn ᶜAlī al-Qaṣrānī who flourished at the courts of Jurjān and Astarābād in the late ninth century. The *Mukhtaṣar* may be identical with the *Kitāb al-ikhtiyārāt* ("Book of Elections) at Alexandria, MS Ḥurūf 12.

4. *Kitāb fi'l-mawālīd* ("Book About Nativities"), a short treatise on genethlialogy preserved in Arabic in only one manuscript (Nuru Osmaniye 2951, ff. 162v–172). This is probably identical with the Latin *De nativitatibus secundum Omar* in three books, translated by Iohannes Hispalensis (and a second time by Salomon with the help of the son of Abaumet the Jew in 1217?); see F. J. Carmody, *Arabic Astronomical and Astrological Sciences in Latin Translation* (Berkeley–Los Angeles, 1956), 38–39 (Carmody's *De iudiciis astrorum* is obviously al-Farghānī's, and *Laurentius Beham de ascensione termini Haomar* does not necessarily have any connection with ʿUmar ibn al-Farrukhān). I have consulted the edition by Nicolaus Prückner, *Iulii Firmici Materni . . . Libri VIII* (Basel, 1551), pt. 2, pp. 118–141. ʿUmar's sources are Ptolemy, Dorotheus, and Māshāʾallāh, as might have been expected.

5. *Kitāb al-ᶜilal.* This work is known to us only through a citation by al-Bīrūnī in his treatise on the solar equation (*Rasāʾil al-Bīrūnī* [Hyderabad, 1948], pt. I, p. 132), in which he gives approximate methods by which the sine of the solar equation corresponding to α is made to vary with sin λ (α) and by which the solar equation corresponding to α is made to vary with the declination of λ (α). These methods are described by E. S. Kennedy and A. Muruwwa, "Bīrūnī on the Solar Equation," in *Journal of Near Eastern Studies*, **17** (1958), 112–121, esp. 118–119. Al-Bīrūnī seems to have devoted a treatise to exposing the ineptitude of ʿUmar's astronomy, as he lists in his bibliography (D. J. Boilot, "L'oeuvre d'al-Beruni: essai bibliographique," in *Mélanges de l'Institut Dominicain d'Études Orientales*, **2** [1955], 161–256) as no. 62 a *Fi'l-faḥṣ ᶜan nawādir abī Ḥafṣ ᶜUmar ibn al-*

Farrukhān ("On Inquiring About the Rarities of Abū Ḥafṣ ʿUmar ibn al-Farrukhān"), which, he claims, covers 240 folios.

NOTES

1. D. Pingree, "The Fragments of the Works of al-Fazārī," in *Journal of Near Eastern Studies*, **29** (1970), 103–123, esp. 104.
2. I have not succeeded in locating this story in the imperfect manuscripts of the *Mudhākarāt* available to me.
3. *Kitāb ṭabaqāt al-umam*, R. Blachère, trans. (Paris, 1935), 111. Ṣāʿid also elsewhere (p. 117) reports that ʿUmar wrote for al-Maʾmūn.
4. *Taʾrīkh al-ḥukamāʾ*, J. Lippert, ed. (Leipzig, 1903), 242.
5. *Ibid.*, the Greek translation is published by F. Cumont in *Catalogus codicum astrologorum graecorum*, V, pt. 1 (Brussels, 1904), 150–151.
6. *Fihrist*, G. Flügel, ed., 2 vols. (Leipzig, 1871–1872), I, p. 273; copied by Ibn al-Qifṭī, p. 242.

BIBLIOGRAPHY

There are short articles on ʿUmar in H. Suter, *Die Mathematiker und Astronomen der Araber und ihre Werke* (Leipzig, 1900), 7–8; and in C. Brockelmann, *Geschichte der arabischen Literatur*, I (Leiden, 1943), 249, and supp. I (Leiden, 1937), 392, where several additional treatises alleged to exist in manuscript are listed.

DAVID PINGREE

AL-UMAWĪ, ABŪ ʿABDALLĀH YAʿĪSH IBN IBRĀHĪM IBN YŪSUF IBN SIMĀK AL-ANDA-LUSĪ (*fl.* Damascus, fourteenth century), *arithmetic.*

Al-Umawī was a Spanish Arab who lived in Damascus, where he taught arithmetic. On the single authority of Ḥājjī Khalīfa, the year of his death is usually given as A.H. 895 (A.D. 1489/1490). But a marginal note on the ninth folio of his arithmetic (MS 1509, 1°, Carullah), written by him to give license to a copyist to teach his work, is dated 17 Dhuʾl-Ḥijja 774 (9 June 1373). The copyist is ʿAbd al-Qādir ibn Muḥammad ibnʿAbd al-Qādir, al-Ḥanbalī, al-Maqdisī. He states that he finished copying the text at Mount Qāsyūn in Damascus on 8 Dhuʾl-Ḥijja 774.

The text referred to is *Marāsim al-intisāb fī ʿilm al-ḥisāb*. A small work in eighteen folios, it is significant in being written by a western Muslim for Easterners, a circumstance that should not discredit the common belief that arithmetic flourished more in eastern than in western Islam. The work represents a trend of Arabic arithmetic in which, as early as the tenth century, the Indian "dust board" calculations had begun to be modified to suit paper and ink; and arithmetic was enriched by concepts from the traditional finger reckoning and the Pythagorean theory of numbers. The trend seems to have started in Damascus; the earliest extant text that shows it is al-Uqlīdisī's *al-Fuṣūl fiʾl-ḥisāb al-hindī*, written in A.H. 341 (A.D. 952/3). But there are reasons to believe that the trend had greater influence in the West than in the East.

The forms of the numerals used in the West differed from those in the East, but al-Umawī avoids using numerals except in a table of sequences, in which the western forms appear. The attempts to modify the Indian schemes resulted in several methods, especially of multiplication. Al-Umawī, however, says little about these methods and describes the principal operations briefly, as if his aim is to show what in western arithmetic is unknown, or not widely known, in the East. Thus he insists that the common fraction should be written as $\frac{a}{b}$, whereas the easterners continued to write it as $\frac{a}{b}$, like the Indians, or as $\frac{a}{b} \, 0$.

He also insists that the numbers operated upon, say, in multiplication, must be separated from the steps of the operation by placing a straight line under them. Such lines appear in the works of Ibn al-Bannāʾ of Morocco (*d.* 1321) but not in the East until late in the Middle Ages.

Like the classical Indian authors, in treating addition al-Umawī dispenses with the operation in a few words and moves on to the summation of sequences. Those he discusses are the following:

1. The arithmetical progression in general and the sum of natural numbers, natural odd numbers, and natural even numbers in particular

2. The geometrical progression in general and 2^r and $\sum_{r=0}^{n} 2^r$ in particular

3. The sequences and series of polygonal numbers, namely $\{1 + (r - 1)d\}$ and $Sn = \sum_{r=1}^{n} \{1 + (r - 1)d\}$

4. The sequences and series of pyramidal numbers, namely $\{S_r\}$ and $\sum_{r=1}^{n} \{S_r\}$

5. Summations of r^3, $(2r + 1)^3$, $(2r)^3$ from $r = 1$ to $r = n$

6. Summations of $r(r + 1)$, $(2r + 1)(2r + 3)$, $2r(2r + 2)$ from $r = 1$ to $r = n$.

The sequences of polygonal and pyramidal numbers were transmitted to the Arabs in Thābit ibn Qurra's translation of Nicomachus' *Introduction to Arithmetic*. Also, al-Karajī had given geometrical proofs of $\Sigma \ r^3$, $(2r + 1)^3$, $(2r)^3$ in *al-Fakhrī* (see T. Heath, *Manual of Greek Mathematics* [Oxford, 1931], 68).

Without symbolism, al-Umawī often takes the sum of ten terms as an example, a practice started by the Babylonians and adopted by Diophantus and Arabic authors.

In subtraction al-Umawī considers casting out sevens, eights, nines, and elevens. All Hindu-Arabic arithmetic books consider casting out nines; and some add casting out other numbers. Some also treat casting out elevens in the way used today for testing divisibility by 11, which is attributed to Pierre Forcadel (1556). Al-Umawī adds casting out eights and sevens, in a way that leads directly to the following general rule:

Take any integer N in the decimal scale. Clearly $N = a_0 + a_1 \cdot 10 + a_2 \cdot 10^2 + \cdots = \Sigma \ a_s \cdot 10^s$. It is required to find the remainder after casting out p's from N, where p is any other integer. Let r_s be the remainder of 10^s, that is $10^s \equiv r_s \pmod{p}$; it follows that if $\Sigma \ a_s \cdot r_s$ is divisible by p so is N. This is a theorem that is attributed to Blaise Pascal (1664); see L. E. Dickson, *Theory of Numbers*, I (New York, 1952), p. 337.

In the text al-Umawī states that the sequence r_s, in the cases he considers, is finite and recurring. Thus for $p = 7$, $r_s = (1, 3, 2, 6, 4, 5)$.

In dealing with square and cube roots, al-Umawī states rules of approximation that are not as well developed as those of the arithmeticians of the East, who had already developed the following rules of approximation.

$$\sqrt{n} = a + \frac{n - a^2}{2a + 1},$$

where a^2 is the greatest integral square in n,

and

$$\sqrt[3]{n} = a + \frac{n - a^3}{3a^2 + 3a + 1},$$

where a^3 is the greatest integral cube in n. These rules do not appear in al-Umawī's text. Instead, we find

$$\sqrt{n} = a + \frac{n - a^2}{2a} \text{ or } (a + 1) - \frac{(a+1)^2 - n}{2(a + 1)}$$

$$\sqrt[3]{n} = a + \frac{n - a^3}{3a^2} \text{ or } (a + 1) - \frac{(a+1)^3 - n}{3(a + 1)^2}.$$

Again, al-Umawī does not consider the method of extracting roots of higher order, which had been known in the East since the eleventh century.

For finding perfect squares and cubes, however, he gives the following rules, most of which have not been found in other texts.

If n is a perfect square:

1. It must end with an even number of zeros, or have 1, 4, 5, 6, or 9 in the units' place.

2. If the units' place is 6, the tens' place must be odd; in all other cases it is even.

3. If the units' place is 1, the hundreds' place and half the tens' place must be both even or both odd.

4. If the units' place is 5, the tens' place is 2.

5. $n \equiv 0, 1, 2, 4 \pmod 7$
    $\equiv 0, 1, 4 \pmod 8$
    $\equiv 0, 1, 4, 7 \pmod 9$

If n is a perfect cube:

1. If it ends with 0, 1, 4, 5, 6, or 9, its cube root ends with 000, 1, 4, 5, 6, or 9, respectively. If it ends with 3, 7, 2, or 8, the root ends with 7, 3, 8, or 2, respectively.

2. $n \equiv 0, 1, 6 \pmod 7$
    $\equiv 0, 1, 3, 5, 7 \pmod 8$
    $\equiv 0, 1, 8 \pmod 9$

Evidently al-Umawī's *Marāsim al-intisāb fī ʾilm al-ḥisāb* is worthy of scholarly interest, especially in connection with the early history of number theory.

Another work by the same author is preserved in MS 5174 ḥ in Alexandria under the name of *Rafʿ al-ishkāl fī misāḥat al-ashkāl* (removal of doubts concerning the mensuration of figures); it is a small treatise of seventeen folios in which we find nothing on mensuration that the arithmeticians of the East did not know.

BIBLIOGRAPHY

On al-Umawī and his work, see C. Brockelmann, *Geschichte der arabischen Literatur*, supp. 2 (Leiden, 1938), p. 379, and II (Leiden, 1949), p. 344; L. E. Dickson, *History of the Theory of Numbers*, 3 vols. (New York, 1952); Ḥājjī Khalīfa, *Kashf alẓunūn . . .*, 2 vols. (Constantinople, 1941); T. L. Heath, *A History of Greek Mathematics*, 2 vols. (Oxford, 1921); Ibn al-Nadīm, *Al-Fihrist* (Cairo); Nicomachus, *Al-Madkhal ilā ʿilm al-ʿadad*, Thābit ibn Qurra, trans., W. Kutch, ed. (Beirut, 1958); and H. Suter, *Die Mathematiker und Astronomen der Araber und ihre Werke* (Leipzig, 1950), no. 453, p. 187.

A. S. SAIDAN

UNANUE, JOSÉ HIPÓLITO (*b*. Arica, Peru [now Chile], 13 August 1755; *d*. Lima, Peru, 15 July 1833), *natural history*.

Unanue, the outstanding figure of the Peruvian enlightenment, began ecclesiastical studies at Arequipa and Lima, but abandoned a church career for one in medicine. He received his medical degree under the direction of Gabriel Moreno around 1784 and by 1789 was professor of anatomy at the University of San Marcos.

From the beginning of his medical career, Unanue devoted himself to the cause of reform in medical and scientific education. In 1792 he succeeded in instituting an anatomical amphitheater in Lima, which the government had authorized nearly thirty-five years earlier. Lacking in equipment and funds, the amphitheater was nevertheless able to provide instruction in dissection for medical students, and Unanue lectured on anatomy there in 1793–1794. The following year Unanue inaugurated a series of clinical lectures in medicine, in which specialists instructed the students on specific diseases. During the same period (1791–1794) he was editor of the *Mercurio Peruano*, a prime conduit for the diffusion of modern scientific ideas in Peru and to which Unanue contributed a number of articles on medical and scientific subjects.

Between 1799 and 1805 Unanue collected data for his major work, *Observaciones sobre el clima de Lima*, a treatise in the Hippocratic tradition, purporting to explicate the climatic causes of disease in the city of Lima. To substantiate his thesis, Unanue correlated meteorological data with clinical observations, combined with traditional and modern medical concepts. In spite of his frequent citations of Newton, Boerhaave, and other modern scientists, Unanue's book has an archaic cast. He denied, for example, the relevance of chemistry to medical practice. The book comprises five sections. The first section describes the climate and physical setting of Lima. The second is an ecological discussion of climate and its influence on vegetation, animals, and human beings. The third expounds the influences of climate on disease. The fourth discusses what dietary and other curative recourses could be had to cure climate-induced diseases. The fifth, a medical profile of the year 1799 in Lima, is perhaps the most interesting part of the book, inasmuch as it provides a meteorological and epidemiological chronicle for that year. The book had tremendous influence, especially in Lima itself, where it appears to have been canonized by the local medical intelligentsia to the point that it inhibited the reception of new medical and scientific ideas.

In 1807 Viceroy José Abascal asked Unanue to submit plans for a new medical school and to serve as its first director. Unanue recommended, in a memorial of the same year, that a medical college be created in one of the hospitals of the city, where students could be instructed in anatomy, physiology, surgery, medicine, and pharmacy. The College of San Fernando opened in 1811 with ten professorships, many held by former students of Unanue. The curriculum, which included mathematics, psychology, and experimental physics, was decidedly modern, the texts having been selected by Unanue personally. At the same time (from 1807), Unanue also served Peru as medical inspector (*protomédico general*).

Like many Latin American men of science of the early nineteenth century, Unanue played a prominent role in his country's struggle for independence, serving as negotiator and cabinet minister.

BIBLIOGRAPHY

I. ORIGINAL WORKS. *Observaciones sobre el clima de Lima, y su influencia sobre los seres organizados, en especial el hombre* (Lima, 1806; 2nd ed., Madrid, 1814). A more recent edition is found in *Obras científicas y literarias del doctor don J. Hipólito Unanue*, Eugenio Larrabure y Unanue, ed., 3 vols. (Barcelona, 1914), I. The standard modern edition is by Carlos Enrique Paz Soldán (Lima, 1940).

Articles of scientific interest originally published in the *Mercurio Peruano*, 12 vols. (1791–1794; facs. ed., Lima, 1964–1966), are reprinted in *Obras científicas*, II.

II. SECONDARY LITERATURE. Various aspects of Unanue's scientific career are discussed in Luís Alayza y Paz Soldán, *Unanue, geógrafo, médico y estadista* (Lima, 1954); Juan B. Lastres, *Hipólito Unanue* (Lima, 1955); and "Hipólito Unanue y *El clima de Lima*," in *Boletín de la Sociedad geográfica de Lima*, **54** (1937), 75–87; Hugo Neira Samanez, *Hipólito Unanue y el nacimiento de la patria* (Lima, 1967); Carlos Enrique Paz Soldán, *Hímnos a Hipólito Unanue* (Lima, 1955); Hermilio Valdizán, "El doctor don Hipólito Unanue (Apuntes bio-bibliográficos)," in *Unanue. Revista Trimestral de Historia de la Medicina Peruana*, II (Lima), nos. 1–2 (Mar.–June 1926), 3–57; and John E. Woodham, "The influence of Hipólito Unanue on Peruvian Medical Science: A Reappraisal," in *Hispanic American Historical Review*, **50** (1970), 693–714.

THOMAS F. GLICK

UNGER, FRANZ (*b*. Der Gute Amthof, near Leutschach, Austria, 30 November 1800; *d*. Graz, Austria, 13 February 1870), *botany*.

The son of a Styrian jurist, Unger received a Gymnasium education at Graz. His father intended that he become a lawyer; but, under the influence of his friend Anton Sauter, Unger turned to medicine. He studied at the universities of Vienna and Prague, qualifying in 1827. After two years at Stockerau as a general practitioner, he became physician to the assize court in Kitzbühel. In 1835 Unger moved to Graz as professor of botany and zoology and as director of the botanical garden at the Johanneum. He received an offer from the University of Vienna in 1849, when a new chair of plant anatomy and physiology was established there. Unger held that post until 1866, when he retired to Graz.

In his own time Unger's fame rested chiefly on the *Grundzüge der Botanik* (1843), which he wrote with Stephen Endlicher. The work contains a description of cell multiplication by division that is based on Unger's St. Petersburg prize essay (1840) on the structure of the flowering plant stem and his *Aphorismen* (1838). The *Grundzüge* made him Schleiden's first opponent on the question of the origin of cells, Schleiden advocating free cell formation, while Unger confined this mechanism to the early stages in the formation of organs and put forward as its successor cell multiplication by division. Unger maintained his position in this area of botany with *Der Anatomie und Physiologie der Pflanzen* (1855).

Unger was an evolutionist before 1859. His conception of the succession of species clearly was influenced by *Naturphilosophie*, but it also was supported by experimental studies of the impact of changes in the conditions of life upon plant variability. These studies, carried out at Kitzbühel, Graz, and Vienna in the 1830's and 1840's, led Unger to oppose the popular link between external influences, especially soil conditions, and variability. His views on evolution were presented in a popular form in a series of articles in the local press in Vienna, and subsequently collected in book form as *Botanische Briefe* (1852). This piece of scientific journalism provoked a violent personal attack upon Unger by the Catholic press. His resignation was prevented by a strong student protest.

Unger's evolutionary views also found expression in his attempt to reconstruct the botanical features of the landscape in earlier geological eras, in *Die Urwelt in ihren verschiedenen Uebergangs-*

perioden (1851). This and other works reflect his deep interest in paleobotany. He was also a pioneer in the study of the early history of cultivated plants as revealed through cultural relics.

Unger also contributed to the understanding of fertilization in the lower plants. Although at first holding the mistaken belief that antherozoids were infusorians, in 1837 he argued effectively for the identification of these bodies in the mosses as the male gametes. No longer did he regard the production of antherozoids as signaling the conversion of plant into animal.

Among Unger's students at Vienna was Gregor Mendel. Unger's involvement in the working out of the cell theory and its application to the fertilization process may well have played a crucial role in equipping Mendel for the cytological interpretation of his breeding experiments.

BIBLIOGRAPHY

I. Original Works. A bibliography of Unger's publications is in A. Reyer's biography cited below. Unger's works include *Über den Einflusse des Bodens auf die Vertheilung der Gewächse* (Vienna, 1836); a series of books on anatomy and physiology: *Aphorismen zur Anatomie und Physiologie der Pflanzen* (Vienna, 1838), *Grundzüge der Anatomie und Physiologie der Pflanzen* (Vienna, 1846), and *Der Anatomie und Physiologie der Pflanzen* (Vienna, 1855); and several books on paleobotany: *Synopsis plantarum fossilium* (Leipzig, 1845); *Genera et species plantarum fossilium* (Vienna, 1850); *Die Urwelt in ihren verschiedenen Bildungsperioden* (Vienna, 1851), translated as *Ideal Views of the Primitive World in Its Geological and Palaeontological Phases* (London, 1863); and *Versuch der Geschichte der Pflanzenwelt* (Vienna, 1852). Unger's important prize essay is *Über den Bau des Dikotyledonenstammes* (St. Petersburg, 1840).

Other works include *Grundzüge der Botanik* (Vienna, 1843), written with S. Endlicher; "Beiträge zur Lehre von der Bodenstätigkeit gewisser Pflanzen," in *Denkschriften der Akademie der Wissenschaften*, **1** (1850), 83–89, written with F. Hruschauer; and *Gratz. Ein naturhistorisch-statistisch-topographisches Gemählde dieser Stadt und ihrer Umgebungen* (Gratz, 1843), written with A. von Muchar, C. Weiglein, and G. F. Schreiner. Unger's best-known popular work is *Botanische Briefe* (Vienna, 1852), translated as *Botanical Letters to a Friend* (London, 1863).

Unger's papers on botany in relation to cultural history appeared in the *Sitzungsberichte der Akademie der Wissenschaften in Wien*, and all the papers are listed in Reyer's biography and in the Royal Society *Catalogue of Scientific Papers*, 6, p. 87; 8, p. 1137.

Unger's correspondence with Endlicher is in G. Haberlandt, ed., *Briefwechsel zwischen Franz Unger und Stephen Endlicher* (Berlin, 1899).

II. SECONDARY LITERATURE. The standard biography of Unger is A. Reyer, *Leben und Werke des Naturhistorikers Dr. Franz Unger* (Graz, 1871). Unger's cytological studies are discussed in Julius Sachs, *History of Botany (1530–1860)* (Oxford, 1906), 325–329, 336–340; and in J. Lorch, "The Elusive Cambium," in *Archives internationales d'histoire des sciences*, **20** (1967), 253–283. The relationship between Unger and Mendel is discussed by R. C. Olby, in "Franz Unger and the Wiener Kirchenzeitung: An Attack on One of Mendel's Teachers by the Editor of a Catholic Newspaper," in *Folia Mendeliana*, no. 2 (1967), 29–37; and in "The Influence of Physiology on Hereditary Theories in the Nineteenth Century," *ibid.*, no. 6 (1971), 99–103. For an evaluation of some of Unger's scientific work, see Johanna Enslein, *Die wissenschaftgeschichtliche Untersuchung und Wertung der anatomischen, physiologischen und ökologischen Arbeiten von Franz Unger* (Vienna, 1956).

ROBERT OLBY

UNZER, JOHANN AUGUST (*b.* Halle, Germany, 29 April 1727; *d.* Altona, Germany, 2 April 1799), *physiology, medicine.*

Unzer began the study of medicine when he was only twelve; his early teacher was Johann Juncker, an ardent disciple of Stahl. He received the M.D. in 1748, but even before then, in 1846, he had begun to publish metaphysical and philosophical works on such physiological problems as life, the emotions, and sleep, in which he defended Stahl's animistic doctrines. Nonetheless, he also seems to have been influenced by the mechanistic and eclectic medicine of Halle's other leading man, Stahl's opponent Friedrich Hoffmann, who was still teaching at the university when Unzer began his studies.

In 1750 Unzer left Halle to take up a busy medical practice, first in Hamburg and then in Altona. (Although some sources suggest that he was for a time professor at the small University of Rinteln, this cannot now be confirmed.) At the same time, he conducted research and, from 1759 to 1764, edited a popular medical weekly, *Der Arzt*, and a series of collections of medical writings that were translated into Dutch, Danish, and Swedish. His writings of this period indicate his gradual abandonment of the Stahlian system and his attempts to work out his own physiology, or "physiological metaphysics," as it was later characterized. While Unzer remained interested in the basic phenomena of life, especially the higher animal functions, he turned from his earlier animism toward a more

anatomical and physiological approach, directed principally to the role of the nervous system in animal functions. His *Erste Gründe einer Physiologie der eigentlichen thierischen Natur thierischer Körper* (1771) is the product of twenty-five years of research and reflection.

The *Erste Gründe* (later translated into English as *The Principles of Physiology of the Proper Animal Nature of the Animal Organism*) marked an attempt to establish the fundamental bases of zoology, considered as a natural science embracing all the animal kingdom, according to the "forces" of each species. In it, Unzer made use of a broad comparative method, which he applied particularly to nerve functions and to motion. He distinguished three types of motion—those that are dependent on the will, those that (although conscious) are independent of the will, and those that are wholly unconscious and involitional. He proceeded from the notion of the animal as a machine to state that some animals (*beseelte Tiere*) have a soul that produces their movements, while others (*unbeseelte Tiere*) have neither soul nor brain, and are instead moved by animal "forces."

Unzer was led to draw this distinction by a series of observations, particularly of decapitated higher animals, which he compared to lower animals that have no brain. He concluded that the brain is the seat of the soul, although animal machines are capable of organic work without the stimulus of a brain or soul, and many animal movements occur through neural stimulus only. He recognized that external stimuli tend to be referred toward the brain but noted that they could be reflected or deviated and localized either in the brain or at a lower level in nerve crossings. He thus distinguished the afferent (*aufleitend*) and efferent (*ableitend*) nerves. He made a thorough study of the nervous reactions, and noted that external stimuli are transmitted in the nervous system by reflection. He also advanced the notion that motor phenomena may be caused by external stimuli that are not consciously perceived and emphasized the difference between voluntary and involuntary movements. Unzer's effort toward defining a rational concept of reflex action was elaborated by Georgius Prochaska in 1784.

Although Unzer's original contribution to science was slight, he nonetheless provided a valuable step in the development of physiology. His careful and essentially correct presentation of the mechanical and material aspects of nerve functions bridged the gap between conflicting views and became the basis of a considerable body of work on

AL-UQLĪDISĪ

AL-UQLĪDISĪ

the nervous system in the nineteenth century. Unzer's wife, Johanna Charlotte Ziegler, was also a writer on natural history.

BIBLIOGRAPHY

I. ORIGINAL WORKS. Unzer's physiological writings include *Gedanken vom Einflusse der Seele in ihrem Körper* (Halle, 1746); *Gedanken vom Schlaf* (Halle, 1746); *Neue Lehre von den Gemüthsbewegungen* (Halle, 1746); *Dissertatio inauguralis medica de sternutatione* (Halle–Magdeburg, 1748); *Philosophische Betrachtung des menschlichen Körpers überhaupt* (Halle, 1750); and *Grundriss eines Lehrgebäudes von der Sinnlichkeit der thierischen Körper* (Rinteln, 1768). The last was a preliminary study for his most important book, *Erste Gründe einer Physiologie der eigentlichen thierischen Natur thierischer Körper* (Leipzig, 1771), which was trans. into English (London, 1851) and is quoted by Fearing, below, and by Edward E. Clarke and C. D. O'Malley in *The Human Brain and Spinal Cord* (Berkeley–Los Angeles, 1968), 342–345.

His medical books include *Sammlung kleiner physikalischen Schriften*: vols. I and III, *Physikalische Schriften*; vol. II, *Zur speculativen Philosophie* (Leipzig, 1768–1769); *Medizinisches Handbuch*, 3 vols. (Leipzig, 1770; 5th ed. 1794); *Über die Ansteckung, besonders der Pocken, in einer Beurtheilung der neuen Hoffmann'schen Pockentheorie* (Leipzig, 1778); *Einleitung zur allgemeinen Pathologie der ansteckenden Krankheiten* (Leipzig, 1782); and *Verteidigung seiner Einwürfe gegen die Pockentheorie des Hrn. Geh. Rath Hoffmann* (Leipzig, 1783).

II. SECONDARY LITERATURE. There are few biographical works about Unzer, but see T. Kirchhoff, in *Deutsche Irrenärzte*, I (Berlin, 1921), 13–15. On his work, particularly in the development of animal physiology and on reflex action, see Georges Canguilhem, *La formation du concept de réflexe aux XVIIᵉ et XVIIIᵉ siècles* (Paris, 1955), 108–114; Franklin Fearing, *Reflex Action. A Study in the History of Physiological Psychology* (London, 1930), 90–93; C. F. Hodge, "A Sketch of the History of Reflex Action," in *American Journal of Psychology*, **3** (1890), 149–167, 343–363; Thomas Laycock, intro. to *The Principles of Physiology of the Proper Animal Nature of the Animal Organism* (his trans. of Unzer's *Erste Gründe*) (London, 1851); and Max Neuburger, *Die historische Entwicklung der experimentellen Gehirn- und Rückenmarksphysiologie vor Flourens* (Stuttgart, 1897).

VLADISLAV KRUTA

AL-UQLĪDISĪ, ABU'L-ḤASAN AḤMAD IBN IBRĀHĪM (*fl.* Damascus, 952–953), *arithmetic*.

No source book mentions al-Uqlīdisī. He is known only from a unique copy of his work entitled *Kitāb al-fuṣūl fi'l-ḥisāb al-hindī* (MS 802, Yeni Cami, Istanbul), the front page of which bears the author's name and the statement that the text was written at Damascus in 952–953. The manuscript was copied in A.D. 1157. In the introduction the author states that he has traveled extensively, read all books on Indian arithmetic that he has found, and learned from every noted arithmetician he has met. The epithet al-Uqlīdisī generally was attached to the names of persons who made copies of Euclid's *Elements* for sale, so it is possible that he earned his living in that way. Internal evidence shows that he had experience in teaching Indian arithmetic, for he knows what beginners ask and how to answer their questions.

The book is in four parts. In the first, Hindu numerals are introduced; the place-value concept is explained; and the arithmetical operations, including extraction of square roots, are described, with many examples applied to integers and common fractions in both the decimal and the sexagesimal systems.

In the second part the subject matter is treated at a higher level and includes the method of casting out nines and several variations of the schemes of operations explained in the first part. In the introduction the author states that in this part he has collected the methods used by noted manipulators, expressed in the Indian way. This section contains almost all the schemes of multiplication that appear in later Latin works.

In the third part, justifications of the several concepts and steps suggested in the first two parts are given, generally in answer to questions beginning "Why" or "How is it."

A few words may be necessary for an appreciation of the fourth part. The first few lines of the text state that Indian arithmetic, as transmitted to the Arabs, required the use of the dust abacus. Later it is said that the operations depended upon shifting the figures and erasing them. For instance, in the example 329 × 456, the numbers are written as shown below:

3 2 9

4 5 6

Then 3 is multiplied by 4 and the product is inserted in the top line as 12; 3 is multiplied by 5, which requires putting 5 above, erasing 2, and putting 3 in its place; 3 is multiplied by 6, making it necessary to remove 3 from the top line and write 8 in its place, to erase the 5 before it, and to put 6 in its

544

place. In preparation for the next step, the lower line is shifted one place to the right. The array is now as shown below:

$$1\ 3\ 6\ 8\ 2\ 9$$
$$4\ 5\ 6$$

456 is to be multiplied by 2, which is above the units place of 456; the position of the units digit of the multiplicand in the lower line indicates the multiplier. The remaining steps can now be followed with ease.

Obviously paper and ink cannot be easily used with such schemes. In the fourth part of the text, modifications of the Indian schemes are suggested whereby the abacus can be dispensed with, and ink and paper used instead. We can now judge that al-Uqlīdisī's modification presents a first step in a long chain of attempts that resulted in discarding the abacus completely, first in western Islam and, many centuries later, in the eastern part.

After suggesting a modification of each operation, al-Uqlīdisī proposed that:

1. Greek letters might replace the nine Indian numerals.

2. The Indian numerals with superimposed dots might form a new Arabic alphabet.

3. There might be calculating dice, with one or two numerals on each face, to use instead of the abacus.

4. There might be a calculating board to be used by the blind.

The second idea is cited in other texts, and the third is reminiscent of Boëthius' apexes. It is as likely as not that here al-Uqlīdisī is describing methods used elsewhere rather than making original suggestions. The book ends with a lengthy discussion of $\Sigma 2^r$ and the method of extracting the cube root.

Al-Uqlīdisī was proud of the following accomplishments in his work:

1. In part 1 he presented the contents of all earlier texts on Indian arithmetic and applied it in the sexagesimal system. We do not have these texts to enable us to judge how far he was correct in this claim. The Latin *Algorismus corpus*, however, indicates that Indian arithmetic as presented by al-Khwārizmī (ninth century) differed basically from that which spread later in the Muslim world. Application of the Indian schemes to the sexagesimal system is found in all later Arabic arithmetic books.

2. In part 2 he gave methods known only to noted arithmeticians, and extended the method of casting out nines to fractions and square roots. On the evidence of later texts, one is inclined to accept this claim of al-Uqlīdisī.

3. In part 4, he showed that Indian arithmetic no longer needed the abacus. This modification was more agreeable to the West than to the East. In support we may note that Ibn al-Bannā' (d. 1321) of Morocco included as a curiosity in one of his arithmetical works the statement that the ancients had used dust for calculation, whereas Naṣīr al-Dīn al-Ṭūsī (d. 1274) of Persia found the dust abacus still important enough to write a book on it.

4. In discussing $\Sigma 2^r$ he distinguished between the nth term and the sum of n terms, which he claimed that some manipulators had confused.

5. He claimed to be the first to have written satisfactorily on the cube root.

There are no documents to decide the last two claims, but we have other reasons to consider al-Uqlīdisī's *Kitāb al-fuṣūl fi'l-ḥisāb al-hindī* the most important of some one hundred extant Arabic arithmetic texts.

First, it is the earliest known text that contains a direct treatment of decimal fractions. The author suggests a decimal sign, a stroke over the units' place, and insists that it must always be used. In a process of successive division by 2 he obtains the sequence 13, 6.5, 3.25, 1.625, 0.8125. He knows how to regain 13 by successive multiplication by 2 and by ignoring the zeros to the right. In a process of repeatedly increasing 135 by one-tenth, he obtains the array

135	148.5	163.35
13.5	14.85	16.335 and so on.
148.5	163.35	179.685

Again, in finding the approximate roots of numbers, he uses the rules

$$\sqrt{a} = \sqrt{ak^2}/k, \qquad \sqrt[3]{a} = \sqrt[3]{ak^3}/k$$

and takes k equal to a multiple of ten.

Although many other arithmeticians used the same rules, all of them rather mechanically transformed the decimal fraction obtained into the sexagesimal system, without showing any sign of comprehension of the decimal idea. Only al-Uqlīdisī gives the root in the decimal scale in several cases. In all operations where powers of ten are involved in the numerator or the denominator, he is well at home.

Second, al-Uqlīdisī's is the first text to tell us clearly that Indian arithmetic depended on the dust abacus. In his introduction, the author compared the Indian system with the then current finger-reckoning and made a correct evaluation of the merits and drawbacks of each. It is now known that Abu 'l-Wafā' (940–997/998) and Ibn al-Bannā' made passing statements about the dust abacus in Indian arithmetic, but these references were too terse to catch the attention of the scholars who first studied their works.

BIBLIOGRAPHY

See A. S. Saidan, "The Earliest Extant Arabic Arithmetic," in *Isis*, **57** (1966), 475–490.

A. S. SAIDAN

URBAN, GEORGES (*b*. Paris, France, 12 April 1872; *d*. Paris, 5 November 1938), *chemistry, mineralogy*.

The son of a professor of chemistry and assistant to Edmond Frémy, Urbain entered the École de Physique et de Chimie in Paris at his father's request and graduated first in his class in 1894. While serving as assistant in the mineral laboratory, he came under the influence of Pierre Curie, who introduced him to scientific research. From 1895 until 1898 he was the private assistant of Charles Friedel and was awarded his doctorate in 1899 from the University of Paris for his thesis on the rare earths. In 1906 Urbain was named assistant professor of analytical chemistry at the Sorbonne and was rapidly promoted to professor of mineral chemistry in 1908. In 1928 he was appointed professor of general chemistry, director of the Institut de Chimie de Paris, and codirector of the Institut de Biologie Physico-chimique. During his term as professor at the Institut he created a mecca for good chemistry students. His lectures were well-delivered and extremely popular.

Urbain's name is linked with his important studies of the rare earths, which occupied him mainly from 1895 until 1912. More than 200,000 fractional crystallizations enabled him to separate rigorously samarium, europium, gadolinium, terbium, dysprosium, and holmium. He found that the ethyl sulfates of the rare earths were the easiest derivatives to separate. The most important single study was his separation of ytterbium (considered an element by Jean Marignac) into ytterbium and the previously unknown lutetium, named after Lutetia, the ancient name of Paris. Urbain's determinations of the atomic weights of these elements were accepted by the authorities and led to his la-

ter election as president of the International Committee on Atomic Weights.

In 1911 Urbain observed another element, not of the rare earth family, which he named celtium. Henry Moseley felt that it was the missing element 72, although X-ray evidence was inconclusive. After World War I, Urbain continued his investigations and, in 1922, confirmed the presence of element 72 in his samples. But Hevesy and Coster isolated larger concentrations of the element that same year and are credited with the discovery of hafnium. For a short period of time the committee accepted both the symbols Ct and Hf for the element.

After 1912 Urbain's interests turned increasingly toward theoretical complex chemistry. He critically evaluated and extended Alfred Werner's coordination theory and proposed his own theory of homeomerism (equal properties). This concept extended the idea of isomorphism beyond the limits of the crystalline state by dropping the condition of equality of interfacial angles. Two substances, then, in order to be homeomeric must have equal molecular coefficients of energy—properties that are generally easy to measure. Thus he defined isotopes as elements that are nearly rigorously homeomeric.

Among Urbain's other deep interests were music and the history and philosophy of science. A fine piano player, he read most of the didactic works on music and composed several brilliant pieces as well as a book on the subject. He keenly analyzed the development of chemistry in a work that has been compared to those of Jean-Baptiste-André Dumas. He firmly believed in the essential unity of inorganic and organic chemistry and felt that by modifying Werner's theory he could achieve this unification for theoretical chemistry.

BIBLIOGRAPHY

I. ORIGINAL WORKS. A complete listing of Urbain's papers is found in Paul Job, "Notice sur la vie et les travaux de Georges Urbain," in *Bulletin de la Société chimique de France*, **6** (1939), 745–766.

Urbain wrote seven books on chemistry. They are, in chronological order, *Introduction à l'étude de la spectrochemie* (Paris, 1911), which is not an advanced treatise on spectrochemistry but is rather an introduction for the beginner on methods of special analysis, including a lengthy historical survey of the subject; *Introduction à la chimie des complexes minéraux* (Paris, 1914), with A. Sénéchal, which is based on Urbain's course at the Sorbonne and, despite its title, is a general text on physical and inorganic chemistry; *Les disciplines d'une science. La chimie* (Paris, 1921), which discusses his attempt to unify inorganic and organic chemistry; *L'énergétique des réactions chimiques* (Paris, 1925), which is a theoretical introduction to chemical thermodynamics based on a course given at the Sorbonne; *Les notions fondamentales d'éléments chimiques et d'atomes* (Paris, 1925); and *La coordination des atomes dans la molecule et la symbolique chimique*, 2 vols. (Paris, 1933), which are two purely theoretical treatises; and *Traité de chimie générale, notions et principes fondamentaux* (Paris, 1939), with P. Job, G. Allard, and G. Champetier, but mostly the work of Urbain.

Urbain places his rare earth studies in their historical perspective in his review article, "Research on Yttrium Earths," in *Chemical Reviews*, **1** (1924), 143–185.

Worthy of note is his book *Le Tombeau d'Aristoxène. Essai sur la musique* (Paris, 1924), in which he proposed that music is more intellectual than sensuous and, consequently, can be the object of a methodical (if not truly scientific) study.

II. SECONDARY LITERATURE. The most detailed biographical sketch of Urbain is Paul Job's obituary notice cited above. An interesting English article written by two of Urbain's former students is Georges Champetier and Charlotte H. Boatner, "Georges Urbain," in *Journal of Chemical Education*, **17** (1940), 103–109.

SHELDON J. KOPPERL

URE, ANDREW (*b.* Glasgow, Scotland, 18 May 1778; *d.* London, England, 2 January 1857), *chemistry.*

A pioneer in the teaching of science to artisans, Ure was also one of the first scientists to earn his living as a consultant. Apart from his teaching and some improvements in the techniques of chemical analysis, he made no significant contributions to the advancement of science. Yet he was an indefatigable writer and encyclopedist, and his major work, the *Philosophy of Manufactures . . .* (1835), while containing ridiculous passages, nevertheless embodies the first clear recognition that what came to be called the industrial revolution was a novel and irreversible alteration in the human condition. Unfortunately, his intemperate scorn for his contemporaries and the self-aggrandizement that characterizes much of his writing obscured his positive qualities and made him many enemies.

Ure was the son of a cheesemonger, Alexander Ure, and his wife Anne Adam. He graduated M.D. at the University of Glasgow in 1801, and after a short period as an army surgeon succeeded George Birkbeck in 1804 as professor of natural philosophy at the Andersonian Institution (now the University of Strathclyde), Glasgow, then in its formative years. Ure's evening lectures in chemistry and mechanics for artisans were extremely popular, although his undoubted success as a teacher was marred by the air of conscious superiority that he adopted.

In 1814 Ure began to lecture at the Royal Belfast Academical Institution during the summer vacations. While in Ireland in 1816 he tried unsuccessfully to interest the Linen Board in a new method of determining the strength of alkaline solutions. His innovation, which he did not publish until much later (*Pharmaceutical Journal*, **3** [1844], 430–450), was to employ solutions of acids and alkalies in such concentrations that these could be expressed in terms of their chemical equivalents. Thus, he was led to originate the concept of normality in volumetric analysis (see W. V. Farrar, "The Origin of Normality," in *Education in Chemistry*, **4** [1967], 277–279).

In 1818 Ure created a sensation by conducting in public a gruesome experiment on the activation by electricity of the muscles of an executed murderer. Of Ure's many papers, one describing improvements in the use of copper oxide in organic analysis was of contemporary importance. His most enduring papers were those relating the composition and densities of aqueous solutions of the mineral acids—the results were quoted in chemist's pocket books until nearly the end of the century. Ure became a fellow of the Royal Society in 1822. The great interest he took in the application of science to the arts and industry bore fruit in his *Dictionary of Chemistry* (1821). This work was originally undertaken at the request of the publishers as a revision of William Nicholson's *Dictionary of Chemistry*, but Ure said that so much of the latter was obsolete that the work had largely to be rewritten. He eventually widened its scope and retitled the work the *Dictionary of Arts, Manufactures and Mines* (1839).

In 1829 Ure published his *System of Geology*, an outdated attempt to reconcile contemporary geological discoveries with the Mosaic account of the Creation. He thought that geologists, by questioning the latter, were undermining the bases of religion and morality. The book was the subject of a devastating attack by Adam Sedgwick at a meeting of the Geological Society of London in 1830 (*Proceedings of the Geological Society of London*, **1** [1834], 208–210). Quite apart from defending a lost cause, Ure had not kept himself up to date and many old errors had been repeated. Moreover, he included considerable extracts from other works without any indication of quotation. Sedgwick concluded that Ure had "shown neither the information nor the industry which might justify him in becoming an interpreter of the labours of others, or the framer of a system of his own."

As Ure's extramural activities increased his teaching seriously deteriorated, leading to many disputes with the managers of the Institution. He resigned in 1830, moved to London, and became probably the first consulting chemist in Great Britain, ready to offer advice on any problem connected with science. His investigations and matters of public concern provided materials for an unceasing flow of writings, including a series of tendentious pamphlets, in which his fellow scientists were frequently castigated. His *Philosophy of Manufactures*, intended as an introductory volume to a series dealing with various industries, was based on a tour of the manufacturing districts of Lancashire, Derbyshire, and Cheshire.

Ure married Catharine Monteath in 1807, but he divorced her in 1819 because of her infidelity. They had two sons and a daughter; Alexander, the elder son, became a London surgeon and wrote several papers. He has sometimes been confused with his father.

BIBLIOGRAPHY

I. ORIGINAL WORKS. Ure's books are *A New Systematic Table of the Materia Medica, With a Preliminary Dissertation, Historical, Critical, and Explanatory, on the Operation of Medicines* (Glasgow, 1813); *A Dictionary of Chemistry on the Basis of Mr. Nicholson* (London, 1821; 4th ed., 1835); *A Dictionary of Arts, Manufactures and Mines* (London, 1839; 4th ed., 1853; 7th ed., 1875); *A New System of Geology* (London, 1829), which was an attempt to reconcile contemporary geological discoveries with the Mosaic account of the Creation; *The Philosophy of Manufactures, or an Exposition of the Scientific, Moral and Commercial Economy of the Factory System of Great Britain* (London, 1835); *The Cotton Manufacture of Great Britain* (London, 1836), which was the first and only one published of an intended series—posthumous editions of this and the preliminary volume were published in 1861, with additions by P. L. Simmonds; and a translation of Claude Louis Berthollet and A. B. Berthollet, *Elements of the Art of Dyeing; With a Description of the Art of Bleaching by Oxymuriatic Acid*, 2 vols. (London, 1824).

Ure also published several pamphlets and a large number of papers, most of which were short and trivial; an incomplete list (though omitting little of any importance) is in *The Royal Society Catalogue of Scientific Papers*, VI (London, 1872), 89–90.

II. SECONDARY LITERATURE. The fullest and most accurate account of Ure is W. V. Farrar, "Andrew Ure and the Philosophy of Manufactures," in *Notes and Records of the Royal Society of London*, **27** (1972–1973), 299–324, with portrait of Ure. See also W. S. C. Copeman, "Andrew Ure, M.D., F.R.S. (1778–1857)," in *Proceedings of the Royal Society of Medicine*, **44** (1951), 655–662. The second article, although based on family papers (the author was a descendant of Ure), is unreliable, particularly with regard to Ure's work. *Dr. Andrew Ure: A Slight Sketch Reprinted From the Times and Other Periodicals, of January, 1857* (anonymous, privately printed, 1875) is eulogistic and misleading.

E. L. SCOTT

URYSON, PAVEL SAMUILOVICH (*b.* Odessa, Russia, 3 February 1898; *d.* Batz, France, 17 August 1924), *mathematics.*

The son of a distinguished Odessa financier, Uryson attended a private secondary school in Moscow in 1915 and entered the University of Moscow, intending to study physics. The same year he published his first scientific work, on Coolidge tube radiation, prepared under the guidance of P. P. Lazarev. Fascinated by the lectures of D. F. Egorov and N. N. Luzin, Uryson began specializing in mathematics and in 1919, after graduating from the university, he remained there to prepare for a teaching career. Uryson's works were at first concerned with integral equations and with other problems of analysis; but in the summer of 1921, being engaged in solving two problems presented to him by Egorov, he turned to topology. In June of that year Uryson was appointed assistant professor at the University of Moscow, where, in particular, he lectured on topology and, later, in 1923–1924, on the mathematical theory of relativity. He was also professor at the Second Moscow University (now the Lenin Moscow Pedagogical Institute).

Uryson's publications on topology first appeared in 1922 in the *Comptes rendus* of the Académie des Sciences, as well as in Soviet and Polish journals. His ideas were also presented in lectures, memoirs, and discourses. The reports he delivered at the Mathematical Society of Göttingen in 1923 attracted the attention of Hilbert; and in the summer of 1924, while touring Germany, Holland, and France, he met L. E. J. Brouwer and Felix Hausdorff, who praised his works highly. Uryson drowned off the coast of Brittany at the age of twenty-six while on vacation.

Although his scientific activity lasted for only

about five years, he greatly influenced the subsequent development of topology and laid the foundations of the Soviet school of topology, which was then led by his friend P. S. Aleksandrov, with whom he carried out several investigations.

The two cardinal aspects of Uryson's works on topology are topological space (abstract topology) and the theory of dimensionality.

In abstract topology his main results are the introduction and investigation of a class of the so-called normal spaces, metrization theorems, including a theorem on the existence of a topological mapping of any normed space with a countable base into Hilbert space.

The principal tool used in all the most recent investigations of normed spaces is the classical "Uryson's lemma," which proves the existence, for any two disjoint closed sets of a normed space, of a continuous function $f(x)$ which is defined over the given space. It satisfies the inequality $0 \leq f(x) \leq 1$ within that space and assumes on one of the two given sets the value zero, whereas on the other set it assumes the value of unity. Based on this lemma is Uryson's theorem on the metrizability of normed spaces having a countable base, and the theorem on the possibility of extending any continuous function defined on a closed set of a normed space R, to a function continuous over the entire space R. Both theorems are fundamental in general topology.

The theory of dimensionality created by Uryson in 1921–1922 was presented in his memoirs on Cantorian varieties, published posthumously in 1925–1926. In this work Uryson first presented an inductive definition of dimensionality that proved highly fruitful and became classical. Uryson then established that dimensionality, in the sense of the new definition of the n-dimensional Euclidean space R^n, actually equals n. In the process Uryson obtained a number of important results.

For $n = 4$ the equality dim $R^n = n$ was proved only by going beyond the limits of the inductive definition of dimensionality. Uryson's proof of the "theorem of equivalence" appeared to be a turning point in the development of the theory of dimensionality and of a considerable part of topology in general. The second part of this work is devoted to the creation of the theory of one-dimensional continua, in particular, their indexes of branching and continua of condensation.

Concurrently with and independently of Uryson, the Austrian mathematician Karl Menger was engaged in the same field; and the theory of dimen-

sionality is often referred to as the Uryson-Menger theory.

BIBLIOGRAPHY

I. Original Works. Uryson's collected works on topology and other branches of mathematics were published as *Trudy po topologii i drugim oblastiam matematiki*, 2 vols. (Moscow–Leningrad, 1951). Separately published writings include "Sur l'unicité de la solution des équations linéaires de M. Volterra," in *Bulletin de l'Académie polonaise des sciences*, ser. A (1922), 57–62; "Sur une fonction analytique partout continue," in *Fundamenta mathematica*, **4** (1923), 144–150; "Ein Beitrag zur Theorie der ebenen Gebiete unendlich hohen Zusammenhanges," in *Mathematische Zeitschrift*, **21** (1924), 133–150; "Zur Theorie der topologischen Räume," in *Mathematische Annalen*, **92** (1924), 258–266, written with P. S. Aleksandrov; "Über die Metrisation der kompakten topologischen Räume," *ibid.*, 275–293; and "Mémoire sur les multiplicitées cantoriennes," in *Fundamenta mathematica*, **7** (1925), 30–137; and **8** (1926), 225–356.

II. Secondary Literature. For a detailed bibliography of Uryson's works, see *Matematika v SSSR za 40 let* ("Mathematics in the U.S.S.R. for Forty Years"), II (Moscow, 1959), 696–697. On Uryson's life and work, see P. S. Aleksandrov, in *Uspekhi astronomicheskikh nauk*, **5** (1950), 196–202.

A. Paplauscas

VAGNER (or WAGNER), EGOR EGOROVICH (*b.* Kazan, Russia, 30 November 1849; *d.* Warsaw, Poland, 27 November 1903), *chemistry.*

Vagner was a student of A. M. Zaytsev and of A. M. Butlerov and was one of the founders of the chemistry of terpenes. He graduated from the University of Kazan in 1874. In his student works, published with Zaytsev, he proposed a new and effective method for the zinc-organic synthesis of secondary alcohols. In 1882 he became professor at the Novo-Aleksandr Agricultural Institute and, in 1886, at the University of Warsaw.

Vagner's scientific research dealt mainly with the natural mono- and bicyclic terpenes and with the synthesis and study of the properties of alicyclic compounds. From 1882 to 1888 he developed a universal method (Vagner oxidation) for determining the number and location of ethylene bonds in the organic molecule by means of hydroxylation with weak aqueous solutions of potassium permanganate to form glycol. It was this simple and fruitful technique that made it possible in the nineteenth century to study the structure of complex unsaturated organic compounds. Despite the later appearance of new methods of establishing molecular structure, especially Harries' ozonization method, the Vagner oxidization has remained important. Having determined the structure of the molecules of limonene and its acid derivatives, Vagner then clarified the more difficult question of the structure of pinene. He specified the structural formulas of pinol, terpene, terpineol, camphene, borneol, isoborneol, carvone, carone, carvestrene, sobrerol, sobreritrite β-camphors and other terpenes. Prior to his work, erroneous formulas had frequently been assigned to these substances.

Having discovered the genetic connection between the hydrocarbons of the terpene series and their acid and halogen derivatives, Vagner established the mechanism of many reactions of terpenes. His discovery of the camphene regrouping of the first class was important for the theoretical development of organic chemistry. This regrouping was later studied in detail by Hans Meerwein and is now called the Vagner-Meerwein rearrangement:

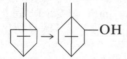

Vagner's proposal for the rational classification of terpenes on the basis of their structural-chemical peculiarities is now accepted by contemporary chemistry.

BIBLIOGRAPHY

I. ORIGINAL WORKS. Vagner's writings include *K reaktsii okislenia nepredelnykh uglerodistykh soedineny* ("On the Oxidization Reaction of Unsaturated Carbon Compounds"; Warsaw, 1888); "Zur Constitution der Pinens," in *Berichte der Deutschen chemischen Gesellschaft*, **24** (1891), 2187–2190; and "K stroeniyu terpenov i im rodstvennykh soedineny" ("On the Structure of Terpenes and Related Compounds"), in *Zhurnal Russkago fiziko-khimicheskago obshchestva*, **26** (1894), 327–362; and **28** (1896), 56–108, 206, 398, 484–501.

II. SECONDARY LITERATURE. On Vagner and his work, see A. E. Arbuzov, "Egor Egorovich Vagner," in *Trudy Instituta istorii estestvoznaniya i tekhniki. Akademiya nauk SSSR*, **4** (1952), 46–61, and V. Lavrov, "Egor Egorovich Vagner, zhizn i deitelnost" ("Egor Egorovich, Life and Work"), in *Zhurnal Russkago fiziko-khimicheskago obshchestva pri Imperatorskago St. Peterburgskago universitete*, **36** (1904), 1337–1339.

V. I. KUZNETSOV

VAILATI, GIOVANNI (*b*. Crema, Italy, 24 April 1863; *d*. Rome, Italy, 14 May 1909), *logic, philosophy of science, history of science.*

Vailati's parents were Vincenzo Vailati and Teresa Albergoni. After attending boarding schools in Monza and Lodi, he enrolled in the University of Turin in 1880, graduating in engineering in 1884 and in mathematics in 1888. Then followed a period of independent study in which he especially studied languages (his writings show a proficiency in Greek, Latin, English, French, German, and Spanish); this was interrupted by the offer of an assistantship at the University of Turin by his former teacher Giuseppe Peano, professor of infinitesimal calculus. Vailati was Peano's assistant from 1892 to 1895, when he became an assistant in projective geometry and later honorary assistant to Volterra. In 1899 he requested a secondary school appointment and was at first sent to Syracuse, transferring to Bari in 1900, to Como in 1901, and to Florence in 1904.

Vailati came of a Catholic family but lost his faith during his early university years. Throughout his life he had affectionate and devoted friends; he never married. His premature death was attributed to heart trouble, complicated by pulmonitis.

Vailati's first ten publications, dealing principally with mathematical logic, were published in the *Rivista di matematica*, founded by Peano in 1891. He also collaborated, especially with historical notes, in the *Formulario* project announced by Peano in 1892. Vailati gained international recognition with the publication of three essays in the history and methodology of science, originally given as introductory lectures to his course in the history of mechanics at the University of Turin (1896–1898).

Vailati was always concerned with tracing ideas back to their origins, and his intimate knowledge of Greek and Latin was invaluable. (In the analytical index to the *Scritti*, "Aristotle" has twice the space of any other entry.) His work in this area will perhaps be his most lasting contribution.

Vailati received most attention during his lifetime as the leading Italian exponent of pragmatism. After his transfer to Florence in 1904 he collaborated, along with his friend and disciple Mario Calderoni, in the publication of the journal *Leonardo*, founded the year before by G. Papini and G. Prezzolini. His philosophical position was closer to that of Charles Sanders Peirce than to the more popular William James, but it remained distinct, individual, and original.

Vailati's wide range of interest included, at various periods, psychic research, economics, and political science (in which he took socialism seriously, but opposed Marx's theory of value.) In all of these areas his acute critical sense allowed him, as was often said, "to succeed in saying in a few words what others had succeeded in *not* saying in many volumes." When the occasion seemed to call for it, he did not hesitate to criticize sharply the opinions of even eminent scientists (for example, he criticized Poincaré's views on mathematical logic).

Finally, Vailati's pedagogical activities must be noted, in recognition of which he was appointed a member of the commission for the reform of the secondary schools. For the work of the commission he established his residence in Rome in 1906, dividing his time between there and Florence, but in 1908 he voluntarily returned to teaching in Florence.

After his death, Vailati's reputation quickly suffered an eclipse; this was partly the result of the form in which his writings appeared. He never published a book-length monograph. Indeed, many of his original ideas appeared in critical reviews, which occupy, by page count, approximately 43 percent of the *Scritti*. After 1950 there was a revival of interest in his work, centering mainly on his philosophical views, but hindered by the general unavailability of his writings. Vailati also carried on a wide correspondence, which is mostly unpublished. Projects announced in 1958 for the publication of his correspondence and a new edition of his writings were not carried out.

BIBLIOGRAPHY

I. ORIGINAL WORKS. With very minor exceptions the published writings of Vailati were collected in the *Scritti di G. Vailati (1863–1909)* (Leipzig–Florence, 1911). The article "Sulla teoria delle proporzioni," appeared posthumously in *Questioni riguardanti le matematiche elementari*, F. Enriques, ed., I (Bologna, 1924), 143–191. There have been three short anthologies, *Gli strumenti della conoscenza*, M. Calderoni, ed. (Lanciano, 1911); *Il pragmatismo*, Giovanni Papini, ed. (Lanciano, 1911); and *Il metodo della filosofia*, Ferruccio Rossi-Landi, ed. (Bari, 1957; repr. 1967).

II. SECONDARY LITERATURE. The *Scritti* contains a biography by Orazio Premoli. Calderoni's preface to *Gli strumenti . . .* (1909) is also valuable. Essential for any study of Vailati is F. Rossi-Landi, "Materiale per lo studio di Vailati," in *Rivista critica di storia della filosofia*, **12** (1957), 468–485; and **13** (1958), 82–108.

An entire number of the *Rivista critica . . .*, **18** (1963), 275–523, contains papers presented by twenty authors for the centenary of Vailati's birth.

HUBERT C. KENNEDY

VAILLANT, LÉON-LOUIS (*b.* Paris, France, 11 November 1834; *d.* Paris, 27 November 1914), *ichthyology, herpetology.*

Vaillant studied medicine and science at Montpellier and obtained both the M.D. and Ph.D. in Paris with theses on human hair (*Essai sur le système pileux dans l'espèce humaine*, 1861) and on the mollusk Tridacna (*Remarques sur l'anatomie de la Tridacna elongata*, 1865). After several years as instructor at the universities of Paris and Montpellier, he became assistant and then full professor at the Muséum National d'Histoire Naturelle in Paris. In 1875 he obtained the chair of herpetology and ichthyology at the Muséum, from which he retired in 1910; he died at work in 1914.

Vaillant's earliest duties at the museum included the installation of new galleries to replace those destroyed by the Prussians in 1871. He identified, labeled, arranged, and exhibited his collections with care and delight. As head keeper of the reptiles, batrachians, and fish in the menagerie (which contained 616 animals when he retired), he had ample opportunity for observation. He taught ichthyology and herpetology for thirty-five years and became a world-renowned specialist.

Vaillant published almost two hundred papers, each but a few pages long, and each containing a new detail that was significant in determining the precise classification of some little-known species. While he was still at Montpellier, his articles appeared mainly in *Mémoires de la Société de biologie* and in *Annales des sciences naturelles*. After the Franco-Prussian War, he published in *Bulletin de la Société philomathique de Paris*. Only after 1895 did he change to a public journal and publish forty-four more papers in the new *Bulletin du Muséum d'histoire naturelle*. During his entire professional life Vaillant kept up a steady flow of one or two communications a year to the Academy of Sciences; yet the Academy rejected his candidacy twice, in 1886 and 1887. He never tried again.

Vaillant spent his life at the Muséum. He concentrated on the classification of new specimens and, in eight instances, helped publish the results of expeditions that he had either participated in or had watched closely.

In 1863–1864 Vaillant traveled to the Gulf of Suez with a government mission (doubtless related to the construction of the canal). His study of a mollusk (*Recherches sur la famille des Tridacnidés*, 1865) won the first Savigny Prize from the Académie des Sciences. In 1880–1883 he participated, as member of a deep-sea dredging commission, in the voyages of the frigates *Travailleur* and *Talisman*, and published his part of the resulting discoveries in a beautifully illustrated volume (*Poissons* [Paris, 1888]). After that, his travels were vicarious.

Vaillant wrote in 1882 a general scientific account of the French mission to Somaliland, established in 1891 the official list of fish brought back from the Algerian Sahara and, in 1893, a list of fish brought back from the Arctic by the frigate *La Manche*. He wrote in 1905 the section on "Fish" for the report of a French expedition to Antarctica, the section on "Turtles" in 1911 for the volume compiled by a military mission to South America, and he left unfinished a study containing the results of a French expedition to Central America.

All Vaillant's writings are technical throughout, with no comments; yet the excitement of the scientist stalking his prey and nailing a precise fact is always present. He explained his methodology as being based on anatomy illuminated by physiology and ethology and aided by microscopic techniques and histology. Sometimes he dealt with extinct species and studied naturalists' descriptions as far back as antiquity, which enabled him, he said, to settle many a dispute. Finally, he was interested in the distribution of species geographically, historically, and at various depths in the ocean.

Vaillant presented several reports of general significance, based on ichthyologic and herpetologic research, to the Académie des Sciences. The fauna of the ocean floor was still quite unknown, and bathymetric studies were just beginning to permit differentiation of "littoral," "coastal," and "abyssal" regions. He also served as a consultant to a national committee on deep-sea fishing and on juries for the World's Fair of 1878, 1889, and 1900. His only official distinction was the *rosette* of the Legion of Honor.

BIBLIOGRAPHY

I. Original Works. Works by Vaillant include *Essai sur le système pileux dans l'espèce humaine* (Paris, 1861), the thesis for the M.D.; "Mémoire pour servir à l'histoire anatomique de la Sirène lacertine," in *Annales des sciences naturelles*, 4th ser., **19** (1863), 295–346;

"Recherches sur la famille des Tridacnidés," in *Annales des sciences naturelles (Zoologie)*, **4** (1865), 65–172; "Remarques sur l'anatomie de la Tridacna elongata," in *Comptes rendus hebdomadaires des séances de l'Académie des sciences*, **61** (1865), 601–603; "Recherches sur les poissons des eaux douces de l'Amérique Septentrionale, désignés par M. L. Agassiz sous le nom d'Etheostomatidae," in *Nouvelles archives du Muséum d'histoire naturelle*, **9** (1873), 5–154; "Sur la disposition des vertèbres cervicales chez les Chéloniens," in *Annales des sciences naturelles*, 6th ser., **10** (1880), no. 7; *Mission G. Révoil aux pays Somalis. Faune et flore. Reptiles et batraciens* (Paris, 1882); "Catalogue raisonné des reptiles et batraciens d'Assinie, donnés par M. Chaper au Muséum d'histoire naturelle," in *Bulletin de la Société zoologique de France*, **9** (1884), 343–354; "Considérations sur les poissons des grandes profondeurs, en particulier sur ceux qui appartiennent au sous-ordre des abdominales," in *Comptes rendus hebdomadaires des séances de l'Académie des sciences*, **103** (1886), 1237–1239; **104** (1887), 123–126; "Matériaux pour servir à l'histoire ichthyologique des Archipels de la Société et des Pomotous," in *Bulletin de la Société philomathique de Paris*, **11** (1887), 49–62; *Poissons* (Paris, 1888), vol. II of Expéditions scientifiques du *Travailleur* et du *Talisman* pendant les années 1880, 1881, 1882, 1883, sous la direction de A. Milne-Edwards; "Rapport présenté au Comité consultatif des pêches sur les morues, la reproduction de la sardine et les causes probables de sa disparition," in *Revue maritime et coloniale*, **97** (1888), 544–554, with L. F. Henneguy; *Rapport adressé au Ministre de la marine au nom du Comité consultatif des pêches maritimes sur la pêche de la montée d'anguilles* (Paris, 1889); *Sur la présence du saumon dans les eaux marines de la Norvège*, in A. Berthoude, *Le Saumon et la loi sur la pêche* (Versailles, 1889); "Les collections d'herpétologie et d'ichthyologie au Muséum d'histoire naturelle," in *Revue scientifique*, **45** (1890), 513–522.

Other works include *Lombriciniens, hirudiniens, bdellomorphes, térétulariens et planariens*, 3 vols. (Paris, 1889–1890), pt. III of *Histoire naturelle des annelés marins d'eau douce*; *Poissons*, sect. IV, pt. II of *L'extrême sud algérien. Contribution à l'histoire naturelle de cette région. Catalogue raisonné et étude des échantillons recueillis dans le Sahara algérien. Nouvelles archives des missions scientifiques*, I (1891), 360; "Sur la délimitation des zones littorales," in *Comptes rendus hebdomadaires des séances de l'Académie des sciences*, **112** (1891), 1038–1040; *Les Poissons d'aquarium. Conférence faite à la Société nationale d'acclimatation* (Paris, 1893); *Les tortues éteintes de l'île Rodriguez, d'après les pièces conservées dans les galeries du Muséum. Centenaire du Muséum d'histoire naturelle de Paris* (Paris, 1893), 254–288; "Essai monographique sur les Silures du genre Synodontis," in *Nouvelles archives du Muséum d'histoire naturelle*, **7** (1895), 233–284; **8** (1896), 87–178; *La Tortue de Perrault (Testudo indica, Schneider), étude historique* (Paris, [1896]); *Guide à la* *ménagerie des reptiles.* Muséum d'histoire naturelle (Paris, 1897); "Contribution à l'étude des Emydosauriens. Catalogue raisonné des Jacaretinga et Alligator de la collection du Muséum," in *Nouvelles archives du Muséum d'histoire naturelle,* **10** (1898), 143–212; "Contribution à l'étude de la faune ichthyologique de la Guyane," in *Leyden Museum Notes,* **20** (1898–1899), 1–20; *Notice sur les travaux scientifiques de Monsieur L.-L. Vaillant* (Paris, 1900); *Poissons* (Paris, 1905), in Expédition antarctique française, 1903–1905, commandée par le Dr. Jean Charcot. Sciences naturelles: documents scientifiques; *Crocodiles et tortues* (Paris, 1910), pt. I of *Histoire naturelle des reptiles,* XVII of *Histoire physique, naturelle et politique de Madagascar,* with G. Grandidier; "Chéloniens et batracien modèle recueillis par le Dr. Rivet," in *Zoologie* (Paris, 1911), IX of *Mission du service géographique de l'armée pour la mesure d'un arc de méridien équatorial en Amérique du Sud, sous le contrôle scientifique de l'Académie des sciences; Études sur les poissons,* pt. IV of *Recherches zoologiques publiées sous la direction de M. H. Milne-Edwards* (Paris, 1883–1915), in Mission scientifique au Mexique et dans l'Amérique Centrale.

See also the Royal Society *Catalogue of Scientific Papers,* for a detailed list of Vaillant's published works.

II. SECONDARY LITERATURE. See Louis Roule, "Allocution prononcée aux obsèques de M. Léon Vaillant," in *Bulletin du Muséum national d'histoire naturelle,* **20** (1914), 374–375.

DORA B. WEINER

VAILLANT, SÉBASTIEN (*b.* Vigny, Val d'Oise, France, 26 May 1669; *d.* Paris, France, 20 May 1722), *botany.*

Vaillant, who came from a family of farmers, was interested in plants from the time of his youth. It is reported that he cured himself of an intermittent fever at the age of eight. An organist at Pontoise when he was eleven, he studied medicine at the hospital there and in 1688 began to practice surgery at Évreux. In 1690 he joined the army as a surgeon and was present at the battle of Fleurus on 1 July. The following year Vaillant moved to Paris, and in 1692 he established himself as a surgeon at Neuilly, working also at the Hôtel-Dieu in Paris. Upon learning that Tournefort was giving courses at the Jardin Royal des Herbes Médicales, usually called Jardin du Roi and now the Jardin des Plantes, he became an assiduous auditor, arriving on foot from Neuilly at five in the morning. Tournefort quickly noticed his gifted and ardent disciple, who brought to class plants collected on his professional rounds and during excursions directed by Tournefort himself.

Vaillant soon left Neuilly to become secretary to Père de Valois, at whose home he met Guy Fagon, first physician of the king, demonstrator of plants, and later superintendent of the Jardin du Roi. When Fagon arrived, Vaillant was classifying mosses; and Fagon engaged him as secretary. This post gave Vaillant valuable opportunities for collecting plants. The herbarium that he established and steadily expanded was preserved in the Cabinet du Roi until the beginning of the nineteenth century, when it was dispersed in the general herbarium of the Muséum d'Histoire Naturelle, as the whole institution became in the Revolution. Vaillant was put in charge of the garden itself, but Fagon, who highly esteemed his honesty, discretion, and broad botanical knowledge, had him appointed—without his having to request it—assistant demonstrator of plants and then demonstrator of plants. (The latter post had several times been denied to Tournefort.) Vaillant not only had his students collect plants but also lent them his research notes to aid in identification and even allowed them to read his manuscripts.

Louis XIV ordered Vaillant to create a Cabinet de Drogues. Vaillant wished to cultivate exotic plants, however, and Fagon obtained permission from the king to build France's first greenhouse (1714). When it proved too small, a second greenhouse, twice as large, was built in 1717. In the latter year Vaillant substituted for the titular professor at the Jardin du Roi, and his opening lecture (at six in the morning) drew a large audience. He was so well liked by the students that the professor allowed him to continue to give the course. Many scientists accompanied Vaillant on botanical excursions over a fourteen-year period, notably along the coasts of Normandy and Brittany.

Vaillant's unstinting dedication to his work undoubtedly aggravated his asthmatic condition, and his premature death from an unidentified pulmonary disease prevented the publication of some of his manuscripts, notably his inaugural lecture at the Jardin du Roi. In it Vaillant established, on the basis of irrefutable evidence—and for the first time in France—the existence of plant sexuality. (A pistachio tree used in his demonstrations is still alive in the Alpine garden of the Muséum d'Histoire Naturelle.) Also notable are the posthumously published *Catalogue des plantes des environs de Paris,* often called the "petit botanicon," and the *Botanicon parisiense,* properly so called, which was published by Boerhaave from Vaillant's notes.

The genus *Vaillantia* (Tournefort) and the species *Galium vaillantii* and *Bulliardia vaillantii* are named for Vaillant, who was also interested in mosses, lichens, and fungi. The most favorable and best-founded judgment of Vaillant was made by Linnaeus. Responding to criticisms by a number of botanists, including Dillenius and Jussieu, he declared: "He was a great observer, and every day I become more convinced that no one has been more skillful in establishing genera."

BIBLIOGRAPHY

Botanicon parisiense, ou denombrement . . . des plantes qui se trouvent aux environs de Paris, Hermann Boerhaave, ed. (Leiden–Amsterdam, 1927), contains beautiful plates executed by Claude Aubriet and is preceded by a detailed biography of Vaillant and a full list of his writings.

The most recent article on Vaillant is Jacques Rousseau, "Sébastien Vaillant, an Outstanding 18th-Century Botanist," in *Regnum vegetabile*, **71** (1970), 195–228. See also Jean-François Leroy, "La botanique au Jardin des Plantes (1626–1970)," in *Adansonia*, 2nd ser., **11**, pp. 225–250.

P. JOVET
J. MALLET

VALDEN, PAVEL IVANOVICH. See **Walden, Paul.**

VALENCIENNES, ACHILLE (*b.* Paris, France, 9 August 1794; *d.* Paris, 13 April 1865), *zoology.*

Valenciennes, whose father had been an aide to Daubenton since 1784, was born in the Muséum d'Histoire Naturelle in Paris and spent all his life associated with that institution. He attended the Collège de Rouen, but the premature death of his father cut short his further education and brought to an end his hopes to attend the École Polytechnique. Instead, in order to help support his family, Valenciennes became a *préparateur* at the Muséum in 1812. He aided successively Geoffroy Saint-Hilaire, Lamarck, and Cuvier with their zoological collections, and he eventually became an *aide-naturaliste* associated with the chair of reptiles and fish held in turn by Lacépède and Constant Duméril.

Early in Valenciennes's career Cuvier obtained for him the task of classifying the animals described by Humboldt on his journey to Latin America from 1799 to 1803. This was the beginning of a lifelong friendship between Humboldt and Valenciennes. Humboldt acted as a patron for Valenciennes, assisting his entry into the Academy of Sciences in 1844.

Valenciennes's major scientific achievement was his collaboration with Cuvier on the classic work *Histoire naturelle des poissons.* After Cuvier chose him, Valenciennes visited the cabinets of Holland, England, and Germany to obtain additional materials for the work. Cuvier and Valenciennes published eight volumes jointly from 1828 to Cuvier's death in 1832. Valenciennes then continued the series until 1849 with fourteen more volumes. Even so, the work remained incomplete, for the classification of cartilaginous fish had not been treated. Cuvier was responsible for the general scheme of classification, a modification of his classification of fish in *Le règne animal.* Valenciennes excelled at the descriptive aspect of the work. Because of his recognized expertise in the classification and description of fish, he was asked to publish the ichthyology of several scientific voyages of navigation.

In 1832, after a bitterly contested election in which he was opposed by Jean René Constant Quoy, Valenciennes succeeded Henri Ducrotay de Blainville in the chair of annelids, mollusks, and zoophytes at the Muséum. Although he greatly increased the collections associated with his chair, Valenciennes did not specialize in the subject area. He continued to write in all areas of zoology, including zoological paleontology. Although best known as an ichthyologist, his memoirs on mollusks and zoophytes include studies of the simplicity of the gills of the corbicula and lucina as compared to other lamellibranch mollusks, a monograph on the panopea, researches with Frémy on the chemical composition of eggshells in the animal series, and his classification of the gorgoniae based on the composition of the axis rather than on the external form.

Although he planned a large work on the sponges, Valenciennes never published a general work on the areas connected with his chair at the Muséum. A protégé of Cuvier, he tended to exaggerate Cuvier's insistence on facts as opposed to hypotheses. Valenciennes was not an original thinker, and most of his work consists of monographs on genera or descriptions and classifications of new species brought to Paris by travelers. He had a wide knowledge of zoology, but he never synthesized it.

In addition to his position at the Muséum, Valenciennes became master of conferences in zoology at the École Normale Supérieure in 1831 and professor of zoology at the École de Pharmacie in

1856. He married Alphonsine Gottis in 1831. Personally a rather brusque man, he was prone to forming enemies. He has been described by detractors as a "bon gros," corpulent, lazy, and hedonistic.

BIBLIOGRAPHY

I. ORIGINAL WORKS. Valenciennes's only major work is the *Histoire naturelle des poissons*, 22 vols. (Paris, 1828–1849). A list of his memoirs can be found in the Royal Society *Catalogue of Scientific Papers*, VI, 95–97, and VIII, 1141. A more complete listing of his works on fish and reptiles, including the ichthyologies he wrote for several voyages of navigation, can be found in Maurice Blanc, "Travaux ichtyologiques et herpétologiques publiés par Achille Valenciennes," in *Mémoires de l'Institut français d'Afrique noire*, **68** (1963), 71–75. Manuscripts left by Valenciennes are catalogued by Théodore Monad, "Achille Valenciennes et l'Histoire Naturelle des Poissons," *ibid.*, 9–45, also see 34–43. Jean Théodoridés has published a series of more than seventy letters written by Alexander von Humboldt to Valenciennes from 1818 to 1858 in "Une amitié de savants au siècle dernier: Alexandre von Humboldt et Achille Valenciennes (correspondance inédite)," in *Biologie médicale*, **54** (1965), i–cxxix.

II. SECONDARY LITERATURE. The entire *Mémoires de l'Institut français d'Afrique noire*, **68** (1963), is devoted to a collection of historical and ichthyological papers dedicated to Valenciennes (*Mélanges ichtyologiques dédiés à la mémoire d'Achille Valenciennes* [1794–1865]). The article by Théodore Monad (see above) contains an account of Valenciennes's entry into the Academy, a useful bibliography (pp. 43–45), an iconography, a list of manuscript sources, and detailed information on the publication of the *Histoire naturelle des poissons*.

Contemporary biographical studies include L. Hallez, "Muséum d'Histoire Naturelle. Cours de M. Lacaze-Duthiers. Valenciennes," in *Revue des cours scientifique*, **3** (1866), 377–384; and Alphonse Milne-Edwards, "Éloge de M. Valenciennes," in *Journal de pharmacie et de chimie*, 4th ser., **5** (1867), 5–17.

TOBY A. APPEL

VALENTIN, GABRIEL GUSTAV (*b.* Breslau, Prussia [now Wrocław, Poland], 8 July 1810; *d.* Bern, Switzerland, 24 May 1883), *embryology, general and comparative anatomy, physiology.*

Valentin is usually known as Purkyně's most important student, but he early cut his ties to his teacher and worked on problems of his own choice. The only child of Abraham Valentin, a silverware merchant and assistant rabbi in Breslau, and Caroline Bloch, Valentin was equally interested in languages and science as a student at the Maria Magdalena Gymnasium. A knowledge of Hebrew enabled him also to study the Talmud. This, together with the religious traditions observed in his parents' home, instilled in Valentin a firm conviction in the beliefs of his forefathers.

At the age of eighteen Valentin began to study medicine at the University of Breslau, where his most influential teachers were the botanist Nees von Esenbeck and the physiologist Purkyně. After four years he received his medical degree with a dissertation on the formation of muscle tissue, and he passed the state medical examination at Berlin in 1833. His father's death obliged Valentin to begin practicing medicine immediately, in order to earn a living. He found greater satisfaction, however, in the time that he was able to devote to microscopic studies.

Perseverance, a gift for observation, and an outstanding memory were the foundations of Valentin's wide-ranging scientific knowledge. A notable additional asset was his mathematical ability, which was of particular service to him in handling physiological problems. Valentin wrote more than two hundred papers and articles, as well as a number of books, some of which are quite long. Although his initial research centered on the formation of plant and animal tissue, he also was interested in the processes of intracellular movement in plants; and in his study of animals he was particularly concerned with embryology. He experimentally produced double malformations in chick embryos, on which he reported to the Versammlung Deutscher Naturforscher und Aerzte meeting at Breslau in 1833. The following year, Valentin undertook a study of the structure of nerve fibers in the brain and spinal cord, in particular measuring their thickness. This research, however, was hampered by a lack of sufficiently developed techniques.

In the spring of 1834, while conducting research designed to detect eggs in vertebrates, Valentin discovered the ciliated epithelium in the oviduct of rabbits; and with Purkyně he investigated its distribution in various classes of vertebrates. They also demonstrated the influence of chemical substances on the ciliary movement and ascertained that the movement is independent of the nervous system. The importance of this research was recognized in Valentin's election to membership in the Leopoldinisch-Karolinische Deutsche Akademie der Naturforscher. Concurrently he wrote *Handbuch der Entwickelungsgeschichte des Menschen* . . . (1835) and worked on a prize question posed by the French Academy of Sciences in 1833: To determine whether the way in which animal tissues develop can be compared with that of plant tissues. In February 1835 Valentin submitted his answer to the Academy under the title "Histiogenia comparata." This Latin manuscript runs to more than 1,000 quarto pages and includes many illustrations by the author.

In the summer of 1835 tensions developed between Valentin and Purkyně over their use of the same microscope in Purkyně's house. Valentin thereupon sought to obtain an independent post. He received an offer from Dorpat; but there, and in Prussia, his Jewish faith proved to be a handicap. His situation soon improved, however; for in December 1835 the jury of the French Academy of Sciences awarded him the Grand Prix des Sciences Physiques for his histology manuscript. The prize, worth 3,000 gold francs, enabled Valentin to buy a large microscope and to travel to Berlin to see Johannes Müller. More important, however, he was recognized as an outstanding microscopist. He accepted a professorship of physiology and zootomy from the University of Bern, after making sure that he would not be required to abandon his religion. At the age of twenty-six Valentin became the first Jewish professor at a German-language university.

Valentin's prize manuscript was not suitable for publication in the form in which he had submitted it, and he was asked to prepare a shortened version. He did not complete it, however, until the beginning of 1838, because of the time taken up by moving. The rapid advances in cytology during this period obliged him to take into account many new findings of other researchers, so that the shorter version no longer answered the original question; and for this reason it was not published. In fact, the essential contents of Valentin's original manuscript were not published until more than a century later.

In his manuscript of 1834 Valentin designated the fundamental structural units of animal tissue as *granula* and *globuli*. Less frequently he called them *corpora* or *corpuscula*, but it is possible that these names refer only to the nuclei. Terms such as the *granulosa* of the ovarian follicle, the "grain" (*Korn*) layers of the cerebellum and of the retina, and the blood "corpuscles" recall the early years of the cell theory. Valentin provided good examples to illustrate cellular structure: the rudimentary form of the hoof (the blastema of the hoof of domestic animals) and fat cells, which he called *cystae et contentum oleosum*. The *cysta* is therefore the cytoplasm surrounding the fat globules. Valen-

tin mentioned that in cartilage and bones he had seen traces of granules, by which he sometimes meant cells and sometimes their nuclei. (Volf mistakenly alleged that Valentin used the term "cell" as early as 1835, but the passage he cited as proof was actually from the shortened version of 1838.) The manuscript of 1835 does contain clear references to certain similarities between animal and plant tissues, but Valentin did not attribute special significance to them; they simply were not important to him. He even concluded from his study that the development of plant tissue is not comparable to that of animal tissue.

At Bern, Valentin had the use of a small but adequately equipped laboratory in the new anatomical institute. He continued to publish a periodical that he had founded at Breslau, *Repertorium für Anatomie und Physiologie*, which appeared from 1836 to 1843. The sole contributor, he reported the results of his own studies and surveyed the latest physiological literature. For example, from 1836 he used the term "cell" in describing many types of epithelium. Among the structural elements of the conjunctiva, he found nuclei and nucleoli; but he did not apply the term "nucleolus" to the latter, calling them, rather, "a kind of second nucleus within the nucleus."

Valentin pursued his microscopic examination of the structure of nerve tissue with great enthusiasm. Since he clung to his notion of terminal loops of nerves and refused to recognize the occurrence of gray (marrowless) nerve fibers, he became involved in controversies with Johannes Müller and Robert Remak, as well as with Friedrich Heinrich Bidder and Alfred Wilhelm Volkmann.

Valentin also made comparative studies of the sea urchin and of the structure of the electric eel. For his research he devised a double-bladed knife for preparing thin sections, and he was the first to use microincineration in the study of animal tissue (bear spermatozoa in 1839). He also made a number of good observations of the structure of the eye, including the cornea and the ganglionic cells in the nerve fiber layer of the retina. His "Grundzüge der Entwicklung der tierischen Gewebe" is still worth reading.

In relation to his teaching duties, Valentin began to do more research in physiology. He designated the glossopharyngeal nerve as the chief nerve of the sense of taste, and he correctly assessed the effect of the electrically stimulated vagus nerve and of the sympathetic nervous system on stomach contraction. He also developed a highly respected method of determining blood volume, but it proved to be inexact. In extensive experiments on himself, Valentin studied the phenomenon of *perspiratio insensibilis* (1843). He also ventured into the unfamiliar fields of biochemistry and biophysics, but in the latter discipline his results were challenged by Emil du Bois-Reymond (1848).

While traveling to Bern, Valentin had made two lifelong friends during a stop at Frankfurt: Gabriel Riesser, a pioneer in the struggle for Jewish emancipation, and the Göttingen mathematician Moritz Abraham Stern. He made other acquaintances in 1837 while in Paris, where, through the recommendation of Humboldt, he met Pierre Flourens, François Magendie, and Gilbert Breschet. In 1839 he traveled to Nice, where his most important contacts were with Rudolf Wagner. Valentin always welcomed visitors, among whom were Jacob Henle of Zurich and Adolph Hannover of Copenhagen.

Valentin was painstaking and conscientious, but he was more critical of the work of others than of his own. The letters that survive give conflicting images of his personality. He joined the Freemasons at an early date, and he was generous and—sometimes, at least—sociable. Occasionally he was boisterous or ironic; yet he himself was very sensitive, easily offended, sometimes mistrustful, and often dissatisfied. He was self-assertive in dealing with his colleagues and co-workers, and thus his relations with them were very strained at times. Valentin served several times as dean of the medical faculty; but despite more than forty years of teaching at Bern, he was never elected rector of the university.

In 1841 Valentin married his cousin Henriette Samosch; they had three children. Over the years the couple became increasingly estranged, and the children had to be sent out to board because of domestic difficulties.

In 1844 Valentin published the two-volume *Lehrbuch der Physiologie des Menschen*, an undertaking for which his previous study of the specialized literature for the *Repertorium* had prepared him well. A novel aspect of the *Lehrbuch* was the frequent attempt to treat problems mathematically. For example, Valentin mentions the then unknown diastasic property of pancreatic juice and reports his observations on the magnitude of the respiratory pressure (see Rothschuh [1952], pp. 13, 51). A second edition of the textbook soon proved necessary (1847–1850), and in it Valentin demonstrated the existence of the threshold of taste (Rothschuh [1952], p. 105). Valentin's *Grundriss der Physiologie des Menschen* (1846), designed for both independent study

and use with courses, went through four editions by 1855 and, like the *Lehrbuch*, appeared in several translations. These textbooks were replaced after about a decade of popularity by Carl Ludwig's *Physiologie des Menschen* (1852–1856). Another important source for Valentin's positions on contemporary problems was his reviews of the physiological literature in Canstatt's *Jahresberichte über die Fortschritte der gesammten Medicin in allen Ländern* (1844–1865).

The respect that Valentin enjoyed in Bern is evident in his becoming the first Jew to be granted citizenship by that city. His scientific standing is revealed not only in the visits by Henle and others but also in Alfonso Corti's six-month stay at Bern in 1849 in order to learn microscopy from him. Corti, moreover, continued to consult with him until 1854.

As director of the Bern Anatomical Institute from 1853 to 1863, Valentin sought to make permanent the provisional arrangement under which it functioned, even though the trend elsewhere was toward a separation of anatomy and physiology. Younger colleagues, working under his supervision, took over part of the teaching in anatomy; but they were more held back than encouraged. Valentin had undoubtedly assumed too heavy a load of responsibilities, and he attempted to lighten his teaching duties in the laboratory courses by composing a pamphlet for students entitled *Die kunstgerechte Entfernung der Eingeweide des menschlichen Körpers* (1857). Of greater scientific significance were the studies he began at this time on the hibernation of the marmot ("Beiträge zur Kenntnis des Winterschlafes der Murmeltiere"), which merit an examination with the aid of the more exact techniques now available. Valentin's *Untersuchung der Pflanzen- und der Tiergewebe in polarisiertem Licht* (1861) was subjected by W. J. Schmidt to a thorough analysis that will be of interest to specialists in the field. Schmidt also points out that Valentin made a number of innovations that contributed to the development of the microscope.

In January 1863 Valentin's wife died after a long illness. At about the same time, the medical faculty sought to put an end to the union of the chairs of anatomy and physiology that he had imposed. Valentin, who was dean at the time, sought to maintain the status quo by appealing to higher authority, and he did not shrink from threats. The government, however, confined his responsibilities to physiology and named Christoph Theodor Aeby professor of anatomy. When the medical faculty declared in December that Valentin still had its support as dean, he allowed himself to be mollified and remained in office.

Until the fall of 1881, when a heart attack rendered him incapable of working, Valentin continued his scientific research, devoting these years primarily to polarization and spectroscopic studies. The results are recorded in "Histologische und physiologische Studien" (1862–1882). The series, which includes forty-five publications, was completed by four "Beiträge zur Mikroskopie" (1870–1875). Parallel with this research, Valentin made seven studies on the effects of curare and other arrow poisons, especially on muscles and nerves ("Untersuchungen über Pfeilgifte" [1868–1873]). The last fruits of his long research career are presented in twelve "Eudiometrisch-toxikologische Untersuchungen" (1876–1881).

Such extensive activity naturally brought Valentin many honors. In addition to being a member of the Leopoldinisch-Karolinische Deutsche Akademie der Naturforscher, he was a foreign corresponding member of the Académie Royale de Médecine de Belgique, of which he became honorary member in 1862. He was also a corresponding member of the Académie de Médecine of Paris; associate member of the Académie Royale des Sciences, des Lettres et des Beaux-Arts de Belgique; and honorary member of the medical societies of Stockholm, Erlangen, Hamburg, Budapest, Turin, Heidelberg, and Copenhagen, and of several scientific societies. The philosophy faculty of Bern awarded him an honorary doctorate, and he was presented with *Festschriften* on his jubilee dates.

BIBLIOGRAPHY

I. ORIGINAL WORKS. Valentin's earlier writings include *Historiae evolutionis systematis muscularis prolulsio* (Breslau, 1832), his dissertation; "Entdeckung continuierlicher, durch Wimperhaare erzeugter Flimmerbewegungen, als eines allgemeinen Phänomens in den Klassen der Amphibien, Vögel und Säugethiere," in Johannes Müller's *Archiv für Anatomie, Physiologie, und wissenschaftliche Medicin*, **1** (1834), 391–400, written with Purkyně; *Handbuch der Entwickelungsgeschichte des Menschen mit vergleichender Rücksicht der Entwickelung der Säugethiere und Vögel* (Berlin, 1835); "De motu vibratorio animalium vertebratorum," in *Verhandlungen der Leopoldinisch-Carolinischen Akademie der Naturforscher*, **17**, Abt. 2 (1835), 841–854, written with Purkyně; "Über den Verlauf und die letzten Enden der Nerven," *ibid.*, **18**, Abt. 1 (1836), 51–240; *De functionibus nervorum cerebralium et nervi sympathici libri quatuor* (Bern–St. Gallen, 1839); and "Über die Spermatozoen des Bären," in *Verhandlungen der Leopoldinisch-Carolinischen Akademie der Naturforscher*, **19**, Abt. 1 (1839), 237–244.

Subsequent works are Valentin's edition of "Hirn-und Nervenlehre," in S. T. von Sömmering, *Vom Baue des menschlichen Körpers*, IV (Leipzig, 1841); "Beiträge zur Anatomie des Zitteraales (*Gymnotus electricus*)," in *Neue Denkschriften der allgemeinen Schweizerischen Gesellschaft für die gesammten Naturwissenschaften*, **6** (1842), 1–74; "Grundzüge der Entwicklung der tierischen Gewebe," in Rudolf Wagner, ed., *Lehrbuch der speziellen Physiologie* (Leipzig, 1842); *Lehrbuch der Physiologie des Menschen*, 2 vols. (Brunswick, 1844; 2nd ed., 1847–1850); *Grundriss der Physiologie des Menschen* (Brunswick, 1846; 4th ed., 1855), translated into English as *A Textbook of Physiology* (London, 1853); *Die kunstgerechte Entfernung der Eingeweide des menschlichen Körpers* (Frankfurt, 1857); and *Die Untersuchung der Pflanzen- und der Tiergewebe in polarisiertem Licht* (Leipzig, 1861).

Later works include "Beiträge zur Kenntnis des Winterschlafes der Murmelliere," in *Untersuchungen zur Naturlehre des Menschen und der Tierre*, **1–13** (1857–1888); "Histologische und physiologische Studien," in *Zeitschrift für rationelle Medicin*, 3rd ser., **14–36** (1862–1869) and in *Zeitschrift für Biologie*, **6–18** (1870–1882); "Untersuchungen über Pfeilgifte," in Pflüger's *Archiv für die gesammte Physiologie*, **1–7** (1868–1873); "Beiträge zur Mikroskopie," in *Archiv für mikroskopische Anatomie*, **6** (1870), 581–597, **7** (1871), 140–156, 220–238, and **11** (1875), 661–687; and "Eudiometrisch-toxikologische Untersuchungen," in *Archiv für experimentelle Pathologie*, **5–13** (1876–1881).

The MS of "Histiogenia comparata" is in the archives of the Paris Academy of Sciences. It has been published by M. B. Volf, in *Věstník Československé zoologické společnosti*, **6–7** (1938–1939), 476–512; and by E. Hintzsche in *Berner Beiträge zur Geschichte der Medizin und der Naturwissenschaften* (Bern), no. 20 (1963).

II. SECONDARY LITERATURE. See Erich Hintzsche, "Gustav Gabriel Valentin (1810–1883)," in *Berner Beiträge zur Geschichte der Medizin und der Naturwissenschaften* (Bern), no. 12 (1953), with complete bibliography of Valentin's writings; Bruno Kisch, "Gabriel Gustav Valentin," in "Forgotten Leaders in Modern Medicine," in *Transactions of the American Philosophical Society*, n.s. **44** (1954), 142–192; W. J. Schmidt, "Gabriel Gustav Valentin," in Hugo Freund and Alexander Berg, eds., *Geschichte der Mikroskopie*, II (Frankfurt, 1964), 413–422; and Karl E. Rothschuh, *Entwicklungsgeschichte physiologischer Probleme in Tabellenform* (Munich–Berlin, 1952).

ERICH HINTZSCHE

VALENTINE, BASIL, or **Basilius Valentinus,** *chemistry, alchemy, iatrochemistry.*

Supposedly a German Benedictine monk born at

Mainz in 1394, Basil Valentine is said to have been a member of St. Peter's in Erfurt in 1413 and to have been elected prior of the same monastery the following year. Other accounts mention that he traveled widely in Europe and that he made a journey to Egypt late in life.

There is no contemporary evidence for any of the facts relating to Basil Valentine and, indeed, the works attributed to him refer to events that occurred after his death (for example, the discovery of America). Although a number of different individuals have been suggested, the authorship of these texts is most commonly attributed to Johann Thölde, a councillor and salt boiler of Frankenhausen in Thuringia, whose *Haligraphia* (1603 and 1612) closely resembles the *Letztes Testament* (1626), one of the principal works ascribed to Basil Valentine.

The actual author was clearly familiar both with laboratory procedures and mining techniques, and he refers to mines located in Central Europe and elsewhere frequently in the *Letztes Testament*. There are long lists of chemical recipes to be found throughout the Basilian corpus, and it is evident that the author was well aware of methods for the preparation of the three mineral acids. He discussed all of the then known metals as well as preparations that might be made from them, and he gave special attention to the precious metals that he believed could be produced through the transmutation of the less perfect metals. He described the precipitation of copper from solution by iron as an example of natural transmutation. Should it be thought that Basil Valentine need be read primarily for his succinct laboratory directions and observations in nature, one need only refer to his *Zwölff Schlüssel* (1602), a traditional book of alchemical symbolism that was to become one of the most frequently reprinted chemical-alchemical treatises of the seventeenth and eighteenth centuries.

Another work attributed to Basil Valentine, the *Triumph Wagen Antimonii* (1604), has a special significance for several reasons. This work contains a wealth of information on antimony, its ores, and other related metals and minerals, as well as on laboratory procedures in general. In addition, the work is important as the primary source for the many controversial antimonial compounds employed as medicines by seventeenth-century chemical physicians.

Indeed, although the chemical compounds described by Basil Valentine have been the subject of considerable research, their medical influence has not been adequately assessed to date. The *Triumph Wagen Antimonii* and other works by this author are clearly related to the Paracelsian treatises of the period. Here may be found a rather typical call for a new investigation of nature so that we might uncover and better understand the secrets of God's creation. The origin of the metals is described in terms of the three principles (mercury, sulfur, and salt), and the origin of these, in turn, is discussed through reference to a macrocosmic distillation. The emphasis is clearly on an understanding of nature as a whole through chemical operations in the laboratory or through chemical analogies. The macrocosm-microcosm analogy is employed throughout and the significance of medicine is sought on both these levels. The true physician is told to seek out the vital spirits in all things with his knowledge of chemistry. Above all, the different preparations of metals are to be found and their effects are to be determined. It is the chemist who can eliminate the poisonous nature of antimony and make it into fit medicines for human ailments. Again in a fashion reminiscent of Paracelsus, Basil Valentine insisted that the physician may utilize these potent chemical medicines only in union with his knowledge of weights; that is, he must pay attention to proper dosage.

Thus, although Basil Valentine may be properly discussed as one of the more significant chemists of the early seventeenth century, he may also be judged in the context of the contemporary iatrochemical literature. In the latter case he emerges as a rather typical Paracelsian who emphasized the macrocosm-microcosm universe with all of its implications. Nevertheless, this corpus of writings, along with those supposedly written by Isaac and John Isaac Hollandus (also then ascribed to the fifteenth century), was employed by chemists of the seventeenth century who sought to destroy the reputation of Paracelsus. Accepting a fifteenth-century date for Basil Valentine, van Helmont and others were able to accuse Paracelsus of having plagiarized the views of his predecessors. It was partially for this reason, partially for their alchemical appeal, and partially for their genuine chemical value that the works attributed to Basil Valentine were frequently published and translated throughout the seventeenth and the eighteenth centuries.

BIBLIOGRAPHY

I. ORIGINAL WORKS. The most thorough bibliography of the various editions of the works of Basil Valentine is found in James R. Partington, *A History of Chemistry*, II (New York–London, 1961), 190–195. The standard collected edition is the *Chymische Schriften*, which appeared first in two volumes at Hamburg in 1677. Corrected editions appeared in 1694, 1700, and 1717, while the fifth edition of 1740 added a 3rd vol. containing additional tracts. The final editions of 1769 and 1775 were essentially reprints of the fifth edition. In addition to the above, the Latin *Basilii Valentini scripta chymica* appeared in Hamburg in 1700.

Of the specific works mentioned, the *Letztes Testament* appeared first at Jena in two parts in 1626. As a five-part work it appeared first at Strasbourg in 1651. An English version by an anonymous translator appeared at London in 1657 and a new translation by J(ohn) W(ebster) was printed in London in 1671. The *Zwölff Schlüssel* was first printed by Johann Thölde in 1599, and it appeared frequently throughout the seventeenth and the eighteenth centuries. It was translated into Latin in Michael Maier's *Tripus Aureus* in 1618, and it was one of the four texts by Basil Valentine to be included in Jean-Jacques Manget, *Bibliotheca Chemica Curiosa*, II (Geneva, 1702), 409–423. This work appeared in French as *Les douze clefs de philosophie* (Paris, 1624), and in a new translation by Eugène Canseliet (Paris, 1956). *The Twelve Keys* appeared in English as the third part of *The Last Will and Testament of Basil Valentine* (London, 1671), and also in A. E. Waite's translation of *The Hermetic Museum*, I (London, 1893; repr. London, 1953), 315–357.

Johann Thölde's edition of the *Triumph Wagen Antimonii* appeared first at Leipzig in 1604 with a forward by Joachim Tanckius. Many separate German editions appeared throughout the seventeenth and the eighteenth centuries until 1770. The first Latin edition was that made by John Fabre (Toulouse, 1646), but the most important is that with the commentary by Theodor Kerckring (Amsterdam, 1671; 1685). The *Triumphant Chariot of Antimony* was translated first into English by I. H. Oxon. (London, 1660), and again by Richard Russell (London, 1678). A third English translation was made by A. E. Waite (London, 1893; repr. London, 1963).

Additional information on these and other works in the Basilian corpus will be found in the Partington bibliography.

II. SECONDARY LITERATURE. By far the most important survey of the chemistry of Basil Valentine will be found in J. R. Partington, *op. cit.*, 183–203, with a survey of the secondary literature, 183, note 1. Those interested in a traditional alchemical life of Basil Valentine may turn to the final leaves (fols. Ccc i and Ccc ii of the 1700 edition) of the *Chymische Schriften* or, in far more detail (and with a bibliography), in Karl Christoph Schmieder's *Geschichte der Alchemie* (Halle, 1832), repr. with an introduction by Franz Strunz (1927), 197–210. The arguments against the fifteenth-century date of the texts were marshaled by Hermann Kopp in his various publications, but see especially his *Beiträge zur Geschichte der Chemie*, 3 pts. (Brunswick, 1869–1875). Both the references in Partington and in the recently

published *ISIS Cumulative Bibliography. A Bibliography of the History of Science formed from ISIS Critical Bibliographies 1–90. 1913–1965*, Magda Whitrow, ed., 2 vols. (London, 1971), testify to the very limited attention given by scholars to the works attributed to Basil Valentine in this century.

ALLEN G. DEBUS

VALERIANUS, MAGNUS. See Magni, Valeriano.

VALERIO (or **VALERI**), **LUCA** (*b*. Naples, Italy, 1552; *d*. Rome, Italy, 17 January 1618), *mathematics*.

Valerio was the son of Giovanni Valeri, of Ferrara, and Giovanna Rodomano, of Greek extraction. He was brought up on Corfu and was educated in Rome at the Collegio Romano, where Clavius was one of his teachers. He studied philosophy and theology, although his main interest was mathematics. Most of his life was spent at Rome as a teacher, both private and public. Valerio taught rhetoric and Greek at the Collegio Greco and, from 1600 until his death, mathematics at the Sapienza in Rome. Among his private pupils were the future Pope Clement VIII and the poet Margherita Sarrocchi, with whom he apparently had a love affair. For a time he was also corrector of Greek in the Vatican Library. On 7 June 1612 he was elected a member of the Accademia dei Lincei and was active in its affairs until 1616. Apparently Galileo and Valerio had met about 1590 in Pisa; and around 1610 they were conducting a brisk and friendly correspondence, replete with expressions of mutual admiration. On 24 March 1616, however, Valerio was expelled from the Lincei for reasons that are now obscure. We do know that he objected to its wholehearted support for Galileo's Copernicanism in the controversy of 1616, but all the facts of the case are not available. Valerio spent the last two years of his life in obscurity and disgrace. It is a supreme irony that a few years later Galileo came to a similar end, but for the opposite reason. Galileo, however, rose above their common fate, for in his *Discorsi* of 1638 he called Valerio "greatest geometer, new Archimedes of our time."

Valerio's *De centro gravitatis* consists of the application of Archimedean methods to the determination of the volumes and centers of gravity of the various solids of rotation and their segments. One of the most interesting lemmas of the book says in effect that if $\lim x = a$ and $\lim y = b$, and if

$\frac{x}{y} = c = $ constant, then $\frac{a}{b} = \frac{\lim x}{\lim y} = \lim \frac{x}{y} = c$, which is basically the same as lemma IV of book I of Newton's *Principia* and as Cavalieri's principle. In *Quadratura parabolae* Valerio used the known center of gravity of a hemisphere to find that of a segment of a parabola. He then used this result to determine the area of the segment. Valerio's method was that of Archimedes, although he introduced general lemmas to dispense with the cumbersome *reductio ad absurdum* process. Some of his theorems may be said to make implicit use of a limit approach, but outwardly he was strictly finitist.

Valerio was strongly influenced by Commandino and apparently, in his method for finding centers of gravity, also by Maurolico. Among the mathematicians who studied him and spoke highly of him were Cavalieri, Torricelli, and J. C. de la Faille. He also had a direct influence on Guldin, Gregorius Saint Vincent, and Tacquet.

BIBLIOGRAPHY

I. ORIGINAL WORKS. Valerio published three books: *Subtilium indagationum seu quadratura circuli et aliorum curvilineorum* (Rome, 1582), of which there is an apparently unique copy in the Alexandrine Library in Rome; *De centro gravitatis solidorum* (Rome, 1604; Bologna, 1661 [with *Quadratura*]); and *Quadratura parabolae* (Rome, 1606; Bologna, 1661). The *De piramidis et conis* mentioned in some accounts is probably a bibliographical ghost. Valerio's letters to Galileo, Cesi, and Baldi are printed in the Edizione Nazionale of Galileo's works.

II. SECONDARY LITERATURE. The standard source of information on Valerio is G. Gabrieli, "Luca Valerio Linceo e un episodio memorabile della vecchia Accademia," in *Atti dell'Accademia nazionale dei Lincei. Rendiconti*, Cl. di scienze morali, storiche e filologiche, 6th ser., **9** (1933), 691–728, which has a good bibliography. The first modern historian to draw attention to Valerio as a mathematician was C. R. Wallner, "Über die Entstehung des Grenzbegriffes," in *Bibliotheca mathematica*, 3rd ser., **4** (1903), 246–259. Later accounts include H. Bosmans, "Les démonstrations par l'analyse infinitésimale," in *Annales de la Société scientifique de Bruxelles*, **37** (1913), 211–228; and A. Tosi, "De centro gravitatis solidorum di Luca Valerio," in *Periodico di matematiche*, **35** (1957), 189–201. See also H. Wieleitner, "Das Fortleben der Archimedischen Infinitesimalmethoden bis zum Beginn des 17. Jahrh., insbesondere über Schwerpunktbestimmungen," in *Quellen und Studien zur Geschichte der Mathematik, Astronomie und Physik*, Abt. B, Studien, **1** (1931), 201–220.

PER STRØMHOLM

VALLÉE-POUSSIN, CHARLES-JEAN-GUSTAVE-NICOLAS DE LA (*b.* Louvain, Belgium, 14 August 1866; *d.* Louvain, 2 March 1962), *mathematics.*

Vallée-Poussin's father was for nearly forty years professor of mineralogy and geology at Louvain. Young Vallée-Poussin entered the Jesuit College at Mons, but he found the teaching in some subjects, notably philosophy, unacceptable. He turned to engineering, although, after obtaining his diploma, he devoted himself to pure mathematics. Since boyhood he had been encouraged in mathematics by Louis-Philippe Gilbert and in 1891 he became Gilbert's assistant at the University of Louvain. Gilbert died in 1892 and, at the age of twenty-six, Vallée-Poussin was elected to his chair. He remained all his life at Louvain.

Vallée-Poussin made a very happy marriage with the gifted daughter of a Belgian family whom he met on holiday in Norway in 1900.

As the outstanding Belgian mathematician of his generation, Vallée-Poussin received many tributes. In accordance with custom, he was honored by celebrations at Louvain in 1928 after thirty-five years in his chair, and again in 1943 after fifty years. On the former occasion, the king of the Belgians conferred on Vallée-Poussin the rank of baron. The Belgian Royal Academy elected him a member in 1909, and he became an associate member of the Paris Académie des Sciences in 1945. He was also a commander of the Legion of Honor and honorary president of the International Mathematical Union.

Vallée-Poussin's earliest investigations were concerned with topics of analysis suggested by his own teaching. He proved in an elegant and general form theorems in the differential and integral calculus. In 1892 his memoir on differential equations was awarded a *couronne* by the Belgian Royal Academy. He quickly showed his analytical power in a spectacular way by his researches into the distribution of primes. After nearly a century of conjectures and proofs of partial results, the prime number theorem—that $\pi(x)$, the number of primes $p \le x$, is asymptotically $x/\log x$—was proved independently by Hadamard and by Vallée-Poussin in 1896. The two proofs look very different, but each is achieved by difficult arguments of complex function theory applied to the zeta function of Riemann. Vallée-Poussin extended his researches to cover the distribution of primes in arithmetical progressions and primes represented by binary quadratic forms. He also made an advance of the first importance in the original prime number theorem by assigning an upper estimate to the difference between $\pi(x)$ and the logarithmic integral li x, which remained for twenty years the closest known. Apart from his two later papers on the zeta function in 1916, Vallée-Poussin left to others the development of the ideas that he had introduced into the theory of numbers.

Although the proof of the prime number theorem was Vallée-Poussin's highest achievement, his main impact on mathematical thought was his *Cours d'analyse*, a model of style, economy, and lucidity. The sweeping changes that Vallée-Poussin made in successive editions of his work reflected his current interests. The first edition expounded the traditional calculus, differential equations, and differential geometry; it was just too early for the Lebesgue integral. Two sizes of type were used, the larger for a basic course and the smaller for supplementary matter suited to mathematical specialists. In the second edition the part in small type was greatly expanded to take in set theory, measure and the Lebesgue integral, bounded variation, the Jordan curve theorem, and trigonometric series up to the theorems of Parseval des Chênes and Fejér. The third edition of volume I (1914) introduced the Stolz-Fréchet definition of the differentiability of $f(x,y)$. The third edition of volume II was burned when the German army overran Louvain. It would have pursued the discussion of the Lebesgue integral.

Vallée-Poussin, invited to Harvard and to Paris in 1915 and 1916, expanded this work into the Borel tract, *Intégrales de Lebesgue* . . ., which bears the marks of successive refinements of treatment. The second edition of the tract included analytic sets (Lusin, Souslin) and the Stieltjes integral. Vallée-Poussin's *Cours d'analyse* itself reverted after 1919 to a basic course without the small print.

In the decade after 1908 Vallée-Poussin made fundamental advances in the theory of approximation to functions by algebraic and trigonometric polynomials. The fact that any continuous function $f(x)$ can be thus approximated uniformly in a closed interval had been proved in 1885 by Weierstrass by integrating the product of $f(u)$ and a peak function $K(u,x)$, which rises steeply to its maximum at $u = x$. Vallée-Poussin (and Landau independently) applied this singular integral method with $K(u,x)$ of the form

$$\{1 - (u - x)^2\}^n \text{ or } \{\cos \tfrac{1}{2}(u - x)\}^{2n}$$

to obtain results about the closeness of approximation to $f(x)$ by polynomials of assigned degree under hypotheses about f and its derivatives.

The Lebesgue integral gave new life to the theory of trigonometric series, and Vallée-Poussin proved a number of results that have become classic, notably his uniqueness theorem, his test for convergence, and a method of summation that is stronger than all the Cesàro methods.

During the first quarter of the twentieth century, Vallée-Poussin's interests were dominated by the Borel-Lebesgue revolution and were centered on the real variable. (His is the one *Cours d'analyse* that contains no complex function theory.) After 1925 he turned again to the complex variable, in particular to potential theory and conformal representation. He collected his contributions in a book *Le potentiel logarithmique* (1949), the publication of which was held up by the war. By the time the book appeared some of his ideas had been superseded by those of a younger school of French analysts.

BIBLIOGRAPHY

I. ORIGINAL WORKS. A list of Vallée-Poussin's important papers is in *Journal of the London Mathematical Society*, **39** (1964), 174–175.

Books by Vallée-Poussin are *Cours d'analyse infinitésimale*, 2 vols. (Louvain–Paris, 1903–1906; 2nd ed., 1909–1912; 3rd ed., vol. I only, 1914; 4th ed., 1921–1922)—with changes in each of these editions and fewer changes in succeeding editions (vol. 2 of the 7th ed., 1938; vol. I of the 8th ed., 1938); *Intégrales de Lebesgue fonctions d'ensemble, classes de Baire* (Paris, 1916); *Leçons sur l'approximation des fonctions d'une variable réelle* (Paris, 1919); *Leçons de mécanique analytique* (Paris, 1924); *Les nouvelles méthodes de la théorie du potentiel et le problème généralisé de Dirichlet*. Actualités scientifiques et industrielles (Paris, 1937); *Le potentiel logarithmique, balayage et représentation conforme* (Louvain–Paris, 1949).

II. SECONDARY LITERATURE. Obituary notices are by P. Montel, in *Comptes rendus . . . de l'Académie des sciences*, 2 April 1962; and J. C. Burkill, in *Journal of the London Mathematical Society*, **39** (1964), 165–175.

J. C. BURKILL

VALLISNIERI (or **VALLISNERI**), **ANTONIO** (*b.* Trassilico, Garfagnana district, Lucca province, Italy, 3 May 1661; *d.* Padua, Italy, 18 January 1730), *biology, medicine.*

Vallisnieri's father, Lorenzo, was governor of the territory of Camporgiano, Garfagnana, and married Maria Lucrezia de' Davini. He later moved to Trassilico, where Antonio spent his first years and was educated by his father. After attending school in Modena he was sent to a Roman Catholic college in Reggio nell'Emilia, where he studied grammar and rhetoric and received a bachelor's degree in Aristotelian philosophy (1682). On the advice of one of his teachers that Vallisnieri learn other philosophic systems more congenial to his interest in nature, he became a pupil of Malpighi, who was then professor at the medical faculty of the University of Bologna. In 1684 Vallisnieri took his doctorate in medicine and philosophy at Reggio, then returned to Bologna for another year of study with Malpighi. He spent 1687 and 1688 at Venice and Parma, where he completed his medical training. He then settled in Reggio, practicing medicine but spending considerable time collecting and dissecting animals and observing natural phenomena. The results of his experiments on and observations of the generation of insects were published as "Sopra la curiosa origine di molti insetti."

Federico Marcello, a magistrate of the Republic of Venice and one of the "Riformatori dello Studio di Padova," read Vallisnieri's work and persuaded the government of Venice to appoint him to a chair at the University of Padua. On 26 August 1700 Vallisnieri was appointed to the chair of modern experimental philosophy, which was soon changed to that of practical medicine. From 1710 until his death he occupied the first chair of theoretical medicine at Padua. After Lancisi's death in 1720, he declined the posts of first physician to the pope and the first chair of medicine at Turin. Most of Vallisnieri's colleagues at Padua still favored the Scholastic philosophy and were dubious about the experimental method that Vallisnieri used in his scientific investigations. He was clever enough, however, to praise the Scholastic tradition in his inaugural lecture (14 December 1700). The text of the lecture has been lost, but the title is significant: "Studia recentiora non evertunt antiquam medicinam, sed confirmant" ("Recent Studies Do Not Subvert the Old Medicine, They Confirm It"). He was active at Padua for the rest of his life as both teacher and physician, and especially as naturalist; and he assembled a rich library and a large collection of mineralogical, geological, zoological, anatomical, and archaeological objects, which after his death was given by his son to the university.

Known throughout Europe, Vallisnieri was a fellow of many learned academies, including the Royal Society of London (1705). In 1718 Duke Rinaldo I of Modena made him a member of the hereditary nobility (knight), and the city of Reggio included his name on the list of nobility. Vallisnieri's exceedingly varied cultural interests were reflected in verses and in his extensive correspondence (both mostly unpublished) with private citizens as well as university professors.

Vallisnieri married Laura Mattacodi; eleven of their children survived childhood but only three daughters and one son survived their father. The son, named for his father, succeeded him in the chair of theoretical medicine and edited his father's collected works (1733).

Vallisnieri's first important scientific contribution was a complement to Redi's demonstration of the fallacy of the hypothesis of spontaneous generation. In 1668 Redi had shown through precise experiments that flies produced in putrefying flesh do not originate by spontaneous generation but derive from eggs previously laid by other flies of the same species. As for the insects forming galls, he was unable to solve the mystery of their origin and left the possibility that they are generated by the vegetative force of the plants that bear the galls. Malpighi, in *Anatomes plantarum* (1675–1679), had already denied the vegetal origin of insects, observing that females lay the eggs in the plant buds by means of a long ovipositor and considering the galls as tumors produced by the presence of the insect eggs. The fact was confirmed by Vallisnieri, who observed that all parasite insects of plants, whether or not they produce galls, derive from eggs. The same is true of entomophagous insects. Thus Vallisnieri enforced his own opinion on the existence of "a perpetual law of nature that like always generates like." His thought was less clear regarding the generation of the parasites of man and domestic animals. The latter belong to two categories: dipteran insect larvae (flies, oestrids) and true worms (ascarids and tapeworms). The former, originating from eggs introduced from outside, eventually metamorphose into flies. While denying the alleged origin of intestinal worms from earthworms or fruit worms Vallisnieri believed that they are transmitted from mother to child "through the passages that carry chyle for the nourishment of the fetus" or through the milk.

His research on the reproductive systems of man and animals led Vallisnieri to observe tubal motility and the movement of the ends of the fallopian tubes to the ovaries. But his general conclusions were mostly mistaken: he denied the function of spermatozoa in fertilization (and was followed by Spallanzani and many others), and he failed to recognize the significance of the Graafian follicle, believing that the mammalian egg is formed in the corpus luteum. In considering the origin of the embryo, he adhered to the ovistic branch of preformism.

Vallisnieri developed to a considerable extent the theory of the "chain of beings"—the progression and connection of all created things, with man at the apex. He was thus a precursor of the "ladder" established by Charles Bonnet (1779). The chain was interpreted not in what modern biologists would call an evolutionary sense, but merely as a realization of a design preexisting in the mind of God. Such ideas were, nevertheless, forerunners of evolutionary concepts. It is remarkable that Vallisnieri considered man to be related to animals. In one of his letters he speculated on the hypothesis that souls progress in such a way that the beast's soul and man's immortal soul are of equal nature. The letter, which remained unpublished by Vallisnieri and by his son because it would have put them into a very difficult position with the Church, was published by G. Brognolico (1895) and then in part by L. Camerano (1905).

Carlo Francesco Cogrossi, a physician from Crema, published *Nuova idea del male contagioso de' buoi* (1714), dedicated to Vallisnieri, in which he proposed the hypothesis of *contagium vivum*— that a contagious disease such as cattle plague is due to microscopic parasites. Vallisnieri replied in a long letter of the same title, published in *Nuove osservazioni fisiche e mediche* (1715), in which he supported Cogrossi's hypothesis with many personal observations and considerations. These works were a very important step toward understanding the etiology of infectious diseases.

Vallisnieri's curiosity about all natural phenomena led him to make excursions on which he did much geological and geophysical work, including a description of salt waters in Emilia-Romagna, studies of a freshwater spring in the Gulf of Spezia, and investigations of earth movements and the origin of alluvial valleys. In *Dei corpi marini* he accepted Fracastoro's concept that fossil shells found on mountains were there because the land had once been under the sea and had not been carried there by the Flood. In *Lezione accademica*, Vallisnieri rejected the theory that spring water originates from seawater that evaporates and recondenses after being percolated through the earth. He demonstrated with sound arguments that it comes from atmospheric precipitation.

In comparison with contemporary scientific thought, Vallisnieri's work has a very modern character. Following—as Redi had already done— the way opened by Galileo (whom he quotes only twice) and Francis Bacon (whom he also quotes) he rejected Scholastic knowledge and trusted solely in direct observation and in experiments. His evaluation of the statements of the ancient naturalists, and especially of Aristotle, was critical and objective. A very important characteristic of Vallisnieri's work was the constant search for general laws and the denial of every miraculous or occultist interpretation of natural phenomena. Even monsters, he believed, must have their laws; even errors have their fixed terms. Vallisnieri was thus one of the first modern naturalists to have a clear awareness of the character of scientific phenomena. Because the static design that he discovered in natural objects reflected the mind of God, Vallisnieri's outlook was essentially still Aristotelian and compatible with Christian belief, while containing the germs of future scientific development.

BIBLIOGRAPHY

I. ORIGINAL WORKS. All of Vallisnieri's works, including many letters on scientific subjects, were reprinted in *Opere fisico-mediche stampate e manoscritte del . . . Antonio Vallisneri raccolte da Antonio suo figliuolo*, 3 vols. (Venice, 1733).

His writings include "Sopra la curiosa origine di molti insetti," in G. Albrizzi, *Galleria di Minerva* (Venice, 1700); *Considerazioni ed esperienze intorno alla generazione dei vermi ordinari del corpo umano* (Padua, 1710, 1726); *Considerazioni intorno al creduto cervello di bue impietrito* (Padua, 1710); *Esperienze ed osservazioni intorno alla origine, sviluppo e costumi dei vari insetti* (Padua, 1713); *Istoria del camaleonte affricano* (Venice, 1713); *Nuove osservazioni ed esperienze intorno alla ovaia scoperta ne' vermi tondi dell'uomo e de' vitelli, con varie lettere* (Padua, 1713); *Varie lettere spettanti alla storia medica e naturale* (Padua, 1713); *Lezione accademica intorno all'origine delle fontane* (Venice, 1715); *Nuove osservazioni fisiche e mediche fatte nella costituzione verminosa ed epidemica seguita nelle cavalle, cavalli e puledri del Mantovano e del Dominio di Venezia* (Venice, 1715); *Dei corpi marini che sui monti si trovano* (Venice, 1721); *Istoria della generazione dell'uomo e degli animali, se sia da' vermicelli spermatici, o dalle* (Venice, 1721); and *Dell'uso e dell'abuso delle bevande e bagnature calde e fredde* (Modena, 1725; Naples, 1727).

A chapter of *Esperienze ed osservazioni intorno all'origine . . .*, "Ragionamento dell'estro dei poeti e dell'estro degli armenti," has been republished separately (Rome, 1885).

The location of the MSS and correspondence of Vallisnieri is given by B. Brunelli (see below).

II. SECONDARY LITERATURE. The best source for Vallisnieri's biography is Giannartico di Porcia, "Notizie della vita e degli studi del Kavalier Antonio Vallisnieri tratte dalle memorie di lui vivente," in *Opere fisico-*

mediche . . ., xli–lxxx. Further information is in Nicolò Papadopoli, *Historia gymnasii Patavini*, I (Venice, 1726), 169 ff.; Angelo Fabroni, *Vitae italorum doctrina excellentium, qui saeculi XVII et XVIII floruerunt* (Pisa, 1778–1805), VII, 9–90; Girolamo Tiraboschi, *Biblioteca modenese* (Modena, 1781–1786), V, 322–338; G. B. Venturi, *Storia di Scandiano* (Modena, 1822), 143 ff.; Camillo Ugoni, biography of Vallisnieri in E. de Tipaldo, ed., *Biografia degli italiani illustri nelle scienze, lettere ed arti*, III (Venice, 1836), 460–466; and Bruno Brunelli, *Figurine e costumi nella corrispondenza di un medico del Settecento (Antonio Vallisnieri)* (Milan, 1938).

On his scientific and medical work, see Luigi Configliachi, *Intorno agli scritti del cav. Antonio Vallisnieri* (Padua, 1836); Ercole Ferrario, *Su la vita e gli scritti di Antonio Vallisneri* (Milan, 1854); Bernardino Panizza, *Di un autografo inedito del Vallisnieri sopra la peste bovina* (Padua, 1864); Lorenzo Camerano, "Antonio Vallisnieri e i moderni concetti intorno ai viventi," in *Atti dell'Accademia delle scienze*, 2nd ser., **55** (1905), 69–112; Joseph Franchini, "Antonio Vallisnieri on the Second Centenary of His Death," in *Annals of Medical History*, n.s. **3** (1931), 58 ff.; and *Il metodo sperimentale in biologia da Vallisneri ad oggi*, symposium held at the University of Padua on the third centenary of Vallisnieri's birth (Padua, 1962), supp. to *Atti e memorie dell'Accademia patavina di scienze, lettere ed arti*, **73**.

On the spelling of the name, see D. Carbone and L. Castaldi, "Vallisnieri o Vallisneri?" in *Rivista di storia delle scienze mediche e naturali*, **19** (1937), 306; B. Brunelli and L. Castaldi, "Ancora su Vallisnieri o Vallisneri," *ibid.*, **20** (1938), 37–38; and P. Capparoni, "Di nuovo su Vallisnieri o Vallisneri," *ibid.*, 85.

GIUSEPPE MONTALENTI

VALMONT DE BOMARE, JACQUES-CHRISTOPHE (*b.* Rouen, France, 17 September 1731; *d.* Paris, France, 24 August 1807), *mineralogy, natural history.*

The extensive writings and public lectures of Valmont de Bomare made him one of the most influential popularizers of natural history studies in France during the later years of the Enlightenment.

Valmont de Bomare's father was an *avocat* of the *parlement* of Rouen and had planned a legal career for his son, who was a brilliant student, particularly of the classics. The works of Aristotle and Pliny influenced Valmont de Bomare to turn to the sciences, however, and he studied pharmacy and chemistry at Rouen before going to Paris in 1751. There, he formulated a plan for developing a comprehensive course of lectures in natural history.

Aware of the fact that he needed to acquire a broader and deeper knowledge of this vast area, he obtained a commission as traveling naturalist for the government from Voyer d'Argenson, then minister of war. This quasi-diplomatic status permitted him to make extended visits to most of Europe during the next twelve years. On these journeys Valmont de Bomare studied the geology and mineralogy of the countries he visited, and he inspected mines and chemical and metallurgical works in addition to meeting foreign scientists. In July 1756 he introduced at the Jardin des Plantes his projected public course in natural history, which was highly successful, and which he continued to offer yearly until 1788. As a result of his activities he met Buffon, Daubenton, Nollet, Guillaume-Francois Rouelle, d'Holbach, d'Alembert, and Diderot.

In 1762 Valmont de Bomare published a two-volume work entitled *Minéralogie, ou nouvelle exposition du règne minéral*. In it, he described minerals and arranged them into nine classes on the basis of their external characteristics and resistance to the action of fire and water, depending to a great extent on the prior classification of Johan Wallerius. His most important work was his *Dictionnaire raisonné universal d'histoire naturelle*, first published in five volumes in 1764. Four enlarged editions of this work subsequently appeared, the last in fifteen volumes in 1800. Valmont de Bomare's *Dictionnaire* was highly successful in encouraging the popular study of natural history, and it served as a model for all similar works.

In 1769 Valmont de Bomare accepted the position as head of the cabinet of physics and natural history of the Prince de Condé at Chantilly. Unfortunately, he merged his own collections with those of the prince, and during the Revolution they were all confiscated. At that time, afraid of being compromised, he destroyed all of the diaries of his various journeys and his correspondence with such luminaries as Linnaeus and Rousseau.

In 1796 Valmont de Bomare was appointed professor of natural history at the École centrale in the Rue Saint-Antoine, and he remained in that position until 1806 when he became assistant headmaster of the Lycée Charlemagne. When the Institut de France was established in 1795 he was named associate member of the mineralogy section. But he failed in his bid to become a member of the first class after the death of Jean d'Arcet in 1801.

Valmont de Bomare did not produce any original

scientific work. In the 1760's he read three papers to the Académie des Sciences, two of which were subsequently published in the *Mémoires de mathématique et de physique*. The first was a description of certain pyrite and marcasite deposits in the Palatinate; the second concerned a process of refining camphor employed in Holland; and the third treated a Dutch method of refining borax. His scientific reputation was earned, instead, through his lectures and scientific writings.

BIBLIOGRAPHY

I. ORIGINAL WORKS. Valmont de Bomare described the mineral and fossil collection that he had accumulated during his travels in his *Catalogue du cabinet d'histoire naturelle de M. Bomare de Valmont* [sic] (Paris, 1758). His *Minéralogie, ou nouvelle exposition du règne minéral*, 2 vols. (Paris, 1762; 2nd ed., 1774), was translated into German and published (Dresden, 1769). His *Dictionnaire raisonné universel d'histoire naturelle* appeared in five editions, 5 vols. (Paris, 1764), 6 vols. (Verdun, 1768–1770), 9 vols. (Paris, 1775), 15 vols. (Lyons, 1791), and 15 vols. (Lyons, 1800). His two published articles were "Mémoire sur les pyrites et sur les vitriols," in *Mémoires de mathématique et de physique, présentés à l'Académie Royale des Sciences*, **5** (1768), 617–630; and "Mémoire sur le raffinage du camphre," *ibid.*, **9** (1780), 470–480.

II. SECONDARY LITERATURE. There is an obituary of Valmont de Bomare in *Le moniteur universel* (23 September 1807). Other biographical articles are *Biographie générale*, XLV (1870), 894–895; *Biographie universelle*, XLII (1854), 513–514; and *Biographie universelle et portative des contemporains*, IV (1836), 1469.

JOHN G. BURKE

VALSALVA, ANTON MARIA (*b*. Imola, Italy, 17 June 1666; *d*. Bologna, Italy, 2 February 1723), *anatomy*.

Valsalva came from a distinguished and well-to-do family. The son of Pompeo Valsalva, a goldsmith, and Caterina Tosi, he was the third of eight children. Valsalva was educated by the Jesuits in the humanities, mathematics, and natural sciences, the latter arousing his interest in animal morphology and entomology. He subsequently moved to Bologna, where he studied philosophy with Lelio Trionfetti, mathematics with Pietro Mengoli, and geometry with Rodelli.

Valsalva may be considered a Galilean through Borelli and thence through Malpighi, founder of microscopic anatomy and Valsalva's teacher at Bologna University. Malpighi deeply respected Valsalva, who was his favorite pupil and who greatly admired Malpighi.

On 10 June 1687, Valsalva became a doctor of medicine and philosophy, defending the dissertation "Sulla superiorità delle dottrine sperimentali." His name was then entered on the roll of Bolognese doctors and, with Santi Giorgio, Guglielmini, Giacomo Beccari, and Albertini, he began to attend scientific meetings at Eustachio Manfredi's house that led to the founding of the Accademia degli Inquieti. In 1697 he became public engraver of anatomy, and in 1704 he published *De aure humana tractatus*. A year later Valsalva was named lecturer and demonstrator in anatomy, a post he held for the rest of his life.

Valsalva was devoted to teaching and scientific research, as well as to the practice of medicine. He spent much time in the anatomical amphitheater, the unhealthy air of which affected his health. Seized by such a *furor studendi* that he even made an organoleptic evaluation of exudates, Valsalva observed that the serum produced by gangrene was so acrid that, after tasting it, its extreme sourness irritated the papillae of his tongue for an entire day.

Valsalva's scientific integrity was noteworthy. When he was elected, with Vittorio Stancari, by the Bologna Academy as censor of the first volume of Morgagni's *Adversaria anatomica*, he asked for time in order to be able to give a considered and precise opinion. When the objection was raised that this would delay publication of the book, Valsalva replied, "That's how I am . . . . I love Morgagni, but I love the truth more."

On 22 April 1709, at the age of forty-three, Valsalva married Elena Lisi, the seventeen-year-old daughter of a noble Bolognese senatorial family; they had six children, three of whom died young. In 1721, during a consultation with Morgagni in Venice, he suffered a temporary dyslalia, a symptom of the fatal apoplexy that struck him two years later.

Valsalva's famous *De aure humana tractatus*, with the anatomical letters that constitute an extensive commentary, is provided with plates that clearly illustrate the parts of the ear. The preparation of these drawings was probably influenced by Eustachi's plates, which Valsalva greatly admired. His strongest incentive for devoting attention to the human ear probably came from Galileo's new methodological approach and from his own interest in revising acoustics.

The treatise is in two parts, each divided into three chapters; the first part is mainly anatomical and the second physiological, in the Galenic sense of the usefulness of the individual parts. Valsalva divides the ear into the outer, middle, and inner parts. He provides the first detailed and precise description of the outer auricular muscles, based on a wax cast of the external auditory duct, and reproduces its course and diameters. In the middle ear he clearly illustrates the hammer and the tube, which he called the Eustachian tube, in which he recognizes cartilaginous, membranous, and bony components, as well as the muscles of the bones in the middle ear. He describes the morphology of the pharyngeal musculature and the muscle fasciae controlling the Eustachian tube, thus anticipating the concept of the unity of otorhinopharyngeal pathology from the morphological standpoint. (The importance of nasopharyngeal conditions in relation to diseases of the ear is fully recognized today.) He next gives careful measurements of the diameter of the eardrum in relation to important formations, such as the windows of the labyrinth wall and the semicircular canals. He was the first to use the term "labyrinth" for the whole of the inner ear, although his idea of the membranous labyrinth was still confused (he did, however, recognize the existence of the labyrinthine liquid).

Valsalva's treatment of the physiology of hearing contains some aspects of particular interest. He emphasizes the usefulness of the structure of the pinna, the auditory tube, and the ceruminous glands. Valsalva does not attribute special importance to the eardrum; in fact, hearing continues even if the membrane is perforated. In the transmission of sound greater importance is given to the bones of the middle ear, considered as a series of levers transmitting the sound to the labyrinth. The function of the labyrinth, similar to that described by Duverney, is distinguished in Valsalva's conception by his failure to consider the lamina cochleae or the semicircular canals as organs that perceive sound; rather, he attributes this function to the *zonae sonorae*, interpreted as the ultimate branches of the auditory nerve. The semicircular canals, as well as the cochlea, are viewed as purely acoustic organs, in accordance with a theory valid until the early nineteenth century. For Valsalva, as for Socrates, the sense of hearing can receive all sounds without becoming overloaded.

Valsalva was an extremely skilled anatomist and pathologist, a fine physician, and an excellent surgeon for a quarter-century in the Bolognese hospitals, especially Sant' Orsola. He was responsible for establishing the hospital institutes and for regulating the courses of study. As a surgeon he antici-

pated the importance of nephrectomy and splenectomy, and did work in ophthalmology, rhinology, and vasal and tumor surgery.

The procedure described in *De aure* and revived by Morgagni in *De sedibus*, which consists of making the patient exhale violently with mouth and nose closed, is still known as Valsalva's test and has acquired importance in modern cardiovascular symptomatology. It was originally used to remove foreign bodies from the ear and to improve hypacusis.

Valsalva has a place in the history of psychiatry for having been among the first to call for, and in part to implement, humanitarian treatment of the insane, preceding Vincenzo Chiarugi and Philippe Pinel. He considered madness to be analogous to organic disease.

BIBLIOGRAPHY

In addition to *De aure humana tractatus* (Bologna, 1704), a complete edition of Valsalva's writings, edited by Morgagni, was published posthumously in 2 vols. (Venice, 1740).

The first and fundamental biography also was written by Morgagni, *De vita et scriptis Antonii Mariae Valsalvae commentariolum* (Venice, 1740). See also the collection *Terzo centenario della nascita di Antonio Maria Valsalva* (Imola, 1966); G. Bilancioni, "La figura e l'opera di Valsalva," in his *Sulle rive del Lete* (Rome, 1930), 77–100; P. Capparoni, "Antonio Maria Valsalva," in *Profili bio-bibliografici di medici e naturalisti celebri italiani dal secolo XV al secolo XVIII* (Rome, 1932), 92–94; and P. Ravanelli, *A. M. Valsalva (1666–1723) anatomico-medico-chirurgo-primo psichiatra* (Imola, 1966).

LORIS PREMUDA

VALTURIO, ROBERTO (*b.* Rimini, Italy, February 1405; *d.* Rimini, August 1475), *military technology, diffusion of knowledge.*

Little is known about Valturio's life. The son of Cicco di Jacopo de' Valturi, he received a good education at Rimini and quickly mastered Greek and Latin. For a long time he served as apostolic secretary to Pope Eugene IV, a post once held by his father. In 1446 or 1447 Valturio entered the service of the ruler of Rimini, Sigismondo Pandolfo Malatesta. As a private secretary with some influence at court, he was an intermediary between Sigismondo and the artists and scholars attracted to his court. Valturio was not, as has sometimes been supposed, a military engineer or an architect.

Nor did he participate in planning the citadel of Rimini, Rocca Malatestiana.

Nevertheless, at Sigismondo's request, Valturio wrote a treatise on the art of war, *Elenchus et index rerum militarium*. Most likely completed between 1455 and 1460, it is known by the briefer title *De re militari*. Valturio undertook the task more as a man of letters and as a humanist scholar than as an expert in the subject. The work consists of twelve books that treat the art of war both generally and from a historical point of view. The most fully illustrated book is the tenth, on offensive and defensive weapons. The work appeared during the transition from the old military technology to the new one based on gunpowder. Valturio treats mainly Roman and medieval military techniques, more recent ones receiving only cursory coverage in the text, although they are somewhat more adequately presented in the illustrations. Book X contains accounts of siege towers, war chariots, screws for breaking iron gratings, catapults, and battering rams; and book XI covers ships, pontoons, and life belts. Firearms are discussed but are relegated to a subordinate role.

Valturio also presents unusual objects of the kind often found in fourteenth- and early fifteenth-century manuscripts on the art of war: an elbow-shaped weapon in which the bolt and chamber are arranged perpendicular to each other; a storming wagon moved by windwheels; a monstrous war machine with a dragon's head, similar to one depicted several decades later in a relief done at Urbino by Francesco di Giorgio Martini; and a completely sealed submarine propelled by paddle wheels, which certainly was never built. Valturio's sources were primarily ancient authors, but he also drew on a few contemporary and—for the fantastic devices—late medieval writers.

The first printed edition of Valturio's work (1472) was a masterpiece of typography and woodcut. The woodcuts (or at least the drawings) were formerly attributed to Matteo de' Pasti; but they may have been done, as E. Rodakiewicz has proposed, by Fra Giovanni Giocondo Veronese. Military leaders of the period held the book in high esteem, and Leonardo da Vinci copied passages of the text and commented on them. Some of the manuscripts, such as those at Dresden and Munich, which contain very fine drawings, may have been produced after the first printed edition and in fact were based upon it.

After Sigismondo's death in 1468, Valturio remained at the court of Rimini under his son and successor, Roberto. According to the investigation made by A. F. Massèra, Valturio died at Rimini in August 1475. In 1484, during the reign of Roberto's successor, Pandolfo IV Malatesta, Valturio's remains were placed in the Church of San Francesco, which in 1446 had been renovated by Leone Battista Alberti into the Tempio Malatestiano.

BIBLIOGRAPHY

I. ORIGINAL WORKS. *De re militari* exists in 22 MSS held at Cesena (Bibl. Malatestiana), Dresden (Landes-Bibl.), Florence (Bibl. Riccardiana and Bibl. Laurenziana), Milan (Bibl. Ambrosiana), Modena (Bibl. Estense), Munich (Bayerische Staatsbibl.), London (British Museum), and seven other libraries (see Rodakiewicz). It has appeared in various eds. and was first printed as *Elenchus et index rerum militarium* (*De re militari*) (Verona, 1472), with 82 woodcuts (Hain-Copinger 15847 = Klebs 1014/1). The 2nd ed. (Verona, 1483) contains 96 woodcuts, copied from those in the 1472 ed. (Hain-Copinger 15848 + Klebs 1014/2). The work also appeared in an Italian trans. (Verona, 1483; Hain-Copinger 15849 = Klebs 1015/1); further Latin eds. (Paris, 1532, 1533, 1534, 1535, 1555); and a French trans. by Loys Meigret, *Les douze livres de Robert Valturin touchant la discipline militaire* (Paris, 1555).

II. SECONDARY LITERATURE. See the following, listed chronologically: C. Yriarte, *Un condottiere au XVe siècle* (Paris, 1882), 128–132, 263–267; M. Jähns, *Geschichte der Kriegswissenschaften*, pt. 1 (Munich, 1889), 358–362; L. Olschki, *Geschichte der neusprachlichen wissenschaftlichen Literatur*, I (Leipzig, 1919), 131–132; A. F. Massèra, "Quando morì Roberto Valturio?" in *Giornale storico della letteratura italiana*, **75** (1920), 118–119; H. T. Horwitz, "Mariano und Valturio," in *Geschichtsblätter für Technik und Industrie*, **9** (1922), 38–40; L. Hain, *Repertorium bibliographicum*, II, pt. 2 (Berlin, 1925), no. 15847 and supp. edited by W. A. Copinger, pt. 1 (Berlin, 1926); A. F. Massèra, *Roberto Valturio* (Pesaro, 1927); A. C. Klebs, "Incunabula scientifica et medica," in *Osiris*, **4** (1938), no. 1014/1; the entry for Valturio in *Enciclopedia biografica e bibliografica italiana*, ser. 50 (Milan, 1939), 314–315; E. Rodakiewicz, "The *editio princeps* of Valturio's *De re militari* in Relation to the Dresden and Munich mss.," in *Maso Finiguerra*, **5** (1940), 14–82; F. Babinger, *Mehmed der Eroberer und seine Zeit* (Munich, 1953), 210, 214–215, 552; and B. Gille, *Les ingénieurs de la Renaissance* (Paris, 1964), 78–80, 235–236.

FRIEDRICH KLEMM

VALVERDE, JUAN DE (*b*. Amusco, Palencia, Spain, *ca*. 1520; *d*. Rome [?], Italy, *ca*. 1588), *medicine, anatomy.*

Few reliable biographical sources are extant, although Valverde's works contain some information. It is believed that he studied humanities and philosophy at Valladolid University but, like most Spanish scholars of his time, went to Italy after graduation. He received anatomical training at Padua for several years under Vesalius and Colombo until 1543 and became assistant to the latter when he went to Pisa in 1544. It may be assumed that Valverde also accompanied Colombo to Rome in 1548 and that he settled there, for he was one of the prosectors at the autopsy of Cardinal Cibò in 1550. By 1551 Valverde had finished *De animi et corporis sanitate tuenda libellus*, dedicated to Cardinal Verallo. Shortly afterward he became physician to Cardinal Álvarez de Toledo, general inquisitor of Rome; and it was while holding this office that he wrote the anatomical treatise *Historia de la composición del cuerpo humano*. While teaching medicine at the Santo Spirito Hospital in 1555, Valverde was among those considered for the post of papal physician, which was given to another Spaniard, Juan de Aguilera.

It has been stated that in 1558 Valverde visited Amusco, carrying special papal indulgences for the town's church. The credit given by Valverde to Antonio Tabo de Albenga in the first Italian version of his *Historia* (1559) could be interpreted to mean that Valverde had married into the Tabo family. He was alive in 1586, when his engraved portrait first appeared in the edition of the *Historia* published in that year; but he probably was dead by 1589, when Michele Colombo, son of Realdo, published the Latin version of the work. The records for 1602 of the St. Sebastian Brotherhood who cared for the sick poor at Amusco contain a grateful mention of "the late" Doctor Juan de Valverde.

Valverde's *De . . . sanitate tuenda* contains sound doctrine on personal hygiene and shows good knowledge of classical sources; but it was the *Historia*, published thirteen years after Vesalius' *Fabrica*, that brought him fame. Valverde based his illustrations on Vesalius', although he offered fifteen new ones and improved Vesalius' with copperplates engraved by Gaspar Becerra; he also made more than sixty corrections and additions to Vesalius' work, including the description of the stapes of the ear, the short palmar muscle, the human uterus, and in particular the true nature of the cardiac septum. On the basis of experiments performed with Realdo Colombo, Valverde corrected Galen's and Vesalius' idea that blood passed through the septum from the right ventricle to the left, and he gave an accurate and correct description of the pulmonary circuit of the blood. His text ran to thirteen editions and was printed in preference to Vesalius'. Arturo Castiglioni stated that Valverde's *Historia* was the most widely read and studied book of the Renaissance.

BIBLIOGRAPHY

I. ORIGINAL WORKS. Valverde's published writings are *De animi et corporis sanitate tuenda libellus* (Paris, 1552; Venice, 1553); *Historia de la composición del cuerpo humano* (Rome, 1556), Italian trans. by Valverde (Rome, 1559, 1560; Venice, 1586, 1606, 1608, 1682), Latin trans. by Michele Colombo (Venice, 1589, 1607); and *Vivae imagines* (Antwerp, 1566, 1572 [colophon dated 1579]), also in Dutch (Antwerp, 1568, 1647).

II. SECONDARY LITERATURE. See Luis Alberti López, *La anatomía y los anatomistas españoles del Renacimiento* (Madrid, 1948); Victor Escribano García, *La anatomía y los anatomistas españoles del siglo XVI* (Granada, 1902); César Fernández-Ruiz, "Estudio biográfico sobre el Dr. D. Juan Valverde, gran anatómico del siglo XVI, y su obra," in *Clínica y laboratorio*, **66** (1958), 207–240; and Francisco Guerra, "Juan de Valverde de Amusco," in *Clio medica*, **2** (1967), 339–362.

FRANCISCO GUERRA

VAN DE GRAAFF, ROBERT JEMISON (*b.* Tuscaloosa, Alabama, 20 December 1901; *d.* Boston, Massachusetts, 16 January 1967), *physics*.

Van de Graaff was born and raised in the cotton country near Tuscaloosa. He studied engineering at the University of Alabama, where he earned the B.S. in 1922 and M.S. in 1923, and physics at the Sorbonne and at Oxford, where he earned the Ph.D. in 1928, and where he conceived the invention of his belt-charged electrostatic high-voltage generator. He was at the threshold of his scientific career when, as a National Research fellow at Princeton, he constructed the first working model of the generator, operating at 80,000 volts, in 1929.

Under the encouragement of Karl T. Compton, then president of Massachusetts Institute of Technology, Van de Graaff came to MIT as a research associate in 1931 to start a series of developments of his invention, for the precisely controllable acceleration of charged nuclear particles and electrons to high velocities for nuclear-physics research. He became associate professor of physics in 1934, continuing in that position until he resigned from MIT in 1960.

With John G. Trump, later to become professor of electrical engineering, Van de Graaff adapted the principles of his high-voltage generator to the production of intense, penetrating X rays for the precise treatment of deep-seated tumors. The first clinical installation was a huge 1-MeV X-ray generator at the Huntington Memorial Hospital in Boston, in 1937. Van de Graaff's association with Trump developed into a close one, enduring until his death.

During World War II, Van de Graaff was the director of the MIT High Voltage Radiographic Project, sponsored by the Office of Scientific Research and Development. In association with one of his protégés, William W. Buechner, he led in the development of the electrostatic generator for the U.S. Navy to use in the radiographic examination of heavy ordnance. Five 2-MeV X-ray generators were constructed for the navy during the war. The experience gained in this project became a basis for the eventual commercial manufacture of Van de Graaff particle accelerators.

Trump and Van de Graaff founded High Voltage Engineering Corporation in late 1946, again with the capable guidance of Compton. Denis M. Robinson, formerly head of the electrical engineering department at the University of Birmingham, England, was appointed president of the company. Van de Graaff served as director and chief physicist (later chief scientist) of the organization, and he devoted his full time to the company after his resignation from MIT.

High Voltage Engineering Corporation was the first company organized with the express purpose of manufacturing particle accelerators. With the counsel of both Van de Graaff and Trump, and under Robinson's leadership, it made a succession of advances in accelerator technology for nuclear physics, radiation therapy, and the industrial applications of electrons and X rays. Van de Graaff urged the company to undertake the important development of the tandem principle of particle acceleration (originally invented by Willard Bennett in 1937 and rediscovered by Luis W. Alvarez in 1951).

In the late 1950's Van de Graaff invented the insulating-core transformer, which can generate powerful direct currents at higher voltages than possible with the conventional transformer-rectifier systems, for application in industrial processing with high-energy electrons. Modifications of this principle are used also for power-factor correction in the transmission of high-voltage power.

Toward the end of his life, Van de Graaff concentrated on the development of a means for accelerating heavy ions, utilizing the tandem principle, with the objective of providing physicists with a complete freedom in choosing target and projectile nuclei. One ambition, frustrated by his death, was to accelerate uranium nuclei to sufficiently high velocities so that they would coalesce with stationary uranium nuclei, thus possibly opening up the field of synthesizing transplutonium isotopes.

BIBLIOGRAPHY

I. ORIGINAL WORKS. Published works by Van de Graaff are "A 1,500,000 Volt Electrostatic Generator," in *Physical Review,* **38** (1931), 1919–1920; "Experiments on the Elastic Single Scattering of Electrons by Nuclei," *ibid.,* **69** (1946), 452–459, with W. W. Buechner and H. Feshbach; "Calorimetric Experiment on the Radiation Losses of 2-MeV Electrons," *ibid.,* **70** (1946), 174–177, with W. W. Buechner; "Further Experiments on the Elastic Single Scattering of Electrons by Nuclei," *ibid.,* **72** (1947), 678–679, with W. W. Buechner, E. A. Burrill, H. Feshbach, and A. Sperduto; "An Investigation of Radiography in the Range From 0.5 to 2.5 Million Volts," ASTM *Bulletin,* no. 155 (1948), 54–64, with W. W. Buechner, E. A. Burrill, H. Feshbach, L. R. McIntosh, and A. Sperduto; "Electrostatic Generators for the Acceleration of Charged Particles," in *Progress in Physics,* **11** (1948), 1–18, with W. W. Buechner and J. G. Trump; "Irradiation of Biological Materials by High-Energy Roentgen Rays and Cathode Rays," in *Journal of Applied Physics,* **19** (1948), 599–604, with J. G. Trump; "Thick-Target X-Ray Production in the Range From 1250 to 2350 Kilovolts," in *Physical Review,* **74** (1948), 1348–1352, with W. W. Buechner, E. A. Burrill, and A. Sperduto; "Secondary Emission of Electrons by High-Energy Electrons," *ibid.,* **75** (1949), 44–45, with J. G. Trump; "Secondary Electron Emission From Metals Under Positive Ion Bombardment in High Extractive Fields," in *Journal of Applied Physics,* **23** (1952), 264–266, with J. G. Trump and E. W. Webster; "Tandem Electrostatic Accelerators," in *Nuclear Instruments and Methods,* **8** (1960), 195–202; "High-Voltage Acceleration Tube Utilizing Inclined-Field Principles," in *Nature,* **195** (1962), 1292–1293, with P. H. Rose and A. B. Wittkower; and "Electrostatic Acceleration of Very Heavy Ions, With Resulting Possibilities for Nuclear Research," in *Bulletin. American Physical Society* (Mexico City meeting, August 29, 1966).

II. SECONDARY LITERATURE. Biographies of Van de Graaff are E. A. Burrill, "Van de Graaff, the Man and His Accelerators," in *Physics Today,* **20** (1967), 49–52; N. Felici, "R. J. Van de Graaff: 1901–1967," in

Bulletin commissariat à l'energie atomique (March-April 1967), p. 20; and P. H. Rose, "In Memoriam: Robert Jemison Van de Graaff," in *Nuclear Instruments and Methods*, **60** (1968), 1–3.

E. Alfred Burrill

VANDERMONDE, ALEXANDRE-THÉOPHILE, also known as **Alexis, Abnit,** and **Charles-Auguste Vandermonde** (*b*. Paris, France, 28 February 1735; *d*. Paris, 1 January 1796), *mathematics*.

Vandermonde's father, a physician, directed his sickly son toward a musical career. An acquaintanceship with Fontaine, however, so stimulated Vandermonde that in 1771 he was elected to the Académie des Sciences, to which he presented four mathematical papers (his total mathematical production) in 1771–1772. Later Vandermonde wrote several papers on harmony, and it was said at that time that musicians considered Vandermonde to be a mathematician and that mathematicians viewed him as a musician. This latter view was unfair in that his mathematical work—although small, not generally well known, and a little delayed in publication—was both significant and influential.

Vandermonde's membership in the Academy led to a paper on experiments with cold, made with Bezout and Lavoisier in 1776, and a paper on the manufacture of steel with Berthollet and Monge in 1786. Vandermonde became an ardent and active revolutionary, being such a close friend of Monge that he was termed "femme de Monge." He was a member of the Commune of Paris and the club of the Jacobins. In 1782 he was director of the Conservatoire des Arts et Métiers and in 1792, chief of the Bureau de l'Habillement des Armées. He joined in the design of a course in political economy for the École Normale and in 1795 was named a member of the Institut National.

Vandermonde is best known for the determinant that is named after him:

$$\begin{vmatrix} 1 & a_1 a_1^2 \cdots a_1^{n-1} \\ 1 & a_2 a_2^2 \cdots a_2^{n-1} \\ \hline 1 & a_n a_n^2 \cdots a_n^{n-1} \end{vmatrix} = \prod_{i>j}(a_i - a_j).$$

The determinant does not seem to occur in Vandermonde's work, although his third paper dealt with factorials and he did work with products elsewhere. Lebesgue believed that the attribution of this determinant to Vandermonde was due to a misreading of his notation. Muir (see Bibliography) did not mention this particuiar determinant, which some also attributed to Cauchy, but Muir asserted that Vandermonde's fourth paper was the first to give a connected exposition of determinants because he (1) defined a contemporary symbolism that was more complete, simple, and appropriate than that of Leibniz; (2) defined determinants as functions apart from the solution of linear equations presented by Cramer but also treated by Vandermonde; and (3) gave a number of properties of these functions, such as the number and signs of the terms and the effect of interchanging two consecutive indices (rows or columns), which he used to show that a determinant is zero if two rows or columns are identical. On this basis, Muir said that Vandermonde was "The only one fit to be viewed as the founder of the theory of determinants." Lebesgue, however, felt that this was neither very original, since there had been earlier workers, nor very important, since others were building equivalent theories, but that Vandermonde's real and unrecognized claim to fame was lodged in his first paper, in which he approached the general problem of the solvability of algebraic equations through a study of functions invariant under permutations of the roots of the equations.

Cauchy assigned priority in this to Lagrange and Vandermonde. Vandermonde read his paper in November 1770, but he did not become a member of the Academy until 1771; and the paper was not published until 1774. During this interval Lagrange published two *mémoires* on the topic. Although Vandermonde's methods were close to those later developed by Abel and Galois for testing the solvability of equations, and although his treatment of the binomial equation $x^m - 1 = 0$ could easily have led to the anticipation of Gauss's results on constructible polygons, Vandermonde himself did not rigorously or completely establish his results nor did he see the implications for geometry. Nevertheless, Kronecker dated the modern movement in algebra to Vandermonde's 1770 paper.

According to Maxwell, Vandermonde's second paper was cited in one of Gauss's notebooks, along with some work of Euler, as being one of two attempts to extend the ideas of Leibniz on the geometry of situation or analysis situs. The paper dealt with the knight's tour and involved the number of interweavings of curves, which Gauss then represented by a double integral and associated with the study of electrical potential.

Unfortunately Vandermonde's spurt of enthusiasm and creativity, which in two years produced four insightful mathematical papers, at least two of which were of substantial importance, was quickly diverted by the exciting politics of the time and, perhaps, by poor health.

BIBLIOGRAPHY

I. ORIGINAL WORKS. Vandermonde's mathematical papers appeared in *Histoire de l'Académie royale des sciences . . .* as follows: "Mémoire sur la résolution des équations" (1771), 365–415; "Remarques sur des problèmes de situation" (1771), 566–574; "Mémoire sur des irrationnelles de différents ordres avec une application au cercle," pt. 1 (1772), 489–498; and "Mémoire sur élimination," pt. 2 (1772), 516–532.

The three algebraic papers were reprinted in C. Itzigsohn, *Abhandlungen aus der reinen Mathematik. In deutscher Sprache herausgegeben* (Berlin, 1888).

II. SECONDARY LITERATURE. The most comprehensive account of Vandermonde's work is Henri Lebesgue, "L'oeuvre mathématique de Vandermonde," in *Thales, recueil des travaux de l'Institut d'histoire des sciences*, IV (1937–1939), 28–42, and in *Enseignement mathématique*, 2nd ser., **1** (1955), 203–223. Also useful are Niels Nielsen, "Vandermonde," in *Géomètres Français sous la revolution* (Copenhagen, 1929), 229–237; Thomas Muir, *The Theory of Determinants in the Historical Order of Their Development*, 2nd ed., I (London, 1906), repr. (New York, 1960), 17–24; and H. Simon, "Vandermondes Vornamen," in *Zeitschrift für Mathematik und Physik*, **41** (1896), 83–85.

PHILLIP S. JONES

VAN DER WAALS, JOHANNES DIDERIK. See Waals, Johannes Diderik van der.

VAN HISE, CHARLES RICHARD (*b*. Fulton, Wisconsin, 29 May 1857; *d*. Milwaukee, Wisconsin, 19 November 1918), *geology*.

A pioneer in the use of the petrographic microscope as a tool for analyzing crystalline rocks and in the application of quantitative methods to the study of geologic phenomena, Van Hise established general principles—still valid a half century later—for deciphering the complexities of Precambrian rocks and understanding the processes of metamorphism. He began his field studies in the Lake Superior region as a geologist of the Wisconsin Geological Survey before 1879, and continued them as a member of the faculty of the department of geology at the University of Wisconsin, where he was an instructor (1879–1883), assistant professor (1883–1886), and professor (1886–1903). His studies were soon extended throughout much of North America under the auspices of the U. S. Geological Survey, by which he was also employed as an assistant geologist (1883–1888), geologist in charge of Lake Superior Division (1888–1900), geologist in charge of Division of Pre-Cambrian and Metamorphic Geology (1900–1908), and consulting geologist (1909–1918).

Van Hise continued his research for several years after he became president of the University of Wisconsin in 1903, but he found it necessary before long to devote his time almost exclusively to administrative responsibilities, which he carried forward with great distinction, and to public affairs.

Early in his career, Van Hise was concerned primarily with mapping ore-bearing formations and determining their structure in order to facilitate mining operations. This soon led him to the enunciation of basic theories concerning ore-deposition and Precambrian history, most of which have been supported by the work of later geologists. His "Principles of North American Pre-Cambrian Geology" (1896) and "Treatise on Metamorphism" (1904) are classics of geologic literature, still useful today. Notable also is the leadership he displayed in the development of a valid rationale for the conservation of natural resources and the wise use of metalliferous ores for human welfare.

BIBLIOGRAPHY

I. ORIGINAL WORKS. Published works by Van Hise include "Crystalline Rocks of the Wisconsin Valley," in *Geology of Wisconsin*, **4** (1882), 627–714, written with R. D. Irving; "The Pre-Cambrian Rocks of the Black Hills," in *Bulletin of the Geological Society of America*, **1** (1890), 203–244; "The Penokee Iron-Bearing Series of Michigan and Wisconsin," in *Monographs of the U.S. Geological Survey*, no. 19 (1892), 1–534, written with R. D. Irving; "Principles of North American Pre-Cambrian Geology," in *Report of the United States Geological Survey*, no. 16 (1896), pt. 1, 573–874; "The Marquette Iron-Bearing District of Michigan," *Monographs of the U.S. Geological Survey*, no. 28 (1897), 1–608, written with W. S. Bayley and H. L. Smyth; "Metamorphism of Rocks and Rock Flowage," in *Bulletin of the Geological Society of America*, **9** (1898), 269–328; "The Iron-Ore Deposits of the Lake Superior Region," in *Report of the United States Geological Survey*, no. 21 (1899–1900), pt. 3 (1901), 305–434; "A Treatise on Metamorphism," in *Monographs of the U.S. Geological Survey*, no. 47 (1904), 1–1286; "Pre-Cambrian Geology of North America," in *Bulletin of* *the United States Geological Survey*, no. 360 (1909), 1–939, written with C. K. Leith; *The Conservation of Natural Resources in the United States* (New York, 1910); and "The Influence of Applied Geology and the Mining Industry Upon the Economic Development of the World," in *Compte-Rendu, International Geological Congress*, XI (1912), 259–261.

II. Secondary Literature. Biographies of Van Hise are T. C. Chamberlin, "Biographical Memoir of Charles Richard Van Hise, 1857–1918," in *Memoirs of the National Academy of Sciences*, **17** (1924), 143–151, including a bibliography of eighty-four titles; and C. K. Leith, "Memorial of Charles Richard Van Hise," in *Bulletin of the Geological Society of America*, **31** (1920), 100–110, including a bibliography of fifty-nine titles.

Kirtley F. Mather

VANINI, GIULIO CESARE (*b.* Taurisano, Lecce, Italy, *ca.* 1585; *d.* Toulouse, France, 9 February 1619), *philosophy.*

The son of a local official and a Spanish noblewoman, Vanini became a Carmelite friar about 1603. The records of the University of Naples show that a doctorate in both canon and civil law was awarded Giulio Cesare Vanini on 6 June 1606. After selling a house and some personal belongings in Naples (16 May 1608), he enrolled in the faculty of theology at Padua University and preached in various places, including Venice.

Under threat of being banished to Naples by the general of his order, Vanini appealed to the English ambassador to Venice, who recommended him to the archbishop of Canterbury (7 February 1612). Five months later in the Italian church in London Vanini publicly renounced Catholicism in the presence of Francis Bacon. But his adherence to Anglicanism was short-lived. On 10 July 1613 his appeal to Rome for permission to reenter the Catholic church as a secular priest, without being required to rejoin the Carmelite order, was granted by the Holy Office and on 22 August by the pope himself.

After escaping from an English prison in the spring of 1614, Vanini made his way to Paris, where (27 August 1614) he was denied permission to publish his work on the Council of Trent, a work that has not survived. In Lyons, in the summer of 1615, he published his *Amphitheatrum aeternae providentiae . . .* with the approval of the local ecclesiastical censor and also with a royal privilege. Likewise with a royal privilege and with the approbation of the Sorbonne, a Parisian publisher, professing that he had surreptitiously procured a copy of Vanini's sixty dialogues dealing

with the secrets of nature, issued (1 September 1616) the philosopher's only other surviving work. A month later the Sorbonne censors claimed that the printed version differed from the manuscript they had approved.

Having studied medicine in Paris, Vanini practiced in Toulouse, where he also taught philosophy privately under an assumed name. In that stronghold of the Catholic counterreformation he was arrested (2 August 1618) and kept in jail more than half a year. On 9 February 1619, exactly nineteen years after Giordano Bruno had been condemned to martyrdom at the stake, Vanini's tongue was pulled out by pincers and cut off; he was strangled and then burned; and his ashes were scattered to the winds. To justify the savage sentence, a host of unscrupulous writers falsified Vanini's biography and maligned his character.

Centuries later, after the historical record had been corrected, the authorities in the capital of Vanini's native province of Lecce unveiled (24 September 1868) a bust of the philosopher.

BIBLIOGRAPHY

I. Original Works. Vanini's two published works are *Amphitheatrum aeternae providentiae divino-magicum christiano-physicum nec non astrologo-catholicum adversus veteres philosophos, atheos, epicureos, peripateticos, et stoicos* (Lyons, 1615); and *De admirandis naturae reginae deaeque mortalium arcanis* (Paris, 1616).

The *Amphitheatrum* in its entirety and extracts from the dialogues were translated into French by Xavier Rousselot, *Oeuvres philosophiques de Vanini* (Paris, 1842). Both works were translated into Italian by Guido Porzio, *Le opere di Giulio Cesare Vanini*, 2 vols. (Lecce, 1913).

II. Secondary Literature. Works on Vanini and his philosophy are Don Cameron Allen, *Doubt's Boundless Sea: Skepticism and Faith in the Renaissance* (Baltimore, 1964), 58–74; J.-Roger Charbonnel, *La pensée italienne au XVIe siècle et le courant libertin* (Paris, 1919), 302–383; Luigi Corvaglia, *Le opere di Giulio Cesare Vanini e le loro fonti*, 2 vols. (Milan, 1933–1934); and *Vanini, edizioni e plagi* (Casarano, 1934); Victor Cousin, "Vanini, ses écrits, sa vie et sa mort," in *Revue des deux mondes*, **4** (1843), 673–728; Francesco Fiorentino, *Studi e ritratti della rinascenza* (Bari, 1911), 423–471; William L. Hine, "Mersenne and Vanini," in *Renaissance Quarterly* (forthcoming); Emile Namer, *Documents sur la vie de Jules-César Vanini de Taurisano* (Bari, 1965); and "Vanini et la préparation de l'esprit scientifique à l'aube du XVIIe siècle," in *Revue d'histoire des sciences*, **25** (1972), 207–220; Andrzej Nowicki, *Giulio Cesare Vanini* (Wrocław, 1968);

John Owen, *The Skeptics of the Italian Renaissance*, 2nd ed. (London–New York, 1893); 3rd ed. (London, 1908); reprint (Port Washington, New York, 1970), 343–419; Raffaele Palumbo, *Giulio Cesare Vanini e i suoi tempi* (Naples, 1878); Guido Porzio, *Antologia Vaniniana* (Lecce, 1908); Victor Ivanovich Rutenburg, *Velikii italianskii ateist Vanini* (Moscow, 1959); Giorgio Spini, *Ricerca dei libertini* (Rome, 1950), 117–135; and "Vaniniana," in *Rinascimento*, 1 (1950), 71–90.

EDWARD ROSEN

VAN SLYKE, DONALD DEXTER (*b.* Pike, New York, 29 March 1883; *d.* Garden City, New York, 4 May 1971), *biochemistry*.

Van Slyke was the son of Lucius Van Slyke, a noted chemist who spent most of his career at the agricultural experiment station in Geneva, New York, and Lucy Dexter. After attending high school in Geneva, he studied for a year at Hobart College before entering the University of Michigan, where he received the B.S. degree in chemistry in 1905. He continued his studies at Michigan and in 1907 received the Ph.D. in organic chemistry under Moses Gomberg. From 1907 to 1914 Van Slyke was a research chemist in the biochemical laboratory of Phoebus A. Levene at the Rockefeller Institute for Medical Research. In 1914 he became chief chemist of the hospital of the Rockefeller Institute, a position he held until 1949, when he moved to Brookhaven National Laboratory. He continued his chemical research at Brookhaven almost until his death. Van Slyke also edited the *Journal of Biological Chemistry* from 1914 to 1925. Among the honors that he received were the Willard Gibbs Medal (1939), the George M. Kober Medal (1942), and membership in the National Academy of Sciences (1921).

Van Slyke's remarkable ability to develop analytical apparatus and methods, especially gasometric methods, proved extremely useful in biochemistry and clinical medicine. For example, in 1911 he developed his famous nitrous acid method for determining the number of free amino groups in a peptide or protein. The method is based on the fact that amino groups react with nitrous acid quantitatively to release gaseous nitrogen, which can be measured. Van Slyke's manometric apparatus for the analysis of gases in blood and other solutions was adapted to the quantitative determination of numerous constituents of body fluids and was widely used in biochemical laboratories. His collaborative effort with John Peters, *Quantitative Clinical Chemistry* (1931–1932), was a classic in its field. Many of the analytical methods presented in the work were developed in Van Slyke's laboratory, and most of the other procedures described were tested there before inclusion in the volume on methods. To honor his contributions in this field, the American Society of Clinical Chemistry created the Donald D. Van Slyke Award and appropriately selected Van Slyke as the first recipient in 1957.

Most of Van Slyke's research concerned acid-base, gas, fluid, and electrolyte equilibriums in body fluids and the relation of these equilibriums to disease states. His post at the Rockefeller Institute hospital probably was largely responsible for focusing his attention on problems of clinical biochemistry. His first effort in this area involved the study of acidosis, a condition that aroused his interest because it often develops in diabetes. In 1914 Lawrence J. Henderson and Walter W. Palmer had defined acidosis as a decrease in the bicarbonate concentration of the blood. In 1917 Van Slyke and Glenn Cullen introduced the term "alkaline reserve" to describe the bicarbonate concentration of blood and developed a quick and accurate method, which became the standard procedure, for determining the level of plasma bicarbonate. The definition of acidosis as a decrease in the body's alkaline reserve actually applies only to metabolic acidosis, however, and not to the condition known as respiratory acidosis. Van Slyke also established the normal and abnormal variations that may be encountered in the acid-base balance of the blood, and developed an exact mathematical definition of buffer value.

In 1919 Henderson and his associates began an investigation of the physicochemical equilibriums of the constituents of blood. Van Slyke's collaboration was solicited for this project; and it was agreed that the equilibriums of the gases, fluids, and electrolytes of blood would be studied in his laboratory. Van Slyke and his co-workers established that the distribution of electrolyte ions between plasma and corpuscles occurs in accordance with the Gibbs-Donnan law. They determined experimentally the buffer values of oxyhemoglobin and reduced hemoglobin, determined that hemoglobin is responsible for much of the total buffer value of blood, and showed how the Gibbs-Donnan law and the acid-base properties of hemoglobin explain the unequal distribution of diffusible ions between red cells and plasma (the chloride-bicarbonate shift).

Van Slyke's other important contributions include his studies on nephritis, his discovery and identification of the amino acid hydroxylysine, and his establishment of the fact that urinary ammonia is derived largely from glutamine rather than from urea.

Van Slyke and his colleagues introduced the concept of "blood urea clearance"—the cubic centimeters of blood per minute cleared of urea by renal excretion—as a measure of the functional ability of the kidney. The urea clearance test that they developed proved to be exceedingly useful in clinical work and in laboratory investigations.

BIBLIOGRAPHY

I. ORIGINAL WORKS. There apparently is no published bibliography of Van Slyke's works. The five books that he wrote alone or in collaboration are *Cyanosis* (Baltimore, 1923), written with Christen Lundsgaard; *Factors Affecting the Distribution of Electrolytes, Water, and Gases in the Animal Body* (Philadelphia, 1926); *Observations on the Courses of Different Types of Bright's Disease and on the Resultant Changes in Renal Anatomy* (Baltimore, 1930), written with nine others; *Quantitative Clinical Chemistry*, 2 vols. (Baltimore, 1931–1932; 2nd ed., 1946), written with John Peters; and *Micromanometric Analyses* (Baltimore, 1961), written with John Plazin. Almost all of his important papers were published in the *Journal of Biological Chemistry*. Particularly noteworthy publications in this journal include the series "Studies of Acidosis," **30–106** (1917–1934); and "Studies of Gas and Electrolyte Equilibria in Blood," **54–105** (1922–1934).

II. SECONDARY LITERATURE. The most substantial biographical article is A. Baird Hastings, "Donald Dexter Van Slyke, 1883–1971," in *Journal of Biological Chemistry*, **247** (1972), 1635–1640. See also the biographical sketch in *Current Biography* (1943), 50–51; and Van Slyke's autobiographical article in *Modern Men of Science*, I (New York, 1966), 495–496. George Corner, *A History of the Rockefeller Institute, 1901–1953, Origins and Growth* (New York, 1964), discusses the work of Van Slyke and his associates at the Rockefeller Institute and hospital—see esp. 274–280, 483–488. A. Baird Hastings, "A Biochemist's Anabasis," in *Annual Review of Biochemistry*, **39** (1970), 3–7, describes some of the work carried out in Van Slyke's laboratory during the 1920's. Van Slyke was interviewed in detail under the Oral History Program of the National Library of Medicine, Bethesda, Md., and the transcript and tape of this memoir are on file at the library.

JOHN PARASCANDOLA

VAN'T HOFF, JACOBUS HENRICUS (*b.* Rotterdam, Netherlands, 30 August 1852; *d.* Steglitz [now Berlin], Germany, 1 March 1911), *physical chemistry.*

Van't Hoff was the third of seven children born to Jacobus Henricus van't Hoff, a physician, and Alida Jacoba Kolff. In 1867, at the age of fifteen, he completed his elementary schooling and entered the fourth class of the five-year secondary school in Rotterdam. In 1869 he passed the final examination and told his parents that he wished to study chemistry. It was agreed that he would study technology at Delft before going to a university. He completed the usual three-year program at the Polytechnic School at Delft in two years; his teachers there included the chemist A. C. Oudemans and the physicist H. G. van de Sande Bakhuyzen.

At Delft, van't Hoff also studied calculus and became interested in philosophy. He immersed himself in Comte's *Cours de philosophie positive*, Whewell's *History of the Inductive Sciences*, and Hippolyte Taine's *De l'intelligence*. He also read Byron's poetic works with great fervor.

In 1871 van't Hoff entered the University of Leiden, where he studied mainly mathematics. From the autumn of 1872 to the following spring he worked with Kekulé at Bonn. In 1873 he passed the doctoral examination in chemistry at the University of Utrecht and early the following year went to Paris for further study under Wurtz. Here he met Le Bel, who later independently published a theory to explain optical isomerism based on stereochemical considerations.

In the summer of 1874 van't Hoff returned to the Netherlands and in September of that year published his theory of the asymmetric carbon atom, a work that inspired the development of stereochemistry. On 22 December 1874 he obtained the Ph.D. at Utrecht under Eduard Mulder's guidance for an undistinguished dissertation on cyanoacetic and malonic acids. In 1876 he was appointed lecturer in physics at the State Veterinary School in Utrecht and began writing his first book, *Ansichten über die organische Chemie* (1878–1881).

In 1877 van't Hoff was appointed lecturer in theoretical and physical chemistry at the University of Amsterdam, where, from 1878 until 1896, he was successively professor of chemistry, mineralogy, and geology and head of the department of chemistry. His appointment was undoubtedly due to J. W. Gunning, professor of chemistry and pharmacy at Amsterdam, who became his lifelong friend. In his inaugural lecture on 11 October 1878 van't Hoff defended the view that in studying the natural sciences both observation and imagination are necessary. Having studied the lives of many scientists, he concluded that the most prominent among them had been gifted with a highly developed imagination.

After 1877 van't Hoff began his studies in chemical thermodynamics and affinity, and in 1884 he stated his principle of mobile equilibrium. From 1885 to 1890 he published the results of his studies on osmotic pressure and explored the analogy between dilute solutions and gases. In 1887 van't Hoff was named professor at the University of Leipzig. Although this invitation catalyzed the authorities at Amsterdam to provide funds for a new chemical laboratory, which was completed in 1891, van't Hoff moved to Berlin in 1896, having been elected to the Royal Prussian Academy of Sciences and appointed professor at the university. Because he lectured only once a week, he was now able to devote himself completely to research. His lectures appeared in *Vorlesungen über theoretische und physikalische Chemie* (1898–1900), which was translated into many languages, and in *Die chemischen Grundlehren nach Menge, Mass und Zeit* (1912). With Wilhelm Ostwald, he was a cofounder of the *Zeitschrift für physikalische Chemie*, the first issue of which appeared in February 1887.

In 1885 van't Hoff was elected a member of the Royal Netherlands Academy of Sciences. He received honorary doctorates from Harvard and Yale (1901), Victoria University of Manchester (1903), and the University of Heidelberg (1908); and was awarded the Davy Medal of the Royal Society of London (1893) and the Helmholtz Medal of the Prussian Academy of Sciences (1911). In 1901 he became the first Nobel laureate in chemistry for his work on osmotic pressure in solutions and on the laws of chemical dynamics. He was also appointed Chevalier de la Légion d'Honneur (1894), senator of the Kaiser-Wilhelm Gesellschaft (1911), and was a member of the Royal Academy of Sciences of Göttingen (1892), the Chemical Society of London (1898), the American Chemical Society (1898), and the Académie des Sciences (1905). In 1911 he died of pulmonary tuberculosis. His body was cremated and the ashes placed in the cemetery at Berlin-Dahlem. He was survived by his wife, Johanna Francisca Mees, whom he had married in 1878, two daughters, and two sons.

Stereochemistry. In 1873 the German chemist Wislicenus published an article on lactic acids, in which he reiterated the view that the only differ-ence between the two optically active forms of the acid must be in the spatial arrangements of the atoms. After van't Hoff had studied this theory, he published a twelve-page pamphlet, *Voorstel tot uitbreiding der tegenwoordig in de scheikunde gebruikte structuur-formules in de ruimte*, which included a page of diagrams. Van't Hoff's name appeared only at the end of the paper, which was dated 5 September 1874.

At the suggestion of Buys Ballot, professor of physics at Utrecht, the paper was soon translated into French, and the following year van't Hoff published his views in extended form as *La chimie dans l'espace*. His revolutionary ideas on the theory of the asymmetric carbon atom did not attract the attention of chemists, however, until Wislicenus asked van't Hoff's permission for a German translation by one of his pupils, Felix Herrmann. The translation was published in 1877 as *Die Lagerung der Atome im Raume*. An English translation by J. E. Marsh appeared in 1891 as *Chemistry in Space*. Then, in 1887, van't Hoff published *Dix années dans l'histoire d'une théorie*, in which he pointed out that Le Bel had independently arrived at the same idea, although in a more abstract form.

Both van't Hoff and Le Bel showed that arrangements of four different univalent groups at the corners of a regular tetrahedron (which van't Hoff defined as an asymmetric carbon atom) will produce two structures, one of which is the mirror-image of the other. The latter is a condition for the existence of optical isomers, already realized in 1860 by Pasteur, who found that optical rotation arises from asymmetry in the molecules themselves. Van't Hoff stated that when the four affinities of one carbon atom are represented by four mutually perpendicular directions lying in the same plane, then we may expect two isomeric forms from derivatives of methane of the type $CH_2(R_1)_2$. Because such isomeric types do not occur in nature, van't Hoff supposed that the affinities of the carbon atom are directed to the corners of a tetrahedron and that the carbon atom is at the center. In such a tetrahedron a compound of the type $CH_2(R_1)_2$ cannot exist in two isomeric forms, but for compounds of the type $CR_1R_2R_3R_4$ it is possible to construct two spatial models that are nonsuperimposable images of one another. In this case there is no center or plane of symmetry for the tetrahedron.

In the first part of the *Voorstel*, van't Hoff discussed the relationship between the asymmetric carbon atom and optical activity. Drawing on several examples he showed that all the compounds of carbon that, in solution, rotate the plane of polarized light possess an asymmetric carbon atom (for example, tartaric acid, maleic acid, sugars, and camphor). Then van't Hoff showed that while the derivatives of optically active compounds lose their rotatory power when the asymmetry of all of the carbon atoms disappears, in the contrary case they usually do not lose this power. Finally he showed that if one makes a list of compounds that contain an asymmetric carbon atom it appears that in many cases the reverse of his first statement is not true, that is, not every compound with such an atom has an influence upon polarized light.

Van't Hoff's concepts of the asymmetric carbon atom explained the occurrence of many cases of isomerism not explicable in terms of the structural formulas then current. Moreover, it pointed out the existence of a link between optical activity and the presence of an asymmetric carbon atom. Van't Hoff also discussed the relationship between the asymmetric carbon atom and the number of isomers. In *La chimie dans l'espace* he showed that the number of possible isomers of a compound with n inequivalent asymmetric carbon atoms is 2^n, and he indicated how the number of isomers decreased if one or more of the asymmetric carbon atoms is equivalent.

Having introduced the concept of the tetrahedral carbon atom to explain the optical isomerism of a number of organic compounds, van't Hoff turned in the second and third part of *Voorstel* to another type of isomerism, which also appeared to be a consequence of the tetrahedral atom, namely, compounds containing doubly and triply linked carbon atoms. A carbon-carbon double bond of the type $R_1R_2C{=}CR_1R_2$ is represented by two tetrahedrons with one edge in common, as in the case of maleic and fumaric acids, bromomaleic and bromoisomaleic acids, citraconic and mesaconic acids, crotonic and isocrotonic acids, and chlorocrotonic and chloroisocrotonic acids. Van't Hoff pointed out that when two tetrahedrons are joined on one edge and R_1, R_2, R_3, and R_4 represent the univalent groups that saturate the remaining free affinities of the carbon atoms, possibilities for isomerism occur when R_1 differs from R_2 and when R_3 differs from R_4. This form of isomerism is now called geometric or cis-trans isomerism. In cases when optical activity was found but the formula was symmetrical, van't Hoff postulated (usually correctly) either an error in the formula or the presence of an optically active impurity. In 1894 he ventured the opinion, later confirmed, that the occurrence of optically active substances in nature

might be the consequence of the action of circularly polarized light in the atmosphere on optically inactive substances.

Although van't Hoff and Le Bel shared certain views concerning the carbon atom, van't Hoff was more imaginative and broader in his conceptions and thus incurred harsher criticism, especially from Kolbe, who saw in van't Hoff's work a regression of German chemical research to the speculative aspects of *Naturphilosophie*:

A Dr. J. H. van't Hoff, of the veterinary school at Utrecht, has as it seems, no taste for exact chemical investigation. He has thought it more convenient to mount Pegasus (obviously loaned by the veterinary school) and to proclaim in his *La chimie dans l'espace* how during his bold flight to the top of the chemical Parnassus, the atoms appeared to him to have grouped themselves throughout universal space ["Zeichen der Zeit," in *Journal für praktische Chemie*, **15** (1877), 473].

He was also criticized by Fittig, Adolf Claus, Wilhelm Lossen, and Friedrich Hinrichsen on the basis that his theories were incompatible with physical laws. Although Wurtz, Spring, and Louis Henry wrote warm acknowledgments, they made no attempt to discuss or criticize his theory. The first to give serious attention to van't Hoff's theory was Buys Ballot, who in the journal *Maandblad voor natuurwetenschappen* (1875) published an open letter to van't Hoff. His reply, in the same journal, discusses a number of interesting points raised in the letter and includes diagrams of the configurations of the ten isomeric saccharic acids.

In volume I of *Ansichten über die organische Chemie* van't Hoff systematically examined the physical and chemical properties of organic substances regarded and classified as derivatives of methane. In volume II he discussed the general relation between the constitution and fundamental properties of organic substances. Especially interested in their physical properties, he attempted to relate stability and reactivity to thermodynamic data, reaction velocities, and chemical equilibriums. Remarkably, van't Hoff made little use here of his stereochemical ideas.

Physical chemistry. In 1884 van't Hoff published *Études de dynamique chimique*, which dealt not only with reaction rates but also with the theory of equilibrium and the theory of affinity based on free energy. In the first section of the book he classified reaction velocities as unimolecular, bimolecular, and multimolecular. He started from the observation (accidentally discovered during his stereochemical researches) that dibromosuccinic acid decomposes at 100°C., a process that he classified as a unimolecular (first-order) reaction. As an example of a bimolecular (second-order) reaction he used the saponification of the sodium salt of monochloric acid, which he had studied in 1883 with his pupil L. C. Schwab: $CH_2ClCOOH + NaOH \rightarrow NaCl + CH_2OHCOONa$.

Van't Hoff recognized the positive-salt effect of the sodium chloride and explained deviations in more concentrated solutions as the variations in volume of the molecules. He also determined the order of chemical reaction for many compounds, for example, the first-order decomposition of arsenic hydride. When arsine is heated, one would expect the chemical equation of its decomposition to indicate a quadrimolecular reaction. But after having determined the velocity of decomposition, van't Hoff found that the reaction is of the first order. Thus he discovered that the order may differ from the molecularity, that is, the number of molecules shown in the ordinary chemical reaction equation. Moreover, van't Hoff found that his researches were complicated by activity factors, reaction milieus, and the movements of the molecules.

Van't Hoff's experiments on the influence of temperature on reaction velocity culminated in his famous thermodynamic relationship between the absolute temperature T and the velocity constant K:

$$\frac{d \ln K}{dT} = \frac{A}{T^2} + B,$$

where A and B are factors dependent on the temperature, and A is now called the activation energy. To make the relation plausible, van't Hoff adopted the notion (first used by Leopold von Pfaundler) of chemical equilibrium as the result of two opposite reactions; but van't Hoff was the first to introduce the double-arrow symbol (still universally used) to indicate the dynamic nature of chemical equilibrium.

After investigating the inflammation temperature at which the reaction takes place, van't Hoff derived the law of mass action on the basis of reaction velocities—the velocities of the forward and reverse reactions being equal at equilibrium. He also established the general equation for the effect of the absolute temperature T on the equilibrium constant K:

$$\frac{d \ln K}{dT} = \frac{q}{2T^2},$$

in which q is the heat of reaction at constant volume. The derivation of this equation is not given in the Études. In 1886 van't Hoff showed that the Clausius-Clapeyron equation (in the form given by Horstmann), which related the temperature coefficient of the vapor pressure to the heat of reaction and volume change, can be generalized in terms of the equilibrium constant, as given above. Since $K = k_1/k_2$, where k_1 and k_2 are the reaction velocities of the forward and reverse directions,

$$\frac{d \ln k_1}{dT} - \frac{d \ln k_2}{dT} = \frac{q}{RT^2}$$

so that

$$\frac{d \ln K}{dT} = \frac{A}{T^2} + B.$$

From this so-called van't Hoff isochor it follows that the increase or decrease of the equilibrium constant with the absolute temperature depends upon the sign of the reaction heat q at constant volume. Van't Hoff applied his relation to both homogeneous and heterogeneous equilibriums, to condensed systems (in which no component has a variable concentration), and to physical equilibriums, that is, changes of state.

Van't Hoff formulated his principle of mobile equilibrium in the limited sense that at constant volume the equilibrium will tend to shift in such a direction as to oppose the temperature change that is imposed upon the system: "Every equilibrium at constant volume between two systems is displaced by fall of temperature in the direction of that system in the production of which heat is developed." In 1884 Le Châtelier cast the principle in a general form and extended it to include compensation, by change of volume, for imposed pressure changes. This principle is known as the van't Hoff–Le Châtelier principle.

In the fifth section of his Études, which dealt with affinity, van't Hoff defined the work of chemical affinity A as the heat q produced in the transformation, divided by the absolute temperature P of the transition point and multiplied by the difference between P and the given temperature T:

$$A = q \frac{P - T}{P}.$$

The quantity A is now called the maximum external work of the system. By differentiating the equation in respect to T, we find the Gibbs-Helmholtz relation for the dependence of the absolute temperature T on the electromotive force at a constant volume:

$$\frac{dA}{dT} = \frac{q - A}{T}.$$

Van't Hoff also established a simple thermodynamic relationship between the osmotic pressure D of the solution and the vapor pressures of pure water S_e and of the solution S_z: $D = 10.5\ T\ \log S_e/S_z$.

At first the *Études* received little attention. It was neither a textbook nor a purely scientific treatise; it included many new formulas that were presented and applied without derivation. Although the same subjects were discussed in his *Vorlesungen über theoretische und physikalische Chemie*, the latter work was better arranged and included the results of subsequent research—and thus became a valuable textbook. The proper derivations of the equations in the *Études* appeared in a number of publications. In "L'équilibre chimique dans les systèmes gazeux, ou dissous à l'état dilué" (1886) van't Hoff showed from quantitative experiments on osmosis that dilute solutions of cane sugar obey the laws of Boyle, Gay-Lussac, and particularly Avogadro.

In his study of solutions, van't Hoff also investigated their properties in the presence of semipermeable barriers. He extended the quantitative investigation of the botanist Wilhelm Pfeffer (1877), who had contained solutions of cane sugar, and of other substances, within membranes of hexacyanocopper II ferrate, which he formed in the pores of earthenware pots by soaking them first in a solution of copper sulfate and then of potassium ferrocyanide. Van't Hoff showed that the osmotic pressure P of a solution inside such a vessel immersed in the pure solvent is in apparently direct proportion to the concentration of the solute and in inverse proportion to the volume V of the solution at a given temperature. At a given concentration, P is proportional to the absolute temperature T. The relation serves the general gas law $pV = kT$.

Van't Hoff then applied this law thermodynamically to various solutions. He found that the laws of Gay-Lussac, Boyle, and Avogadro are valid only for ideal solutions, that is, those solutions that are diluted to such an extent that they behave like "ideal" gases and in which both the reciprocal actions of the dissolved molecules and the space occupied by these molecules compared with the volume of the solution itself can be neglected.

To the analogy that exists between gases and solutions van't Hoff gave the general expression $pV = iRT$, in which the coefficient i expresses the ratio of the actual osmotic effect produced by an electrolyte to the effect that would be produced if it behaved like a nonelectrolyte. He also arrived at the important generalization that the osmotic pressure that the dissolved substance would exercise in the gaseous state if it occupied a volume is equal to the volume of the solution. Thus he applied Avogadro's law to dilute solutions. Van't Hoff determined that the coefficient i has a value of nearly one for dilute solutions and exactly one for gases. He reached this value by various methods, including the vapor pressure and Raoult's results on the lowering of the freezing point. For dilute solutions of binary electrolytes, such as sodium chloride and potassium nitrate, he found values ranging from 1.7 to 1.9. Hugo de Vries's experiments with plant cells and Donders' and Hartog Jacob Hamburger's experiments with red blood corpuscles produced isotonic coefficients that agreed with van't Hoff's.

Thus van't Hoff was able to prove that the laws of thermodynamics are valid not only for gases but also for dilute solutions. His pressure law gave general validity to the electrolytic theory of Arrhenius, who recognized in the values of i the magnitude that he had deduced, from experiments on electrical conductance, as the number of ions in which electrolytes are divided in solution. Consequently, van't Hoff became an adherent of the theory of electrolytic dissociation.

In "Lois de l'équilibre chimique dans l'état dilué, gazeux ou dissous" (1886) van't Hoff showed that for many substances the value of i was one, thus validating the relation $pV = RT$ for osmotic pressure. It then became possible to calculate the osmotic pressure of a dissolved substance from its chemical formula and, conversely, the molecular weight of a substance from the osmotic pressure. In "Conditions électriques de l'équilibre chimique" (1886), van't Hoff gave a fundamental relation between the chemical equilibrium constant and the electromotive force (the free energy) of a chemical process:

$$\ln K = \frac{-E}{2\ T},$$

in which K is the chemical equilibrium constant, E is the electromotive force of a reversible galvanic cell, and T is the absolute temperature.

While at Amsterdam, van't Hoff worked on physicochemical problems with a number of his pupils (Johan Eykman, Pieter Frowein, Arnold Holleman, Cohen, and Willem Jorissen) and with foreign chemists who came to Amsterdam to study under him (Arrhenius and Wilhelm Meyerhoffer). Besides his fundamental contributions to thermodynamics of chemical reactions, van't Hoff also studied solid solutions and double salts. In an important paper on solid solutions, "Ueber feste Lösungen und Molekulargewichtsbestimmung an festen Körpern" (1890), he determined, with the aid of his laws, the molecular weights of the dissolved substance—a solution of carbon in iron or a solution of hydrogen in palladium.

In *Vorlesungen über Bildung und Spaltung von Doppelsalzen* (1897) van't Hoff outlined the theoretical and practical treatment of the formation, separation, and conversion of many double salts, especially the tartrates of sodium, ammonium, and potassium. The book also gave a survey of the work in this field by van't Hoff and by a number of his pupils in the laboratory at Amsterdam.

At Berlin, van't Hoff studied the origin of oceanic deposits and the conditions of the formation of oceanic salt deposits, particularly those at Stassfurt, from the point of view of Gibbs's phase rule. He investigated phase equilibriums that form when various quantities of individual salts from the Stassfurt minerals are placed in water that is evaporated at a constant temperature. He also studied the form, order, and quantities of these equilibriums and the effect on them of time, temperature, and pressure. This important theoretical study was of special benefit to the German potash industry. Van't Hoff's method generally consisted in determining the fundamental nonvariant equilibriums (consisting of vapor, solution, and three solid phases) that characterize a four-component system at each particular temperature. In this study he was assisted chiefly by Meyerhoffer. Their results were published in the *Sitzungsberichte* of the Prussian Academy of Sciences and were summarized in van't Hoff's two-volume *Zur Bildung der ozeanischen Salzablagerungen.*

Chemistry is indebted to van't Hoff for his fundamental contributions to the unification of chemical kinetics, thermodynamics, and physical measurements. He was instrumental in founding physical chemistry as an independent discipline.

BIBLIOGRAPHY

I. ORIGINAL WORKS. Van't Hoff's doctoral thesis, *Bijdrage tot de kennis van het cyanazijnzuur en malonzuur* (Utrecht, 1874), was preceded by the publication, a few months earlier, of his important *Voorstel tot uitbreiding der tegenwoordig in de scheikunde gebruikte structuur-formules in de ruimte; benevens een daarmeê samenhangende opmerking omtrent het verband tusschen optisch actief vermogen en chemische constitutie van organische verbindingen* ("Proposal for the Extension of the Formulas Now in Use in Chemistry Into Space; Together With a Related Remark on the Relation Between the Optical Rotating Power and the Chemical Constitution of Organic Compounds"; Utrecht, 1874). It was translated into French as "Sur les formules de structure dans l'espace," in *Archives néerlandaises des sciences exactes et naturelles*, **9** (1874), 445–454; and an English version, "Structural Formulas in Space," appeared in G. M. Richardson, ed., *The Foundations of Stereo Chemistry. Memoirs by Pasteur, van't Hoff, Lebel and Wislicenus* (New York, 1901), 37–46.

Van't Hoff's views were published in extended form as *La chimie dans l'espace* (Rotterdam, 1875), trans. into German by F. Herrmann as *Die Lagerung der Atome im Raume* (Brunswick, 1877, 1894, 1908); and into English by J. E. Marsh as *Chemistry in Space* (Oxford, 1891) and by A. Eiloart as *The Arrangement of Atoms in Space* (London–Bombay–New York, 1898).

An enl. ed. of *La chimie dans l'espace* appeared as *Dix années dans l'histoire d'une théorie* (Rotterdam, 1887); new ed., *Stéréochimie* (Paris, 1892). Van't Hoff's reply to Buys Ballot is "Isomerie en atoomligging," in *Maandblad voor natuurwetenschappen*, **6** (1875), 37–45.

Subsequent writings are *Ansichten über die organische Chemie*, 2 vols. (Brunswick, 1878–1881); *Études de dynamique chimique* (Amsterdam, 1884); and "L'équilibre chimique dans les systèmes gazeux, ou dissous à l'état dilué," in *Archives néerlandaises des sciences exactes et naturelles*, **20** (1886), 239–302; "Lois de l'équilibre chimique dans l'état dilué, gazeux ou dissous," in *Kungliga Svenska vetenskapsakademiens handlingar*, **21**, no. 17 (1886), 3–41; "Une propriété générale de la matière diluée," *ibid.*, 42–49; and "Conditions électriques de l'équilibre chimique," *ibid.*, 50–58; were translated into English in *The Foundations of the Theory of Dilute Solutions*, Alembic Club Reprints no. 19 (Edinburgh, 1929), 5–42.

Later works are "Die Rolle des osmotischen Druckes in der Analogie zwischen Lösungen und Gasen," in *Zeitschrift für physikalische Chemie*, **1** (1887), 481–508; *Vorlesungen über Bildung und Spaltung von Doppelsalzen* (Leipzig, 1897); *Vorlesungen über theoretische und physikalische Chemie*, 3 vols. (Brunswick, 1898–1900; 2nd ed., 1901–1903), with English trans. by R. A. Lehfeldt as *Lectures on Theoretical and Physical Chemistry*, 3 vols. (London, 1899–1900); "Ueber feste Lösungen und Molekulargewichtsbestimmung an festen Körpern," in *Zeitschrift für physikalische Chemie*, **5** (1890), 322–339; *Acht Vorträge über physikalische Chemie, gehalten auf Einladung der Universität Chicago, 20 bis 24 Juni 1901* (Brunswick, 1902), with English trans. by A. Smith as *Physical Chemistry in the Service of the Sciences* (Chicago, 1903); *Zur Bildung der ozeanischen Salzablagerungen*, 2 vols. (Brunswick, 1905–1909); and *Die chemischen Grundlehren nach Menge, Mass und Zeit* (Brunswick, 1912).

Van't Hoff contributed to E. Cohen and H. Precht, eds., *Untersuchungen über die Bildungsverhältnisse der*

*ozeanischen Salzablagerungen, insbesondere des Stass-
furter Salzlagers* (Leipzig, 1912), published after his
death. His 1901 Nobel Prize lecture, "Osmotic Pressure
and Chemical Equilibrium," is in *Nobel Lectures.
Chemistry, 1901–1921* (Amsterdam–London–New
York, 1966), 5–10.

II. SECONDARY LITERATURE. The most comprehensive study of van't Hoff's life and work is E. Cohen,
Jacobus Henricus van't Hoff. Sein Leben und Werken
(Leipzig, 1912), with complete bibliography, 598–622.
His professorship at Amsterdam is extensively described in W. P. Jorissen and L. T. Reicher, *J. H. van't
Hoffs Amsterdamer Periode 1877–1895* (Den Helder,
1912). Achille Le Bel's 1874 article is "Sur les relations
qui existent entre les formules atomiques des corps organiques et le pouvoir rotatoire de leurs dissolutions," in
Bulletin de la Société chimique de Paris, **22** (1874),
337–347; C. H. D. Buys Ballot's open letter is "Open-
bare brief aan Dr. J. H. van't Hoff," in *Maandblad voor
natuurwetenschappen*, **6** (1875), 21–28.

There are obituary notices by H. C. Jones, in *Proceedings of the American Philosophical Society*, **50**
(1911), iii–xii; W. Ostwald, in *Berichte der Deutschen
chemischen Gesellschaft*, **44** (1911), 2219–2252; F. G.
Donnan, in *Proceedings of the Royal Society of London*,
86A (1912), xxxix–xliii; and J. Walker, in *Journal of the
Chemical Society*, **103** (1913), 1127–1143. See also
H. A. M. Snelders, "The Birth of Stereochemistry. An
Analysis of the 1874 papers of J. H. van't Hoff and J. A.
le Bel," in *Janus*, **60** (1973), 261–278; and "The Reception of J. H. van't Hoff's Theory of the Asymmetric
Carbon Atom," in *Journal of Chemical Education*, **51**
(1974), 2–7.

H. A. M. SNELDERS

VANUXEM, LARDNER (*b.* Philadelphia, Pennsylvania, 23 July 1792; Bristol, Pennsylvania, 25 January 1848), *geology.*

Vanuxem was the son of James Vanuxem, a
shipping merchant of Philadelphia, formerly of
Dunkirk, France. Young Vanuxem left his father's
business at the age of twenty-four and studied for
the next three years in Paris at the École des
Mines with the mineralogists Alexandre Brongniart, René-Just Haüy, and others. Upon his return
to the United States in 1819, Vanuxem became
professor of chemistry and mineralogy at South
Carolina College, a post that he held until 1826,
when he retired to practice geology as a profession.

Among Vanuxem's activities during the next few
years was a visit to Mexico to examine gold-min-
ing properties; he also made geologic investigations in New Jersey, New York, Ohio, Kentucky,
Tennessee, and Virginia. In his work Vanuxem

substituted paleontological criteria for classification based on lithology and attitude, correcting
Maclure's and Eaton's erroneous assignment of the
"western country, and the back and upper parts of
New York, with secondary rocks" (1829).

Vanuxem was one of the geologists appointed by
Governor William L. Marcy of New York in 1836
to carry out the geologic survey of the state. Of the
principal geologists of that famous survey, William
Williams Mather, Ebenezer Emmons, Timothy A.
Conrad, and James Hall—all of whom proved
highly competent—Vanuxem was the oldest, the
most experienced in the field, and the only one
with any formal training in geology. From this survey came his major scientific contribution: his report on the geology of the third geologic district of
New York (1842). The slenderest of the four reports, Vanuxem's was a model of organization,
presentation, and economy of words without loss
of significant detail. Even more than a century later
his report is still the starting point for any geologic
work in central New York State. Much of the stratigraphic classification adopted by the survey for
the New York rocks, long the standard for the
eastern United States, may be attributed to Vanuxem's sensible influence. It was in this report that
he introduced into stratigraphy the concept of type
locating.

The most important result of Vanuxem's studies
of the Atlantic coastal plain was his demonstration
in 1828, based upon fossils, of the presence of strata distinct from the Tertiary and equivalent to the
Cretaceous of Europe—the first recognition of this
system in North America and one of the first secure intercontinental correlations.

BIBLIOGRAPHY

I. ORIGINAL WORKS. *Geology of New York. Part III,
Comprising the Survey of the Third Geological District*
(Albany, 1842).

II. SECONDARY LITERATURE. "Sketch of Professor
Lardner Vanuxem," in *Popular Science Monthly*, **46**
(1895), 833–840, with a portrait.

JOHN W. WELLS

VARĀHAMIHIRA (*fl.* near Ujjain, India, sixth
century), *astronomy, astrology.*

The best-known and most respected astrologer
of India, Varāhamihira was the son and pupil of
Ādityadāsa, a Maga Brāhmaṇa and descendant of
Iranian Zoroastrians who immigrated to northern
India in the centuries about the beginning of the

Christian era and who, while retaining some traces of the solar worship of their forebears, were absorbed into Hinduism. Varāhamihira himself stated that he was a native of Avantī or Western Mālwā (the region about Ujjain) and that he resided in the village Kāpitthaka, which is probably to be identified with the ruins at Kayatha about twelve miles from Ujjain. His date is established by his own adaptation in the *Pañcasiddhāntikā* of Lāṭa's epoch, 505, and by the references to him as an authority in the *Brāhmasphuṭasiddhānta* composed by Brahmagupta in 628. It has further been suggested that he was connected with the Aulikara court at Daśapura (Mandasor), and in particular with Yaśodharman, who was reigning in 532.

His numerous writings covered all of the traditional fields of astrology and astronomy in India, generally in pairs. It is evident from internal cross-references that he composed the *Pañcasiddhāntikā* and *Bṛhatsaṃhitā* simultaneously toward the beginning of his career, although some additions were made to the latter after his other major works were completed. The *Bṛhajjātaka* was probably composed toward the end of his life, and the other treatises fall somewhere in between.

Varāhamihira was not original in his writings. In genethlialogy he depended primarily on Sphujidhvaja's and Satya's expositions of an Indianized Greek system, in divination on the Indian adaptations by Garga and others of Mesopotamian omen-series, and in astronomy on representatives of three traditions: the Mesopotamian-influenced *vedāṅga*-astronomy as represented in the first century *Paitāmahasiddhānta*, the Indian versions of Greco-Babylonian solar, lunar, and planetary theory in the *Vasiṣṭhasiddhānta* and *Pauliśasiddhānta*, and the essentially Hellenistic astronomy of the *Romakasiddhānta* and Lāṭa's *Sūryasiddhānta*. Since we have very few other sources for studying these traditions in India in the period before 500, Varāhamihira's work is extremely valuable; and as we know little else about the Greek traditions that the sources of the *Pañcasiddhāntikā* depend on, it affords us a most useful if somewhat problematic insight into pre-Ptolemaic Greek astronomy.

Varāhamihira's works are as follows:

1. The *Pañcasiddhāntikā*, edited with translation and commentary by O. Neugebauer and D. Pingree, 2 pts. (Copenhagen, 1970–1971). This difficult text deals with solar, lunar, and planetary theory; problems of time and terrestrial latitude; eclipses; astronomical instruments; and cosmology. Something has been said of its sources and its importance above.

2. The *Bṛhatsaṃhitā* on divination, edited with the commentary of Utpala (966) by Sudhākara Dvivedin, 2 vols. (Benares, 1895–1897; repr., Benares, 1968); there are several English translations, of which the best is H. Kern, "The Bṛhat-Saṇhitā," in *Journal of the Royal Asiatic Society* (1870), 430–479; (1871), 45–90, 231–288; (1873), 36–91, 279–338; and (1875), 81–134; this was reprinted in H. Kern, *Vespreide Geschriften*, 16 vols. (The Hague, 1913–1929), I, 169–319, and II, 1–154. This extensive treatise, besides being one of the most complete extant Sanskrit treatises on divination, is very valuable for the information it contains about Indian geography and society; see, for instance, J. F. Fleet, "The Topographical List of the Brihat-Sanhita," in *Indian Antiquary*, 22 (1893), 169–195; and A. M. Shastri, *India as Seen in the Bṛhatsaṃhitā of Varāhamihira* (Delhi-Patna-Varanasi, 1969).

3. The *Samāsasaṃhitā*, Varāhamihira's shorter work on divination. This is now lost, but many of the quotations from it can be found in A. M. Shastri, "Contribution Towards the Reconstruction of the Samāsa-Saṃhitā of Varāhamihira," in *Bhāratīya Vidyā*, 23 (1963), 22–39.

4. The *Vaṭakaṇikā*, a third work on divination, is also lost save for some quoted verses; see P. V. Kane, "The Vaṭakaṇikā of Varāhamihira," in *Vishveshvaranand Indological Journal*, 1 (1963), 63–65.

5. The *Bṛhajjātaka*, Varāhamihira's major work on genethlialogy; it has often been commented on and often translated. The most useful commentary is that of Utpala (966), published, for example, at Bombay in 1864. This is still the standard work on natal horoscopy in India. For its relation to Greek astrology, see *The Yavanajātaka of Sphujidhvaja*, D. Pingree, ed., which is to appear in the Harvard Oriental Series.

6. The *Laghujātaka* is the shorter treatise on genethlialogy. It also was commented on by Utpala, and it was translated into Arabic by al-Bīrūnī, who inserted it into his *India*. There are many editions: for example, with the Hindī *orṭikā* of Kāśīrāma (Bombay, 1936). Unfortunately, there exists no critical edition of either of these popular textbooks on genethlialogy.

7. The *Bṛhadyātrā* is a major treatise on military astrology. An edition of it with the surviving fragment of Utpala's commentary, prepared by D. Pingree, is in *Bulletin of the Government Oriental Manuscripts Library, Madras*, 20 (1972), 1, app., 1–92; 2, app., i–xiv; and 93–130; repr. (Madras, 1972).

8. The *Yogayātrā* is a shorter text on military astrology. The first nine chapters were published by H. Kern, "Die Yogayātrā des Varāhamihira," in *Indische Studien*, **10** (1868), 161–212; **14** (1876), 312–358; and **15** (1878), 167–184; and the whole, in imperfect fashion, by J. Lal (Lahore, 1944). A critical edition of the text with the commentary of Utpala has been prepared by D. Pingree.

9. The *Ṭikaṇikāyātrā* is a third treatise on military astrology. It was edited by V. R. Pandit, "Ṭikanikayātrā of Varāhamihira," in *Journal of the University of Bombay*, **20** (*Arts*, No. 26) (1951), 40–63.

10. The *Vivāhapaṭala*, a text on astrology as related to marriage, is preserved in a unique manuscript at Baroda. An edition has been prepared by V. R. Pandit.

BIBLIOGRAPHY

Additional bibliographical references to those given above will be found in O. Neugebauer and D. Pingree, *Pañcasiddhāntikā*, II, pp. 152–154; A. M. Shastri, *India as Seen in the Bṛhatsaṃhitā*, pp. 504–515; and D. Pingree, *Census of the Exact Sciences in Sanskrit*, series A, V (forthcoming).

DAVID PINGREE

VARENIUS, BERNHARDUS (**Bernhard Varen**) (*b.* Hitzacker, in the district of Hannover, Germany, 1622; *d.* Amsterdam, Holland, 1650), *physical geography*.

Son of the court preacher to the duke of Brunswick, Varenius spent his early years at Uelzen, the home of the duke. From 1640 to 1642 he studied in the Gymnasium of Hamburg, and from there he went to the universities at Königsberg (1643–1645) and Leiden (1645–1649), devoting himself to mathematics, medicine, and natural history. He took his medical degree at Leiden in 1649, and settled in Amsterdam with the intention of practicing medicine.

From some remarks in his writing it is evident that Varenius felt he had little future in Hannover, which had been devastated by the Thirty Years' War. In Amsterdam the recent discoveries of Abel Tasman, Willem Schouten, and other Dutch navigators, and his friendship with Willem Blaeu as well as other geographers led him to concentrate on geography rather than medicine, much to his own economic detriment.

Varenius was a prolific writer, although two of his early works, an academic treatise on motion according to Aristotle, which he wrote at Hamburg in 1642, and a table of universal history written at Amsterdam in 1649, were probably never published and are not now extant. His first significant works were the *Descriptio regni Japoniae* and the *Tractatus de religione Japoniae*. These works of special geography are usually regarded as a single book in part because they were published under the title of *Descriptio regni Japoniae et Siam, cum brevi informatione de diversis omnium religionibus* (Amsterdam, 1649). In actuality, the volume consisted of five separate works—a description of Japan by Varenius, a Latin translation of Jodocus Schouten's account of Siam, the discourse on religion in Japan by Varenius, excerpts from Leo Africanus on religion in Africa, and a short *Dissertatio de Rebuspublica in genere*.

The best known of Varenius' works is his *Geographia generalis* (Amsterdam, 1650), which established a framework for physical geography capable of including new facts of discovery as they arose. The work became the standard geographic text for more than a century. Varenius believed that there were three ways by which the truth of geographical propositions could be established, first by geometrical, arithmetical, and trigonometrical means; second by astronomical precepts and theorems; and third by experience. In the case of special geography, only celestial properties can be proven, and the remainder must rest on the experience either of the writer or of other observers. His *Geographia generalis* was divided into three sections. In the first he examined the mathematical facts relating to the earth, including its figure, dimensions, motions, and measurements. In the second part he examined the effect of the sun, stars, climates, and seasons on the earth and the differences of apparent time at various places. In the third part he treated briefly the actual divisions of the surface of the earth and laid down the principles of what is now known as regional geography. Each area was to be classified according to terrestrial information, including longitude, the nature of the terrain, and fertility; by celestial information, including the distance of the place from the pole, the climate, and the length of day and night; and finally by human information, including the status of the inhabitants, and their art, trade, virtues, vices, ceremonies, speech, and religion. Varenius' work long held the position as the best treatise on scientific and comparative geography. Humboldt and others were much impressed by it, and Newton revised parts of it for an edition published in England.

BIBLIOGRAPHY

I. ORIGINAL WORKS. Varenius' *Descriptio regni Japoniae et Siam, cum brevi informatione de diversis omnium religionibus* went through four editions, the last published in 1673. There was also a German summary of the description of Japan published at Jena in 1670. The brief treatise on religions of the world was included as an appendix in Alexander Ross, *Pansebeia* (London, 1653).

The *Geographia generalis*, according to the research of Gottfried Lange, went through fifteen complete and four partial editions in five European languages, plus ten in a summarized French version. There was also a summarized Japanese version published in 1932. Four editions were published by Elzevir in Amsterdam in 1650, 1664, 1671, and 1672. Newton's revision was published at Cambridge in 1672 and 1681, and at Jena in 1693. Another edition edited by James Jurin was published at Cambridge in 1712 and at Naples in 1715. The first English translation was by Richard Blome (London, 1682), and this was reprinted twice before 1693. A second English translation based upon Jurin's edition, translated by Dugdale and revised by Shaw, went through four editions between 1733 and 1765. A Dutch translation appeared in 1755 and a French translation by Philippe-Florent de Puisieux in that same year. A Russian version was published in Moscow in 1718 and a second one at St. Petersburg in 1790. The ten French summaries by Guillaume Sanson appeared between 1681 and 1743. In addition, Varenius wrote several brief works on human ecology published in Amsterdam in 1650.

II. SECONDARY LITERATURE. For discussions of Varenius and his work see J. N. L. Baker, "The Geography of Bernhard Varenius," in *Transactions of the Institute of British Geographers*, no. 21 (1955), 51–60; and Gottfried Lange, "Das Werk der Varenius: Eine kritische Gesamtbibliographie," in *Erdkunde*, **15** (1961), 10–18. See also Gottfried Lange, "Varenius über die Grundfragen der Geographie: Ein Beitrag zur Problemgeschichte der geographischen Wissenschaft," in *Petermanns geographische Mitteilungen*, **105** (1961), 274–283; and Hans Offe, "Bernard Varenius (1622–1650)," in *Geographisches Taschenbuch und Jahrweiser zur Landeskunde* (1960–1961), 435–438.

The most detailed study of Varenius' life was done by Siegmund Günther, *Varenius* (Leipzig, 1905), but his study has been much supplemented by works cited above. The brief biography by F. Ratzel, "Bernard Varenius," in *Allgemeine Deutsche Biographie*, XXXIX (Leipzig, 1895), must now be regarded as somewhat inaccurate.

VERN L. BULLOUGH

VARIGNON, PIERRE (*b.* Caen, France, 1654; *d.* Paris, France, 23 December 1722), *mathematics, mechanics.*

It is due to Lagrange that Varignon's name gained recognition in the teaching of mechanics in France in the nineteenth century, and until rather recently his name was linked with a theorem on the composition of forces that is now identified with the properties of the vector product. The passage of time diminishes this kind of fame; but historians are discovering in Varignon's work—which, admittedly, is of second rank with regard to substantive results—an importance for the philosophy of science. Expressive of the attempt to reduce the number of basic principles in mechanics in order to improve the organization of the subject, Varignon's accomplishments illustrate the relationship between this effort and progress made in notation and in operational procedures in pure mathematics.

The son and brother of contracting masons, Varignon stated that his entire patrimony consisted of his family's technical knowledge; it proved, however, to be of considerable importance for his later career. He probably studied at the Jesuit *collège* in Caen, which he would have entered at a relatively late age. The only certain information about this period of his life, however, is that relating to his entrance into the religious life: he submitted to the tonsure on 19 December 1676, earned his Master of Arts degree on 15 September 1682, and became a priest in the St.-Ouen parish of Caen on 10 March 1683. An ecclesiastical career enabled him to study at the University of Caen, where he was certainly one of the oldest students.

One of Varignon's fellow students was Charles Castel, Abbé de Saint-Pierre (1658–1743), who later achieved fame for his philanthropy. Saint-Pierre soon offered to share his lodgings and income with Varignon. The two left Caen for Paris in 1686. When Varignon reached Paris, he had already done considerable scientific research; and the contacts he made through Saint-Pierre accomplished the rest. As early as 1687 he had access to Pierre Bayle's periodical, *Nouvelles de la république des lettres*, for the publication of his memoir on tackle blocks for pulleys, and his first published book, *Projet d'une nouvelle méchanique*, was dedicated to the Académie des Sciences.

Although not to be compared with Newton's *Principia*, which appeared in the same year as Varignon's *Projet*, their simultaneous publication perhaps brought the latter work a greater success among French scientists than it would otherwise have had. In any case, the success of the *Projet* brought Varignon nomination as geometer in the Académie des Sciences in 1688, as well as the first appointment to the newly created professorship of mathematics at the Collège Mazarin. Within two years, therefore, Varignon was set in his career. He taught—and resided—at the Collège Mazarin until his death. In 1704 the former secretary of the Academy, Jean-Baptiste du Hamel, resigned in Varignon's favor from the chair of Greek and Latin philosophy at the Collège Royal (now the Collège de France). The title of the chair in no way restricted the scientific topics that could be taught by its holder, who had sole discretion in this regard.

Fully occupied by his teaching duties and his responsibilities as an academician, Varignon had no leisure to prepare works for publication. After a short second work, *Nouvelles conjectures sur la pesanteur* (1690), his literary production consisted of articles for learned journals and a large number of memoirs submitted to the Academy. His correspondence, however, particularly with Leibniz and Johann I Bernoulli, bears witness to his role in the scientific life of his age. From the papers he left at his death, most of which are now lost, his disciples assembled several posthumous works: *Nouvelle mécanique* (announced in the *Projet* of 1687) and *Éclaircissemens sur l'analyse des infiniment petits*, both published in 1725, and *Élémens de mathématiques* (1731), which was based on his courses at the Collège Mazarin.

Varignon's intense pedagogical activity, extending over more than thirty years, constituted his chief contribution to the progress of science and was the source of his fame. By inaugurating a chair devoted specifically to mathematics at the Collège Mazarin, he joined the handful of men who were then teaching advanced mathematics; and it is in this context that his work was of great importance.

Bossut and Montucla, writing the history of mathematics half a century later, were unable to ignore Varignon; but, lacking the necessary historical distance, they were unjustly severe. Bossut, for example, wrote: "Endowed with an excellent memory, Varignon read a great deal, closely examined the writings of the pioneers [*inventeurs*], generalized their methods, and appropriated their ideas; and some students took disguised or enlarged reformulations to be discoveries." But since the essential precondition of a teacher's effectiveness is that he constantly broaden his knowledge and keep it current, Bossut should have praised Varignon for having done just that, instead of condemning him for not sufficiently citing his sources. The latter judgment is, of course, possible; but Varignon's writings offer no incontrovertible support for it. Montucla's evaluation was more penetrating; he criticized Varignon primarily for what may be called a mania for "generalization." Certainly, Varignon had neither a precise nor an acceptable notion of that process and often confused it with the mere use of algebraic language. Viewed in its historical context, however, this failing is not at all astonishing.

The pejorative assessments of Bossut and Montucla were echoed by Pierre Duhem, who in his *Origines de la statique* (1905–1906) wrote ironically of Varignon's naïve belief in his own originality in mechanics. Yet, like earlier criticisms, Duhem's is not wholly justified. The audacity that average intellects must needs muster in order to fight for progressive ideas always presupposes a certain naïveté on their part. Indeed, the more it becomes evident that Varignon was not a genius, the less the defects of his thought ought to be allowed to weigh against estimates of his real accomplishments.

From this point of view, Lagrange underscored the essential point. In the posthumous edition of the *Nouvelle mécanique* he found the text of a letter from Johann Bernoulli to Varignon (26 January 1717) marking the emergence of the principle of virtual velocities, and he realized that in this matter Varignon deserves credit on two counts: for preparing the way for and eliciting Bernoulli's statement, and for attempting to provide the broadest justification of the principle. Thus the period between the *Projet* of 1687 and the *Nouvelle mécanique* witnessed the development of what appeared a century later to be the very foundation of classical mechanics.

Lagrange was not mistaken, either, about Varignon's active role in the initial development of the principle of the composition of forces. The technique of composing forces by the rule of the parallelogram had undergone more than a century of development when it was published, simultaneously, in 1687 in Newton's *Principia*, Varignon's *Projet*, and the second edition of Bernard Lamy's *Traitez de méchanique*. The enunciation of the principle, which appeared as a consequence of the composition of infinitely small movements and not of finite ones, eliminated a troublesome confusion that had hampered progress in the subject.

The simultaneous publication of the principle makes difficult any judgment regarding priority. Nevertheless, it was Varignon alone who grasped two important points. The first is that the law of the lever does not hold a privileged position in statics, and that the unification of "mechanics" (the science of simple machines) was to be carried out on the basis of the composition of forces. The second concerns the inclined plane: that the real reason for the equilibrium observed is that the resultant of the applied forces is orthogonal to the possible displacement. These two points provide a good indication of Varignon's contribution to the development of the principle of virtual velocities.

It must, of course, be added that his contribution was limited to general statics; but this was the point of departure for d'Alembert's subsequent extension of the principle to dynamics. In the latter field Varignon did not solve any of the important problems of his time—as Bossut correctly observed. Nevertheless, in his memoirs to the Academy, he showed how to apply infinitesimal analysis to the science of motion and how, in specific cases, to use the relationship between force and acceleration. The laborious nature of this work does not detract from its historical importance.

In working with the model of falling bodies, Varignon encountered difficulties in obtaining acceleration as a second derivative. This problem had the advantage, however, of obliging him to reassess the importance of the new differential and integral calculus. His acceptance of the new procedures occurred between 1692 and 1695, and he was among those who gave the most favorable reception to the publication of L'Hospital's *Analyse des infiniment petits* in 1696. The *Éclaircissemens* is composed of critical notes that Varignon, as a professor, considered necessary in presenting L'Hospital's pioneering work to young mathematicians—further evidence of his constructive role in the movement to transform the operations used in mathematics. But Varignon accomplished even more: in 1700–1701 he refuted Rolle's arguments against the new calculus, challenged the cabal that had formed within the Academy, and obliged Leibniz to furnish a more precise account of his ideas. Leibniz, to be sure, did not give him all the aid desired. Nevertheless, he encouraged Varignon to cease debating principles and to start developing mechanical applications of the new mathematics. The questions that Varignon subsequently treated show how faithfully he followed Leibniz' advice.

In his course at the Collège Royal for 1722–1723, Varignon planned to discuss the foundations of infinitesimal calculus but was able to do no more than outline his ideas. Although he died before he could present what was undoubtedly the core of a lifetime's experience, that experience had already borne fruit.

BIBLIOGRAPHY

I. Original Works. Varignon's books include *Projet d'une nouvelle méchanique* (Paris, 1687); *Nouvelles conjectures sur la pesanteur* (Paris, 1690); *Éclaircissemens sur l'analyse des infiniment petits* (Paris, 1725); *Nouvelle mécanique ou statique* . . ., 2 vols. (Paris, 1725); *Traité du mouvement et de la mesure des eaux coulantes et jaillissantes* . . . (Paris, 1725); and *Élémens de mathématiques* . . . (Paris, 1731).

His major published articles are "Démonstration générale de l'usage des poulies à moufle," in *Nouvelles de la république des lettres* (May 1687), 487–498; a sequel to the preceding article containing "une nouvelle démonstration du paradoxe de M. Mariotte," in *Histoire des ouvrages des sçavans*, **1** (Oct. 1687), 172–176; "Règles du mouvement en général," in *Mémoires de mathématiques et de physique tirés des registres de l'Académie* . . . (1692), 190–195; "Des cycloïdes ou roulettes à l'infini," *ibid.* (1693), 43–47; "Règles des mouvemens accélérés suivant toutes les proportions imaginables d'accélérations ordonnées," *ibid.*, 93–96; "Méthode pour trouver des courbes le long desquelles un corps tombant s'approche ou s'eloigne de l'horizon en telle raison des temps qu'on voudra . . .," in *Mémoires de l'Académie royale des sciences* (1699), 1–13.

Later works are "Du mouvement en général par toutes sortes de courbes et des forces centrales tant centrifuges que centripètes, nécessaires aux corps qui les décrivent," *ibid.* (1700), 83–101; "Application au mouvement des planètes," *ibid.*, 218–237; "De la figure ou curvité des fusées des horloges à ressort," *ibid.* (1702), 192–202; "Du mouvement des eaux . . .," *ibid.* (1703), 238–261; "Du mouvement des planètes sur leurs orbes en y comprenant le mouvement de l'apogée on de l'aphélie," *ibid.* (1705), 347–361; "Différentes manières infiniment générales de trouver les rayons osculateurs de toutes sortes de courbes . . .," *ibid.* (1706), 490–507; "Des mouvements faits dans des milieux qui leur résistent en raison quelconque," *ibid.* (1707), 382–476; "Des forces centrales inverses," *ibid.* (1710), 533–544; "Réflexions sur l'usage que la mécanique peut avoir en géométrie," *ibid.* (1714), 77–121; and "Précaution à prendre dans l'usage des suites ou séries infinies . . .," *ibid.* (1715), 203–225.

II. Secondary Literature. See Pierre Costabel, "Contribution à l'histoire de la loi de la chute des graves," in *Revue d'histoire des sciences et de leurs applications*, **1** (1947), 193–205; "Le paradoxe de Mariotte," in *Archives internationales d'histoire des sciences*, **2** (1948), 864–886); "Pierre Varignon et la diffusion en France du calcul différentiel et intégral," *Conférences du Palais de la découverte*, ser. D, no. 108 (1965); and "Varignon, Lamy et le parallélogramme des forces," in *Archives internationales d'histoire des sciences*, **19**, nos. 74–75 (1966), 103–124; J. O. Fleckenstein, "Pierre Varignon und die mathematischen Wissenschaften in Zeitalter des Cartesianismus," *ibid.*, **2** (1948), 76–138; and Bernard de Fontenelle, "Éloge de M. Varignon," in *Histoire et mémoires de l'Académie des sciences* for 1722, 189–204.

PIERRE COSTABEL

VAROLIO, COSTANZO (*b.* Bologna, Italy, 1543; *d.* Rome, Italy, 1575), *medicine.*

Varolio, the son of Sebastiano Varolio, a Bolognese citizen, studied medicine at the University of Bologna. He displayed interest and aptitude in particular for anatomy, which he pursued under the direction of Giulio Cesare Aranzio. Varolio received his medical degree in 1567, and in 1569 was given the extraordinary chair of surgery, which carried with it the responsibility of teaching anatomy as well. He held this position until 1572, when he went to Rome. There is little positive biographical information about Varolio and, consequently, some difference of opinion as to whether or not he went to Rome upon invitation to join the medical faculty of the Sapienza, the papal university. Contrary to former positive assertions, Varolio's name appears not to have been listed in the *rotuli* of that institution. Moreover, there is also question as to whether he had been invited to become the physician or surgeon of Pope Gregory XIII or, indeed, had any appointment at all in the papal medical service. In any case, Varolio was esteemed by the pope and enjoyed his patronage during the three years that he was in Rome. According to a contemporary commemorative inscription—which refers to Varolio's anatomical lectures and demonstrations "*in gymnasio Romano*"—he is declared to have died "from an unknown ailment."

During his short life Varolio wrote two books, *De nervis opticis nonnullisque aliis praeter communem opinionem in humano capite observatis* (Padua, 1573), illustrated with three views of the brain drawn by the author, and the posthumously published *Anatomiae sive de resolutione corporis humani libri IIII* (Frankfurt, 1591), which has been described as a teleologic physiology of man, but which contains a reprint of *De nervis opticis*. It has furthermore been asserted that Varolio was the author of a work entitled *De cerebro*, published at Frankfurt in 1591, and of a large anatomical treatise in four books with many illustrations that was being printed at the time of his death. Neither attribution appears to be correct; in both instances there was apparently confusion with the existing posthumous *Anatomiae libri IIII*, which contains no illustrations except for the three figures of the brain that appeared originally in the earlier work of 1573.

De nervis optics, the source of Varolio's anatomical reputation, consists of a letter to Girolamo Mercuriale dated 1 April 1572, the latter's reply, and a response by Varolio. The book was published without Varolio's consent or knowledge through the efforts of Paolo Aicardi, a disciple of Mercuriale.

From Galenic times onward the brain had been dissected *in situ* by means of a series of horizontal slices begun at the uppermost part of the cerebral hemispheres. Varolio, "considering most organs of the brain to be near the base of the head, and the brain by its weight, especially in the dead body, to compress them between itself and the skull," judged the usual method of dissection "to be hindered by many obstacles." In consequence he used a new method by which he first removed the brain from the skull, turned it over, and dissected it from below, beginning at its base. "If one proceeds in this way," he wrote, "each of [the brain's] organs may be observed as completely as desirable." Although he referred to his new method of dissection as "unusual" and "very difficult," it did permit a better observation of the structures of the brain, notably the cranial nerves, and was widely followed. It was in consequence of his new technique that Varolio was able for the first time to observe and describe the pons, still known as the *pons Varolii*, so called because the spinal marrow was "carried under this transverse spinal process as a flowing stream is carried under a bridge." Although Varolio considered the pons to be part of the cerebellum, it has more recently been attributed to the brain stem.

As a result of this new method of dissecting the brain, Varolio was able to make some contributions to the knowledge of the course and terminations of the cranial nerves. In the instance of the optic nerve, which provided the title of the book, he traced its course approximately to the true termination. He also suggested that the spinal cord had four tracts, two anterior serving sensation and two posterior for cerebellar functions.

BIBLIOGRAPHY

Varolio's two books, mentioned above, are very rare, *De nervis opticis* especially so. This work has been reprinted in facsimile (Brussels, 1969).

Works giving biographical information about Varolio are scanty and many data must be used with caution. They are, in chronological order, Gaetano Marini, *Degli archiatri pontifici*, I (Rome, 1784), xxxviii, 429; Giovanni Fantuzzi, *Notizie degli scrittori bolognese*, VIII (Bologna, 1790), 158–160; Michele Medici, *Compendio storico della Scuola Anatomica di Bologna* (Bologna, 1857), 84–90; Umberto Dallari, *I rotuli dei lettori legisti e artisti dello Studio Bolognese dal 1384 al 1799*, II (Bologna, 1889), 176, 179, 182; and Ludwig Choulant, *History and Bibliography of Anatomic Illustration*, Mortimer Frank, trans. (Chicago, 1920), 214–215. There is also some information on Varolio as an anatomist in Antoine Portal, *Histoire de l'anatomie et de la chirurgie*, II (Paris, 1770), 28–38.

C. D. O'MALLEY

VARRO, MARCUS TERENTIUS (*b.* Reate, Italy, 116 B.C.; *d.* Rome, 27 B.C.), *encyclopedism, polymathy, biology.*

Varro, whom Quintilian dubbed "the most learned of the Romans," came from an obscure equestrian family at Reate in the Sabine country. He studied under the Stoic grammarian L. Aelius Stilo at Rome and with the Academic philosopher Antiochus of Ascalon at Athens. Varro devoted most of his life to public service. From 86 B.C. to 43 B.C., he proceeded through the ranks of the *cursus honorum* until he reached the office of praetor. During the Civil War he led Pompeian forces in Spain; after the death of Pompey he was pardoned by Caesar. In 47 B.C. Caesar appointed him director of the proposed public library at Rome. Proscribed by Antony in 43 B.C., Varro's villa and library were seized. Having escaped the death sentence, he devoted the remainder of his life to scholarship.

Varro was the most prolific of all Roman authors, writing more than 620 books under seventy-four different titles. Of these works, only the three books of *De re rustica* are substantially complete. Books V to X are extant from the twenty-five-book study *De lingua Latina*. For Varro's other writings, only fragments are extant. His lost works include the 150 books of the popular *Saturae Menippeae*, the treatises of the *Logistoricon libri LXXVI*, the 700 illustrated biographies of famous Greeks and Romans in the *Imagines*, the *Antiquitatum rerum humanarum et divinarum libri XLI*, and the highly influential *Disciplinarum libri IX*.

Varro began his agricultural treatise *De re rustica* when he was eighty years old. Written in the form of a dialogue, this handbook on husbandry discusses general agricultural practices, domestic cattle, and small livestock—poultry, game birds, bees, and fish. The three books of this study were based on Greek and Latin sources and on Varro's own agricultural experiences. It presents a comprehensive view of Roman farming techniques.

De lingua Latina is a philological study of the Latin language. In its entirety it contained an examination of etymology, inflections, and syntax. While its etymology is often fanciful, it does contain perceptive comments on early Latin words. The extant portions of this treatise include approximately half of the books on etymology and inflections.

Varro's most lasting scientific legacy was the orientation he gave to later scholarship. In his lost *Disciplinarum libri IX*, Varro introduced the Greek encyclopedic tradition into Roman thought. The *Disciplinae* was an encyclopedia of the liberal arts based on Greek sources. Containing chapters on the traditional Greek *trivium* (grammar, rhetoric, and logic) and *quadrivium* (arithmetic, geometry, astronomy, and music), along with sections on medicine and architecture, it was designed to provide a survey of the knowledge needed by a free man. Later scholars deleted medicine and architecture, which became professional studies, and retained the subjects of Varro's *trivium* and *quadrivium* as the basis for medieval education.

Varro's work popularized both the encyclopedic tradition and the liberal arts. Ultimately, handbooks and encyclopedias based on excerpts from the writings of earlier authorities became a fundamental part of Roman scientific thought.

BIBLIOGRAPHY

I. ORIGINAL WORKS. From antiquity to the present, Varro's *De re rustica* has usually appeared with Cato's agricultural treatise. The *editio princeps* of Varro's study was published by Nicolas Jenson at Venice in 1472. Other editions soon followed at Bologna in 1494 and Venice in 1514. Modern editions include those published at Leipzig in 1884 and 1929, and at Cambridge in 1935.

De lingua Latina has also appeared in a number of editions. The date and place of publication of the *editio princeps* by Pomponius Laetus is unknown. There were a number of fifteenth- and sixteenth-century editions: Rome, 1474; Venice, 1475, 1483, 1492, 1498, 1513; Milan, 1510; and Paris, 1529. There have also been a number of modern editions: Berlin, 1826; Leipzig, 1910; and Cambridge, 1938.

II. SECONDARY LITERATURE. Accounts of Varro's life and works may be found in Conrad Cichorius, *His-*

torische Studien zu Varro (Bonn, 1922), 189–241; Gaston Boissier, *Étude sur la vie et ouvrages de M. T. Varron* (Paris, 1861); Hellfried Dahlmann, "M. Terentius Varro" in Pauly-Wissowa, *Real-Encyclopädie der classischen Altertumswissenschaft*, supp. vol. VI (1935), 1172–1277; Jens Erik Skydsgaard, *Varro the Scholar* (Copenhagen, 1968); and William H. Stahl, *Roman Science* (Madison, Wis., 1962).

Numerous bibliographical references may be found in *L'année philologique*.

PHILLIP DRENNON THOMAS

VASSALE, GIULIO (*b.* Lerici, Italy, 22 June 1862; *d.* Modena, Italy, 3 January 1913), *endocrinology.*

One of the outstanding endocrinologists of his generation, Vassale contributed to the early development of that science in Italy. He began to study medicine at the University of Modena but transferred to Turin, from which he graduated in 1887 with a thesis on regeneration of the gastric mucous membrane. In the same year he was appointed assistant to the professor of general pathology and pathological anatomy at Modena, and in 1889 he was employed at the asylum of Reggio nell'Emilia as a dissector. In 1894 he was named substitute teacher of general pathology at Modena, and in 1898 full professor. He died, a bachelor, of cancer at the age of fifty.

A pupil of Bizzozero, Vassale began his scientific activity as a histologist at Turin, with microscopic observations of the gastric mucosa, *Sulla riproduzione della mucosa gastrica* (1888). This work, started in 1887 as his doctorate thesis, demonstrated that the canine gastric epithelium and gastric glands were regenerated, after aseptic excision of the mucous coat, by proliferation from elements of the glands contiguous to the edges of the excision. By 1889, however, Vassale had become interested in neurology. He spent twenty years (1890–1910) in experimental research on internal secretions, principally those of the thyroid, parathyroid, and adrenal glands.

In 1890 Vassale studied the changes in the canine pancreas following the ligature of Wirsung's duct, and the following year he demonstrated the independence of the islands of Langerhans from the pancreatic digestive gland. In contrast with the pancreatic digestive gland (which underwent atrophy), the islands of Langerhans were not damaged by ligature of Wirsung's duct; and there was no glycosuria. This observation marked the beginning of the insular theory of diabetes.

In November 1890, Vassale demonstrated that an aqueous extract of the thyroid gland quickly suppresses the serious results of thyroid failure. His conclusions were confirmed in animals in 1891 by M. E. Gley and in man by George B. Murray in the same year. Vassale had been anticipated, however, by Gustavo Pisenti of Perugia, who had administered intravenous injections of aqueous extracts of thyroid early in 1890.

In 1892 Vassale demonstrated the cachexia following experimental destruction of the hypophysis; and his experiments on animals were contemporary with those of Gley and Gheorgi Marinescu. From 1896 to 1906 he studied the effects of a total parathyroidectomy and demonstrated, in dogs, that acute tetany was not due to insufficiency of the thyroid but resulted from the inadvertent ablation of the parathyroid when the thyroid was removed.

From 1898 to 1908 Vassale investigated the physiopathology of the adrenal glands and helped to differentiate their medullary and cortical components. In 1902 he demonstrated that acute adrenal insufficiency is due to insufficiency of the medulla alone. Three years later he showed that adrenaline, the substance active in the elevation of blood pressure, was produced only by the medullar cells of the adrenal glands.

BIBLIOGRAPHY

I. ORIGINAL WORKS. Vassale's writings include *Sulla riproduzione della mucosa gastrica* (Modena, 1888); "Intorno agli effetti della iniezione di succo di tiroide nei cani operati di estirpazione della tiroide," in *Rivista sperimentale di freniatria e medicina legale delle alienazioni mentali*, **16** (1890), 439–455; *Ricerche microscopiche e sperimentali sulle alterazioni del pancreas consecutive alla legatura del dotto di Wirsung* (Reggio nell'Emilia, 1891); "Sulla distruzione della ghiandola pituitaria," *ibid.*, **18** (1892), 525–561; "Sugli effetti dell'estirpazione delle ghiandole paratiroidee," in *Rivista di patologia nervosa e mentale*, **1** (1896), 95–99; "Sugli effetti dello svuotamento delle capsule soprarenali," in *Bollettino della Società medico-chirurgica di Modena* (meeting of 12 Feb. 1898); and *Fisiopatologia delle ghiandole a secrezione interna* (Modena, 1914), a reprint of all Vassale's works on endocrinology, issued by the Medical School of Modena.

II. SECONDARY LITERATURE. See R. Abderhalden, "Le secrezioni interne," in *Ciba Review*, **5** (1951), 916; L. Castaldi, "Il precursore della preparazione della insulina," in *Riforma medica*, **15** (1929); E. Centanni, "Giulio Vassale," in *Biochimica e terapia sperimentale*, **4** (1913), 193–198; J. Derrien, *Étude historique et critique sur le traitement du myxoedème par les injections de liquide thyroïdien* (Paris, 1893), a doctoral dissertation; V. Diamare, "Documenti per la storia della teoria insulare del diabete, e sui precedenti dell'insulina," in *Archivio di fisiologia*, **22** (1924), 141–157; U. Lombroso, "Sugli elementi che compiono la funzione interna del pancreas," in *Archivio di farmacologia sperimentale e scienze affini*, **7** (1908), 170–218, a critical and precise review with a rich bibliography; G. Pisenti, "Le basi dell'opoterapia tiroidea," in *Terapia* (Milan), **20** (1930), 193–195; and M. Segale, "Giulio Vassale," in *Pathologica*, **5** (1913), 137–145, with bibliography and portrait.

PIETRO FRANCESCHINI

VASTARINI-CRESI, GIOVANNI (*b.* Taranto, Italy, 1870; *d.* Naples, Italy, 14 April 1924), *anatomy, histology.*

Vastarini-Cresi was lecturer, assistant professor, and then from 1905 in charge of microscopic anatomy in the Naples Anatomical Institute. In 1919 Vastarini-Cresi was appointed head of the institute and was succeeded by Giovanni Antonelli, Giunio Salvi, and Riccardo Versari. Vastarini-Cresi led an austere life, entirely devoted to scientific activity and to teaching numerous pupils, especially in the histological field. A scrupulous and intelligent researcher, and the author of appreciated works on morphology, he studied arteriovenous anastomosis and the hypopharynx in man. He made excellent contributions to histological technique, especially with the method of glycogen-staining in tissues that bears his name. Lambertini reported that in studying the taste organ Vastarini-Cresi (1) asserted that vallate papillae can also arise from the rear part of the tongue, contrary to His's doctrine, which restricts the territory of origin of the taste buds to the *tuberculum impar* only; (2) demonstrated the presence of a double vallate papilla rising from the declivity of Morgagni's foramen cecum and observed the presence of retrocecal vallate papillae; and (3) described that in the lingual innervation, in addition to branches going to the taste buds on its own sides, the glossopharynx also sends fibers passing to the opposite side and reaching the central circumvallate papilla of the foramen cecum. On Vastarini-Cresi and his work, see Gastone Lambertini, *Dizionario anatomico* (Naples, 1949), 216, 279, 564; and "Necrologio di Giovanni Vastarini-Cresi," in *Monitore zoologico italiano*, **35** (1924), 104.

BRUNO ZANOBIO

VAṬEŚVARA (*b.* 880 at Ānandapura [modern Wadnagar], Gujarat, India), *astronomy.*

The son of Mahadatta Bhaṭṭa, Vaṭeśvara wrote a *Vaṭeśvarasiddhānta* at the age of twenty-four (that is, in 904), in which he frequently follows, but at times severely criticizes, the *Brāhmasphuṭasiddhānta* of Brahmagupta (born 598); basically Vaṭeśvara's text belongs to the Āryapakṣa (see essay in Supplement). The manuscripts of this work are exceedingly rare so that its contents beyond the first three chapters, which have been published, remain obscure; but what is known makes it clear that this is an extremely important work for understanding the developments that took place in Indian astronomy between Brahmagupta and Bhāskara II (born 1115), particularly because of Vaṭeśvara's explicit criticisms of his predecessors modeled on Brahmagupta's eleventh chapter, the *Tantraparīkṣā.*

The only other work of Vaṭeśvara that we know of is an astronomical handbook, *Karaṇasāra*, which is lost in Sanskrit, but which was often cited by al-Bīrūnī (born 973) in his *India*, his *Transits*, and his *Al-Qānūn al-Masʿūdī*. From the former (chap. 49 and 53) we learn that the epoch of the *Karaṇasāra* was A.D. 899; this is confirmed by the *Karaṇasāra's* computation of the assumed motion of the Saptarṣis (Ursa Major) in the *India* (chap. 45) and in the *Qānūn* (IX, 1). Al-Bīrūnī, however, calls the author of the *Karaṇasāra* "Batīshfar ibn Mahadatta from the city of Nāgarapūr," which Sachau erroneously translates "Vitteśvara, the son of Bhadatta" (*India*, chap. 14); the name Nāgarapura refers to the fact that Anandapura was the center of the Nāgara Brāhmaṇas. There is, then, no doubt about the identity of the authors of the *Vaṭeśvarasiddhānta* and of the *Karaṇasāra.*

BIBLIOGRAPHY

A first volume of an edition of the *Vaṭeśvarasiddhānta* with Sanskrit and Hindī commentaries was published by Ram Swarup Sharma and Mukund Mishra (New Delhi, 1962); many errors in the commentary are corrected by T. S. Kuppanna Shastri, "The System of the *Vaṭeśvara Siddhānta*," in *Indian Journal of History of Science*, **4** (1969), 135–143. See also R. N. Rai, "Sine Values of the *Vaṭeśvarasiddhānta*," *ibid.*, **7** (1972), 1–15; and "Calculation of *Ahargaṇa*, in the *Vaṭeśvarasiddhānta*," *ibid.*, 27–37; and K. S. Shukla, "Hindu Astronomer Vaṭeśvara and His Works," in *Gaṇita*, **23** (1972), 2, 65–74.

DAVID PINGREE

VAUBAN, SÉBASTIEN LE PRESTRE DE (*b.* St.-Léger-de-Fougeret [now St.-Léger-Vauban], near Avallon, Burgundy, France, 15 May 1633; *d.* Paris, France, 30 March 1707), *military engineering.*

France's greatest military engineer—the famous "taker of cities"—and a dedicated public servant of Louis XIV, Vauban scarcely deserves to be called a scientist. Although made an honorary member of the Royal Academy of Sciences in his old age, it was less for any scientific attainments than for his long, devoted, and manifold services to France. He never distinguished himself in mathematics or physics like Lazare Carnot or Coulomb, both trained as military engineers. Vauban was a practical man of little culture and sparse scientific training who was skilled in the application of simple arithmetic and geometry and the elementary principles of surveying and civil engineering to fortification and siegecraft. Above all he had range and flexibility of mind, common sense, and the tact and insight that comes from long experience.

Vauban's family was of modest origin—notaries and small merchants of Bazoches in the climatically rugged Morvan. In the sixteenth century one member of Vauban's family entered the lesser nobility through the purchase of a small fief. Vauban's father boasted the title of "Écuyer, Seigneur de Champignolle et de Vauban." Saint-Simon from his lofty social eminence called Vauban a "petit gentilhomme de Bourgogne, tout au plus."

Of Vauban's youth little is known. At first he was taught by the village curate of St.-Léger-de-Fougeret, where he was born during the reign of Louis XIII and the administration of Cardinal Richelieu. At the age of ten Vauban was sent to the Carmelite collège of Semur-en-Auxois; here he acquired the rudiments of mathematics, a smattering of history, and showed some talent for draftsmanship. In 1651, when he was seventeen, he entered upon his military career as a cadet in the forces of Louis II de Bourbon, prince de Condé, then in rebellion against the king. Under Condé he served his apprenticeship by working on the fortifications of Clermont-en-Argonne. Captured by the king's forces in 1653, he shared in the pardon of Condé and his troops and entered the royal army. Cardinal Mazarin, learning of Vauban's knack for fortification, placed him under the chevalier de Clerville, a man of mediocre gifts who was then regarded as the foremost military engineer of France. Two years later Vauban earned the rank of *ingénieur ordinaire du roi*.

Between the end of the war with Spain in 1659 and Louis XIV's first war of conquest in 1667, Vauban worked under Clerville repairing and improving the fortifications of the kingdom. During the brief War of Devolution, he so distinguished himself—notably by his talent for siegecraft—that Louvois, his direct superior, promoted him over the head of Clerville to the rank of *commissaire*

général, in effect making him the virtual director of all the engineering work in Louvois's department.[1] The conquests of the War of Devolution in Hainaut and Flanders launched Vauban on a building program involving such conquered towns as Bergues, Furnes, Tournai, and Lille, the outposts of the future expansion.

Nine years of peace had succeeded the war with Spain. Vauban returned briefly to his native Morvan, where he married Jeanne d'Osnay, daughter of the baron d'Epiry. Yet soon after the wedding he returned to garrison duty at Nancy, leaving his wife behind. Until late in life, his visits home were rare, although he fathered two daughters and a son who died in infancy. In 1675 he bought the nearby Château de Bazoches, but until his last years his stays were brief in this, his favorite residence. He was constantly in the field. As Daniel Halévy put it, Vauban's true family was the army.[2]

This, then, was the tireless rhythm of Vauban's life: constant repairs and construction of fortress towns in time of peace; in war, sieges and new conquests; then more feverish construction during the ensuing intervals of peace, always with an eye towards the strategic goal of giving France the maximum security.[3] Until the year of his death, Vauban was constantly on the move, traveling from one end of France to the other on horseback, or, in his later years, carried in a famous sedan chair borne by horses. Although he sedulously avoided the court and was rarely seen in Paris or Versailles for any length of time, he kept in steady communication with his superiors, deluging Louvois, for example, with innumerable letters and reports written in pungent and undoctored prose. This "vie errante" of over forty years gave him an unrivaled knowledge of the state of France, and led to many of the proposals he set forth in his letters or in his ironically mistitled *Oisivetés*, a collection of papers written during intervals of repose at Bazoches or while traveling.

In his long and active life Vauban directed some fifty sieges, and Sir Reginald Blomfield lists nearly a hundred towns and strong points fortified or radically strengthened by Vauban. In the seventeenth and eighteenth centuries, sieges were usually the focal operations of a campaign and the inevitable preliminary to invading foreign territory; indeed they were more frequent than infantry combat in open country, and were begun as readily as pitched battles were avoided or broken off. In siegecraft, the art of reducing fortified places, Vauban made his reputation as early as 1658–1659 at Montmédy, Ypres, Gravelines, and Oudenaarde in the

Low Countries. His most famous success was the siege of Namur in 1692, defended by the great Dutch engineer, Cohorn, and immortalized by Uncle Toby in Laurence Sterne's *Tristram Shandy*. Here the French troops were commanded by the king in person, and Vauban's conduct of the siege was recorded by the official historian, the playwright Racine, in three letters to the poet Boileau. But it was at the earlier siege of Maastricht that Vauban, always concerned with the welfare of his troops, and hoping to reduce casualties, introduced the system of parallel trenches by means of which the assailants could approach under cover within close range of the ramparts of a fortress. [4] Less concerned about the fate of the defenders, at the siege of Philippsburg he first used the ricochet fire of mortars, where the propelling charge was so greatly reduced that the projectile was gently lobbed into the enemy's stronghold, where it would rebound this way and that, a peril to man and machine.

In the design of fortified places, Vauban owed a considerable debt to his predecessors. He was the heir of nearly a century and a half of progress, during which the profile was lowered and the bastioned trace (a polygonal outline marked by projecting bastions) reached a high degree of perfection at the hands of men like Jean Erard of Bar-le-Duc, the founder of the French school of fortification,[5] and Blaise Pagan (1604–1665), a theorist rather than a practical engineer and an astronomer of some repute. Pagan's *Traité des fortifications* (1645) strongly influenced Vauban; indeed his earliest forts were based on Pagan's designs, but with minor improvements and adaptations to differences in terrain, a characteristic feature of Vauban's work.[6]

It has been claimed that Vauban followed three different "systems" in the course of his career. This claim has rightly been challenged. He never published anything about his methods, or wrote anything except to stress the importance of accumulated experience, flexibility of mind, and a distrust of bookish formulas. Many later writers have agreed with Lazare Carnot who admired Vauban, yet who gave him little credit for striking originality. "The fortification of Vauban," Carnot wrote, "reveals to the eye only a succession of works known before his time, whereas to the mind of a good observer it offers sublime results, brilliant combinations, and masterpieces of industry."[7] Later studies, by Lieutenant Colonel Lazard and by Sir Reginald Blomfield have altered our perspective. Blomfield, while unable to praise Vauban's architectural taste (he severely criticizes the design

of gateways into some of Vauban's fortified towns), fully agrees with Lazard that, strictly speaking, Vauban did not follow sharply defined systems; instead, as his experience grew and deepened, we detect distinguishable periods in which he favored modified designs, all variations of the polygonal trace with bastions. His major works were the citadel of Lille (his earliest honor was to be made its governor); Maubeuge, considered one of the best examples of a fortified town; and his masterpiece and last major work, Neuf-Brisach, designed as a wholly new fortified town,[8] octagonal in shape with elaborate outworks. Vauban's tendency was increasingly to rely "on the outworks of his forts more than on the traditional rampart, bastion, moat, covered way and glacis."[9] The main body of his fort was protected by demilunes (detached triangular works erected in the moat), detached bastions, or hornworks (*ouvrages à cornes*),[10] which pushed the defense out into the surrounding country. Such detached works first appear timidly in forts of what was once called his "second system," for example, at Belfort and Besançon; but the culmination of this development is to be seen in the outline of Neuf-Brisach, which deserves also an important place in the history of city planning.

During Vauban's lifetime there was not yet, in any real sense, an organized corps of army engineers. The engineers were men of diverse training and background: some were civilians (architects or mathematicians) of known ability; others held commissions in the infantry or cavalry and, like Vauban, had served a novitiate under an established practitioner. To see created a true corps of engineers, as a regularly constituted arm of the service with its own specially trained officers, with troops (including sappers and miners) under their command, and with a distinctive uniform, was an objective Vauban strove to attain throughout his career, although with little success. His recommendations did not bear fruit until later in the eighteenth century.

Vauban's concerns were not limited to his own branch of the military profession. He was one of the most indefatigable military reformers of his age, and his proposals left few areas untouched. He was keenly interested in improving artillery; disliking bronze cannon, he urged the army to emulate the navy in the use of iron. He was a tireless advocate of the flintlock musket, and wished to abolish the pike and substitute for it the bayonet fitted with a sleeve or socket, in order to align the blade at the side of the barrel, thereby allowing the piece to be fired with bayonet fixed.

In a long paper of the *Oisivetés* on the reorganization of the army, he gives his views on war in general and the French army in particular.[11] War, he wrote, has "interest" (in the sense of our phrase "vested interest") as father; its mother is ambition and for its close relatives it has all the passions that lead us to evil. The French, nevertheless, like war if it can be carried out with honor; they are courageous and intelligent; yet service in the army is hated: desertions are constant, even though they are cruelly punished on the gallows. Recruitment by force and the press gang is a source of constant complaint; and Vauban finds it a grave social evil, taking husbands away from their families and driving some wives to beggary. The mode of recruitment was to be reformed, and the special categories of men who are exempted should be sharply reduced. The pay (*solde*) must be increased and the conditions of service drastically improved. To Vauban's influence is at least partly due the restriction, if not elimination, of the practice of quartering troops on the civilian population. After the treaty of Aix-la-Chapelle, this practice was supplemented by barracks (*casernes*), many of which were built by Vauban, chiefly used in frontier regions and recently conquered territory.

Vauban's reformist impulses were far from limited to military matters. Deeply sensitive to the woes of others, shocked by the inefficiency and distress he encountered in town and country on his travels, his official correspondence and his *Oisivetés* contain blunt criticism on all manner of topics. His proposals were sometimes farfetched but at other times bold and farsighted. He wrote about the need to preserve the forests of France and urged that lumbering be regulated by the state. He proposed that the *caprerie*—those freelance, piratical raids on enemy shipping—should be systematized and supported by the government. Surely his most courageous proposal was to urge the recall of the Huguenots. He pointed out not only that the Revocation of the Edict of Nantes was an injustice to the Protestants, but that it brought grave injury upon France, which thereby lost excellent craftsmen, veteran soldiers, and eight or nine thousand of *the* finest sailors.[12]

Best known, of course, are Vauban's economic views. Like his contemporaries, Pierre Boisguilbert and Henri Boulainvilliers, he had antimercantilist sentiments and was fully as well informed as they about the impoverishment of the kingdom and the need, above all, to reform the system of taxation, the unfairness of which was matched only by the arbitrariness and corruption of the tax collec-

tors (*maltôtiers*). About 1680 Vauban drafted a memoir on the salt tax (*gabelle*), and in 1695 in his *Projet de capitation* he outlined a whole new scheme of direct taxation. His last words on the subject, and his chief published work, was his clandestine *Dîme royale*, published anonymously and without a license in 1707.[13] It reviews the poverty and misery of the French people, the causes of which, he wrote, "are sufficiently well known," and which he documents with statistics. Instead of the current forms of taxation he proposes a single tax to fall on all the king's subjects, taking the form of one-tenth of the produce of landed wealth, or one-tenth of other forms of income. Basing his proposal on historical precedent, including the Bible, but modeling his proposal specifically on the *Dîme ecclésiastique*, by which the church contributed to the national treasury, he argued that this would be the simplest to collect, and a form of levy less likely to arouse the ire of the people. It would, indeed, fall on all persons regardless of privilege or rank with the sole exception of the clergy.

When Fontenelle, who delivered Vauban's eulogy before the Academy, spoke of Vauban as chosen by the Academy of Sciences as a mathematician, who more than anyone else had "drawn mathematics down from the skies," this can be thought of in terms of Vauban's keen interest in, and constant recourse to, statistics. Here, perhaps, he deserves to be mentioned along with his older contemporaries in Britain, William Petty and John Graunt.

To his superiors, and to many who have written about him, he was admired less perhaps for his recognized genius than as a model of the ideal public servant. Indeed the word *citoyen*, in the sense of a good citizen, a man devoted to the welfare of his country, was first used in reference to him. Voltaire said of Vauban: "He proved, by his conduct, that there can be citizens under an absolute government."[14]

Yet despite his achievements, the honors he most desired were slow to come. He was sixty-five when he was made an *académicien honoraire* of the Academy of Sciences at the time of its reorganization (and installation in the Louvre) in 1699.[15] In 1703, while inspecting the fortifications of Namur, he learned that he had been made a marshall of France. This high honor, for which he had been several times passed over, had never, according to Saint-Simon, been attained before by anybody "of this sort," by which the great nobleman must have meant a man of middling origin or a mere engineer. Finally, in 1705, he received the highest distinction his sovereign could bestow, membership in the select Ordre du Saint Esprit.

Despite these belated honors, Vauban's last years were a disappointment. The king refused to assign him to conduct a major siege (that of Kehl), probably because of his age, but officially because the task was unworthy of his new illustrious rank. Although he led a successful attack on another fortress in 1703, he was in effect put out to pasture. His health began to fail and he suffered increasingly from chronic bronchitis and other ailments. The last months of his life were spent in his Paris house near the Palais-Royal. In early 1707 he fell dangerously ill with pneumonia and on Wednesday, 30 March, not long after the publication of his influential *Dîme royale*, he died in the arms of his son-in-law. After a modest funeral service his body was brought to Bazoches and buried, with his heart in a separate lead casket, in the family vault in the chapel that Vauban had himself built.[16]

NOTES

1. The administration of military engineering, which had been centralized in the time of Sully, was divided in 1661. One department was under the minister of war (first Michel Le Tellier, then his son, the Marquis de Louvois). This department supervised work in the provinces of Flanders, Hainaut, Artois, and along the eastern frontier. The other department was headed by Colbert, first as controller general of finance and later (1669) as secretary of the navy. Until his death in 1683, Colbert was responsible for fortification in Picardie, Champagne, the Three Bishoprics, Provence, and Languedoc.
2. Halévy, *Vauban*, p. 104.
3. For the strategic consideration of Vauban's fortress building, and the concept of the *pré carré* (a fleshed-out defensable frontier), see H. Guerlac, in E. M. Earle, ed., *Makers of Modern Strategy: Military Thought From Machiavelli to Hitler*, 44–47.
4. Voltaire ascribed the invention, or the first use of, the system of parallels to Italian engineers serving the Turks in the siege of Candia (now Iráklion) in Crete; see *Oeuvres complètes de Voltaire*, XIV (Paris, 1878), 263–264.
5. Erard's famous work with his *La fortification démontrée et réduite en art* (Paris, 1594; repr., 1604).
6. On Pagan, see Blomfield, ch. 4.
7. See his *Éloge de Vauban* (1784). For this appraisal the reader may consult Charles Coulston Gillispie, *Lazare Carnot Savant* (Princeton, 1971). This passage has been frequently cited.
8. For a plan of the town of Neuf-Brisach, see Bélidor, *La science des ingénieurs*, bk. 4, plate 25, p. 60. Bélidor takes Vauban's scheme for defending the town as his model for military architecture, and illustrates its defenses in bk. 6. plate 52, p. 40. A model of Neuf-Brisach is in the Musée des Plans Reliefs in the Invalides in Paris. A photograph is reproduced by Hebbert and Rothrock, "Marshal Vauban," in *History Today*, 24, pt. 1, p. 156. A colored aerial view is published in Michel Parent and Jacques Verroust, *Vauban*, p. 15.
9. Blomfield, pp. 53–54.
10. A hornwork is so named because of the acute angles, facing the point of attack, of the two detached half bastions.

11. Rochas d'Aiglun, ed., *Vauban–Oisivetés et Correspondance*, I, p. 267.
12. *Ibid.*, p. 466.
13. The first edition of the *Dîme Royal* was published without indication of place. According to Rochas d'Aiglun, it was probably printed at Rouen in 1706, under the supervision of the Abbé Roget de Beaumont, a longtime collaborator of Vauban. There have been a number of later editions, and an English trans. has appeared.
14. "Catalogue de la plupart des écrivains français qui ont paru dans le siècle de Louis XIV," in *Oeuvres complètes de Voltaire*, XIV (Paris, 1878), 141. Fontenelle had called Vauban "Un Romain, qu'il semblait que notre siècle eut dérobé aux plus heureux temps de la république," in *Éloges de Fontenelle*, Francisque Bouillier, ed. (Paris, n.d.), p. 31. According to James Kip Finch, *Engineering and Western Civilization* (New York, 1951), p. 36, n. 3, it was Saint-Simon who is "said to have coined the word citizen and applied it to Vauban." I have not found that Saint-Simon in fact uses the term, at least in referring to Vauban.
15. The other honorary members besides Vauban were the Abbé de Louvois, the Chevalier Renau, Father Thomas Gouye, Jean Truchet, otherwise known as Father Sébastien, and the aged Malebranche. Most had reputations as mathematicians including, of course, Malebranche. See Ernest Maindron, *L'Académie des sciences* (Paris, 1888), p. 27.
16. For the ceremonial reburial of Vauban's heart, in the Invalides during the reign of Napoleon, see Hebbert and Rothrock, "Marshal Vauban," in *History Today*, 24, pt. 2 (1974), 264.

BIBLIOGRAPHY

I. ORIGINAL WORKS. Vauban wrote voluminously and published hardly anything in his own lifetime. Many works attributed to him (like the small manual entitled *Directeur général des fortifications* [The Hague, 1785]) are probably spurious. It is debated whether he ever wrote a treatise on fortification. Unquestionably his, however, is the *Traité de l'attaque de la défense des places* (The Hague, 1737; repr., 2 vols., 1742), written for the Duc de Bourgogne. This work was republished by Latour-Foissac in 1795, and by Lieutenant Colonel Augoyat in 1829; a German trans., 2 vols. in 1, appeared in Berlin, 1751. A similar work, written earlier (perhaps as early as 1667) is his *Mémoire pour servir d'instruction dans la conduite des sièges et dans la défense des places* (Leiden, 1740), trans. by George A. Rothrock as *A Manual of Siegecraft and Fortification* (Ann Arbor, Mich., 1968). Of the mass of Vauban MSS that survive, a significant portion have been reprinted, notably in the nineteenth century. The *Abrége des services du maréchal de Vauban, fait par lui en 1703* was printed under the editorship of Augoyat, who also published the first 4 vols. of *Oisivetés* in 1842–1845. Vauban's *De l'importance dont Paris est à la France, et le soin que l'on doit prendre de sa conservation* was first printed in Paris in 1821.

Vauban's most famous book, *Projet d'une dixme royal*, was published first in 4° in 1707 with neither place nor date of publication, then in Brussels in 1708. It was reprinted by Eugène Daire, in *Economistes français du dix-huitième siècle* (Paris, 1843). Its interesting preface was included by Rochas d'Aiglun in his own *Vauban—*

Sa Famille et ses Ecrits—Ses Oisivetés et sa Correspondance, 2 vols. (Paris–Grenoble, 1910), which is a major source. D'Aiglun's work begins with a genealogy of Vauban, and in the first volume includes the most important memoirs in the 12 vols. of MSS to which Vauban gave the title of *Oisivetés.* The second volume of this work is devoted to Vauban's correspondence with Louvois and others.

II. SECONDARY LITERATURE. For a laudatory view of Vauban by a contemporary, see Charles Perrault, *Les hommes illustres qui ont paru en France pendant ce siècle,* 2 vols. (Paris, 1696). Still valuable is the early sketch of Vauban given by Fontenelle in his *éloge;* see *Oeuvres Complètes de Fontenelle,* I (Paris, 1818), 95–103, and *Éloges de Fontenelle, avec introduction et notes,* Francisque Bouillier, ed. (Paris, n.d.), 22–31. As indicated in our text there are interesting references to Vauban by Saint-Simon in his *Mémoires* and by Voltaire in his *Siècle de Louis Quatorze.* Lazare Carnot's appraisal, *Éloge de Vauban* (Paris, 1784), aroused much contemporary debate among the military, and was viciously attacked by Cholerlos de Laclos. A fine study in English, by an architect and architectural historian, is Sir Reginald Blomfield, *Sébastien le Prestre de Vauban, 1633–1707* (London, 1938), making good use of Colonel de Génie Pierre Elizir Lazard, *Vauban* (Paris, 1934), which covers the many aspects of Vauban's career. Both works are well illustrated—Blomfield's with his own drawings of Vauban forts in their modern state of preservation, and Lazard with sketches by Vauban and with photographs of models from the Musée des Plans Reliefs of the French army's geographical service. Two recent general studies deserve especially to be cited: Marcel Parent and Jacques Verroust, *Vauban* (Paris, 1971), sumptuously illustrated and splendidly printed; and F. J. Hebbert and G. A. Rothrock, "Marshal Vauban," in *History Today,* **24** 1974), 149–157, 258–264. Among nineteenth-century works, George Michel, *Histoire de Vauban* (Paris, 1879), is a useful connected narrative, but not much of an improvement on J. J. Roy, *Histoire de Vauban* (1844).

More specialized aspects are Jacques Guttin, *Vauban et le corps des ingénieurs militaires* (Paris, 1957); Humbert Ricolfi, *Vauban et le génie militaire dans les alpes-maritimes* (Nice, 1935); Ferdinand Dreyfus, *Vauban économiste* (Paris, 1892); Walter Brauer, *Frankreichs wirtshaftliche und soziale Lage von 1700; dargestellt unter besonderer Berüchsichtigung der Werke von Vauban und Boisguillebert* (Marburg, 1968); and Félix Cadet, *Histoire de l'économie politique. Les précurseurs. Boisguilbert, Vauban, Quesnay, Turgot* (New York, 1970), repr. of the early 1869 ed. Henry Guerlac, "Vauban: The Impact of Science on War," in Edward Meade Earle, *Makers of Modern Strategy* (Princeton, 1943), 26–48, with bibliography on pp. 522–523, draws upon—for its discussion of Vauban strategic aims—H. Chotard, "Louis XIV, Louvois, Vauban et les fortifications du Nord de la France, d'après les lettres inédites de Louvois adressées à M. de Chazerat, Gentilhomme

d'Auvergne," in *Annales du Comité Flamand de France,* **18** (1889–1890), and on Gaston Zeller, *L'organisation défensive des frontières du Nord et de l'Est au XVIIᵉ siècle* (Paris, 1928).

HENRY GUERLAC

VAUCHER, JEAN PIERRE ÉTIENNE (*b.* Geneva, Switzerland, 27 April 1763; *d.* Geneva, 5 January 1841), *botany.*

Vaucher was the son of a carpenter, and he expected to follow that trade; but by the age of twelve he knew that he wanted an academic career. He entered college, where he found a general education, including theology and physical sciences, but not botany, which he began to study as a leisure pursuit following interest aroused by his exploration of the mountains around Geneva. He was ordained in 1787 and worked as a parish priest from 1797 to 1822, carrying out his duties conscientiously, but always giving much time and energy to botany, which increasingly fascinated him.

A founder member of the Société de Physique et d'Histoire Naturelle de Genève, he was asked in 1794 to give a course of lectures on botany for the Society. These were attended by A. P. de Candolle who became a close friend. By 1798 Vaucher was sufficiently recognized as a botanist and an exceptionally good teacher to be appointed honorary professor of botany in the university, and he held this post until 1807 when he transferred to the chair of ecclesiastical history, which he held until 1839, undertaking additional responsibilities as rector from 1818 to 1821. He married and had children.

Vaucher's most important work was his observation and interpretation of conjugation and spore formation in algae, particularly in *Ectosperma,* later renamed *Vaucheria* by de Candolle. Although the cell theory had not yet been developed, he drew and described the cells showing that they were bounded by separate walls and had a certain degree of independence. He showed how conjugation can occur between cells of threads lying side by side, or cells of a single thread folded over on itself, by means of the communication channel through which the contents of one cell pass to fuse with the contents of the other cell. He also showed male organs, or anthers, protruding to meet other cells and was sure that this was a sexual act, comparable to that found in higher plants and to the copulation of animals. His optical equipment did not allow him to see the actual fertilization, but he correctly inferred it. The newly formed grains, or spores, dropped to the bottom of the ditches in which the algae were found, and in order to verify that they would germinate to give new filaments of *Ectosperma* in the spring he had to culture them in the laboratory, an uncommon practice at that time. He showed similar conjugation in other primitive algae, and the formation of new nets in old cells of *Hydrodictyon*.

Other work published by Vaucher was wide-ranging. Perhaps the most comprehensive was the *Histoire physiologique des plantes d'Europe* (1804–1841), mainly a taxonomic compilation arranged by the system of Candolle. He wrote monographs on *Equisetum* (1822) and broomrape (1827) and a paper on leaf fall (1826) that was the first to examine in detail the structure of the base of the petiole.

As a member of the agriculture section of the Société des Arts de Genève from 1796, he carried out some useful investigations on diseases of vines and of wheat, the effects of temperature on plant growth, culture of the potato, and management of woodlands.

BIBLIOGRAPHY

I. ORIGINAL WORKS. The descriptions of conjugation and germination in filamentous algae were published as "Sur les graines des conferves," in *Journal de physique*, **52** (1801), 344–358, and more fully in *Histoire des conferves d'eau douce . . . des Tremelles et des Ulves* (Geneva, 1803). *Histoire physiologique des plantes d'Europe*, t.l. (Geneva, 1804), was reissued in 1830 and the complete work was published in 4 vols. in Paris a few days before Vaucher's death in 1841. *Monographie des Prêles* (Geneva–Paris, 1822) was followed by *Monographie des Orobranches* (Geneva–Paris, 1827). The "Mémoire sur la chute des feuilles" was published in *Mémoires de la Société de physique et d'histoire naturelle de Genève*, **1** (1821), 120–136, and a report of the work, followed by discussion, appeared in *Edinburgh Journal of Science*, **5** (1826), 330–338.

Vaucher's sermons were printed as *Souvenir d'un pasteur genevois* (Geneva, 1842).

II. SECONDARY LITERATURE. The most comprehensive biography of Vaucher is an anonymous obituary in *Verhandlungen der Schweizerischen Naturforschenden Gesellschaft bei ihrer Versammlung zu Zürich*, **26** (1841), 308–313. There is another anonymous obituary in *Mémoires de la Société de physique et d'histoire naturelle de Genève*, **10** (1843), xxiv–xxvi, and one by A. de Candolle in *Annals and Magazine of Natural History*, **10** (1842), 161–168, 241–248, translated from the *Bibliographie universelle de Genève* (1841). The *Souvenir* has a 22-page biographical preface by Vaucher's son.

Two modern evaluations of his work are by C. Baehni, "Il y a 150 ans, le Genevois, J. P. Vaucher découvrait la fécondation chez les algues" in *Les Musées de Genève*, **10** no. 10 (1953), and by G. de Morsier, "Contribution à l'histoire de la genétique," in *Physis*, **7** (1965), 497–500.

His relations with the university may be found in C. Borgeaud, *Histoire de l'Université de Genève*, II (Geneva, 1909); and Candolle's tributes are in his *Histoire de la botanique Genevois* (Geneva, 1830), which includes a bibliography of 14 items, and in his *Mémoires et souvenirs de Genève* (Geneva, 1862).

Vaucher's publications can be traced through the *Royal Society Catalogue*, which lists 15 items, and G. A. Pritzel, *Thesaurus literaturae botanicae* (Leipzig, 1872), entries 9704–9710.

DIANA M. SIMPKINS

VAUQUELIN, NICOLAS LOUIS (*b.* St. André d'Hébertot, Normandy, France, 16 May 1763; *d.* St. André d'Hébertot, 14 November 1829), *chemistry*.

The son of Nicolas Vauquelin, an estate manager, and Catherine Le Chartier, Vauquelin became assistant to a pharmacist in Rouen when he was about fourteen, but left after he was reprimanded for taking notes of the scientific lectures given by his master. He went to Paris and eventually worked for a pharmacist named Chéradame, a cousin of the chemist Fourcroy. About 1784 Vauquelin became Fourcroy's laboratory and lecture assistant and at his invitation began to lecture at the lycée. But his voice was weak and he lacked confidence; and although he later occupied several chairs he never achieved fame as a lecturer. It soon became clear that he was a first-class experimental chemist, however, and his relationship with Fourcroy developed into an association of equals. Their first joint research was published in 1790, but political events interrupted their collaboration.

Vauquelin left Fourcroy's laboratory by 1792 and became the manager of a pharmacy. In 1793 he spent several months as a hospital pharmacist at Meaux, near Paris. In September 1793 he was sent to the region around Tours by the government in order to organize the production of saltpeter, urgently needed for gunpowder. Vauquelin returned to Paris and resumed his association with Fourcroy late in 1794, when he was appointed assistant professor of chemistry at the new École Centrale des Travaux Publics (later, École Polytechnique). In 1795 he received the title of master in pharmacy and was elected to the Institut de France. He had apparently been elected to the old Académie des

Sciences on 31 July 1793, a few days before its suppression, but his appointment had not been confirmed by the government.

Vauquelin left the École Polytechnique when its staff was reduced in 1797, but he continued as inspector of mines (a post he had held since 1794), and he retained his position as professor of assaying at the École des Mines, which he had entered after its reorganization in 1795. He also became official assayer of precious metals for Paris, and in 1799 he published a useful *manuel de l'essayeur*. He left the École des Mines in 1801 to succeed Jean d'Arcet as professor of chemistry at the Collège de France; in addition, he became director of the École de Pharmacie on its foundation in 1803.

In 1804 he moved again, from the Collège de France to the Muséum d'Histoire Naturelle, where he followed Antoine-Louis Brongniart as professor of applied chemistry. At the Muséum he was once more a colleague of Fourcroy, whose death in 1809 left a vacant chair in chemistry at the Faculté de Médecine. Much of Fourcroy's research had been done in collaboration with Vauquelin, who was his obvious successor. However, the professor had to be medically qualified, so Vauquelin obtained his doctorate with a thesis on the chemical analysis of the human brain; he received his appointment in 1811. Along with several other professors he was dismissed in 1822 during a politically inspired reform of the Faculté, but he retained his posts at the Muséum and the École de Pharmacie. In 1828 he was elected to parliament as a deputy for Calvados, his native district.

In the course of his numerous analyses of minerals, Vauquelin discovered two new elements in 1798. By boiling the rare Siberian mineral crocoite (lead chromate) with potassium carbonate he obtained the yellow salt of an unknown acid. On reduction with carbon the acid yielded a metal that he named chromium on account of its colorful compounds (Greek, *chroma*-color). In beryl (beryllium aluminum silicate) he found an earth (oxide) that superficially resembled alumina (aluminum oxide) but was insoluble in alkali and did not form alum. At the suggestion of the editors of *Annales de chimie*, he originally called it glucina, from the sweetness of its sulfate, but later it was renamed beryllia. Metallic beryllium was not obtained until 1828, when Friedrich Wöhler and, independently, Antoine Bussy first isolated it.

The most important of Vauquelin's many analyses of vegetable and animal substances were done with Fourcroy. In 1804 the two friends set up a small factory in Paris for the manufacture of high-quality chemicals. Vauquelin, the more active partner, was personally involved in its management for several years and retained a financial interest until 1822.

Vauquelin never married, and Fourcroy's sisters, Madame Le Bailly and Madame Guédon, kept house for him from about 1790 until they died in 1819 and 1824 respectively.

BIBLIOGRAPHY

I. ORIGINAL WORKS. Vauquelin's 305 contributions to periodicals that he wrote himself and the seventy-one that he wrote jointly with Fourcroy or others are listed in *The Royal Society Catalogue of Scientific Papers*, VI (London, 1872), 114–128; a less complete list is given in Poggendorff, II, cols. 1182–1190. His only book is *Manuel de l'essayeur* (Paris, 1799). This was reprinted in 1812 and a new ed., revised by A. D. Vergnaud, appeared in 1836; there is a German trans. by F. Wolff, with notes by M. H. Klaproth (Königsberg, 1800) and a Spanish trans. (Paris, 1826).

While working on the production of saltpeter he wrote, with Trusson as coauthor, a 32-page pamphlet, *Instruction sur la combustion des végétaux, la fabrication du salin, de la cendre gravelée, et sur la manière de saturer les eaux salpêtrées* (Tours, 1794); trans. into Portuguese as *Instrucçao sobre a combustaõ dos vegetaes . . .* (Lisbon, 1798). Vauquelin wrote articles on apparatus in Fourcroy's *Encyclopédie méthodique chimie*, II (Paris, 1792), and he was co-author, with Fourcroy, of VI (Paris, 1815). He also supervised the preparation of the two vols. of plates (1813, 1814). Reports made by Vauquelin to various institutions are listed in the author catalogue of the Bibliothèque Nationale, Paris, vol. 204, cols. 206–207.

II. SECONDARY LITERATURE. The earliest accounts of Vauquelin's life are A. Chevallier and Robinet, *Notice historique sur N. L. Vauquelin* (Paris, 1830); and G. Cuvier, "Éloge historique de Louis Nicolas (*sic*) Vauquelin," in *Mémoires de l'Académie Royale des Sciences de l'Institut*, **12** (1833), xxxix–lvi. Additional information is given by A. Chevallier, "Notice biographique sur M. Vauquelin," in *Journal de chimie médicale*, ser. 3, **6** (1850), 542–549; and E. Pariset, *Histoire des membres de l'Académie Royale de Médecine*, I (Paris, 1850), 317–350.

Vauquelin's baptismal certificate, now in the town hall of St. André d'Hébertot, shows that he was named Nicolas Louis, and not Louis Nicolas, as is often stated. This certificate has been published, with some other manuscripts, by M. Bouvet, "Documents encore ignorés sur Vauquelin," in *Revue d'histoire de la pharmacie*, **16** (1963), 17–20. Vauquelin's election to the Académie des Sciences in 1793 is discussed by M. Bouvet, "Vauquelin fut-il membre de l'Académie des Sciences?" *ibid.*,

12 (1955), 66–70. Information about the chemical factory is given in three papers by G. Kersaint, "L'Usine de Vauquelin et Fourcroy," *ibid.*, 14 (1959), 25–30; "Sur la fabrique de produits chimiques établie par Fourcroy et Vauquelin," in *Comptes rendus hebdomadaires des séances de l'Académie des sciences*, 247 (1958), 461–464; and "Sur une correspondence inédite de Nicolas Louis Vauquelin," in *Bulletin. Société chimique de France* (1958), 1603.

For Vauquelin's work on saltpeter manufacture in 1793–1794, see C. Richard, *Le comité de salut public et les fabrications de guerre sous la terreur* (Paris, 1922), 429. For accounts of his research on chromium and beryllium, see M. E. Weeks and H. M. Leicester, *The Discovery of the Elements* (Easton, Pa., 1968), 271–281, 535–540. See also "Fourcroy," in *DSB, V*, 92–93.

W. A. SMEATON

VAVILOV, SERGEY IVANOVICH (*b.* Moscow, Russia, 24 March 1891; *d.* Moscow, 25 January 1951), *physics*.

Vavilov, the son of a manufacturer and trader, and the youngest brother of the botanist Nikolay Ivanovich Vavilov, received his secondary education at the Moscow Commercial School, concentrating on physics and chemistry. In 1909 he entered the Faculty of Physics and Mathematics of Moscow University, and by the end of the first year he had chosen a subject on which to work in Lebedev's laboratory, under the supervision of P. P. Lazarev. Vavilov did not finish this work, however, for in 1911 Lebedev and Lazarev left Moscow University to protest the violation of the university's autonomy by the minister of education, L. A. Kasso. Vavilov's scientific work was transferred to Shanyansky City University, a small private institution in Moscow, where Lebedev's laboratory was set up.

In 1913 Vavilov published his first scientific work, on the photometry of polychromatic light sources; at the same time he carried out research on a subject proposed by Lazarev, who was then studying the discoloration by light of collodion films colored with cyanine dyes. Assigned to investigate the discoloration of these dyes through heating, Vavilov constructed an ingenious experimental device and discovered the essential differences between the discolorations caused by light and by heat. The work was published in 1914, and Vavilov received a gold medal for it (1915). At the beginning of World War I, he was drafted into the army and sent to the front. Throughout the conflict he served mainly in the technical units; and in his mobile radio laboratory he was able to conduct research in radiotechnology, the results of which were published in 1919.

Discharged from the army in 1918, Vavilov began independent scientific work on photoluminescence and physical optics in general at the Institute of Physics and Biophysics, which was directed by Lazarev. At the same time he was a *Privatdozent* at the Moscow Higher Technical School, where in 1920 he became professor of physics. In 1929 Vavilov was named professor and head of the department of general physics at Moscow University, and from 1930 all of his work was carried out there. He was elected corresponding member of the Academy of Sciences of the U.S.S.R. in 1931, and the following year was named scientific director of the State Optical Institute now named for him. At this time Vavilov moved to Leningrad but retained his affiliation with Moscow University. At the State Optical Institute he conducted wide-ranging and fruitful work in a new laboratory for luminescence.

In 1932 Vavilov was elected full member of the Academy of Sciences of the U.S.S.R. and became director of the Physics Institute of the Academy of Sciences in Leningrad. Two years later, when the Academy of Sciences of the U.S.S.R. was transferred to Moscow, this institute came with it and, through Vavilov's efforts, became the important P. N. Lebedev Physical Institute.

During World War II, Vavilov worked on problems connected with national defense, although the State Optical Institute was evacuated to Yoshkar-Ola and the Physics Institute to Kazan. These institutes provided much of the high-quality optical equipment needed by the Soviet armed forces. In 1943 Vavilov was named commissioner of the State Committee for Defense of the U.S.S.R. and was awarded the Order of Lenin and the State Prize. He was elected president of the Academy of Sciences of the U.S.S.R. while retaining all of his other positions, and in 1945 was awarded a second Order of Lenin. As president of the Academy of Sciences, Vavilov was particularly concerned with the relation of science to the national economy and aided the development of scientific institutions in the national republics and in the major industrial regions.

Vavilov conducted important research aimed at determining what proportion of absorbed light is converted into fluorescent light. Although it had been assumed that this portion is extremely small, Vavilov showed that the energy output of fluorescence reaches 70–80 percent and in some cases approaches 100 percent. In his research on the polarization of fluorescence, he was the first to show that the degree of polarization depends on the wavelength of the light that stimulates the fluorescence. This finding led to the creation of the study of the spectra of fluorescence. Under Vavilov's leadership a detailed method of luminescent analysis was elaborated and luminescent lamps were developed. His research was described in *Mikrostruktura sveta* ("Microstructure of Light"), an original proof of the quantum nature of light.

A major discovery made under Vavilov's supervision was the Vavilov-Cherenkov effect, a special kind of luminescence that occurs when charged molecules in a medium move at a velocity exceeding the velocity of light in that medium. For this work P. A. Cherenkov, I. Y. Tamm, and I. M. Frank were awarded the Nobel Prize in 1958, seven years after Vavilov's death.

Vavilov's works in the history of science include a Russian translation and commentary on Newton's *Optiks* and his *Lectures on Optics*, a work on Galileo's place in the history of optics, and a popular biography of Newton.

BIBLIOGRAPHY

I. ORIGINAL WORKS. Vavilov's collected works were published as *Sobranie sochineny*, 5 vols. (Moscow, 1952–1956), with biographical sketch by V. L. Levshin. See also *Mikrostruktura sveta* ("The Microstructure of Light"; 2nd ed., rev. and enl., Moscow–Leningrad, 1945); and *Glaz i solntse* ("The Eye and the Sun"; Moscow–Leningrad, 1950).

II. SECONDARY LITERATURE. See N. I. Artobolevsky, *Vydayushchysya sovetsky ucheny i obshchestvenny deyatel S. I. Vavilov* ("The Distinguished Soviet Scientist and Social Activist S. I. Vavilov"; Moscow, 1961), which includes a bibliography of his basic scientific works; and E. V. Shpolsky, *Vydayushchysya sovetsky ucheny S. I. Vavilov* (Moscow, 1956). A collection of articles commemorating his seventieth birthday was published in *Uspekhi fizicheskikh nauk*, **75**, no. 2 (1961).

J. DORFMAN

VEBLEN, OSWALD (*b*. Decorah, Iowa, 24 June 1880; *d*. Brooklin, Maine, 10 August 1960), *mathematics*.

Veblen's parents were both children of immigrants from Norway. His mother (1851–1908) was born Kirsti Hougen; his father, Andrew Anderson Veblen (1848–1932), was professor of physics at the University of Iowa; and his uncle, Thorstein Veblen (1857–1929), was famous for his book *The Theory of the Leisure Class*. Veblen himself had two B.A. degrees (Iowa, 1898; Harvard, 1900) but was most influenced by his graduate study (Ph.D., 1903) at the University of Chicago under E. H. Moore. He had a happy marriage (1908) to Elizabeth Mary Dixon Richardson. His influential teaching career was at Princeton, both at the University (1905–1932) and at the Institute for Advanced Study (1932–1950).

The axiomatic method, so characteristic of twentieth-century mathematics, had a brilliant start in Hilbert's *Grundlagen der Geometrie* (1899). In this book, precise and subtle analysis corrected the logical inadequacies in Euclid's *Elements*. Veblen's work, starting at this point, was devoted to precise analysis of this and many other branches of geometry, notably topology and differential geometry; his ideas have been extensively developed by many younger American geometers.

The initial step was Veblen's thesis (1903, published 1904), which gave a careful axiomatization for Euclidean geometry, different from that of Hilbert because based on just two primitive notions, "point" and "order" (of points on a line), as initially suggested by Pasch and Peano. With this systematic start on the axiomatic method, Veblen's interests expanded to include the foundations of analysis (where he emphasized the role of the Heine-Borel theorem, that is, of compactness) and finite projective geometries. His work in projective geometry culminated in a magnificent two-volume work, *Projective Geometry* (vol. I, 1910; vol. II, 1918), in collaboration with J. W. Young. This book gives a lucid and leisurely presentation of the whole sweep of these geometries over arbitrary fields and over the real number field, with the properties of conics and projectivities and with the classification of geometries by the Klein-Erlanger program. It includes a masterful exposition of the axiomatic method (independence and categoricity of axioms), which had extensive influence on other workers in algebra and geometry.

Veblen's greatest contribution probably lies in his development of analysis situs. This branch of geometry deals with numerical and algebraic measures of the "connectivity" of geometric figures. It was initiated by Poincaré in a famous but difficult series of memoirs (1895–1904). It came naturally to Veblen's attention through his earlier work on the Jordan curve theorem (that is, how a closed curve separates the plane) and on order and orientation to Euclidean and projective geometry. Veblen's 1916 Colloquium Lectures to the American Mathematical Society led to his 1922 *Analysis Situs*, which for nearly a decade was the only systematic treatment in book form of the pioneering ideas of Poincaré. This book was carefully studied by several generations of mathematicians, who went on to transform and rename the subject (first "combinatorial topology," then "algebraic topology," then "homological algebra") and to found a large American school of topology with wide international influence.

Veblen also did extensive work on differential geometry, especially on the geometry of paths (today treated by affine connections) and on projective relativity (four-component spinors). His more important work in this field would seem to be his part in the transition from purely local differential geometry to global considerations. His expository monograph (1927) on the invariants of quadratic differential forms gave a clear statement of the usual formal local theory; and it led naturally to his later monograph with J. H. C. Whitehead, *The Foundations of Differential Geometry* (1932). This monograph contained the first adequate definition of a global differentiable manifold. Their definition was complicated; for example, they did not assume that the underlying topological space is Hausdorff. Soon afterward H. Whitney, starting from this Veblen-Whitehead definition, developed the simpler definition of a differentiable manifold, which has now become standard (and extended to other cases such as complex analytic manifolds). In this case the Veblen-Whitehead book had influence not through many readers, but essentially through one reformulation, that of Whitney.

Veblen had an extensive mathematical effect upon others; in earlier years through many notable co-workers and students (R. L. Moore, J. W. Alexander, J. H. M. Wedderburn, T. Y. Thomas, Alonzo Church, J. H. C. Whitehead, and many others) and in later years by his activities as a mathematical statesman and as a leader in the development of the School of Mathematics at the Institute for Advanced Study.

BIBLIOGRAPHY

I. Original Works. Veblen's thesis was published as "A System of Axioms for Geometry," in *Transactions of the American Mathematical Society*, 5 (1904), 343–384. His other works include *Projective Geometry*, I (New York, 1910), written with J. W. Young; II (Boston, 1918); *Analysis Situs*, in *Colloquium Publications. American Mathematical Society*, 5, pt. 2 (1922); 2nd ed. (1931); "Invariants of Quadratic Differential Forms," in *Cambridge Tracts in Mathematics and Mathematical Physics*, 24 (1927); "The Foundations of

Differential Geometry," *ibid.*, 29 (1932), written with J. H. C. Whitehead; and "Projective Relativitätstheorie," in *Ergenbnisse der Mathematik und ihrer Grenzgebiete*, 2, no. 1 (1933).

II. Secondary Literature. On Veblen and his work, see *American Mathematical Society Semicentennial Publications*, 1 (1938), 206–211, with complete list of Veblen's doctoral students; Saunders MacLane, in *Biographical Memoirs. National Academy of Sciences*, 37 (1964), 325–341, with bibliography; Deane Montgomery, in *Bulletin of the American Society*, 69 (1963), 26–36; and *Yearbook. American Philosophical Society* (1962), 187–193.

Saunders Mac Lane

VEJDOVSKÝ, FRANTIŠEK (*b*. Kouřim, Bohemia [now Czechoslovakia], 24 October 1849; *d*. Prague, Czechoslovakia, 4 December 1939), *zoology*.

For a detailed study of his life and work, see Supplement.

VEKSLER, VLADIMIR IOSIFOVICH (*b*. Zhitomir, Russia, 4 March 1907; *d*. Moscow, U.S.S.R., 22 September 1966), *physics, engineering*.

Veksler was the son of an engineer, Iosif Lvovich Veksler. After working as an apparatus assembler in a factory, Veksler graduated from the Moscow Energetics Institute, and held a post at the All-Union Electrotechnical Institute and, later, at the Lebedev Physics Institute of the Academy of Sciences of the U.S.S.R.

In 1954 Veksler became director of the electrophysics laboratory of the Academy of Sciences, and from 1956 he headed the high-energy laboratory of the Joint Institute for Nuclear Research. He was elected an associate member of the Academy of Sciences of the U.S.S.R. in 1946 and a full member in 1958.

Veksler began his career with studies of cosmic rays and discovered a new type of interaction between high-energy particles and atomic nuclei. He is best known, however, for his work on the theory of the accelerator, an apparatus for artificially obtaining the charged particles of great energy that usually are necessary for investigations of the atomic nucleus.

In 1944, simultaneously with E. M. MacMillan, Veksler established the principle of phase stability of accelerated particles. This discovery, which is applied to all modern accelerators, proved to be a turning point in nuclear physics and in the physics of elementary particles. The largest Soviet accelerators were planned and constructed under Veksler's direction. For his fundamental investigations regarding accelerators he received the Lenin and State prizes of the U.S.S.R.

Veksler was a creator of the large groups of scientists and engineers at the Joint Institute for Nuclear Research, the Lebedev Physics Institute, and at Moscow University. He also was active in international scientific collaboration, serving for many years as chairman of the Commission on High-Energy Physics of the International Union of Pure and Applied Physics. His services were noted abroad by the award of the U.S. Atoms for Peace Prize in 1963.

BIBLIOGRAPHY

Veksler's writings include *Eksperimentalnye metody yadernoy fiziki* ("Experimental Methods in Nuclear Physics"; Moscow–Leningrad, 1940); "Novy metod uskorenia relyativistskikh chastits" ("A New Method of Accelerating Relativistic Particles"), in *Doklady Akademii nauk SSSR*, **43**, no. 8 (1944), 346; "On the Stability of Electron Motion in the Induction Accelerator of the Betatron Type," in *Fizicheskii zhurnal*, **9**, no. 3 (1945), 153; "Elektronno-yadernye livni kosmicheskikh luchey i yaderno-kaskadny protsess" ("Electronuclear Showers of Cosmic Rays and the Nuclear-Cascade Process"), in *Zhurnal eksperimentalnoi i teoreticheskoi fiziki*, **19**, no. 9 (1949), 135; *Ionizatsionnye metody issledovania izlucheny* ("Ionization Methods in the Study of Radiation"; Moscow, 1950); and "Kogerentny metod uskorenia zaryazhennykh chastits" ("The Coherent Method of Accelerating Charged Particles"), in *Atomnaya energiya*, **11**, no. 5 (1957), 427.

A. T. GRIGORIAN

VELLOZO, JOSÉ MARIANO DA CONCEIÇÃO (*b.* San José, Minas Gerais, Brazil, 1742; *d.* Rio de Janeiro, Brazil, 13 June 1811), *botany.*

Vellozo, the father of Brazilian botany, entered the Franciscan order in 1761 and, although largely self-educated in the sciences, became instructor in geometry at São Paulo ten years later. In 1782 he was commissioned by the viceroy, Luis de Vasconcelos, to prepare a study of the flora of Rio de Janeiro province. He roamed the countryside for eight years, turning his monastic cell into a herbarium where he analyzed his specimens. His companion in the field and fellow Franciscan, Francisco Solano, prepared drawings of many of the plants for the completed work, *Flora fluminensis.*

In 1790, his work on the *Flora* completed, Vellozo accompanied his patron Vasconcelos to Lisbon, where he was named director of the Tipografia Calcográfica e Tipoplástica do Arco do Cego, a printshop later absorbed into the National Press of Portugal. There he directed the publication of numerous scientific works, many of which he had written or translated. Although he was summoned to organize the herbarium of the Royal Museum in 1797–1798, Vellozo spent most of the 1790's producing works of scientific and economic popularization, the majority of which were characterized by the utilitarian motive so typical of the Enlightenment. Particularly noteworthy was his essay on alkaloids (1798), the first part of which was a treatise on popular chemistry and the second a description of Brazilian plants from which alkaloids could be derived. Between 1798 and 1806 Vellozo published a multivolume work on economic botany, *O fazendeiro do Brazil*, in which he discussed plants that could contribute to the economic development of Brazil: sugarcane, dyes, coffee and cocoa, spices, and textile fibers.

Vellozo also was interested in zoology. In 1800 he published a descriptive treatise on the birds of Brazil, *Aviário brasílico*; in the first chapter, a history of ornithology from the sixteenth through the eighteenth centuries, Vellozo discussed the contributions of European naturalists from Konrad Gesner to George Edwards.

In the two decades following his fieldwork, Vellozo discovered that collecting the data for his *Flora* was a good deal easier than getting the work into print—a fate he shared with the members of the contemporaneous Spanish botanical expeditions. In 1808 the imminent publication of the *Flora* was aborted when Geoffroy Saint-Hilaire went to the National Press and, under orders from General Andoche Junot, took the plates to Paris, where he and Candolle later used them. This bizarre incident delayed publication until 1825, when Emperor Pedro I ordered the printing of the text. Two years later the engravings of 1,640 plants were published at Paris. In the introduction to his masterpiece, Vellozo included a terse description of his achievement: "I observed, had drawn, and reduced to Linnean nomenclature according to the sexual system, fully seventeen hundred species of plants." The *Flora fluminensis* is regarded as the greatest creation of Enlightenment science in Brazil.

BIBLIOGRAPHY

I. ORIGINAL WORKS. *Flora fluminensis, seu descriptionum plantarum praefectura fluminensi* appeared in two parts: text (Rio de Janeiro, 1825), 2nd ed. as *Archuivos do Museu nacional* (Rio de Janeiro), **5** (1881), and plates *Florae fluminensis icones*, Antonio da Arrabida, ed., 12 vols. (Paris, 1827). The ornithological treatise is *Aviário brasílico ou galeria ornitológica das aves indígenas do Brasil* (Lisbon, 1800). Among the more important works on economic botany are *Alografia dos álcales fixos* (Lisbon, 1798); *Memória e extratos sôbre a pipereira negra* (Lisbon, 1798); *O fazendeiro do Brazil*, 11 vols. in 5 (Lisbon, 1798–1806); *Quinografia portuguêsa* (Lisbon, 1799); and the didactic *O naturalista instruído nos diversos métodos, antigos e modernos, de ajuntar, preparar e conservar as producões dos três reinos de natureza* (Lisbon, 1800).

II. SECONDARY LITERATURE. Biographical data are in Augusto Vitorino Sacramento Blake, *Dicionario bibliográfico brasileiro*, 7 vols. (Rio de Janeiro, 1883–1902), V, 64–70; José Saldanha da Gama, "Biographia do botánico brasileiro José Mariano da Conceição Velloso," in *Revista do Instituto histórico e geográfico brasileiro*, **37** (1868), 137–305; Carlos Stellfeld, *Os dois Vellozo* (Rio de Janeiro, 1952); and "A biografia de Frei Vellozo," in *Tribuna farmacéutica* (Curitiba), **21** (1953), 119–124. A valuable collection of documents on the *Flora fluminensis* is *Flora fluminensis de Frei José Mariano da Conceição Vellozo. Documentos*, Thomaz Borgmeier, ed. (Rio de Janeiro, 1961). On Vellozo's role in the Brazilian Enlightenment, see José Ferreira Carrato, *Ingreja, iluminismo e escolas mineiras coloniais* (São Paulo, 1968).

THOMAS F. GLICK

VENEL, GABRIEL FRANÇOIS (*b.* Tourbes, near Pézenas, France, 23 August 1723; *d.* Montpellier, France, 29 October 1775), *chemistry, medicine.*

The son of Étienne Venel, a physician, and Anne Hiché, Venel qualified as a doctor of medicine at the University of Montpellier in 1742. About 1746 he went to Paris to gain further experience in hospitals, and there he attended Guillaume-François Rouelle's chemistry lectures and soon decided to devote himself to chemistry. He secured the patronage of Louis, duc d'Orléans, who put him in charge of his laboratory at the Palais Royal, and he was appointed a royal censor for books on natural history, medicine, and chemistry.

Venel was interested in the composition of vegetable matter; in 1752 he compared fire analysis with the recently introduced method of solvent extraction, praising the latter and saying that it showed some principles—extract and resin, for example—to be common to the entire vegetable kingdom, whereas others, including essential oils and gums, were constituents of only certain plants. He never achieved his aim of examining each prin-

ciple separately, for his attention was diverted to the analysis of mineral waters.

In 1750 Venel described his analysis of the effervescent mineral water of Selz, in Germany. Evaporation yielded only common salt and a little lime, and he was more interested in the effervescence, which was, he thought, caused by the escape of common air. All water contained a small amount of dissolved air, but Selzer and other effervescent waters contained superabundant air, as Venel called it. He made artificial Selzer water by adding the correct amounts of marine (hydrochloric) acid and soda to pure water, and he called the product aerated water, a term that is still in use. Stephen Hales had thought that effervescent mineral waters contained "sulphurous spirit"; Venel's experiments proved the absence of the gas now called sulfur dioxide, but he failed to notice that the "superabundant air" differed in any way from common air. It was, of course, carbon dioxide, characterized in 1754 by Joseph Black, who called it fixed air. Fourcroy later commented that no one had ever been so close to making a discovery without actually making it as was Venel.[1]

The government wanted a report on all French mineral waters, and in 1753 Venel and Pierre Bayen were appointed to prepare it. They traveled widely, but when the Seven Years' War started in 1756, Bayen became an army pharmacist[2] and there were insufficient funds for Venel to continue alone.

While living in Paris, Venel met Diderot, one of the editors of the *Encyclopédie*. Most chemical articles in the first two volumes were by Paul-Jacques Malouin, but Venel contributed a few to the second volume (1751), and then became the principal author on chemistry and materia medica. Venel, who was unknown outside a small Parisian circle, was a strange choice as successor to so distinguished an academician as Malouin, but he rose to the occasion and wrote more than 700 articles in volumes three to seventeen (1753–1765). Many were short accounts of preparations, properties, and medicinal uses of substances, but in some articles, including "Menstrue," "Mixte," and "Principes," he expounded his ideas on the nature of matter—ideas that were based on an extensive and critical reading of recent chemical literature. He followed Hales in regarding air as a common constituent of solids, and he generally approved of Stahl's phlogiston theory, but, curiously, he wrote no article on "Phlogistique" (although cross-references were given to such an article), perhaps because of his uncertainty about the properties of phlogiston.

In his longest article, "Chymie," Venel criticized the Newtonians who saw chemistry merely as a branch of physics. The chemist was concerned with relationships between corpuscles and principles, and these were not necessarily subject to the same forces as the large masses studied by physicists. Even though they lacked mathematical precision, chemical theories could be as valid as physical laws, but Venel admitted that chemistry had not yet progressed as far as physics and that it awaited a "new Paracelsus" who would bring about a revolution in his subject.

Upon returning to the Languedoc, his native province, in 1758, Venel was elected to the Société Royale des Sciences de Montpellier; in 1759 he became a professor at the University of Montpellier, where he gave an annual course on materia medica. He recognized two classes of medicament—external and internal—with a further division into those that acted mechanically (including external ligatures or metallic mercury taken internally) and those that affected the body chemically. He admitted that there was not yet a satisfactory theory of the chemical action of medicaments, so the physician had to rely largely on observation.

Each year Venel gave a chemistry course, but this was outside the university, in the laboratory of Jacques Montet, who provided the accompaning demonstrations.[3] In sixty-four lectures Venel gave a comprehensive account of the vegetable, animal, and mineral kingdoms, treating them in the same order as Rouelle. He did not discuss chemical theories in depth, but he expressed an opinion about phlogiston, which, he believed, did not gravitate toward the center of the earth but, on the contrary, levitated and thus diminished the weight of anything containing it.[4] Its release from a metal during calcination, therefore, caused the observed increase in weight. This theory was compatible with Venel's belief that principles did not necessarily behave like large masses, but he never published it and, according to Bayen, did not hold it strongly.[5] By the end of his life Venel had doubts about the whole doctrine of phlogiston, writing in 1775 that it was "beginning to age a little."[6]

Diderot said that Venel "vegetated" in Languedoc.[7] Certainly he lived a comfortable bachelor life and cultivated his tastes for good food, wine, and conversation, but he was not idle between lecture courses, for he carried out agricultural experiments on his estate near Pézenas and he became interested in other practical matters.

Wood was scarce in Languedoc and at the request of the provincial government Venel wrote in 1775 a long treatise on the advantages of coal, which was abundant there. He recommended it for domestic use and also for local industries, including the manufacture of silk and olive oil (both of which required much boiling water) and the distillation of alcohol. He also resumed his work on mineral waters in 1773, and by 1775 had visited all the remaining French provinces, but he died before completing his book on the subject. This book, like other work done in his later years, remained unpublished. Fourcroy wrote a fitting epitaph: "Venel was better known by what he promised the sciences than by what he really did for them."[8]

NOTES

1. Antoine François de Fourcroy, *Encyclopédie méthodique, chimie . . .*, III (Paris, 1796), 364.
2. Bayen was attached to the French expedition to Minorca in March 1756, and became chief pharmacist to the army in Germany in October 1756. See A. Balland, *Les pharmaciens militaires français* (Paris, 1913), 35–36, 39.
3. Jacques Montet (1722–1782), a pharmacist who had attended Rouelle's chemistry lectures, was a leading member of the Société Royale des Sciences de Montpellier. See J. Poitevin, "Éloge de M. Montet," in R. N. D. Desgenettes, ed., *Éloges des académiciens de Montpellier* (Paris, 1811), 242–249.
4. "Cours de chymie fait, chez Monsieur Montet apoticaire; par Monsieur Venel," in the library of the Wellcome Institute for the History of Medicine, London, MS 1516, p. 164.
5. P. Bayen, *Observations sur la physique . . .*, 3 (1774), 282.
6. G. F. Venel, *Instructions sur l'usage de la houille* (Avignon-Lyons, 1775), 495–496.
7. D. Diderot, "Voyage à Bourbonne et à Langres," in *Oeuvres complètes*, R. Lewinter, ed., VIII (Paris, 1971), 600–627 (quotation from p. 606).
8. Fourcroy, *op. cit.*, 262.

BIBLIOGRAPHY

I. ORIGINAL WORKS. Before graduating from Montpellier, Venel defended a thesis, *Dissertatio de humorum crassitudine* (Montpellier, 1741). When applying for the vacant chair in 1759 he wrote *Quaestiones chemicae duodecim* (Montpellier, 1759), twelve essays on medicochemical topics that were judged better than similar collections submitted by the other candidates.

Venel's account of seltzer water was published in two parts, as "Mémoire sur l'analyse des eaux de Selters ou de Selz, Première (Seconde) Partie," in *Mémoires de mathématique et de physique, présentés à l'Académie Royale des Sciences, par divers Savans*, 2 (1755), 53–

79, 80–112; his first (and only) paper on vegetable analysis is "Essai sur l'analyse des végétaux. Premier mémoire," *ibid.*, 319–332. An abridged version of the work on seltzer water appeared in one of the rare early issues of *Observations sur la physique* . . . (August 1772), 60–71; it was reprinted in *Introduction aux observations sur la physique* . . ., **2** (1777), 331–334. Venel's only other publication on mineral waters is a pamphlet, written with P. Bayen, *Examen chimique d'une eau minérale nouvellement découverte à Passy dans la maison de Monsieur et de Madame de Calsabigi* (1755); repr. with other descriptions of the same water in the anonymously edited *Analyses chimiques des nouvelles eaux minérales, vitrioliques, ferrugineuses, découvertes à Passy dans la maison de Madame de Calsabigi* (1757), 19–52.

More than 700 articles by Venel appeared in Diderot's *Encyclopédie*, from II (1751) to XVII (1765), and he contributed two articles to the *Supplément*, I (1776). These are listed in R. N. Schwab, W. E. Rex, and J. Lough, "Inventory of Diderot's *Encyclopédie*," in *Studies on Voltaire and the Eighteenth Century*, LXXX (1971), LXXXIII (1971), LXXXV (1972), XCI–XCII (1972), with an author index in XCIII (1972). The important article "Chymie" in *Encyclopédie*, III (Paris, 1753), 408–437, was reprinted by A. F. Fourcroy, *Encyclopédie méthodique, chimie*, III (Paris, 1796), 262–303; a substantial extract (omitting Venel's account of the history of chemistry) is in J. Proust, *L'encyclopédisme dans le Bas-Languedoc au XVIIIᵉ siècle* (Montpellier, 1968), 106–140.

The last work by Venel to appear in his lifetime was *Instructions sur l'usage de la houille, plus connue sous le nom impropre de charbon de terre* . . . (Avignon-Lyons, 1775). His course on materia medica was published posthumously as *Précis de matière médicale*, 2 vols. (Paris, 1787), with many notes and additions by Joseph Barthélemy Carrère. Students' MS notes of Venel's courses on materia medica and chemistry are in the libraries of the University of Montpellier, MSS 563–564; and the Wellcome Institute for the History of Medicine, London, MSS 1516–1517 (both courses, dated 1761) and MS 347 (materia medica, dated 1767).

II. SECONDARY LITERATURE. Two valuable biographical accounts by men who knew Venel well are J. J. Menuret de Chambaud, *Éloge historique de M. Venel . . . par M. J. J. M.* (Grenoble-Paris, 1777); and E. H. de Ratte, "Éloge de M. Venel," in *Observations sur la physique* . . ., **10** (1777), 3–14, repr. in J. B. Carrère's edition of G. F. Venel, *Précis de matière médicale*, I (Paris, 1787), vii–xxxviii, and also in R. N. D. Desgenettes, ed., *Éloges des académiciens de Montpellier* (Paris, 1811), 194–203.

Additional information is given by J. Castelnau, *Mémoire historique et biographique sur l'ancienne Société Royale des Sciences de Montpellier* (Montpellier, 1858), 74–76, 154.

Venel's association with the *Encyclopédie* is discussed by J. Proust, *L'encyclopédisme dans le Bas-Languedoc au XVIIIᵉ siècle* (Montpellier, 1968), 23–27, 33–35. Venel's theory of the levity of phlogiston is put in its historical context by J. R. Partington and D. McKie, "Historical studies in the phlogiston theory. I. The levity of phlogiston," in *Annals of Science*, **2** (1937), 361–404. Venel's criticism of Newtonian chemistry is discussed by Arnold Thackray, *Atoms and Powers* (Cambridge, Mass., 1970), 193–197.

W. A. SMEATON

VENETZ, IGNATZ (*b.* Visperterminen, Valais, Switzerland, 21 March 1788; *d.* Saxon-les-Bains, Valais, Switzerland, 20 April 1859), *civil engineering, glaciology.*

Venetz was the son of Peter Ignatz Venetz, who, although said to be descended from Venetian nobility, was a poor carpenter all his life. His mother was Anna Maria Stoffel. Although his parents wished him to become a priest, Venetz was attracted to science and mathematics and studied these subjects at the Collège de Brig. During the French occupation of the Valais he entered the Service des Ponts et Chaussées, in which he rose to become chief engineer for the district. His engineering career was, however, marred by a disaster in 1818, when the Gétroz glacier in the Val de Bagnes had grown, after three years of heavy snow, to dam up a stream which quickly became a lake. It was feared that warm weather would melt the glacier and cause a flood. Venetz tried to obviate the menace by making a channel through the ice through which the water might drain gradually. Unfortunately, the channel so weakened the ice dam that it gave way. Five hundred million cubic feet of water poured into the valley below, causing great loss of life and property.

Venetz' work in the Val de Bagnes led to a happier result through his conversations with a local chamois hunter, Jean-Pierre Perraudin, who had noticed that the striations left by glaciers extended as far as Martigny, a dozen miles away. Although skeptical, Venetz made his own observations and found that the hunter was correct. He presented his findings in a paper, read in 1821, which included evidence of earlier advances and retreats of glaciers and which won the prize offered by the Swiss Natural Science Society for an explanation of climatic deterioration. The work was nonetheless generally ignored until it was finally published in 1833 by Jean Charpentier, who had been convinced by another work of Venetz (written in 1829 but not published until 1861) that glaciers had extended more widely in earlier ages. Venetz thus provided the link between the observations of a peasant and the great discovery of a scientist—the Ice Age.

BIBLIOGRAPHY

Venetz' works include "Mémoire sur les variations de la température dans les Alpes de la Suisse," in *Denkschriften der allgemeinen Schweizerischen Gesellschaft für die gesammten Naturwissenschaften*, **1**, sec. 2 (1833), 1; and "Mémoire sur l'extension des anciens glaciers, renfermant quelques explications sur leurs effets remarquables," in *Nouvelles mémoires de la Société helvétique des sciences naturelles*, **18** (1861), 1.

On his life and work, see Ignace Mariétan, "La vie et l'oeuvre de l'ingénieur Ignace Venetz (1799–1859)," in *Bulletin murithienne de la Société valaisanne des sciences naturelles*, **76** (1959), 1.

GAVIN DE BEER

VENING MEINESZ, FELIX ANDRIES (*b.* Scheveningen, Netherlands, 30 July 1887; *d.* Amersfoort, Netherlands, 10 August 1966), *geodesy, geophysics.*

The son of Sjoerd Vening Meinesz, burgomaster of Rotterdam and later of Amsterdam, and Cornelia den Tex, Vening Meinesz studied civil engineering at the Technical University of Delft, obtaining a degree in 1910. Shortly afterward J. J. A. Muller of the Rijkscommissie voor Graadmeting en Waterpassing asked him to join that government bureau and participate in a gravimetric survey of the Netherlands. Vening Meinesz agreed immediately; the survey would take a few years at most, and after that there would still be time to go into practice as a civil engineer. Gravity, however, held him in its grip for life.

It is not surprising that Vening Meinesz, who never married, became enamored of geodesy. Imbued as a child with the importance of solemn governmental affairs, he felt at home among the geodesists' formal courtesy in a tradition of international cooperation that was over a century old. In 1911 he participated in the measurement of a base near Lyons by the Service Géographique de l'Armée. He was later elected president of the Association Géodésique Internationale (1933–1955) and of the International Union of Geodesy and Geophysics (1948–1951), in each case for his contributions to these sciences and for his continued efforts to bring order to their entangled relations. That both geodesy and solid-earth geophysics were needed to interpret the results of Vening

Meinesz' gravity measurements, and that geology had its role as well, became abundantly clear after his first cruises. His strenuous efforts to achieve scientific interplay, however, elicited only a meager response.

One is struck by a strictly logical line of development in Vening Meinesz' scientific achievements; everything seems to follow a careful plan, although of course no one could have foreseen that grave obstacles would yield to ingenuity and perseverance, or that salient features of the field of attraction of the earth exist—the Vening Meinesz belts of negative anomalies.

Vening Meinesz' first measurement of gravity in the Netherlands confronted him with what appeared to be an insurmountable obstacle. At many stations it proved impossible to find a stable support for the pendulums; the continuous vibration of the peaty subsoil would lead to unacceptable errors in the results. Vening Meinesz' efforts to overcome this difficulty were typical of the manner in which he confronted a problem. Far from trusting to luck in trying modifications of the experiments, he started with the thorough theoretical investigation embodied in his doctoral dissertation *Bÿdragen tot de theorie der slingerwearnemingen* (1915). In the introduction Vening Meinesz disparaged the originality of his own work; most of the disturbances had already been investigated when various authors had been confronted with them. His work, however, presents a systematic treatment starting from the fundamental equation

$$\frac{g}{l}\vartheta + \ddot{\vartheta} + S = 0,$$

where S represents the sum of all disturbances (*storingen*) the squares and products (second-order corrections) of which generally are negligible, so that, for instance, it is not necessary to introduce the temperature-dependence of the correction for finite amplitude.

For practical observations the most important conclusion of this theoretical work is that the mean of the periods of two isochronous pendulums swinging in the same plane with equal amplitude in opposite phases is not affected by the troublesome S-term, $\ddot{y}$, the horizontal acceleration in that plane. Vening Meinesz had to use an apparatus in which two pairs of pendulums swung in two mutually perpendicular planes. For each pair the above conditions could be fulfilled with sufficient precision; and, using this method, by 1921 he had measured gravity at fifty-one stations covering the territory of the Netherlands at intervals of about forty kilometers. It was claimed that the mean-square error of the difference of the values for g from that obtained at the central station at De Bilt was somewhat less than 2 milligals. Gravity at De Bilt was compared, both before and after the survey, with the absolutely determined value at Potsdam, where Vening Meinesz had been instructed in the practice of pendulum observations by the director of the Geodetic Institute, Ludwig Haasemann. During the survey the chronometers were compared with the clock at the Leiden astronomical observatory by telephone and after 1919 the radio time signals from Paris were used.

While working to solve the problems of unstable support, Vening Meinesz was tempted to direct his efforts more boldly to the apparently overambitious plan of measuring gravity at sea. In his *Theory and Practice of Pendulum Observations at Sea*, he again began with the first equations of motion for two pendulums affected by the same horizontal accelerations:

$$\ddot{\vartheta}_1 + \frac{g}{l_1}\vartheta_1 + \frac{\ddot{y}}{l_1} = 0, \ddot{\vartheta}_2 + \frac{g}{l_2}\vartheta_2 + \frac{\ddot{y}}{l_2} = 0,$$

then jubilantly exclaimed:

It is clear that $\ddot{y}$ can be eliminated from these two equations, and this is the fundamental principle of the method. If the pendulums are isochronous, so that $l_1 = l_2$, the result of this elimination is very simple: the difference of the equations gives

$$(\ddot{\vartheta}_1 - \ddot{\vartheta}_2) + \frac{g}{l}(\vartheta_1 - \vartheta_2) = 0.$$

which has the same shape as the equation of motion of an undisturbed pendulum of the same mathematical length *l* and an angle of elongation $(\vartheta_1 - \vartheta_2)$. We reach in this way the important conclusion that the difference of the angles of elongation may be considered as the angle of elongation of a fictitious pendulum, which is not disturbed by the horizontal accelerations of the apparatus, and which is isochronous with the original pendulums.

A shipboard attempt proved a complete failure, however, for even tiny surface waves striking the hull cause fairly high accelerations. It was necessary to wait for so exceptional a calm that the method was totally impractical. Vening Meinesz gratefully acknowledged the suggestion of F. K. T. van Iterson, chief engineer of the state coal mines, who, while on a submarine training dive conducted by the Dutch navy, had been struck by the profound tranquillity during submersion. Waves are in fact damped exponentially with depth, so that only 2 percent of the amplitude remains at a depth equal to the wavelength. The brisk movements of shorter waves were therefore imperceptible at the moderate depth then attainable by submarines, while the disturbance caused by the longer waves was handled by the fictitious pendulum. (See Figure 1.)

The first voyage to measure gravity at sea, from the Netherlands to Java in 1923, began under adverse circumstances. The small submarines moved slowly when submerged and could cover only limited distances. As a rule dives were restricted to the demands of the gravity observations. A heavy six-day storm wreaked the usual hardships on a

TABLE I
VENING MEINESZ' GRAVITY EXPEDITIONS AT SEA

Year	Submarine H.M.S.	Route	Number of Observations
1923	K II	Holland – Suez – Java	32
1925	K XI	Holland – Alexandria	10 (experiments with new pendulum apparatus)
1926	K XIII	Holland – Panama – Java	128
1927	K XIII	Java Deep	26
1929–30	K XIII	Indonesia	237
1932	O 13	Atlantic	60
1934–35	K 18	Holland – Buenos Aires – Cape Town – Freemantle – Java	237
1937	O 16	Holland – Washington – Lisbon	93
1937	O 12	Curaçao – Holland	20 (experiments on
1938	O 13	Channel	wave motion
1939	O 19	North Sea	and Browne terms)
		Total	843

boat of 630 tons, aggravated by the limited room, by water coming through the hatch, and by clothes refusing to dry. But, Vening Meinesz reported, "The worst thing of all was that the pendulum apparatus could not be used." (The rolling at a depth of thirty meters was still heavy enough to endanger the pendulums.) Finally, off the coast of Portugal with a smooth sea, three dives afforded an opportunity for observations. It now became clear that the apparatus, if it was to operate under normal waves, would have to be fitted in a kind of cradle to counteract the roll of the boat.

The harbor of Gibraltar was entered, and Vening Meinesz quickly developed the pendulum records; they showed good results, suggesting that no difficulties would arise if the tilt of the instrument could be kept small enough. The British commander gave permission for the naval yard to construct a suspension about an axis parallel to the keel. On the voyage to Java this tenacity was rewarded with thirty successful observations.

The Sterneck apparatus dealt separately with each pendulum, and the horizontal accelerations gave rise to irregular records that required days to interpret. Vening Meinesz constructed an entirely new instrument that was admirable for its ingenuity as well as for exquisite craftsmanship. The fundamental principle, elimination of $\ddot{y}$ by subtraction,

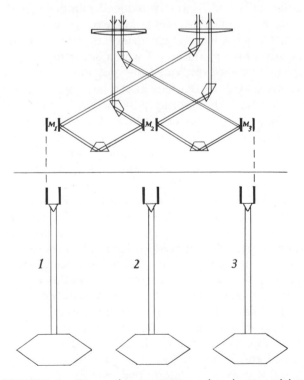

FIGURE 1. Top section represents a plan above pendulum mirrors Mi, prisms, lenses, and light paths. Lower section represents elevation of the three pendulums.

is applied in a beam of light reflected from one pendulum mirror onto the opposite mirror of a second pendulum, thus recording the desired fictitious pendulum (Figure 1). This device proved highly successful; from an engagingly regular pattern the value of gravity can be derived in a few hours. Furthermore, the strictly regular records have the advantage of showing at a glance that some conceivable disturbances affecting amplitude do not exist. Actually there are three pendulums swinging in the same plane; the outer two, each combined with the middle one, yield the records of two fictitious pendulums. The amplitude of the middle pendulum is kept as small as possible, and therefore the periods of the outer pendulums enter preponderantly into the result. Hence their stability can be relied upon as long as the slight difference between the two fictitious periods remains the same. The small amplitude of the middle pendulum is recorded separately against a short auxiliary damped pendulum, and this record is used to evaluate the correction for finite amplitude. A second damped pendulum records the tilt of the swinging plane. (In the Sterneck instrument the latter expedient was unnecessary; each pair of pendulums indicated the tilt of the swinging plane of the other pair.)

A cruise from Holland to Egypt to test the new apparatus (1925) gave satisfactory results. On the first cruise to Java the recording apparatus was separately mounted at the distance of one meter required for an easily measurable deflection of a light spot on the records. Thus a fixed direction was necessary for the registering beam of light, which therefore was directed through the axis of the cradle, made hollow for this purpose. This axis, being constantly perpendicular to the swinging plane, had to be kept horizontal with a tolerance of thirty minutes. This requirement demanded extremely careful trimming of the boat, and placed a great strain on the helmsman and the crew, who were not allowed to move about.

Suspension in gimbals seemed unavoidable, which necessitated rearrangement of the recording piece so that it could be joined firmly to the pendulum box. To retain its full length, the light path was "folded" by introducing more prisms. A good example of Vening Meinesz' attention to details is seen in the length of this path's being 1,162 millimeters, whereas the focal distance of the exit lens is 1,110 millimeters. This excess length compensates for the loss of convergence by refraction of the rays as they enter a prism. (For the collimator these figures are 653 and 616 millimeters.)

His equipment now being shipshape, Vening Meinesz strongly desired to take it to sea. Fortunately he combined technical skill with a rare gift for persuasion. His tenacious politeness succeeded in convincing government officials and the admiralty of the urgent need for gravity values on all oceans. He next inspired the Dutch submarine service to unheard-of achievements. At that time it was still thought impossible for submarines to travel long distances without escort ships on the surface. K XIII, however, crossed both the Atlantic and Pacific oceans unescorted. Several longer and shorter cruises followed over the southern Atlantic and the Indian Ocean and the seas of Indonesia, yielding hundreds of observations (see Table I).

While Vening Meinesz was on his 1937 cruise, B. C. Browne, a young geodesist at Cambridge, sent him a letter that might be summarized as "Dear Sir, you have made a mistake." On studying Browne's arguments, Vening Meinesz had to admit that the numerous regular corrections failed to cover some of the disturbances due to the motions of the boat. He made this admission gracefully, without vexation or excuses. It is even possible that he enjoyed the opportunity to work again with the mechanics of the pendulum and to produce in corroboration three papers on "Browne terms" and the second volume of *Theory and Practice.*

With the primitive cradle, the single axis of which was fixed in the direction of the keel, an acceleration $\ddot{z}$, parallel to the axis and hence to the knife-edges, clearly could not affect the motion of the pendulums. The effect of the other component of horizontal acceleration, $\ddot{y}$, had been dealt with by the fictitious pendulum device. On the other hand, it is equally clear that suspension in a complete gimbal system requires consideration of the resultant of gravity and acceleration given by vector addition: $g + \ddot{x} + \ddot{y} + \ddot{z}$.

A piece of good luck—as Vening Meinesz put it—made it possible for the vertical acceleration to be recovered from the old records. Assuming a circular wave movement, as was concurrently deduced from several wave theories, the horizontal acceleration should be equal—$|\ddot{x}| = |\ddot{y} + \ddot{z}|$—and thus Browne's correction could be introduced. For the future, however, a more direct determination seemed worth trying. If the angle between apparent gravity and the true vertical could be found, the horizontal accelerations would be known. This would be no easy task, for the whole apparatus in its gimbals follows apparent gravity.

Vening Meinesz may well have been equally pleased with the opportunity to show that his skill in tackling such problems had not deteriorated during twelve years of making routine measurements. In close cooperation with Browne the "slow pendulums" were designed and used as a highly simplified but effective artificial horizon. A slow pendulum consists of a horizontal brass beam balanced on a knife-edge. The center of gravity being only a few tenths of a millimeter beneath this edge, the pendulum's period amounts to about half a minute. Therefore, waves going round in less than ten seconds can set it in motion to only an insignificant degree. Keeping a steady position in space, two such pendulums thus afford a means for registering the tilt of the apparatus in the gimbals (or, rather, of the damped pendulums, which, because of their short periods, follow exactly the changing direction of apparent gravity). For recording the slow pendulums, three lenses and thirteen prisms had to be added to the four mirrors, four lenses, and twenty-three prisms already in use. The housing of the new pendulums could be fitted into the eighty millimeters left between the main box and the recording box, and the whole instrument now appeared to have been made all of a piece.

The instrument was used for only a short time, however, because the outbreak of World War II suspended the peaceful use of submarines. After the war the Royal Dutch Navy was again helpful, although it had a greatly reduced number of submarines. Vening Meinesz, however, had to delegate the work to younger observers. For over thirty years his apparatus (of which some five copies are in existence) provided the only means for measuring gravity at sea, but in the late 1950's it was superseded. Then spring gravimeters mounted on stabilized platforms on surface ships began to record gravity values along continuous profiles. American investigators used the Vening Meinesz method until 1959, the number of stations then amounting to nearly 3,000.

Vening Meinesz' Observations in Relation to Geodesy. Geodesy seeks to ascertain the shape and dimensions of the earth. Altitudes and depths must refer to a certain curved surface called the geoid, which is the gravity-equipotential surface coinciding with the mean surface of the sea and its continuation on land. The geoid is approximately an ellipsoid of revolution, minor deviations being due to irregularities in the distribution of masses. These deviations are therefore closely linked to the values of gravity as measured by pendulum observations. If gravity is determined everywhere on the earth, the shape of the geoid with reference to the ellipsoid can be calculated according to a formula deduced by Stokes. This calculation greatly occupied Vening Meinesz. For instance, *Gravity Expeditions at Sea,* II, 13–17, concludes with "In the future it will become possible to apply the Theorem of Stokes in its full accuracy and to solve in this way the central geodetic problem: the determination of the Figure of the Earth."

Values of gravity averaged over regions extending some tens of kilometers are appropriate for this purpose. Observations on land have the disadvantage that a nearby irregular mass may cause a severe deviation from the mean. At sea this problem does not arise, since no irregularity can be nearer than the sea floor. Through Vening Meinesz' and English and American observations, approximation was already possible for about half the globe. Recently the central problem was solved by observing the trajectories of satellites. Their acceleration at any moment is that of gravity averaged over a region the radius of which is proportional to the distance of the satellite from the earth (about 100 kilometers).

Since the eighteenth century geodesists have asked whether the geoid, instead of being represented by an ellipsoid of revolution, should rather be seen as a triaxial ellipsoid—that is, whether the equator was a circle or an ellipse, the latter shape involving a systematic variation in the values of gravity. Having closed a ring of observations around the globe, Vening Meinesz could rule out the possibility of regular deviations and therefore establish that the equator must be represented by a circle.

Isostasy. The principle of isostasy is usually elucidated by analogy with blocks of wood or a mass of ice floating on stagnant water. The experiments by which we try to understand the origin of the geographic and geologic structure of the earth are perforce on a small scale. Small-scale models are very deceptive because of the strength of materials factor. In order to imitate real rocks on a continental scale the tensile strength has to be practically zero. Hans Cloos and P. H. Kuenen were among the first to experiment with wet clay or soft wax, but in general it is impossible to get all the mechanical parameters to scale and difficulties multiply. These problems do not affect Vening Meinesz' numerous calculations in applied mechanics. For large nonplastic deformations and for disruptions, calculations are hardly possible. For small strains seismic data are very useful and allow fairly accurate estimates of the specific weight of materials at depth.

In the latter half of the nineteenth century the earth came to be seen as originally a molten sphere, which at an early stage of cooling came to be enclosed in a strong crust of consolidation. Vening Meinesz constantly had in mind an earth model with an elastic crust on a viscous substratum. This led to his preference for interpretation in terms of regional isostasy, reducing observed gravity by applying the so-called regional isostatic compensation. For such a calculation a number of assumptions are tried regarding the thickness of the crust (twenty or thirty kilometers) and its strength, resulting in a bend area with a radius of 232, 174, 116, 58, or 29 kilometers (also 0 kilometers: local compensation). An assumption resulting in a complete reduction of the anomaly may be true—at least it cannot be said to be wrong. The great drawback of gravity measurements, however, is that although a value can be calculated from a given repartition of masses, the reverse calculation is impossible. A given set of gravity values can result from a wide range of depth configurations that depart in many ways from a simplified assumption. In addition, in some instances none of the regional isostatic assumptions made by Vening Meinesz can be said to give satisfactory results.

The Vening Meinesz Belts. The most striking feature shown by the earth's gravity field was discovered by Vening Meinesz during his earlier cruises. The "Vening Meinesz negative gravity anomaly belts of island arcs," as they were called by H. H. Hess (*Gedenkboek*, 183), with their bold, steeply descending lows of gravity, are not reduced to zero by any of the common suppositions. Winding for thousands of miles in gentle curves, along deep-sea trenches and rows of mostly volcanic islands, the belts often follow the outcrop of a roughly stratiform cluster of shallow and deep earthquake foci dipping at about forty-five degrees landward.

The regular concurrence of these conspicuous phenomena challenged every inventive mind to discover their significance. Vening Meinesz directed his attention chiefly to the gravity anomalies; his explanation of them by means of the buckling hypothesis brought strong reactions from geologists. Throughout he used the classic tool of compression in a rigid crust. Strong enough to overcome the resistance of the crust, the compression would cause a thickening along a line of weakness that apparently coincides with the frontier between a continent or shallow sea and the ocean. This thickened part of the crust, representing increased mass, naturally sinks to restore isostasy, thus causing the compressive forces to deviate downward. On further compression the crust will be folded and the folded parts pressed downward, thus causing light crustal rocks to take the place of heavy mantle materials. This process explains the observed negative gravity anomalies. The Dutch geologist Kuenen, who often did model experiments to explain geological phenomena, illustrated this buckling by compressing a floating layer of soft wax, which behaved exactly as Vening Meinesz had predicted. The downward buckling was soon interpreted as a geosyncline receiving sediments because of the compensating rise of the borders, which led to emergence of land at the continental edge and its subsequent attack by erosion. The resulting sediments, filling in the depression, would then be folded by continued pressure. The deep-sea trenches often are situated somewhat farther from the continent than the most strongly negative anomaly; this situation is explained by the sediments' having filled part of the trench.

A strong departure from isostasy cannot be of unlimited duration. In due course the base will be buoyed, thus producing an elevated strip of folded sediments. In Vening Meinesz' view, folded mountain chains, such as the Alps, represent buckles of an older period that now reach great altitudes because of isostatic compensation by the remnants of a base of crustal rocks. The view that the Indonesian archipelago was comparable with an initial stage of Alpine mountains had long been considered by geologists. This view, joined with Kuenen's experiment, secured a favorable reception for the buckling hypothesis.

Areas of strong anomalies are necessarily of limited size, at least in breadth. A large, round domain could not depart from isostasy to a degree comparable with the negative anomaly belts, unless one accepted an exorbitant value for the strength of the crust. An example of an extensive area about 1,000 kilometers across having moderate negative anomalies is in Scandinavia and is readily interpreted in connection with the thick ice cap formerly present there. That ice cap would have been brought into isostatic equilibrium during the long glacial epoch by weighing down the crust of the earth. It melted rather suddenly, a short geological time (6,000 years) ago. In correspondence with the remaining negative anomaly, the land is now rising. In combination these two facts, numerically assessed, enabled Vening Meinesz to calculate the resistance of the substratum, which, expressed in terms of viscosity, yields a value of 10^{22} poises. He used this value for calculations concerning the velocity of the movement that other departures from isostatic equilibrium may cause.

Convection Currents in the Mantle. In the 1920's Arthur Holmes, among others, had used convection currents to explain continental drift. By general agreement, however, the geoscientists of the northern hemisphere had also dismissed the sound arguments offered by Wegener, bluntly denying the possibility of wandering continents. For Vening Meinesz the crust was so rigid that he had no choice but to state that the continents were firmly fixed, while the interior of the earth became the site of great activity. He often thought in terms of a cooling earth and accepted an increase in temperature with depth greater than the adiabatic gradient. The resulting departure from equilibrium led to convection currents, about the velocity of which the Scandinavian viscosity could give information. The drag of the currents on the crust, in Vening Meinesz' view, led to no more than a buckle here and there, notably along the Vening Meinesz belts—which, therefore, had to be located near a descending branch of the currents.

Vening Meinesz was strongly convinced that he had derived an unshakable argument for the reality of convection currents from a regularity apparent in the development of the earth's relief in spherical harmonics. He showed this regularity to be present, at first, in the development calculated in 1922 by Adelbert Prey up to the sixteenth order, which, at his request, was extended to the thirty-first order by the Mathematical Center of Amsterdam. Its numerical result reflects mainly the contrasting heights of oceans and continents, whereas it is their distribution on the globe that must be closely linked with the system of convection currents: around sinks in this system patches of light continental rocks had floated together in the formation of the land on the surface of the globe. This all had taken place in a primordial stage, when the earth was still largely molten. Through cooling, the crust soon became so rigid as to resist further rearrangement; throughout the whole of geological time the continents retained their shapes and relative positions despite continued convection underneath. (When, in the early 1960's, continental drift was held to be established by paleomagnetism, the currents were still there, serving as a motor.)

Convection had been challenged; and seismic data led to the view that a lower part of the mantle, because of higher specific weight, could not be involved in those currents. Vening Meinesz argued that the high density at depth was probably due to the presence of olivine in the spinel modification. The reversible transition between the olivine and the spinel phases could not be an obstacle, yet the boundary between them ought to be sharp—and, according to the seismologists, it was not. This objection was met by the plausible assumption of a fayalite component that caused phase equilibrium to persist through a certain range of pressures. These ideas were worked out with the physicochemists J. L. Meijering and C. S. M. Rooymans, and were likewise taken up by A. E. Ringwood.

Problems like these, clearly needing information from many different fields, strengthened Vening Meinesz' conviction that interdisciplinary cooperation is necessary when fundamental principles are involved. He felt this to be especially the case in geophysics and geology, and he had some success. Certain chapters in volume II of *Gravity Expeditions at Sea* written by the prominent Dutch geologists J. H. Umbgrove and Kuenen resulted in a genetic interpretation of the Indonesian archipelago. Twenty years later B. J. Collette submitted a doctoral dissertation concerning the effect of gravity on the geology of the Sunda Islands. In 1955–1957 Collette measured gravity on the North Sea, the shallower parts with a static gravimeter lowered to the bottom and the deeper northern part, up to 61° north latitude, with the Vening Meinesz instrument.

Vening Meinesz maintained a keen interest in the ocean floor. Later investigators did not forget the grand old pioneer: his honors steadily increased, culminating in the Vetlesen Prize in 1962. In 1963 the new institute for geophysics and geochemistry at Utrecht University was named for him.

BIBLIOGRAPHY

I. ORIGINAL WORKS. A list of Vening Meinesz' publications to 1957 is included in the jubilee volume, *Gedenkboek F. A. Vening Meinesz*, which is *Verhandelingen van het Nederlandsch geologisch-mijnbouwkundig genootschap*, Geol. ser., **18** (1957), with portrait. His most important works are *Theory and Practice of Pendulum Observations at Sea*, 2 vols. (Delft, 1929–1941), with illustrations of apparatus and records; *The Gravity Measuring Cruise of the U.S. Submarine S-21* (Washington, 1930), written with F. E. Wright, which includes illustrations of apparatus and records as well as a full explanation of the instruments and method; and *Gravity Expeditions at Sea*, 5 vols. (Delft, 1932–1960; II, repr. 1964), vol. II written with J. H. Umbgrove and P. H. Kuenen.

II. SECONDARY LITERATURE. See B. J. Collette, "In Memoriam Dr. Ir. Felix Andries Vening Meinesz," in *Geologie en mijnbouw*, **45** (Sept. 1966), 285–290, in English, with portrait and complementary bibliography to that in the jubilee volume (see above); J. L. Meijering and C. J. M. Rooymans, "On the Olivine-Spinel Transition in the Earth's Mantle," in *Proceedings of the K. nederlandsche akademie van wetenschappen*, Ser. B, **61** (1958), 333–344; and J. Lamar Worzel, "Pendulum Gravity Measurements at Sea, 1936–1959," *Contributions. Lamont Geological Observatory*, no. 807 (1963), which contains the most important continuation of Vening Meinesz' observations and interpretations.

W. NIEUWENKAMP

VENN, JOHN (*b.* Hull, England, 4 August 1834; *d.* Cambridge, England, 4 April 1923), *probability, logic*.

Venn's family was one of a group belonging to the evangelical wing of the Church of England that was noted for its philanthropic work. This group, which included the Macaulays, Thorntons, and Wilberforces, was centered in the London suburb of Clapham and was nicknamed the "Clapham Sect." A pivotal figure was Venn's grandfather, Rev. John Venn, rector of Clapham.

After attending two London schools, at Highgate and Islington, Venn entered Gonville and Caius College, Cambridge, in 1853; took his degree in mathematics in 1857; and was elected a fellow of his college, holding the fellowship until his death. He took holy orders in 1859, but after a short interval of parochial work he returned to Cambridge as college lecturer in moral sciences and played a considerable part in the development of the newly established moral sciences tripos examination. In 1883 Venn resigned his clerical orders, being out of sympathy with orthodox Anglican dogma but remained a devout lay member of the church. He received the Cambridge Sc.D. in 1883 and in that year was elected a fellow of the Royal Society.

Besides his scientific works, Venn conducted much research into historical records and wrote books on the history of his college and on his family. He also undertook the preparation of *Alumni Cantabrigienses*, a tremendous task in which he was assisted by his son, J. A. Venn; two volumes appeared in his lifetime.

Venn's volumes on probability and logic were highly esteemed textbooks in the late nineteenth and early twentieth centuries. The historian H. T. Buckle had discussed the validity of statistical studies of human activities, and De Morgan and Boole had written on the foundations of probability theory; this work stimulated Venn to write his *Logic of Chance*. In this book he disclaimed any attempt to make extensive use of mathematical techniques; he believed that there was a need for a thorough and logical discussion of principles, and his work was an essay in that direction. British predecessors were critically discussed. Venn thought that De Morgan's *Formal Logic* provided a good investigation, but he was not prepared to accept his principles; he was dubious about Boole's *Laws of Thought*, for he was not entirely happy with certain aspects of Boole's algebraic analysis of logic.

Venn attempted to deal with the notorious Petersburg paradox by insisting on the concept of "average gain," which is connected with his revision of the basic definition of probability. The classical definition, given in the early eighteenth century by De Moivre, considers the situation in which there are s successes in m trials and defines the probability of a success as s/m. One weakness of that definition is that if a possible ambiguity is to be evaded by specifying that the m possibilities are all equally likely, we may be led into a circular argument. Venn offered the following definition: If in a large number m of trials there are s successes (and $m - s$ failures), the probability of a success is the limit of s/m as m tends to infinity. This definition avoids the difficulties that arise when the classical definition is applied to, say, a die with bias, but is itself not free from defects. The existence of the limit cannot be proved from the definition; Venn implicitly assumes that a unique limit must exist. In the twentieth century R. von Mises improved Venn's work by adding explicit postulates on the existence of the Venn limit that effectively restrict the nature of the possible trials. The Venn definition also has been criticized on the practical grounds that it alone cannot provide a specific numerical value for the probability and that further hypotheses must be added in order to arrive at such values.

Venn's books on logic were based on a thorough study of earlier works, of which he had a very large collection that is now in the Cambridge University Library. His writings can still be consulted with profit but are chiefly remembered for the use of logical diagrams, although *Symbolic Logic* is largely an attempt to interpret and correct Boole's work. The use of geometric diagrams to represent syllogistic logic has a long history, but Leibniz was the first to use them systematically rather than as casual illustrations. "All A is B" is represented by a circle marked A placed wholly inside another circle marked B; "Some A is B" is represented by two overlapping circles; and the standard syllo-

gisms are depicted by means of three circles. The procedure was further developed by Euler, and in the early nineteenth century many writers offered varieties of diagrammatic representation. In preparing his book Venn had made a careful survey of such writings, and his chapter discussing them is severely critical. Boole's *Laws of Thought* (1854) was the first efficient development of an algebra of logic, but he did not use diagrams.

Venn was strongly influenced by Boole's work, and in his books he clarifies some inconsistencies and ambiguities in Boole's ideas and notations; but his chief contribution to logic was his systematic explanation and development of the method of geometrical representation. He pointed out that diagrams that merely represent the relations between two classes, or two propositions, are not sufficiently general; and he proposed a series of simple closed curves (circles or more elaborate forms) dividing the plane into compartments, such that each successive curve should intersect all the compartments already obtained. For one term, compartments x, $\bar{x}$ (the negation or complement of x) are needed; for two terms, four compartments are needed; for three terms, eight; and so on. By the time five classes are under consideration, the diagram is becoming complicated to the point of uselessness. To illustrate the principles of symbolic logic, Venn deliberately provided a variety of concrete instances, often of the type now found in collections of mathematical puzzles, for he remarked that the subject is sufficiently abstract to present difficulty to the average student, who must be helped by a supply of realizable examples.

Since the null class was not then accepted as a class, Venn also had to discuss whether the diagrams represented compartments or classes—that is, whether compartments could be regarded as unoccupied. A compartment known to be unoccupied could be shown by shading it, and a universal proposition could be represented by a suitable unoccupied compartment: Thus "No A is B" could be represented by shading the area common to the two intersecting circles (or closed curves) representing A and B. Venn's treatment of the "universe of discourse" was somewhat indefinite and was criticized by C. L. Dodgson in his *Symbolic Logic* (published under the pseudonym by which he was better known, Lewis Carroll); Dodgson insisted, in Carollian style, on the use of a closed compartment enclosing the whole diagram to delimit the universe of discourse. Venn diagrams, as they are now generally called, have recently been much used in elementary mathematics to encourage logical thinking at a fairly early stage of a child's education.

BIBLIOGRAPHY

I. ORIGINAL WORKS. Venn's books include *The Logic of Chance* (London–Cambridge, 1866); *Symbolic Logic* (London–Cambridge, 1881); and *The Principles of Empirical Logic* (London–Cambridge, 1889).

II. SECONDARY LITERATURE. A detailed obituary notice of Venn by his son, J. A. Venn, is in *Dictionary of National Biography* for 1922–1930, 869–870. For a critical discussion of definitions of probability, see Harold Jeffreys, *Theory of Probability*, 2nd ed. (Oxford, 1948). A succinct but valuable account of Venn diagrams is M. E. Baron, "A Note on the Historical Development of Logic Diagrams: Leibniz, Euler and Venn," in *Mathematical Gazette*, **53** (May 1969), 113–125.

T. A. A. BROADBENT

VERANTIUS, FAUSTUS (also known as **FAUSTO VRANČIĆ** or **VERANZIO**) (*b.* Šibenik, Dalmatia, 1551; *d.* Venice, Italy, 20 January 1617), *engineering.*

Son of Michael Vrančić, a diplomat and poet, and of Catherine Dobroević, Verantius came from a noble Croatian family; its members, aristocracy of the city of Šibenik, were related to several Church dignitaries and to a viceroy of Croatia. His uncle, Anthony Verantius (1504–1573), was archbishop of Esztergom, primate of Hungary, cardinal, and an influential statesman. He took charge of Verantius' education, sending him to study philosophy and law at Padua (1568–1570) and initiating him into the political intrigues of the day. Although Anthony Verantius was principally a man of letters, he was greatly interested in the art of fortification and supervised the construction of the fortress at Eger. It is possible that his uncle's enthusiasm for technical problems influenced Verantius.

In 1579, Verantius became commander of the citadel at Veszprim. Two years later he resigned this post to accept an offer from Emperor Rudolf II to become secretary of the royal chancellory of Hungary. Thus from 1581 to 1594 Verantius was a diplomat, working at times for the emperor at Prague as well as for Archduke Ernest at Vienna. In his leisure time Verantius studied mechanics and mathematics.

In 1594 Verantius resigned his position at the Hapsburg court. From then until 1598 he lived in Dalmatia and Italy, mainly Venice, where, in 1595, he published a dictionary in five languages (Latin, Italian, German, Croatian, and Hungarian). Verantius had two children, and following the death of his wife, he took religious vows. In 1598 Rudolf II granted him the title of bishop of Csanad, an honorary office since the bishopric was then occupied by the Turks. Nevertheless, Verantius interrupted his literary and scientific work in order to accept an important political assignment, as imperial counselor for Hungarian and Transylvanian affairs. Although he was a skillful courtier and an able administrator, his career was hampered by his impetuous nature. Disappointed in his political ambitions, he left the court at Prague in 1605 and became a member of the Congregation of St. Paul, in Rome.

Verantius became friendly at Rome with Giovanni Ambrogio Mazenta, a Barnabite like himself and, from 1611, general of the Congregation of St. Paul. Very possibly it was Mazenta who interested Verantius in the construction of machines and in architectural problems. Verantius undoubtedly had an opportunity to see many of Leonardo da Vinci's technical drawings, of which Mazenta had prepared a list about 1587. During his stay at Rome, Verantius had drawn and engraved a series of "new machines." At his request on 9 June 1614 Louis XIII granted him a privilege for printing a "book of machines." According to its terms, for fifteen years no one would be permitted to publish another edition; and for thirty years no French subject would be allowed, without Verantius' permission, to "put into use . . . the said machines of his invention [which have] never been seen before." Cosimo II de' Medici, grand duke of Tuscany, granted Verantius an analogous privilege (June 1615) for the book "that the latter wishes to publish."

During this period Verantius fell gravely ill; and his doctors advised him to leave Rome. He drew up his will on 12 June 1615 and decided to return to Šibenik to await his death. His efforts to publish the book on machines in France, Rome, or Florence were unsuccessful. He was so intent on carrying out his project, however, that on his way to Dalmatia he stopped at Venice, where in 1616 he published a treatise on logic (which he called "ars discendi et docendi scientias") and, most important, a splendid folio volume entitled *Machinae novae.* Too ill to continue his trip, Verantius died in Venice; but in accordance with the provisions of his will, his body was taken to Šibenik and placed in the family burial vault on the isle of Prvić.

Machinae novae poses some bibliographic problems, since it is undated and the surviving copies are not identical. The work consists of a title page, forty-nine plates, and five sets of explanations of the plates. Each set has a new pagination and is written in a different language (Latin, Italian, Spanish, French, and German). Although there are at least two different title pages and some copies do not contain explanations in five languages, it can be assumed that the work was published only once and, in particular, that all the plates are from a single printing. The publication dates of 1595, 1605, and 1617 found in the literature and in certain library catalogs must be considered erroneous. The printing of the *Machinae novae* was completed during the first half of 1616 (or perhaps the last two months of 1615), for in July 1616 several of Verantius' friends thanked him for sending them the book.

Some of Verantius' inventions are applicable to the solution of hydrological problems, for example, the project for preventing the Tiber from overflowing its banks at Rome and that of providing Venice with fresh water. Others concern the construction of clepsydras, sundials, mills, presses, and bridges and boats destined for widely different uses. Unlike Leonardo da Vinci, Verantius had no interest in machines of war; rather, he devoted himself especially to perfecting agricultural implements. He foresaw the advantages of the assembly line, and in his many designs for mills he was especially concerned with the rational use of various sources of energy. In this connection his idea of utilizing the motive force of the tides is particularly important. His devices demonstrate an intuitive grasp of the principle of the mechanical moment and of the triangle of forces. His designs for a wind turbine, a funicular railway, and a bridge suspended by iron chains represent a definite advance over contemporary techniques. Although some of Verantius' "machines" are not wholly original or independent inventions, many of them are explained for the first time in print in *Machinae novae*. One example is *homovolens*, the first published mention of a parachute.

BIBLIOGRAPHY

I. ORIGINAL WORKS. The original ed. of *Machinae novae* is rare, but the work is now available in two fasc. eds., edited by F. Klemm and A. Wissner (Munich, 1965) and by U. Forti (Milan, 1968). *Dictionarium quinque nobilissimarum Europae linguarum* (Venice, 1595) is also available in modern editions (Bratislava, 1834; Zagreb, 1971). The treatise on logic is *Logica nova suis ipsius instrumentis formata et cognita* (Venice, 1616).

II. SECONDARY LITERATURE. There is still no critical study of Verantius' life, ideas, and inventions. The best sources for biographical details are the obituary by J. T. Marnavich, *Oratio habita in funere ill. ac rev. viri Fausti Verantij* (Venice, 1617); and the study by G. Gyurikovits, "Biographia Verantii," in Verantius' *Dictionarium pentaglottum* (Bratislava, 1834), ix–xx. On his scientific and technical work, see G. Boffito, *Scrittori barnabiti*, IV (Florence, 1937), 148–152; H. T. Horwitz, "Ueber Fausto Veranzio und sein Werk *Machinae novae*," in *Archeion*, **8** (1927), 169–175; V. Muljević, "Faust Vrančić kao fizičar i konstruktor," in *Hrvatsko sveučilište* (Zagreb), **1**, no. 6 (1971), 13–15; and F. Savorgnan di Brazza, "Un inventore dalmata del 500: Fausto Veranzio da Sebenico," in *Archivio storico per la Dalmazia*, **13** (1932), 55–73.

M. D. GRMEK

VERDET, MARCEL ÉMILE (*b.* Nîmes, France, 13 March 1824; *d.* Nîmes, 3 June 1866), *physics.*

Verdet was one of the outstanding physics teachers of mid-nineteenth-century France, holding professorships at the École normale supérieure, the École polytechnique, and the Faculté des sciences in Paris. He introduced into the French scientific world the thermodynamics of Joule, Clausius, Helmholtz, and William Thompson, and conducted important experiments on the effects of a magnetic field on plane-polarized light.

Little is known of Verdet's background except that he came from a leading Protestant family in the south of France. An early preference for teaching led him to attend the École normale supérieure, rather than the École polytechnique, to which he was also accepted. At the close of his studies he scored so high on the *concours d'agrégation* that he was spared the customary tour of duty in the provinces and appointed directly to the Lycée Henri IV in Paris. In 1848 he received his *doctorat* from the Sorbonne and was appointed lecturer in physics at the École normale, a position he held for the rest of his life. Four years later he became entrance examiner at the École polytechnique; then examiner in physics (1853) and professor of physics (1862). Later his fame as a teacher gained him the chair of mathematical physics at the Paris Faculté des sciences.

Verdet educated his colleagues as well as his students. French physicists of his time were ignorant of much of the research going on outside their country, so Verdet undertook to publish abstracts of the most important articles appearing in foreign journals. From 1852 to 1864 every volume of the *Annales de chimie* contained ten or more of his synopses. Since much of the work being done in England and Germany in this era centered on the development of the mechanical theory of heat, Verdet soon became the French expert in this subject. In 1864–1865 he taught the new thermodynamics at the Sorbonne, and the notes from his course were compiled by two students and published as *La théorie mécanique de la chaleur*, a textbook which has become a classic.

Verdet's original scientific papers, although limited in quantity by his extensive academic duties, his short life, and poor vision, reveal a talent not as an innovator but, rather, as a painstaking investigator who filled in the details of others' discoveries. His early research included a series of experiments on electromagnetic induction and a theoretical treatise on the image-forming power of lenses. In his major effort Verdet investigated the phenomenon now known as the "Faraday effect": the rotation of the plane of polarization of a ray of light by a transparent solid or liquid in a magnetic field (this effect was discovered by Michael Faraday in 1845). Verdet studied the dependence of the Faraday effect on the strength of the magnet causing the rotation, the medium in which the light is traveling, and the color of the light. He found that the magnetic power of rotation was directly proportional to the strength of the magnet, inversely proportional to the square of the wavelength of the light, and related to the index of refraction of the material. In recognition of the importance of this work a measure of the power of magnetic rotation was named "Verdet's constant."

BIBLIOGRAPHY

I. ORIGINAL WORKS. Verdet's entire scientific output is collected in *Oeuvres de Verdet*, 8 vols. (Paris, 1868–1872), which includes all his scientific papers and the lecture notes from his courses. His writings include "Mémoires sur la physique publiés à l'étranger, extraits par M. E. Verdet," in *Annales de chimie*, 3rd ser., **34–69**, and 4th ser., **1–4** (1852–1864); *La théorie mécanique de la chaleur* (Paris, 1868); "Recherches sur les phénomènes d'induction produits par les décharges électriques," in *Annales de chimie*, 3rd ser., **24** (1848), 377–405; "Note sur les courants induits d'ordres supérieurs," *ibid.*, **29** (1850), 501–506; "Recherches sur les phénomènes d'induction produits par le mouvement des métaux . . .," *ibid.*, **31** (1851), 187–217; "Sur l'intensité

des images lumineuses formées au foyer des lentilles et des miroirs," *ibid.*, 489–503; and "Recherches sur les propriétés optiques développées dans les corps transparents par l'action du magnétisme," *ibid.*, **41** (1854), 370–412; **43** (1855), 37–44; **52** (1858), 129–168; and **69** (1863), 415–491.

II. SECONDARY LITERATURE. The two best biographies of Verdet are by M. A. Levistal, in *Annales scientifiques de l'École normale supérieure*, **3** (1866), 343–351; and A. de La Rive, in *Mémorial de l'Association des anciens élèves de l'École normale 1846–1876* (Paris, 1877).

EUGENE FRANKEL

VER EECKE, PAUL (*b.* Menin, Belgium, 13 February 1867; *d.* Berchem, Belgium, 14 October 1959), *mathematics.*

Ver Eecke attended the *collège* in Menin until he was fifteen and completed his secondary education at Bruges. After graduating as a mining engineer from the University of Liège in 1891 and following a short period in private industry, he entered the Administration du Travail in 1894, where he served until his retirement in 1932. His many honors included membership in the Société Mathématique de Belgique, the Académie Internationale d'Histoire des Sciences, and the Comité Belge d'Histoire des Sciences.

While quite young, Ver Eecke became interested in ancient Greek mathematics, especially in the works of Archimedes, and his first publication (1921) was a French translation of the complete works of Archimedes. Nearly all his scholarship concerned the translation of Greek mathematical works into French, the only exceptions being his translations from the Latin into French of the *Liber quadratorum* of Leonardo Fibonacci (written in 1225) and a treatise by Vito Caravelli. He carried out this work not as a philologist but as a scientist, adhering closely to the Greek text. His translations were preceded by surveys of the periods in which the mathematicians lived; and in the footnotes Ver Eecke gave the proofs in modern notation. Ver Eecke thus provided historians of science with a fairly accurate reflection of thought in antiquity and the scientific significance of the works.

In addition to translations Ver Eecke also wrote articles. In "Le théorème dit de Guldin considéré au point de vue historique" he defended the assumption that the law bearing his name was original with Guldin. Ver Eecke's arguments were, however, rejected by R. C. Archibald (*Scripta mathematica*, **1** [1932], 267).

BIBLIOGRAPHY

Ver Eecke's works include *Les oeuvres complètes d'Archimède* (Brussels, 1921); *Les Coniques d'Apollonius de Perge* (Bruges, 1923; repr. Paris, 1963); *Diophante d'Alexandrie. Les six livres arithmétiques et le livre des nombres polygones* (Bruges, 1926); *Les Sphériques de Théodose de Tripoli* (Bruges, 1927); *Serenus d'Antinoë. Le livre "De la section du cylindre" et le livre "De la section du cône"* (Paris–Bruges, 1929); "Note sur le procédé de la démonstration indirecte chez les géomètres d l'antiquité grecque," in *Mathesis*, **44** (1930), 382–384; "Note sur la théorie du plan incliné chez les mathématiciens grecs," ibid., **45** (1931), 352–355; "Le théorème dit de Guldin considéré au point de vue historique," ibid., **46** (1932), 395–397; "La mécanique des Grecs d'après Pappus d'Alexandrie," in *Scientia* (Milan), **54** (1933), 114–122; *Pappus d'Alexandrie. La Collection mathématique* (Paris–Bruges, 1933); "Le traité des hosoèdres de Vito Caravelli (1724–1800)," in *Mathesis*, **49** (1935), 59–82; "Le traité du métrage des divers bois de Didyme d'Alexandrie," in *Annales de la Société scientifique de Bruxelles*, ser. A, **56** (1936), 6–16; "Note sur une démonstration antique d'un théorème de lieu géométrique," in *Mathesis*, **51** (1937), 11–14; *Euclide. L'Optique et la Catoptrique* (Paris–Bruges, 1938); "Note sur une interprétation erronée d'une définition pythagoricienne de la ligne géométrique," in *Antiquité classique*, 7 (1938), 271–273; *Les opuscules mathématiques de Didyme, Diophane et Anthemius, suivis du fragment mathématique de Bobbio* (Paris–Bruges, 1940); *Proclus de Lycie. Les commentaires sur le premier livre des Éléments d'Euclide* (Bruges, 1948); and *Léonard de Pise. Le livre des nombres carrés* (Bruges, 1952).

H. L. L. BUSARD

VERHULST, PIERRE-FRANÇOIS (*b.* Brussels, Belgium, 28 October 1804; *d.* Brussels, 15 February, 1849), *statistics, sociology, probability theory, mathematics.*

According to Adolphe Quetelet, Verhulst, while on a trip to Rome, "conceived the idea of carrying out a reform in the Papal States and of persuading the Holy Father to give a constitution to his people." The project was, in fact, considered; and Verhulst, ordered to leave Rome, was almost besieged in his apartment.

Verhulst first thought of publishing the complete works of Euler but abandoned this idea in order to study with Quetelet, with whom he eventually collaborated on social statistics. The two did not, however, always share the same views in this field, in which the theoretical foundations were uncertain and observations far from abundant. It was generally assumed, following Malthus, that the tendency of a population to increase follows a geometric progression. Quetelet, however, believed he had grounds for asserting that the sum of the obstacles opposed to the indefinite growth of population increases in proportion to the square of the rate at which the population tends to grow. Verhulst showed in 1846 that these obstacles increase in proportion to the ratio of the excess population to the total population. He was thus led to give the figure of 9,400,000 as the upper limit for the population of Belgium (which, in fact, has grown to 9,581,000 by 1967). Verhulst's research on the law of population growth makes him a precursor of modern students of the subject.

Verhulst was a professor at the Université Libre of Brussels and later at the École Royale Militaire. He was elected to the Académie Royale de Belgique in 1841 and became its president in 1848.

BIBLIOGRAPHY

There are articles on Verhulst by J. Pelseneer, in *Biographie nationale publiée par l'Académie royale de Belgique*, XXVI (Brussels, 1936–1938), cols. 658–663, with bibliography; and A. Quetelet, in *Annuaire de l'Académie r. des sciences, des lettres et des beaux-arts de Belgique*, **16** (1850), 97–124, with a bibliography of Verhulst's works and a portrait.

J. PELSENEER

VERNADSKY, VLADÍMIR IVANOVICH (*b.* St. Petersburg, Russia, 12 March 1863; *d.* Moscow, U.S.S.R., 6 January 1945), *mineralogy, geochemistry, biogeochemistry.*

Vernadsky's father, Ivan Vasilievich Vernadsky, a member of the gentry, was a professor at Kiev and Moscow universities and later at the Main Pedagogical Institute and the Aleksandrov Lycée in St. Petersburg. From 1857 to 1864 he edited liberal economic journals, in which he spoke against serfdom. His mother, Anna Petrovna Konstantinovich, came from a Ukrainian landowning family and taught singing.

While still at the classical gymnasium, Vernadsky became interested in chemistry but was also attracted by history, philosophy, and Slavic languages. From 1881 to 1885 he was a student in the Natural Sciences Section of the Physics and Mathematics Faculty at St. Petersburg University. According to Vernadsky, while he was there, Mendeleev's brilliant lectures awakened a strong desire for knowledge and its application. Dokuchaev, who lectured on mineralogy and crystallography, supervised Vernadsky's first scientific research. After graduation Vernadsky remained at the university to prepare for a teaching career, and from 1886 he was curator of the mineralogical collection at the university. In the latter year he married Natalia Egorovna Staritskaya; they had two children. From 1888 to 1890 Vernadsky traveled abroad. Interested in the structure of crystal substances, he worked in Groth's crystallographic laboratory at Munich and in Le Châtelier's and Fouqué's laboratories at the Collège de France. He also made geological excursions in Italy, Germany, Switzerland, Austria, France, and England. Vernadsky subsequently traveled widely in Europe and North America in order to become acquainted with areas of geological and mineralogical interest, to participate in international scientific congresses, and to study the organization of scientific research and higher education.

In the fall of 1890 Vernadsky became a *Privatdozent* in mineralogy and crystallography at Moscow University. In 1891 he defended his master's thesis, "O gruppe sillimanita i roli glinozema v silikatakh" ("On the Sillimanite Group and the Role of Alumina in Silicates") and, in 1897, his doctoral dissertation, "O yavleniakh skolzheniya kristallicheskogo veshchestva" ("On the Phenomena of Gliding in Crystal Substances"). Vernadsky was appointed professor at Moscow University in 1898. The St. Petersburg Academy of Sciences elected him associate member in 1909 and academician in 1912.

Vernadsky was among those professors and teachers who, in response to the reactionary treatment of the university by the Ministry of National Education, left Moscow in 1911 and moved to St. Petersburg. In 1914 he became director of the Geological and Mineralogical Museum of the Academy of Sciences and a year later joined the Commisssion to Study the Natural Productive Forces of Russia, serving as its president in 1915–1917 and in 1926–1930. From June 1917 to the beginning of 1921 Vernadsky lived in the Ukraine. He was responsible for the creation of the Ukrainian S.S.R. Academy of Sciences in 1919 and was its first president. Following his return to Leningrad from Paris and Prague in 1926, he continued his scientific and organizational activity at the Academy of Sciences. In 1926 he founded and headed the Commission on the History of Knowledge of the Academy of Sciences of the U.S.S.R. and, the following year, the Section on Living Substances (now the V. I. Vernadsky Institute of Geochemistry and Analytical Chemistry). At Ver-

nadsky's suggestion, at the Seventeenth International Geological Congress, held at Moscow in 1937, an international commission was created to determine the absolute age of geological rock by radioactive methods; he was elected vice-president of this commission.

In the first twenty-five years of his scientific career, Vernadsky was concerned with crystallography and, primarily, mineralogy, which he also studied later, when he turned to geochemistry, radiogeology, and biogeochemistry. Two important works devoted to the structure of crystalline substances were Vernadsky's doctoral dissertation (1897) and *Osnovy kristallografii* ("Fundamentals of Crystallography"; 1904), in which he developed the relation of crystal form to physicochemical structure and emphasized the importance of energetics in studying crystals.

Vernadsky opened a new, evolutionary direction in mineralogy. His research was presented in *Opyt opisatelnoy mineralogii* ("Experiment in Descriptive Mineralogy"; 1908–1922) and *Istoria mineralov zemnoy kory* ("History of Minerals of the Earth's Crust; 1923–1936). Defining mineralogy as the chemistry and history of the minerals in the earth's crust, he believed that "mineralogy, like chemistry, must study not only the products of chemical reactions but also the very processes of reaction" (*Izbrannye sochinenia*, II, 9)—and in the concept of mineral he included gases and water. In his works on mineralogy Vernadsky started from the premise that the purposes of mineralogy as a science are to establish the chemical composition of minerals; to explain the conditions necessary for chemical reactions involved in the genesis and paragenesis of minerals, and to study the conditions under which minerals change in the various zones of the earth.

Vernadsky's works stated the laws of paragenesis of minerals, the concept of which had been introduced into mineralogy in 1849 by J. F. A. Breithaupt. In *Paragenezis khimicheskikh elementov v zemnoy kore* ("Paragenesis of Chemical Elements in the Earth's Crust"; 1910), Vernadsky, starting from the capacity of isomorphic compounds to produce isomorphic mixtures—solid solutions—introduced the concept of natural isomorphic series of chemical elements. His table of elements in the earth's crust consisted of eighteen series, each of them related to definite thermodynamic zones. Vernadsky distinguished three such zones: the weathering crust, the area of low temperature and low pressure; the area of metamorphism, the area of high pressure and moderate temperature; and the deep layers of the lithosphere—the area of magmatization—the area of high temperature and high pressure. He emphasized that "isomorphic series are transformed and change under the influence of changes of temperature and pressure" (*Izbrannye sochinenia*, I, 404). Vernadsky's position was the basis for the development of the theory of paragenesis of elements and minerals, which was of great importance in the search for useful mineral deposits.

Vernadsky's great contribution to mineralogy was his research on silicates and aluminosilicate minerals, which constitute a major part of the earth's crust. The aluminosilicates had previously been considered to be salts of silicic acid and their acid properties to be attributable only to alumina. Vernadsky refuted this view in his master's dissertation and showed experimentally a different structure of aluminosilicates, according to which aluminum in the most important rock-forming minerals—feldspars and micas—is chemically analogous to silicon. He proposed the theory of the kaolin nucleus, composed of two atoms of aluminum, two of silicon, and seven of oxygen, and constituting the basis of many minerals. This theory has played an important role in explaining the structure, genesis, and classification of minerals. It was later confirmed by X-ray structural analysis, and it is now considered an established fact that silicon and aluminum in aluminosilicates are joined by atoms of oxygen placed at the points of tetrahedrons, which represent the framework of the aluminosilicates, the cavities of which are filled with large cations.

Vernadsky's basic works in geochemistry are of great importance. Geochemistry is a science of the twentieth century, although the term was introduced into the literature in 1838 by C. F. Schonbein. Defining geochemistry as a science, Vernadsky wrote:

> Geochemistry scientifically studies . . . the atoms of the earth's crust and, as much as possible, of all the planets. It studies their history, distribution, and motion in space-time, their genetic relationships on our planet. It is sharply distinguished from mineralogy, which studies the history of the earth in the same space and the same time only as the history of compounds of atoms—molecules and crystals [*Izbrannye sochinemia*, I, 14].

Vernadsky's geochemical research, which he conducted intensively from 1908 to 1910, was generalized in *Ocherki geokhimii* ("Sketches in Geochemistry"; 1927, 1934), which first appeared in French as *La géochimie* (Paris, 1924). Directly connected with this work is *Biosfera* ("Biosphere"; 1926). Examining the early period of geochemistry, Vernadsky showed the importance of the contributions of many scientists in different countries, including Robert Boyle. In his geochemical works he gave remarkable descriptions of many elements of the earth's crust. He prepared precise data on the chemical composition of the earth's crust to a depth of twenty kilometers and tabulated the chemical elements of this layer in weight percentages.

The history of the chemical elements in the earth's crust, Vernadsky showed, can be reduced to their migrations: the motion of atoms in the formation of compounds; their transformation into mobile liquids, gases, and solid bodies; and their assimilation into the respiration, nourishment, and metabolism of organisms.

These migrations in the crust of the earth create large systems of chemical equilibria or modes of occurrence of chemical elements. Vernadsky distinguished four such modes: molecules and compounds in minerals, rocks, liquids, and gases; elements in living organisms; elements in magmas, occurring under conditions of high pressure and temperature; and dispersed elements. He paid much attention to the geospheres (the earth's layers), between which the migration of chemical elements also occurs. Material on geospheres occupies a large portion of *Ocherki geokhimii* ("Sketches in Geochemistry").

Vernadsky considered inaccurate the widely accepted view that the earth's crust is the remnant of the first crust of a once-liquid molten mass. In studying it, he found it convenient to distinguish, in a simplified form, the following layers: the biosphere, the layer occupied by all living things; the stratisphere, the layer of sedimentary rock; the metamorphic layer; the granite layer; and the basalt layer. The layers have a close genetic relation to each other, and cyclical transfers of chemical elements occur among them. Vernadsky believed that these processes have formed "burial layers," including the granite, that have gone through the biosphere stage and thus should be called ex-biospheres.

Vernadsky classified the elements of Mendeleev's periodic system into six groups according to their role in the geochemical history of the earth's crust: noble gases, noble metals, cyclical elements, "scattered" elements, strongly radioactive elements, and rare earths. The cyclical elements, which constitute about 99.7 percent of the weight of the earth's crust, play the main role in the processes originating there.

Each element in a given geosphere enters into the compounds appropriate to it under given thermodynamic conditions. These compounds are broken down in the transition to another geosphere, where other compounds are formed. In this process, "after more or less prolonged and complex changes the element returns to the first compound and begins a new cycle, which is completed for the element by a new return to its primary condition" (*Izbrannye sochinenia*, I, 40). These cycles are partly reversible, however, and some of the atoms constantly leave the cycle. Vernadsky examined the sources of energy under the influence of which tectonic motions and transfers of substances in the earth's crust take place. On the basis of work by Joly and Strutt (Lord Rayleigh), as well as his own research, he considered the energy released by the radioactive decomposition of elements to be one of the main sources of these processes: "The heat effect of radioactive decomposition has been so substantial that it allows us to discard the hypothesis of the once molten planet and provides a basis for a new scientific consideration of atomic heating of the substance of the planet, sharply distinct in its various localities" (*Izbrannye sochinenia*, I, 225).

Vernadsky was one of the first to recognize radioactivity as a powerful source of energy. When even physicists did not clearly recognize its practical significance, he pointed out the responsibility of scientists for the consequences of the use of their discovery. He wrote in 1922:

> We are approaching a great revolution in the life of humanity, with which nothing . . . earlier . . . can be compared. The time is not far away when man will take atomic energy into his hands. . . . This can occur in the near future; it may happen after a century. But it is clear that it will inevitably happen. Does man know how to use this power, to direct it to good and not to self-destruction? Has he . . . the ability to use this force, which science will inevitably give him? Scientists must not close their eyes to the possible consequences of their . . . work, of . . . progress. They must consider themselves responsible for the consequences of their discoveries. They must relate their work to the best organization of all humanity [*Ocherki i rechi*, II, foreword].

In 1910 Vernadsky and his colleagues began to seek radioactive minerals and to study them in the laboratory. Greatly concerned with radioactivity, Vernadsky later laid the foundations of a new science, radiogeology.

In the last twenty years of his scientific career Vernadsky and his colleagues, especially A. P. Vinogradov, concentrated on the chemical composition of plants and animals. At the same time he clarified the role of living organisms in reactions and transformations of chemical elements in the biosphere. He introduced into geochemistry the concept of living matter as the totality of living organisms expressed in terms of weight, chemical composition, and energy. Such an approach to the study of living matter allowed Vernadsky to express in mathematical form certain regularities of the multiplication of organisms. He showed the primary importance of living organisms as accumulators, transformers, and carriers of solar radiation — the second powerful source of energy in geochemical cycles.

The analysis of biogeochemical processes led Vernadsky to conclude that the main gases of the earth's atmosphere — oxygen, nitrogen, and carbon dioxide — are created by living things. He indicated the immediate role of living matter in the concentration of many chemical elements in the earth's crust, especially carbon, silicon, calcium, nitrogen, iron, and manganese. Living matter, he asserted, influences the entire chemistry of the earth's crust and determines the history of almost every element in it. He also considered the possibility that the quantity of living matter on the earth apparently has been constant throughout geological time. There is another possibility, however: that the mass of living matter grows over geological time. Vernadsky is thus considered the founder of the theory of the biosphere and of a new area of geochemistry: biogeochemistry.

Vernadsky gave great attention to the hydrosphere. His research in this field is presented in *Istoria prirodnykh vod* ("History of the Waters of Nature"; 1931), in which he treats the mineralogy of water and explains the relation between water and the solid crust of the earth. In the first volume of *Opyt opisatelnoy mineralogii* ("Experiment in Descriptive Mineralogy"; 1908–1914), and in later works Vernadsky showed the substantial effect of human activity on the history of the earth. As a result of this activity the face of the planet is increasingly changing as are the chemical properties of its surface.

BIBLIOGRAPHY

I. ORIGINAL WORKS. Vernadsky's writings include "O gruppe silliamanita i roli glinozema v silikatakh" ("On the Sillimanite Group and the Role of Alumina in

Silicates"), in *Byulleten Moskovskogo obshchestva ispytatelei prirody*, **5** (1891), 1–100, 165–169; *Ocherki i rechi* ("Sketches and Speeches"), 2 vols. (Petrograd, 1922); *Biosfera* ("The Biosphere"; Leningrad, 1926; Moscow, 1967); *Biogeokhimicheskie ocherki. 1922–1932 gg.* ("Biogeochemical Sketches . . ."; Moscow–Leningrad, 1940); *Izbrannye sochinenia* ("Selected Works"), 6 vols. (Moscow, 1954–1960); and *Khimicheskoe stroenie biosfery Zemli i ee okryzhenia* ("The Chemical Structure of the Earth and Its Environs"; Moscow, 1965). A work still in MS is "Nauchnaya mysl kak planetnoe yavelnie" ("Scientific Thought as a Planetary Phenomenon"), Moscow, Archives of the Academy of Sciences, fond 518.

II. SECONDARY LITERATURE. See A. E. Fersman, *Zhiznenny put akademika Vladimira Ivanovicha Vernadskogo* ("The Career of Academician . . . Vernadsky"; Moscow, 1946); B. L. Lichkov, *Vladimir Ivanovich Vernadsky. 1863–1945* (Moscow, 1948), with bibliography on 83–102; *Materialy k biobibliografii uchenykh SSSR* ("Materials for a Biobibliography of Scientists of the U.S.S.R."), Chem. ser., no. 6 (Moscow–Leningrad, 1947), devoted to Vernadsky; K. V. Vlasov, "Vladimir Ivanovich Vernadsky," in *Lyudi russkoy nauki* ("People of Russian Science"; Moscow, 1962), 135–157; and A. P. Vinogradov, *Vladimir Ivanovich Vernadsky* (Moscow–Leningrad, 1947).

I. A. FEDOSEYEV

VERNEUIL, PHILIPPE ÉDOUARD POULLETIER DE (*b.* Paris, France, 13 February 1805; *d.* Paris, 29 May 1873), *geology, paleontology.*

Édouard de Verneuil, the son of Antoine César Poulletier de Verneuil and Genevieve Pauline Flore Laurens de l'Ormeon, prepared for the law, received a license, and in 1833 entered the employment of the French Ministry of Justice. He studied the geological lessons of Élie de Beaumont and then in 1835, being of independent means, devoted himself to science.

Verneuil's scientific career was concerned with describing the geological formations and fossil groups of the Paleozoic era. His extensive knowledge of these fossils enabled him to make his major theoretical contribution to stratigraphy—the hypothesis that the Paleozoic deposits of the United States and Spain are parallel to those of Europe.

Verneuil made his principal researches in five areas in Europe and North America. From 1835 to 1838 he traveled in Europe from England to the Crimea; in 1840 and 1841 he toured European Russia with the English geologist Roderick Murchison; in 1846 he briefly visited the United States; from 1849 to 1862 he traveled almost annually in Spain; and in the years after 1864, he studied the activity of Mount Vesuvius. He made

his first tour in 1835 to Wales. His objective was to study the formations that had recently led Murchison and his colleague Adam Sedgwick to break down Abraham Werner's Transitional Formations (specifically, the graywacke) into the Silurian and Cambrian systems. Verneuil's observations led to his support for an extension of the classification. In the summer of 1836, he traveled along the Danube to Turkey and the Crimea, neither of which had received extensive geological examination. He was primarily interested in the prominent Tertiary terrains, but he described the Silurian system around Constantinople.

Verneuil's adoption of Murchison's theories, his defense of them before the Geological Society of France, and his knowledge of the fossils of the older strata inevitably brought him into personal contact with the English scientist. In 1839 Murchison and Sedgwick were in northern Germany, Belgium, and northern France to gather evidence for a new system—the Devonian—that they had described in England. Verneuil, who had earlier followed the Silurian system in northern France, was invited to join their French tour. Verneuil charmed Murchison with his sophistication and his piano playing, and their professional acquaintance became a lifelong friendship.

The geological tours and perhaps personal contact with Murchison stimulated the beginning of Verneuil's theoretical contribution to geology. In 1840 Verneuil suggested that the Silurian system, which had then been observed in England, Europe, and Turkey, was universal in extent. This suggestion was the germ of his generalization of the uniformity of Paleozoic laws. Proving the generalization provided the research for his mature scientific career.

Verneuil's first opportunity to verify the universality of the new Paleozoic systems came later in 1840. Murchison desired to travel in Russia, where he expected he could easily observe the Silurian, Devonian, and Carboniferous layers; and he asked Verneuil to accompany him. Tours were made in the summer of 1840 and 1841. Not only did the two geologists—who were intermittently joined by the Russian naturalist Alexandr Keyserling—verify Murchison's systems for European Russia, but on the second tour Murchison discovered, and Verneuil made the fossil analysis of, a new formation in Perm, hence called the Permian system. These strata, which paralleled the Zechstein of Germany and Magnesian Limestone of England, were proved by Verneuil to constitute the upper limit of the recently defined Paleozoic era. Verneuil was quickly able to demonstrate the same fossil group in western Europe and thus the existence of the Permian system there as well.

Upon the publication of the results of the Russian expeditions in the two-volume *Geology of Russia in Europe and the Ural Mountains*, with Murchison and Keyserling (London–Paris, 1845), in which he was chiefly responsible for the volume on paleontology, Verneuil could turn his attention to verifying the Paleozoic order elsewhere. The outstanding problem, as he had recognized in 1840, was to bring the geological structure of the Americas into correspondence with that of Europe. In 1846 he journeyed to the United States primarily to study formations in New York and Ohio, where American geologists had already described the strata in detail, although in local perspectives. He sought to answer two questions: Did the fossil species in America and Europe present themselves in the same order? And was it possible to trace between the American Paleozoic stages the divisions established in Europe under the names of the Silurian, Devonian, and Carboniferous systems? Verneuil's research immediately provided affirmative answers. He announced in his important essay "Note sur le parallélisme des roches des dépôts paléozoïques de l'Amerique septentrionale avec ceux de l'Europe" (in *Bulletin de la Société géologique de France*, 2 [1846–1847], 646–709) that the Paleozoic deposits of the two continents are parallel and that the distribution of fossils in each had been made according to a common law.

In his remaining career, Verneuil was largely concerned with the geology of Spain. Spanish stratigraphy had been brought to his attention as early as January 1844 by a colleague who sent fossils to him for identification. Beginning in 1849, Verneuil traveled often to the Iberian Peninsula and was able to prove that its Paleozoic order corresponded to that east of the Pyrenees. In 1858, and frequently after 1864, Verneuil studied Mount Vesuvius.

Verneuil was elected president of the Geological Society of France three times, in 1840, 1853, and 1867. In 1854 he was elected to the Académie des Sciences, and he was a foreign associate of the Royal Society of London and the academies of science of St. Petersburg and Berlin.

BIBLIOGRAPHY

I. ORIGINAL WORKS. A list of the principal publications is given in Daubrée, "Notice nécrologie sur Édouard de Verneuil," in *Bulletin de la Société géologique de France*, 3, ser. 3 (1875–1876), 317–328. A complete list of articles is in the Royal Society *Catalogue of Scientific Papers (1800–1900)*, VI, VIII. Scattered pieces of correspondence are listed in Ministère de l'éducation nationale, *Catalogue générale des manuscrits des bibliothèques publiques en France* (Paris, 1885–), VIII, XXXIX, XLIX, LV; and the *Catalogue of Manuscripts in the American Philosophical Society Library* (Westport, Conn., n.d.), IX.

Verneuil's fossil collection, left to the École des Mines, Paris, is described by J. Barrande, "Collection paléontologique de M. Edouard de Verneuil," in *Annales des mines, mémoires*, 7, ser. 4 (1873), 327–338.

II. SECONDARY LITERATURE. The best biographical memoir, from which most other such memoirs are derived, is Daubrée, "Discours sur M. Édouard de Verneuil," in *Annales des mines, mémoires*, 7, ser. 4 (1873), 318–326. Other memoirs are listed in the Royal Society *Catalogue of Scientific Papers (1800–1900)*, VIII, XI. Verneuil's relationship with Murchison is discussed in Archibald Geikie, *Life of Sir Roderick I. Murchison*, 2 vols. (London, 1875).

RONALD C. TOBEY

VERNIER, PIERRE (*b*. Ornans, France, 19 August 1584; *d*. Ornans, 14 September 1638), *military engineering, scientific instrumentation.*

From his father, Jean, who was castellan of the château of Ornans, a lawyer by training, and probably an engineer, Vernier inherited an interest in all sorts of measuring instruments. At an early age he studied the writings of contemporary scientists and learned how measuring instruments work. After becoming adept at using them, Vernier worked as a military engineer for the Spanish Hapsburgs, then rulers of Franche-Comté. His reading of the works of Nuñez Salaciense (Nonius), Clavius, and Tycho Brahe, combined with his experience in helping his father survey and prepare an excellent map of Franche-Comté, led him to seek a new way to read off angles on surveying instruments.

Around 1540 Nuñez, a Portugese mathematician who was trying to improve the accuracy of the astrolabe, a sixteenth-century preoccupation, hit upon the idea of engraving on the face of the astrolabe a series of scales laid out along concentric circles. The scale on any circle was determined by dividing the circumference of the circle into an equal number of parts, one less than that dividing the next circle out and one greater than that dividing the next circle in. Thus in shooting a star, the line of sight would inevitably fall very close to a whole division on one of the scales. By an elementary calculation or by use of a table, one could easily determine the number of degrees, minutes, and seconds of an angle being measured. In theory Nuñez' method could bring great accuracy, but it was extremely difficult to engrave with precision a different scale on each concentric circle. Brahe remarked that in practice Nuñez' method failed to live up to its promise (*Astronomiae instauratae mechanica* [Nuremberg, 1611], p. 2).

About fifty years later Clavius, who had studied under Nuñez, found a way to facilitate the engraving of the various scales on the concentric circular segments. His associate Jacobus Curtius further simplified Nuñez' method by placing the same scale on the concentric segments in such a way that the zero of the scale on any segment started one degree away from that of the scale on the preceding segment. It thus became possible to read off degrees and minutes directly if the outer scale were divided into degrees and if there were sixty concentric circular segments. These methods were described by Clavius in his *Geometria practica* (Rome, 1604), which Vernier surely read and meditated on.

Vernier replaced the fifty-nine inner concentric circular segments with a mobile concentric segment, thereby giving a mobile scale rather than a series of static ones. Thus he solved the difficulty of engraving many different concentric scales. By this time (1630) he had acquired a reputation as an excellent engineer and was *conseiller et général des monnaies* for the count of Burgundy. He made a special trip to Brussels to present his invention to Isabelle-Claire-Eugénie, the infanta of Spain, the ruler of Franche-Comté, who had him publish a description of it. Throughout the seventeenth century this work remained on the whole unknown to the European scientific community. Certainly the declining importance of the Spanish Hapsburgs within Western Europe did not facilitate diffusion of Vernier's treatise nor did the development of technology favor the vernier because the extra precision it brought could not make seventeenth-century instruments more accurate than was allowed by open sights, which were commonly used, and by the imprecise methods of marking scales. Indeed, at the start of the eighteenth century, as soon as the technological situation became propitious, the vernier began to be used; but Vernier's name did not become associated with his invention until around the middle of the century.

After publishing his treatise in 1631, Vernier returned to Dôle, where he designed and directed the construction of fortifications. His other engineering projects included the design of a building for the harquebusiers of Dôle. In 1636 illness forced him to discontinue the practice of engineering; and he returned to Ornans, where he died a few years later.

BIBLIOGRAPHY

I. ORIGINAL WORKS. Vernier's writings are *La construction, l'usage, et les propriétez du quadrant nouveau de mathématique: Comme aussi la construction de la table des sinus . . .* (Brussels, 1631); "Traité d'artillerie" (MS at the Bibliothèque Nationale, Paris, according to Michel, p. 349); a map prepared by Vernier's father with the aid of Vernier is described in Claude François Rolland, "Études sur la cartographie ancienne de la Franche-Comté . . .," in *Mémoires de la Société d'émulation du Doubs*, 8th ser., **7** (1912), 187–299; and **8** (1913), 375–429 (see 404–421); the plan of a mill that Feuvrier attributes to Vernier in his study on him (see below) figures in J. Feuvrier, "Les derniers moulins à bras et à chevaux en Franche-Comté," in *Procès-verbaux et mémoires de l'Académie des sciences, belles-lettres et arts de Besançon* (1909), 125–131; that of the building for the harquebusiers that he also attributes to Vernier is in J. Feuvrier, "Les chevaliers du noble et hardy jeu de l'arquebuse de la ville de Dôle," in *Mémoires de la Société d'émulation du Jura*, 6th ser., **2** (1897), 1–70, plan on plate between 24–25, discussion on 27–28.

II. SECONDARY LITERATURE. The Archives Départementales du Doubs confirmed the correctness of Vernier's dates of birth and death. Henri Michel, "Le 'vernier' et son inventeur Pierre Vernier d'Ornans," in *Mémoires de la Société d'émulation du Doubs*, 8th ser., **8** (1913), 310–373, gives a comprehensive history of the vernier and the salient features of Vernier's life; Julien Feuvrier, "L'ingénieur Pierre Vernier à Dôle," in *Procès-verbaux et mémoires de l'Académie des sciences, belles-lettres et arts de Besançon* (1912), 293–302, which contains a facsimile of a handwritten report by Vernier, adds to Michel details concerning Vernier's family and his activity as an engineer in Dôle. Wilhelm Lührs, "Ein Beitrag zur Geschichte der Transversalteilungen und des 'Nonius,'" in *Zeitschrift für Vermessungswesen*, **39** (1910), 177–191, 209–223, 241–254, gives details of the background to the vernier; A. Breusing, "Nonius oder Vernier?" in *Astronomische Nachrichten*, **96** (1879), 131–134, is superseded by the above studies; Maurice Daumas, *Les instruments scientifiques aux XVIIe et XVIIIe siècles* (Paris, 1953), 250–255, briefly discusses the history of the vernier; and J. B. J. Delambre, *Histoire de l'astronomie moderne*, II (Paris, 1821), 119–125, gives extensive extracts from Vernier's treatise on the vernier.

ROBERT M. McKEON

VERONESE, GIUSEPPE (*b.* Chioggia, Italy, 7 May 1854; *d.* Padua, Italy, 17 July 1917), *mathematics.*

Giuseppe Veronese, professor of geometry at the University of Padua from 1881 until his death, was one of the foremost Italian mathematicians of his time. He took part also in political life, first as a member of Parliament for Chioggia (1897–1900), then as a member of the City Council of Padua, and finally as a senator (1904–1917).

Veronese's father was a house painter in Chioggia, then a small fishing town not far from Venice; his mother, Ottavia Duse, was a cousin of the celebrated actress Eleonora Duse. In 1885 Veronese married the Baroness Beatrice Bartolini; they had five children. Veronese was a handsome man, tall and commanding, but in his last years his health was undermined by influenza, which he had contracted in 1912 and which left him with grave cardiovascular disorders.

Because of his parents' poverty, Veronese had to interrupt his studies when he was eighteen and take a minor job in Vienna; but through the generosity of Count Nicolò Papadopoli he was able to resume his studies a year later, first at the Zurich Polytechnic, where he studied engineering and mathematics under Wilhelm Fiedler, and later, following a correspondence with Luigi Cremona, at the University of Rome, from which he graduated in 1877. In the previous year he had become assistant in analytical geometry, an unheard-of distinction for an undergraduate, after demonstrating his exceptional abilities in a paper on Pascal's hexagram, a work he had begun at Zurich. In 1880–1881 Veronese did postgraduate study at Leipzig. Immediately afterward, he won the competition for the professorship of complementary algebra and algebraic geometry at the University of Padua, where he succeeded Giusto Bellavitis. The latter had shown personal liking for Veronese but was fiercely opposed to the new approaches to geometry, which Veronese supported.

Veronese published only about thirty papers; but some of them, also available in German, were extremely important in the history of geometry. In particular he may be considered the main founder of the projective geometry of hyperspaces with n dimensions, which had previously been linear algebra presented geometrically, rather than geometry. Hyperspaces began to assume a more truly geometrical aspect when Veronese used an original recursion method to produce them: a plane can be obtained by projecting the points of a straight line from a point outside it, and a three-dimensional space by projecting the points of a plane from a point outside it, and so on. He is also remembered for "Veronese's surface," a two-dimensional surface of a five-dimensional space, which in its simplest expression can be represented by the parametric equations $x_1 = u^2$, $x_2 = uv$, $x_3 = v^2$, $x_4 = u$, $x_5 = v$, where $x_1, . . ., x_5$ are the nonhomogeneous coordinates of the space and u and v are two independent parameters. The study of this surface is equivalent, from the point of view of projection, to the study of all the conics of a plane; and one of its projections in ordinary space is Steiner's Roman surface.

Veronese was also one of the first to study non-Archimedean geometry, at first arousing strong opposition, and he demonstrated the independence of Archimedes' postulate—which states that among the multiples of a given magnitude there is always one greater than every fixed magnitude—from the other postulates of geometry. Veroneses also wrote useful books for the secondary schools.

Veronese was a member of the Accademia Nazionale dei Lincei and of other Italian academies; and his pupils included Guido Castelnuovo and Tullio Levi-Civita.

When a member of Parliament, Veronese campaigned strenuously for the conservation of the Lagoon of Venice.

BIBLIOGRAPHY

An obituary is C. Segre, "Commemorazione del socio nazionale Giuseppe Veronese," in *Atti dell' Accademia nazionale dei Lincei. Rendiconti*, 5th ser., **26**, pt. 2 (1917), 249–258, with a bibliography of Veronese's publications.

F. G. TRICOMI

AMERICAN COUNCIL OF LEARNED SOCIETIES

Dictionary
of Scientific
Biography
cSs